THE ENCYCLOPEDIA OF
BASIC MATERIALS
FOR PLASTICS

REINHOLD ONE-VOLUME ENCYCLOPEDIAS

THE ENCYCLOPEDIA OF
BASIC MATERIALS
FOR PLASTICS

EDITED BY

HERBERT R. SIMONDS

Consulting Engineer
Monroe, Connecticut

AND

JAMES M. CHURCH

Professor of Chemical Engineering
Columbia University, New York

2030

REINHOLD PUBLISHING CORPORATION
A subsidiary of Chapman-Reinhold, Inc.

NEW YORK   AMSTERDAM   LONDON

CONTRIBUTORS

R. AARONS, Industrial and Biochemicals Dept., E. I. DuPont De Nemours & Co., Wilmington, Del. *Azo Initiators.*

WILLIAM B. ANDERSON, Titanium Pigment Corp., National Lead Co., New York, N.Y. *Titanium Dioxide Pigment.*

JOHN S. AUTENRIETH, Pine and Paper Chemicals Dept., Hercules Inc., Wilmington, Del. *Rosin Esters.*

JOHN K. BACKUS, Mobay Chemical Co., Pittsburgh, Pa. *Urethane Materials.*

CLARE E. BACON, Owens Corning Fiberglas Corp., Toledo, Ohio. *Glass Reinforcements.*

JOSEPH W. BAKER, Organic Chemicals Div., Monsanto Co., St. Louis, Mo. *Phosphorus Esters.*

T. F. BANIGAN, JR., Director of Research, Pilot Chemical Co., Los Angeles, Calif. *Phosphonitrilic Chloride.*

ROBERT M. BARTH, Price-Driscoll Corp., Farmingdale, L.I., N.Y. *Mold Release Materials.*

IRVING S. BENGELSDORF, U.S. Borax Research, Anaheim, Calif. *Boric Acid Esters.*

E. PETER BENZING, Mgr. Research and Development, Organic Chemicals Division, Monsanto Co., St. Louis, Mo. *Flame Retardants.*

DOUGLAS J. BOLTON, Manager Technical Service, Lucidol Div., Wallace and Tiernan, Inc., Buffalo, N.Y. *Ketone Peroxides.*

SIDNEY A. BRESLER, Chemical Engineering Associates, New York, N.Y. (Formerly with The Borden Chemical Co., New York, N.Y.) *Acetylene.*

H. A. BROWN, Central Research Labs., 3M Company, St. Paul, Minn. *Fluorocarbon Monomers.*

GEORGE L. BROWNELL, U.S.S. Chemicals, Division of United States Steel Corp., Pittsburgh, Pa. *Maleic Acid and Derivatives.*

HALSEY BUELL, General Development Dept., The Carborundum Company, Niagara Falls, N.Y. *Abrasive Materials.*

FRANCIS M. BURESH, Textile Consultant, Au Sable Forks, N.Y. *Nonwoven Materials.*

RICHARD D. CADLE, Chemistry and Microphysics Dept., National Center for Atmospheric Research, Boulder, Colo. *Particle Size for Plastic Ingredients.*

CHARLES E. CHASTAIN, High Strength Plastics Corp., Chicago, Illinois. *Epoxy Intermediates; Epoxy Resin Ingredients; Silicone, Ingredients of; Silicone Mold Release Agents.*

D. F. CHICHESTER, Chas. Pfizer and Co., Inc., New York, N.Y. *Sorbitol.*

JOHN CORNELL, Director of Research, Sartomer Resins Inc. Essington, Pa. *Catalyst, Promoter; Monomers, Polyfunctional.*

LEE CRAMPTON, Plastics Div., Dow Chemical Co., Midland, Mich., *Methylstyrenes.*

G. H. CRAWFORD, Mgr. Polymer Research, 3M Company, St. Paul, Minn. *Fluorocarbon Monomers.*

ANDREW DAVIES, Mgr. Edgewater Laboratory, Plastics Div. Allied Chemical Corp. Edgewater, N.J. *Phenolic Resins, Ingredients.*

J. W. DAVISON, Director Process Development, Phillips Petroleum Co., Bartlesville, Okla. *Olefin Monomers.*

JOHN DELMONTE, President, Furane Plastics, Inc., Los Angeles, Calif. *Powdered Metals.*

ROBERT P. DEL VEECHIO, Erickson Research Chemicals, Sartomer Resins Inc., Chicago, Ill. *Ethylene Glycol Dimethacrylate.*

JOHN M. DEMPSTER, Project Manager, Sohio Chemical Co., Cleveland, Ohio. *Fillers, Hollow Glass Spheres.*

ELLIOTT DORMAN, Ciba Products, Summit, N.J. Reviewer: *Epoxy Hardeners; Epoxy Intermediates, Epoxy Ingredients:*

STEVENS S. DRAKE, Scientific Projects Lab., Dow Chemical Co., Midland, Mich., *Methylstyrenes.*

MORRIS DUNKEL, Director of Research, UOP Chemical Division, East Rutherford, N.J. *Anhydrides, Acid.*

JAMES P. DUX, Fibers Research and Development, American Viscose Div., FMC Corp., Marcus Hook, Pa. *Cellulose and Derivatives.*

P. J. EHMAN, Chemical Products Division, The Ansul Co., Marinette, Wis. *Methyl Chloride.*

IRVING N. EINHORN, Assoc. Prof. Chem. Eng., Wayne State University, Detroit, Mich. *Blowing Agents.*

GEORGE W. EWALD, Synthetic Industrial Fabric Dept., J. P. Stevens and Co., Inc., New York, N.Y. *Fabrics for Vinyl Coating and Laminating.*

JOHN D. FARR, Organic Chemicals Division, Emery Industries, Inc. Cincinnati, Ohio. *Azelaic Acid and Derivatives.*

THOMAS H. FERRIGNO, United Sierra Division, Cyprus Mines Corp., Trenton, N.J. *Fillers, Properties and Uses; Reinforcements.*

H. C. FREEMAN, JR. (Formerly with Industrial and Biochemicals Dept., E. I. DuPont De Nemours & Co., Wilmington, Del.) *Azo Initiators.*

J. THURMAN FREEZE, Tech. Service and Product Development, Chas. Pfizer and Co. Inc., New York, N.Y. *Itaconic Acid.*

MILTON FREIFELD, Dyestuff and Chemical Div., General Aniline and Film Corp., New York, N.Y. *Methyl Pyrrolidone.*

MARK E. FRENCH, Vice President, General Foam Corp., Hazleton, Pa. *Polyurethanes, Ingredients.*

KURT C. FRISCH, Polymer Research and Development, Wyandotte Chemicals Corp., Wyandotte, Mich. *Foam Ingredients.*

WARREN J. FRISSELL, Saran Products Lab., Dow Chemical Co., Midland, Mich. (Formerly with Rohm and Haas Co.) *Polymeric Plasticizers.*

WESLEY M. GERMON, Chemical Division, The Goodyear Tire and Rubber Co., Akron, Ohio, *Vinyl Chloride Latex.*

MELVIN M. GERSON, Mgr. Technical Services, Podell Industries, Inc., Saddle Brook, N.J. *Organic Colorants, Soluble Dyes.*

MARCELLO T. GIACHINO, Research Division, W. R. Grace and Co., Clarksville, Md. *Urea.*

CONTRIBUTORS

GEORGE T. GMITTER, Manager Plastics Research, The General Tire and Rubber Co., Akron, Ohio *Diisocyantes.*

ALBERT GOLDSTEIN, Devro Division, Johnson and Johnson, Sommerville N.J. (Formerly with Chemical Corp., East Brunswick, N.J.) *Ethylenimine.*

GABRIEL F. GOLDSTEIN, Finishes Division, Interchemical Corp., Clifton, N.J. *Decorative Coatings.*

ADRIAN J. GOOD, Minnesota Paints, Inc., Fort Wayne, Ind. *Epoxy Resins, Novolak.*

DAVID A. GORDON, Geigy Industrial Cnemicals, Yonker, N.Y. *Stabilizers, Light.*

H. A. GREEN, Houdry Process and Chemical Co., Air Products and Chemicals, Allentown, Pa. *Imidazoles and Derivatives.*

RICHARD GREENHAUS, Plastics Division, Monsanto Co., Springfield, Mass. *Fillers, Conductive, for Epoxy Resins.*

GLENN C. GRIMES, Senior Research Engineer, Southwest Research Institute, San Antonio, Tex. *Prepregs—Preimpregnated Laminate Materials.*

FREDERICK M. HALL, Cordo Division, Ferro Corp., Norwalk, Conn. *Fabrics, Lead Coated.*

B. FRANK HANTZ, American Insulator Corp., New Freedom, Pa. *Cold Molding Materials.*

J. V. E. HARDY, Plastics Dept., E. I. Du Pont DeNemours & Co., Wilmington, Del. *Nylon Intermediates.*

JAMES W. HAWKINS, Silicone Products Dept., General Electric Co., Waterford, N.Y. *Potting and Encapsulating Materials.*

GEORGE J. HEH, Famco, Inc., Commercial Glass Div., American Air Filter Co., Inc. Louisville, Ky. *Glass Fibers, Milled.*

NORMAN L. HEWITT, Chemical Division, Pittsburgh Plate Glass Co., Pittsburgh, Pa. *Pigments, Extender.*

ROBERT C. HICKERSON, Industrial Chemicals Div. Velsicol Chemical Corp., Chattanooga, Tenn. *Sucrose Benzoate.*

DONALD G. HUGGINS, Oronite Industrial Chemicals Div., Chevron Chemical Co., San Francisco, Calif. *Fumaric Acid and Esters; Phthalic Acids: Isophthalic.*

FREDERICK J. IHDE, JR., Nopco Chemical Co., Harrison, N.J. *Stabilizers, Vinyls.*

R. W. INGWALSON, Industrial Chemicals Div., Velsicol Chemical Corp., Chattanooga, Tenn. *Benzoguanamine; Benzonitrile.*

FREDERICK M. KAFKA, Vice President, Superior Materials Inc., New York, N.Y. *Fillers, Inorganic.*

OTTO S. KAUDER, Argus Chemical Co., Witco Chemical Co., Inc., Brooklyn, N.Y. *Stabilizers, Organotin.*

W. G. KAYSER, JR., Mgr. Organic Chemicals Dept., Pennsalt Chemicals Corp., Philadelphia, Pa. *Amyl Phenols.*

THOMAS J. KELLY, The Avisun Corp., New Castle, Del. *Polypropylene Monomers.*

W. B. KINNEY, Casein Dept., The Borden Chemical Co., Bainbridge, Conn, *Casein.*

CHARLES E. KLEIMAN, Industrial Chemicals Div.,

Mallinckrodt Chemical Works, St. Louis, Mo. *Stabilizers, Heat.*

CHARLES J. KNUTH, Chemical Division, Chas. Pfizer and Co., Inc., New York, N.Y. *Citric Acid and Esters.*

ERNST KÖHNLEIN, Badische Anilin & Soda-Fabrik AG. Ludwigshafen, Germany, *Polyisobutylenes.*

THEODORE O. J. KRESSER, Chemicals Dept., Gulf Oil Corp., Orange, Texas. *Antiblock and Slip Agents.*

J. H. KURTZ, Product Manager, ICI Organics Inc. Providence, R. I. *Antistatic Agents.*

ROBERT E. LALLY, Nuodex Division, Tenneco Chemicals Inc., Piscataway, N.J. (Formerly with Nopco Chemical Co.) *Stabilizers, Vinyl.*

L. C. LANE, Research Laboratories, American Cyanamid Co., Stamford, Conn., *Dicyandiamide; Melamine.*

F. H. LAUCHERT, JR., Technical Service Dept., Lucidol Div. of Wallace and Tiernan Inc. Buffalo, N.Y. *Ketone Peroxides.*

E. LAWSON (Deceased) Perfume Division, Fritzsche Brothers, Inc., New York, N.Y. *Odors and Perfumes.*

HENRY LEE, Technical Director, The Epoxylite Corp., South ElMonte, Calif. *Stripping Agents.*

MARTIN K. LINDEMANN, Mobile Chemical Co., Metuchen, N.J., (Formerly with Air Reduction Chem. Co.) *Polyvinyl Alcohol; Vinyl Acetate.*

FRANK W. LONG, Consultant, Princeton, N.J. (Formerly with Princeton Chem. Research) *Pyromellitic Dianhydride.*

LEO S. LUSKIN, Special Products Dept., Rohm and Haas Co., Philadelphia, Pa. *Acrylic and Methacrylic Acids and Esters.*

ROBERT M. LUSSKIN, Vice President of Research, UOP Chemical Div. East Rutherford, Pa., *Anhydrides, Acid.*

W. N. MACLAY, Asst. Mgr. of Plastics Research, Koppers Co., Inc., Monroeville, Pa. *Divinylbenzene.*

WILLARD H. MADSON, Pigments Dept., E. I. DuPont DeNemours & Co., Inc., Wilmington, Del. *Pigments, White.*

HERMAN F. MARK, Director, Institute of Polymer Research, Polytechnic Institute of Brooklyn, Brooklyn, N.Y. *Additives; Catalysts, Polymerization.*

MARTIN E. MARKS (Formerly with U.S. Peroxygen Corp., Richmond, Calif.). *Organic Peroxides for Polyester Resins.*

CHARLES R. MARTENS, Director Products Laboratory, The Sherwin-Williams Co., Cleveland, Ohio. *Surfactants.*

JAY R. MARTIN, Plastics Technical Service, Marbon Chemical Division, Borg-Warner Corp. Washington, W.Va. *ABS Modifiers for PVC Compounds.*

GUY A. MARTINELLI, President, Dimensional Pigments, Inc., Bayonne, N.J. *Dyes and Pigments.*

D. M. MAYER, Industrial Chemicals Div., Shell Chemical Co., New York, N.Y. *Allylamines.*

C. P. MCCLELLAND, Chemical Division, Union Carbide Corp., *Alcohols, Mono- and Polyhydric.*

W. R. McElroy, Vice President, Research, Conap Inc., Allegany, N.Y. *Polyurethane Elastomer Materials.*

Robert N. Meals, Silicone Products Dept., General Electric Co., Waterford, N.Y. *Silicone Intermediates.*

J. Gilbert Mohr, Fiber Glass Division, Johns-Mansville Co., Waterville, Ohio. *Glass Fiber Mats.*

Louis F. Moormeier, Market Research and Development Dept., U.S. Industrial Chemical Co., New York, N.Y. *Methylene Glutaronitrile.*

Kris Neville, Program Manager, Epoxylite Corp., South ElMonte, Calif. *Stripping Agents.*

Milton Nowak, Research Director, Troy Chemical Corp., Newark, N.J. *Fungicides.*

H. F. Oehlschlaeger, Organic Chemicals Division, Emery Industries, Inc., Cincinnati, Ohio. *Azelaic Acid and Derivatives.*

Harold F. O'Keefe, Bureau of Medicine, Food and Drug Administration, Washington, D.C. *F.D.A. Regulations for Plastics.*

Frank J. Olsen, Kensol-Olsenmark, Inc., Melville, L.I., N.Y. *Roll Leaf.*

J. Tracy O'Rourke, Director Research and Development, Liquid Nitrogen Processing Corp. Malvern, Pa. *"Teflon" Sponge Powders.*

Hans Osborg, President, The Chemirad Corp., East Brunswick, N.J. *Ethylenimine.*

L. L. R. Phillips, Industrial Papers Division, The Mead Corp., South Lee, Mass. *Papers used in Plastics.*

F. J. Prescott, Dyestuff and Chemical Div. General Aniline and Film Corp. New York, N.Y. *Methyl Pyrrolidone.*

Harry Raech, Jr., Defense Technology Labs., FMC Corp., Santa Clara, Calif. *Allylic Resin Intermediates.*

Victor H. Rampelberg, Vice President, Marketing, Bee Chemical Co., Lansing, Ill. *Paint Materials.*

Robert W. Reardon, Nalco Chemical Co. (Formerly with The Quaker Oats Co., Chicago, Ill.) *Furfural and Derivatives.*

Ronald J. Reid, Jr., General Development Dept., The Carborundum Co., Niagara Falls, N.Y. *Abrasive Materials.*

J. L. Rendall, Manager Research and Development, Hitco, Inc., Gardena, Calif. *Carbons.*

Philip H. Rhodes, Castleberry Industries, Mallinckrodt Chemical Works, St. Louis, Mo. *Stabilizers, Heat.*

Michael A. Ricciardi, General Foam Corp., Hazleton, Pa. *Polyurethanes, Ingredients.*

William F. Ringk, Dir. Research & Development, Benzol Products Division, Cowles Chemical Co., Newark, N.J. *Benzyl Alcohol; Phenylethyl Alcohol.*

Michael Robin, Catalin Corp., Div. Ashland Oil and Refining Co., Fords, N.J. *Antioxidants.*

D. V. Rosato, Technical Editor, *Plastics World*, Waban, Mass. *Filament Winding Materials.*

J. H. Ross, Chemicals Division, Union Carbide Corp. South Charleston, W.Va. *Antifoam Agents.*

H. K. Salzberg, Consultant for The Borden Chemical Co., Bainbridge, N.Y. *Casein.*

Samuel G. Salzinger, Mgr. of Manufacturing, Heath Tecna Corp., Kent, Washington, *"Prepregs"—Preimpregnated Laminate Materials.*

Arthur M. Schiller, Plastics and Polymers Research Dept., American Cyanamid Co., Stamford, Conn. *Aliphatic Acids and Esters.*

D. C. Schreck, Sonneborn Division, Witco Chemical Co., Inc., New York, N.Y. *Petroleum Products.*

Herbert S. Schwartz, Non-Metallic Materials Div., Air Force Materials Lab. Wright-Patterson Air Force Base, Ohio. *Boron Fibers.*

R. T. Schwartz, Chief, Non-Metallic Materials Div., Air Force Materials Lab., Wright-Patterson Air Force Base, Ohio. *Boron Fibers.*

Raymond B. Seymour, Assoc. Prof. of Chemistry, University of Houston, Houston, Tex. *Fillers and Reinforcements; Plasticizers; Propylene Oxide; Vinyl Monomers.*

W. E. Shackelford, Technical Service Dept., Chemical Div., General Mills Inc., Kankakee, Ill. *Thixotropic Materials.*

Peter T. B. Shaffer, Senior Research Associate, The Carborundum Co., Niagara Falls, N.Y. *Silicon Carbide Whiskers.*

Donald E. Smith, Industrial Division, High Voltage Engineering Corp., Burlington, Mass. *Radiation of Plastics.*

M. K. Smith, Technical Division, The Baker Castor Oil Co., Bayonne, N.J. *Castor Oil.*

Willard F. Spengeman, Pigments Dept., E. I. DuPont DeNemours & Co., Chestnut Run, Wilmington, Del. *Coloration of Plastics.*

M. A. Spina, Manager Specialty Dept., Interchemical Corp., New York, N.Y. *Decoration of Plastics.*

Clinton J. Starke, Product Manager, FMC Corp., New York, N.Y. *Diallyl Phthalate.*

Paul M. Steginsky, Director of Sales, Nuclear Research Assoc. Inc., Long Island City, N.Y. *Phototropic Additives.*

Robert Steinman, President, Ram Chemicals, Inc., Gardena, Calif. *Waxes.*

Sharan Stellrecht, Consultant, Morton Salt Co., Chicago, Ill. *Sodium Chloride and Salt Chemicals.*

J. Pat Sterry, Vice President (Formerly with H. I. Thompson Fiber Glass Co., Gardena, Calif.) *Silica Fibers.*

David W. Stutz, Chemical Product Sales Dept., American Can Co., Neenah, Wis. *Dispersing Agents.*

Vincent Sussman, Epoxy Products Division. Allied Products Corp., New Haven, Conn. *Fillers, Conductive, for Epoxy Resins.*

Willard H. Sutton, Mgr. Metallurgy and Ceramics Research, General Electric Co., King of Prussia, Pa., *Reinforcements: Ceramic Whiskers.*

Norman W. Touchette, Organic Chemicals Div., Monsanto Co., St. Louis, Mo. *Phosphorus Esters.*

R. L. Tusch, Enjay Polymer Laboratories, Humble Oil and Refining Co., Linden, N.J. *Polypropylene Additives.*

CONTRIBUTORS

DOUGLAS E. TUTTLE, Pamavco Inc., Roselle, N.J. (Formerly with Interchemical Printing Inks). *Printing Inks, for Films.*

R. W. VAIL, Stabilizer Sales Manager, Ferro Corp., Chemical Division, Bedford, Ohio. *Catalysts, Urethane Foam.*

ROBERT H. VARLAND, Plastics, Chemicals Division, Atlas Chemical Industries, Wilmington, Del. *Polyethers for Urethane Foam.*

JOHN M. VERDI, Senior Project Manager, Mobil Chemical Co., New York, N.Y. (Formerly with Nicolet Industries) *Asbestos Fibers.*

HAROLD G. VESPER, Chemist, Shell Development Co., Emeryville, Calif. *Allyl Alcohol and Its Esters.*

DALE P. VOGEL, Chemical Purchasing Dept., The Goodyear Tire and Rubber Co., Akron, Ohio. *Vinyl Chloride Latex.*

H. C. VOGT, Polymer Research and Development, Wyandotte Chemicals Corp., Wyandotte, Mich. *Foam Ingredients.*

CARL VON DOENHOFF, Senior Research Associate, The Carborundum Co., Niagara Falls, N.Y. *Abrasive Materials.*

FRANK S. WAGNER, JR., Technical Center, Celanese Chemical Co., Corpus Christi, Tex. *Acetic Acid.*

ALLAN A. WAHL, Mgr. Quality Control, Cadet Chemical Corp., Burt, N.Y. *Organic Peroxides, General.*

JOHN F. WALKER, Synthetics Research Div., Hercules Co., Wilmington, Del. *Dimethyltereph-thalate and Terephthalic Acid.*

W. L. WAMPNER, Vice President of Development Reichhold Chemicals, Inc., White Plains, N.Y. *Formaldehyde.*

ELBERT C. WEAVER, Chemistry Dept., Southern Connecticut State College, New Haven, Conn. *Essential Oils; Ethylene.*

J. ARNDT WEICKSEL, Organic Chemicals Division, American Cyanamid Co., Bound Brook, N.J. *Ultraviolet Absorbers.*

EDWARD R. WELLS, Mobay Chemical Co., Pittsburgh, Pa. *Urethane Materials.*

EDWARD L. WHITE, Manager, Plastics Dept., National Lead Co., Hightstown, N.J. *Stabilizers, Electrical; Stabilizers, Lead.*

H. JAMES WHITE, Mgr. Specialty Products, Amicon Corp., Cambridge, Mass. *Epoxy Curing Agents.*

RICHARD S. WILNER, Wilner Wood Floor Co., Norway, Maine, *Wood Flour.*

PHILIP F. WOERNER, Specialty Chemicals Div. Diamond Alkali Co., Cleveland, Ohio. *Fillers, Calcium Carbonate.*

ARTHUR K. WOERNLE, Minerals, Pigments and Metals Div., Chas. Pfizer and Co., New York, N.Y. *Iron Oxide Pigments.*

IVAN A. WOLFF, Chief, Industrial Crops Lab., Agricultural Research Service, U.S. Dept. Agriculture, Peoria, Ill., *Crambe Vegetable Oil.*

PREFACE

Research chemists have at their disposal more than 5000 established chemicals. Of this large number of primary materials, perhaps one-fifth, or 1000 chemicals, form the basis of the plastics industry, which today produces some 30 different types of plastics.

This book is about the materials from which the various plastics are made. However, it is something more, because it describes such functions as those of plasticizers and catalysts, as well as the basic materials involved in plastics production.

In fact, the aim of the editors has been to cover in one book everything about plastics except the plastic products themselves. Therefore, polymers and formulated plastic compounds are not emphasized, except in relation to the basic materials from which they are made.

The articles have been written by authorities on the various materials. In most cases the authors are active in the industries producing these materials and have taken time to write for this encyclopedia because they believe it will provide a new approach to a segment of the plastics industry—an approach both necessary and useful but heretofore not generally available.

The articles are arranged in alphabetical order, the so-called encyclopedia method. To save space, there are no formal bibliographies. Instead, pertinent references are placed as footnotes.

To keep the book within reasonable limits in size, the contributors were asked to condense their articles as much as possible without sacrificing useful information. In some cases, the editors have further condensed them to avoid duplication. Because of differences in terminology in the industry, the problem of eliminating duplication has been one of the most difficult the editors have faced. For example, such terms as "curing agents" and "hardening agents," "fillers" and "extenders," are often used interchangeably.

Because of these and other editorial difficulties, the editors have included a complete index, and the reader should make use of it in seeking complete information about a given subject. Many articles have cross references to guide the reader to more extensive treatment of subjects perhaps too briefly described in an article that had to be drastically condensed because of duplication.

Monroe, Conn.
New York, N.Y.
August, 1967

HERBERT R. SIMONDS
JAMES M. CHURCH

ACKNOWLEDGMENTS

The completion of this encyclopedia has depended upon the interest and contributions of many people, the majority of whom are technical specialists in the chemical and plastics industries. The response to our requests for articles was very encouraging, with most of the individuals approached welcoming our invitation to write about their special products. Their enthusiasm and willingness to cooperate in this venture was most unusual, indicating a strong desire to make valuable information about their products available to others in these industries. In several instances, more than one article was written by an author, as noted in the List of Contributors.

All of the correspondence and typing, as well as assistance in the general organization of the book, was the work of our respective secretaries, Mrs. Charlotte C. Warren and Mrs. Libby Rubin, to whom we are much indebted.

To our numerous contributors, we extend our sincere appreciation and gratitude for their excellent articles which made this encyclopedia possible. The book, if it proves as useful to the plastics industry as the editors hope it will, stands as a tribute to these individuals.

Monroe, Conn.   HERBERT R. SIMONDS

New York, N.Y.   JAMES M. CHURCH

August, 1967

A

ABRASIVE MATERIALS

A "coated abrasive" consists of a flexible backing material, to which is added a coating of an abrasive material bonded to one or both sides of the backing with an adhesive. The backing may be cloth, paper, vulcanized fiber, or combinations of cloth and paper or cloth and fiber. The abrasive may be a natural material such as flint, emery or garnet, or a synthetic product, such as fused aluminum oxide or silicon carbide. The adhesive used to bond the abrasive to the backing material may be various grades of animal hide glue or synthetic resins, normally of the phenol-formaldehyde or urea-formaldehyde type.

The first documented coated abrasive was probably one produced by the Chinese, sometime prior to the 15th century, which consisted of crushed shells bonded to parchment with a natural adhesive. Actual production of coated abrasives started in England early in the 19th century, and in the United States about 30 years later. For many years, the only coated abrasive products manufactured and sold were emery, flint and garnet paper and cloth, but with the development of fused aluminum oxide and silicon carbide synthetic abrasives, the utility and variety of coated abrasives expanded rapidly. Today, upward of 30,000–40,000 different varieties of coated abrasive products are available on the market with a yearly sales value of over 100 million dollars.

Another of the major factors contributing to the growth of the coated abrasive industry has been the development of synthetic resin adhesives to replace the traditional animal glue binders for holding the abrasive grains on the backings. Animal glue, while an excellent type of adhesive for many applications, has a number of short-comings as an abrasive binder. Among these are lack of water resistance, stability at the high temperatures reached during grinding, and the tendency to become sticky or tacky during use which results in what is termed as "loading" of the abrasive product.

Many coated abrasive applications are such that animal glue-bonded products are perfectly satisfactory. However, because of the superiority of resin-bonded coated abrasives for applications involving coolants, or where high grinding temperatures are generated, numbers of new uses for coated abrasives, especially in the form of endless belts, have developed. It is estimated that several million pounds of phenolic resins go into the manufacture of coated abrasive products of this type annually.

Manufacture of Coated Abrasives

In order to outline the function of the bond system in the overall picture of a coated abrasive product, a brief description of the manufacturing process seems important.

A coated abrasive manufacturing machine consists of eight separate and distinct units, each performing a definite function and so arranged that the backing is fed into one end of the machine and a finished or semi-finished product comes out at the other end. These units are, in order, the unwind stand, printing press, making adhesive coater, grain application unit, making dry oven, sizing adhesive coater, sizing dry oven, and winder. The manufacturing process consists of the following steps:

(1) From the unwind stand, which holds a large roll of the backing material, the backing passes through the printing press which prints pertinent information such as product type and grit size on the backing.

(2) At the making adhesive coater a coating of adhesive is applied on one side of the backing, called the making coat.

(3) Abrasive grain is immediately deposited in the wet adhesive layer by means of the grain application unit.

(4) The making adhesive is dried, or in the case of resin binders, B-staged, in the making dry oven.

(5) A second coating of adhesive is applied over the top of the abrasive coating, called the sizing coat.

(6) The sizing adhesive is dried, or B-staged in the sizer drying oven as above.

(7) The product is rewound in large diameter continuous rolls for final processing, such as re-drying or curing.

Several specific bond systems are used in resin-bonded and waterproof coated abrasives. These are outlined below.

(1) *Resin over glue bond*, which consists of an animal glue making coat and a phenolic or urea formaldehyde sizing coat.

(2) *Resin over resin bond*, which consists of a phenolic resin making and sizing coat.

(3) *Waterproof cloth bond*, which consists of a phenolic resin making and sizing coat on a waterproof cloth backing.

(4) *Waterproof paper bond* which consists of a varnish making coat and either a varnish or a phenolic resin sizing coat.

These bond systems are used to produce products for definite end uses and are naturally designed to result in a product which will give optimum performance in the use for which it is intended.

The phenolic resins employed for coated abrasive bonding are low molecular weight polymers produced by reacting phenol and formaldehyde in the presence of a catalyst to produce a water-soluble condensation product. The actual water solubility is determined by the number of methylol groups present in relation to the average size of the polymer molecule. Both the type and amount of catalyst are varied, as is the mole ratio of formaldehyde to phenol to result in finished resins having particular properties. In general, the more alkaline the catalyst used or the higher percentage of catalyst employed, the faster gelling and more tightly cross-linked the resin will be, so that the net result is a fast gelling, brittle, low temperature curing product which can be used successfully for resin over glue bonds. Condensation products prepared with less alkaline catalysts, at lower levels, tend to chain extend further before cross-linking which results in tougher, stronger bonds which can be used for resin over resin or waterproof cloth products.

In many cases the phenolic resins are modified with finely ground inert fillers such as calcium carbonate or calcium silicate to reduce cost and to reinforce the cured bond structure. Other additives such as pigments, dyes, dispersing agents, wetting agents and the like are also added to the resins during processing.

The urea-formaldehyde resins used for coated abrasive bonding are mixtures of methylol ureas produced by reacting urea and formaldehyde in the presence of mild alkali. These adhesives are normally used only as a sizing coat over a glue making coat primarily to result in improved heat and moisture resistance. An acid catalyst is added to the urea-formaldehyde resin so that an extremely fast cure cycle at relatively low temperature can be obtained. To prevent stress cracking or crazing of the urea-formaldehyde bond layer, the resin is usually plasticized with 20–30%

furfuryl alcohol. Other compounding ingredients such as pigments, dyes, inert fillers, shell flours, etc., are also often added to enhance the properties of the finished adhesive.

The final general type of resinous adhesive which is used in the manufacture of coated abrasives falls in the category of alkyd and oleoresinous binders. These adhesives are used on a product line known as "Waterproof Paper," which has application for the wet sanding of primed and painted surfaces during the finishing of furniture, appliances, and automobile bodies.

The oleoresinous binders are similar to common spar varnishes, and usually consist of a cooked blend of a drying oil or mixtures of two or more drying oils, and one or more oil-soluble phenol aldehyde resins. The particular phenolic resins are usually based on *para*-substituted phenols. In general, 30 gal. or less of oil per 100 lb of phenolic resin are used so aromatic solvents are required to obtain good solutions of the resin-oil combinations. Standard metallic soap dryers are added to aid the drying process.

The alkyd-type adhesives, which may also be used for the manufacture of "Waterproof Paper," are based very generally on polyesters formed by co-reacting a polybasic acid with a polyhydric alcohol and an unsaturated monobasic acid derived from a drying oil glyceride. These adhesives can be designed to give practically any desired hardness, toughness or degree of flexibility in the finished coated abrasive product, and like the oleoresinous binders, can be further modified by the addition of alkyl modified urea or melamine formaldehyde resins.

Finishing of Plastics with Coated Abrasives

In most cases, some finishing operations are necessary in the fabrication of plastics parts, regardless of the process used in forming the part itself. With molded parts, usually the removal of flash, gates or risers is required. Where a flat surface is desired, grinding to the required degree of flatness may become necessary because of shrinkage of the part during the curing process. Often it may be more economical to produce a particular shape or contour on a plastic part by grinding rather than by the mold design used in the molding or casting process. Precision parts must be ground and finished to the required tolerances.

Coated abrasives are an effective means of obtaining both desired finishes and tolerances. Different techniques, however, must be used when mechanically finishing thermosetting and thermoplastic materials, if the desired surface characteristics and tolerances for each type are to be achieved. Generally speaking, in grinding or finishing these two types of materials, parts fabricated from thermosetting resins tend to powder, while those fabricated from thermoplastics tend to melt and string. Therefore, under optimum conditions, good dust removal facilities are required when grinding thermosetting resin parts; wet grinding is required when finishing thermoplastic parts.

Two basic general types of grinding equipment are used for the finishing of plastic parts. Where the parts are small and can be adapted to semi-automated finishing operations, a variety of stationary grinding machines can be used. These stationary grinding machines can be described as follows:

(1) Lathe and backstand.
(2) Slack of belt.
(3) Platen.
(4) Through-feed conveyorized.
(5) Vonnegut brush sander.
(6) Centerless.

Where the parts to be finished are large, such as fiber-glass boat hulls, a large variety of portable tools with coated abrasives in the form of belts, discs, sleeves, pads, cartridge rolls, sheets and the like can be used.

Silicon carbide grain is recognized as the best mineral to use for abrasive grinding and finishing of plastics. The extreme hardness of the SiC crystals, the sharpness of the grain, plus the brittle characteristics of the abrasive which causes fracture and continuously exposes new, sharp-cutting points are characteristics which make it desirable for use on plastics.

The effectiveness and life of a coated abrasive product used on plastics, normally, is proportional to the amount and rate of loading, or build up of ground material on the abrasive surface, during grinding. For this reason, where wet grinding is possible, optimum abrasive life is obtained through the use of this process rather than by dry grinding.

Use of Plastics in Bonded Abrasives

Abrasive bonds for grinding wheels are commonly classified into the two broad categories of inorganic and organic bonds, each of which represents roughly half of the total dollar volume of grinding wheel manufacture. In general, the use of inorganic bonds is confined to those applications which require maximum dimensional precision and minimum heat developed in grinding. Surface grinding, tool room grinding, and cylindrical grinding are examples of such applications. Wheels made from organic bonds are tougher and stronger, permitting them to be operated at higher wheel speeds. Organic-bonded wheels are therefore more suitable for foundry work, steel billet conditioning, and cutting-off operations.

The organic bonding agents include three types of bonding materials: synthetic resins, rubbers, and shellac. Shellac bonds are of relatively minor importance, and therefore not discussed here. By far the most important organic bonding agents are the synthetic resins, which are almost entirely of the phenolic type. Typical resin wheel compositions contain, by weight, from 6–12% of phenolic resin, up to 3% of "plasticizers" or dispersing agents, and up to 25% of inorganic fillers, with the remainder being the abrasive grit.

The resins used for this purpose are novolak-type phenolics in powder form, containing 6–10% of hexamethylene tetramine. These phenolic resins for the abrasive industry frequently carry a premium price because of the exceptionally severe requirements for uniformity with respect to particle size distribution and flow characteristics. Advance samples are frequently supplied by the resin supplier, and each shipment may be given an acceptance test by the wheel manufacturer, in which a standardized abrasive composition is prepared from the resin and tested for physical characteristics such as tensile strength. Many of the phenolics for abrasive use have been modified by the incorporation of up to 10% of a thermoplastic material such as polyvinyl butyral.

"Plasticizers" and dispersing agents are used in order to obtain mix uniformity and to obtain specific mix-handling, molding, and curing characteristics. The granular abrasive mix must be capable of being charged into the wheel molds without caking or packing and without appreciable segregation of bond and grits. It must further be capable of being molded to a specified density within the available molding pressure limitations, usually from 1000–5000 p.s.i. depending upon wheel size. Furfural and low molecular weight phenolic resins are the two most frequently used "plasticizers." When the abrasive grains are wet with these materials the powdered resin and fillers can then be firmly attached as a coating of relatively uniform thickness around each individual abrasive grit. There is an alternative type of mix in which the loose dry bond materials are kept in relatively uniform suspension between the grit particles by the addition of small amounts of a dispersing agent such as creosote oil.

The harder grades of resinoid abrasive wheels require the use of large amounts of inorganic filler in the mix compositions to increase the strength and wear resistance of the wheels. Cryolite, calcium sulfate, and iron pyrites are the materials most frequently used for this purpose. Anhydrous lime is used as a dehydrating agent and curing aid.

The abrasive grain in resonoid wheels is primarily alumina for metallic grinding applications, with silicon carbide being used for grinding non-metallic materials, and diamond grit for special applications on very hard materials. The abrasive grain size may range from the 10-mesh abrasive needed for billet conditioning wheels to the 400-

mesh abrasive in roll-finishing wheels. In designing wheel performance characteristics for specific applications, in addition to the choice of abrasive grain size, the wheel manufacturer may make selections from among several degrees of grain friability and shape characteristics.

In the manufacture of resinoid wheels one of two alternative molding methods is used; either hot-pressing at temperatures up to 350°F, or cold-press preforming followed by oven curing. In both methods the molds are cylindrical compression molds capable of closing from both ends to a fixed-volume mold cavity. Long oven curing cycles are prevalent with overnight schedules using temperatures up to 350°F or higher.

Rubber, the other major organic bonding material for grinding wheels, is used for those grinding applications in which smooth finish, free-cutting characteristics, or wheel flexibility and resilience are of greater importance than long wheel life with high stock removal rates. Some representative applications for rubber-bonded wheels are: the grinding of hardened steel ball-bearing races, the cutting-off of metallurgical specimens, and the polishing of drill flutes. The unique characteristics which make them suitable for these applications are their resilience at grinding temperatures and the ease with which the mix compositions can be formed into thin sheets of uniform structure and high strength. For example, the .005 in. thin wheels used for slotting pen points could not be made from the granular type mixes required for the resinoid bonds, but instead they are made from calendered sheets of rubber-bonded abrasive mix compositions.

Rubber bonds for grinding wheels are pre-dominantly of the ebonite or hard-rubber type, utilizing both natural and synthetic rubbers. Typical compositions may contain, by weight, from 6–15% of rubber, from 3–8% of sulfur and vulcanizing agents, up to 4% of resins, plasticizers and modifiers, and up to 25% of inorganic fillers, the remainder consisting of abrasive grain which may range from 16-mesh to about 240-mesh. For the more rigid bonds the principal rubber types used are natural rubber, polyisoprene, and styrene-type copolymers, while for resilient wheel bonds neoprene is generally preferred.

Bond mixing is done either on a two-roll rubber mill or in a Banbury-type mixer. The abrasive grain, however, is usually incorporated by folding it into the bond and passing it through a two-roll mill with no differential roll speed. In this manner mix compositions containing as much as 90% of abrasive can be prepared. After blending until uniform, the mix is calendered to any desired thickness, up to about 1 in. Thin wheels do not require a subsequent molding operation and are merely cut from the calendered slab and then oven cured. Thicker wheels, such as those used for centerless grinding, are hot-pressed from several layers of discs cut from thick calendered slabs. The trimmings are reprocessed to form new slabs.

All grinding wheel structures must be carefully designed and closely controlled in grade "hardness" in order to properly adjust the balance between wheel wear rate on the one hand and dulling and glazing of the abrasive grit on the other hand. The composition and processing factors most frequently used as controlled variables in the design of organic-bonded wheel structures are: the amount of porosity in the structure, the volume concentration of abrasive grain, the type and proportion of primary bonding resin or rubber, the type and proportion of inorganic filler, the curing cycle, and the choice of bond modifier to produce various degrees of strength, heat resistance, toughness and resilience. One of the major advantages of organic bonds over inorganic bonds is the fact that the organic wheels can readily be reinforced with internal molded-in plies of strong materials such as glass fabric. These reinforced wheels provide additional safety in grinding operations in which exceptionally severe side-stresses and impact loads may be encountered. Rapid progress has been evident in recent years in the design of this type of reinforced abrasive wheel structure.

HALSEY BUELL
RONALD J. REID, JR.
CARL VON DOENHOFF

ABS MODIFIERS FOR PVC COMPOUNDS

The use of ABS polymers* as a modifier of polyvinyl compounds is a major application for these versatile plastic materials. The original use of ABS in this application was as an impact modifier for rigid compounds; while ABS is still used for this purpose it is also used extensively in semi-rigid and flexible compounds as a processing aid and property modifier. ABS has the added advantage of being the most economical of the polymeric resin additives for PVC compounding.

The Mechanism of Reinforcement

ABS provides a convenient method for adding a rubber phase to the inherently brittle PVC. ABS forms a two-phase system with PVC which is necessary for reinforcement. One way of looking at the mechanism is to consider that the particle size of the rubber phase is "built into" the ABS molecule and surrounded by a compatible (with PVC) thermoplastic shell. This controlled rubber particle size is responsible for the relative insensitivity of ABS/PVC blends to variations in

* ABS = terpolymers of acrylonitrile-butadiene-styrene.

mixing. ABS/PVC compounds can be reground and recycled through process equipment with a minimal loss in properties due to changes in the dispersion of the rubber phase. Rubber-PVC blends, on the contrary, are very sensitive to the time and intensity of mixing and the optimum impact reinforcement is attained over a very narrow range of time and temperature mixing. It follows then, that problems may be anticipated upon re-processing these rubber-modified PVC compounds. The same is true of many other rubber/PVC blends.

The grades of ABS vary in the nature and degree of their reinforcement, not only with respect to their compositions but also in regard to the particle size of the rubber phase, the molecular weight and composition of the non-rubber phase, and the amount of cross-linking of the ABS. There is little improvement in impact strength beyond the 20% ABS level. Increasing the ABS content improves the processing and modifies other characteristics, such as heat distortion and tensile modulus. Having a range of products to select from, it is possible to select an ABS modifier which will confer properties ranging from impact reinforcement of a rigid compound, to improving the hot tear properties of a highly plasticized compound.

Applications in Rigid Compounds

Type II PVC pipe provides an example of impact modification by ABS in what is probably its simplest, practical form. The economics of the plastic pipe industry dictate that the cost of the product be kept to a minimum while the physical properties and dimensions must conform to certain standards. The profile of pipe is, of course, simple and regular. This allows the selection of a modifier which is most efficient in terms of impact. It is also necessary to consider the effect of the modifier upon the stress rating of the pipe, the heat distortion point, chemical resistance, toxicity and stability of the compound.

Optimum impact at minimum ABS levels is achieved in an ABS/PVC blend by the selection of the highest molecular weight PVC which can be uniformly and thoroughly blended with the ABS modifier. Normally, the highest molecular weight PVC that can be successfully utilized in a rigid compound is a GP-5* resin. Processing and design considerations, in the case of pipe, set a practical upper limit of about GP-4 for the molecular weight of PVC. The most efficient ABS for this product is a relatively "soft" ABS such as BLENDEX 301. The BLENDEX 301 will confer the desired impact modification and sufficient processability for a product as geometrically simple as pipe. The optimum amount of ABS for this application is approximately 15% of the total polymer system.

* ASTM D-1755 designation for PVC.

(So that the normal stabilizer levels are not disturbed, it is preferable to consider the *total* polymer system as 100% when writing the formula for an ABS/PVC blend. Replacing PVC with ABS results in minimal changes in compound stability. If the compounder prefers to base his compound on 100% PVC he should be alert for the need to increase his stabilizer level.) The use of ABS levels of less than 15% for pipe application should be approached with caution. As can be seen in the accompaning graph, the impact resistance of ABS/PVC blends is very sensitive to the modifier level in the range of 10–12% modifier. Any error in weighing or inhomogeneity in a powder blend may cause a drastic reduction in impact strength. If, instead of a simple profile such as pipe, a complex channel is to be extruded, it will probably be necessary to compromise impact strength with processability. Even if impact is not a consideration, unmodified PVC is difficult to successfully and economically extrude into complex shapes. As the level of ABS in an ABS/PVC compound is increased, the processing becomes more similar to that of ABS. Proper selection of ABS and PVC in approximately a 1 : 1 ratio, will produce a compound which can be injection molded in conventional ram machines. If the compound is intended

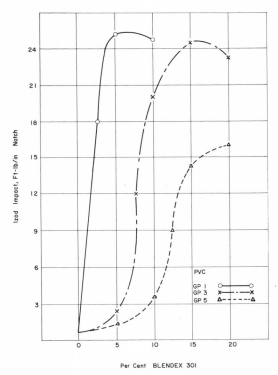

FIG. 1. Effect of concentration of BLENDEX on PVC's of varying molecular weight.

for use in a screw machine then there is considerably more latitude in the design of the compound. It is possible, when designing for screw machines, to use higher molecular weight PVC and lesser amounts of ABS.

ABS is well suited to the modification of rigid PVC compounds for calendering. BLENDEX 401, an ABS modifier which is specifically designed for clear compounds, facilitates the production of clear, high impact sheet, resistant to stress-marking. The improved processing characteristics and hot strength conferred by ABS make it a valuable additive for the production of both extruded and calendered sheet. ABS modified sheet also exhibits improved embossing retention and vacuum forming properties compared to unmodified PVC sheet.

ABS is also successfully compounded with PVC/PVAc copolymers. Copolymer resins are used primarily for their comparative ease of processing but they lack impact, flex modulus and hot strength. Proper selection of an ABS modifier enables the compounder to take advantage of the easy processing copolymers while maintaining a good balance of physical properties.

Applications in Flexible Compounds

ABS is used in flexible PVC compounds for the following reasons:
(1) Improved processing.
(2) Improved hot strength.
(3) Improved embossing retention.
(4) Improved thermo-forming.

Some flexible ABS/PVC compounds contain such a high proportion of ABS that they may be more properly termed PVC modified ABS compounds. In these cases ABS is selected for its processing characteristics and the compound is modified with PVC to reinforce the tear and abrasion properties. An example of this type compound is automotive crash pad skin.

The basic reason for the modification of flexible PVC compounds with ABS is the ability of ABS to enhance the hot strength of these compounds. ABS is used in PVC sponge to regulate the modulus and improve the uniformity of cell structure. In PVC shoe soles, ABS increases flex modulus without adversely affecting the low temperature properties of the compound. Soft compounds, modified with ABS, can be successfully blow molded, thereby economically competing with plastisol processes. Low "Durometer" profiles are easier to extrude because the ABS content improves the "hot strength" characteristics of the compound.

When designing a flexible compound the amount and type of ABS are not, of course, chosen for their effect on impact, but rather for their effect on the hardness, modulus and melt rheology of the compound. The plasticizer system must be selected with care. Plasticizers may not have the same compatibility with ABS as with PVC. Generally speaking, the more common ester types such as DOP, DIDP and TCP are acceptable in ABS/PVC compounds.

SUGGESTED STARTING FORMULATIONS

(1) *Rigid Sheet for Vacuum Forming*

Material	Parts
BLENDEX 101[a]	20
PVC (GP-3 or GP-4)	80
Color pigments	Q. S.
Metallic stearate	0.5
Ethylene bis stearamide	0.5
Organo tin mercaptide	1.5-2.0

(2) *Transparent or Translucent Extruded Rigid Sheet*

Material	Parts
BLENDEX 401 or 301	15–20
PVC (GP-3)	85–80
Color pigments	0.5
Ethylene bis stearamide	0.5
Organo tin mercaptide	1.5-2.0
Metallic stearate	0.5

(3) *Semi-flexible Sheet*

Material	Parts
BLENDEX 101	40
PVC (GP-5)	60
Plasticizer	30
Organo tin mercaptide	1.5-2.0
Antioxidant	0.5
Metallic stearate	0.5
Color pigments	Q.S.

(4) *Injection Molding – Opaque*

Material	Parts
BLENDEX 111	40
PVC (GP-1 or GP-2)	60
Color Pigments	Q. S.
Metallic stearate	0.75
Organo tin mercaptide	2.00
Ethylene bis stearamide	0.75

[a] BLENDEX Registered Trademark of Borg-Warner.

J. R. MARTIN

ACETIC ACID

Acetic acid, CH_3COOH, is a waterlike colorless liquid, with a sharp odor, and a biting, fiery taste. Its dilute aqueous solution, vinegar, has a characteristic sour taste. Vinegar obtained by souring of wine or beer has been known from antiquity, and has been used for food flavoring and preservation. Current industrial production of acetic acid and vinegar amounts to more than a billion pounds annually.

Acetic acid is manufactured mainly by synthesis, and finds application chiefly in the production of cellulose acetate, esters, pharmaceuticals, and metallic acetate salts. Although it is a normal constituent of many foods, and is used as a condiment, solvent, and preservative, highly concentrated acetic acid—*glacial* acetic acid—acts as a powerful irritant to mucous membranes.

Physical Properties

The physical properties of acetic acid are shown in Table 1. Methods for obtaining absolutely pure acetic acid, the solvent properties, electrolytic and related properties are reported.

Chemical Properties

Esterification of acetic acid is easily accomplished with mineral acid or ion exchange resin catalysis. Thus, an alcohol dissolved in a large

TABLE 1. PHYSICAL PROPERTIES OF ACETIC ACID.

Melting point	16.635°C
Boiling point	118.1°C/760 mm of Hg
Density, 20/4	1.04923
Refractive index, 20°C	1.37160
Surface tension, 20°C/air	27.6 dynes/cm
Viscosity	
20°C	1.22 cps.
50°C	0.80 cps
100°C	0.43 cps
Open-cup flash point	135°F
Specific heat	0.534 (liquid) cal/g/°C
Heat of vaporization at boiling point	96.8 cal/g
Heat of combustion at 25°C	208.7 kcal/mol

excess of acetic acid can react to yield the acetate ester with a very low level of acid catalyst concentration:

$$R—OH + CH_3COOH \rightarrow CH_3COO—R + H_2O$$

The reaction can be accelerated by addition of an entraining agent, e.g., benzene, toluene, etc., to the reaction mixture and distilling over the water as it forms. Acetate esters are used as solvents for plastics and resins, as plasticizers and conditioning agents, and lubricants. Unsaturated acetates, especially vinyl acetate, are important monomers.

Acetate salts are formed by neutralization of the acid or by saponification of the esters. Sodium acetate has some application as a dyestuff mordant, in photography, and, when crystallized from glacial acetic acid to furnish sodium diacetate, it serves as a bread mold inhibitor. A number of antifungal agents are made from other acetate salts, e.g., lead acetate, copper acetate, zinc acetate.

Pyrolysis of acetic acid yields ketene, which can be condensed with more acetic acid to give acetic anhydride:

$$CH_3COOH \rightarrow CH_2 : C : O + H_2O$$

$$CH_2 : C : O + CH_3COOH \rightarrow (CH_3CO)_2O$$

Neutralization of acetic acid with ammonia gives ammonium acetate, which can be distilled to yield acetamide, a mousy-smelling, crystalline solid used to some extent as a solvent and softener:

$$CH_3COOH + NH_3 \rightarrow CH_3COONH_4$$

$$CH_3COONH_4 \rightarrow CH_3CONH_2 + H_2O$$

Further dehydration of acetamide to acetonitrile occurs at higher temperatures:

$$CH_3CONH_2 \rightarrow CH_3CN + H_2O$$

Acetonitrile is important as a solvent in organic syntheses because of its good solvency coupled with a high dielectric constant, an uncommon trait among organic liquids.

Olefins combine with acetic acid in two important ways. Anhydrous acetic acid containing traces of perchloric acid or sulfuric acid combine with olefins to make secondary acetate esters:

$$R—CH : CH_2 + CH_3COOH \rightarrow CH_3COOCH—R \overset{\displaystyle CH_3}{|}$$

In the presence of sodium acetate, sodium persulfate, and acetic acid, olefins combine with acetic acid to give higher carboxylic acids, thus ethylene yields butyric acid:

$$CH_3COOH + CH_2 : CH_2 \rightarrow CH_3CH_2CH_2COOH$$

Small quantities of higher, even-numbered carboxylic acids are produced at the same time.

The reactions of acetic acid are usually considered to be the characteristic reactions of all aliphatic, carboxylic acids.

Synthesis of Acetic Acid. Most of the acetic acid produced in the U.S. is made by air oxidation of acetaldehyde, according to the reaction:

$$CH_3CHO + 1/2O_2 \text{ (air)} \rightarrow CH_3COOH$$

Acetaldehyde is also an important intermediate for many other organic chemicals, such as *n*-butanol, and is made by a variety of processes.

Acetaldehyde from Acetylene. Acetylene, made by hydrolyzing calcium carbide, or from cracking lower petroleum hydrocarbons, is hydrated by absorbing in 20% sulfuric acid. The reaction is catalyzed by mercuric sulfate.

$$CH \equiv CH + H_2O \rightarrow CH_3CHO$$

The product is absorbed in water and recovered by distillation.

Acetaldehyde from Ethylene. Ethylene, obtained from petroleum cracked gases, is first converted to ethanol by absorption in hot concentrated sulfuric acid to form ethyl hydrogen sulfate, and then hydrolyzed with steam to yield the alcohol, as follows:

$$CH_2 : CH_2 + H_2SO_4 \rightarrow CH_3CH_2SO_4H$$

$$CH_3CH_2SO_4H + H_2O \rightarrow CH_3CH_2OH + H_2SO_4$$

Ethanol is partially oxidized with air at high

temperatures, e.g. 500°C, by passing an alcohol-rich air mixture over silver gauze catalyst. Acetaldehyde is thus obtained by an oxidative dehydrogenation:

$$CH_3CH_2OH + 1/2O_2 \text{ (air)} \rightarrow CH_3CHO + H_2O$$

The crude product is absorbed in water and distilled to obtain pure, anhydrous acetaldehyde.

Recently, acetaldehyde has been made directly by oxidation of ethylene with palladium-copper chloride catalysts. The precise mechanism of the sequence of reactions still remains to be cleared up, but the results may be pictured as follows:

In aqueous solutions, ethylene reacts to yield acetaldehyde:

$$(1) \ CH_2 : CH_2 + PdCl_2 + H_2O \rightarrow$$
$$CH_3CHO + Pd + 2HCl$$

The metallic palladium is oxidized then by cupric chloride:

$$(1) \ Pd + 2CuCl_2 \rightarrow PdCl_2 + 2CuCl$$

and the cuprous chloride obtained reacts with oxygen in the presence of hydrochloric acid to regenerate cupric chloride:

$$(3) \ 4CuCl + 4HCl + O_2 \rightarrow 4CuCl_2 + 2H_2O$$

The easy re-oxidation of the cuprous chloride to cupric chloride with air makes the process fully cyclic, and permits very low palladium concentrations to be used. Moiseev and co-workers has proved that substitution of acetic acid for water in this reaction leads to formation of vinyl acetate instead of acetaldehyde.

Oxidation of Acetaldehyde to Acetic Acid. Liquid phase oxidation of acetaldehyde to acetic acid is one of the major production phases. It is operated continuously in a flooded column reactor containing acetic acid solvent and a catalyst, e.g., manganous acetate, by sparging air into the bottom. Pressures of 1–10 atm are used, and the temperature may be controlled by refluxing the mixture gently. Manganese or cobalt acetates are the most favored catalysts, though a considerable number of other substances have been mentioned in patents. The presence of small quantities of copper promotes formation of acetic anhydride in this oxidation.

Other processes for Acetic Acid. Oxidation of aliphatic hydrocarbons such as butane in the liquid phase to furnish acetic acid is a comparatively recent innovation (see Fig.1). Air is sparged into the reaction vessel *a*, which contains an acetic acid solution of butane. The reaction is carried out under high pressure and at a temperature near the critical temperature for butane—hence the acetic acid reaction solvent is particularly important. Cobalt acetate, stearate, or naphthenate may be employed more or less interchangeably as the catalyst, either alone or in combination with other metallic ions. Product is removed as a vapor stream, condensed in the condenser *b*, fed into a surge tank *c*, then delivered to the separator *d*. Water made during the reaction causes the homogeneous liquid phase to separate into two liquid phases and thus creates operating problems. The phase equilibrium under these conditions is quite significant to practical opera-

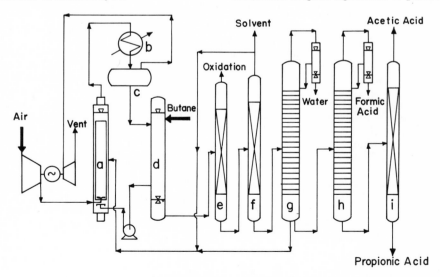

FIG. 1. Acetic acid from butane liquid phase oxidation.

a. Reactor   d. Separator
b. Condenser   e,f,i. Raschig Ring Columns
c. Surge Tank   g,h. Azeotropic Distillation Columns.

tion[9]. The butane-rich layer is returned to the oxidation vessel and the acetic acid-rich layer is passed on to columns *e* and *f* for distillation of butane and the solvents mixture.

In the heavy-ends columns *g* and *h*, water is first removed azeotropically, then formic acid. Finally, the residue from *h* is passed into a finishing column *i* where glacial acetic acid is produced overhead and propionic acid recovered from the bottoms.

Hydroformylation of methanol is another route to acetic acid, now in limited commercial use. Discovered in the 1920's by Henry Dreyfus, this method requires high pressures and temperatures and techniques for handling highly corrosive gases and liquids. A methanol solution of cobalt acetate and potassium iodide containing water is treated with carbon monoxide under about 300 kg/cm² at about 200–260°C, and after a suitable reaction time the acetic acid is recovered.

Recovery of acetic acid from dilute water solutions is very difficult. Although acetic acid has a boiling point 18°C higher than water, sharp separation is not readily achieved owing largely to the unfavorable relative volatility coefficient. The possibility of lowering, in effect, the boiling point of water through the addition of an azeotropic agent has been considered, and several such systems have been developed. Ethyl acetate has been used for acetic acid extraction and azeotropic water removal for a long time. The temperature has little effect on the extraction, and excess water is easily removed on distillation.

A number of other solvents have also been successfully tried.

Uses of Acetic Acid. The greatest single use for acetic acid is in the production of acetic anhydride, which is further consumed in the manufacture of cellulose acetate, cellulose acetate-butyrate, and cellulose acetate-propionate. Lesser amounts of acetic anhydride are used in making vinyl acetate, cellulose triacetate, aspirin and other pharmaceuticals. Indeterminate amounts of acetic acid are used in production of vinyl acetate, saturated esters for solvents, salts, various chlorinated acetic acids, acrylic acid, and acrylate esters.

Manufacture of Acetic Anhydride. One method of making acetic anyhdride is the ketene process. Acetic acid, vaporized under 150 mm pressure, is mixed with triethyl phosphate catalyst and passed into pyrolysis tubes heated to 550-660°C where it is decomposed into ketene and water. Ammonia is injected into the gas stream to neutralize the catalyst, and the gaseous mixture is chilled in coolers kept at −20°C to freeze out the water, catalyst, and unchanged acetic acid. Gaseous ketene is passed into absorbers where it combines with acetic acid to yield acetic anhydride. Figure 2 illustrates the general flow pattern.

Ketene may be made alternatively from acetone according to the equation:

$$CH_3COCH_3 \rightarrow CH_2 : C : O + CH_4$$

Since methane is comparatively inert and has a lower formula weight than water, this route has both chemical and economic advantages.

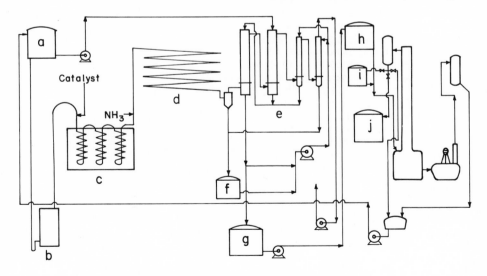

FIG. 2. Acetic anhydride from acetic acid by pyrolysis.

a. Acetic Acid Storage	e. Ketene Absorbers	i. 30% Anhydride
b. Vaporizer	f. 50% Acid	j. 95% Anhydride
c. Furnace	g. 85% Anhydride	
d. Gas Coolers	h. Feed Tank	

Acetic anhydride may also be prepared by direct oxidation of acetaldehyde in acetic acid solvent. A copper-containing catalyst is used. Isopropyl acetate may be employed as a solvent instead of acetic acid, if desired. This Usines de Melle process is commercially used in France, Mexico, Norway, and the USSR.

Cellulose Acetate. Cellulose acetylation is analogous to esterification of simple alcohols, but differs owing to the high degree of association within the cellulose molecules, the necessity for avoiding excessive degradation, and the need for complete acetylation of the cellulose molecules. Cellulose is usually presoaked with acetic acid to condition it for reaction. It is then suspended in methylene chloride and acetic anhydride containing a catalytic quantity of sulfuric acid mixed into it. The amount of acid catalyst is particularly important, inasmuch as combined sulfate causes poor stability and heat resistance of the finished cellulose acetate.

Cellulose is sometimes acetylated in acetic acid solvent. The normal procedure is to charge the presoaked cellulose to the reaction vessel, and add a mixture of acetic anhydride, sulfuric acid, and acetic acid chilled to about 0°C. The liquid is first absorbed, then the mixture becomes semi-solid as the temperature rises, and finally it turns to a viscous syrup. The temperature is allowed to rise to about 35°C where the reaction is usually terminated.

Excess anhydride remaining in the reaction mixture is decomposed with water. Enough additional water is put in to accomplish hydrolysis of the cellulose triacetate to secondary cellulose acetate. Water is usually added as a dilute acetic acid solution. The cellulose acetate dilute acetic mixture is allowed to react slowly in shallow pans at constant temperature and under a controlled atmosphere for several days until the acetyl value falls to the necessary figure. Addition of small amounts of sulfuric acid and heating to slightly higher temperatures permits completion of the hydrolysis in only 3-12 hours. Temperatures up to 60°C are used, though higher temperature increase the rate they also increase the cellulose degradation. When hydrolysis is complete, the methylene chloride is distilled off.

The cellulose acetate is then precipitated with a large volume of water, diluted with acetic acid. Gelatinous and gravy-like precipitates are occasionally obtained through lack of careful control of this step. The precipitate is centrifuged and the dilute acid returned for recycling. Such dilute acid recovery is essential to the economic operation of cellulose acetate processes.

Vinyl Acetate. Vinyl acetate is also made from acetic acid. It is mainly used for production of polyvinyl acetate homopolymer, which finds application in waterbased paints, adhesives, and textile sizing. Substantial amounts of the monomer are used in production of polyvinyl chloride copolymers for films and sheeting, flooring, coatings, etc. Hydrolysis of polyvinyl acetate yields polyvinyl alcohol,* which is used in water-soluble plastic films and adhesives. Acetalization of polyvinyl alcohol furnishes wire-coating material and safety glass interlayer adhesives. Approximately half a billion pounds of vinyl acetate monomer are currently manufactured annually in the United States. Most vinyl acetate is manufactured by passing vaporized acetic acid and acetylene through coke impregnated with cadmium or zinc slats, at about 200°C. The process is clearly described in the literature, and recent patents chiefly mention improvements in catalysts.

An increasing proportion of vinyl acetate production is being supplied by the direct oxidation of ethylene in acetic acid solution with the use of palladium-copper catalysts. Ethylene and oxygen are passed into a solution containing palladium chloride, lithium chloride, and cupric acetate dissolved in anhydrous acetic acid.

Acetate Esters. The saturated esters of acetic acid which find use as solvents or plasticizers for plastics are listed in Table 2.

Most of the simple acetates are good solvents for polyvinyl acetate, cellulose esters and ethers, polymethyl methacrylate, and similar plastics.

TABLE 2. ACETATE ESTER SOLVENTS AND PLASTICIZERS.

	Boiling point/atm	Density D_4^{20}	Refractive index, 20°
Methyl acetate	57.2°	0.928	1.3593
Ethyl acetate	76.7°	0.902	1.3719
Propyl acetate	101.6°	0.887	1.3844
Isopropyl acetate	88.7°	0.870	1.3791
Butyl acetate	126.6°	0.882	1.3942
sec-Butyl acetate	112.2°	0.872	1.3890
tert-Butyl acetate	96.0	0.890	
Isobutyl acetate	116.4°	0.871	1.3997
2-Methoxyethyl acetate	145.1°	1.0067	1.4019
Amyl acetates (mixed)	110–150°	0.857–0.865	
2-Ethoxythyl acetate	156.4°	0.9748	1.4058
Ethylene glycol diacetate	190.8°	1.104	1.415
2-(2-ethoxyethoxy) ethyl acetate	217°	1.0114	1.4213
2-(2-batoxyethoxy) ethyl acetate	246.8°	0.9812	
Triacetin (glyceryl triacetate)	258–260°	1.1560	1.4305

* For details see Polyvinyl Alcohol, page 378.

Esters with higher carbon numbers have increasingly good solvency for nitrocellulose, polystyrene, chlorinated rubber, etc. Some of the higher acetates are also used in ballpoint and printing ink formulations. Several complex esters of acetic acid are used in plasticizers, such as glyceryl monolactate triacetate, acetyl triethyl citrate, butyl acetyl ricinoleate, etc. These compounds often serve in diminishing the volatility of the plasticizer constituents, as well as improving low-temperature flexibility properties of the plastics. Acetates of glycerol, pentaerythritol, sorbitol, and sucrose have been found useful in plasticizing cellulose derivatives. Most of these esters are resistant to hydrocarbon oils, gasoline, kerosine, etc., and impart this resistance to the plastic.

These esters may be prepared by direct esterification with acetic acid, acetic anhydride, or by "transesterification" under comparatively mild conditions with another acetate ester. Direct esterification with acetic acid can be done without a catalyst, but proceeds most efficiently with 0.1–0.5% by weight of toluenesulfonic acid, and with azeotropic removal of the water of reaction. "Transesterification" of a polyol can be done using a reactive ester, e.g., isopropenyl acetate, without a catalyst, or using a less reactive ester, e.g., ethyl acetate, in the presence of zinc acetate or similar catalysts. Most of these esters are not appreciably water-soluble, so they are conveniently recovered by addition of sufficient water to the reaction mixture.

FRANK S. WAGNER, JR.

ACETYLENE

Acetylene (C_2H_2), under normal conditions, is a colorless, odorless, highly reactive and hazardous gas. Burned with oxygen or air, it produces a bright, intense flame suitable for metal working. Its triple bond can be utilized for the production of an extremely broad range of chemicals, although economic considerations currently limit major industrial applications to some five compounds.

In 1836, Edmund Davy, adding water to a mixture of materials containing potassium carbide, was the first man to produce acetylene. Commercial production, by reaction with calcium carbide, began in 1895. All of the acetylene made was used as an illuminant. The manufacture of acetylene-based chemicals began in 1910, and today absorbs approximately 85% of the total acetylene output of the United States.

Production of acetylene from hydrocarbons began in 1940 in Germany and in 1952 in the United States. Twelve years later (1964), more than 40% of the acetylene made in this country was derived from natural gas or heavier hydrocarbons.

Physical Properties

Name	Acetylene (ethyne)
Formula	HC≡CH
Molecular weight	26.04
Sublimation point at 1 atm	−118°F (−83.5°C)
Boiling point at 24.7 psia (1.68 atm)	−103°F (−75°C)
Critical temperature	96°F (35.6°C)
Critical pressure	907 psia (61.6 atm)
Critical density	14.35 lb/ft³ (0.23 g/ml)
Triple point-temperature	−114°F (−81.1°C)
Triple point-pressure	17.7 psia (1.2 atm)
Vapor pressure at 32°F (0°C)	400 psia (27.2 atm)
Flame temperature (approx.)-air	4215°F (2325°C)
Flame temperature (approx.)-oxygen	5430°F (3000°C)
Heat of formation at 64°F (18°C)	3,800 Btu/lb (54.8 kcal/g. mole)
Gross heat of combustion at 68°F (20°C)	21,600 Btu/lb (312.0 kcal/g mole)
Free energy at 77°F (25°C)	3,460 Btu/lb (50.0 kcal/g. mole)
Solubility at 59°F (15°C)	
Water–1 atm	1.1 Vol. of gas (STP) per vol. solvent
Acetone–1 atm	20 Vol. of gas (STP) per vol. solvent
Acetone–12 atm	240 Vol. of gas (STP) per vol. solvent

Manufacture

Aproximately 570,000 tons of acetylene were produced in 1965, a 4% increase over 1964, and a 36% increase over 1960.

The traditional method of making acetylene has been to react calcium carbide with water, and this method still is used to manufacture half of the acetylene produced in the US. However, increasing amounts are being produced from hydrocarbon feedstocks. The trend also is evident in other countries. For example, it was estimated that in 1966 almost 70% of acetylene production in West Germany was based on hydrocarbons, and in England most major producers use naphtha. Factors to be considered in deciding which process to use include not only the capital and operating requirements of the production plant and its gas purification facilities, but also the reliability of electrical versus hydrocarbon energy, the value assigned to the by-product gases produced when acetylene is made from a hydrocarbon, and the supporting technological and economic environment of the country in which the plant is to be located.

From Calcium Carbide. Calcium carbide is formed by passing an electric current through a mixture of lime and coke. Calcium carbide when reacted with water forms acetylene.

$$3C + CaO \rightarrow CaC_2 + CO$$

$$CaC_2 + 2H_2O \rightarrow HC \equiv CH + Ca(OH)_2$$

The slaked lime can be calcined and recycled. To minimize the problem of acetylene purification, both lime and coke must contain minimum amounts of arsenic, sulfur, phosphorus and silicon.

Acetylene generators function either by adding calcium carbide to an excess of water or by adding water to the carbide. In the former case, the slaked lime is discharged as a 10-15% solution, whereas in the latter it is generally recovered substantially dry. Approximately three pounds of CaC_2 are required per pound of acetylene produced. All generators are designed to prevent local overheating of the carbide, which may cause an explosion of the gases; or overheating of the acetylene which, even if not high enough to create a hazardous condition, might result in polymerization or other undesired side reactions.

The crude acetylene must be purified to remove traces of phosphine, silane, arsine, sulphur compounds and undesired hydrocarbons. The extent and type of purification process may vary greatly, depending upon the quality of the raw materials used to produce the acetylene and the end use to which it is put, i.e., for welding or for specific chemical reactions.

From Hydrocarbons. Three basically different methods are used to obtain the energy needed to increase the temperature of a hydrocarbon to the point at which acetylene formation becomes significant, and to supply the endothermic heat of reaction. These may be characterized as partial combustion, indirect heating, and electric arc processes.

In all instances, the gases leaving the reaction zone are quenched immediately to stabilize the acetylene which has been formed.

Partial Combustion or Oxidation. Several processes are in commercial operation today, and others are in the pilot-plant stage. Almost all require the use of oxygen rather than air. A single- or a two-stage reactor may be employed.

In a single-stage reactor, the hydrocarbon feedstock is mixed with oxygen, and undergoes a partial oxidation to produce the desired chemicals. In a two-stage reactor, a hydrocarbon fuel, which may not be the same as the feedstock, is burned with oxygen and the feedstock injected into the hot combustion gases.

Specific processes differ in reactor design and operating conditions, feedstock requirements, extent of co-product ethylene production, and selection of solvents used to separate and purify the reactor effluent.

(1) BASF Process. The most widely used process in 1965 for producing acetylene from hydrocarbons, particularly from natural gas, was that developed by BASF and first placed in commercial operation in 1952. Pre-heated oxygen and methane are piped to the burner at atmospheric pressure, mixed, partially oxidized, and immediately quenched.

The products of reaction are scrubbed to remove carbon, and selective solvents are used to recover the acetylene from the remaining reaction products. These consist of small amounts of unreacted methane and higher hydrocarbons, plus a significant quantity of carbon monoxide and hydrogen. Very little ethylene is formed.

The same basic process, incorporating a modified quench system utilizing a high boiling oil, is used in a commercial plant to produce acetylene from a light naphtha. Ethylene content of the reacted gas remains very low. Again, the effluent gases contain hydrogen and carbon monoxide.

A further modification of the process, designed to produce a mixture of acetylene and ethylene from heavier hydrocarbons (including crude oils) by partial oxidation in a submerged flame under pressure, has been studied in a pilot-plant but has not been employed commercially.

(2) SBA Process. Although the burner design is different, the basic concept of the SBA process is similar to that of the BASF process, particularly when used to produce acetylene from methane. However, when a heavier feedstock is used, not all of the hydrocarbon is mixed with oxygen. Instead a fuel gas is mixed and burned in a combustion chamber, and then the process hydrocarbon injected into the hot gas stream.

After quenching, the reacted gases contain acetylene and ethylene, the ratio of which can be varied, plus carbon monoxide, hydrogen, and hydrocarbon impurities. The gases are separated and purified. Solvents used are not the same as those employed by the BASF process.

(3) Montecatini Process. The reactor is operated at a pressure of approximately four atmospheres. In other basic aspects, this process is similar to the SBA process, although there are major differences in the design of the reactor and of the purification system.

(4) Other Processes. A number of other processes have been developed. Generally, the preferred hydrocarbon feedstock is heavier than methane, a two-stage reactor is used, and ethylene is produced as well as acetylene.

Installations have been based on designs of Dow, Union Carbide, Hoechst, Eastman and Chiyoda. Other reactors have been developed and tested by DuPont, Shell, Delhi-Taylor-HRI and Grinenko (USSR), as well as by Phillips, whose reactor can use either oxygen or air, and by Tsutsumi, whose reactor operates at subatmospheric pressure.

Indirect Heating:

(1) Wulff Process. This is the only process in commercial operation which utilizes indirect heating to produce acetylene. The first semi-

commercial unit was installed in California in 1950, then modified and enlarged in 1952.

The basic feature of the Wulff process is a checkerwork refractory furnace. During the combustion phase, a hydrocarbon fuel is burned with air to heat the refractory. During the production phase, the process hydrocarbon passes over the heated checkerwork and is cracked to produce acetylene and ethylene.

Conditions for the desired reaction are favored by low hydrocarbon partial pressure and short residence time in the furnace, these being achieved by operation under partial vacuum and the addition of diluent steam. Not less than two furnaces are used to provide a continuous flow of all process streams.

Leaving the furnace, the cracked gases are quenched, compressed, and purified, Selected solvents are used to remove acetylene and ethylene, separating them from carbon monoxide, hydrogen and hydrocarbon impurities. The process is particularly suitable for use with feedstocks heavier than methane, and can be operated over a very wide ratio of acetylene to ethylene.

(2) Happel-Kramer-Othmer Process. A number of pilot-plants have been used to test this process. Methane, or other hydrocarbon having a molecular weight not exceeding that of a light naphtha, is passed through a heated annular reactor. A low partial pressure of reactants is attained by vacuum operation and/or hydrogen dilution. High yields per pass simplify the purification step of the process.

To insure accurate temperature control and facilitate experimentation, all reactors are heated electrically. However, in a commercial unit, it may be possible to supply the required energy by burning a hydrocarbon fuel. The quenched product consists almost entirely of acetylene and hydrogen, although some ethylene can be produced if so desired.

(3) Kunugi Process. This process is similar to the Wulff process. The regenerative furnace is operated at close to atmospheric pressure and uses hydrogen as a diluent. Both methane and higher hydrocarbons have been used as the hydrocarbon feed stream.

Electric Arc. There are only two commercial processes which apply the energy of an electric arc to the production of acetylene. Both employ direct current. A number of other processes have been pilot-planted, including some which use an alternating current arc or a plasma jet (compressed arc).

(1) Huels Process. The first commercial plant to produce acetylene from hydrocarbons was placed in operation in Germany in 1940, utilizing a Huels arc furnace. Any of a wide variety of gaseous hydrocarbons may be used as a feedstock.

As the gas enters a furnace, a swirling motion is imparted to the stream, and it is passed through an elongated electric arc. This motion causes the striking point of the arc to rotate, stabilizing the arc and tending to equalize temperatures.

Liquid hydrocarbons, introduced below the arc, quench the gas stream and are pyrolyzed to form ethylene. The gaseous mixture is subsequently quenched with water. Leaving the furnace, the gases are scrubbed to remove carbon and to recover acetylene, ethylene, and hydrogen. Remaining hydrocarbons are recycled to the furnace.

When methane is fed to the furnace, and the hydrocarbon quench eliminated, the cracked gas mixture contains essentially acetylene, hydrogen, and unreacted methane.

(2) DuPont Process. The basic concept of the arc furnace is similar to that used in the Huels process. However, the DuPont process uses a rotating electromagnetic field to extend and stabilize the arc.

(3) Other Processes. The Knapsack process uses an alternating current electric arc to heat and partly disassociate hydrogen. This hot gas serves as an intermediate fluid which transmits energy to a hydrocarbon stream, splitting it to produce acetylene, ethylene, hydrogen, and methane.

The Schoch process uses a rotating electrode to blow a hydrocarbon gas stream between the electrodes of an alternating current arc. The Brno process employs an alternating current arc, a gaseous hydrocarbon feed and a liquid hydrocarbon quench.

The Ediger and other processes are based on the discharge of an alternating current arc submerged in a liquid hydrocarbon bath.

Because of the very high temperatures which are generated by constricting an electric arc, thus forming a plasma jet, this procedure is a potentially attractive means of producing acetylene. A number of processes have been studied. The most promising methods, at this time, are based on the production of an argon plasma, followed by introduction of methane into the jet.

Industrial Usage

Of the total acetylene consumed, approximately 85% is used to produce other organic chemicals and the remainder burned in a torch, using either oxygen or air, to cut or weld metals. In both applications, acetylene faces strong competition—in the first, primarily from the use of ethylene or propylene as raw materials; and in the second, primarily from the use of electric arc equipment. At the present time, the price of acetylene is higher than that of the olefins with which it competes, and an increasing number of processes are being developed, and plants built, to utilize these lower cost, higher molecular weight compounds.

However, before a process selection is made, two additional factors must be reviewed:

First, every plant constructed to produce acetylene will also produce a valuable c-o product, which may be ethylene, hydrogen or a hydrogen-carbon monoxide synthesis gas mixture.

Second, a process based on acetylene may require fewer steps and therefore be less costly and more efficient than one based on olefins.

Over half the acetylene used by the chemical industry is converted into vinyl chloride and neoprene. Other significant amounts are used to manufacture acrylonitrile, vinyl acetate, and trichloroethylene. Relatively small amounts are used to produce Reppe chemicals, carbon black, and other materials.

Very brief descriptions of the methods used industrially to produce these chemicals from acetylene and from alternate raw materials are noted below. All production figures apply to the United States.

Vinyl Chloride

Approximately 940,000 tons of vinyl chloride were manufactured in 1965, a 20% increase over 1964, and almost double the production of five years ago. Substantially all of this material was utilized in 1965 to produce 915,000 tons of homopolymers and copolymers, or approximately 80% of the total production of vinyl plastics. Vinyl chloride-based polymers are processed chiefly by calendering operations, forming sheet, film and flooring. Substantial amounts are extruded to produce wire, cable, hose, pipe, and, recently, fiber. Additionally, substantial amounts are used as coating, bonding, or adhesive materials for paper, textile, and flooring materials; molded to produce records and blow-molded to manufacture bottles. It is anticipated that large amounts of these polymers will be used in the construction and packaging industries in the next few years.

Vinyl chloride is produced from acetylene by a catalytic vapor phase reaction with hydrogen chloride:

$$HC\equiv CH + HCl \rightarrow H_2C=CHCl$$

In contrast, there are two alternate processes for producing vinyl chloride from ethylene:

(1) The first consists of reacting ethylene with chlorine to produce ethylene dichloride ($ClCH_2-CH_2Cl$), followed by dehydrochlorination to produce vinyl chloride. In this process, a method must be found for disposing of the liberated hydrogen chloride. If the plant complex contains a hydrocarbon cracking process which produces both acetylene and ethylene, the hydrogen chloride can be utilized by reacting it with acetylene, as noted in the process above.

(2) The second, and newer process, consists of reacting ethylene, hydrochloric acid and oxygen (or air) over an oxyhydrochlorination catalyst to produce ethylene dichloride and water. As before, the ethylene dichloride is then dehydrochlorinated, and the hydrochloric acid by-product recycled to the first step. Fresh feed may be chlorine, in a "balanced" process, or by-product hydrochloric acid from other chlorination processes.

Neoprene

Approximately 170,000 tons of neoprene were produced in 1965, a 12% increase over 1964 and a 40% increase over 1960. Consumption is not expected to increase substantially in the next few years.

Neoprene is used as a synthetic rubber which is resistant to attack by oil, grease, heat, and sunlight. At one time, neoprene was used extensively as a covering for wire and cables, but in recent years its application in this area has been superseded by other elastomers.

Neoprene is produced by: (1) the catalytic polymerization of acetylene in an aqueous solution of chlorides, forming dimers and trimers. (2) The separated dimer, vinylacetylene, is reacted with hydrogen chloride to form chloroprene, and (3) the latter polymerized to produce neoprene:

(1) $\quad 2HC\equiv CH \rightarrow H_2C=CH-C\equiv CH$

(2) $\quad H_2C=CH-C\equiv CH + HCl \rightarrow$
$$H_2C=CH-CCl=CH_2$$

(3) $\quad n(H_2C=CH-CCl=CH_2) \rightarrow$
$$-(H_2C-CH=CCl-CH_2)-_n$$

At present, substantially all neoprene is produced from acetylene. However a new process based upon the chlorination of butadiene is being developed.

Acrylonitrile

Approximately 385,000 tons of acrylonitrile were produced in 1965, a one-third increase over 1964 and more than three times the production of five years ago.

Homopolymers and copolymers of acrylonitrile are used to produce acrylic fibers such as Orlon and Acrilan; to produce oil resistant rubbers; and as a coating for cotton fabrics. Production of acrylonitrile-butadiene-styrene (ABS), used for automobile and appliance parts, is growing rapidly; as is the production of styrene-acrylonitrile (SAN) and butadiene-acrylonitrile polymers. Also some acrylonitrile is converted electrolytically into adiponitrile, used to produce nylon.

Acrylonitrile is produced from acetylene by the catalytic addition of hydrocyanic acid:

$$HC\equiv CH + HCN \rightarrow H_2C=CH-CN$$

In addition, some acrylonitrile is produced by reacting ethylene oxide with hydrocyanic acid to produce ethylene cyanohydrin, which is subsequently dehydrated.

Alternative processes have been developed

recently which utilize propylene as the basic raw material, reacting it catalytically with ammonia and oxygen (air).

Vinyl Acetate*

Approximately 250,000 tons of vinyl acetate were produced in 1965, a one-quarter increase over 1964, and twice the production of five years ago.

Homopolymers of vinyl acetate are used primarily as adhesives and as paint emulsions. The polymer also is converted into polyvinyl alcohol,* which is used as a sizing agent, and also converted into polyvinyl butyral and polyvinyl formal. Copolymers with vinyl chloride and with ethylene are molded and also are processed into film and sheeting.

Vinyl acetate is produced from acetylene by the catalytic addition of acetic acid:

$$HC \equiv CH + CH_3-COOH \rightarrow CH_2 = CHOCOCH_3$$

In addition some vinyl acetate is manufactured by reacting acetaldehyde and acetic anhydride to form ethylidene diacetate, the latter being cracked to produce acetic acid and vinyl acetate.

Two processes have been developed recently for the direct production of vinyl acetate from ethylene and acetic acid.

Trichloroethylene

Approximately 220,000 tons of trichloroethylene and 215,000 tons of perchloroethylene were produced in 1965, 20% more than that produced in 1964.

The principal use of trichloroethylene is as a solvent to remove oil and grease from metal surfaces. It is also used as an intermediate in the production of perchloroethylene, a dry cleaning agent.

Trichloroethylene is produced from acetylene by the catalytic addition of chlorine to form tetrachlorethane, followed by dehydrochlorination:

$$HC \equiv CH + 2Cl_2 \rightarrow HCl_2C-CCl_2H$$

$$HCl_2C-CCl_2H \rightarrow HClC = CCl_2 + HCl$$

Perchloroethylene is produced from trichloroethylene by the addition of chlorine to form pentachloroethane, followed by dehydrochlorination:

$$HClC = CCl_2 + Cl_2 \rightarrow HCl_2C-CCl_3$$

$$HCl_2C-CCl_3 \rightarrow Cl_2C = CCl_2 + HCl$$

An alternate process for producing trichloroethylene utilizes ethylene as the basic raw material, adding and substituting chlorine and then dehydrochlorinating. Perchloroethylene also may be made by chlorination of olefins.

* For a more detailed account, see Vinyl Acetate, p. 487, and Polyvinyl Alcohol Ingredients, p. 378.

Carbon Black

Carbon produced by the pyrolysis of acetylene exhibits good electrical properties. Its principal use is as a component in the manufacture of dry-cell batteries.

SIDNEY A. BRESLER

ACRYLIC AND METHACRYLIC ACIDS AND ESTERS

Acrylic acid, $CH_2 = CHCOOH$, and methacrylic acid, $CH_2 = C(CH_3)COOH$, along with crotonic acid, are the simplest members of the family of α, β-unsaturated acids. Though the acids and their esters have long been known, study of the polymers goes back to the doctoral thesis of Otto Röhm in 1901. The serious investigation of commercial possibilities by Dr. Röhm and his associates began after World War I and led to the first commercial production of acrylates and polyacrylates in 1927. Since then, an extensive group of monomers has become available, and applications for the polymers have found a steady growth. In 1964, American capacity for methyl methacrylate and acrylates was estimated to be 300 and 175 million pounds, respectively. Other facilities are in operation in England, France, Germany, Italy, and Japan. Well documented reviews on the chemistry, polymerization, and applications of acrylic monomers have appeared, and should be consulted for a more extensive coverage of this subject, as well as bibliographies.

Commercially Available Monomers

The physical properties of the acids and the principal esters, as reported by American manufacturers, are listed in Tables 1 and 2. Most of the products are single species supplied in high (95–99.9%) purity. Lauryl and stearyl methacrylates are mixtures obtained from the corresponding mixed alcohols whose major components are lauryl or stearyl alcohols. Both solvent-free and solution grades of the hydroxyalkyl methacrylates are supplied; the solution grades contain xylene and minor amounts of methacrylic acid. Though uninhibited grades are available in limited areas, the commercial monomers normally contain small amounts of phenolic inhibitors, such as hydroquinone (HQ) or its monomethyl ether (MEHQ), to insure stability and safety during shipping and storage. The tables cite the principal inhibitor grades offered by American suppliers.

Manufacturing Processes

Acrylates. The first commercial process was based on the stepwise hydrolysis and alcoholysis of ethylene cyanohydrin under strongly acidic conditions. The cyanohydrin is obtained from the base-catalyzed addition of hydrogen cyanide to

15

TABLE 1. PROPERTIES OF ACRYLIC ACID AND ACRYLATE ESTERS.

Compound	Acrylic acid	Methyl acrylate	Ethyl acrylate	n-Butyl acrylate	Isobutyl acrylate	2-Ethylhexyl acrylate
Formula	$CH_2{=}CHCOOH$	$CH_2{=}CHCOOCH_3$	$CH_2{=}CHCOOC_2H_5$	$CH_2{=}CHCOOC_4H_9$	$CH_2{=}CHCOOCH_2CH(CH_3)_2$	$CH_2{=}CHCOOCH_2CH(C_2H_5)C_4H_9$
Formula weight	72.06	86.09	100.11	128.17	128.17	184.27
Boiling range, °C	140–142	79–81	98–100	146–148	61–63 (50 mm)	130 (50 mm)
Freezing point, °C	13	$<{-}75$	−77	−64	−61	−90 (glass)
Refractive index n_D^{25}	1.4185	1.4003	1.4034	1.4160	1.4124	1.4332
Specific gravity, 25/15.6°C	1.045	0.950	0.917	0.894	0.884	0.880
Flash point, °F Tag. open cup		50	50		86	
Cleveland open cup	155			120		195
Explosive limits in air, % By volume, 25°C Lower limit	2.4[a]	2.8	1.8	1.5	1.9	0.9[a]
Upper limit		25	Saturation	9.9	8.0	

TABLE 1 (continued). PROPERTIES OF ACRYLIC ACID AND ACRYLATE ESTERS.

Solubility, g/100 ml of soltuion, 25°C						
In water	∞	5	1.5	0.2	0.2	0.01
Of water	∞	2.5	1.5	0.7	0.6	0.15
In organic solvents	Soluble in most common solvents					
Heat of vaporization, cal/g	151.5	92	83	67	71	61
Heat capacity cal/g/°C	0.50	0.48	0.47	0.46	0.46	0.46
Inhibitor Grades, ppm						
HQ[b]	200, 1000	1000	200, 1000	100		100
MEHQ[c]	200, 1000	15, 50, 200, 1000	15, 50, 200, 1000	5, 50, 100	100	50, 100
Phenothiazine	1000					

[a] Does not explode at 25°C.   [b] HQ = Hydroquinone.   [c] MEHQ = Monomethyl ether of HQ.

TABLE 2. PROPERTIES OF METHACRYLIC ACID AND METHACRYLATE ESTERS.

Compound	Methacrylic acid	Methyl methacrylate	Ethyl methacrylate	n-Butyl methacrylate	Isobutyl methacrylate	Lauryl methacrylate
Formula	$CH_2{=}CCOOH$ $\mid$ CH_3	$CH_2{=}CCOOCH_3$ $\mid$ CH_3	$CH_2{=}CCOOC_2H_5$ $\mid$ CH_3	$CH_2{=}CCOOC_4H_9$ $\mid$ CH_3	$CH_2{=}CCOOCH_2CH(CH_3)_2$ $\mid$ CH_3	$CH_2{=}CCOO(CH_2)_nCH_3$ [a] $\mid$ CH_3
Formula weight	86.09	100.11	114.14	142.19	142.19	262
Boiling range, °C	159–163	100–101	116–119.5	162–163	155	230–349
Freezing point, °C	14					−22
Refractive index, n_D^{25}	1.4288	1.4120	1.4116	1.4220	1.4170	1.444
Specific gravity, 25/15.6°C	1.015	0.939	0.909	0.889	0.883	0.868
Flash point, °F Tag open cup		55	80		120	
Cleveland open cup	170		95	150		270
Explosive limits in air, % by volume, 25°C Lower limit		2.12	1.8			
Upper limit		12.5	Saturation			

TABLE 2 (*continued*). PROPERTIES OF METHACRYLIC ACID AND METHACRYLATE ESTERS.

Solubility, g/100 ml of solution, 25°C						
In water	∞	1.5	Essentially insoluble			
Of water	∞	1.25				
In organic solvents	Soluble in most common solvents					
Heat of vaporization, cal/g	86	83				
Heat capacity, cal/g	0.50–0.55	0.45	0.45			
Inhibitor grades, ppm						
HQ[b]	1000	25, 60	25, 60, 100	25, 100	25, 60	100
MEHQ[c]	100, 250	10, 50, 100	15	10	10	
BHT[d]	35					

[a] n = 11–13. [b] HQ = Hydroquinone. [c] MEHQ = Monomethyl ether of HQ. [d] BHT = Butylated Hydroxytoluene.

TABLE 2 (*continued*). PROPERTIES OF METHACRYLIC ACID AND METHACRYLATE ESTERS.

Compound	Stearyl methacrylate	2-Hydroxyethyl[f,g] methacrylate	Hydroxypropyl[f,h] methacrylate	2-Dimethylaminoethyl methacrylate	2-t-Butylaminoethyl methacrylate
Formula	CH_2=$CCOO(CH_2)_nCH_3$[e] $\vert$ CH_3	CH_2=$CCOOCH_2CH_2OH$ $\vert$ CH_3	CH_2=$CCOO(C_3H_6)OH$[i] $\vert$ CH_3	CH_2=$CCOOCH_2CH_2N(CH_3)_2$ $\vert$ CH_3	CH_2=$CCOOCH_2CH_2NHC(CH_3)_3$ $\vert$ CH_3
Formula weight	332	130.14	144.17	157.20	185.25
Boiling range, °C	206–370	95 (10 mm)	96 (10 mm)	68.5 (10 mm)	93 (10 mm)
Freezing point, °C	15	−12	<−70	ca−30	<−70
Refractive index, n_D^{25}	1.4502	1.4505	1.4456	1.4376	1.4400
Specific gravity, 25/15.6°C	0.864	1.064	1.027	0.933	0.914
Flash point, °F Tag. open cup				165	
Cleveland open cup	>300	227 (closed)	250		205
Solubility, g/100 ml of solution, 25°C	Insoluble	∞	Limited	Very soluble	1.8
Of water		∞			
In organic solvents			Soluble in most common solvents		
Heat of vaporization, cal/g	100			75	
Inhibitor grades, ppm HQ[b]		200[f]	200[f]		
MEHQ[c]		380[g]	450[h]	2000	1000

[e] n = 15–17. [f] 96% grade. [g] Also supplied as 30% solution in xylene containing 3% methacrylic acid, 300–400 ppm MEHQ.
[h] Also supplied as 40% solution in xylene containing 6% methacrylic acid, 450 ppm MEHQ.
[i] Approximately 70–30 mixture of 2-hydroxypropyl and (2-hydroxy-1-methyl)-ethyl isomers.

TABLE 2 (*continued*). PROPERTIES OF METHACRYLIC ACID AND METHACRYLATE ESTERS.

Compound	Glycidyl methacrylate	Glycol dimethacrylate	1,3-Butylene dimethacrylate
Formula	$CH_2{=}CCOOCH_2CH{-}CH_2$ with CH_3, O	$[CH_2{=}CCOOCH_2]_2$ with CH_3	$CH_2{=}CCOOCH_2CHOOC{=}CH_2$ with CH_3, CH_3, CH_3
Formula weight	142.15	198.21	226.26
Boiling range, °C	75 (10 mm)	96–98 (4 mm)	110 (3 mm)
Refractive index, n_D^{25}	1.4482	1.4520	1.4502
Specific gravity, 25/15.6°C	1.073	1.048	1.011
Flash point, °F Tag. open cup	183		
Cleveland open cup		235	255
Solubility, g/100 ml of solution, 25°C In water		Essentially insoluble	
In organic solvents		Soluble in most common solvents	
Inhibitor grades, ppm HQ[b]		60	
MEHQ[c]	50		100

ethylene oxide:

$$CH_2\text{---}CH_2 + HCN \xrightarrow{base} HOCH_2CH_2CN \xrightarrow[H+]{H_2O,ROH}$$
$$\underset{O}{\diagdown\diagup}$$
$$CH_2\text{=}CHCOOR \quad (1)$$
$$(R\text{=}H \text{ or alkyl})$$

Acrylic acid can be isolated from the crude reaction mixture before the addition of an alcohol.

The carbonylation of acetylene with alcohols or water and carbon monoxide in the presence of nickel compounds is a more recently developed route. The reaction may proceed stoichiometrically in acidic media under mild conditions using nickel carbonyl as the source of carbon monoxide (Eq. 2), or catalytically with carbon monoxide and nickel salts under pressure at elevated temperature (Eq. 3). The two processes can be combined in a semicatalytic operation when the stoichiometric process is established first and the reaction is then continued by adding the reactants continuously in carefully controlled proportions. If acrylic acid is isolated, subsequent esterification with alcohols provides the esters:

$$4CH\text{=}CH + 4ROH + 2H^+ + Ni(CO)_4 \rightarrow$$
$$4CH_2\text{=}CHCOOR + Ni(II) + 2(H) \quad (2)$$

$$CO + CH\text{=}CH + H_2O \xrightarrow[tetrahydrofuran]{Ni(II)}$$
$$CH_2\text{=}CHCOOH \xrightarrow[H+]{ROH} CH_2\text{=}CHCOOR \quad (3)$$

In another process, propiolactone produced from ketene and formaldehyde is polymerized and hydrolytically depolymerized to acrylic acid or is converted to the esters by reaction with alcohols under pyrolytic conditions:

$$CH_2\text{=}C\text{=}O + CH_2O \rightarrow \underset{\underline{\quad\quad O\quad\quad}}{CH_2\text{---}CH_2\text{---}CO} \rightarrow$$

$$\underset{\underline{\quad\quad O\quad\quad}}{CH_2\text{---}CH_2\text{---}CO_x} \xrightarrow{H_2O} CH_2\text{=}CHCOOH \quad (4)$$

The oxidation of propylene to acrylic acid and the acidic alcoholysis of acrylonitrile have been described:

$$CH_2\text{=}CHCH_3 \xrightarrow[cat]{O_2,H_2O} CH_2\text{=}CHCOOH$$

$$CH_2\text{=}CHCN \xrightarrow[H_2O]{H+} CH_2\text{=}CHC\overset{\displaystyle O}{\diagup}\underset{\diagdown NH_3^+}{} \xrightarrow{ROH} \quad (5)$$

$$CH_2\text{=}CHCOOR + NH_4^+ \quad (6)$$

Methacrylates. The principal manufacturing method is the hydrolysis and alcoholysis of acetone cyanohydrin. Methacrylic acid or methacrylamide can be isolated by modification of the workup procedures:

$$(CH_3)_2C\text{---}CN \xrightarrow{H_2SO_4}$$
$$\underset{OH}{|}$$
$$\underset{CH_3}{\overset{|}{CH_2\text{=}CCONH_3^+HSO_4^-}} \xrightarrow[H+]{ROH} \underset{CH_3}{\overset{|}{CH_2\text{=}C\text{---}COOR}} \quad (7)$$

The oxidation of isobutylene with nitric acid and oxides of nitrogen is a new process whereby methacrylic acid is obtained after several intermediate stages:

$$CH_2\text{=}C(CH_3)_2 \xrightarrow{N_2O_4,H_2O}$$
$$\underset{OH}{\overset{|}{(CH_3)_2CCOOH}} \rightarrow \underset{CH_3}{\overset{|}{CH_2\text{=}CCOOH}} \quad (8)$$

Special Methods. The above methods are the industrial sources of the acids and of the methyl and ethyl esters as primary products. Esters of higher alcohols, substituted alcohols, or polyhydric alcohols are obtained by direct esterification of the acids or by transesterification of the lower esters using appropriate catalysts chosen from mineral acids or from the alkoxides of alkali metals, aluminium, or titanium:

$$\underset{R'}{\overset{|}{CH_2\text{=}CCOOH}} + ROH \xrightarrow{H^+}$$
$$\underset{R'}{\overset{|}{CH_2\text{=}CCOOR}} + H_2O \quad (9)$$

$$\underset{R'}{\overset{|}{CH_2\text{=}CCOOCH_3}} + ROH \xrightarrow{cat.}$$
$$\underset{R'}{\overset{|}{CH_2\text{=}CCOOR}} + CH_3OH \quad (10)$$

$$(R'\text{=}CH_3\text{---} \text{ or } H\text{---})$$

The addition of the acids to epoxy compounds provides the hydroxyalkyl esters:

$$\underset{CH_3}{\overset{|}{CH_2\text{=}CCOOH}} + CH_2\text{---}CH_2 \rightarrow$$
$$\underset{\diagdown O \diagup}{}$$
$$\underset{CH_3}{\overset{|}{CH_2\text{=}C\text{---}COOCH_2CH_2OH}} \quad (11)$$

Glycidyl methacrylate forms from the reaction of epichlorohydrin and the alkali salts of the acids:

$$\underset{CH_3}{\overset{|}{CH_2\text{=}C\overset{-\ +}{COONa}}} + CH_2\text{---}CHCH_2Cl \rightarrow$$
$$\underset{\diagdown O \diagup}{}$$
$$\underset{CH_3}{\overset{|}{CH_2\text{=}CCOOCH_2CH\text{---}CH_2}} + NaCl \quad (12)$$
$$\underset{\diagdown O \diagup}{}$$

Chemical Reactions

Though the principal interest of acrylic compounds lies in their conversion to polymeric products, they have an extensive chemistry which is founded on the reactivity of the unsaturated site and the carbonyl group. The displacement of the ester function by higher alcohols, mentioned above, has commercial importance. Substances capable of addition to the double bond include dienes (Diels–Alder reaction), active hydrogen compounds, such as hydrogen halides, alcohols and phenols, amines and ammonia, thiols, acids, nitroparaffins, etc., halogens and active halogen compounds, active methylene compounds, such as certain esters, nitriles, and ketones, acetylene, and olefins. The esters can condense with themselves to form oligomers, and they can react with telogens such as mercaptans or carbon tetrahalides. They can also undergo electrolytic hydrodimerization with themselves or other α, β-unsaturated compounds to give difunctional derivatives. Certain simultaneous reactions of both reactive sites are also known.

The acids undergo reactions typical of carboxylic acids to provide derivatives such as acyl chlorides, anhydrides, esters, and salts. The chlorides and anhydrides are frequently utilized in the laboratory preparation of substituted amides, esters, and other compounds.

Polymerization

Acrylic monomers can be polymerized by free radical or anionic processes. Anionic initiation has been studied intensively, because crystalline acrylic polymers may be obtained in this way. Industrial processes using free radical formers, such as peroxides, hydroperoxides, persulfates, and azo compounds are by far the most important. Illumination with electromagnetic radiation or electron beams has also been widely examined. Photoinitiated processes may be in use for special applications, as in the manufacture of printing reliefs or in photography, and in the preparation of graft copolymers. Since homogeneous or heterogeneous media may be used, the selection of a process is usually decided by the requirements of the ultimate applications.

Acrylics are easily homopolymerized and enter readily into copolymerizations with acrylic and other monomers. Table 3 lists the initial rates of polymerization measured in bulk or solution at 44.1°C and 60°C and the heats of polymerization for the more common acrylic materials. Table 4 gives their monomer reactivity ratios with styrene and the Price-Alfrey copolymerization parameters. This table also contains the glass transition temperatures, T_g, of acrylic homopolymers, since many properties of polymeric products, such as hardness, flexibility, flow, and the temperature of film formation are related to T_g. An approximate calculation of T_g for copolymers is obtained from the values for the homopolymers using the relation:

$$\frac{1}{T_g} = \frac{w_1}{T_{g1}} + \frac{w_2}{T_{g2}} + \cdots \frac{w_n}{T_{gn}} \qquad (13)$$

where T is expressed in degrees Kelvin, and w is the weight per cent of each component. Consideration of the property contributions and T_g relations of copolymer systems furnishes a guide to the selection of appropriate compositions for applications.

The high purity of commercial acrylic monomers permits their use in most polymerization reactions without preliminary treatment. The more highly inhibited grades may exhibit long induction periods and may require the addition of large amounts of initiators to overcome the inhibitor. These disadvantages are alleviated by the use of the lowest inhibitor grades. Although they are fully inhibited and therefore stable in storage, the low inhibitor grades of acrylic monomers are converted with maximum efficiency to polymers. The practice of removing shipping inhibitors before reaction is therefore needless in all save the most demanding applications. If uninhibited monomers are really necessary, the inhibitors can be removed, with varying efficiency,

TABLE 3. RATES AND HEATS OF POLYMERIZATION OF ACRYLIC ESTERS.

Monomer	$k_p k_t^{-1/2}$		k^a		ΔH, kcal/mole
	44.1°C	60°C	44.1°C	60°C	
Methyl acrylate	0.982[b]	1.93[b]	250[b]	1480[b]	18.8
Ethyl acrylate	1.23[b]	2.27[b]	313[b]	1730[c]	18.6
Butyl acrylate	1.27[b]		324[b]		18.5
2-Ethylhexyl acrylate	1.52[b]		457[b]		14.5
Methyl methacrylate	0.105[c]	0.161[c]	27[c]	123[c]	13.8
Ethyl methacrylate	0.123[b]	0.167[c]	25[b]	128[b]	13.8
Butyl methacrylate	0.182[c]	0.207[c]	41[b]	158[c]	14.2
Isobutyl methacrylate					14.3
Dodecyl methacrylate	1.34[c]		346[c]		
Dimethylaminoethyl methacrylate	0.260[c]		66[c]		
t-Butylaminoethyl methacrylate	0.195[c]	0.291[c]	50[c]	222[c]	
Methacrylic acid	0.278[c]		71[c]		13.5

[a] From the equation, initial rate of polymerization (in % per hr) $= k\sqrt{[\text{AIBN}]}$ where $k = 3.6 \times 10^5 \dfrac{k_p}{k_t^{1/2}} (fk_d)^{1/2}$, k_p and k_t being the rates of propagation and termination of the polymer chains, respectively, k_d the rate of dissociation of the initiator, and f the efficiency of the initiator, all at the temperature of measurement.
[b] Measured in solution.
[c] Measured in bulk.

TABLE 4. MONOMER REACTIVITY RATIOS AND PRICE-ALFREY COPOLYMERIZATION
PARAMETERS FOR ACRYLIC MONOMERS (M_1) AND STYRENE (M_2).
GLASS TRANSITION TEMPERATURES (T_g) OF ACRYLIC POLYMERS.

Monomer, M_1	r_1	r_2	Q	e	T_g, °C
Methyl acrylate	0.18 ± 0.02	0.75 ± 0.07	0.43	0.60	8
Ethyl acrylate	0.16 ± 0.04	1.01 ± 0.14	0.34	0.58	−22
n-Butyl acrylate	0.18 ± 0.01	0.88 ± 0.03	0.38	0.56	−54
2-Ethylhexyl acrylate	0.26 ± 0.02	0.94 ± 0.07	0.41	0.39	−85
Acrylic acid	0.19 ± 0.02	0.22 ± 0.01	1.09	0.98	—
Methacrylic acid	0.74 ± 0.04	0.09 ± 0.01	2.37	0.83	—
Methyl methacrylate	0.46 ± 0.02	0.52 ± 0.02	0.74	0.40	105
Ethyl methacrylate	0.33 ± 0.03	0.55 ± 0.06	0.64	0.50	65
n-Butyl methacrylate	0.47 ± 0.06	0.52 ± 0.06	0.74	0.39	20
Isobutyl methacrylate	0.40 ± 0.02	0.55 ± 0.02	0.68	0.43	48
Lauryl methacrylate	0.52 ± 0.02	0.56 ± 0.03	0.71	0.32	−65
2-Hydroxyethyl methacrylate	0.65^a	0.57^a	0.93	0.4	55
Hydroxypropyl methacrylate	0.65 ± 0.02	0.56 ± 0.02	0.79	0.20	—
Glycidyl methacrylate	0.55	0.45	0.86	0.38	—
Dimethylaminoethyl methacrylate	0.37 ± 0.01	0.53 ± 0.02	0.68	0.48	18
t-Butylaminoethyl methacrylate	0.83 ± 0.06	0.47 ± 0.05	0.98	0.17	33

Calculated from the values $r_1 = 1.25$, $r_2 = 0.89$ (M_2 = methyl methacrylate).

by extraction with alkaline solutions, distillation, or adsorption on Amberlyst ion exchange resins. Since the Amberlyst resins readily adsorb hydroquinone, uninhibited monomers are conveniently obtained by starting with grades containing this inhibitor.

Oxygen is also an effective inhibitor which may cause long induction periods. Acrylic monomers are usually stored in contact with the atmosphere so that the removal of oxygen prior to polymerization is usually advisable. Before the addition of initiators, the monomers are normally degassed *in vacuo* or by passage of a stream of inert gas (nitrogen, carbon dioxide) through the reaction mixture, and an inert atmosphere is then maintained. Reaction under reflux is another effective way to exclude oxygen, though this is usually combined with an inert atmosphere.

The reaction conditions are important not only in controlling the evolution of heat, but also for their effect on molecular weight and particle size (in dispersion processes). Discussions of these effects are available in the standard treatises on polymerization. The selection of solvents, however, has specific interest. The solubility parameter, θ, of acrylic ester polymers and copolymers, ranges from about 8–9.7. Acrylic polymers are soluble in the corresponding monomers and in organic solvents having similar values of θ, such as aromatic hydrocarbons, esters, and aliphatic ketones. These solvents are acceptable media for polymerization and for lacquers.

Poly(acrylic acid) and poly(methacrylic acid) are insoluble in the monomeric acids. The degree of solubility in water can be affected by the mode of preparation and varies with the molecular weight, temperature, and tacticity; they dissolve more readily in aqueous solutions of bases such as alkalis, ammonia, and amines. The aqueous solubility of copolymers containing these acids is similar to the homopolymers, but at a reduced level related to the carboxyl content. Aqueous solutions or dispersions of the polyacids or acidic copolymers increase dramatically in viscosity with increasing pH. Such products are normally prepared at mildly acidic pH, because the undissociated acid polymerizes much more rapidly than the corresponding anion. The pH is therefore adjusted to provide the desired solubility and viscosity after the conversion of monomers is completed.

Applications

Castings. A major application is the manufacture of sheets, tubes, rods, and embedded products from methyl methacrylate. These shapes are used in shatter-resistant glazing for aircraft and buildings, signs, decorative panels, electrical lighting fixtures, showcases, and other applications which take advantage of the brilliance, sparkling clarity, high transparency, and weathering resistance of poly(methyl methacrylate). Colored products of great beauty can be produced by the incorporation of colorants and pigments into the casting mixtures. Other shapes can be made readily by forming the heated plastic under vacuum or with air pressure in suitable molds. The plastics can also be machined and polished with conventional machine tools.

The smooth surfaces of acrylic sheets result from manufacture in clamped molds made up from sheets of glass which are separated and sealed with flexible spacers and gaskets. The duration of the polymerization, which is carefully programmed between 45–90°C, depends on the thickness of the mold and the composition of the casting mixture. Casting mixtures may be composed of monomers containing a peroxide or azo initiator; a catalyzed syrup of partially polymerized monomer may also be used. The shrinkage occurring during the cure is about 20% after starting from monomer and a correspondingly smaller amount when syrups are employed. For special applications preshrunk or annealed grades of sheet may be needed. In most cases, however, unshrunk sheets are preferred for their flatness and freedom from warping.

Rods can be cast by the addition of monomer or syrups to cylindrical aluminum or nylon molds which are gradually lowered into a water bath. Tubes are made similarly in a spinning mold. Biological specimens and metal objects are embedded in acrylic plastic by immersing the dried materials in a casting mixture within a mold. When embedded biological substances are to be sliced for examination, softer polymers or copolymers obtained from higher alkyl methacrylates or hydroxyalkyl methacrylates are convenient.

Molding Powders. Polymerization of methyl methacrylate or its mixtures with other monomers by a suspension process provides polymers in the form of tiny beads. A small amount of surfactant or colloidal dispersant is added to the mixture of monomer, water, and oil-soluble initiator. The rate of agitation and the concentration of dispersant are the primary factors which govern the average size of the beads. The dried beads are extruded into rods which are then chopped up into pellets used for molding operations. Three ASTM grades of acrylic molding powders, classified in accordance with their heat distortion temperature, are available commercially. Colorants, pigments, and fillers can be incorporated by preblending and extrusion before use in injection molding processes. Flat, patterned, corrugated, and embossed sheets, as well as a wide variety of other shapes, are made conveniently from acrylic molding powders by extrusion or injection processes.

Rubbers. Vulcanizable rubbers, based on polymers of ethyl or butyl acrylates or their copolymers with acrylonitrile, styrene, or dienes, are prepared by emulsion processes. Though the latexes may serve in coating and adhesive applications, the principal interest is in the coagulated dried polymers. To facilitate the curing process, minor amounts of halogen-containing monomers, such as chloroethyl vinyl ether, are usually incorporated into the acrylic polymer. Various curing recipes have been described, but a recent tendency is toward rapid mild cures. The most important feature of acrylic rubbers is their excellent resistance to sulfur-containing lubricants at temperatures up to 350°F, and they are therefore used in automotive gasket and sealant applications.

Coatings and Related Applications. Most acrylic resins for coatings and related applications are copolymers composed entirely of acrylic monomers or of mixtures with other common comonomers and are available as aqueous latexes or organic solutions. Latexes have the advantages of high molecular weight, freedom from the hazards and expense of solvents, and speed in film formation and drying. Because of their lower molecular weight and nonparticulate nature, solution coatings show better flow, gloss, and transparency. The wide-ranging copolymerizability of the family of acrylic monomers offers a broad selection of copolymer products whose physical properties can thus be modified to fit consumers' requirements. Many acrylic products are thermoplastic copolymers of the esters, into which minor amounts of acrylic or methacrylic acids are incorporated to improve adhesion. In latexes, the acids also impart mechanical and storage stability and increase resistance to freeze-thaw cycling.

Thermosetting or self-curing compositions constitute a major new extension of the utility of acrylic resins in coatings and other fields of application. The resins, which can be prepared in solution or emulsion, are basically thermoplastics into which minor amounts of monomers bearing carboxyl, amido, hydroxyl, amino, or epoxy functions are incorporated. After formulation and application of the coating to the substrate, a cross-linked network forms by reaction of the functional groups with themselves or with those of other added chemicals or polymers. The cure may proceed under ambient conditions or may be forced to completion by the use of catalysts and elevated temperature. Thermoset acrylic coatings show excellent resistance to chemical agents, climatic conditions, and abrasion and outstanding hardness and strength. Similar compositions are used as pigment binders for coating textiles and paper, binders for nonwoven fabrics and wool, rug backings, modifiers for cementitious materials, and impregnants for leather. Polymers having acid or basic components contribute the unique property of removability to floor polishes.

Acrylic monomers and mixtures with styrene can themselves be used as curing agents for unsaturated polyester resins, by copolymerization and cross-linking of the unsaturated sites, and for alkyd resins, by a complex mixture of chain transfer and addition reactions. The cured polyesters have outstanding resistance to weathering and sunlight and, when used as binders in laminates reinforced with glass fabrics, excellent resistance to erosion of the fibers. Methacrylated alkyds dry rapidly in air or on baking to tough, durable, and resistant coatings. A related application for dimethacrylates is their use as reactive plasticizers for poly(vinyl chloride). The processing of vinyls is thereby facilitated and results in moldings with improved surface perfection and increased impact strength.

Thickeners. The effect of pH on the viscosity of poly(acrylic acid) and poly(methacrylic acid) has been mentioned above. This phenomenon is utilized for the thickening of latexes of natural or synthetic polymers used in the backing of rugs and upholstery fabrics, the manufacture of gloves by dipping, and paints.

Storage and Handling

Premature polymerization during storage and shipping is prevented by the addition of shipping inhibitors and the maintenance of a blanket of dry air over the surface of the monomer. Under normal climatic conditions, the fully inhibited grades (Tables 1 and 2) are stable for prolonged periods.

To prevent runaway reactions during the manufacture of polymers, the rate at which the heat of polymerization (Table 3) is evolved and removed must be controlled by various means dependent on the process. In bulk reactions, the temperature schedule is adjusted in accordance with the size and thickness of castings; for very thick pieces, the polymerization may be run under pressure. The rate of heat liberation in solution processes can be governed by gradual addition of the monomers and catalysts and by refluxing of the solvent. Heat is controlled or dissipated during dispersion processes by incremental addition and refluxing of monomers or by absorption in the aqueous phase.

The methyl and ethyl esters of acrylic or methacrylic acid are classed as inflammable materials, and shipping containers must therefore carry ICC Red Labels. The higher acrylates, the methacrylates, and the acids, though less hazardous, are combustible. Within certain limits of concentration, the lower esters form explosive mixtures with air. Adequate precautions, such as flame arresters, static-free hoses and dip pipes, and proper electrical grounding of equipment and lines, must be maintained to avoid a source of ignition. All installations and procedures should conform to local ordinances and the regulations of underwriters and insurance companies.

The esters are noncorrosive materials and are normally stored in mild steel vessels. Though most esters can be stored outdoors, provisions should be made to protect drummed materials from the direct rays of the sun. Storage sheds for drums should be constructed of noncombustible materials and be well ventilated. The presence of moisture tends to promote the formation of popcorn polymer and of rust particles which, in

contact with wet monomer, may also initiate polymerization. Moisture must therefore be excluded from storage facilities by keeping the air blanket in a dry condition and by preventing the seepage of water into storage vessels, lines, and auxiliary equipment. Acrylic and methacrylic acids are highly corrosive to many metals and are stored only in resistant vessels of stainless steel or aluminum or in drums with polyethylene liners. They should be kept from freezing; frozen material must be thoroughly and carefully thawed, preferably at 70–85°F. Acrylic acid forms a dimer whose amount depends on the temperature and duration of storage; dimerization is minimized by storage at 60–75°F.

Acrylic monomers range in toxicity from slight to moderate (Table 5); they may be safely handled without difficulty in appropriate equipment when established safety procedures are followed by properly trained personnel. Methyl acrylate and ethyl acrylate are the most toxic of the esters; the eyes and respiratory mucosa are most liable to injury by these monomers in liquid or vapor form. The maximum recommended concentration of the vapors of methyl acrylate or ethyl acrylate in air is 10 ppm and 25 ppm, respectively. The higher acrylates and the methacrylates are less irritating. The aminoalkyl methacrylates, however, have toxicities on the order of methyl acrylate and are skin irritants. The liquid acids are stongly corrosive to the skin and eyes; the vapors of acrylic acid are also irritating—methacrylic acid much less so.

Protective clothing, such as goggles, face shields, boots, gloves, and aprons should be worn. Damaged protective clothing should be discarded, and clothes wetted by monomers should be removed and laundered before rewearing. If contact with acrylic monomers occurs, the eyes and skin must be flushed or washed with generous amounts of water. Medical attention should be obtained at once after such accidents, especially if the eyes are involved. Personnel displaying toxic symptoms should be removed to an uncontaminated area, and a physician should be summoned promptly.

Analysis of Acrylic Monomers

Gas liquid chromatography provides a convenient, rapid, and specific assay for acrylic esters. Precise chemical methods are also used to determine the unsaturation and saponification equivalent of the esters and the neutralization equivalent of the acids and aminoalkyl esters. Impurities, such as acidity and water, are measured volumetrically with alkali and Karl Fischer reagent, respectively. The principal procedures for inhibitor contents involve spectrophotometric determination of colored derivatives. Polarography is useful for low concentrations of inhibitors and for the residual monomer content of poly-

TABLE 5. TOXICITY OF ACRYLIC MONOMERS.

Monomer	Acute Oral Toxicity Species	LD_{50} mg/kg	Inhalation Toxicity Species	LD_{50} mg/kg	PPM[a]	Time Hr	Acute Percutaneous Toxicity Species	LD_{50} mg/kg	Other Remarks
Methyl acrylate	Rats Mice Rabbits	300 840 180–280	Rats Rabbits	3.8 8.7	1000 2300	4 1	Rabbits	1300	Liquid and vapor corrosive to eye
Ethyl acrylate	Rats Mice Rabbits	1020 1800 280–420	Rats	7.4	1800	4	Rabbits	1800	Liquid corrosive to eye
Butyl acrylate	Rats	3730	Rats[b]	5.3	1000	4	Rabbits	3000	Liquid corrosive to eye
2-Ethylhexyl acrylate	Rats	5660	Rats[c]	1.9	250	8	Rabbits	7500	Inhalation dosage is saturation point
Methyl methacrylate	Rats Dogs Guinea pigs	7900 4700 5900	Rats	50–70	12500– 16500	1/2	Rabbits[c]	35500	Acute intraperitoneal toxicity (LD_{50}): mice 940 mg/kg guinea pigs 1900 mg/kg rats 1700 mg/kg
Ethyl methacrylate	Rats	13300	Rats Rabbit, Guinea pig[c]	12.4–15.0 17.7	2700– 3200 3800	8 8			Acute subcutaneous (LD_{50}): rats about 20000 mg/kg
Butyl methyacrylate	Rats	18000	Rats[c]	5.0		8			
1,3-Butylene dimethacrylate	Rats	14500							
Hydroxypropyl methacrylate	Mice	11200							
t-Butylaminoethyl methacrylate	Rats	1550							Skin irritant[c]
Dimethylaminoethyl methacrylate	Rats	1500							Skin irritant[c]
Acrylic acid	Rats	2655	Rats	c	d	8	Rabbits	1010[c]	Skin irritant, corrosive to eye
Methacrylic acid	Rats	2200	Rats	c			Rabbits Local irritant[c]		Slight eye irritation

[a] Concentration in air.   [b] Killed 5 of 6.   [c] Not lethal.   [d] Concentration not given.

mers. Small amounts of polymer in the monomers can be detected by precipitation from solvents such as aqueous acetic acid, methanol, or "Ultrasene."

LEO S. LUSKIN

ACRYLONITRILE

Before 1940, acrylonitrile was mainly a laboratory curiosity, with no commercial product available and very few known uses for this compound. It first came into prominence in the early years of World War II, when, because of the shortage of natural rubber, it was used in the development of one of the first of the synthetic rubbers, known as "nitrile rubber." Some of this rubber is still being produced, but most of the synthetic rubber is made from styrene-butadiene copolymers.

The real development which has brought about a rapid expansion in the production of acrylonitrile has been its use as the main constituent in acrylic fibers. In the early 1950's, the first of the synthetic acrylic fibers was brought on the market under the tradename of "Orlon," by du Pont. This was quickly followed by similar acrylic fibers under the tradenames of "Acrilan" by Chemstrand, "Dynel" by Union Carbide, "Creslan" by American Cyanamid and "Zefran" by Dow. Since then the production of acrylonitrile has increased rapidly from 50 million pounds in 1955, to 260 million pounds in 1960 and nearly 500 million pounds in 1965. It was not until the late 1950's that acrylonitrile found a use in plastics, and this too has expanded rapidly during the past few years with the development of the ABS (acrylo-butadiene-styrene) and the AS (acrylo-styrene) types. About 20% of the acrylonitrile produced is used as a co-monomer in plastics, with 60% going into synthetic acrylic fibers, 10% into nitrile rubbers and 10%, for miscellaneous uses.

Production of Acrylonitrile

There have been several processes developed for the production of acrylonitrile over the past 30 years, but only two of these are now used commercially. One of the original processes has only recently been declared obsolete, but it is still considered a commercial possibility with minor improvements.

(1) From Ethylene via Ethylene Oxide. This was one of the first of the commercial processes, which utilizes ethylene oxide, the same intermediate used in the production of ethylene glycols and derivatives. Ethylene oxide is produced cheaply in large quantities, mainly by the air oxidation of ethylene, using a mild oxidation catalyst such as silver and low contact times for a low conversion per pass, according to the following equation:

$$CH_2=CH + 1/2O_2(air) \rightarrow CH_2-CH_2 + CO_2 + H_2O$$
$$\diagdown O \diagup$$

Temperatures in the range of 250–300°C with low pressures of 200 psi are employed. A large excess of ethylene is used to prevent overoxidation. In some of the newer processes, 100% oxygen or enriched air (40% O_2) is being used. Conversions of 20–30% of the ethylene per pass is permitted, giving yields of 70–80% of the oxide, based upon the ethylene consumed.

The second step of the process is the cyanation of the ethylene oxide by addition of aqueous hydrogen cyanide, as shown in the following equation:

$$CH_2-CH_2 + HCN \rightarrow HOCH_2CH_2CN$$
$$\diagdown O \diagup$$

The ethylene oxide is bubbled into the slightly alkaline cyanide solution at 60°C for a nearly quantitative yield of the cyanohydrin product. This is then stripped from the reaction solution by steam distillation and dehydrated in the third step, in vapor phase over alumina at 250–300°C for a 90% yield of the acrylonitrile, according to the following equation:

$$HOCH_2CH_2CN \xrightarrow{-H_2O} CH_2=CHCN + H_2O$$

The acrylonitrile is separated from the water by an azeotropic distillation and further refined by a fractional distillation. This process, devised by American Cyanamid Co., operated successfully for over 20 years but was declared obsolete in 1965.

(2) From Acetylene by Direct Cyanation. Until recently, most acrylonitrile was manufactured from the reaction of acetylene with hydrogen cyanide, according to the following equation:

$$CH\equiv CH + HCN \rightarrow CH_2=CHCN$$

The earlier process employed a liquid-phase batch process, with the acetylene bubbled under slight pressure into hot (80°C), aqueous hydrocyanic acid containing appreciable amounts (25%) of dissolved cuprous chloride, acting as the catalyst. A large molar ratio (10:1) of acetylene was used, with most of it passing through the solution unreacted. Later, the batch process was transformed into a continuous countercurrent tower process. The products and excess acetylene are removed continually from the top of the reactor, absorbing the acrylonitrile in a water scrubber along with traces of by-products such as acetaldehyde, vinylacetylene, etc., and allowing the unreacted acetylene to be recycled to the tower for further reaction. The water scrubber solution containing 1.5% acrylonitrile is stripped by distillation, the crude acrylonitrile dehydrated azeotropically and then refined by a vacuum fractionation. Yields of about 80% have been reported for this process.

Following World War II, it was discovered that the Germans were using a vapor-phase process employing temperatures of 350–400°C and a cuprous cyanide catalyst, with a 10:1 molar ratio of acetylene to hydrogen cyanide for a 90% yield of the acrylonitrile product. Adaptations of this vapor phase process are now in use in the United States.

(3) From Propylene by Amino Oxidation. In 1960, Sohio Chemical Co. announced a new process for the production of acrylonitrile by the combination of oxidation and amination of propylene. By using a mixture of air and ammonia with the propylene, the reaction is carried out at high temperature (450°C/50 psi) and low pressure in vapor phase, as shown in the equation below:

$$CH_2\!=\!CHCH_3 + 1\,1/2\,O_2(air) + NH_3 \rightarrow$$

$$CH_2\!=\!CHCN + 3\,H_2O$$

A slight excess (20–30% or 8–10 moles) of air is used, along with equal molar ratios of propylene, ammonia and steam. A variety of catalysts have been suggested, with the Sohio process using a bismuth phosphomolybdate-type catalyst. Another competitive process reports the use of a silver catalyst precipitated on silica granules. Weight yields of 70–75% are claimed, with considerable amounts (10–15%) of acetonitrile and hydrogen cyanide being formed as by-products.

As in the acetylene process, the products from the reactor are quenched in a series of water scrubbers to absorb the acrylonitrile along with acetonitrile, hydrogen cyanide and any unreacted ammonia. The excess air, nitrogen and unreacted propylene are discharged into the atmosphere. The water scrubber solution is then stripped to recover the acrylonitrile and acetonitrile as the distillate, and these are further refined by fractional distillation. One pound of propylene yields 0.73 lb acrylonitrile, 0.11 lb of acetonitrile and 0.13 lb hydrogen cyanide. The costs of producing acrylonitrile by this process are much less than those of the acetylene process, because of the lower cost of propylene as compared to acetylene. Consequently several of the manufacturers have recently converted to the propylene process.

(4) From Acetaldehyde via Cyanohydrin. This is a new process recently announced in Germany which uses acetaldehyde as the starting material, in a manner similar to the original process using ethylene oxide. Both processes involve a cyanohydrin intermediate, and the basic raw material is ethylene. However, this process makes use of the direct conversion of ethylene to acetaldehyde by the "Wacher Process," developed recently in Germany. The series of reactions involved are shown as follows:

(a) $CH_2\!=\!CH_2 + 1/2\,O_2 \xrightarrow[\text{PdCl}_2\text{ cat.}]{100°C} CH_3CHO$

(Wacher Process)

(b) $CH_3CHO + aq.\ HCN \xrightarrow[\text{alk. cat.}]{60°C} CH_3\overset{\displaystyle OH}{\underset{\displaystyle CN}{CH}}$

(cyanohydrin)

(c) $CH_3\overset{\displaystyle OH}{\underset{\displaystyle CN}{CH}} - H_2O \xrightarrow[\text{H}_3\text{PO}_4\text{ cat.}]{250°C} CH_2\!=\!CHCN$

(acrylonitrile)

Yields of over 80% are claimed.

Properties and Uses

The properties of acrylonitrile are shown in the following table:

Appearance	Colorless liquid
Boiling point, °C/atm	78.5
Melting point, °C	−82
Specific gravity (20°/4°C)	0.8075
Flash point (open cup), °F	32
Ignition temperature, °F	898
Explosive range in air	3.05–17.0%
Toxicity (mm allowable in air)	15 ppm

As mentioned above, most of the acrylonitrile is being used as a monomer in the manufacture of various acrylic fibers, which make up about 20% of the total synthetic fiber market. These acrylic fibers are copolymers containing 80–90% acrylonitrile polymerized with methyl acrylate, vinyl chloride, vinylidene chloride and other co-monomers. Only about 20% of the total production of acrylonitrile is finding its way into plastics, but this outlet has been steadily increasing in recent years. Most of this is used in polymers of the acrylonitrile-butadiene-styrene (ABS) combination. So far, the homopolymers of acrylonitrile have not been found suitable for use in plastics, but efforts are being made to produce high-acrylonitrile co-polymers which may increase the consumption of acrylonitrile in plastics.

J. M. CHURCH

ADDITIVES

Experience has shown that most polymers should not be applied in their original state but are assisted in their usefulness for many purposes by the addition of various ingredients, which, in general, are referred to as *additives*.

This article attempts to enumerate the most important classes of additives and to point out their influence on the properties of the polymers in which they are employed.

Plasticizers.* Many polymers (PVC, Cellulose acetate, etc.) are too hard and brittle for certain commercial moldings, castings and extrusions and have to be *plasticized* by the incorporation of compatible, high boiling, nontoxic, colorless and odorless liquids. The *plasticizers* are usually medium molecular weight (200–1000) hydrocarbons, chloro-carbons, ethers, esters or ketones and are added in amounts from 5–50 w %; they reduce the modulus of rigidity and the glass transition temperature and improve moldability and extrudibility of the mass and impact strength and flexibility of the final products.

Fillers.* The hardness, abrasion resistance, impact strength and solvent resistance of many polymers can be substantially improved by the addition of *fillers*, which are, in general, finely

* For more detailed account see:
  "Plasticizers", page 360
  "Fillers", page 198, etc.

divided powders (particle size varying from 0.1–50μ) such as carbon black, silica ("Cabosil"), alumina ("Alon"), bentonite, clay or iron oxide. They are incorporated either by the addition to a solution of the polymer or by such mechanical means as mixing ("Banbury"), rolling or extruding and are applied in amounts from 5–50 w %.

Lubricants.* Many polymers have the tendency to adhere to the walls of an extruder, die, spineret or hopper which slows down production rate and makes frequent cleaning necessary. This disadvantage can be avoided by the addition of certain *lubricants* (abhesives, stripping agents or die releasers) which have surface active character and, therefore, migrate to the interface of the polymer and the metal equipment in which the material is processed. Long chain salts, esters, amides, ethers and ketones of medium molecular weight (200–2000) such as stearic acid salts and amides, polyethyleneoxides and fluorinated fatty acid esters are examples for these additives which are usually applied in small quantities (0.05–0.5%).

Antistatic Agents.* Related to the lubricants are the *antistatic agents*, which have the very important task of preventing the accumulation of static charges not only during processing but during the ultimate use, as well, where static behavior is particularly undesirable in the textile and film application. The antistatic agents must possess a certain *hydrophilicity* without being water-soluble; i.e., they have to contain water compatible groups (OH, COOH, COOR, H_2COCH_2, CONH), but must be so firmly anchored in the polymer that they are not removed even by repeated washing. One attempts to arrive at successful compromises by using surface active agents of somewhat higher molecular weight, such as the reaction product of bisphenol with ethylene oxide:

$$H\text{-}(O\text{---}CH_2\text{---}CH_2)_8O\text{---}\overset{\displaystyle CH_3}{\underset{\displaystyle CH_3}{\overset{|}{\underset{|}{C}}}}$$
$$H\text{-}(O\text{---}CH_2\text{---}CH_2)_8O$$

The terminal hydroxyl groups of which are esterified with lauric or stearic acid. Additives of this type are usually applied in amounts from 0.1–1.0%.

Heat Stabilizers.* Most polymers deteriorate at elevated temperatures (above 100°C) rather rapidly and even at ambient temperatures (20–40°C) gradually. Two types of *stabilizers* are

* For more detailed account see:
  "Mold release Materials", page 288
  "Antistatic Agents", page 76
  "Stabilizers", page 433

necessary; one which protects the polymer during the short period (a few seconds to several minutes) of high temperature (150–300°C) processing (molding, extruding, blowing, spinning, etc.), and one which prevents slow *aging* during the use of the material over longer periods (up to 20 years) at ambient temperatures. Representative for the first class are compounds containing heavy metals such as Ba, Zn, Cd, Sn, Sb and Pb and organic groups which render these compatible with the polymeric system; dibutyltindilaurate and basic lead maleate may be named as examples; the second class contains amongst others salts and esters of ortho alkylated phenols, such as the barium salt of *o*-nonylphenol combined with sebacic or adipic acid

$(x = 4 \text{ or } 8)$

Other, very effective stabilizers contain amine, imine and amide groups or reducing species of sulfuric and phosphoric acid salts or esters; they are all usually applied in quantities between 0.2 and 1.0%.

Light Stabilizers.* Similar compounds are effective in delaying discoloration and embrittlement of many polymers under the prolonged exposure to intense light in the presence of oxygen and moisture. It seems that free radical scavengers (phenolic, naphthylaminic, disulfidic, mercaptic), together with reducing agents (hydroxylamines, aldehydes, sulfinic esters, phosphorous acid esters, etc.), provide for relatively good protection. Very small percentages of such ingredients (0.05–0.10) can already be effective.

Ultraviolet Absorbers. The protection against radiation damage can be enhanced by the use of certain aromatic ketones and hydroxyketones which have the capacity to absorb UV-radiation selectively and to disperse its energy in harmless manner as thermal vibrations.

HERMAN MARK

Cross-references: PLASTICIZERS, ULTRAVIOLET ABSORBERS, FILLERS, STABILIZERS.

ALCOHOLS—MONO- AND POLYHYDRIC

Alcohols are organic compounds having the general structure ROH, in which the R is an alkyl, acyclic or alkaryl group, and —OH is the hydroxyl group. The more common alcohols, such as methyl, ethyl, etc., are classified as monohydric alcohols, since they contain only one hydroxyl group. The polyhydric alcohols are illustrated by ethylene glycol with two hydroxyl groups, glycerine with three hydroxyl groups, etc.

Only the more common and industrially

important alcohols, used as raw materials or solvents in the plastics industry are presented here. Many of these are used in esterification reactions to form simple esters like ethyl acetate or polyesters like polyethylene terephthalate, combining the hydroxyl group with a carboxyl group of an acid. Monomers such as the acrylic esters are made similarly from the corresponding acrylic acids and alcohols, making a large group of starting materials which may be polymerized to form acrylic resins. Other alcohols such as allyl alcohol may be esterified with acids such as phthalic and the diallylphthalate ester product serves as the monomer for the polyallylphthalate resins. The various classes of resins made from alcohols include: acrylics, alkyds, polyesters, epoxy, urea and melamine, polyurethanes and vinyl ethers. The most important alcohols are listed in Table 1, showing their formula, molecular weight and more common physical properties. Table 2 contains a list of the various mono- and polyhydric alcohols and the classes of resins made from them.

In addition to their use in the manufacture of plastic resins, the alcohols find uses by themselves, or by conversion to ketones, ethers and esters, as solvents useful for the preparation of lacquers, enamels, protective coatings, and many other specialty products, acting as the vehicle or medium for the solution of the plastic resin. In other instances they are used as non-solvents for resins, added to solvent solutions to precipitate the resins out of solution. Perhaps one of the biggest use of alcohols in the plastic industry is for the manufacture of plasticizers, which for the most part are simple and mixed esters of the higher alcohols and larger molecular weight organic acids. Examples of these are dioctyl phthalate and dihexyl sebacate.

The two most important chemical properties of alcohols for their use in plastic products are esterification, mentioned above, and oxidation. The formation of alkyd resin, polyesters, acrylic esters, phthalate esters and similar ester compounds is based upon the reaction of the hydroxyl group of the alcohol with a carboxyl group of an acid. Characteristic of most esterification reactions, water is evolved as the reaction product and its removal essential for the completion of the reaction. Acid catalysts are commonly employed for speeding up the equilibrium, but do not aid in the removal of the water by-product, which really controls the ultimate speed and completion of the reaction. Azeotropic distillation is one common method used for the removal of the water of reaction. Here an excess of the alcohol can be used, providing it forms a separable azeotrope with the water. Such is usually the case with the higher alcohols. Otherwise a third component capable of forming an azeotrop may be employed.

The other method of water removal is by entrainment in an inert gas or alcohol vapor, sometimes under diminished pressure, where a gas such as nitrogen is bubbled through the reaction mixture removing the water as an entrained vapor.

Alcohols are converted to aldehydes, ketones and acids by the oxidation reaction. The largest use of methyl alcohol is its oxidation to formaldehyde, an essential raw material for phenolic, urea, melamine and polyformaldehyde resins. Another example is the oxidation of cyclohexanol to cyclohexanone and further oxidation to adipic acid, the basic ingredient for nylon 66. Likewise isopropyl alcohol is oxidized to acetone, an important solvent for plastic solutions.

Manufacture of Alcohols

Industrial processes for the manufacture of the simple alcohols, glycols and polyhydric alcohols are summarized below, as well as in Tables 3, 4, and 5. A more detailed description of the processes may be found in any of the industrial chemical texts.*

Simple Alcohols. Commercial methods for the manufacture of alcohols are chiefly synthetic, with a few made by fermentation. The reduction of carbon monoxide to methanol, the aldol condensation of acetaldehyde with subsequent dehydration and hydrogeneration to *n*-butanol, the reaction of carbon monoxide with olefinic hydrocarbons to form aldehydes which are subsequently reduced to the corresponding alcohols (the oxo process), and the more recently developed method for making long chain fatty alcohols by the reaction of olefines with alkylaluminum compounds, are some of the synthetic methods used for the production of a great variety of alcohols.

One of the earliest and still widely used processes for alcohols is the hydration of olefines either directly by use of catalysts, or more commonly by first the absorption of the olefine in sulfuric acid and hydrolysis of the resulting alkyl hydrogen sulfate to form the alcohol. Outside of ethyl alcohol from ethylene, all of the other alcohols made from the higher olefines by this method, are secondary and tertiary alcohols. Some alcohols are still obtained from natural products, such as the straight chain fatty alcohols C_8 to C_{14} by the reduction of the corresponding coconut fatty acid esters, or caustic splitting of castor oil.

Glycols or Dihydric Alcohols. These are mainly

* Industrial Chemicals, Keyes, Faith, and Clark, John Wiley & Sons, Inc., "Riegel's Industrial Chemistry," Kent, J. A., Reinhold Publishing Corp., ACS Monograph No. 114, "Glycols," Curme and Johnston, Reinhold Publishing Corp.

TABLE 1. PHYSICAL PROPERTIES OF ALCOHOLS.

Name	Formula	Mol w	Boiling point, °C, 760 mm	Freezing point, °C	Specific gravity, 20/20°C	n_D^{20}	Solubility in H_2O, w % 20°C
Monohydroxy							
methanol	CH_3OH	32.04	64.5	−97.7	0.7924	1.3286	∞
ethanol	CH_3CH_2OH	46.07	78.3	−114.1	0.7905	1.3614	∞
1-propanol	$CH_3CH_2CH_2OH$	60.1	97.2	−126.2	0.8046	1.3856	∞
2-propanol (isopropyl alcohol)	$CH_3CH(OH)CH_3$	60.1	82.3	−88.5	0.7861	1.3772	∞
1-butanol	$CH_3(CH_2)_2CH_2OH$	74.12	117.7	−89.3	0.8108	1.3993	7.7
2-methyl-1-propanol (isobutyl alcohol)	$(CH_3)_2CHCH_2OH$	74.12	107.9	−108	0.8030	1.3959	8.7
1-hexanol	$CH_3(CH_2)_4CH_2OH$	102.18	157.1	−44.6	0.8205	1.4181	0.58
1-octanol	$CH_3(CH_2)_6CH_2OH$	130.23	195.2	−14.9	0.8268	1.4295	0.03
2-ethyl-1-hexanol	$CH_3(CH_2)_3CH(C_2H_5)CH_2OH$	130.23	184.7	−70[a]	0.8340	1.4316	0.07
isooctyl alcohol[b]	$C_8H_{17}OH$	130.23	186.5	−100[a]	0.8323	1.4308	0.07
1-decanol	$CH_3(CH_2)_8CH_2OH$	158.29	230	6.9	0.8310	1.4373	
isodecyl alcohol[b]	$C_{10}H_{21}OH$	158.29	220.1	−60[a]	0.8406	1.4390	0.01
1-dodecanol (lauryl alcohol)	$CH_3(CH_2)_{10}CH_2OH$	186.34	261	24	0.8355[c]	1.4428[c]	
isotridecyl alcohol[b]	$C_{13}H_{27}OH$	200.37	274	30.6	0.8344[c]	1.4450[c]	
1-octadecanol (stearyl alcohol)	$CH_3(CH_2)_{16}CH_2OH$	256.48	332	53.9	0.8397[c]	1.4516[c]	
2-propen-1-ol (allyl alcohol)	$CH_2=CHCH_2OH$	58.08	97.0	<−129	0.8537	1.4133	∞
Dihydroxy							
1,2-ethanediol (ethylene glycol)	$HOCH_2CH_2OH$	62.07	197.6	−12.7	1.1155	1.4316	∞
2,2'-oxydiethanol (diethylene glycol)	$HOCH_2CH_2OCH_2CH_2OH$	106.12	245.8	−7.8	1.1184	1.4474	∞
triethylene glycol	$HOCH_2(CH_2OCH_2)_2CH_2OH$	150.17	288	−4.3	1.1255	1.4561	∞
tetraethylene glycol	$HOCH_2(CH_2OCH_2)_3CH_2OH$	194.23	231_{50}	−6.2	1.1247	1.4598	∞

TABLE 1 (*continued*). PHYSICAL PROPERTIES OF ALCOHOLS.

1,2-propanediol (propylene glycol)	HOCH(CH₃)CH₂OH	76.10	187.3	−60ᵃ	1.0381	1.4329	∞
dipropylene glycolᵈ	[HOCH(CH₃)CH₂]₂O	134.18	231.9		1.0252	1.4440	∞
1,3-propanediol	HOCH₂CH₂CH₂OH	76.10	214.8	−30	1.0548	1.4396	∞
1,3-butanediol	CH₃CH(OH)CH₂CH₂OH	90.12	207.3		1.0059	1.4401	∞
1,4-butanediol	HOCH₂CH₂CH₂CH₂OH	90.12	218	19	1.0178	1.4460	∞
1,5-pentanediol	HOCH₂(CH₂)₃CH₂OH	104.15	242.4	−15.6	0.9921	1.4489	∞
Polyhydroxy							
glycerol (1,2,3-propanetriol)	HOCH₂CH(OH)CH₂OH	92.10	209.4	181.1	1.2620	1.4747	∞
1,1,1-trimethylolethane (2-hydroxymethyl-2-methyl-1,3-propanediol)	CH₃C(CH₂OH)₃	120.14					
1,1,1-trimethylolpropane (2-ethyl-2-hydroxymethyl-1,3-propanediol	CH₃CH₂C(CH₂OH)₃	134.16	295	59			∞
pentaerythritol (2,2-bis(hydroxymethyl)-1,3-propanediol)	C(CH₂OH)₄	136.13	276₃₀	260			6
sorbitol (D-glucitol)	HOCH₂(CHOH)₄CH₂OH	185.15		97.7			∞
1,2,6-hexanetriol	HOCH₂(CH₂)₃CH(OH)CH₂OH	134.18	178₅	32.8	1.1063	1.4771	∞
methyl glucoside	CH(OCH₃)CHOHCHOHCHOHCH(CH₂OH)	194.18		167	1.46ᵉ		52

ᵃ Sets to a glass below this temperature.
ᵇ Mixture of isomers obtained by the oxo process. Properties of commercial product will vary slightly from different manufacturers.
ᶜ Supercooled liquid.
ᵈ Mixture of principally disecondary and primary-secondary hydroxy isomers.
ᵉ 30/40°C.

TABLE 2. USES OF ALIPHATIC ALCOHOLS IN RESINS.

Alcohol	Resin classes
Monohydroxy	
methanol	acrylic, methacrylic, vinyl ether
ethanol	acrylic, methacrylic, vinyl ether
2-propanol (isopropyl alcohol)	melamine–formaldehyde, urea–formaldehyde
1-butanol	acrylic, epoxy, melamine–formaldehyde, methacrylic, polyester, urea–formaldehyde, vinyl ether
2-methyl-1-propanol (isobutyl alcohol)	acrylic, melamine–formaldehyde, urea–formaldehyde, vinyl ether
1-hexanol 1-hexanol	methacrylic
1-octanol	methacrylic
2-ethyl-1-hexanol	acrylic, polyester, urea–formaldehyde
isooctyl alcohol[a]	acrylic
1-decanol	methacrylic
isodecyl alcohol[a]	acrylic
1-dodecanol (lauryl alcohol)	acrylic, methacrylic
1-octadecanol (stearyl alcohol)	methacrylic
2-propen-1-ol (allyl alcohol)	epoxy
Dihydroxy	
1,2-ethaneoliol (ethylene glycol)	alkyd, polyester, urea–formaldehyde
2,2-oxydiethanol (diethylene glycol)	alkyd, polyester
triethylene glycol	alkyd, polyester
tetraethylene glycol	polyester
1,2-propanediol (propylene glycol)	alkyd, polyester
dipropylene glycol[b]	polyester
1,3-propanediol	polyester
1,4-butanediol	polyester
1,5-pentanediol	polyester
Polyhydroxy	
glycerol (1,2,3-propanetriol)	alkyd, epoxy, polyurethan
1,1,1-trimethylolethane (2-hydroxymethyl-2-methyl-1,3-propanediol)	alkyd, polyurethan
1,1,1-trimethylolpropane (2-ethyl-2-hydroxymethyl-1,3-propanediol)	alkyd
pentaerythritol (2,2-bis(hydroxymethyl)-1,3-propanediol)	alkyd
sorbitol (D-glucitol)	alkyd, polyurethan
1,2,6-hexanetriol	polyurethan
methyl glucoside	alkyd, melamine–formaldehyde, polyurethan, urea–formaldehyde

[a] Mixture of isomers obtained by the oxo process. Properties of commercial product will vary slightly from different manufacturers.
[b] Mixture of principally disecondary and primary-secondary hydroxy isomers.

ethylene and propylene glycols and their higher polyglycols such as diethylene glycol or tripropylene glycol. These are manufactured from ethylene or propylene oxides, which are made by direct oxidation of ethylene or from the corresponding chlorohydrin, obtained by the reaction of hypochlorous acid ($Cl_2 + H_2O$) with the olefine, by dehydrochlorination. Each of the longer chain glycols has a unique method of manufacture as shown in Table 4.

Polyhydric Alcohols. Glycerol is the most widely used of all of the polyhydric alcohols. It is still recovered in large volume as a by-product of soap manufacture. In recent years, synthetic methods have been developed for its manufacture; from propylene via allyl alcohol or acrolein.*

Another synthetic method is by the hydrogenolysis of sugars which also produces ethylene and propylene glycols, as well as manitol and sorbitol which are hexahydric alcohols. The aldol condensation of formaldehyde with acetaldehyde is used to produce pentaerythritol $C(CH_2OH)_4$, a tetrahydric alcohol.

* See Glycerine, p. 256.

Commercial specifications for some of the more common alcohols are given in Table 6.

Uses of Alcohols in the Production of Plastic Resins

Reactions important for the use of alcohols of all types in the synthesis of polymer products are outlined below:

Synthesis of Acrylate and Methacrylate Esters. In the equations below, various alcohols (ROH) are reacted with acrylic and methacrylic acids to form a large number of acrylic esters. The R group ranges from methyl to stearyl, with the more common esters being the methyl, ethyl, butyl and 2-ethylhexyl acrylates and methacrylates.

(a) $CH_2{=}CHCOOH + ROH{\longrightarrow}$
Acrylic acid
$$CH_2{=}CHCOOR + H_2O$$
Acrylate ester

(b)
$$\overset{\displaystyle CH_3}{\underset{\displaystyle |}{CH_2{=}CCOOH}} + ROH{\longrightarrow}$$
Methacrylic acid
$$\overset{\displaystyle CH_3}{\underset{\displaystyle |}{CH_2{=}CCOOR}} + H_2O$$
Methacrylate ester

Polyester Formation. The reaction of a polyhydric alcohol with a polybasic acid results in the formation of a polyester resin, as shown below:

$nHOCH_2CH_2OH + nHO \cdot CO(CH_2)_8CO \cdot OH{\longrightarrow}$
Ethylene glycol   *Sebasic acid*

$(-OCH_2CH_2O \cdot CO(CH_2)_8CO{-})_n + 2nH_2O$
Polyethylene sebcaate

Production of Alkyd Resins. A more involved reaction is the esterification of a polyhydric alcohol with a mixture of a dibasic acid and a fatty acid, as shown in the equation below:

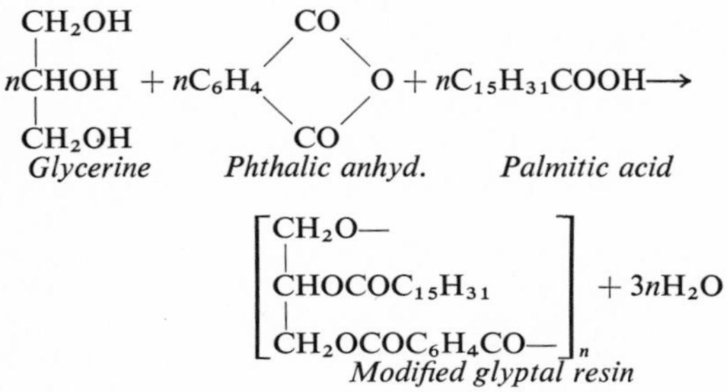

$$n\overset{\displaystyle CH_2OH}{\underset{\displaystyle CH_2OH}{\overset{|}{\underset{|}{CHOH}}}} + nC_6H_4\diagup\!\!\!\overset{CO}{\underset{CO}{}}\!\!\!\diagdown O + nC_{15}H_{31}COOH{\longrightarrow}$$
Glycerine   *Phthalic anhyd.*   *Palmitic acid*

$$\left[\begin{matrix} CH_2O- \\ | \\ CHOCOC_{15}H_{31} \\ | \\ CH_2OCOC_6H_4CO- \end{matrix}\right]_n + 3nH_2O$$
Modified glyptal resin

Modifications of Amino Resins. The inclusion of alcohols in the polycondensation reactions of urea and melamine with formaldehyde provides a means of modifying the amino resin to provide an increased solubility for use in lacquer and coating formulations:

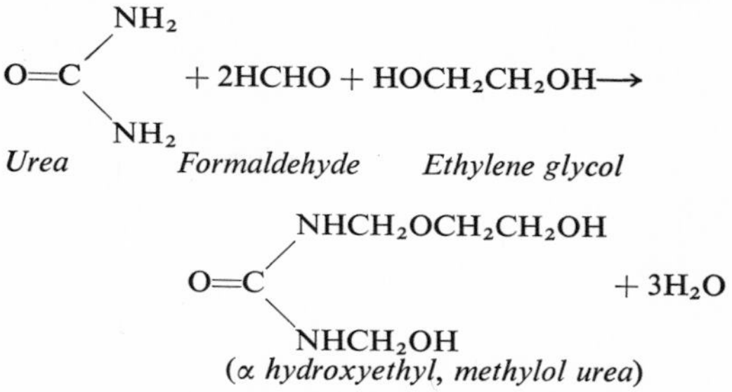

$$O{=}C\overset{\displaystyle NH_2}{\underset{\displaystyle NH_2}{\big\langle}} + 2HCHO + HOCH_2CH_2OH{\longrightarrow}$$
Urea   *Formaldehyde*   *Ethylene glycol*

$$O{=}C\overset{\displaystyle NHCH_2OCH_2CH_2OH}{\underset{\displaystyle NHCH_2OH}{\big\langle}} + 3H_2O$$
(α hydroxyethyl, methylol urea)

Formation of Polyurethanes. This is the reaction of a polyhydric alcohol with a diisocynate for the formation of a polyurethane as shown below:

$nR(OH)_2 + nR^1(NCO)_2{\longrightarrow}$
Glycol   *Diisocyanate*
$$[-NHR^1NHCO \cdot OROCO{-}]_n$$
Polyurethane

Synthesis of Polyvinylethers. The reaction of a simple alcohol with acetylene in the presence of alkali yields a vinyl ether, which then may be polymerized to the corresponding resin:

$CH{\equiv}CH + ROH{\longrightarrow}ROCH{=}CH_2{\longrightarrow}$
Acetylene   *Alcohol*   *Vinyl ether*
$$\left[\begin{matrix} -CH{-}CH_2 \\ | \\ OR \end{matrix}\right]_n$$
Polyvinylether

Production of Polyallylphthalate Resin. Here an unsaturated alcohol is esterified with a dibasic acid thus forming the monomer, diallylphthalate which is polymerized to the resin.

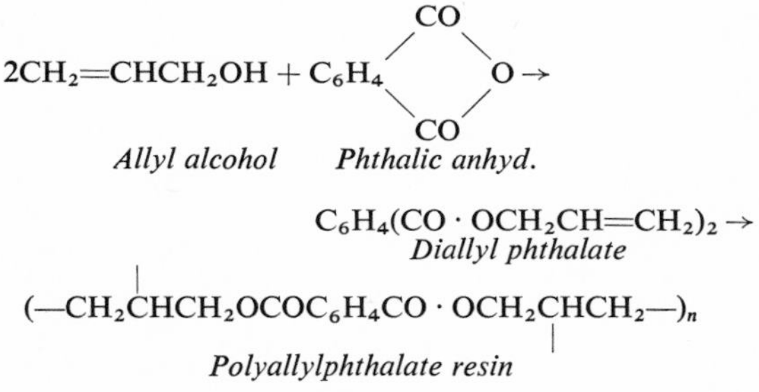

$$2CH_2{=}CHCH_2OH + C_6H_4\diagup\!\!\!\overset{CO}{\underset{CO}{}}\!\!\!\diagdown O \rightarrow$$
Allyl alcohol   *Phthalic anhyd.*

$$C_6H_4(CO \cdot OCH_2CH{=}CH_2)_2 \rightarrow$$
Diallyl phthalate

$$(-CH_2CHCH_2OCOC_6H_4CO \cdot OCH_2CHCH_2{-})_n$$
Polyallylphthalate resin

Epoxy Resin Reactants. Alcohols may be reacted with epichlorohydrin to form reactive diluents, which are added to the usual Bisphenol-A epichlorohydrin epoxy compound, to form a modified epoxy resin:

(a) $CH_2{-}CHCH_2Cl + ROH{\longrightarrow}$
        $\diagdown O \diagup$
Epichlorohydrin   *Alcohol*

$$CH_2{-}CHCH_2OR + HCl$$
$$\diagdown O \diagup$$
Alkyl glycidylether

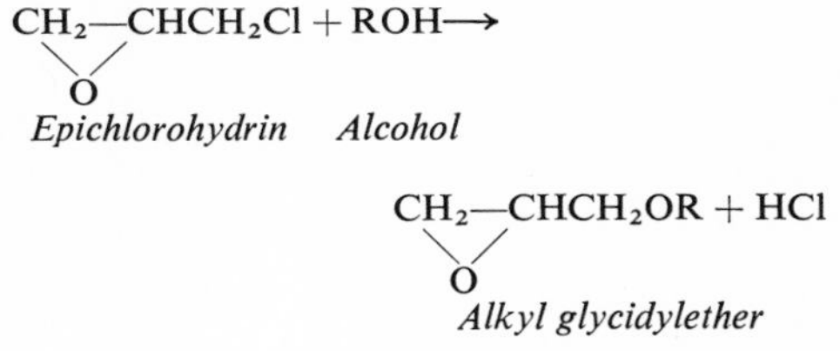

TABLE 3. PREPARATION OF MONOHYDROXY ALCOHOLS.

Reaction	Reaction conditions
Methanol $CO + 2H_2 \rightarrow CH_3OH$	vapor phase, 350–375°C, 250–350 atm, typical catalyst $ZnO\text{-}Cr_2O_3$
Ethyl, isopropyl, sec-butyl, tert-butyl alcohol $RCH{=}CH_2 + H_2SO_4 \rightarrow RCHCH_3 \xrightarrow{H_2O} RCHCH_3 + H_2SO_4$ $\qquad\qquad\qquad\qquad\ \ OSO_3H \qquad\quad\ OH$	typical values[a] 60–70°C, 225–350 psig; H_2SO_4 strength about 96–99% for C_2 and 65–80% for C_3 and C_4; for hydrolysis, 25–50% H_2SO_4
1-Butanol, 2-ethyl-1-hexanol, branched-chain alcohols[b] $2\,CH_3CHO \rightarrow CH_3CHCH_2CHO \xrightarrow{-H_2O} CH_3CH{=}CHCHO \xrightarrow{H_2} CH_3CH_2CH_2CH_2OH$ $\qquad\qquad\qquad\quad OH \qquad\qquad\qquad\qquad\qquad\qquad\qquad\qquad\qquad$ 1-butanol $2\,CH_3CH_2CH_2CHO \rightarrow CH_3CH_2CH_2CHCHCHO \xrightarrow{-H_2O} CH_3CH_2CH_2CH{=}CCHO \xrightarrow{H_2}$ $\qquad\qquad\qquad\qquad\qquad\quad HO\ \ C_2H_5 \qquad\qquad\qquad\qquad\qquad\ C_2H_5$ $\qquad\qquad\qquad CH_3(CH_2)_3CHCH_2OH$ $\qquad\qquad\qquad\qquad\qquad\quad C_2H_5$ $\qquad\qquad\qquad$ 2-ethyl-1-hexanol	aldolization: 5–25°C, aqueous caustic; dehydration: 95°C, 30–35% sodium acid phosphate; hydrogenation: 200°C, vapor phase with Cu on pumice or liquid phase, Ni catalyst

TABLE 3 (*continued*). PREPARATION OF MONOHYDROXY ALCOHOLS.

C₃–C₁₃ alcohols[c]

$$RCH{=}CH_2 \xrightarrow{CO+H_2} RCHCH_3 + RCH_2CH_2CHO \xrightarrow{H_2} RCHCH_3 + RCH_2CH_2CH_2OH$$
$$\quad\quad\quad\quad\quad\quad | \quad\quad\quad\quad\quad\quad\quad\quad\quad\quad\quad\quad | $$
$$\quad\quad\quad\quad\quad\quad CHO \quad\quad\quad\quad\quad\quad\quad\quad\quad\quad CH_2OH$$

liquid phase, cobalt carbonyl catalyst, 140–175°C CO to H₂ ratio 1:1, 1500–4000 psig

Straight-chain primary alcohols[d]

$$Al{-}CH_2CH_3 + (x+y+z)CH_2{=}CH_2 \rightarrow Al{-}(CH_2CH_3)_{y+1}H \xrightarrow{O_2} Al{-}OR'' \xrightarrow{H2SO4}$$

with branches $(CH_2CH_2)_{x+1}H$ / OR', (CH_2CH_3), $(CH_2CH_2)_{n+1}H$ / OR'''

$$R'OH + R''OH + R'''OH + Al_2(SO_4)_3$$

displacement: 265°C, 10 atm; oxidation, 30–95°C, 1 atm; hydrolysis: 40°C, 1 atm, 98% H₂SO₄

Allyl alcohol

$$CH{=}CHCH_3 \xrightarrow{O_2} CH_2{=}CHCHO \xrightarrow{(CH_3)_2CHOH} CH_2{=}CHCH_2OH + (CH_3)_2CO$$

oxidation: vapor phase, 400°C, CuO catalyst, propylene to oxygen ratio 7.5; reduction; vapor phase, isopropyl alcohol reacted over a MgO–ZnO catalyst, 350–450°C

$$CH_3CHCH_2 \rightarrow CH_2{=}CHCH_2OH$$
$$\quad\backslash\;/$$
$$\quad O$$

isomerization: vapor phase, catalyst such as Li₃PO₄, 280°C

[a] Reaction conditions vary widely for absorption of the olefin.
[b] Produced through aldol condensation.
[c] Produced from the oxo process.
[d] Produced from the Alfol process.

37

TABLE 4. PREPARATION OF DIHYDROXY ALCOHOLS.

Reaction	Reaction conditions
Ethylene glycol $CH_2{=}CH_2 \xrightarrow{O_2} CH_2CH_2(O) \xrightarrow{H_2O} HOCH_2CH_2OH$	vapor phase, 220°C, Ag catalyst, vol ratio of air to ethylene 10:1, 1 atm
$HOCH_2CH_2Cl \xrightarrow{lime} CH_2CH_2(O) \xrightarrow{H_2O} HOCH_2CH_2OH$	dehydrochlorination: liquid phase, 45–50°C, 1 atm, pH 8; hydration: dil H_2SO_4, 50–70°C, or neutral soln, 190–200°C, 300 psig
Propylene glycol $CH_3CH{=}CH_2 \xrightarrow{HOCl} CH_3CHOHCH_2Cl \xrightarrow{Ca(OH)_2} CH_3CHCH_2(O) \xrightarrow{H_2O} CH_3CHCH_2OH\ \ OH$	hypochlorination: liquid phase, 35°C, 1 atm; dehydrochlorination: liquid phase, excess lime 90–100°C, 1 atm; hydration: H_2SO_4, 50–75°C
Diethylene, triethylene, and higher oxyethylene glycols $HOCH_2CH_2OH + n(CH_2CH_2) \rightarrow HOCH_2CH_2(OCH_2CH_2)_nOH$	liquid phase, NaOH or KOH catalyst, 80–140°C, 30–75 psig
Dipropylene, tripropylene, and higher oxypropylene glycols $CH_3CH(OH)CH_2OH + n(CH_3CHCH_2) \rightarrow HOCH(CH_3)CH_2[OCH_2CH(CH_3)]_nOH$	liquid phase, NaOH or KOH catalyst, 80–140°C, 30–75 psig
1,3-Butanediol $2CH_3CHO \xrightarrow{alkali} CH_3CH(OH)CH_2CHO \rightarrow CH_2CH(OH)CH_2CH_2OH$	aldol condensation: see synthesis of 1-butanol; hydrogenation: Cu–Cr catalyst, 50–150°C, 4500 psig
1,4-Butanediol $CH{\equiv}CH + CH_2O \rightarrow HOCH_2C{\equiv}CCH_2OH \xrightarrow{H_2} HOCH_2CH_2CH_2CH_2OH$ $H_2C{-}CH_2,\ H_2C{-}CH_2{-}O \xrightarrow{H_2O} HOCH_2CH_2CH_2CH_2OH$	ethynilation: 100°C, 75–90 psig, Cu acetylide catalyst; hydrogenation: Ni or Co catalyst on pumice, high pressure, 80–130°C
1,5-Pentanediol (10) $CH_2{=}CHCHO + CH_2{=}CHOC_2H_5 \xrightarrow{heat} CH{=}CH{-}CH_2CH_2CHOC_2H_5 \xrightarrow{H_2O}$ $OHCCH_2CH_2CH_2CHO \xrightarrow{H_2} HOCH_2CH_2CH_2CH_2CH_2OH$	addition: 200–250°C, 400–500 psig; hydrolysis: 100–200°C; hydrogeneration: Ni catalyst, 100–250°C, 1500 psig

38

TABLE 5. PREPARATION OF POLYHYDROXY ALCOHOLS.

Reaction	Reaction conditions
Glycerol $CH_2=CHCH_3 \xrightarrow{Cl_2} CH_2=CHCH_2Cl \xrightarrow{HOCl} ClCH_2CHCH_2Cl \xrightarrow{lime}$ $\qquad\qquad\qquad\qquad\qquad\qquad\qquad\qquad\quad \underset{OH}{\mid}$ $CH_2CHCH_2Cl \xrightarrow{NaOH} HOCH_2CH(OH)CH_2OH$ $\underset{\diagdown\,O\,\diagup}{}$	high-temperature chlorination to allyl chloride: vapor phase, 500–530°C, 10–15 psig; addition of hypochlorous acid: liquid phase, 25–35°C; dehydrochlorination to epichlorohydrin: liquid phase, 80–90°C; hydrolysis: liquid phase, 10–12% aq alkali, 150°C
Trimethylolethane, trimethylolpropane, pentaerythritol (14,14a,14b) $CH_3CH_2CHO + 3\,CH_2O + MOH \rightarrow CH_3C(CH_2OH)_3 + HCOOM$ trimethylolethane $CH_3CH_2CH_2CHO + 33H_2O + MOH \rightarrow CH_3CH_2C(CH_2OH)_3 + HCOOM$ trimethylolpropane $CH_3CHO + 3CH_2O + MOH \rightarrow C(CH_2OH)_3CHO \xrightarrow{CH_2O} C(CH_2OH)_4 + HCOOM$ pentaerythritol	liquid phase, aq Ca(OH)$_2$, mole ratio CH$_2$O to CH$_3$CHO 5:1, 30–35°C for all three reactions
1,2,6-Hexanetriol $2CH_2=CHCHO \xrightarrow{heat} CH=CHCH_2CH_2CHCHO \xrightarrow{H_2O}$ $HCOCHCH_2CH_2CH_2CHO \xrightarrow{H_2} HOCH_2CH(CH_2)_3CH_2OH$ $\qquad\underset{OH}{\mid} \qquad\qquad\qquad\qquad\qquad\qquad\qquad \underset{OH}{\mid}$	dimerization: 210°C, 600–700 psig; hydrolysis, 25°C, dil H$_2$SO$_4$; hydrogenation: Ni catalyst, 100–150°C, 500–1000 psig
Sorbitol carbohydrates (particularly glucose) $\xrightarrow{H_2}$	hydrogeneration: high pressure (1500–2000 psig) or electrolytically (3,3a)

39

TABLE 6. COMMERCIAL SPECIFICATIONS FOR SOME ALCOHOLS.

Alcohol	Specific gravity 20/20°C	Distillation range, °C	Acidity, % by w, max	Alcohol, % by w	Water, % by w, max	Ash % by w, max	Color, Pt–Co, max	Aldehydes, % by w, max
Monohydric								
methanol	0.79268 max	within 0.5°C	0.003	99.85 min	0.05	0.001[a]	5	
ethanol	0.7905–0.7914		0.002		0.2	0.0025[a]	10	
2-propanol	0.7862–0.7869	within 1.0°C including 82.3	0.002	99.8 min	0.2	0.002[a]	10	
1-butanol	0.8100–0.8120	within 1.5°C including 117.7	0.005		0.10	0.005[a]	10	none
isobutyl alcohol	0.802–0.804	within 1.5°C including 107.9	0.003		0.2	0.001[a]	5	
1-hexanol	0.8190–0.8230	153 min 160 max	0.01	530 min[d]	0.3		15	
2-ethyl-1-hexanol	0.8325–0.8345	182.0 min 186.0 max	0.01		0.10		5	0.10 as 2-ethyl-hexaldehyde
isooctyl alcohol[e]	0.835	192.0	0.001	99.0 min	0.10		5	0.05 as octanal
isodecyl alcohol[e]	0.837–0.842	215–225	0.002	98.5 min	0.10		10	0.5 as decanal
allyl alcohol	0.852–0.855	95–98		98.0	0.3		15	
Dihydric								
ethylene glycol	1.1151–1.1156	193.0–205.0	0.005		0.30	0.005	10	
diethylene glycol	1.1170–1.1200	242.0–250.0	0.005		0.20	0.005[a]	15	
triethylene glycol	1.124–1.126	278.0–300.0	0.01		0.1	0.01	25	
tetraethylene glycol	1.122–1.132	305.0–340.0	0.01		0.2		70	
propylene glycol	1.0375–1.0390	185.0–190.0	0.005		0.2	0.005	10	
dipropylene glycol	1.020–1.025	222.0–238.0	0.01		0.1		15	
1,3-butanediol	1.004–1.008	200.0–210.0	0.01		0.5		20	
Polyhydric								
glycerol	1.2626 min		neutral to litmus	99.5 min	0.3	0.01	20	
1,1,1-trimethylolethane				41.75[d]	0.3	0.01	100	
1,1,1-trimethylolpropane		57–59[b]	0.002	37.5 min[d]	0.05	0.01	5[c]	
pentaerythritol				49.0 min[d]	0.5	0.01	100	
methyl glucoside	1.46[f]			48.5[d]	0.5	0.05		

[a] Grams/100 ml.
[b] Melting point.
[c] 10% aqueous soln.
[d] Hydroxyl content.
[e] Mixture of isomers obtained by the oxo process.
[f] 30/40°C.

(b) $2CH_2—CHCH_2Cl + HOCH_2CH_2OH \rightarrow$

$$\underset{O}{\overset{\diagdown\diagup}{}}$$

Epichlorohydrin   *Ethylene glycol*

$$CH_2—CHCH_2OCH_2CH_2OCH_2CH—CH_2$$

$$\underset{O}{} \qquad\qquad\qquad \underset{O}{}$$

Diglycidyl ether of ethylene glycol

DR. C. P. MCCLELLAND

ALIPHATIC ACIDS AND ESTERS

There are many aliphatic acids, both mono-carboxylic and dicarboxylic, saturated and unsaturated. This article deals only with the mono- and dicarboxylic saturated aliphatic acids and their esters, since the others are discussed elsewhere.*

Monocarboxylic Acids

The known saturated straight-chain monocarboxylic acid ($C_nH_{2n+1}COOH$) series from formic (C_1) to octatriacontanoic (C_{38}) is complete except for two or three odd-numbered acids above C_{31}. All of the even-numbered acids occur either in the free or combined state in nature, and all of them from butyric to octatriacontanoic are present either as glycerides or as monoesters in fats or waxes. Palmitic acid (C_{16}) is the most abundant saturated acid, and is present in practically all plant and animal fats. Stearic acid (C_{18}) is less abundant, but has a wide distribution.

Properties. The naturally occurring saturated fatty acids, with few exceptions, do not exhibit any isomerism. Although only a few branched-chain, hydroxy, and keto acids have been detected in naturally occurring fatty substances in appreciable amounts, a considerable number of these and also of odd-numbered acids have been prepared synthetically. The lower members of the saturated fatty acid series are liquids at ordinary temperatures, but as the series is ascended the individual members become increasingly more viscous and ultimately pass to crystalline solids.

Some of the most frequently used physical constants of representative mono-carboxylic acids are listed in Table 1.

Preparation. Several general methods available for both laboratory and industrial synthesis of the carboxylic acid group are given below.

(1) Oxidation of primary alcohols or aldehydes:

$$RCH_2OH + O_2 \rightarrow RCOOH + H_2O$$

$$RCHO + 1/2O_2 \rightarrow RCOOH$$

(2) Hydrolysis of nitriles, which are readily prepared from the alkyl halides. Strong acid is usually employed as catalyst for the hydrolysis,

* See articles on Maleic Anhydride, p. 270, Fumaric Acids, p. 242, Anhydrides, Acid p. 61.

but a basic catalyst may also be used:

$$RX + KCN \rightarrow RCN + KX$$

$$RCN + 2H_2O + HX \rightarrow RCOOH + NH_4X$$

Hydrogen peroxide converts nitriles to amides under alkaline conditions. The amides may then be converted to acids by hydrolysis:

$$RCN + H_2O_2 \overset{OH^-}{\longrightarrow} RCONH_2 RCOOH$$

(3) Hydrolysis of esters, amides, acid chlorides, and acid anhydrides. However, except for the saponification of glycerides, this method is of limited importance, since these compounds are generally prepared from the acids.

(4) Reaction of Grignard reagents with carbon dioxide:

$$RMgX + CO_2 \rightarrow RCOOMgX$$

$$RCOOMgX + H_2O \rightarrow RCOOH + MgXOH$$

(5) Reaction of carbanions with carbon dioxide (M = alkali metal)

$$RM + CO_2 \rightarrow RCOOM$$

$$RCOOM + HCl(aq) \rightarrow RCOOH + MCl$$

Laboratory methods for preparation of substituted acetic acids are the acetoacetic ester synthesis and the malonic ester synthesis. The Reformatsky reaction can be used to prepare -hydroxy acids, and from them, -unsaturated acids can be prepared. Additional methods include pyrolysis of barium salts of acids with a chain length greater by one carbon atom than that desired, and the oxidation of hydrocarbons and of unsaturated compounds.

Many of the monocarboxylic acids discussed in this article are derived from naturally occurring fats and oils. The words *Fats* and *Oils* as used herein refer to that class of lipid materials consisting of the glyceride esters of the fatty acids and associated materials. They are obtained from plants or animals by such processes as extraction with hot water, steam, or organic solvents, by pressing, or by combinations of these processes. Specifically, fats and oils consist of the triglycerides (glycerol esters) of the fatty acids (see also Drying Oils) and have the general formula:

$$R'COO—CH_2$$
$$R''COO—CH$$
$$R'''COO—CH_2$$

In the naturally occurring triglycerides R′, R″, and R‴ may be the same or different fatty acid residues. For the most part, synthetic triglycerides are made with all three residues identical. The major difference in usage between the words fat and oil is the physical state of the material—a fat is solid and an oil is liquid at ambient

TABLE 1. PHYSICAL PROPERTIES OF SATURATED ALIPHATIC MONOCARBOXYLIC ACIDS.

Common name	Systematic name	Formula	Formula wt.	M.P., °C	B.P., °C	$d\frac{20}{4}$	$n\frac{20}{D}$
Formic	methanoic	HCOOH	46.03	8.4	100.5	1.220	1.3714
Acetic	ethanoic	CH_3COOH	60.05	16.6	118.1	1.049	1.3718
Propionic	propanoic	CH_3CH_2COOH	74.08	−22	141.1	0.992	1.3874
Butyric	butanoic	$CH_3(CH_2)_2COOH$	88.10	−7.9	163.5	0.959	1.39906
Caproic	hexanoic	$CH_3(CH_2)_4COOH$	116.16	−1.5	205	0.929	1.41635
Enanthic	hepatanoic	$CH_3(CH_2)_5COOH$	130.18	−10.5	223.0	0.922	1.4230
Caprylic	octanoic	$CH_3(CH_2)_6COOH$	144.21	16	237.5	0.910	1.4285
Pelargonic	nonanoic	$CH_3(CH_2)_7COOH$	158.24	12	254	0.9055	1.4330
Capric	decanoic	$CH_3(CH_2)_8COOH$	172.26	31.4	270	$0.8858^{(40°)}$	1.42855^{40}
Lauric	dodecanoic	$CH_3(CH_2)_{10}COOH$	200.31	43.5	$225_{(100mm.)}$	0.883	1.42665^{60}
Myristic	tetradecanoic	$CH_3(CH_2)_{12}COOH$	228.37	53.8	$250.5_{(100mm.)}$	$0.8622^{(53.8°)}$	1.43075^{60}
Palmitic	hexadecanoic	$CH_3(CH_2)_{14}COOH$	256.42	62.9	$271.5_{(100mm.)}$	$0.8527^{(62°)}$ (liq)	$1.4284^{74.5}$
Stearic	octadecanoic	$CH_3(CH_2)_{16}COOH$	284.47	71.5	$291_{(100mm.)}$	0.9408	1.43003^{80}
Arachidic	eicosanoic	$CH_3(CH_2)_{18}COOH$	312.52	77	328	$0.824^{(100°)}$	
Behenic	docosanoic	$CH_3(CH_2)_{20}COOH$	340.58	84	$306_{(60mm.)}$		
Lignoceric	tetracosanoic	$CH_3(CH_2)_{22}COOH$	368.63	86	dec		
Cerotic	hexacosanoic	$CH_3(CH_2)_{24}COOH$	396.68	79		0.8359^{79}	1.4440^{79}

temperatures. This definition has little scientific foundation because the familiar fats are in reality plastic solids, or at least semisolids, consisting of a liquid in admixture with microcrystalline solid particles.

In the distribution of *Fatty Acids*, including unsaturated acids, in the common fats and oils, only fatty acids with an even number of carbon atoms occur in nature.

The fatty acids are manufactured from the naturally occurring fats and oils by one of several "splitting" or hydrolytic processes, which produce, in addition to the acids, a stoichiometric quantity of glycerol (Eq. 1). The earliest method used was complete saponification using either sodium or potassium hydroxide. This process is still widely applied in soapmaking. The most popular method in use today is the Twitchell process, dating back to 1890, which makes use of an alkylated benzene-sulfonic acid to catalyze the aqueous hydrolysis of the triglycerides. Another process, "autoclave splitting," consists of carrying out the reaction either with a mild oxide catalyst at 75–150 psi or noncatalytically at 425–450 psi. It has the advantages of shorter reaction times and production of a lightercolored fatty acid than the other processes.

$$
\begin{array}{llll}
R'COO{-}CH_2 & & R'COOH & CH_2OH \\
| & & & | \\
R''COO{-}CH + 3H_2O \rightarrow & R''COOH + & CHOH & (1) \\
| & & & | \\
R'''COO{-}CH_2 & & R'''COOH & CH_2OH \\
& & \text{Mixed fatty} & \textit{Glycerol} \\
& & \text{acids} &
\end{array}
$$

The process that is destined to find widest application is continuous, countercurrent, high-temperature, high-pressure splitting. This method was developed in the 1940's independently by Colgate-Palmolive-Peet, Procter and Gamble, and Emery Industries. Hydrolysis by continuous methods is capable of producing a 97–99% yield at a rate of 3000–5000 lb fat/hr. Continuous countercurrent hydrolysis is not as satisfactory as batch processing for highly unsaturated fats such as fish oil, since the products are less useful in coatings.

The fatty acids produced by either batch or continuous hydrolysis are a mixture of several components. Various fractionation methods have been developed to produce fatty acids of specific chain lengths. These include crystallization and distillation techniques.

Fatty acids can be synthesized in the laboratory by the various methods discussed above. Fatty acids can also be prepared commercially by way of the oxo process, in which aldehydes are obtained from olefins by catalytic reactions with carbon monoxide and hydrogen. The aldehydes, in turn, may be oxidized to carboxylic acids.

Some higher aliphatic saturated acids of interest in the polymer field are discussed in detail below.

For discussions of the shorter-chain members of this group, see the works cited in the General References.

Caproic Acid, $CH_2(CH_2)_4COOH$, occurs as a constituent (2%) of milk fats and in small amounts in coconut and palm oils (1%). It was first isolated from butterfat in 1816 by Chevreul. Oxidative rancidification of butterfats converts caproic acid to propyl ketone (4-heptanone), which has an unpleasant odor. Caproic acid has an odor characteristic of goats, hence its name from the Latin *Caper*, goat. The acid is manufactured commercially from hexanol by oxidation and from capronitrile by hydrolysis. It can be prepared by both the malonic ester synthesis and the acetoacetic ester synthesis from 1-bromobutane.

Caprylic Acid, $CH_3(CH_2)_6COOH$, occurs naturally and has a fairly wide distribution in animal and vegetable fats. However, it rarely exceeds 8% of the total fatty acids. It is commercially available as a 90% pure product obtained by fractional distillation of coconut oil fatty acids.

Pelargonic Acid, $CH_3(CH_2)_7COOH$, derives its name from the essential oil of geranium (*Pelargonium Roseum*), in which it has been reported to be present. It has also been isolated from secretions of the sebaceous glands. It may, however, be a product of oxidative cleavage of C_{18} unsaturated acids during preparation, rather than an original component. It is a primary product of oxidative fission of oleic acid and other acids unsaturated in the 9,10 position, and is manufactured by oxidation of oleic acid.

Capric Acid, $CH_3(CH_2)_8COOH$, is a minor component in the same fats that contain caprylic acid. It is a major constituent of elm seed oil (50%) and bay tree seed oil (37%). It is produced commercially as a 90% pure product by fractional distillation of coconut oil fatty acids.

Lauric Acid, $CH_3(CH_2)_{10}COOH$, is one of the three most widely distributed saturated fatty acids in nature, along with palmitic and stearic. It is also the shortest-chain saturated acid found abundantly in nature. It derives its name from the seed fats of the laurel (*Lauraceae*). It is available commercially in the form of mixed acids of coconut oil, or as the mixture from which caproic, caprylic, and capric have been removed by distillation.

Uses. The monocarboxylic acids are used extensively in alkyd resins and polyesters, and as plasticizers. Cellulose esters are important raw materials for fibers, plastics, and films.

Alkyd Resins and Polyesters are derived from fatty acids, which are used as such, as well as in the form of esters and oils (triglycerides) to impart flexibility and drying properties to surface coatings. Variation of the "oil length" (related to per cent of oil used) allows a wide range in

TABLE 2. PHYSICAL PROPERTIES OF ESTERS OF MONOCARBOXYLIC ACIDS $CH_3(CH_2)_xCOOR$.

Ester	Mol. wt.	M.P., °C	Specific gravity $\frac{20}{4}$	
Formiate Esters				
($CH_3 + x{=}0$)				
Methyl	60.05	−99	32	0.974
Ethyl	74.08	−79	54	0.923
n-Propyl	88.10	−93	81	0.901
n-Butyl	102.13	—	107	0.911
n-Amyl	116.16	−73	132	0.902
Acetate Esters				
($x{=}0$)				
Methyl	74.08	−99	57	0.933
Ethyl	88.10	−84	77	0.901
n-Propyl	102.13	−95	102	0.886
n-Butyl	116.16	−73	126	0.882
n-Amyl	130.18	−71	149	0.876
Propionate Esters				
($x{=}1$)				
Methyl	88.10	−87	80	0.915
Ethyl	102.13	−74	99	0.898
n-Propyl	116.16	−75	123	0.883
n-Butyl	130.18	−89	146	0.885
n-Amyl	144.21	−73	169	0.875
n-Butyrate Esters				
($x{=}2$)				
Methyl	102.13	−85	103	0.901
Ethyl	116.16	−101	122	0.876
n-Propyl	130.18	−95	166	0.872
n-Amyl	158.23	−73	186	0.870
n-Valerate Esters				
($x{=}3$)				
Methyl	116.16	−91	127	0.895
Ethyl	130.18	−91	145	0.877
n-Propyl	144.21	−71	167	0.874
n-Butyl	158.23	−93	186	0.872
n-Caproate Esters				
($x{=}4$)				
Methyl	130.18	−71	152	0.888
Ethyl	144.21	−68	167	0.873
n-Propyl	155.23	−74	188	0.860
n-Butyl	172.26	−63	208	0.858
n-Amyl	186.29	−50	226	0.856
n-Octyl	228.35	−28	275	0.853
n-Caprylate Esters				
($x{=}6$)				
Methyl	158.24	−34	194	0.890
Ethyl	172.26	−32	209	0.881
n-Propyl	186.29	−46	226	0.860
n-Butyl	200.31	−43	245	0.857
n-Amyl	214.33	−35	260	0.855
n-Octyl	256.41	−15	307	0.853
n-Laurate Esters				
($x{=}10$)				
Methyl	214.33	+4	142 (18mm)	—
Ethyl	228.35	−2	163 (25mm)	0.868
n-Butyl	256.41	−15	307	0.853
Stearate Esters				
($x{=}16$)				
Methyl	298.49	+39	215 (15mm)	—
Ethyl	312.51	34	200 (10mm)	0.854
n-Butyl	340.56	28	222 (25mm)	0.860
n-Amyl	354.59	30	360	0.858
n-Octyl	396.63	34	235 (6mm)	0.841

TABLE 3. PHYSICAL PROPERTIES OF SATURATED ALIPHATIC DICARBOXYLIC ACIDS.

Common name	Systematic name	Formula	Formula wt.	M.P., °C	B.P., °C	d_4^{20}	Solubility in water, g/100 g
Oxalic	ethanedioic	$HOOCCOOH.2H_2O$	126.07	101 / 189 (anhyd)	150 (subl)	1.653^{20}	$9.5^{at\ 15°C}$
Malonic	propanedioic	$HOOCCH_2COOH$	104.06	135.6	dec	1.631^{15}	73.5^{20}
Succinic	butanedioic	$HOOC(CH_2)_2COOH$	118.09	185	235 (dec)	1.564^{15}	6.8^{20}
Glutaric	pentanedioic	$HOOC(CH_2)_3COOH$	132.11	97.5	304 (dec)	1.429^{15}	63.9^{20}
Adipic	hexanedioic	$HOOC(CH_2)_4COOH$	146.14	152.1	330.5 (dec) / 265.1_{100}	1.366^{20}	1.5^{15}
Pimelic	heptanedioic	$HOOC(CH_2)_5COOH$	160.17	106	272_{100}	$1.329^{14.5}$	5^{20}
Suberic	octanedioic	$HOOC(CH_2)_6COOH$	174.19	144	279_{100}		0.14^{16}
Azelaic	nonanedioic	$HOOC(CH_2)_7COOH$	188.22	106.5	360 (dec)	1.029^{20}	0.2^{15}
Sebacic	decanedioic	$HOOC(CH_2)_8COOH$	202.24	134.5	295_{100}		0.11^{17}

properties, from a soft film to a hard, tough tack-free film. In 1956, 59.9 million lb of fatty acids went into plastic, resin, and paint use.

Plasticizers, are another product of fatty acids; in 1958, 27 million lb of fatty acids were used to make plasticizers. Oleic and stearic acids are the most widely used fatty acids. Pelargonic acid is also used to make plasticizers; production from this source is 3–4 million lb per year. Other acids such as palmitic, lauric, ricinoleic, and myristic, have small roles in the plasticizer field. Collectively, they account for 5 million lb of plasticizer acids.

Monocarboxylic Acid Esters (RCOOR′)

These are the reaction products of acids or acid derivatives with alcohols or phenols. A summary of the physical properties of representative esters of the more common monocarboxylic acids is given in Table 2. The lower esters are colorless volatile liquids, usually with a pleasant fragrant odor, while the esters of the higher saturated acids are white, odorless, crystalline solids.

In general, the boiling and melting points of the lower esters are below those of the corresponding acids. With an increase in the alcohol chain length, the values increase and become higher than those of the parent acids. Since the lower esters are readily distillable and have favorable solubilities for many other type compounds, they are widely used as solvents in lacquers, paints, coating compounds, plastic mixtures and in extraction processes. They are generally insoluble in water, but quite soluble or miscible with other organic liquids.

Although esters do occur widely in nature, all except the fatty acid glycerides and higher natural esters are synthesized commercially in large tonnage quantities for a great variety of industrial uses. The main methods for the preparation of esters are shown below. Generally speaking, esterification is any reaction by which an ester is produced as the principal product.

(1) Reaction of an alcohol directly with an acid or acid anhydride or acid chloride:

$$RCO \cdot OH + R′OH = RCO \cdot OR′ + H_2O$$

(2) Alcoholysis or ester-interchange:

$$RCOOR′ + R″OH = RCOOR″ + R′OH$$

(3) Acidolysis or acid-interchange:

$$R′COOR + R″COOH = R″COOR + R′COOH$$

(4) Trans-esterification:

$$RCOOR″ + R′COOR‴ = RCOOR‴ + R′COOR″$$

(5) Reaction of an acid amide with an alcohol:

$$RCO \cdot NH_2 + R′OH = RCO \cdot OR′ + NH_3$$

(6) Auto-oxidation and reduction of aldehydes (Cannizaro reaction):

$$2RCHO = RCH_2CO \cdot OR$$

(7) Carbonylation of alcohols:

$$3ROH + CO = RCO \cdot OR + HCOOR + H_2O$$

(8) Alcoholysis of nitriles:

$$RCN + 2R'OH = RCO \cdot OR + RNH_2$$

It can be readily seen that from the numerous methods available for the preparation of esters, there is no absolute best way to prepare any one ester. The route chosen depends on scale of operation, purity desired, availability of raw materials and of course the economics of the process. Direct esterification of an acid or acid derivative with an alcohol is usually the simplest and least expensive method for large scale production of esters. Where water is evolved as the by-product, this tends to limit the degree of esterification, or completion of the reaction, unless removed from the reaction equilibrium. This may be done in various ways. Use of a large excess of the more volatile component, usually the alcohol, will permit the water to be removed under reflux temperatures, by azeotropic distillation or entrainment in the alcohol vapors. Otherwise a third component, an entrainer or withdrawing agent, has to be added which will azeotrope or entrain the water, in order to remove it from the system. Sometimes the use of vacuum, particularly with high boiling esters and inert gases sparged through the reaction mixture, will assist in the removal of the water of reaction.

Esters of monocarboxylic acids are neutral substances and undergo hydrolysis to form the free acid and alcohol. Heat and acid or base catalyst speed up the hydrolysis. The ease of hydrolysis decreased with increasing molecular weight, with the higher esters being difficult to hydrolyze.

Dicarboxylic Acids

Properties. The straight-chain C_4—C_{10} saturated aliphatic dicarboxylic acids, general formula $(HOOC)C_nH_{2n}(COOH)$, where n is 2–8, are crystalline materials exhibiting an alternating variation in melting point and water solubility as the number of carbon atoms is increased (Table 3). These contrasts become less marked as the number of carbon atoms increases. Chains with an odd number of segments do not fit favorably into the crystal structure; hence the acids having an odd number of carbon atoms have lower melting points than those having an even number. The alternating relationship is also evident in the decarboxylation temperatures (Table 4); the even numbered acids are more difficult to decompose than the odd ones preceding them. Boiling points, however, rise steadily with increasing molecular weight.

The diacids having fewer than four carbon atoms (i.e., oxalic and malonic) are of little commercial interest in plastics and resins because they

TABLE 4. DECARBOXYLATION TEMPERATURES.

Acid	Decarboxylation Temp., °C	Acid	Decarboxylation Temp., °C
Oxalic	170	adipic	310
Malonic	150	suberic	350
Succinic	300	azelaic	330
Glutaric	285	sebacic	360

decompose on heating. Succinic and glutaric acids, having four and five carbon atoms, respectively, yield cyclic anhydrides when heated alone, and this reaction frequently interferes with their use in polycondensations. Higher acids yield polymeric anhydrides upon being heated alone. Branched diacids are not readily available.

A dicarboxylic acid useful in plastics and resins is "dimer acid." It is not a pure compound, but a mixture resulting from the polymerization of mixed unsaturated fatty acids. One mixture contains 95% of a C_{36} dibasic acid, 4% of a C_{54} tribasic acid, and 1% C_{18} monobasic acids. Reported physical properties[10] are: sp. gr. 25°C/20°C, 0.95; n_D^{60}, 1.4706.

Dicarboxylic acids react readily, mostly without decomposition, with polyols and polyamines to give polymeric materials useful in the manufacture of plastics and resins. They also undergo reactions characteristic of all carboxylic acids, such as salt formation, esterification, amidation, and formation of peracids. The methylene group adjacent to the carboxylic acids group, the methylene group, is susceptible to radical reactions (abstraction of a hydrogen atom) and to attack by nucleophilic reagents. The susceptibility toward nucleophilic attack is greatest in malonic acid derivatives with at least one hydrogen atom on the carbon atom; it decreases as the distance between carboxylic acid groups increases.

Preparation. In general, dicarboxylic acids are prepared industrially by controlled oxidation of alicyclic and other aliphatic compounds. The acids having an even number of carbon atoms are generally more accessible than are the acids with an odd number of carbon atoms. It is for this reason that the odd-numbered diacids have found relatively little application.

Dicarboxylic acids can be prepared by the usual methods of synthesis of the carboxylic acid group.

Succinic Acid, $HOOCCH_2CH_2COOH$, occurs widely in nature in both plant and animal matter. It is used as an intermediate in the synthesis of a variety of organic compounds by utilizing the reactivity of the α-methylene groups.

The acid was first obtained by Agricola in 1550 by distilling amber. It was recovered in 3–8% yields. It is also found in some varieties of lignite, in natural resins, turpentine oils, and animal fluids. Succinic acid is formed in both the chemical and biochemical oxidation of fats, in the fermentation of calcium malate or ammonium tartrate, and in the alcoholic fermentation of sugar.

Succinic acid is generally produced by the hydrogenation of maleic anhydride or fumaric acid (see *Acids, Maleic and Fumaric*, pp. 242, 270). It is isolated either as the free acid or as the anhydride. There are several different processes available for this purpose and all give excellent commercial yields. They include, for example, treating an aqueous solution of sodium maleate with hydrogen gas at 100°C under 2500 psi pressure in the presence of a Raney nickel catalyst, electrolytic reduction, and reduction with sulfuric acid and zinc. The acidic or basic hydrolysis of succinonitrile has also been used for the preparation of the acid:

$$NCCH_2CH_2CN + H_2O \xrightarrow{H+ \text{ or } OH-}$$
$$HOOCCH_2CH_2COOH$$

Oxidative methods may be employed for preparation of succinic acid. Treatment of glutamic acid or esters of butyric acid with hydrogen peroxide, or with acetic acid and potassium peroxydisulfate, or with acetylperoxide gives succinic acid. Oxidation of petroleum wax or of butyrolactone with vanadium oxide or copper oxide catalyst yields mixtures of the acid and anhydride. Potassium malonate, tetrahydrofurfuryl alcohol, and tetrahydrofuran give the acid on electrolytic oxidation.

Caustic fusion of corn cobs yields succinic acid as does treatment of milk sugar (lactose), gum arabic, or cinnamic acid with hydrated lime.

Glutaric Acid, $HOOC(CH_2)_3COOH$, is so named because of its relationship to *glut*amic acid and tar*taric* acid. It is less available than the other dicarboxylic acids. The acid has been found in beet juice and in the water in which raw sheep's wool has been washed. It was obtained from the latter source by Biusine and Biusine in 1888. Glutaric acid is now prepared by the oxidation of cyclopentanone by nitric acid, or by air in the presence of catalyst.

Vapor-phase catalytic oxidations of methylcyclohexane or petroleum fractions rich in cyclohexanes also yield glutaric acid A good laboratory preparation is the hydrolysis of glutaronitrile, which can be obtained from 1,3-dibromopropane (tri-methylene dibromide) and an alkali cyanide.

Adipic Acid, $HOOC(CH_2)_4COOH$, was originally found as a natural constituent of sugar beets. It occurs in natural products that have become rancid due to oxidation. It is also a reaction product of the oxidation of Russian mineral oil, which is rich in cyclohexane. The acid was first synthesized in 1902 through the dinitrile from 1,4-dibromobutane (tetra-methylene dibromide), and described by Thorpe in 1909. The name adipic acid is derived from the Latin word for fat, *Adeps*. The first commercial production of adipic acid in the United States was begun in 1937 by E. I. duPont de Nemours & Company.

Commercially,* adipic acid is manufactured from one of two basic raw materials, either phenol or cyclohexane. Essentially the process consists of a two step air oxidation of cyclohexanol, obtained by hydrogenation of phenol, or by oxidation of cyclohexane. This is followed by further oxidation of the cyclohexanol to cyclohexanone. And finally air oxidation of the latter to adipic acid in an acetic acid solution completes the synthesis.

Since a high degree of purity is required for production of polymers from adipic acid, the crude adipic acid is usually purified by recrystallization from water. The catalysts used in the oxidation may be metallic oxides, such as those of vanadium, mercury, manganese, or molybdenum; salts such as mercuric sulfate or ammonium vanadate; or copper salts. The temperature of the reaction may vary from 35–275°C. A recent method of great potential is the electroreductive dimerization of acrylonitrile to form adiponitrile, which may then be hydrolyzed to adipic acid:

$$2CH_2{=}CHCN \xrightarrow{\text{electrolysis}} NC(CH_2)_4CN$$
$$NC(CH_2)_4CN \xrightarrow{H_2O} HOOC(CH_2)_4COOH$$

Pimelec Acid, $HOOC(CH_2)_5COOH$, derives its name from the Greek word for fat, *Pimele*. Pimelic acid was obtained in 1884 by Ganttner and Hell, as a product of oxidation of ricinoleic acid. It has also been found in the urine of herbivorous animals. It was first synthesized by nitric acid oxidation of cycloheptanone. It is conveniently prepared from 3-tetrahydrobenzonitrile, which in turn is made from acrylonitrile and butadiene:

$$CH_2{=}CHCN + CH_2{=}CH{-}CH{=}CH_2 \rightarrow$$

Chlorination of cyclohexanone, followed by preparation of the cyanide and treatment with sodium hydroxide, also yields pimelic acid:

$$HOOC(CH_2)_5COOH$$

(*See Nylon Intermediates, p. 293).

It can also be made by treatment of salicylic acid with sodium in amyl alcohol, and by heating 1,1,5,5-pentanetetracarboxylic acid, derived from trimethylene dibromide and sodium malonic ester:

$$Br(CH_2)_3Br + 2NaCH(COOC_2H_5)_2 \longrightarrow$$
$$(H_5C_2OOC)_2CH(CH_2)_3CH(COOC_2H_5)_2 \xrightarrow[H+]{H_2O}$$
$$HOOC(CH_2)_5COOH$$

Suberic Acid, $HOOC(CH_2)_6COOH$, is named from its preparation by the oxidation of cork, from the Latin *suber*. In 1841 Tilley obtained the acid by nitric acid oxidation of castor oil. It can be prepared by prolonged oxidation of castor oil (mainly glyceryl ricinoleate) and ricinoleic acids or esters with relatively dilute nitric acid at high temperature. These conditions favor the production of suberic acid over that of azelaic acid, which is produced at the same time. The two acids are separated by distillation of the methyl esters. Suberic acid can also be prepared by oxidation of cyclooctene, which is prepared by partial hydrogenation of cyclooctatetraene. The latter, in turn, is obtained from acetylene. The acid has also been prepared by the electrolysis of potassium ethyl glutarate and by the reaction of the Grignard reagent from trimethylene dibromide with carbon dioxide:

$$Br(CH_2)_3Br + 2Mg \quad BrMg(CH_2)_3MgBr \xrightarrow{CO_2}$$
$$HOOC(CH_2)_6COOH$$

Azelaic Acid, $HOOC(CH_2)_7COOH$, is the C_9 straight-chain dicarboxylic acid. Its name is derived from Azotic (nitric) and elaidic acid (an acid isomer of oleic acid), because the acid is obtained from oleic acid by nitric acid oxidation. Azelaic acid is found in natural products only after exposure to the oxidative influence of the atmosphere. Crushed castor beans, when rancid, contain azelaic acid.

The acid was prepared by Ganttner and Hell in 1881, and by Saytzeff in 1885 by oxidation of oleic acid with potassium permanganate. Oxidative fission of oleic acid can be carried out to give relatively good yields of azelaic acid but the reaction cannot be controlled to produce stoichiometric quantities of the primary fission

TABLE 5. PHYSICAL PROPERTIES OF DICARBOXYLIC ACID ESTERS, $ROOC(CH_2)_xCOOR$.

Ester	Formula wt.	M.P., °C	B.P., °C	d_4^{20}	n_D^{20}
Succinic acid esters (n = 2)					
Dimethyl	146.14	19.5	192.8	1.202[18]	1.41976[18.3]
Diethyl	174.19	−21	217.7	1.0402	1.42007
Di-*n*-butyl	230.30	−22	255	0.974[26]	1.428[25]
Dibenzyl	298.33	36	238[14]		
Glutaric acid ester (n = 3)					
Diethyl	188.22	−24.1	237	1.025	1.4241
Pimelic acid esters (n = 5)					
Dimethyl	188.22	−20.6	121–122[11]		
Monoethyl	188.22	10	181–182[18]		
Diethyl	216.27	23.8	139–141[15]	0.99448	
Suberic acid esters (n = 6)					
Monomethyl	188.22	10	146–150[1]	1.047	
Dimethyl	202.24	−3.1	130–131[9]	1.0217	1.43408
Monoethyl	202.24	21–22	186–188.5[16]	1.037[23]	1.4412[23]
Diethyl	230.30	−5.9	251–253[320]	0.9822	1.43278
Azelaic acid esters (n = 7)					
Dimethyl	216.27	−3.9			
Monoethyl	216.27	28–29	178–179[5.5]		
Diethyl	244.32	−18.5	291	0.9766[15]	
Di-2-ethylhexyl	300.43	−105	237[5]	0.918[20/20]	1.446
Diisooctyl	300.43	−90	235[5]	0.920[20/20]	1.448
Di-2-ethylbutyl	272.38	−105	230[5]	0.934[20/20]	1.443
Sebacic acid esters (n = 8)					
Monomethyl	216.27	40–41	208[20]		
Dimethyl	230.30	26.4	175[20]	0.98818[28]	1.43549[28]
Monoethyl	230.30	35	202–203[15]		
Diethyl	250.35	5.1	308	0.96461	1.43589
Di-*n*-butyl	314.45	−19.5	344–345	0.933[15]	1.4391
Di-*n*-hexyl	370.56		184[2]	0.920	
Di-*n*-octyl	426.66		284[4]	0.910[25]	1.447[28]
Dibenzyl	382.49	28	265[4]	1.05[25]	1.521

products indicated:

$$CH_3(CH_2)_7CH{=}CH(CH_2)_7COOH \xrightarrow{O_2}$$
$$CH_3(CH_2)_7COOH + HOOC(CH_2)_7COOH$$

pelargonic acid   *azelaic acid*

Both of the primary fission products undergo further oxidation to produce shorter-chain acids prior to the complete oxidation of the oleic acid. Ozonization of oleic acid also yields azelaic acid. The so-called malonic ester synthesis has also been used in the laboratory to prepare azelaic acid via pentamethylene dibromide and diethyl sodiomalonate:

$$Br(CH_2)_5Br + 2NaCH(COOOC_2H_5)_2 \longrightarrow$$
$$(H_5C_2OOC)_2CH(CH_2)_5CH(COOC_2H_5)_2$$
$$\xrightarrow[H+]{H_2O} HOOC(CH_2)_7COOH$$

Sebacic acid, $HOOC(CH_2)_8COOH$, appears to be named from the Latin *Sebaceus* (tallow candle) because of its tallowy feel, and its use in the manufacture of candles. The acid was first prepared by Boius in 1885 by the dry distillation of castor oil (mainly ricoleic acid) in the presence of caustic soda. This method was improved to meet the increasing industrial demand for the acid. The improvements consist of carrying out the reaction with caustic soda either in the solid form, in aqueous solution, or as a suspension in mineral oil.

Sebacic acid can be prepared by various other methods, such as the oxidation of 10-undecenoic acid and the electrolysis of an aqueous solution of potassium ethyl adipate.

Dimer acid is produced by the thermal polymerization of mixed C_{18} monobasic unsaturated acids. It is produced in several grades, containing minor amounts of tribasic acid.

Dicarboxylic Acid Esters

Diesters of dicarboxylic acids appear extensively in the polymer field as polyesters such as poly (ethylene terephthalate), and in alkyd resins. An important reaction for their preparation is ester interchange, basic catalysts usually being preferred over acid catalysts since they yield products with less discoloration. Alcoholysis is used in the preparation of superpolyesters to form bis-hydroxyethyl) esters of dibasic acids, usually from the methyl esters (see esters above under mono-carboxylic acids).

Properties. The diesters of dicarboxylic acids are for the most part colorless, high-boiling liquids. Some physical properties of representative esters of dicarboxylic acids are listed in Tables 5 and 6.

TABLE 6. PHYSICAL PROPERTIES OF ADIPIC ACID ESTERS, $ROCO(CH_2)COOR$.

Ester	Formula wt.	M.P., °C	B.P., °C	$d\frac{20}{4}$	$n\frac{20}{D}$
Monomethyl	160.17	3	160_{82}		
Monoethyl	174.18	28–29	169–170_{17}	1.081	1.4384
Monopropyl	188.21		146_4	1.0574	1.4401
Monobutyl	202.25		155.5_4	1.0377	1.4418
Dimethyl	174.18	8.5	110_{92}	1.0625	1.4284
Diethyl	202.25	−21.4	127_{13}	1.0261	1.4272
Dipropyl	230.30	−20.3	155_{10}	0.9790	1.4314
Diisopropyl	230.30		136_{14}		
Dibutyl	258.35	−37.5	154_4	0.9652	1.4369
Diisobutyl	258.35			0.957	1.428^{25}
Di-*sec*-butyl	258.35		153–154_{10}	0.9543	1.4301
Di-*tert*-butyl	258.35	10	$116_{1.5}$		
Diamyl (mixture of *n* and *iso*)	286.40	−14			
Diisoamyl (di(3-methylbutyl))	286.40		190_{15}	0.9455	1.4343
Di-*n*-hexyl	314.45	−8		0.933^{25}	1.439^{25}
Di(1,3-dimethylbutyl)	314.45			9.926	1.433^{25}
Dioctyl	342.49	9.7	175_2	0.9135	1.4402^{25}
Diisooctyl	342.49			0.915	1.440^{25}
di(2-ethylhexyl)	342.49			0.927	1.447
Dinonyl	370.54	21.6		0.914^{25}	1.445^{25}
Di(3,5,5-trimethylhexyl)	370.54	−10	206_5	0.9130^{25}	1.4455^{25}
di-*n*-decyl	398.59	26	244_5	0.896	1.4481^{25}
Ditridecyl	482.75	45.9		0.891	1.459^{25}
Dicyclohexyl	312.44	36–88	212_{12}	1.013^{40}_{25}	1.4702^{25}
Di(2-methoxyethyl)	262.30		185–190_{11}	1.075^{25}	1.439^{25}
Bis(2-methoxymethoxyethyl)	322.35		199_{215}	$1.112^{15.6}_{15.6}$	1.4402^{25}
Di(2-ethoxyethyl)	290.35		165_4	1.036^{25}	1.439^{25}

Uses. The dicarboxylic acids find much more widespread uses in the polymer field than the monocarboxylic acid derivatives.

Polyesters and Alkyd Resins which are industrially important are based primarily on phthalic anhydride (coating resins) and terephthalic acid (fibers). These are modified in certain instances with an aliphatic dicarboxylic acid to improve the flexibility. The modifying acid is usually adipic acid because it is the most readily available and the most economical. As a general rule, the use of acids of shorter chain length than adipic will stiffen the product and of longer chain length will increase the flexibility. The odd-numbered carbon atom acids will tend to flexibilize more than the next higher even-numbered acid.

The most important industrial application for aliphatic saturated polyesters is in the field of polyurethan elastomers (see *polyurethanes*). Polyurethan foam based on polyesters is not widely accepted except in rigid foams because of inherently poor resistance to moisture. Again adipic acid is the major dicarboxylic acid used. In 1960, the production figure for polyurethan-type elastomers was 6,798,000 lb at an average price of 94¢ per lb. This use required about 2,700,000 lb of adipic acid in 1960. Polyester-based polyurethan foams (nonelastomeric) used 8,000,000 lb of adipic acid in 1960. Laminating resins, polyesters, and alkyd reins consumed about 8–9 million lb of adipic acid in 1960.

The polyesters used for polyurethan elastomers are based on the reaction of adipic acid with various glycols such as ethylene glycol, diethylene glycol, propylene glycol, 1,4-butanediol, and blends of these glycols. The resulting elastomers exhibit high tensile strength, good resilience, excellent aging characteristics, and outstanding abrasion resistance. Foams are made from polyesters containing adipic acid, a glycol, and a triol (about 4% by weight of total) (see *Alcohols, Mono- and Polyhydric,* p. 30).

Succinic acid will impart flexibility to coatings and plastics when polymerized in combination with other dicarboxylic acids. Commercial production figures for succinic acid have not appeared in recent years. The U.S. Tariff Commission Reports show that 29,000 and 60,000 lb of succinic acid were produced in 1946 and 1947, respectively.

Azelaic acid is used to a very minor extent in polyesters and alkyd resins. It is sold by Emery Industries, which in 1960 produced 4–5 million lb. Its chief use is in plasticizers, however. It is expected to find greater usage in polyesters in the future.

Sebacic acid was produced at a level of 14 million lb per year in 1960 and 1961. Of this, 11% went into alkyd resin uses.

Hexahydrophthalic anhydride has found use in alkyd resins. It imparts rigidity and toughness to the cured resin without the poor weathering characteristics of phthalic anhydride-based alkyd resins.

"Dimer acid" is finding great use in surface-coating applications where ti is used to replace a portion of the fatty acid. Improved flexibility is the result. Polyesters based on "dimer acid" are used in both rigid and flexible foam formulations.

Polyamides, whose predominant single type is nylon-6,6 poly(hexamethylene adipamide), is, as with polyesters, the major dicarboxylic acid in use. The major outlet for nylon is as a textile fiber. Recently, modified nylon-6,6 has become available for use in various molding applications, nontextile filament uses, in sheets, rods, and tubes. Of the approximately 500 million lb per year capacity for adipic acid, some 290 million lb is used to make nylon-6,6. The Chemstrand Corp. (180 million lb per year and E. I. duPont de Nemours & Co. (170 million lb per year use almost all of their adipic acid capacity for the production of nylon-6,6.

A major use for the 14 million lb per year of sebacic acid is in the production of nylon-6,10. In 1960 and 1961, 5 million lb was used for this purpose. Nylon-6,10 was used for molding, and as sheet, rod, etc.

A class of polyamides available under the trademark "Versamid" (General Mills) is based on "dimer acid"; these polyamides are finding use as flexibilizing curing agents for epoxy resins, as hot-melt adhesives, and in coatings.

Plasticizers are used to render rigid plastics, particularly poly(vinyl chloride), more flexible. Most plasticizers are esters. There are some 300 different types on the market, including simple monoesters, diesters, polyesters, and esters of inorganic acids. The plasticizer market has a projected growth rate of 7% a year. In 1961, 630 million lb of plasticizer was produced, of which 437 million lb went into poly(vinyl chloride). A breakdown of plasticizer production is given in Table 7.

It can be easily seen that the aliphatic dicarboxylic acids comprise only a small fraction of the total plasticizer market. These plasticizers are

TABLE 7. 1961 PRODUCTION OF PLASTICIZERS.

Type	Production, 1000 lb	Sales, 1000 lb	Average unit value, $/lb
Phthalic esters	375,566	320,677	0.25
Adipic esters	25,742	20,538	0.37
Azelaic esters	7335	5972	0.42
Sebacic esters	11,500	9181	0.59

used where low-temperature flexibility of the plasticized product is necessary. Another major use for aliphatic diesters is as synthetic lubricants; 30% of the production went into that market in 1961. The U.S. Tariff Commission report does not separate plasticizer usage from synthetic lubricant usage. The azelates are more efficient than the adipates for low-temperature uses, and as such are displacing the adipates. The sebacates are also higher in cost and are largely relegated to specialty uses.

The polymeric plasticizers represent the fastest growing segment of the plasticizer market. The output was 38 million lb in 1960, and about 45 million lb in 1961. Practically all is used in vinyl chloride polymers. The polymeric plasticizers are made from a dicarboxylic acid (or mixture of acids), a glycol, and a fatty acid. They are classified as secondary plasticizers, since these are materials that are not soluble enough in a resin to be the sole plasticizer and hence are blended with others.

ARTHUR M. SCHILLER

Cross reference: PLASTICIZERS.

ALLYL ALCOHOL AND ITS ESTERS

Allyl alcohol (CH_2=$CHCH_2OH$) is a colorless liquid with a characteristic pungent odor, known to science since 1856, when the first descriptions of its preparation were published. The name *allyl* (from the Latin *allium*, garlic) had been coined as early as 1844.

Allylalcohol is of considerable importance to plastics manufacturers because of its use as a basic material for allyl plastics.

The first synthesis of allyl alcohol was based on glycerol, which reacts with phosphorus iodide to form allyl iodide, which in turn was converted into allyl alcohol via the oxalate or other ester. In 1870, a more direct synthesis from glycerol was developed employing oxalic acid, which was later modified by employing formic acid. In recent years the Shell Chemical Company has been preparing allyl alcohol from the high-temperature chlorination of polypropylene, producing allyl chloride from which the alcohol is obtained by acidic or basic hydrolysis.

Properties

Allyl alcohol boils at 96.9°C (atmospheric pressure) and congeals at −129°C. At lower temperatures it forms a "glass." It is moderately volatile (vapor pressure 23.8 mm at 25°C), and is lighter than water but denser than the saturated alcohols: $d_4^{25} = 0.8476$, weight 7.05 lb per US gal at 25°C. Allyl alcohol is completely miscible with water at room temperature, and forms a constant boiling mixture with water, boiling at 88.89°C and

containing 72.3% by weight of allyl alcohol. It is likewise miscible with all common organic solvents, and forms azeotropes with a number of them.

In its chemical properties allyl alcohol is both reactive and versatile. Direct derivates obtainable from allyl alcohol include oxidation and reduction products, chlorohydrins, ethers, esters from a great variety of organic and inorganic acids, polymers, condensation products, complex amino-derivatives, and the like. This versatility results from the presence of both a primary alcohol group and an olefinic double bond; either may react, or both simultaneously, depending upon reagents and conditions. Each derivative is of course capable of undergoing modification to produce further derivatives; for example, from the chlorohydrins many useful compounds may be obtained, including glycerol ethers and esters, amino compounds, sulfonates, etc. Among the most valuable derivatives of allyl alcohol are the resinous polymers obtainable from the alcohol itself and from its esters.

Allyl Alcohol and its Esters

Nearly all of the allyl esters of saturated monobasic acids thus far prepared have been polymerized to resins. A brief review of such polymerizations follows.

Allyl alcohol is quite stable at ordinary temperatures, undergoing neither polymerization nor other changes for long periods. When heated to about 100°C in the presence of oxygen, however, allyl alcohol undergoes reaction, yielding viscous polymers of relatively low molecular weight. A polymer prepared in this way has been reacted with gum rosin (abietic acid) to form a polymer with fast-drying properties when incorporated into varnishes, and with drying oil fatty acids to produce drying oils of improved properties.

Polyallyl alcohol, which contains one double bond per molecule, may be made by saponifying a polymer of diallyl oxalate. Polyallyl alcohol is soluble in water, alcohols, glycols, etc., and only slightly soluble in hydrocarbons. It readily forms polyesters and alkyd resins, and undergoes other known reactions of polyhydroxy compounds; for example, such a product has been reacted with acrylic acid, giving a polyallyl acrylate.

Monoallyl Esters

The polymerization of monoallyl esters of saturated acids proceeds in a manner like that of allyl alcohol itself; the ester polymers are likewise linear and hence thermoplastic. These monoallyl esters are sometimes used as copolymerizing agents in alkyd or other resins, and as polymerizable plasticizers. Thus allyl acetate has been copolymerized with an unsaturated alkyd resin (diethylene glycol maleate or itaconate); allyl formate with N-n-butylmaleimide; allyl caproate or allyl chloroacetate with vinylidene chloride, and allyl acetate, butyrate, or caproate with vinyl chloride. The copolymers with vinyl resins have been suggested as permanent thermoplastic adhesives. Allyl acetate has been reported to act as a polymerization inhibitor for diallyl phthalate partial polymer, although copolymers have also been made.

Allyl esters containing two or more unsaturated groups, such as the monoesters of unsaturated acids or the diesters of dibasic acids, give thermosetting resins, which generally combine good solvent resistance, transparency, toughness, hardness, and dimensional stability even at temperatures considerably higher than the boiling point of water—properties which make them valuable in many applications such as cast or molded objects, surface coatings, and constituents of safety glass.

Monoallyl esters of unsaturated acids that have been used to make simple polymers include allyl acrylate, allyl chloroacrylate, allyl methacrylate, allyl crotonate, allyl cinnamate, allyl cinnamalacetate, allyl furoate, and allyl furfurylacrylate. Copolymers include those of allyl acrylate with acrylic acid, allyl methacrylate with butadiene, allyl crotonate with methyl methacrylate, allyl cinnamate with vinylidene chloride or styrene, and allyl furoate with styrene or vinylidene chloride.

Diallyl Esters

Similarly extensive use has been made of diallyl esters. Simple polymers include those from diallyl oxalate, diallyl malonate, diallyl succinate, diallyl sebacate, diallyl maleate, diallyl fumarate, diallyl itaconate, allyl ether of diallyl malate, diallyl phthalate, diallyl 9,9-fluorenedipropionate, diallyl carbonate, diethylene glycol bis-allyl carbonate, and diethylene glycol bis-allyl phthalate. Corresponding copolymers include those of diallyl oxalate with vinylidene chloride, diallyl malonate with vinylidene chloride, diallyl succinate with vinyl acetate, diallyl adipate with vinylidene chloride, diallyl maleate with methyl methacrylate or styrene, etc., and diallyl phthalate with p-chlorostyrene, divinylbenzene, or vinylidene chloride, or with a glycol maleate resin, or with such polymer and linseed oil or these and sebacic acid or castor oil.

In the plastics industry, the principal allylics are the diallyl esters of phthalic and isophthalic acids—diallyl phthalate (DAP) and isophthalate (DAIP). They are available commercially as monomers or as partially polymerized prepolymers. Both monomers and prepolymers or mixtures of the two are converted to the cured thermoset stage by free radical sources, usually selected peroxides. Other monomers of commercially significant importance are diallyl maleate (DAM) and diallyl chlorendate (DAC). Diethylene glycol bis-allyl carbonate finds its major use in colorless, optically clear castings. Triallyl cyanurate (TAC) is the most reactive allylic monomer in copolymerizations with vinyl-type monomers. Dapon 35 (a trademark of the Food Machinery & Chemical Corporation) is the prepolymer resin derived from diallyl orthophthalate, and "Dapon M" is the isophthalate analogue. Table 1 gives the typical physical properties of diallyl castings and laminates.

TABLE 1. DIALLYL PHTHALATE, TYPICAL RANGES OF PHYSICAL PROPERTIES OF CASTINGS AND LAMINATES[a].

	Clear casting	Muslin laminate	Duck laminate	Fortisan laminate	Glass cloth laminate[b]	Mitscherlich paper laminate
Specific gravity, 20/4 C	1.27	1.29–1.30	1.3–1.4	1.29–1.41	1.73–1.79	1.32
Resin content, % wt.	100	50.0–52.0	67	59–61	....	30.5
Tensile strength, psi	6000–8000	7900–9900	8000–8800	14,300–19,600	31,300–45,900	27,100
Modulus in tension, psi $\times 10^{-6}$	0.37–0.46	0.77–0.93	0.75–0.86	1.2–1.4	1.6–2.5	2.4
Elongation, %	1.7–2.2	4–5	4–5	3–3.5	2–3	1.6
Compressive strength (edgewise) psi	20,000–26,000	22,200–26,500	23,000–32,500	....	13,100–28,800	17,700
Impact strength Izod (ft lb/in. of notch)	0.4–0.5	3.6	3.0	10.1–11.4	22.2	....
Barcol hardness	45–47	45–50	43–56	45–52	60–66	58
Rockwell M hardness	118	....	....	101–103	113–119	....
Heat distortion point, °C	106–121	....	105–170	160–175	>180[c]	....
Refractive index, n_D^{20}	1.572	....	....	....	....	....
Light transmission at 425 mu (%)	77–84	....	....	....	....	....

[a] Tests conducted by appropriate ASTM procedures. All laminate plies crossed.
[b] ECC-127 glass cloth.
[c] 0.015–0.045 mm at 170–180°C.

Reaction with Inorganic Acids, Anhydrides, Etc.

The reaction of concentrated hydrobromic or hydrochloric acid with allyl alcohol in the presence of sulfuric acid gives almost quantitative yields of allyl bromide or allyl chloride. With other dehydrating agents (zinc chloride, calcium chloride), the reaction with HCl leads to allyl ether as well as allyl chloride. The conversion of allyl alcohol to halide (chloride, bromide, or iodide) by reaction with the hydrogen halide also proceeds in the absence of dehydrating agents, especially if the water formed is continuously removed by distillation and the reaction has been conducted at room temperature for several days. The allyl halides are especially valuable chemical intermediates—from them are produced allyl esters and ethers, mono- and dihalohydrins, epihalohydrins, trihalopropanes, allyl mustard oil (allyl isothiocyanate), allylamines, allylurea, allylbenzene, allylmalonic acid, allyl-substituted barbituric acids (sedatives), cyclopropane (anesthetic), allyl starch (resin), and many other useful products.

Toxicity

Allyl alcohol is toxic. The vapors are quite irritating to the eyes, nose, and throat. Local contact with the skin may cause first- and second degree burns with blister formation. Fortunately, the characteristic odor and "tear-gas" effects of allyl alcohol provide warning of its presence.

HAROLD G. VESPER

ALLYLAMINES

The term *allyl* refers to the univalent radical —$CH_2CH=CH_2$, or similar arrangement of carbon and hydrogen atoms. *Amino group* refers to the group-NH_2 united to a radical other than an acid radical. The allylamines or alkenyl amines combine the amino group with one, two, or three allyl radicals and for this reason are highly reactive materials, forming salts, amides, imines, imides, etc., as do the corresponding alkylamines, but in addition undergoing a variety of reactions that are not possible with the latter. The physical properties of the three allylamines are given in Table 1.

Additions to the Double Bond

With hydrogen halides. The allylamines, as salts, can add halogens or hydrogen halides to the double bond to form halopropyl amines.

With hydrogen sulfide. Other addition products can be made by the reaction of allylamines with hydrogen sulfide. Diallylamine, for example, can be reacted with H_2S to form 2,6-dimethyl-1,4-thiazane.

With benzene. Another interesting reaction of the allylamines utilizes the reactive double bond to add alkylamine groups to an aromatic nucleus, thus:

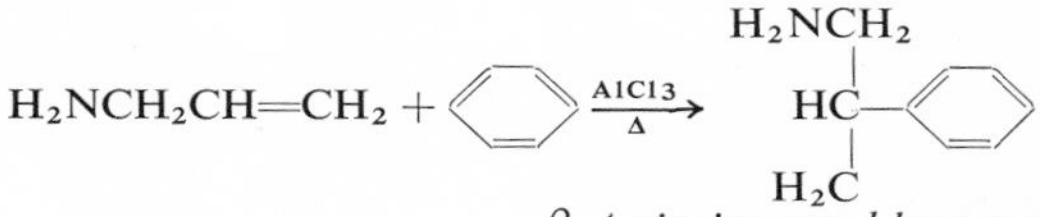

β-*Aminoisopropyl benzene*

With cyclopentadiene. Although allylamines, as free bases, are not readily polymerized with free radical catalysts, the Diels-Alder reaction of allylamine and cyclopentadiene has been carried out, to form 2,5-endomethylene-1,2,5,6-tetra-hydrobenzylamine.

Polymerization

The hydrohalides and quaternary ammonium salts derived from diallylamine and triallylamine have been employed to make both soluble and cross-linked homopolymers. The free radical polymerization of diallylamine hydrohalides is of special interest since a novel type of chain propagation is involved:

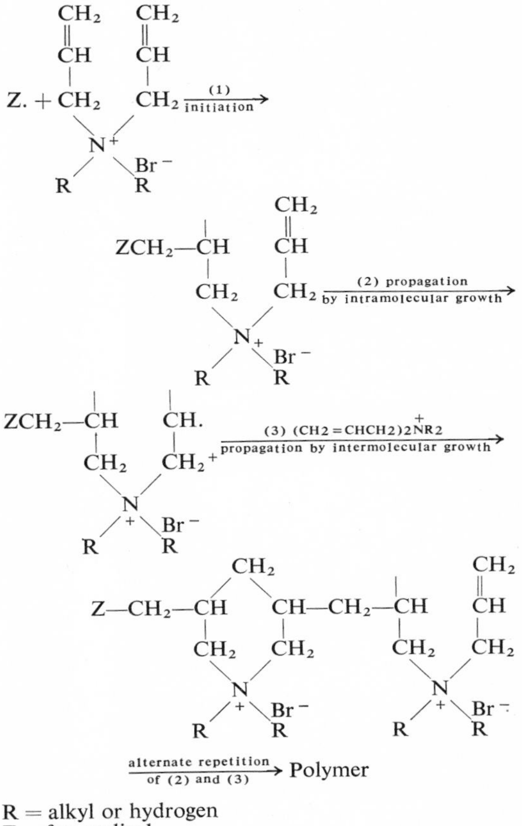

R = alkyl or hydrogen
Z = free radical

The products derived from polymerization are

TABLE 1.

Physical properties (of the pure compound)	Monoallylamine $CH_2=CH—CH_2NH_2$	Diallylamine $(CH_2=CH—CH_2)_2NH$	Triallylamine $(CH_2=CH—CH_2)_3N$
Molecular weight	57.09	97.16	137.22
Boiling point, °C	52.9	110.4	149.5
Melting point, °C	−88.2	−88.4	< −70
Flash point, tag open cup, °F (approx.)	−20	60	103
Specific gravity, 20/4°C	0.7627	0.7874	0.800
Solubility at 20°C, %wt.			
in water	complete	8.6	0.25
in toluene	complete	complete	complete
in acetone	complete	complete	complete
in octane	complete	complete	complete
pH of 0.1M aqueous solution	11.2	11.5	

water-soluble, linear polymers. The reactions of the polymeric free base are typical of a poly-(secondary)amine. Triallylalkylammonium halides or tetraallylammonium halides, on the other hand, form cross-linked, insoluble, infusible resins when polymerized under free-radical conditions.

Reactions Involving the Amino Group

Mannich reactions. Monoallylamine reacts as a typical primary amine in the Mannich reaction with ketones, acids, and esters. For example (allylaminomethyl)benzyl malonic acid is formed from allylamine, formaldehyde and benzylmalonic acid.

With ethylene oxide. Di(2-hydroxyethyl)-allylamine is readily prepared from monoallylamine and ethylene oxide.

With chloroacetic acid. Monoallylamine reacts with chloroacetic acid to form allylamino-acetic acid hydrochloride.

With carbon disulfide. Diallylamine reacts with carbon disulfide to form the sodium salt of allyl dithiocarbamic acid.

With chloroformates. When reacted with an alkyl chloroformate, diallylamine forms a carbamic acid ester.

With alkyl halides. When allylamine is heated with an alkyl iodide or bromide and KOH, the corresponding nitrogen-substituted alkyl allyl-amine is formed:

$$H_2NCH_2CH=CH_2 + CH_3I \xrightarrow[\Delta]{KOH} CH_3NHCH_2CH=CH_2$$

Applications of the Allylamines

Monoallylamine is useful in pharmaceutical applications, where it has been employed as an intermediate in making sedatives, diuretics, and antiseptics. It has also found applications in agricultural chemicals for making bactericides and fungicides. Monoallylamine-ethylene oxide

derivative may be considered as a polyurethane intermediate that functions as a polyol, yet has double bonds available for subsequent cross-linking. The thiuram derivatives have been investigated as rubber-curing accelerators. Small amounts of monoallylamine incorporated in acrylonitrile polymers are said to improve the dyeability of the resultant fibers. Other possible uses for monoallylamine include its use as an intermediate in resin manufacture.

Diallylamine has been reacted with diethylene-melamine to produce a resin that is water-repellent and may possibly be used for treating fabrics or plasticizing other resin systems. Another potential use of diallylamine is as an intermediate for making neoprene rubber plasti-cizers. In addition, it has been suggested that the carbamate derivative of diallylamine be used as a rubber-vulcanization accelerator. Diallylamine has been investigated in preparing dyestuffs, pharmaceuticals, and agricultural chemicals. The soluble polymers derived from diallylamine are suggested for use in binding weatherproof coatings to cellophane to improve wet strength of paper produced under neutral or alkaline conditions, and as "Epon"* curing agents.

Triallylamine is of potential interest as an intermediate for preparation of quaternary ammonium salts, which have been copolymerized by free-radical mechanism to form cross-linked polymers and have been suggested as being potentially useful as ion-exchange resins.

D. M. MAYER

ALLYLIC RESIN INTERMEDIATES

Allylic resins are generally thought of as esterification products of allyl alcohol and an acid, although the manufacturing process may not envolve this particular step. The simplest

* Registered trademark, US Patent Office.

representative process is that for the manufacture of diallyl *ortho*-phthalate monomer, which is condensed as shown below:

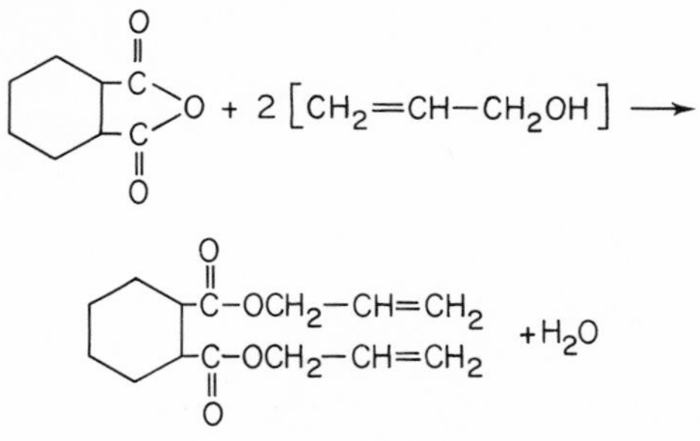

ILLUSTRATION 1.

This reaction is typical for the manufacture of other allylic esters such as diallyl *meta*-phthalate, diallyl maleate, diallyl chlorendate, diallyl adipate and diallyl diglycolate.

On the other hand, the manufacture of diethylene glycol bis(allyl carbonate) is somewhat more involved. The schematic mechanism is generally considered to be:

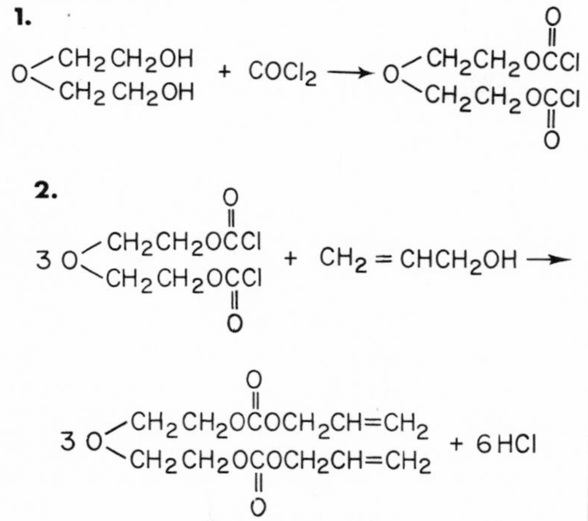

1.

2.

ILLUSTRATION 2.

Triallyl cyanurate is manufactured in two stages. In the first, an appropriate triazine is made:

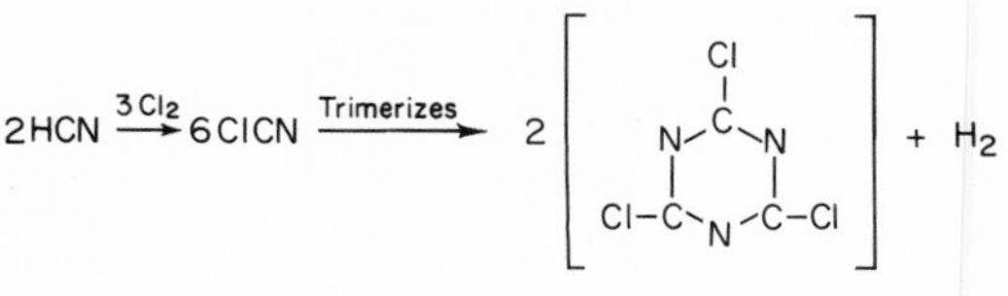

ILLUSTRATION 3.

This is then reacted with alcohol to form the ester using sodium hydroxide plus chloro-*s*-triazine.

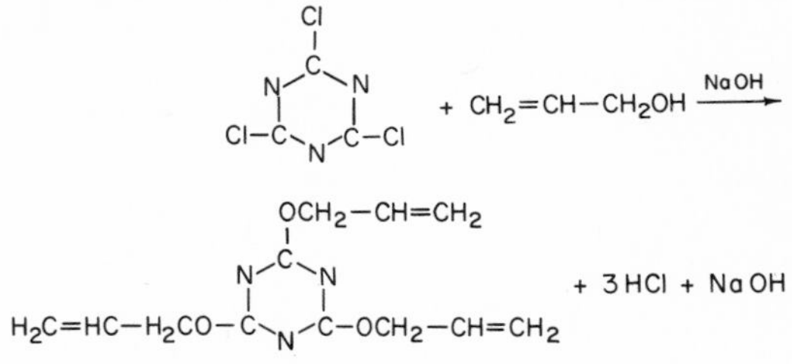

ILLUSTRATION 4.

Using the methods described above, many other allylic esters have been prepared, including allyl acrylate, allyl itaconate and methyl allyl methacrylate.

Some of the representative dibasic acids used in the manufacture of allylics are given in Fig. 1, while the structural formulas of some typical allylic monomers are shown in Fig. 2.

Characteristic allylic monomers are low viscosity fluids at room temperature. Both diallyl chlorendate and triallyl cyanurate are exceptions, having melting points just above room temperature. The characteristic properties of allylic monomers are given in Table 1.

Allylic monomers, with the exception of diethylene glycol bis(allyl carbonate) are rarely homopolymerized *in situ*. More commonly, they are copolymerized with other unsaturated materials such as polyesters. However, it is possible to prepare a resinous material from allylic monomers by advancing the molecular weight to the point that the materials are solids, yet possess residual unsaturation. Such materials, when catalyzed with appropriate organic peroxides, are easily molded and utilized as laminating, molding and casting resins, as well as varnishes.

Preparation of solid resinous, or "prepolymer" allylics, is conducted by reaction at elevated temperature in the presence of an organic peroxide. Usually, the process is limited to a yield of about 25%, at which point the solid is precipitated with alcohol, washed and dried.

Allylic molding compounds are nearly always formulated to include fibrous, particulate and resinous materials. Most allylic compounds are covered by military specifications, and are commonly so identified. For example, GDI-30 is the most widely used type of allylic molding compound, and utilizes long (1/4-in.) glass fibers as reinforcement. Table 2 gives the formulations of common allylic compounds. There are three basic methods for making allylic molding compounds, these being the solvent system, the dry system and the fusion system. The solvent system is the most widely used and the oldest method. This system utilizes the allylic in its prepolymer form. The products of the system are free-flowing granules, chips or flakes.

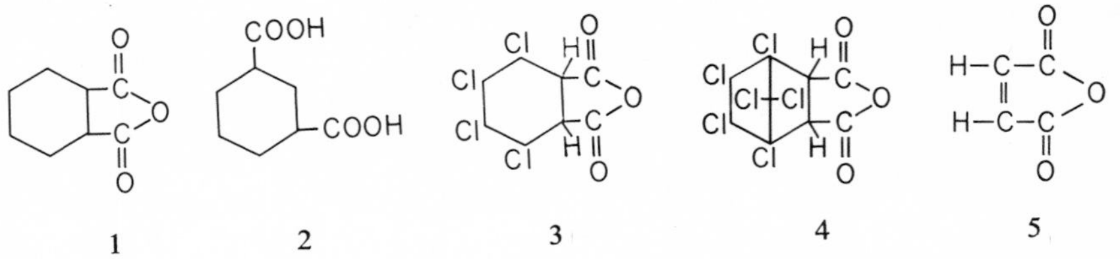

FIG. 1. Some dibasic acids used in manufacture of allylic monomers.

1. phthalic anhydride
2. isophthalic acid
3. tetrachlorophthalic acid

4. chlorendic anhydride
5. maleic anhydride

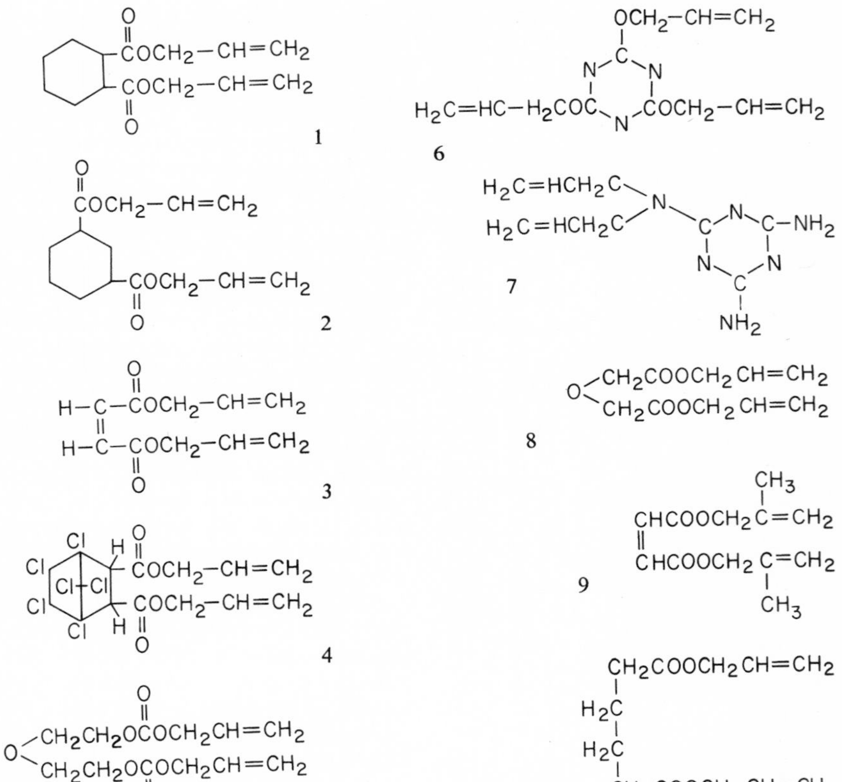

FIG. 2. Structural formulas of some allylic monomers.

1. diallyl (*ortho*)phthalate
2. diallyl (*meta*)phthalate (isophthalate)
3. diallyl maleate
4. diallyl chlorendate
5. diethylene glycol bis(allyl carbonate)

6. triallyl cyanurate
7. N, N-diallyl melamine
8. diallyl diglycollate
9. dimethallyl maleate
10. diallyl adipate

TABLE 1. PROPERTIES OF ALLYL ESTER MONOMERS.

	Diallyl phthalate	Diallyl isophthalate	Diallyl maleate	Diallyl chlorendate	Diallyl adipate	Diallyl diglycollate	Triallyl cyanurate	Diethylene glycol bis-(allyl carbonate)
Density, @ 20°C	1.12	1.12	1.076	1.47	1.025	1.113	1.113	1.143
Molecular weight	246.35	246.35	196	462.76	226.14	214.11	249.24	274.3
Boiling pt., 4 mm Hg °C	160	181	111		137	135	162	160
Freezing point, °C	-70	-3	-47	29.5	-33		27	-4
Flash point, °C	166	340	122	210	150	146	>80	177
Viscosity @ 20°C, cps	12	16.9	4.5	4.0	4.12	7.80	12	9
Vapor pressures @ 20lC mm Hg	27							
Surface tension @ 20°C dynes/cm	34.4	35.4	33		32.10	34.37		35
Solubility in gasoline, %	24	100	23		100	4.8	80	—
Thermal expansion in./in./°C	0.00076							

Solvent System Formulations are prepared by having the prepolymer, monomer and catalyst first dissolved in an equal weight of solvent such as acetone or methyl ethyl ketone. This operation may be conducted in a simple pony or even propeller mixer.

In an intensive mixer, the solid materials-fibers, fillers and release agents are well mixed. This mixer may be the single curve double bladed type operating in a bifurcated, jacketed body. After the solid materials are thoroughly mixed, the previously formulated resin solution is added and the entire system well mixed with the lid of the mixer closed. When mixing is complete, a vacuum may be applied, thereby removing the solvent, until the mix has reached a putty-like consistency.

If glass fiber reinforcement is used, a variation of this method is used in order to avoid degradation of the glass fibers. In this variation, the glass is added last, and a minimum of subsequent mixing is employed in order to avoid breaking down the glass length.

Subsequent to mixing, two finishing approaches are available, dependent upon whether the type of product desired is flake or granule.

If the flake product is desired, the compound is removed from the mixer and spread on drying trays in a low temperature drying oven to remove residual volatiles. Following the drying operation, the matted resultant compound is fed into a hammer mill which breaks the dry matted material into small flakes, the size dependent upon the screen size chosen.

When non-flake compound is desired, a two-roll mill is usually employed to densify and consolidate the compound, and in this case, shorter fibers are used. The putty-like product of the intensive mixer is placed upon a two-roll mill having one roll cooled and the other heated to about 180°F. Using this technique, the milled batch will tend to adhere to the heated roll. The roll heat plus heat of milling then advances the compound to the required point.

This end point of advancement must be determined experimentally, but once found, may be repeated consistently by maintaining consistent roll gap, temperature, and time.

Subsequent to milling, the material is granulated, and is then ready for blending and molding.

Dry formulation system employs a ball mill, and because of this, does not lend itself to the formulation of long fiber materials which are unduly broken down in milling. In addition to this, the dry system does not densify as does two-roll milling, and yields a product of high bulk factor.

From the positive viewpoint, ball milling is potentially the least expensive method of compound manufacture, requires a relatively low capital investment and minimizes fire hazard

TABLE 2. FORMULATION OF TYPICAL SOLVENT-MIX ALLYLIC MOLDING COMPOUNDS.

Ingredient, % by w	MDG	SDG	SDG-F	GDI-30	GDI-30F	SDI-5	SDI-30
Short asbestos fibers	49	—	—	—	—	—	—
1/4in. glass fibers	—	46	37	—	—	—	—
1/2in. glass fibers	—	—	—	36	28	—	—
Acrylic fibers	—	—	—	—	—	26	—
Polyethylene-terphthalate fibers	—	—	—	—	—	—	25
Diallyl phthalate prepolymer	49	43	34	53	38	59	60
Diallyl chlorendate	—	—	10	—	10	—	—
Peroxide	1	1	1	1	1	1	1
Release agent	1	1	1	1	1	1	1
Antimony oxide	—	—	19	—	22	—	—
Kaolinite	—	9	—	9	—	13	13

from dust or solvent fires. Of profound importance is the ability of ball milling to produce a product of minimum color and metal contamination, since there is no abrasive and rubbing contact with metal as there is in two-roll milling.

The ceramic ball mill used for this operation utilizes flint stones loaded to about one-fourth the capacity of the mill. A typical formulation is given in Table 3.

TABLE 3. FORMULATIONS OF TYPICAL NON SOLVENT-MIX ALLYLIC MOLDING COMPOUNDS.

Ingredient, % by w	Allylic dry blend	Allylic fusion blend	Alkyd-diallyl phthalate
Diallyl phthalate pre-polymer	36	28	—
Diallyl phthalate Monomer	2	10	3
Alkyd,	—	—	22
Faolinite	45	45	—
Calcium carbonate	—	—	58
Peroxide	1	1	.75
½in. glass fibers	15	15	12.5
Release agent	1	1	.75
Titanium dioxide	—	—	3

The ball mill should be charged in the following order: Allylic prepolymer, fillers, monomer, catalyst, mold release, color pigments and fibers. All materials except reinforcing fibers should be milled together for about 5 hr. At the end of this period, fibers should be added and the mix milled for an additional 1/2 hr.

Densification of the compound can be conferred by mild baking, although the end result does not compare with that yielded by mill densification. An advantage of this system is the unusually low resin levels which can be achieved. Recipies with resin levels as low as 10% exhibit molding properties and physical properties quite adequate

for many applications. However, the electrical properties are inferior and do not meet military specifications.

Fusion formulation takes advantage of the low melting point of allylic prepolymer-monomer blends. The technique can also be used with alkyd (polyester) allylic formulations.

Typical recipies for both allylic and alkyd allylic blends are given in Table 3.

The mixer used for fusion blending is the same intensive mixer previously described, but using a jacket heated to 120°F–150°F. Mixing procedure is as follows: The resin and monomer are charged into the heated mixer and the mixing proceeds until the formulation has fused into a liquid mass. Next, the catalyst, usually *tert*-butyl perbenzoate, is added and mixed in well. This is followed by fillers and pigments, and the whole mass mixed well. Lastly, reinforcing fibers are added and mixed for a period of time just adequate to achieve good wetting and intimate mixing. The product as produced by this method is putty-like, and can be hand preformed. Variations are possible by increasing filler or fiber reinforcing so as to achieve stiff, fibrous or even boardy compounds.

Any of the compounds described above should be blended after manufacture. The purpose of this is to assure uniformity, inasmuch as single batches are bound to vary from one another. By the use of a large capacity blender, relative uniformity can be assured, and the batch-to-batch variation smoothed out.

Premix is a damp, sometimes sticky variation of molding compound differing technically from so-called "molding compound" only in the ratio of monomer which is used. Because of the high levels of monomer, solvents are commonly not used, and the formulating technique is simplified. In addition, densification is not commonly employed, further simplifying the manufacturing technique. Premix commonly uses resin systems comprised of about 65 parts of alkyd or allylic prepolymer and 35 parts of monomer, commonly diallyl phthalate. When the premix uses diallyl phthalate monomer, it has low volatility and ambient reactivity, and can be stored for protracted periods, frequently months, without requiring refrigeration.

Premixes are usually prepared in intensive mixers, using precisely the steps and techniques described for the manufacture of fusion-type molding compound preparation, except that no heat is used. Typical recipes for this class of compound are given in Table 4.

TABLE 4. FORMULATIONS OF TYPICAL POLYESTER-DIALLYL PHTHALATE PREMIX.

Ingredient, % by w	Fibrous compound	Putty-like compound
Alkyd	24	18
Diallyl phthalate	6	5
Peroxide	.6	.6
Release agent	1	1
Kaolinite	48.4	40
Wollastonite	—	35.4
1/4in glass fibers	20	—

Dependent upon the fiber and filler content, the premix compound may vary in consistency from putty-like materials to tough fibrous dry appearing ones. Generally speaking, they will have large bulk factors, commonly as great as two, and are difficult to preform or to consolidate if the fiber content is at all high.

When fiber content and resin content are low, i.e., fiber contents 10% and under, and resin content 20% and under, it is quite convenient to densify the product by extrusion. In this manner, a continuous rope can be produced, and such compound products are marketed commercially. Bulk factors of these products are quite close to one, and the handling properties are excellent.

A wide variety of mineral fillers can be employed in premixes, and there is substantial data in the literature on this subject. The bulk of the mineral fillers fall into three major categories: Calcium carbonate, aluminum silicates, and magnesium silicates. Large numbers of subclasses exist under each of the above classes, and the potential combinations are endless. In addition, silica is commonly used in sub-micron sizes to impart thixotropy to mixes. Silica in larger than micron sizes is usually avoided owing to its excessive abrasion on compounding equipment and molds.

Allylic Laminates

For the preparation of laminates using allylic resins, it is common practice to preimpregnate the broadgoods used, whether paper, fabric or non-woven material. The advantage of pre-impregnation, rather than impregnation *in situ*, lies in the better control of resin ratio and of volatile contents. Thus, product laminates are of higher quality and have reduced reject rates. Furthermore, the handling of dry sheet material is far easier than that of wet tacky systems.

Impregnation is normally accomplished by means of a continuous horizontal-type machine commonly used for impregnation of papers. Such a machine is excellent for the purpose, because the impregnating solution does not tend to run on the surface and leave streaks or dry portions. However, the carrying bars used on horizontal machines tend to leave "bar marks," and if it is necessary to change recipies frequently, there is danger of contamination.

The contamination problem is surmounted by use of the vertical impregnation machine. This is designed so that the impregnating solution is deposited in a solution tank at the bottom of the machine, and the wet impregnated goods then rises vertically through a heating and drying tower, traveling 15 to 20 ft or more before touching the top roll, over which it travels downward through another section of drying oven. Before it reaches the top roll, the prepreg is tack free, and thus does not mark off or contaminate the equipment.

Paper impregnation of allylics uses an allylic prepolymer dissolved in acetone. A typical recipe will be as follows:

	Parts by Weight
Diallyl phthalate prepolymer	93
Diallyl phthalate monomer	7
tert-Buryl perbenzoate (catalyst)	2
Lauric acid (release agent)	3
Acetone	100

Impregnation level is controlled by the viscosity of the solution, thus the higher the solids, the heavier the deposit. Naturally there is a limit to the amount of material that can be deposited at one pass without running and streaking, thus it is sometimes desirable to make two passes in order to deposit an adequate amount of resin.

Paper used in allylic decorative laminates is usually 65 lb-per-ream basis weight super-callendered alpha cellulose. Impregnation is commonly held at 52–65% of total impregnated weight. When non-woven materials, for example, "Orlon" or rayon, are impregnated, the impregnation level is considerably higher, usually 85% of the total composite.

Fabric impregnation presents entirely different problems from impregnating paper. Resin levels are usually considerably lower on a weight basis. Typical glass cloth treating levels range from between 35 and 50% resin in the total composite.

TABLE 5. TYPICAL ALLYLIC PREPREG FORMULATIONS.

Component	Conventional "polyester"	Flame-resistant polyester	Diallyl ortho-phthalate	Diallyl metaphthalate	Flame-resistant diallyl metaphthalate	Low-pressure decorative laminate
Diallyl ortho-phthalate monomer, %	2.5–10	2.5–10	2.5–10			
Diallyl meta-phthalate monomer, %				2.5–10		3.5
Diallyl chlorendate, %					25	
Bisphenol A or isophthalate alkyd, %	47.5–40					
Chlorendic alkyd, %		47.5–40				
Diallyl ortho-phthalate prepolymer, %			47.5–40			
Diallyl meta-phthalate prepolymer, %				47.5–40	25	46.5
t-Butyl perbenzoate, %	1	1	1	1	1	1
Lauric acid, %						0.5
Acetone, %	49	49	49	49	49	48.5
Hydroquinone, ppm	50					50

Owing to the lower absorption of fabric as compared with paper, treating speeds are considerably lower. For this reason and the possibility of contamination on a typically short production run of allylic impregnated fabric, vertical impregnators or treators are usually employed.

Problems of fabric impregnation revolve around the rather rigid specification usually imposed by the consumer. Close stipulations of volatile content, resin content, flow, tack and drape are usually made, placing a premium on the skill of the prepreg manufacturer.

Resin formulations for allylic prepreg manufacture tend to be rather involved, and generally three types are manufactured. These are diallyl *ortho*-phthalate, diallyl *meta*-phthalate and alkyd (polyester) diallyl *ortho*-phthalate monomer. Typical recipes for such prepregs are given in Table 5.

Generally, *tert*-butyl perbenzoate is the peroxide catalyst used, owing to the storage stability conferred. However, there is a trend at the time of this writing to the use of lower temperature peroxides such as benzoyl peroxide, and to peroxide combinations such as benzoyl plus decumyl, in order to acquire versatility in curing techniques.

HARRY RAECH, JR.

AMYLPHENOLS

Amylphenols are an important group of alkylphenols which are intermediate in chemical characteristics between the methylphenols (cresols) and the octylphenols. Applications of amylphenols range from coatings resins to polymer antioxidants. Physical forms include flaked solids and oily liquids. Several isomeric forms are in commercial use and have been produced in substantial volume for over twenty-five years.

Amylphenols are made by alkylating phenol with amyl chlorides or amylenes. The preferred method for making them commercially is by reacting amylenes with phenol with the aid of an acid catalyst. This process is carried out in two steps. In the first step, conditions are applied which favor the reaction of the tertiary amylene with phenol to give tertiary amylphenols. In the second step, the unreacted primary and secondary amylenes are brought into contact with phenol under more strenuous conditions to produce the secondary amylphenols. The crude mixed tertiary amylphenols are separated by distillation into *ortho*-, *para*- and di-*tert*-amylphenols. The secondary amylphenols are separated into *ortho*- and di-*sec*-amylphenols, since the amount of *para* isomer is quite small.

para-tert-Amylphenol is the most important

product in this group from the standpoint of the volume used in resins and plastics. It is a white solid having a freezing point of 90°C minimum, which is packaged in flake form or shipped molten in tankcars. It is not soluble in water but is soluble in most of the common organic solvents, and moderately soluble in strong aqueous potassium hydroxide. The boiling point of commercial *para-tert*-amylphenol is 256°C, and its flash point determined by the open cup method is 230°F. Two types of resins are made from *para-tert*-amylphenol and formaldehyde or paraformaldehyde depending on the catalyst used to carry out the condensation. One type does not react with drying oils when cooked with them in the varnish making process and is called "non-oil reactive". This resin is obtained by reacting a slight molar excess of amylphenol with formaldehyde using an acid such as hydrochloric, sulfuric, oxalic, toluene sulfonic or other acid as a catalyst. The resin is a hard brittle pale amber solid which has a high melting point (270°F) and is soluble in drying oils. It is non-reactive to drying oils because it contains relatively few methylol groups. The other type resin is called "oil-reactive" because it reacts with drying oil when cooked in a varnish. This resin is prepared using an alkali such as sodium carbonate or hydroxide as the catalyst. After careful neutralization of the alkali and further reaction at a low acidity, the resin is obtained in the form of a viscous syrup which is soluble in drying oils. Since the resin contains a high proportion of methylol groups in its structure it reacts with the drying oils when heated. When the alkali catalyst employed is a tertiary amine, such as triethylamine, the neutralization and washing steps to remove the catalyst are unnecessary, and the resulting resins have superior electrical properties. Varnishes made from these amyl phenol resins exhibit excellent water resistance and good acid alkali resistance even when lower cost drying oils such as oiticica, linseed, or soybean are used. Such varnishes, either clear or pigmented, are especially suitable for marine wood finishes, durable furniture finishes, and primers for wood surfaces. Both types of amylphenol resins are used in making insulating varnishes for wire coating and for impregnating coils in transformers and armatures for electric motors. In addition to heat stability and moisture resistance, these resins contribute flexibility and lower power factors to insulating varnishes.

para-tert-Amylphenol is effective as a plasticizer-stabilizer in hot melt adhesives formulations based on ethylcellulose. An example of this type product contains about 25% by weight of the amylphenol with about 20% of ethylcellulose and 50% hydrocarbon resin (such as Pentalyn H). The virtues of the amylphenol are

high melting point (90°F), good stabilization against heat effects, and good compatibility with the cellulose ether and hydrocarbon.

Di-*sec*-amylphenol is used in the manufacture of bis(di-*sec*-amylphenol) sulfide which functions as a non-staining anti-oxidant in a variety of plastics.

W. G. KAYSER, JR.

ANHYDRIDES, ACID

Carboxylic anhydrides are prepared most readily by eliminating a molecule of water between two carboxyl groups. The reaction is reversible, and usually is carried to completion by removing the water, either through azeotropic distillation or through reaction with reagents such as acetyl chloride, thionyl chloride and phosphorus trichloride. Other general preparative methods include the reaction of carboxylic acids or their salts with acid chlorides, the addition of ketenes to carboxylic acids, the reaction of esters with acid chlorides in the presence of zinc chloride, and the exchange reaction between acid chlorides and anhydrides.

The chemical structure of specific anhydrides may be modified by processes which do not involve the carbonyl function yet considerably alter the structure and physical properties of the polymer. For example, unsaturated anhydrides may undergo Diels-Alder reactions and both aliphatic and aromatic anhydrides may be halogenated or otherwise substituted.

General Reactions

The reactions of carboxylic anhydrides most applicable to polymers are those which involve nucleophilic attack on the carbonyl carbon to yield an acyl derivative. In this fashion esters result from the reaction with alcohols (1), with phenols (2), or with epoxy compounds (3), and amides (4) or imides (5) result from reaction with amines:

$$
\begin{array}{lll}
R'OH & \longrightarrow & RCOOR' \quad (1)\\
C_6H_5OH & \longrightarrow & RCOOC_6H_5 \quad (2)
\end{array}
$$

$$
R-C(=O)-O-C(=O)-R
$$

$$
\begin{array}{lll}
& \longrightarrow & -C-C- \\
& & |\quad\ | \\
& & RCOO\ \ OCOR \quad (3)
\end{array}
$$

$$
\begin{array}{lll}
R'R''NH & \longrightarrow & RCONR'R'' \quad (4)\\
R'NH_2 & \longrightarrow & \begin{matrix}RCO\\ RCO\end{matrix}\!\!>NR' \quad (5)
\end{array}
$$

When polycarboxylic anhydrides are treated with polyfunctional nucleophilic reagents under the proper conditions, polymeric products are obtained. The molecular weight of the polymer is influenced by the proportion of the main reactants, but it also may be controlled by adding predetermined quantities of monocarboxylic anhydrides which halts growth of the polymer chain. Monocarboxylic anhydrides also may be used to stabilize polymers by "end capping," i.e., reaction with chains containing terminal nucleophilic groups. Polyformaldehyde, for example, is stabilized in such a manner.

Use in Polyesters. Under comparatively mild conditions the addition of a hydroxyl-containing compound to an anhydride yields the acid half ester. The reaction is accelerated by acidic or basic catalysts such as pyridine, phosphoric acid, boron trifluoride, or metallic salts of carboxylic acids. When using polyhydric alcohols and dicarboxylic anhydrides the initially formed half esters contain hydroxyl end-groups which may be attacked by a second molecule of anhydride. Similarly, a tetracarboxylic dianhydride reacting with a dihydric alcohol will yield a low molecular weight polyester containing free carboxyl groups. In either case, the terminal carboxylic acid groups then may be esterified to further increase the molecular weight. Polyesterification, which is acid catalyzed, may be driven to completion by removing the water of reaction either azeotropically or thermally. At elevated temperatures the rate of esterification is sufficiently rapid and catalysis usually is not required. The rate of reaction may be followed by observing the decrease in acid or hydroxyl value with time.

To obtain high molecular weight polyesters exact stoichiometry of anhydride and alcohol is required. In practice, however, an excess of the lower boiling constituent usually is added to compensate for material lost during the reaction. Ethylene or propylene glycol is employed in most commercial formulations and the excess that remains when the acid number reaches the desired level is removed by distillation. Saturated polyesters depend upon degree of polymerization to obtain desired properties but unsaturated polyesters may also utilize cross-linking through copolymerization of carbon-carbon double bonds with vinyl monomers. The vinyl monomers usually are styrene or methyl methacrylate. Unsaturation in the polyester backbone often is derived from unsaturated anhydrides of which maleic anhydride is the most common example.

It has been found that polyesters derived from fumaric acid tend to have better physical properties than those with the maleate configuration. However, the maleic esters (which are more available commercially) isomerize to this favored geometric form, fumaric, during the preparation of the polymers. The extent of isomerization may be determined by infrared spectroscopy since maleate polyesters exhibit a moderately intense band at 7.17μ, compared to the fumarate absorption at 7.45μ. Itaconic and citraconic esters likewise tend to undergo isomerization and styrenated, cured itaconic polyesters have approximately the same physical properties as maleic polyesters.

Other acids and anhydrides are used in varying proportions with maleic anhydride to obtain specific properties. Phthalic anhydride has found general utility due mainly to its relatively low cost. Although at a given styrene content, cured resins having higher phthalic to maleic ratios give lower heat distortion temperatures and poorer abrasion resistance, they do show higher flexural strength, Izod impact strength, and modulus of elasticity. Dodecenyl succinic anhydride imparts greater flexural strength and the introduction of small amounts of cyclopentanetetracarboxylic-, pyromellitic-, trimellitic-, or other anhydrides containing more than two carboxylic groups, decreases the flexibility but increases the toughness of the cured, styrenated polyester.

Polyesters have found wide use as architectural panels, in automobile and truck bodies, in theatre and bus seats, and in printed circuits, aircraft radomes and other areas where fire retardance is desirable. This important property may be incorporated into a polyester formulation by introducing a highly halogenated anhydride. If chlorine, the least expensive halogen, is employed, it must be present in at least 30% in order to impart sufficient flame retardance to the final product. The concentration of chlorine may be reduced by partially substituting another fire-retardant material such as one of the phosphite esters. Among the halogenated raw materials, dicarboxyendomethylenehexachlorooctahydronaphalene anhydride, chlorendic anhydride, dichloromaleic anhydride, and tetrabromophthalic anhydrides all are useful for the preparation of materials having high fire retardance. Ultraviolet stabilizers must be added to the polyesters prepared from each of these halogenated anhydrides if a light-stable product is desired. Polyesters based on dicarboxyendomethylenehexachloro-octahydronaphthalene anhydride seem to require less stabilizer than do the others.

One of the major classes of polyesters is that of the alkyd resins, usually of lower molecular weight, which are parpared from anhydrides (or polycarboxylic acids), polyols and monobasic acids frequently obtained from natural oils or fats. These resins are particularly useful in the coatings industry. For this application phthalic is the most widely used anhydride, although all of the commercially available anhydrides are used to impart specific properties to coatings. Maleic anhydride, when added to an alkyd cook, reacts with conjugated diolefinic fatty acids and, to a lesser extent, with the nonconjugated fatty acids to yield a cross-linked, and, therefore, tougher, product system. Trimellitic anhydride, and pyromellitic-, cyclobutanetetracarboxylic di-anhydrides and other polyanhydrides when added in limited quantities result in improved polymers. For example, about ten mole percent of these anhydrides based on the total acidic compounds imparts a high degree of water dispersibility to a resin. Fire retardance, another important property for certain coating applications, may be achieved by employing chlorinated or brominated anhydrides.

Hydroxyl-terminated polyesters have been used for the preparation of rigid foamed polyurethanes almost from the inception of the technology. Polyethers have, in large replaced polyesters in flexible foamed polyurethanes. Adipic acid and Dimer acid are generally used. Alkyd resins and other unsaturated polyester resins containing hydroxyl groups find utility as chain extenders and polyols. The saturated polyesters find application in the urethane elastomer field and some have been used as plasticizers. Special properties, such as fire retardance, are derived from the anhydride portion of the polyester.

Use in Epoxy Resins. The reaction of an anhydride with an epoxide is generally catalyzed by acids, bases or hydroxyl-containing materials. The catalyst reacts with the anhydride to produce the reactive carboxylate ion. If the epoxide contains hydroxyl groups or if an alcohol is used to catalyze the reaction, the anhydride is opened to form an ester and the carboxylic acid. Either the acid or the carboxylate ion can attack an epoxy group yielding an ester function and an alcohol or alcoholate ion capable of reacting further with anhydride. This sequence of reactions continues until the resin is polymerized to a high molecular weight. A side reaction that probably also occurs is the attack of an alcoholate ion on an epoxy linkage, causing etherification and consuming epoxide function. This has been postulated to explain optimum physical properties usually obtained by using less than stoichiometric quantities of anhydride to cure epoxy resins.

In comparison to amine curing agents, anhydrides react relatively slowly with epoxy resins, require higher cure temperatures, generally longer cure times and have lower peak exotherms. The anhydrides are difficultly soluble in the resins and may require special techniques for forming homogeneous dispersions. When higher temperatures are required to obtain solubility, diminished pot-life results. In some cases problems due to lack of solubility can be avoided by using anhydrides that are liquid at room temperature. Among those are dodecenyl succinic anhydride and methyl bicyclo [2,2,1]-5-heptene-2,3- dicarboxylic anhydride (Methyl Nadic Anhydride[R]). Eutectic mixtures of anhydrides also have been employed and are more easily dispersed and dissolved in the resin. Alternatively, solid anhydrides may be ground to a fine particle size so they disperse more readily and settle out more slowly. The anhydride-cured epoxy resins usually are characterized by high heat distortion temperatures, good thermal stability, and toughness.

TABLE 1. PHYSICAL PROPERTIES OF ANHYDRIDES.

	Molecular wt.	Equivalent wt.	Melting point, °C
Dodecenyl succinic anhydride	266	133	Oil
Citraconic anhydride	130	65	7–8
Methyl bicyclo(2,2,1)-5-heptene-2,3-dicarboxylic anhydride	178	89	< 12
Cyclohexane-1,2-dicarboxylic anhydride	154	77	35–6
Maleic anhydride	98	49	52.8
Itaconic anhydride	130	65	67–8
Cyclohex-4-ene-1,2-dicarboxylic anhydride	152	76	104
Dichloromaleic anhydride	167	83.5	119–20
Succinic anhydride	100	50	120
Phthalic anhydride	148	74	128
Bicyclo (2,2,1)-hept-5-ene-2,3-dicarboxylic anhydride	164	82	164–5
Trimellitic anhydride	192	64	168
Cyclopentanetetracarboxylix dianhydride	210	52.5	220–1
Benzophenonetetracarboxylic dianhydride	322	80.5	236
Chlorendic anhydride	370	185	239
Dicarboxyendomethylenhexachloro-octahydronaphthalene anhydride	425	212.5	240–60
Tetrachlorophthalic anhydride	286	143	255–7
Tetrabromophthalic anhydride	464	233	265
Pyromellitic dianhydride	218	54.5	286

The use of dodecenyl succinic anhydride as a curing agent results in a product of relatively high flex strength. Cyclopentanetetracarboxylic dianhydride, benzophenone tetracarboxylic dianhydride, pyromellitic anhydride and ethylene glycol bis trimellitate have utility in high-temperature stable epoxy systems and adhesive formulations. Phthalic anhydride finds wide use mainly due to its low cost. It has the disadvantages of subliming out of the resin mixture and possessing a relatively low heat distortion temperature; however, the product has good electrical properties. Maleic anhydride is used mainly as a secondary anhydride. Resins cured with maleic anhydride alone are too friable for most uses. Bicycloheptene dicarboxylic anhydride cures epoxy resin to a thermally stable product with good heat distortion temperature. Dicarboxyendomethylenehexachlorooctahydronaphthalene anhydride, chlorendic anhydride and the other halogenated anhydrides are important flame retardants.

Use in Polyimides and Polyamides. The reaction of an anhydride with an amine initially yields the -amic acid. If a primary amine has been the reactant, cyclization to an imide may occur. When pyromellitic dianhydride and diamines are reacted in solvents such as dimethyl formamide or dimethyl acetamide, high molecular weight polyamic acids are formed at the relatively low temperatures of 15°–75°C. The polyamic acid is soluble in these solvents and the solutions themselves may be used directly to cast films. By heating the film carefully above 150°C cyclization takes place, and the polyimide is formed. The reaction may be followed analytically by the disappearance of the N—H band at 3.0μ in the infrared spectrum, and the concomitant growth of the bands attributable to the imide linkage at 5.63 and 13.85μ. Benzophenone dianhydride, cyclopentanedianhydride, glycol bis trimellitate, as well as the product obtained by the photochemical addition of two molecules of maleic anhydride to benzene, have been used for the preparation of polyimides. Excellent thermal and hydrolytic stability, and zero strength temperatures over 700°C are characteristic of these materials.

The polyimides also have been prepared first by converting the dianhydride to the diester-diacid through treatment with alcohol. Upon subsequent reaction with diamine at elevated temperatures the insoluble, infusable product was obtained.

Strict adherance to stoichiometric quantities is required to form high molecular weight products. Consequently it is essential that the starting diamines and dianhydrides be of high purity.

Reaction of anhydrides with secondary amines produces amides. With polyfunctional starting materials, polymeric amides are obtained. However, due to their inability to hydrogen bond, the polymers are of little use as fibers.

Polyanhydrides

Polymeric anhydrides are obtained by treating dicarboxylic acids with acetic anhydride. In some cases, a mixed anhydride of the acid and acetic acid is obtained. Further heating at 250–300°C *in vacuo* splits off acetic anhydride and forms the polymeric anhydride. Depending upon the structure of the diacid, either a high-molecular weight polymer or a cyclic product is obtained. For example, malonic acid yields a polymer, whereas succinic and glutaric acids, under similar conditions, yield cyclic anhydrides. Dehydration of adipic acid produces a mixture both of cyclic and of linear materials. The dicarboxylic acids containing seven or more carbon atoms all form linear polymers.

The aliphatic polyanhydrides generally have poor hydrolytic stability and, at the temperatures required for fabrication, tend to degrade. The polyanhydrides prepared from the bis alkyl ethers of p-hydroxy benzoic acid are reported as having excellent film and fiber forming properties and good stability toward hydrolytic degradation. Mixed aromatic and aliphatic dibasic acids have been used for the preparation of polyanhydrides; and although fibers spun from them had interesting properties, they too were susceptible to hydrolysis. Aromatic polyanhydrides containing a methylene or ether linkage between aromatic rings have better flexibility and lower melting points than those prepared from terephthalic acid.

Morris Dunkel
Robert M. Lusskin

ANTIBLOCK AND SLIP AGENTS

Slip agents are materials which are added to plastic compounds for the purpose of reducing the coefficient of friction of the surface of products, especially films, made from the compounds. Antiblock agents are materials which are added to a plastic compound for the purpose of preventing the adhesion of the surfaces of products made from the compounds, to each other, or to other surfaces. They are distinct from coatings, dusts, or sprays which are used for similar purposes and are applied to the surface after the product has been made.

Antiblock and slip agents may be used with practically all plastic materials but are of particular importance in polyolefins and vinyls.

General Nature of Slip Additives

Slip additives are part of the large group of molecules classed as surface active agents, which have a polar group, or groups joined to non-polar groups. Following the general principle that like prefers like, or is compatible with like, this gives these molecules one end which will be compatible with polar materials, and one compatible with nonpolar materials, which means that when they are mixed with a resin there will be a tendency to eject the end that is incompatible, and retain the end that is compatible. The results are a concentration of the additive on the surface, in an even and firmly adherent layer. Amounts up to that required to form an monomolecular layer will have the compatible end of the molecule anchored into the polymer surface, while the incompatible end will protrude from the surface, changing its nature from that of uncoated resin surface.

If one considers the theory of friction developed for metallic materials, which is that the frictional force is the force required to shear off the "asperities" or high spots on the contacting surfaces, one can then see that the function of a slip additive is to coat these asperities with a film of material with a shear strength appreciably lower than that of the base polymer. When this is done, relative movement of the surfaces produces shear in the weak additive layer rather than in the stronger resin body, resulting in lower friction. If amounts larger than needed for a monomolecular layer are used, there will be a tendency for the excess material to be forced completely out of the resin and form a loose unattached layer. This excess may have undesirable side effects such as interfering with sealing or printing, or may transfer to other materials in contact with the product, and generally will have little effect on the slip coefficient.

The exact nature of the slip additive will of course depend on the base resin in which it is to be used. This will be discussed under each resin.

The General Nature of Antiblock Additives

Antiblock additives generally consist of finely divided solid infusible materials, usually mineral in nature. The particle size is generally larger than that of pigments, and must be large enough to produce a slight roughening of the surface.

If the same sort of analysis of antiblock action as that used for slip additive action is employed, it can be seen that by the addition of antiblock additives, the "asperities" on the film surface, which are the only areas in actual contact when two films are put together, have been greatly altered in nature. In the absence of antiblock additives the film asperities made of soft thermoplastic resin readily fused together with relatively light pressures. However, when antiblock is added, at least a high proportion of the asperities are hard, infusible mineral which will not under

any ordinary circumstances become fused together on contact. In addition these hard asperities are not readily deformed by pressure, and therefore they maintain a small air space between adjacent film layers, which assures ready access of air to the main film surfaces area, thus preventing adhesion due to air exclusion. Some plastic film surfaces have on them a thin liquid layer, which may be an additive, low molecular weight resin, or exuded plasticizer. In the absence of antiblock agent the liquid layers from adjacent films may merge contributing to air exclusion and also causing blocking by cohesion of the liquid layer (liquid block).

The antiblock additive, by maintaining the separation of the films, prevents the liquid layers on adjacent surfaces from merging and so prevents the liquid block. In some cases the antiblock agent may actually absorb small amounts of liquid and so remove it from the film faces.

Antiblock additives need to be matched to a resin as closely as slip additives, and the same material will function as antiblock for a variety of resins. In those cases where it is necessary to as far as possible avoid interference with the optical properties of the product, it is necessary to use an additive with a refractive index closely matching that of the base resin, and to use a particle size which minimizes optical effects.

Another widely used type of antiblock additive is a high melting point, hard natural or synthetic wax. Antiblock additives of this type are generally compatible with the polymer melt, but quite incompatible with the solid polymer. This means that they exude to the surface on cooling and form a surface layer which is harder than the plastic, thus resisting fusion of asperities. The wax coating is relatively weak, so any fused asperities break readily. The materials used with each resin will be noted under the resin headings.

Antiblock and Slip Additives in Polyolefins

The technology of antiblock and slip additives is probably most highly developed in the field of polyolefin film resins, since this application presents some of the most critical problems for such agents. In addition to their primary function the additives must also meet a number of other requirements, the most serious of which are:

(1) They must not spoil the optical properties of the film.

(2) They must not interfere with the adhesion of printing ink to the film.

(3) They must not prevent the sealing of the film.

(4) They must be odorless, colorless, and nontoxic.

The optical properties most important in polyolefin films are haze, gloss and transparency. Gloss represents specular reflection from the surface, so is strongly influenced by the nature of the surface. In order to avoid damaging gloss a slip additive must produce a very thin, firmly adherent layer with no tendency to spew or form a liquid or greasy surface film. In order to avoid damage to gloss an antiblock additive must have a particular size small enough so that the surface roughness produced does not scatter an appreciable amount of light, and its refractive index must be very close to that of the polymer. Haze and transparency are functions of the light transmission of the film, the slip additive must be small enough in quantity, and sufficiently compatible with the polymer so that it does not form a separate phase within the film, while antiblock must have a refractive index close enough to that of the polymer so that the interphase boundary does not scatter light. It is obvious that these requirements cannot be met completely, and that there will always be some interference with optical properties, however, the interference can be minimized.

In order to avoid interference with print adhesion, or with sealing of the film, it is also necessary to avoid a loose surface film of slip additive. In addition even a thin adherent film of slip additive can cause trouble unless it is sufficiently soluble in ink solvents, and compatible with ink solids, to permit ink adhesion, and sufficiently compatible with molten resin to go into solution during the heat sealing operation. These detailed requirements, in conjunction with acceptability of the food and Drug Administration in regard to toxicity, eliminate practically all slip additives except certain fatty acid amides such as oleamide, stearamide, and erucamide. Exactly which of these amides is to be used depends on the rate of "blooming" required (exuding to the surface), which in turn depends on the processing temperatures to be encountered, as well as other details of the process.

Color and odor are not matters of chemical composition, but rather of purity. All of these amides can be obtained commercially in any form, from a dark odorous grease up to an almost pure white powder with a very mild odor. For high grade applications only the very purest amide can be used. When discussing purity, it is not intended to imply that commercial slip additives consist exclusively of any one chemical species. These fatty acid amides are all produced from natural oils containing several different acids in proportions which differ according to the source of the oil, time of the year, etc. The chemical name under which such is sold will generally represent the largest single constituent, but sometimes this will not even constitute 50% of the total. A supplier will generally try to keep the composition of his product reasonably constant, by using oils from the same source, or by blending

to a constant composition, but material of the same nominal designation from different suppliers may be quite different. This will, of course, affect its action in the resin, so that alternative suppliers cannot be assumed to be equivalent without careful checking.

Chromatographic techniques have recently been developed which make possible the analysis of complex mixtures of fatty amides. As these come into common use they will make it possible to specify slip additive unequivocably on the basis of actual molecular species and this should do a great deal to advance slip agent technology.

Before the analytical procedures have their full effect, it must be possible to produce amides of fixed composition. Separation procedures are known, but as yet they are too expensive to justify use on slip additives. As the improved analytical procedures become more generally used, it may be able to demonstrate differences which will justify work on producing additives consisting of pure molecular species.

The maximum reduction of frictional coefficient can generally be achieved by the use of enough additive to give a layer one molecule thick on the surface of the film. This varies with film thickness.

For 1 mil film about 0.01% of the typical slip additive, oleamide will do this. Losses in processing and incomplete "blooming" may require somewhat more in some cases, but too much of an excess should be avoided to prevent some of the difficulties previously discussed. In many cases the maximum reduction of slip coefficient is not required and a smaller amount of additive is used.

Antiblock additives are usually silica, because the excellent match between the refractive index of silica and the polyolefins gives the least possible disturbance of optical properties. The low cost and availability in suitable well controlled particle sizes, makes diatomaceous earth the preferred form of silica. The exact particle size used is a balance between the amount of antiblock action required and the optical distortion that is acceptable; coarser particles are more effective, but finer ones cause less distortion. The same balance must be struck in quantity. The usual amounts are about the same percentage as used for slip additives, but this is varied depending on the specific requirements of each application.

Slip additives have a limited use in polyolefin applications other than film. They are used in coating resins for the same reasons that they are used in film resins; here again the same agents are used. Because of the high extrusion temperatures used in coating operations, loss of slip additive by volatilization may be quite great and problems such as deposits on the chill roll of the coating line may be severe.

In some cases slip additives are used in poly-olefin molding compounds to prevent the sticking together of nested moldings. Generally the same additives are used but the amounts will vary depending on the application. In this application it is also possible to use waxes of various sorts because many of the restrictions found in the film application do not apply.

Antiblock and Slip Agents in Vinyls

This is a much more difficult matter than in the polyolefins because vinyl compositions are much more complex than polyolefin compositions. Frequently some constituent of the vinyl compound that also serves another primary purpose can be made to affect the resin surface.

For instance the blocking of vinyl sheeting is strongly influenced by the nature of the plasticizer used. A plasticizer of the most active type will produce a sticky sheet, while a similar degree of flexibility produced by a less active, extender type plasticizer will produce a dry and tack free surface. This means that the exact plasticizer mixture used can often be used to control vinyl film and sheet blocking, although the materials used are not primarily antiblock agents.

Since most vinyls are colored and opaque, the restrictions regarding the type and amount of antiblock or slip additive that hold for poly-olefins are not important. In addition to the slip additives used in polyolefins it is possible to use a wide variety of natural and synthetic waxy materials, metal salts of fatty acids, fatty acids themselves, and surface active agents of many sorts to reduce the coefficient of friction, the specific material used depending on details of the application. One example is the use of sodium lauroyl sulfate as slip additive in "Saran" coatings.

Calcium carbonate is frequently used as a filler in vinyl compounds where it acts as antiblock agent, although its primary purpose is generally to reduce the cost of the compound and improve its processing characteristics, rather than simply reducing blocking. It is also often possible to prevent blocking in vinyl sheeting by purely mechanical means, such as embossing the surface.

Antiblock and Slip Agents in Cellulosics

The problem of slip and antiblock agents in cellulosic plastics is similar to that in vinyls in that these properties are frequently best controlled by choice of plasticizer rather than by the addition of an agent specifically present for surface property control. However, when a specific agent is used, they are similar to those used in polyolefins, that is, fatty amides for slip, and silica for antiblock with occasional use of waxes for both.

Antiblock and Slip Agents in Thermosetting Resins

While slip and antiblock agents are primarily associated with films, it is sometimes necessary to put them into resins used for molding in order to prevent the sticking together of molded pieces, or to achieve a low coefficient of friction on parts used for bearing purposes.

Many thermosetting compounds are formulated with metal stearates primarily for the purpose of facilitating preforming, and many also contain waxes for mold release purposes. These materials will have the additional function of slip and antiblock agents in the final part.

The incorporation of graphite, molybdenum disulfide, soft metal powders, and similar materials serves to decrease the coefficient of friction of bearing materials, which brings them into our definition of slip additives, however, this is an entirely separate technology so will not be discussed in detail.

Evaluating the Effectiveness of Antiblock and Slip Additives

The laboratory tests used to evaluate the effectiveness of slip and antiblock agents are quite straightforward; however, unless certain details are understood, it is quite possible to be misled by them. Slip additives are judged by their effect on the coefficient of friction of the products made from the resin.

Coefficient of friction is theoretically one of the simplest of physical measurements, yet an accurate and reproducible value depends on close adherence to a standard procedure. The most generally accepted standard is ASTM D1894. In this a metal block or sled weighing 200 ± 5 g and wrapped with 1/8 in. of medium density foam rubber is held in a stationary position by means of a force measuring device, while a horizontal table supporting the block is drawn under the block at a constant speed of 0.5 ± 0.1 ft per min. Figure 1 is a diagram of this

Fig. 1. Apparatus for measuring coefficient of friction.

        A. Moving plane
        B. Sled
        C. Inelastic connector
        D. Force Measuring device

method. To measure the coefficient of friction of film, a piece of the film is fastened to the block, and another to the table. The force measured on the force measuring device is used to calculate the coefficient of friction. There are two different frictional coefficients, the static coefficient of friction, and the dynamic coefficient of friction. The static coefficient is calculated by using the force recorded at the first relative motion between the film on the sled and that on the plate. The kinetic coefficient is calculated using the average force reading during smooth sliding between the two surfaces:

$$\text{Static } c/f = \mu s = \frac{Fs}{200}$$

$$\text{Kinetic } c/f = \mu K = \frac{F_A}{200}$$

where:

Fs = force at first motion, g.
F_A = average force of sliding, g.
200 = weight of sled, g.

Static coefficient of friction is quite variable from one determination to the next, so it is a very unsatisfactory value for most purposes. When a coefficient of friction is reported without specifying static or kinetic, kinetic is commonly meant, because this is a much more reproducible figure, and therefore more useful for comparisons.

Slip additives also influence the coefficient of friction between the film and metals or other solids, and can be determined on the same apparatus by drawing across the other material. This is of interest in some film converting operations which involve sliding the film against metal guides.

Blocking is measured in two different ways which are not comparable because somewhat different factors are involved. The simplest and most straightforward is merely to take two pieces of film as they come from a roll without separating them, fastening one to one flat plate, the other to another flat plate, separating the edges where they extend beyond the plates, and then measuring the force required to separate the plates. Figure 2

is a diagram of this process. While this test is widely used it has not been standardized by ASTM or any other standards making body. This means that there is no industry agreement on the details of the test and results from different laboratories are not comparable. A partial list of the factors that influence the value obtained on this test are:

(1) Rate of application of load.

(2) Method of applying load, continuous or stepwise.

(3) The method of fastening the film to the plates.

(4) The smoothness of the plates, and whether or not the plates are perforated.

(5) Whether or not the edges of the film are separated before starting test.

The main difficulty with this test is that if the two pieces of film are fastened firmly to flat plates without edge separation, air cannot enter between the films, and the applied load must exceed the pressure of the atmosphere before it can begin to act on the adhesive force between the films. Since atmospheric pressure is large as compared to commonly found adhesive forces, this method of doing the test tends to disguise any real adhesion differences. The preferred way is to bring the film samples around two edges of the plate and fasten them on the back of the plate, thus starting separation at the two folded up edges. If perforated plates are used so that the film does not cling to them, this essentially converts the test into a double peel test with the separation moving in from the attached edges to the center. While this is no longer what the test appears to be in principle, it is much more

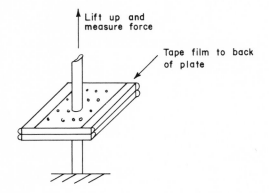

FIG. 2. Blocking by plate separation method.

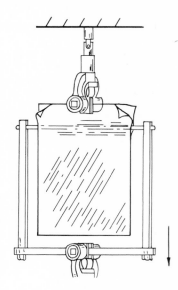

FIG. 3. Blocking by rod stripping method.

In Figure 2, labels read:
"Lift up and measure force"
"Tape film to back of plate"

informative regarding the practical use of the film.

Within one laboratory, on one piece of equipment, reasonably consistent results can be obtained on this test, and with one modification or another it is the most widely used blocking test.

The other widely used blocking test consists of separating the edges of two pieces of film, inserting a metal rod between the pieces and then measuring the force required to draw the rod through the unseparated portion. This has been standardized under ASTM D1893, and is diagrammed in Fig. 3. It can be seen that this test is somewhat influenced by the frictional coefficient of the film, so is not strictly comparable to the flat plate method, however, since blocking is very often used as an indication of the ease of opening a bag, for instance, it can be seen that coefficient of friction enters into this as well, so the rod technique is a good indication of behavior in practice.

THEODORE O. J. KRESSER

Cross-reference: ADDITIVES.

ANTIFOAM AGENTS

The purpose of an antifoam, as the name implies, is to quell, prevent, suppress and/or control foaming in systems subject to foam formation. The prefix "anti" denotes a condition which is unwanted. Foaming is certainly a serious and intolerable problem in many process operations involving the manufacture and use of plastics. It is often a problem in the preparation of latexes and in polymerization reactions of many resin types, such as coumarone-indene, alkyd, melamine, phenolic and urea. This discussion is confined to the antifoams that alleviate the foaming condition which causes a partial loss of product and relatively poor control in reactions and processing of plastics. Antifoaming agents employed in the preparation of cellular plastics such as the urethane foams are, of course, a necessary item used in the control of cell size. This use of antifoaming agents is not discussed here except to point out that the foams must be stabilized with an antifoam for a relatively short but critical time period until changes occur in the foaming material that permit it to support itself.

Fortunately the foaming problem can be solved, or at least minimized in most cases, by additives which in very small amounts in many systems effectively combat or eliminate it. A large number of these antifoam materials are now available, and much is known about their action.

Although the properties required for an antifoam are now known, only by trial can the most

effective agent or combination of agents be found for a given process. An excellent summary of the behavior and industrial use of surface active agents, give the requirements for an antifoam as follows: (a) limited solubility, (b) low surface tension, and (c) low interfacial tension with the foaming liquid. Any distinction between the terms "antifoaming" and "defoaming" one of semantics. To understand the action of an antifoam an understanding of the formation and stabilization of foams is helpful.

Pure liquids do not foam. A foaming liquid must contain a surface active agent (surfactant). This agent performs the following functions: (a) lowers the surface tension of the system, (b) produces film elasticity under dynamic conditions, and (c) produces surface plasticity. A simplified view of such a surfactant (nonionic) is that shown in Fig. 1(a). The hydrophobic portion of the

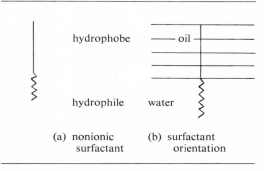

FIG. 1(a and b). Simplified view of a nonionic surfactant and its orientation in a water-oil mixture.

molecule is depicted as having an affinity for, or being oriented to the oil side of the oil-water interface, shown in Fig. 1(b). The hydrophilic portion of the molecule is depicted as having an affinity for, or being oriented to, the water side of the oil-water interface. In a molecule such as an alkyl aryl sulphonate, the sulphonate group is hydrophilic, whereas the alkyl aryl groups are hydrophobic. Monolayers of some of these surfactants containing as little as 10^{-10} mole per cm² are able to impart foaming tendencies to some liquids. In somewhat higher concentrations the surfactant imparts sufficient film elasticity and surface plasticity that the foam life-time is extended for correspondingly longer periods.

The most important action of a completely effective antifoam agent is to eliminate surface elasticity. To do this it must displace any foam stabilizer which may be present. Therefore, it must have a low intrinsic tension in the pure state, and possess high spreading power. It must be present in sufficient quantity to maintain a high surface concentration even under dynamic conditions. Low solubility is, therefore, an advantage. Many antifoams are insoluble oils having a large and positive spreading coefficient.

Film rupture starts with a thinning area on the bubble wall. The surfactant operates to make the liquid move toward the thin area, restoring the original thickness. Thus, an antifoam, spreading rapidly on the surface of a liquid film, is believed to pull away the liquid and replace it with a liquid (itself) incapable of sustaining a film.

By far the most popular antifoams are the dimethyl polysiloxanes. These fluids appear to be highly efficient in reducing foaming and bumping during the heating of many types of materials. The amounts of the dimethyl polysiloxanes required are normally in the parts per million range. Generally, for any new industrial application, it is desirable to start with a concentration of 20–50 then increase or decrease this amount until the most economical use level is reached. The dimethyl polysiloxanes have the added advantage of exhibiting a very low order of toxicity to animals by all routes of administration. They do not irritate the skin, and are odorless.

The quantity and particular antifoam required should be determined by trial for each system. The different agents which are recommended for different foams have been developed largely empirically. A laboratory method of evaluating antifoams involves the production of voluminous quantities of foam by passing finely divided air bubbles, at a constant rate (by means of a gas dispersion tube), through 100 cc of foaming solution. The total volume of foam plus liquid is recorded with time after the addition of the antifoam.

Some of the more common chemical antifoams which have been employed with success in many systems are shown in Table 1. It is preferable to consult the supplier and his literature for the proper antifoam and the use characteristics because each individual case may have certain special requirements. For example, in the preparation of adhesive compounds, the antifoam may substantially reduce adhesion. Some antifoams have less effect on adhesion than others. However, generally, it is customary to use the minimum amount of the antifoam required to eliminate the foam.

Another reason to consult the supplier is to obtain the most technically advanced product. Continued improvements are being made in the development of new and better antifoams tailored to the foaming problem. For example, silicone polyoxyalkylene copolymers have been developed which, because of their inverse water solubility characteristics with temperature, can function as antifoaming agents above their cloud points, and as profoamers below. They are water-soluble and low in viscosity, designed for defoaming aqueous systems above room temperature. These have found use in the dyeing of synthetic fabrics in hot water dye baths where several other silicone types of antifoams were found to plate out on the fabric and interfere with the dyeing process. Block copolymers of these antifoams have different properties and may have value as antifoams in other systems.

Special problems are encountered in preventing foaming in the compounding and processing of neoprene latex. Some common antifoams suggested for use in the prevention of foaming and webbing in the compounding and processing of neoprene latexes are listed among the antifoams in Table 1.

TABLE 1. CHEMICAL ANTIFOAMS FOUND SUITABLE FOR MANY SYSTEMS.

Silicone greases (dissolved in kerosene and emulsified)
Whole milk, skim milk, cream and powdered milk
Octanol
2-Ethylhexanol
Cyclohexanol
Capryl alcohol
Lauryl alcohol
Cetyl alcohol
1,2 and 1,3 Glycols
Tricresyl phosphate in suitable solvent
Tributyl phosphate in suitable solvent (pine oil)
Ceresin wax (emulsions)
Heavy metal stearates (with other antifoams), dissolved in oil and emulsified or dispersed in water along with an inert filler
Glyceride oils
Fatty acids
Pine oil
Lard oil
Vegetable oils
Dimethyl polysiloxanes
Aliphatic ethers
Dimethylsilicone polyoxyalkylene glycol copolymers
1,3-Dimethybutyl alcohol

There are, of course, many proprietary antifoams whose identifications are not always disclosed. A list of some of these and their suppliers are given in Table 2.

The physical form and the method of application of the particular antifoam are dictated by the nature of the foam and the system involved. For aqueous systems (latexes) it is usually convenient to add the antifoam as a dilute aqueous emulsion; whereas, in non-aqueous systems, the antifoam dissolved in an organic solvent may be employed. The antifoams are usually employed in the liquid phase, but they may be spread on the inside of the reaction vessel at the level of the liquid surface. When used in this manner they may be emulsified, the solid or viscous antifoams

TABLE 2. SELECTED PROPRIETARY ANTIFOAMS USED IN RUBBER LATEXES AND PLASTICS MANUFACTURE[a].

Name	Active ingredients, %	Supplier
AP foam reducer	43	Adhesive Products Corp.
Foamnix	—	Crusader Chemical Co.
Dow Corning Antifoam A	100	Dow Corning Corp.
Dow Corning Antifoam C	30	Dow Corning Corp.
Dow Corning 200 Fluid	100	Dow Corning Corp.
SF-96 Silicone	100	General Electric Corp.
Viscasil Silicone	100	General Electric Corp.
CW-4	—	General Latex and Chem. Corp.
J-114 Emulsion	50	Heveatex Corp.
Hodag Antifoam PV-45B	—	Hodag Chemical Corp.
Hodag Antifoam FD-82	—	Hodag Chemical Corp.
Hodag Antifoam PV-48	—	Hodag Chemical Corp.
Hodag Antifoam TBX	—	Hodag Chemical Corp.
Nopco JMK	85	Nopco Chemical Co.
Nopco NDW	100	Nopco Chemical Co.
Antifoam P-C	10	Para-Chem, Inc.
Antimussol WL	100	Sandoz, Inc.
Sag 47 Silicone antifoam	100	Union Carbide Corp.
Sag 530 Silicone antifoam	100	Union Carbide Corp.
Sag 5440 Silicone antifoam	100	Union Carbide Corp.
Sag 5441 Silicone antifoam	30	Union Carbide Corp.
Sag 472 Silicone antifoam	30	Union Carbide Corp.
Surfynol 104E	—	Air Reduction Co., Inc.
Surfynol TG	—	Air Reduction Co., Inc.

[a] These materials are often available in several viscosity ranges.

having first been dissolved in a material of low volatility such as kerosene or other oil. In some cases the antifoams are dissolved in solvents such as alcohols and are added directly to the system. The higher alcohols and glycols have slight effectiveness as antifoams themselves. The particular diluent used will often affect the performance of the defoamer. However, no generalizations can be made as to the best diluent to use in all cases, since this varies with each foam. In many processes one of the ingredients of a foaming system can serve as a dispersant for the antifoam.

Occasionally the antifoams diminish in effectiveness as the compound ages. In that case, of course, it is necessary to replenish with an additional amount. To defoam large continuous process operations, a metering pump may be used to add the silicone continuously to the process lines.

J. H. Ross

ANTIOXIDANTS

Most plastics materials are subject to degradation by the action of oxygen during manufacture, processing, storage and in service, with adverse effect upon their appearance and properties. The speed of such deterioration depends on a number of factors, among which are the composition of the polymer and the conditions of exposure to oxygen, heat and light. These adverse effects may be greatly retarded in most plastics materials by the use of antioxidants. An antioxidant is defined as a substance that opposes oxidation, or inhibits or retards reactions promoted by oxygen or peroxides. In the specific case of antioxidants for polymeric materials, they are substances that retard atmospheric oxidation or the degradative effect of oxidation and extend the polymer's useful temperature range and service life, when they are added in very low concentrations on the order of fractions of 1%. Structure, processing conditions, impurities and end use of the polymer must be considered in choosing the best stabilizer or antioxidant system.

Mechanisms of Oxidation and Inhibition

The mechanisms of oxidation and antioxidant action are still the subject of investigation. Oxidation has been described as a free radical, chain type reaction. At processing temperatures and more slowly at ambient temperatures, polymer (or impurity) free radicals ($R°$) are formed. These react with oxygen to form peroxy radicals ($ROO°$), which can abstract a hydrogen atom from the polymer to form a hydroperoxide (ROOH) and another polymer free radical. The cycle repeats itself with the addition of oxygen to the new free radical. The unstable hydroperoxides left along the polymer molecule are the major source for degradation. Under the influence of heat, light, and certain metals, they decompose to form carbonyl groups. When this happens, the polymer chain breaks and splits off another polymer free radical. Ultimately, this type of degradation can lead to discoloration, embrittlement, loss of strength, etc.

The antioxidants used in plastics act either to tie up the peroxy radicals so that they are incapable of propagating the reaction chain, or to decompose the hydroperoxides in such a manner that carbonyl groups and additional free radicals are not formed. The former, which are called chain breaking antioxidants, free radical scavengers, or inhibitors are usually phenols or amines. The latter, called peroxide decomposers, are generally sulfur compounds (i.e., mercaptans, sulfides, sulfoxides, sulfones), or metal complexes of dithiocarbamates and dithiophosphates.

A general outline of the reactions involved in oxidation and inhibition is as follows: where:

$$RH = \text{polymer molecule}$$
$$AH = \text{antioxidant}$$
$$ROOH = \text{polymer peroxide}$$
$$R^\circ = \text{polymer radical}$$
$$A^\circ = \text{antioxidant radical}$$
$$RO_2{}^\circ = \text{polymer peroxy radical}$$

Initiation:

$$RH \xrightarrow[\text{heat, light, etc.}]{\text{activation}} R^\circ + H^\circ$$
$$RH + O_2 \to R^\circ + HO_2{}^\circ$$
$$AH + O_2 \to A^\circ + HO_2{}^\circ$$
$$ROOH \to RO^\circ, RO_2{}^\circ, HO^\circ$$

Propogation:

$$R^\circ + O_2 \to RO_2{}^\circ$$
$$RO_2{}^\circ + RH \to ROOH + R^\circ$$

Chain Transfer:

$$RO_2{}^\circ + AH \to ROOH + A^\circ$$
$$A^\circ + RH \to AH + R^\circ$$

Termination:

$$A^\circ + RO_2{}^\circ \to \text{stable products}$$
$$2A^\circ \to \text{stable products}$$
$$2RO_2{}^\circ \to \text{stable products}$$

Peroxide Decomposition:

$$ROOH \to \text{stable products}$$

Synergism

By using two or more different types of antioxidants or additives, the resistance to oxidation or deterioration of an organic material may be improved to a greater extent than would be predicted on the basis of strict additivity. The two additives are then said to show a "synergistic" effect toward one another. The converse of synergism is "antagonism."

Probably the most generally effective mixtures of antioxidants in plastics are those in which one compound functions as a decomposer of peroxides, and the other as an inhibitor of free radicals. Although the latter retards the formation of long reaction chains, some hydroperoxide is nevertheless formed. If this hydroperoxide then reacts with a decomposer of peroxides, instead of decomposing into free radicals, the two antioxidants act together to complement each other. Moreover, the peroxide decomposer may itself be subject to oxidation by peroxy radicals, and its efficiency will therefore be increased in the presence of an inhibitor of free radicals. In the case of phenol sulfide mixtures, the sulfide (peroxide decomposer) also continuously regenerates the phenol (radical scavenger) to accentuate the synergistic nature of the mixture.

The high efficiency of many antioxidants containing two or more functional groups (i.e., OH and NH, OH and S, etc.) is undoubtedly connected with the occurrence of a different inhibiting reaction at each group. Some heterocyclic compounds that contain nitrogen and sulfur (i.e., phenothiazine), and phenols that contain sulfur (i.e., thiobis phenols), can fulfill the role of a synergistic mixture alone. However, difficulty is being encountered when attempting to build into one molecule all the desirable properties required of a good antioxidant, however, the problem is still being investigated.

A large variety of amines which do not themselves function as inhibitors of free radicals, can apparently fulfill the role of a decomposer of peroxides with sterically hindered phenols, nonhindered phenols, and with aromatic amines. Of considerable interest are combinations of what are regarded as strictly inhibitors of free radicals. The effects observed may be additive, antagonistic, or synergistic depending on the inhibitors chosen and the substrate.

In addition to being capable of chemically preventing unwanted reactions in the polymer, antioxidants must be sufficiently heat stable to withstand processing temperatures. The use of higher temperatures, especially with polyolefins, has created a demand for antioxidants to meet these conditions. The antioxidants being developed in this area are mainly polyphenolic in nature.

In addition, the stabilizers must be compatible with the plastic, should have low volatility, and should react to give colorless products.

Polymers vary in their ability to resist oxidation. Unsaturated polymers are most susceptible. Saturated hydrocarbons are less reactive. Polystyrene and polymethyl methacrylate are quite stable even at fabrication temperatures. The type and quantity of antioxidant to be employed will be dependent on the type of polymer, the application, and to some extent on the other additives present. The same type of polymer from different producers may exhibit different responses.

Polymers which oxidize most readily are those with structural unsaturation, such as natural rubber, polybutadiene, isoprene polymers and copolymers, petroleum based resins, such as coumarone indene, rosin and its derivatives, etc. The high-impact plastics, such as ABS, impact polystyrene, impact acrylics, and impact PVC, also fall into this class. The oxidation mechanism is complex. Peroxides and peroxy radicals are formed and lead eventually to chain splitting and the formation of aldehydes and acids with attendant loss in molecular weight. Incidental effects include development of color, odor, bloom, softening or stiffening of the composition, etc. Butadiene-based polymers tend to cross-link, with a reduction in elongation and elastic properties.

Aryl amines and phenolic compounds function well as antioxidants in this type of polymer. The amines may be used where color development may be tolerated, the phenolics where discoloration is objectionable. In general, alkylation of a phenol lowers the oxidation-reduction potential and enhances the stabilization action. Therefore, hindered phenols are effective antioxidants. 2,6-di-*tert*-butyl-*para* cresol and 2,2'-methylene-bis-(4-methyl-6-*tert*-butylphenol) are effective non-discoloring, non-staining antioxidants. Aryl phosphites and aryl alkyl phosphites also function as nondiscoloring antioxidants, either by themselves or in synergistic combination with the phenolics. All may be incorporated into the polymer either during the hot melt stage or by addition to the latex.

Saturated hydrocarbon polymers (i.e., polyethylene, polypropylene, polyisobutylene, and polystyrene) are more resistant than unsaturated polymers, but they oxidize rapidly at elevated temperatures and in thin films during processing and later use. Once the reaction starts, it activates nearby spots in the molecule so that degradation is progressive in character. The net effects are very similar to those with unsaturated polymers of similar structure. Many of these products are used in electrical insulation so that the effects of ozone are important. Because of the build-up of oxygenated species during the oxidation process, a deterioration of electrical properties can be detected before physical degradation becomes apparent.

Polyethylene. During processing, polyethylene is often exposed to air while the polymer is above its melting point. This results in oxidation of the polymer initiated at the branched sites. Because of the minimal amount of branching and high degree of crystallinity, especially in high-density polyethylene, oxidation at service temperatures is relatively slow. Oxidation leads to deterioration

in physical properties, loss of electrical and mechanical properties, cracking, splitting, and formation of color and odor.

The antioxidants for the inhibition of thermal oxidation of polyethylene are similar to those for rubber (i.e., phenols and amines). However, the amines produce color and are rarely used. In some cases, mixtures of phenols and sulfides, such as dilaurylthiodipropionate (DLTDP), or phenols and organic phosphites, or combinations of all three have given improved or synergistic results.

Oxidation due to light is a more serious problem and the normal thermal antioxidants are unsatisfactory. Substituted benzophenones have been found effective. The most satisfactory is carbon black, which acts as an ultraviolet light screen. The general effects are the same as for thermal oxidation. The addition of carbon black causes a loss in activity of the conventional alkylated phenol and amine thermal antioxidants.

In contrast, their thioether derivatives provide more protection against oxidation than the sum of the separate contributions of carbon black and sulfur compounds. Such an antioxidant is 2,2'-thiobis-(4-methyl-6-*tert*-butylphenol). The antioxidants may be added before fabrication of the polyethylene on open rolls, internal mixers, or screw type extrusion machines.

Polypropylene. The polypropylene molecule differs from the polyethylene molecule in that there is a methyl group attached to every other carbon atom in the polypropylene chain, whereas high-density polyethylene has practically no branches on the chain, and low density polyethylene has perhaps two or three side chains per hundred chain carbon atoms in its molecule.

It is well known that a hydrogen atom which is attached to a tertiary carbon atom (one which is connected to three other carbons, as it would be at a branch in the chain) is more reactive than hydrogen attached to carbon atoms which are connected with only one or two other carbons. These tertiary hydrogen atoms are easily lost under the influence of heat and light to form free radicals that initiate the oxidation reaction. The oxygen uptake of polypropylene is therefore greater than that of polyethylene. In contrast to polyethylene, polypropylene is extremely susceptible to oxidation at processing temperatures. Even under normal use conditions, the rate of oxidation is appreciable. Therefore, antioxidants are necessary for the utility of the polymer, especially since polypropylene, because of its higher softening point, can be used at higher temperatures than polyethylene and therefore can be expected to encounter more exacting service conditions in its end uses.

Polypropylene can be effectively stabilized against thermal oxidation both at elevated and normal temperatures. The antioxidants used are of the same general class as for polyethylene. Synergistic mixtures of alkylated phenols or alkylidenebisalkylated phenols and sulfur compounds give good processing results. DLTDP has been used extensively as the sulfur component. Distearylthiodipropionate (DSTDP) shows somewhat higher synergistic activity and is gaining acceptance. Certain nickel organic complexes used as light stabilizers and dye site sources also act as effective antioxidants on long term aging, while the finished material is in use.

The type and quantity of antioxidants required depends largely on the intended method of fabrication and end-use. In applications where FDA approval is required, certain approved antioxidants, such as 2,6-di-*tert*-butyl-*para*-cresol and dilaurylthiodipropionate, possibly in combination with some approved organo-phosphites, may be used. Where a higher order of stabilization is required, alkylidene-bis-alkylated phenols and thiobis-alkylated phenols can be used along with DLTDP and DSTDP. For longterm heat stability, synergistic combinations of the phenolic and sulfur antioxidants have proven to be most effective safeguards.

Polystyrene. Polystyrene is relatively stable to oxidation both at processing and room temperatures, and retains good physical properties at all temperatures below the point of heat distortion. Thermal antioxidants are only occasionally used. However, polystyrene is very sensitive to degradation by light. It has to be stabilized to prevent yellowing in indoor use and is not practical for outdoor use. The light stabilizers include aliphatic and cyclic amines, amino alcohols, cyclic alcohols, hydroxybenzophenones, and hydroxy benzotriazoles, also in combination with hindered phenols (i.e., 2,6-di-*tert*-butyl-*para*-cresol).

High-impact polystyrene (styrene-rubber copolymer), containing unsaturated linkages, is more susceptible to oxidation. Antioxidants used as inhibitors in the monomers are generally removed prior to emulsion or bead polymerization. Protection is not usually necessary during the polymerization since this is usually done under nitrogen. Hindered phenols (i.e., 2,6-di-*tert*-butyl-*para*-cresol) are incorporated during milling or extrusion to prevent yellowing and retard degradation of the material when it is fabricated into finished products and exposed to oxidizing conditions.

Vinyls. Polyvinyl chloride and chlorine-containing polymers, in general, degrade under the influence of heat and light by autocatalytic dehydrohalogenation that produces unsaturation. Heat and light stabilizers, which are not antioxidants, are effective in preventing the initial decomposition (i.e., stearates, laurates, ricinoleates of calcium, barium, strontium, organo-tin

compounds, etc.). Once the double bonds are formed, oxidation of the molecule proceeds as with other unsaturated compounds, so that antioxidants may be advantageously used in combination with the conventional vinyl stabilizers. Alkylated phenols have been suggested for this use.

In plasticized PVC, the presence of antioxidants becomes more important due to the fact that certain plasticizers oxidize readily; 4,4'-isopropylidene-bisphenol is commonly used.

Other Polymers. Polyamides, polyesters and polyurethanes are not subject to rapid oxidation. Polyesters are generally more stable than polyamides toward oxidative changes. Phosphite esters have been used as stabilizers for polyesters, polyamides and other polymer types.

The discoloring and aging properties of polyurethanes may be improved by the addition of the conventional polyolefin antioxidants (i.e., hindered phenols, alkylidene-bis-alkylated phenols, etc.), in conjunction with phosphoric acid, phosphites or U.V. absorbers.

Polyoxymethylenes are susceptible to oxidation at elevated temperatures and alkylidene-bisalkylated phenols (i.e., 2,2'-methylene-bis-(4-methyl-6-*tert*-butylphenol)) are recommended as satisfactory stabilizers in this particular situation.

Although plastics materials use only a comparatively small amount of antioxidants, the rate of production of plastics materials continues to increase sharply and will contribute largely to the increased demand for stabilizing materials. Virtually every major plastic is expected to hit a new high in production and use in 1966. Even the volume leader, polyethylene, will show gains estimated at 20%, to well over the 2.8 billion lb per year mark. Polypropylene is closing the gap between sales and production capacity. The vinyl family, second in size only to polyethylene, should pass the 2.5 billion lb per year mark in 1966. United States production of antioxidants for all purposes, which were introduced in the 1920's, should exceed 100 million lb in 1966.

MICHAEL ROBIN

ANTISTATIC AGENTS

Antistatic agents for permanent attachment to thermoplastics has become an important consideration by plastic processors and consumers. This trend has initiated a considerable amount of research and development to synthesize the "ideal" permanent antistatic agent with very encouraging results. The sum total has been a flood of new internal antistatic agents, along with a vast improvement in the testing equipment and procedures. In spite of all the recent improvements, very little is known about the mechanism involved.

During the processing and subsequent storage

of thermoplastics, electrostatic charges are built up on the surface. The strengths of these charges vary between plastics and are also dependent upon other factors, such as, processing conditions, the shape of objects, and relative humidity of the surrounding atmosphere.

Any electrostatic charge, regardless of its magnitude, ionizes the surrounding atmosphere with the following results:

(1) Dust attraction to finished parts.

(2) Plastic beads, pellets, and powders will adhere while being processed, resulting in clogged chutes and conveyor equipment.

(3) Adhesion to converting equipment, such as rolls, which eventually results in uneven feeding through cutters, bag making machines.

(4) In extreme cases, shocks to operators in film processing plants.

(5) Occasional fires may break out in the presence of flammable solvents.

The actual mechanism of electrostatic charges in the thermoplastics is not too well known. Some authorities believe that an electrostatic charge is conducted throughout the plastic, although most feel that it is entirely a surface phenomenon. It is believed that an electrostatic charge is accumulated when the thermoplastic is being processed, by a combination of pressure and rubbing where the atoms are put in intimate contact with each other thus increasing the possibility of electron transfer. Thermoplastics, in general, are insulators and will not dissipate the charge which has been induced, thus remaining on the surface permanently.

Requirements of an Ideal Permanent Antistatic Agent

A permanent antistatic agent must be able to withstand repeated washing and rubbing which a plastic may undergo during its lifetime. Many surface treatments have been tried and at best are considered semi-permanent. The most effective method is the use of chemicals that are mass-incorporated into the plastic without changing its physical properties, processing characteristics, etc. An ideal permanent antistatic agent should be able to do the following:

(1) Eliminate electrostatic charges at low concentrations (0.1% or lower).

(2) Should not contribute to color development at elevated processing temperatures and subsequent usage.

(3) Should be non-corrosive to the processing equipment.

(4) Should have no adverse effects on processability, printability, stress cracking, odor and optical clarity (in film).

(5) The product should be easy to handle in production.

(6) United States F.D.A. approval is preferable

(7) Should be economical at normal levels of use.

(8) Should be effective in a wide range of plastics.

Plastics Requiring Antistatic Agents

Theoretically, most thermoplastics are capable of maintaining an electrostatic charge. At the present time, static elimination concerns primarily the large volume thermoplastics such as polyolefins, polyvinyl chloride (PVC), polystyrene, and acrylonitrile butadiene styrene (ABS). This is due to the many molded articles manufactured from these polymers requiring a positive sales appeal (e.g., detergent bottles).

The greatest demand for permanent antistatic agents is in the high and low density polyethylene market. High density polyethylene requires antistatic agents in blow molded bottles for the elimination of dust attraction, and low density polyethylene requires antistatic agents for blow molded bottles and film applications.

Polypropylene requires antistatic agents for specially molded articles and film applications, while polystyrene requires antistatic agents for molded articles, vacuum formed articles, and film. PVC requires antistatic agents for hi-fi records and specialty unplasticized formulations. Generally speaking, molded products require antistatic agents for sales appeal and film for the elimination of processing problems due to adhesion, electrostatic discharge.

Methods of Elimination

The two basic methods of static elimination are mechanical and chemical. Mechanical methods afford temporary protection, while the chemical method will eliminate static temporarily, semi-permanently, and permanently, depending upon the chemical and method of application.

Mechanical elimination is the oldest method used. The simplest consists of grounded metallic points placed very close to the plastic requiring neutralization. This method will eliminate enough of the electrostatic charge to enable trouble-free production. Electrostatic eliminators completely neutralize a plastic by placing a static bar close to the plastic. This static bar is attached to a power unit which supplies energy with a low amperage and high voltage. There are other devices such as radioactive static eliminators, etc., which neutralize a charge accumulated on the surface of a plastic.

Chemical additives are the most effective permanent antistatic agents, in addition to being used for temporary and semi-permanent protection. The method of application will determine whether or not the antistatic agent is permanent or temporary. Surface active agents are used for static protection, but when applied to the plastic surface, they will eventually wash, wear or rub off. The surface active agents can be applied as a coating by either spray, dip, or wiping onto the plastic surface.

Mass incorporation of the proper surface active agents will impart permanent antistatic protection. These materials must have a limited compatibility in the plastic mix which enables them to form a monomolecular film on the surface. This monomolecular film provides static protection which when rubbed off will be replaced by more of the antistatic agent from within the plastic.

The principal products used for mass incorporation into plastics are ethoxylated aliphatic amines and amides. Others currently being used are ethylene oxide adducts of aliphatics, phosphate esters, quaternary ammonium salts, aliphatic esters and glycol esters.

These chemicals, if they are effective in a particular plastic, have a partial incompatibility enabling them to form a monomolecular film on the plastic surface. They are hydroscopic and will pick up moisture from the atmosphere forming a monomolecular water layer on the plastic surface. This layer of water dissipates any electrostatic charge built up on the plastic. In addition to dissipating this charge, some of the aliphatic and glycerol based chemicals act as internal and external lubricants thus reducing the coefficient of friction within the plastic and also between the plastic and processing equipment.

According to the definition of an ideal permanent antistatic agent discussed earlier, ethoxylated aliphatic amines and amides have been found most effective. They can be used effectively at low concentrations (0.1–0.2%), develops a minimum amount of color, are essentially non-corrosive at low concentrations, can be used over a wide range of plastics, do not affect processing clarity, odor, stress cracking, and some are F.D.A. approved at 0.1%.

Table 1 illustrates a typical ethoxylated aliphatic amine mass-incorporated into high density polyethylene film and molded discs. It should be noted that 0.2% is highly effective in reducing

an electrostatic charge. In more general tests such as the "Soot Chamber" like results were obtained.

Test Methods

The prime reason for the market improvements in developing antistatic agents has been the improvement and development of more meaningful test methods. Prior to these improvements there was no way to determine whether or not a prospective antistatic would function under actual use conditions.

Although there are many sophisticated tests being used today. they are all based on the following:

Ash Tray Test. This was the earliest method and although not very scientific and not reproducible, this method is used by many laboratories as a screening test.

The test consists of spreading cigarette ashes on a paper, rubbing the plastic object and lowering the object to the ashes until they begin to jump and adhere to the plastic. The distance between the charged plastic and the paper is measured.

Static Test for Molded Objects. The static test for molded objects enables a laboratory to examine articles which will actually be used in the field (e.g., blow-molded polyethylene bottles). Test pieces are pre-conditioned 48 hr at 60% relative humidity at 72°F. These pieces are exposed to a high voltage and the surface resistivity is measured in ohms.

Static Test for Film. The film test method which can be used to examine film taken off of the production line consists of a turntable on which the film is layed. An arm covered with some fabric is placed on the film and the table is rotated for a total of 180 sec, which builds up an electrostatic surface charge on the film. The electrostatic charge is measured at the start, 30 sec, 60 sec, and 180 sec. After 180 sec the turntable is stopped and the time to decay to 1/2 of the maximum charge recorded is recorded.

Dust Chamber Test. This test is probably the most practical one for measuring blow-molded

TABLE 1. ANTISTATIC PROTECTION OF AN ETHOXYLATED ALIPHATIC AMINE [a].

Sample	High density polythene discs surface			High density polyethylene film			
	Concentration	restivity (ohms)		Charge after rubbing /			Time of decay to ½ max. charge in sec.
		Side 1	Side 2	0 sec	30 sec	60 sec	
Control	0	4×10^{14}	4×10^{14}	140	2000	2400	180
Ethoxylated aliphatic amine	0.2%	2.6×10^{14}	1.0×10^{14}	12	60	80	4

[a] All tests were conducted on samples that were conditioned 48 hr. at 60% relative humidity and 72°F.

plastic bottles which will be stored on super-market shelves. The soot which is used in this test simulates dust which settles on the bottles during the storage period.

Blow-molded bottles, pre-conditioned to a certain temperature and humidity, are placed on a shelf enclosed in a dust chamber where fine soot particles are blown in. The dust chamber is conditioned to a low relative humidity to simulate forced hot air which warms a supermarket in the winter. Soot is then attracted to the bottles with no static protection. The bottles are examined visually for the degree of soot attracted and rated on a 1–10 scale.

Soot for this test is made and distributed evenly about the dust chamber by burning a toluene soaked filter paper in an adjacent enclosure and driven into the dust chamber by a fan.

Other tests are used but in general, they are derived from the ones described. The test methods will undoubtedly improve in the future and improved antistatic agents will eventually be developed as a result.

J. H. KURTZ

ASBESTOS FIBERS

Origin and Properties of Asbestos

The word "asbestos," derived from ancient Greek, means "inconsumable," and is a technical or commercial designation for a variety of naturally occurring fibrous mineral silicates. There are some 30 known varieties, but there are only 6 which have commercial significance. They may be divided into two general classifications; the serpentine group which contains chrysotile, and the amphibole group which includes antho-phyllite, an *ortho*-rhombic mineral, and the monoclinic minerals-tremolite, actinolite, amosite, and crocidolite. Both *ortho*-rhombic and mono-clinic structures have been reported for chrysotile. Both classes of asbestos have silicon-oxygen tetrahedra as the basis of the structural unit. In chrysotile the tetrahedra form Si_2O_5-double layers (laminar structure), and in the amphiboles they combine to produce Si_4O_{11}-double chains (banded structure).

Asbestos is a metamorphic product of other minerals or rocks. Original igneous or sedimentary rocks were greatly changed in character by tem-perature, pressure, or other factors acting within the Earth's crust, and these complex geologic processes lasting over millions of years and occurring in an irregular and repetitious manner transformed original rocks such as peridotites, pyroxenites or carbonates into asbestos fibers.

Chrysotile constitutes about 93% of the current world production. Serpentinized peridotite, which is composed primarily of olivine, a ferromagnesian mineral, is the host rock for the most important

regions of chrysotile in the world. Serpentiniza-tion of carbonates such as dolomite led to an iron-free serpentine, and eventually to a low iron content chrysotile as is found in Arizona. Further hydrothermal reaction under certain conditions led to the crystallization of chrysotile asbestos and the formation of veins within the serpentine rock. There are two main types of veins, the first and generally most common are cross-fiber veins, i.e., the fiber lies at a high angle or normal to the walls of the vein. A less common variety is the slip-fiber vein, in which the fiber lies parallel to the walls of the vein. Most chrysotile mines are of the cross-fiber variety.

Chrysotile is a hydrated magnesium ortho-sili-cate containing a high percentage of magnesia and water. Its chemical formula is $3MgO \cdot 2SiO_2 \cdot 2H_2O$. Chrysotile can be subdivided into exceptionally fine fiber. The basic single fiber is a smooth cylinder approximately 0.02μ (7.1×10^{-7} in.)-0.04μ, compared with the fiber diameter of 40μ for human hair. The surface area of chrysotile, which will depend upon the degree of fiberization, has been measured at 13–22 sq m per g by nitrogen absorption, compared to 0.31 sq m per g for nylon. In general, chrysotile fibers are soft and silky although harsh and semi-harsh grades are not uncommon. The actual structure of the basic fiber has been the subject of considerable research. Current opinion is that the fiber is a hollow tube but the center may be filled with crystalline or amorphous forms of chrysotile, or other minerals.

Chrysotile fibers will absorb up to 3% surface moisture depending upon the ambient humidity. Ignition losses at elevated temperatures are somewhat higher than the theoretical 13% water of crystallization due to other decomposition losses. Weight losses versus temperature, after 2 hr exposure, increase gradually from 400°F, show a sharp increase at 1100°F, and reach a final maximum at 1800°F. It is postulated that chrysotile begins to undergo rearrangement to form fosterite at approximately 1000°F, and that the transformation is complete at around 1500°F. Chrysotile's high temperature capabilities depend upon exposure time. After short exposure time to 1000°F, the fiber will retain approximately 60% of its original strength. At 600°F, it is rela-tively unaffected by long term exposure.

Canadian chrysotile has been reported to exhibit average tensile strengths of 281,000 psi and a Young's modulus of 23.1×10^6 psi for 2.5 cm length samples. Strength increases as the fiber length decreases. Chrysotile exhibits good resistance to caustics and organic solvents, but it is readily attacked by acids.

Various impurities are present in chrysotile, the most important being magnetite (Fe_3O_4) in concentrations from nil to 6%. The presence of magnetite can be objectionable in electrical applications, but its effect is a function of the actual amount present, as well as the grain size. A low concentration of large grain size can be more troublesome than a higher concentration of small grain size, for example. It should also be noted that a chemical analysis for total iron content is inadequate since iron can be present as a silicate or as Fe_2O_3. The Mapes analyzer as described in ASTM D-1187-57 is often used to estimate magnetite content.

The major deposits of chrysotile are located in Canada, the Soviet Union, Southern Rhodesia, Union of South Africa, Swaziland, and the United States. Chrysotile is also produced in various parts of Europe, Asia and South America. On an average, the asbestos content of the host rock varies from 4%–10% with fiber lengths varying up to 2 in. However, the bulk of the fiber is less than 1/4-in. long. After separation by hand of the long fibers, the ore is processed through a mill in order to separate the fiber from the rock. In general, the separation of the fibers from the rock consists of a repetitive breaking and return of the not yet disintegrated rock, drying, separation into fibers, sieving and removal of the fiber by suction. The milled fibers are classified according to color, strength, and length. One basis of classification in both Canada and the Soviet Union is a mechanical sieving test conducted on the Quebec Standard Testing Machine No. 2.

The classification system used by the Canadian asbestos producers is shown in Table 1. The values indicate the ounces retained from a 16-oz sample in each of 4 boxes. The screens in the top three boxes have 1/2 in., 0.187 in., and 0.063 in. holes, respectively. The shorter and least expensive grades are used for filling plastic compositions such as tile and molding compounds. Longer grades are used where higher strengths are required. Papers, millboards, felts or mats, and fabrics which are produced from the longer grades are also used as plastic reinforcements, as well as papers composed of asbestos and glass fibers. Asbestos papers are generally produced on a cylinder-type machine, although Fourdrinier-type machines are also used. Various inorganic and organic binders at a general level of 15% are used. Asbestos felts are produced on garnets or carding machines with approximately 5% or less binder level. Asbestos rovings spun into yarn are woven into fabrics by wet or dry processes using textile operations. Up to 25% of non-asbestos fibers may be used.

Neither tremolite or actinolite is used to a significant extent as a plastic reinforcement or filler, and the usage of amosite is relatively minor. Crocidolite and amosite are found in metamorphosed ferruginous sedimentary formations and account for 5–6% of the world production.

Crocidolite asbestos is produced in South Africa and Australia, and deposits also exist in Bolivia. Amosite is mined only in South Africa.

TABLE 1. CANADIAN CLASSIFICATION SYSTEM.

Group No. 1 Crude No. 1	Consists basically of crude 3/4 in. staple and longer.
Group No. 2 Crude No. 2	Consists basically of crude 3/8 in. staple up to 3/4 in.
Crudes, run-of-mine	Consists basically of unsorted crudes.
Crudes, sundry	Consists of crudes other than specified above.

MILLED ASBESTOS

Standard designation of grades	Guaranteed minimum shipping test			
	Group No. 3			
(Spinning fibers)				
3F	10.5	3.9	1.3	0.3
3K	7	7	1.5	0.5
3R	4	7	4	1
ST	2	8	4	2
3Z	1	9	4	2
	Group No. 4			
(Shingle fibers)				
4A	0	8	6	2
4D	0	7	6	3
4H	0	5	8	3
4K	0	4	9	3
4M	0	4	8	4
4R	0	3	9	4
4T	0	2	10	4
4Z	0	1.5	9.5	5
	Group No. 5			
(Paper fibers)				
5D	0	0.5	10.5	5
5F	0	0	13	3
5K	0	0	12	4
5M	0	0	11	5
5R	0	0	10	6
5Z	0	0	8.6	7.4
	Group No. 6			
6D	0	0	7	9
	Group No. 7			
(Shorts)				
7D	0	0	5	11
7F	0	0	4	12
7H	0	0	3	13
7K	0	0	2	14
7M	0	0	1	15
7R	0	0	0	16
7T	0	0	0	16
7W	0	0	0	16
	Group No. 8			
8S	Less than 50 lb per cu ft loose measure			
8T	Less than 75 lb per cu ft loose measure			
	Group No. 9			
9T	Over 75 lb per cu ft loose measure			

TABLE 2. PROPERTIES OF ASBESTOS FIBERS.

	Chrysotile	Amosite	Anthophyllite	Crocidolite	Tremolite	Actinolite
Specific gravity	2.4–2.6	3.1–3.25	2.85–3.1	3.2–3.3	2.9–3.2	3.0—3.2
Tensile strength[a]	80,000–440,000	16,000–200,000	4000 and less	100,000–600,000	1000–8000	1000 and less
Acid resistance	Poor	Good	Good	Good	Good	Fair
Fusion point, °F	2770	2550	2675	2180	2400	2540
Temp. at max. ignition loss, °F	1800	1600–1800	1800	1200	1800	—
Resistance to heat	Good	Good	Very good	Poor, fuses	Fair to good	—
Specific heat, Btu/lb/°F	0.266	0.193	0.210	0.201	0.212	0.217
Elec. Charge	Pos.	Neg.	Neg.	Neg.	Neg.	Neg.
pH	9.2–10.3	8.5	7.0	8.4	—	—
Ionizable Salts, micromhos (Relative elect. conductance)	1.82	1.34	0.58	0.84	—	—
Magnetite content	0–6.0	0	0	3.0–5.9	0	—
Mineral impurities present	Iron, chrome, nickel, lime	Iron	Iron	Iron	Lime	Lime, iron
Hardness	2.5–4.0	5.5–6.0	5.5–6.0	4	5.5	6$^+$
Flexibility	High	Good	Poor	Good	Poor	Poor
Spinnability	Very Good	Fair	Poor	Fair	Poor	Poor
Color	Green, grey to white, yellowish	White to yellowish brown	Yellow-brown, white, grey, or green	Blue, lavender, or greenish	White, greenish, yellowish, or bluish	Greenish

[a] Depends upon source, type of sample, fiber length, and method of test.

Crocidolite and amosite fibers are much coarser than chrysotile fiber, approximately 0.1 μ in width. The basic fiber structure is a straight, solid, narrow strip, and in general the fibers occur in longer lengths than chrysotile asbestos. The theoretical formula for crocidolite is

$$Na_2O_3 \cdot FeO \cdot Fe_2O_3 \cdot 8SiO_2 \cdot H_2O,$$

and the presence of iron gives the fiber a characteristic blue color. The theoretical formula for amosite is $1.5MgO \cdot 5.5FeO \cdot 8SiO_2 \cdot H_2O$. Average tensile strengths of 148,000–203,000 psi, and 409,000–605,000 psi have been reported for amosite and crocidolite, respectively. Corresponding Young's moduli were 23.6 and 27.1×10^6 psi. Both fibers exhibit good resistance to acids, alkalies and organic solvents. Crocidolite fiber exhibits a maximum weight loss of approximately 1% at temperatures of 1200°F, but it undergoes structural changes and tends to fuse. Amosite is superior to crocidolite in heat resistance, and exhibits a maximum weight loss of 1.5% at 1800°F. Crocidolite is used in the form of paper, felts and fibers for plastic reinforcement.

Anthophyllite is produced in Finland and the United States of America. Its theoretical formula is $(MgFe)_7Si_8O_{22}(OH)_2$. The fiber is weak, exhibiting only 4,000 psi tensile strength, but it possesses good chemical resistance and is the most heat resistant of the asbestos fibers. Weight loss is less than 1% at temperatures up to 1500°F. In addition, it contains little or no magnetite as an impurity. It is used in short fiber form as a filler in plastic composition.

In general, the amphiboles will be used in plastic compositions where some unique property such as good acid resistance, low water absorption which obtains as a result of the different fiber structure, more neutral pH, or freedom from magnetite is required.

TABLE 3. PERCENTAGE COMPOSITION OF ASBESTOS.

Variety	SiO_2	MgO	Iron oxides Fe_2O_3	CaO Na_2O	H_2O
Chrysotile	35–44	36–44	0–9	0–2	12–15
Crocidolite	49–57	0–15	20–40	2–8	2–4.5
Amosite	45–56	1–7	31–46	1–2	1–5
Anthophyllite	52–64	25–35	1–10	0–1	1–5
Tremolite and actinolite	50–63	18–33	2–17	1–10	1–4

Plastics Applications of Asbestos

Floor Coverings. The single largest application for asbestos in plastics is vinyl asbestos floor tile.

Short chrysotile fibers (Grade 7) are compounded with a vinyl-chloride-acetate copolymer of approximately 13% vinyl acetate content, plasticizers, stabilizers, pigments, and other fillers in a banbury of sigma-type mixer, and then further processed in a continuous web through mills and calenders to produce a finished sheet which is cut into tiles. Vinyl asbestos tile is typically 1/16-in. thick, as contrasted with the weaker asphalt tile which is typically 1/8-in. thick. Asphalt time, the older product, is made in a similar fashion. In fact, tile plants can produce either. Asphalt tile formulations are similar to those used with vinyl asbestos, except that various petroleum resins or coumarone-indene resins from coal tar and pitches such as cottonseed pitch are used for the binder system. Vinyl asbestos tile has grown much more rapidly, however, due to lighter colors, improved wearability, easier maintenance, and better chemical and grease resistance.

A typical tile compound is shown below:

Vinyl Chloride-acetate copolymer	15–25%
Plasticizer	6–8
Asbestos (Grade 7)	15–27
Calcium carbonate	40–60
Pigments	1–10
Stabilizers	0.7–0.9

Phthalate ester plasticizers are generally used and processing temperatures seldom exceed 250°F. Asbestos fibers impart strength, abrasion resistance and cold flow resistance to the tile. The presence of free iron in the chrysotile asbestos requires special stabilizing systems which chelate the iron and prevent it from discoloring and degrading the vinyl resin. Stabilizer systems containing various nitrogen based compounds are generally preferred. The reinforcing action of the asbestos and its color are important since these characteristics determine the amount of lower cost calcium carbonate which can be tolerated, as well as the amount of relatively expensive pigments which must be used in the formula.

Chrysotile paper is used as an inert and dimensionally stable substrate for vinyl sheet floor covering. Cubes or other granular forms of a plasticized vinyl homopolymer or low acetate content copolymer filled with calcium carbonate and clay are fused to the paper and overlaid with a clear plasticized vinyl. The finished sheet is permanently affixed to the floor with appropriate adhesives.

Friction Materials. Brake linings, clutch facings and similar products are a major application for resin bonded, chrysotile asbestos. Powdered and liquid phenolic resins at concentrations of 15–25% are generally used. Other ingredients such as metal particles or mineral fillers are also used in the compounds. Both dry and wet processes are used and asbestos can be in the form of short fibers, in mixes which are molded or extruded, or as woven fabric or millboard which is impregnated. Final curing is done at pressures up to 4000 psi and approximately 300°F. Phenolic-asbestos brake linings generally exhibit frictional coefficients of 0.35–0.60. Temperature requirements generally exceed 500°F.

Cold Molded Plastics. Highly viscous phenol-formaldehyde resins (as well as other binders such as asphalts, pitches, gilsonite, or polymerizable oils) are used as binders with loadings up to 85% of short fibers. The compounds are prepared in a heater mixer and then cold molded at pressures up to 4000 psi. Post baking may or may not be required depending upon the binder. Heater plug parts and housings for the shielding of electrical units are produced by this process. Tensile strengths up to 3000 psi and load deflection temperatures in excess of 400°F are typical.

Thermosetting and Thermoplastic Molding Compounds. Asbestos is used as a filler or reinforcement in thermosetting and thermoplastic molding compounds for a variety of reasons. Improved hardness, heat resistance, burning rate, mechanical properties, dimensional stability and cold flow resistance of thermoplastic resins are some of the advantages which obtain with the use of asbestos fiber. The type of fiber, as well as fiber length and amount of loading, will depend upon the application. Maximum mechanical properties will be obtained with long fibers, for example, but appearance properties such as finish and smoothness tend to be impaired.

Vinyl polymers and copolymers, polyolefins, polyamides, fluropolymers and ethyl cellulose have all been compounded with asbestos fibers. Banburies, heated rolls, or extruders are generally used. Special techniques are required to minimize degradation of long fibers, however. Anthophyllite has been preferred for polypropylene compounds since this fiber type apparently exhibits minimal effect on heat stability. Long-fibered chrysotile has been used to reinforce modified rigid vinyl sheet which can be laminated to substrates or used without support for building, engineering and chemical applications.

Premix or dough molding compounds containing various proportions of polyester resin, asbestos, mineral filler and glass fiber or sisal reinforcements are mixed in a sigma-type mixer and then preformed through an unheated extruder. Molding is generally accomplished at approximately 300°F and pressures less than 1000 psi and typical applications include automotive heater parts, appliance parts and electrical equipment parts. At concentrations of approximately 5–10% short chrysotile fibers act as a flow control agent by preventing the polyester resin from flowing away from the glass reinforcement, thus improving appearance and uniformity Asbestos also aids in producing a drier and more handleable mix. Asbestos may also be used as the reinforcement at levels up to 50% in polyester, phenolic and epoxy premix-type compounds. Crocidolite fibers are employed where corrosion resistance properties are required.

TABLE 4. ASBESTOS REINFORCED THERMOPLASTICS.

Resin	Nylon 6/6	Polypro-pylene	Vinyl
Specific gravity	1.5	1.2	1.75
Hardness, Rockwell M	M75	M95	—
Tensile strength, psi	11,000	4200–5000	10,500
Elongation, %	16	6	—
Flexural strength, psi	17,600	8000–12,000	17,000
Flexural modulus, psi	650,000	370,000–1,000,000	1,600,000
Load deflection temp. @ 264 psi, °F	365	170–230	158
Izod impact strength Ft lb/in. notch	0.5	0.3–2.2	3.2
Coefficient of linear thermal expansion (per °C $\times 10^{-5}$)	—	3.8	1.2–2.6
Water absorption (24 hr), %	0.4–0.7	0.02	—

Asbestos is also used along with other mineral fillers in filling various phenolic, melamine, alkyd, diallyl phthalate, and silicone molding compounds. Asbestos content and fiber length will vary with each resin system and properties desired. When using short fibers, properties will vary little over the range of 30–60%. With longer fiber, however, maximum strengths are obtained at the 25% level with phenolics, and 45% with silicone, for example. The compounding technique will depend upon the material. Banburies, heated rolls, sigma-type mixers and other types of internal mixes are used.

Phenolic molding compounds are generally reinforced with asbestos when service conditions up to 500°F are required. Typical examples include heater plugs, utensil handles, toaster handles and similar applications. Typical asbestos reinforced melamine applications include ignition parts, electrical components, terminal blocks, circuit breakers, and similar applications where high arc resistance and dielectric strength, low shrinkage and good insert retention are required. These compounds are granular and are molded at pressures in excess of 2000 psi.

Asbestos filled silicone parts are used in applications where structural or dielectric properties are to be maintained at temperatures up to 600°F. High performance compounds based upon alkyds or diallyl phthalate resins exhibiting good electrical performance at high temperatures are also reinforced with asbestos. These materials are generally in granular or putty form, and are molded at pressures less than 1500 psi.

Anthophyllite and chrysotile grades are used, with the former being preferred in applications where electrical properties and low water absorption are preferred. Anthophyllite is also used where the alkalinity of chrysotile will interfere with acid cures as in the case of melamine formaldehyde.

Acid leached anthophyllite fibers are used as reinforcements for corrosion resistant structures. Acid leaching removes chemically combined complex magnesium and non-silicates. The fiber is compounded in a sigma blade-type mixer with furfuryl alcohol-formaldehyde or phenol formaldehyde resins, and the resulting putty after shaping onto a mold is cured in an autoclave or metal dies at elevated temperatures. Chemical resistant equipment and pipe which will withstand non-oxidizing acids, salt of these acids and strong alkalies at temperatures up to 300°F is produced by this process. Wall thicknesses are generally 1/2-in., but can be reduced by filament winding glass reinforced epoxy around the structure.

Laminates. Asbestos papers, mats, felts, fabrics, and millboards are all used as reinforcements with a wide variety of thermosetting resins. Good bonds are obtained without the use of special coupling agents as are required with glass reinforcements. The webs are impregnated on a standard treater and dryer with liquid phenolformaldehyde, melamine-formaldehyde, polyester (diallyl phthalate and triallyl cyanurate modified), silicone and epoxy resins and then laminated under heat and pressure. Typical applications include printed circuits, insulation boards, oven parts, pump parts and electric appliance insulation. Carefully cleaned fiber with low magnetite content is required for good electrical properties.

Corrosion resistant pipe for 300°F, 150 psi service is made from impregnated crocidolite paper which is wound onto a mandrel under pressure and then cured at elevated temperatures. Alternatively, crocidolite mat, impregnated with 80–90% of a corrosion resistant resin, is used as a corrosion protection barrier in epoxy, and glass filament wound pipe or tanks.

Chrysotile papers, felts and tapes, as well as composites of asbestos and glass fibers, are impregnated with heat resistant resins such as phenol formaldehyde and are laminated, wound or molded at moderate pressures and temperatures of approximately 300°F into missile parts such as nose cones and nozzles. They exhibit

TABLE 5. ASBESTOS REINFORCED THERMOSETTING COMPOUNDS.

	Phenol-formaldehyde	Melamine formaldehyde	Furfuryl alcohol-formaldehyde	Polyester	Silicone (MSG)[b]	Alkyd (MAG)[b]	Diallyl phthalate (MDG)[b]
Specific gravity	1.55–1.90	1.70–2.00	1.7	1.4–2.3	1.6–1.9[a]	2.1–2.2[a]	1.65–1.95[a]
Tensile strength, psi	4000–7,500	5500–7000	4100	5000–10,000	—	—	—
Tensile modulus, psi	$1.5–1.6 \times 10^6$	2×10^6	0.9×10^6	$1.5–2.5 \times 10^6$	—	—	—
Flexural strength, psi	6000–17,000	9000–12,000	—	8000–15,000	6000	7500	6800
Compressive strength, psi	15,000–35,000	25,000–30,000	15,800	13,000–27,000	—	—	—
Impact, strength, ft/in. of notch	0.23–4.5	0.25–0.8	—	1–25	0.25	0.25–0.35[a]	0.2
Load deflection temp. @ 264 psi, °F	350–400	265	265–330	315	—	350–400[a]	350–420[a]
Continuous operating temp., °F	300–500	250–400	—	350–600	—	350–400[a]	350–400[a]
Water absorption, %	0.2–0.5	0.08–0.14	—	0.1–0.2	0.50	0.50	0.70
Dielectric strength, S/T volts/mil	150–300	350–400	—	200–400	—	—	—
Dielectric strength, step-by-step, volts/mil	—	—	—	—	275	—	140
Dielectric constant, 1 MC	5–7	5.0–6.7	—	—	5.0	6.0	6.0
Dissipation factor, 1 MC	0.04–0.25	0.03–0.50	—	—	0.015	0.03	0.14
Arc resistance, sec	Tracks	120–200	—	—	210	175	115

[a] Typical   [b] Grades MSG, MAG and MDG requirements per US Military Specification MIL-M-14 "Molding Plastics and Molded Plastics Parts, Thermosetting."

TABLE 6. ASBESTOS REINFORCED LAMINATES.

	Polyester, mat	Polyester, mat	Melamine formaldehyde, fabric or paper	Phenol-formaldehyde, fabric	Phenol-formaldehyde, paper	Phenol-formaldehyde, felt/mat	Silicone, fabric or paper
Laminating temperature, °F	—	300	270–320	300–350	300–350	300–320	350
Laminating pressure, psi	Hand lay-up	300	1000–1,800	300–1800	1000–1800	200–1000	300–2000
Specific gravity	1.4	1.7	1.75–1.85	1.55–1.80	1.65–1.83	1.7–2.8	1.6–1.75
Reinforcement content, %	15–20	60	40–60	40–60	40–60	50–70	50–60
Tensile strength, psi	8000–10,000	25,000	6000–12,000	10,000–12,000	5000–15,000	11,000–60,000	—
Tensile modulus, psi	$0.8–1.0 \times 10^6$	3.0×10^6	$1.6–2.2 \times 10^6$	$1.0–1.7 \times 10^6$	$1.6–2.5 \times 10^6$	$2.8–3.5 \times 10^6$	—
Flexural strength, psi	12,000–23,000	45,000	12,000–14,000	10,000–35,000	15,000–30,000	16,000–90,000	12,000–25,000
Flexural modulus, psi	—	—	—	$1.0–1.5 \times 10^6$	$1.4–2.3 \times 10^6$	$1.5–5.0 \times 10^6$	—
Izod impact, ft lb/in. Notch	—	—	0.75–4.0	3–5	0.6–1.5	1–6	6.0–90.
Load deflection temp. at 264 psi, °F	—	—	—	>320	>320	>320	>320
Continuous operating temperature, °F	—	—	225–275	275	275	>300	>300
Dielectric strength, S/T, volts/mil	—	—	50–150	50–100	160–250	—	50–380
Dielectric constant, 1 MC	—	—	8.0–9.6	5.0–10.0	5.0	—	4.3
Power factor, 1 MC	—	—	0.12–0.22	0.10–0.15	0.08–0.14	—	—
Water absorption, %	—	—	1.0–5.0	0.3–2.5	0.4–2.0	—	0.5–1.5

good high temperature and ablative characteristics, which are due in part to the water of crystallization, and retain significant strength after long exposure at 700°F. Asbestos reinforced laminates are reported to have withstood temperatures up to 10,000°F for several seconds.

Asbestos mats can also be fabricated into boats, furniture and similar products with typical polyester hand lay-up techniques.

JOHN M. VERDI

Cross-references: FIBERS, ASBESTOS; FILLERS, ASBESTOS.

AZELAIC ACID AND DERIVATIVES

Azelaic acid (nonanedioic acid) is a 9 carbon, saturated aliphatic dibasic acid represented by the following formula:

$$HOOC—(CH_2)_7—COOH$$

It is produced along with other products by the oxidative cleavage of a number of naturally occurring fatty acids or their derivatives. Oxidation of oleic acid or 9, 10 dihydroxystearic acid with potassium permanganate, chromic acid, or sodium dichromate and sulfuric acid yields azelaic acid, and the nine carbon straight chained monobasic acid, pelargonic acid, as a co-product. Subjecting 9,10-dihydroxystearic acid to a high temperature caustic fusion with potassium hydroxide or a mixture of potassium and sodium hydroxides, yields the same products. Azelaic acid also can be produced by the reaction of ricinoleic acid with alkaline permanganate, or by the reaction of castor oil or ricinoleic acid with oxides of nitrogen or nitric acid. In the latter case suberic acid is produced as a by-product. Azelaic acid has been synthesized by the action of carbon dioxide on the Grignard reagent, 1,7-heptamethylene magnesium bromide, and by the hydrolysis of the corresponding dinitrile, 1,7-dicyanoheptane.

Recently a unique process for the production of both azelaic and pelargonic acids on a commercial scale utilizing ozonolysis has been described. In this process, technical grade oleic acid, the "red oil" of commerce, is reacted with a gaseous stream of ozone and oxygen to yield a viscous intermediate, oleic acid ozonide. In this reaction pelargonic acid is added as a diluent primarily to increase fluidity of the resulting ozonide. The thermal decomposition of the ozonide with simultaneous oxidation of the intermediate cleavage products (chiefly aldehydic in nature) with molecular oxygen yields the desired carboxylic acids. The over-all reaction can be illustrated as follows:

$$CH_3—(CH_2)_7—CH=CH—(CH_2)_7—COOH + O_3 \longrightarrow$$

Oleic acid

$$CH_3—(CH_2)_7—\underset{\underset{O——O}{|}}{\overset{\overset{H \quad O \quad H}{|}}{C}} \quad \overset{}{C}—(CH_2)_7—COOH + 1/2O_2 \longrightarrow$$

Oleic acid ozonide

$$CH_3—(CH_2)_7—COOH + HOOC—(CH_2)_7—COOH$$

Pelargonic acid   *Azelaic acid*

Polyunsaturated acids such as linoleic and linolenic acid, from safflower oil, linseed oil or tall oil are also suitable feed stock for this process. In this case monobasic acids of less than nine carbon atoms are obtained as co-products.

Types and Properties

Pure azelaic acid is a white, solid material of formula weight 188.22. It has a melting point of 107°C and boiling points of 225.5°C at 10 mm Hg and 286.5°C at 100 mm Hg. Azelaic acid is only slightly soluble in cold water (0.1 g in 100 cu cm water at 0°C; 0.212 g in 100 cu cm at 22°C) but is infinitely soluble at the boiling point of the aqueous solution.

Azelaic acid is soluble in alcohol and other relatively polar organic solvents with the solubility increasing as the solvents are heated. Because of the presence of the two polar carboxyl groups it is only very slightly soluble in non-polar solvents such as petroleum ether and carbon tetrachloride. Being an odd carbon fatty acid, azelaic acid has a lower melting point and somewhat greater solubility than even carbon dibasic acids of similar molecular weight; e.g., suberic acid melting point —144°C, azelaic acid melting point —107°C, sebacic acid melting point —133°C. This general rule is also applicable to simple derivatives of the dibasic fatty acids (e.g., n-methyl amides, etc.).

Specifications and characteristics are listed in Table 1*.

Azelaic acid is a rather strong organic acid (ionization constant $K_1 = 2.5 \times 10^{-5}$) which enters into all reactions characteristic of compounds containing the carboxyl group. Thus, azelaic acid can be readily converted into salts, esters, amides, acid chlorides, nitriles, alcohols, and anhydrides. Because of the difunctionality of the molecule interesting mixed derivatives such as acid salts, acid esters, ester amides, etc., can be prepared. In addition polymers can be readily formed by the reaction of azelaic acid with polyols and polyamines.

Azelaic acid readily reacts with alkali metal hydroxides, carbonates or bicarbonates to form

* Several grades of azelaic acid are available from Emery Industries, Inc., under the trademark of "Emerox Azelaic Acid."

TABLE 1. CHARACTERISTICS OF AZELAIC ACID.

Specifications	Test method	Commercial grade	Polymer grade
Acid value	ASTM-D1980-61	580–595	588–594
Color (molten)	Coleman Jr.	15/71	82/96 min.
% Transmission 440/550 mmu	Spectrophotometer		
Properties			
Appearance		White flakes	White flakes
Color stability, molten	Coleman Jr.		
% Transmission 440/550 mmu	Spectrophotometer		
2 Hr/205°C	(air)	8/40	78/96
Color, molten	APHA	500	30
Equivalent w	—	96	95
Average molecular w	—	192	190
Melting range	Fisher-Johns	96–103	101–102
Solubility, g/100 g at 27°C			
H_2O			0.24
Acetone			1.40
Ethyl ether			2.70
Toluene			5.70
Ethanol			54.00
Di methyl formamide			137.00
Ash content, ppm	ASTM-D482-59T	50	1
Iron content, ppm	Emery Method	2.5	1
Composition (w % of methyl ester by gas liquid chromatography)			
C_9 Dibasic		83.0	92.00
C_{10} Dibasic		1.50	1.20
C_{11} Dibasic		5.50	5.60
Other dibasics		8.50	1.16
Monobasics		1.50	0.04

salts or soaps. These soaps are extremely water soluble but exhibit no surface active properties. The salts of other metals such as calcium, magnesium, aluminum, etc., are usually prepared by the double decomposition of precipitation method in which an aqueous solution of the metal salt is reacted with a solution of a soluble alkali salt of azelaic acid. The metal azelate being insoluble in water precipitates and is collected by filtration, washed and dried.

Amides of azelaic acid can be prepared by dehydration of an ammonium or amine salt of the acid. Passing ammonia gas through molten azelaic acid at 200°C for 10–12 hr so that water is continuously removed produces azelamide (mp 175°C) in good yields. The reaction time in this reaction can be greatly reduced by operating under a moderate pressure (100 psi) of ammonia gas. Dimethylamide, the anilide and other substituted amides of azelaic acid can be prepared similarly. Azelaic acid, being dibasic, can react with diamines to form linear polymers. In general, the polyamides formed from azelaic acid possess somewhat lower melting points than those prepared from adipic or other even carbon dibasic acids.

If the above mentioned reaction of gaseous ammonia and azelaic acid is carried out in the neighborhood of 300°C especially in the presence of a catalyst such as alumina, the product is not the diamide but the corresponding dehydration product, azelanitrile. Azelanitrile can be converted to a useful polymer similar in characteristics to those of commercial polyhexamethylene adipamide by reaction with formaldehyde. Azelanitrile can be reduced to the corresponding diamine nonamethylene diamine or 1,9-nonanediamine, by conventional methods.

Azelaic acid or the simple diesters can be reduced by hydrogenation under 5000 psi pressure using a copper chromite catalyst to the corresponding glycol, 1,9-nonanediol. This dialcohol has a melting point of 45°C and is insoluble in both water and hydrocarbon solvents. The acid-alcohol (9-hydroxy pelargonic acid) can also be formed but is difficult to isolate in the pure state because of a tendency to polymerize when heated.

Other derivatives of azelaic acid such as anhydrides, acid chlorides, etc., can also be prepared but by far the most important derivatives of azelaic acid are the esters. The monohydric alcohols of azelaic acid (particularly the di-2-ethyl hexyl and isooctyl esters) are relatively high boiling and are extremely efficient plasticizers for vinyl and cellulosic plastics and neoprene, nitrile and butadiene styrene rubbers. They also find application as base fluids for greases and synthetic lubricants particularly for jet aircraft.

Reaction of azelaic acid with polyfunctional alcohols produces polyesters of varying chain lengths and properties depending on the alcohol and reaction conditons used. Polyurethane resins result from the reaction of these azelaic polyesters and diisocyanates. These products are finding usage in flexible and rigid foams and in synthetic rubbers with improved wear characteristics. More detailed information on the uses of the esters of azelaic acid is given in the following section on applications of azelaic acid.

Applications of Azelaic Acid

Simple diesters of azelaic acid find broad application as base stocks for synthetic lubricants and greases, and for plasticizers, whereas the polyesters are used for plasticizers, for manufacture of isocyanate derivatives, for laminating and coating resins, and for film. Probably the outstanding application for azelaic acid esters is in the field of polyvinyl chloride, nitrocellulose, cellulose acetate butyrate, and synthetic rubber plasticization. Here, the azelaic acid diesters are widely accepted for their compatibility, low temperature performance, low water extraction, low volatility, good efficiency and excellent light stability. Polyester type plasticizers prepared by the esterification of azelaic acid with selected difunctional glycols, possess a high degree of performance, low migration properties, outstanding compatibility, and unique low temperature

TABLE 2. COMPARATIVE PERFORMANCE OF AZELAIC ACID DERIVED PLASTICIZERS WITH BIS-2-ETHYLHEXYL PHTHALATE (DOP) IN POLYVINYL CHLORIDE.

Plasticizer Concentration (parts/hundred of resin)	Bis-2-ethyl-hexyl phthalate (DOP) 50	Bis-2-ethyl-ahexyl zalate (DOZ) 45	Azelaic poly-ester MW-1000 (Plastolein[a] 9722) 60	Azelaic poly-ester MW-1800 (Plastolein[a] 9750) 65	Azelaic poly-ester MW-3000 (Plastolein[a] 9765) 68
75 mil sheet					
Elongation, %	340	390	360	390	370
Modulus, psi (100% elongation)	1390	1330	1400	1320	1370
Tensile, psi	3035	3015	2955	2860	2820
Hardness (10 sec durometer A)	89/81	86/82	84/78	86/78	86/79
A.S.T.M. D-746 brittle point	−29	−60	−23	−23	−17
20 mil sheet					
Masland impact, °C	−25	−55	−20	−15	−10
Volatility					
1 day at 70°C	0.9	1.1			
7 days at 90°C	15.2		4.1	2.4	1.4
Extraction, % loss					
Soapy water, 1 day at 90°C	4.4	0.4	4.0	2.6	2.6
Mineral oil, 1 day at 50°C	4.7	8.2	2.8	2.5	1.3
Hexane, 1 day at 25°C	20.4	—	3.8	2.3	0
Migration					
Nitrocellulose, % softening	85	—	80	60	40
Polystyrene, extent of marring	Severe	Severe	Trace	None	None
SBR Paper, % loss from vinyl, 7 days at 70°C	8.5	—	1.5	0.4	0.2
Aging					
Fadeometer, 400 hr at 60°C Degradation	Trace	Trace	Slight	Slight	Slight
Florida, 600 sun hr, degradation	Trace	Moderate	Trace	Trace	Trace
Heat, min. to failure at 400°F	20	25+	25	25	25

[a] Registered trademark Emery Industries, Inc.

characteristics for their type. These polyesters may or may not be chain stopped (generally with monobasic acids such as pelargonic) depending upon the desired molecular weight.

The "work horses" of the plasticizer field are bis 2-ethyl hexyl phthalate or DOP, as it is commonly known, and bis iso-octyl phthalate or DIOP. In 1964. these esters, because of their all-around performance and low cost, accounted for nearly 40% of the plasticizers used in the United States. Azelaic based esters and polyesters are generally higher in cost than DOP and DIOP and, hence, are used in constructions that require special performance not available through the use of phthalates or other types. An examination of Table 2 comparing the performance of selected azelaic acid diesters and polyesters with DOP will indicate why these specialty plasticizers are gaining broad use in the field.

In comparing bis 2-ethylhexyl azelaic (DOZ) with DOP, the major area of difference is in low temperature performance. Many use areas of plasticized plastics require outstanding low temperature performance. Examples of such uses are in automotive coated fabrics and instrument panel covers, rain wear, garden hose, food packaging film, and footwear. Use of DOZ permits this specialty performance requirement to be met.

Comparison of DOP with the complex linear polyesters of varying molecular weights (see Table 2) will show many points of difference. These points generally relate to those performance factors that are associated with improved permanence of plasticized polymers. In fact, this type of plasticizer is now commonly referred to as a permanent type. The polyesters are outstanding in terms of low volatility and migration, and high resistance to extraction. These factors are of extreme importance in formulating, for example, PVC refrigerator gaskets that come in contact with ABS or polystyrene door panels, PVC films

TABLE 3. TYPICAL USE FORMULATIONS REQUIRING SPECIALTY (AZELAIC) PLASTICIZERS.

Automotive upholstery	Parts by wt
PVC (Polyvinylchloride)	100
DOP (Bis-2-Ethylhexyl phthalate)	40
DOZ (Bis-2-Ethylhexyl azelate)	30
Stabilizer (Cd-Ba type)	3
Colorants	As needed

Rainwear	
PVC	100
DOP	20
DOZ	20
Stabilizer (Cd-Ba type)	3

Storm window film	
PVC	100
DOZ	40
Stabilizer (Cd-Ba type)	3

TABLE 3 (continued)

Pool liners	
PVC	100
DOP	30
DOZ	15
Stabilizer (Cd-Ba type)	3
Colorants	As needed

Garden hose	
PVC	100
DOP	35
DOZ	15
Stabilizer (Cd-Ba type)	3
Colorants	As needed

High temperature wire coating	
PVC (electrical grade)	100
Polymeric (MW-1800)	50
Stabilizer (Pb type)	10
Clay	7
Colorants	As needed

Refrigerator gasketing	
PVC	100
Polymeric (MW-3000)	85
Epoxy soya	10
Filter	20
Colorants	As needed

SBR Impregnated paper coatings	
PVC	100
Polymeric (MW-1000)	55
Stabilizer (Cd-Ba type)	3
Colorants	As needed

Truck upholstery	
PVC	100
Polymeric (MW-1800)	70
Stabilizer (Cd-Ba type)	3
Colorants	As needed

Adhesive back film	
PVC	100
Polymeric (MW-3000)	60
Stabilizer (Pb type)	5
Colorants	As needed

Furniture upholstery	
PVC	100
Polymeric (MW-1000)	40
DOP	30
Stabilizer (Cd-Ba type)	3
Colorants	As needed

Automotive instrument panel cover	
PVC	50
ABS	50
Polymeric	20
Epoxy soya	10
Colorants	As needed

Food film	
PVC	84
Bis-di normal hexyl azelate	15
Nontoxic stabilizer	1

to be used for baby accessories, adhesive tapes, high temperature wire insulation, vinyl to metal coatings, truck upholstery and high quality furniture coverings.

Formulations utilizing azelaic esters in PVC, typical of those used in the industry, are presented in Table 3. In general, azelaic acid esters find uses similar to esters based on adipic and sebacic acids; however, the odd-carbon configuration of azelaic acid is responsible for some uniqueness, particularly in low temperature performance and fluidity of its derivatives.

Progress in aircraft design has increased the speed and range of both military and civilian aircraft and has created a need for improved lubrication at both high and low temperature. High altitude flying with temperatures of $-65°F$ being common has introduced a severe low temperature problem. The newer turbojet and turboprop aircraft engines with higher compression ratios and increased power outputs require oils which can withstand relatively high temperatures (up to 450°F).

Modern military greases must also withstand wide temperature ranges ($-100°F$–$400°F$) and have greater oxidation stability, improved corrosion resistance and extreme pressure properties.

Azelate diesters (particularly the di-2-ethyl-hexyl and di-isooctyl esters mentioned previously) are used commercially as base stocks for the manufacture of synthetic lubricants and specialty greases. As lubricants they possess excellent low temperature properties, good lubricity and thermal stability and superior viscosity-temperature relationships. Selected azelate esters also show promise as base stocks in the field of automotive engine lubrication.

The methyl ester of the polymer grade of azelaic acid is finding use as an intermediate in the production of polyester film. Modification by way of the azelaic moiety increases toughness and low temperature performance of these films. Similar use of azelaic polyesters with appropriate isocyanates provide a means of obtaining spandex fibers with improved performance.

Other suggested uses include polyamide molding powders, dielectric fluids, special alkyds, isocyanate resins for foam and elastomer applications.

JOHN D. FARR
H. F. OEHLSCHLAEGER

AZO INITIATOR

2,2′-azobisisobutyronitrile (azobis) is the best known member of a series of compounds containing an azo group ($-N{=}N-$) which thermally decomposes into free radicals capable of initiating polymerization. Nitrogen is evolved as a by-product. The family of compounds, which can be described as azobisalkyl nitriles, is represented by the following formula:

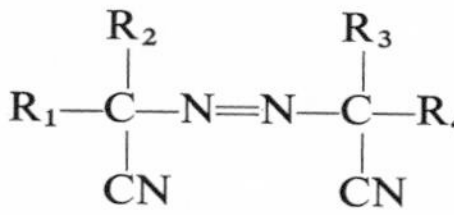

$$R_1-\underset{\underset{CN}{|}}{\overset{\overset{R_2}{|}}{C}}-N{=}N-\underset{\underset{CN}{|}}{\overset{\overset{R_3}{|}}{C}}-R_4$$

where R_1, R_2, R_3 and R_4 may be alkyl, substituted alkyl, cycloalkyl or aromatic, or where R_1, R_2 and R_3 and R_4 respectively, may be alkylene groups forming homocyclic derivatives. In the case of 2,2′-azobisisobutyronitrile, R_1, R_2, R_3 and R_4 are methyl groups.

A number of such derivatives has been prepared and their properties and kinetics of decomposition studied. However, since 2,2′-azobisisobutyronitrile is the only member of the series offered commercially, further comments will be limited to this compound.

Azobis has been known since 1896 but its use as a source of free radicals was not recognized until the early nineteen forties. Since that time it has been found in the trade under various trade names and synonyms including "Vazo" vinyl polymerization catalyst, "Porophor" N, AIBN, AZDN, and Lucin. The Chemical Abstract nomenclature is 2,2′-azobis (2-methyl propionitrile).

Azobis decomposes by the absorption of thermal or photochemical energy into two free radicals (isobutyronitrile or isopropyl cyanide) and nitrogen as shown below:

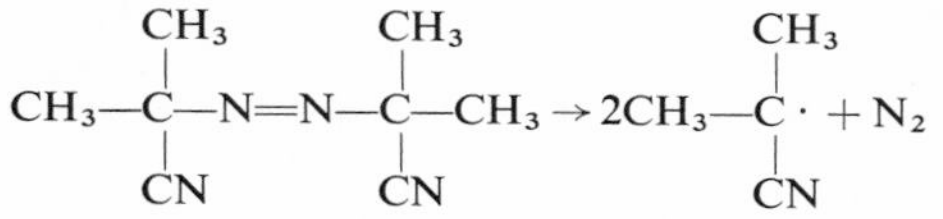

$$CH_3-\underset{\underset{CN}{|}}{\overset{\overset{CH_3}{|}}{C}}-N{=}N-\underset{\underset{CN}{|}}{\overset{\overset{CH_3}{|}}{C}}-CH_3 \rightarrow 2CH_3-\underset{\underset{CN}{|}}{\overset{\overset{CH_3}{|}}{C}}\cdot + N_2$$

The decomposition in solution is strictly first

TABLE 1. RATE OF DECOMPOSITION OF AZOBIS AT 176°F (80°C) IN VARIOUS ORGANIC SOLVENTS.

Solvent	Rate constant, sec.$^{-1}$ $k \times 10^4$	Half-life, min $t_{\frac{1}{2}}$[b]
Aniline	1.68	68.7
N,N-dimethylaniline	1.83	63.1
Dodecyl mercaptan	1.46	79.0
t-amyl alcohol	1.40	82.5
Isobutyl alcohol	1.72	67.2
Toluene	1.5–1.8[a]	78–64[a]
Xylene	1.533	75.5
Nitrobenzene	1.98	58.3
Glacial acetic acid	1.52	76.0

[a] Range reported in literature.

[b] $t_{\frac{1}{2}} = \dfrac{0.693}{k}$

order, being little influenced by the medium. The rate of free radical formation can be controlled by regulating the temperature. The rate of decomposition in toluene expressed in half-life, showing the temperature dependency of the decomposition, is given in Fig. 1, where the ordinate is the reciprocal of the absolute temperature. The rate of decomposition in various solvents is given in Table 1.

Physical Properties

Azobis is a white crystalline powder with the following physical properties:

Molecular W	164.14
Melting point	105°C.
Solubility in Water	Nil

Solubilities of azobis in various solvents are to be found in Table 2.

Chemical Properties

The only chemical reaction of consequence for azobis is its thermal decomposition to yield free radicals and gaseous nitrogen. This reaction, though simple, kinetically speaking, is quite complex. Dimethyl-N-(2-cyano-2-propyl)ketenimine, isobutyronitrile, methacrylonitrile and tetramethylsuccinonitrile have been identified as decomposition products. However, the last named chemical is the principle product. The photochemical decomposition of azobis to initiate polymerization has also been reported.

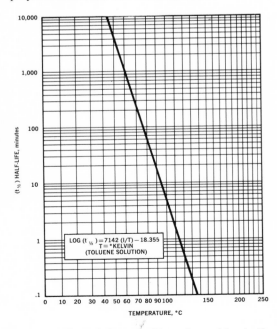

FIG. 1. Thermal decomposition of azobis half-life temperature curve.

TABLE 2. SOLUBILITY OF AZOBIS IN VARIOUS SOLVENTS.

Solvent	Solubility, g/100 g. at 32°F (0°C)	at 77°F (25°C)
Acetone	12.0	—
Benzene	< 1.0	11.0
Carbon tetrachloride	—	0.7
Chloroform	17.0	25.0
Dichloromethane	21.5	40.0
N,N-dimethylacetamide	7.0	20.5
Dioxane	< 1.0	—
Ethanol (absolute)	—	2.7
Ethanol 2B	—	2.7
Ethyl acetate	5.0	14.0
Ethyl ether	—	4.0
Ethylene chloride	4.0	23.0
Formamide	—	0.5
Freon[a] 113	< 1.0	—
Heptane	—	0.45
Isopropyl alcohol	—	0.65
Methanol (absolute)	2.5	7.5
Methyl formate	10.0	26.0
Methyl methoxyacetate	8.5	20.0
Styrene	—	8.0
Toluene	2.0	7.0
Xylene	—	2.5
Water	< 0.01	—
Mixtures (50%–50% by wt)		
Benzene + N,N-dimethyl-acetamide	8.0	20.5
Benzene + methyl formate	15.0	33.0
Benzene + methyl methoxyacetate	8.0	20.0

Azobis is also soluble in many vinyl monomers.

[a] DuPont's registered trademark for its fluorinated hydrocarbons.

Use as Vinyl Polymerization Initiator

Azobis has been used successfully for bulk, solution, and suspension polymerization of all of the common vinyl monomers, including styrene, ethylene, acrylonitrile, vinyl chloride, vinyl acetate, vinylidene chloride, methyl methacrylate and methyl acrylate. It is also useful in the polymerization of unsaturated polyesters and in copolymerizations of vinyl compounds.

In general, the most useful temperature range for azobis as a polymerization initiator is 113°–194°F (45°–90°C) though under some conditions it can be used at higher temperatures. The amount of azobis used will vary from 0.01% or less to 0.5–1.0% of monomer depending upon the type and purity of the monomer, the speed of reaction desired, the temperature, etc.

Although the decomposition and rate of production of free radicals is not influenced by the chemical environment, the isobutyronitrile free radicals will react with substances normally considered to be free radical scavengers. These, of course, include polymerization inhibitors, oxygen, chain transfer agents and certain metallic ions. As with other types of free radical initiators it is necessary to exclude or control such substances in the system in order not to interfere with the reaction of the free radicals and the vinyl monomers.

The literature contains hundreds of reports of laboratory studies in which azobis was used to initiate polymerization of a wide variety of vinyl type monomers which are too numerous to review here. Practical industrial applications are also numerous. Azobis is ideally suited for initiating bead polymerization of vinyl chloride where it is used at levels between 0.06–0.15% based on monomer, depending on the temperature and the molecular weight desired. Typical polymerization curves for laboratory "coke bottle" reactions are shown in Fig. 2.

Likewise, vinyl acetate is polymerized in solution type processes using azobis in amounts ranging from 0.1–1.0% depending on conditions. Improved process control is claimed for azobis as compared to other types of initiators.

Azobis is used to initiate polymerization in the manufacture of some grades of low density polyethylene where amounts less than 0.1% based on ethylene are sufficient. It is selected for this application for reasons of process control and effect on product quality.

Azobis has a long history of use for polymerizing methyl methacrylate in suspension, solution and bulk polymerizations. In suspension polymerization, amounts in the order of 0.1–0.4% are employed. In bulk polymerization to produce cast sheeting, where azobis gives exceptionally uniform and controllable initiation, the level of use is about 0.05%.

The curing at elevated temperatures of unsaturated polyesters modified with either styrene or methacrylates can be catalyzed with azobis. Amounts will vary with resin composition, temperature, and time of cure, but will usually be less than 0.5% based on the polyester. Mixtures of azobis and benzoyl peroxide have been found to give advantageous effects in some instances.

Although azobis can be added directly in solid form to the reaction vessel in some polymerizations, it is sometimes advantageous or necessary to dissolve or suspend it in a liquid which is then added at the beginning of the reaction or added continuously as the reaction proceeds. In high pressure processes care must be taken to select solvents which do not freeze under pressure at ambient temperature (see Table 2). Forming a paste with butyl phthalate or tricresyl phosphate greatly accelerates solution in unsaturated polyesters.

Advantages of Azobis in Vinyl Polymerizations

(1) Azobis is usually a more efficient initiator than the organic peroxides and therefore can be used at lower concentrations (up to 8 times less) without sacrifice in conversion or polymerization rate. The greater efficiency is due to low molecular weight (M.W. = 164) and lack of side reactions.

(2) Because there is less tendency for the isobutyronitrile free radical to abstract hydrogen from the growing chain than the peroxide free radicals, azobis generally produces more linear polymers, which are often desired.

(3) The rate of decomposition of azobis to form free radicals is not influenced by chemical environment.

Use as a Blowing Agent

Azobis has been used as a blowing agent for making polyvinyl chloride foams. It decomposes between 100 and 104°C, evolving 135 cc of nitrogen per gram. However, the principal decomposition product of azobis, namely, tetramethylsuccinonitrile (TMSN), a highly toxic material, volatilizes during the foaming operation, creating a hazardous condition in the surrounding working area. The toxicology of TMSN has been reported in some detail.

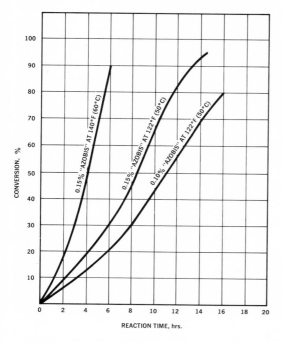

FIG. 2. Effect of temperature and "Azobis" concentration on rate of vinyl chloride polymerization.

Stability of Azobis

The normal handling and storage of azobis in containers is not hazardous. However, it tends to cake on prolonged storage at elevated temperatures; thus storage at or below 75°F (24°C) is recommended. When stored at 75°F or lower azobis possesses a high degree of stability. At any given temperature, the crystalline solid decomposes one-tenth as fast as it would in solution. At 75°F, it decomposes to the extent of about 0.6% of its weight in a month. This rate doubles for each 9°F rise in temperature.

Unlike peroxide catalysts, azobis will not detonate or explode on impact nor can it be ignited by an instantaneous electrical spark. However, since the decomposition of azobis is an exothermic reaction, it can accelerate itself at elevated temperatures. Self-heating begins in sealed 100 lb fiber drums when heated to about 120°F (49°C) with momentary ignition and mild explosion occurring as the temperature reaches 140°F (60°C).

Dry, solid azobis can be ignited readily with an open flame or a continuous electrical arc. As long as air is available for combustion, azobis burns brightly, though mildly, and completely, with no sudden release of pressure.

Toxicity of Azobis

Azobis has a low acute inhalation toxicity for rats, the approximate lethal concentration (ALC) for 4 hr being greater than 12 mg/liter nominal concentration in air. The approximate lethal dose (ALD) of azobis administered orally to rats is 670 mg/kg of body weight, classifying this chemical as moderately toxic. It is not irritating to the skin and does not produce skin sensitization.

Tetramethylsuccinonitrile (TMSN), formed by the recombination of two of the isobutyronitrile free radicals, is a residue which is present to varying degrees in polymers catalyzed with azobis.

TMSN is a highly toxic chemical, whether introduced orally, subcutaneously or by inhalation.

TMSN can be present in a resin, at most, only to the extent that the azobis has decomposed and that the free radicals are available to recombine with themselves. Most of the free radicals are consumed in initiating polymer chains and remain part of the polymer molcule. Although TMSN is a high-melting solid (334°F or 168°C) it has an appreciable vapor pressure and will sublime. Because TMSN sublimes, part or all of any residue present will be lost by volatilization in the finishing steps and in the further processing of the resin into finished product forms. The final TMSN level will depend upon the amount of catalyst used, its efficiency in the particular polymerization involved, the conditions of washing and drying of the polymer and the temperatures and times involved in the further processing of the resins to finished articles. The presence and type of plasticizers also have an influence. A gas chromatographic method of analysis for determining TMSN levels in polymers is available from azobis suppliers.

TMSN residues in samples of polyethylene film made with azobis were found to be less than 0.5 ppm. Higher levels have been found in polyvinyl chloride film made with azobis; however, extractability by simulated foods in standard ASTM tests was essentially nil.

F. D. A. Status

Azobis has received F.D.A. sanction as a polymerization catalyst both in substances used as components of paper and paperboard in contact with aqueous and fatty foods, and in adhesives used as components of articles intended for use in packaging, transporting or holding food.

H. C. FREEMAN, JR.
R. AARONS.

B

BENZOGUANAMINE

Benzoguanamine is the common name which is used for the weak organic base more correctly known as 2,4-diamino-6-phenyl-s-triazine. It is a high-melting (227°C), colorless, free-flowing, crystalline solid, having limited solubility in the common solvents such as water, ether, acetone, benzene and petroleum ether.

The guanamine name was first used by Nencki when he prepared acetoguanamine by heating guanidine acetate. The structure was later determined to be 2,4-diamino-6-methyl-s-triazine. Benzoguanamine may be prepared by a similar technique, the heating of guanadine benzoate.

Benzoguanamine, also known in Germany as "Benzamin," was manufactured there on a rather large scale during World War II from benzonitrile and dicyandiamide and was used to make the amino resin "Meprenal BC."

Structure

The accepted structure for benzoguanamine is:

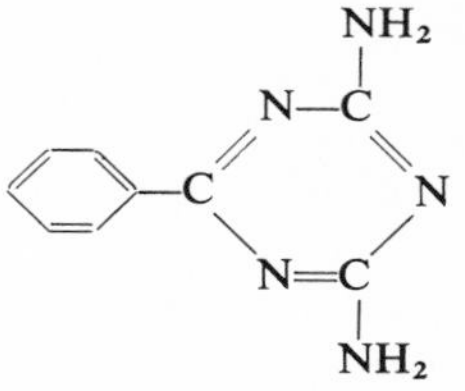

and three other resonance structures which contribute to the true structure are:

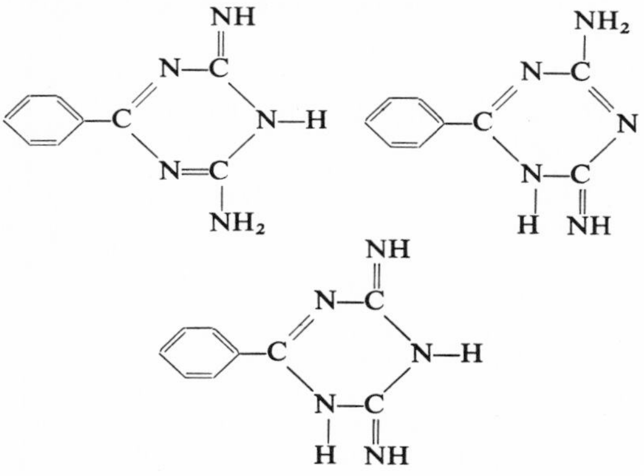

There is a close similarity between benzoguanamine and melamine, and the amino groups of both materials behave alike chemically. This similarity may be easily noted by comparing the melamine structure to that of benzoguanamine.

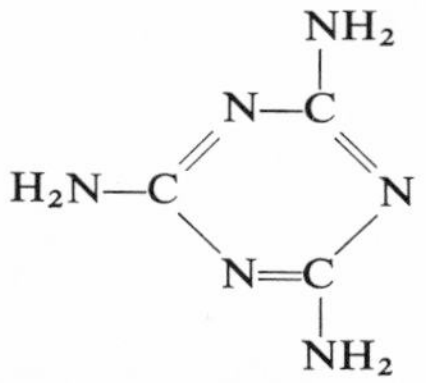

Melamine (2,4,6-triamino-s-triazine)

Reactions

Benzoguanamine undergoes many reactions, most of them taking place at the amino groups. In some cases (formation of salts) the two amino groups are not equivalent in reactivity, one behaving chemically as a neutral amido group rather than a basic amino group. Upon inspection of the above resonating structures this difference in reactivity might be predicted.

(1) Condensation with urea using dimethylformamide for a solvent, 2-phenyl-4,6-diureido-s-triazine is formed.

(2) Reaction with carbonates a polymer may be formed:

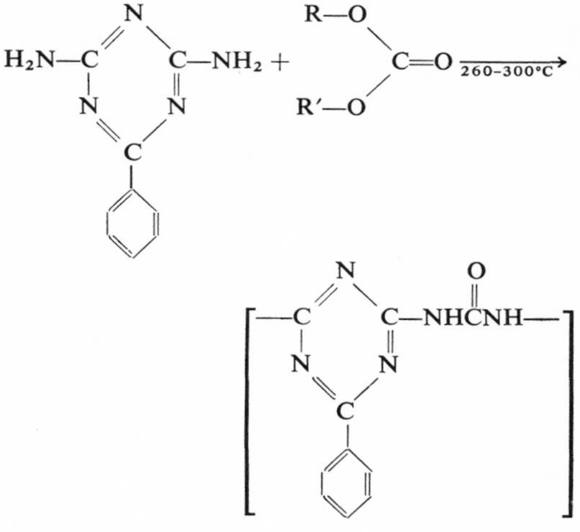

(3) Cyanoethylation. From 1–4 cyanoethyl groups may be substituted on the 2 amino nitrogen atoms giving an intermediate expected to find some application in alkyd resins, polyesters, plasticizers and surface active agents.

(4) Reaction with formaldhyde. This produces thermosetting amino resins having unusual properties. The bulk of the information available, including numerous patents, concerns this important condensation reaction with formaldehyde in which methylol groups are readily formed at pH of 8–9. The primary over-all reaction is:

$$R—NH_2 + HCHO \rightarrow R—NHCH_2OH$$

where R is C_6H_5—C

$$
\begin{array}{c}
NH_2 \\
| \\
N—C \\
\diagup \quad \diagdown \\
N \\
\diagdown \quad \diagup \\
N=C \\
|
\end{array}
$$

This reaction may continue until all amino hydrogen, or the formaldehyde, has been reacted. The reactive monomer containing the methylol groups may be modified by etherification with various alcohols for the purpose of imparting some physical property which adapts the resin to a particular application, such as improved compatibility, flexibility, viscosity, etc., in some resin system. These modified reactive monomers may be further reacted by condensation polymerization forming resinous, heat reactive, fusible products, which may be further polymerized to heat stable, good colored resins. Consequently they are of prime importance in white baked finishes. With slight modifications, a wide variety of useful resins for coating, adhesive, textile, laminating, molding and ink applications may be produced. The advantages of the amino resins in plastic applications are: good heat stability, good water resistance, good stain resistance, light colors, and hardness. Benzoguanamine is used in melamine and urea resins for imparting excellent water, alkali, and stain resistance, as well as a higher gloss to the molded article.

Equipment suitable for the production of the melamine resins may also be used for producing benzoguanamine resins.

Physical Properties

The commercial grade of benzoguanamine has a minimum freezing point of 224°C, a maximum water content of 1% by w, and an ash under 0.1% by w.

Pure benzoguanamine has a freezing point of 227°C, a bulk density of 1.40 g/cc, and its cryoscopic constant is 1.3 mole %/°C.

Benzoguanamine is insoluble in water, benzene and ether. It is slightly soluble in acetone and soluble in THF, DMF and methyl cellosolve.

R. W. INGWALSON

BENZONITRILE

Benzonitrile (cyanobenzene, phenylcyanide), C_6H_5CN, is a colorless, high boiling liquid with a mild aromatic odor resembling that of benzaldehyde. The accepted structure is:

C≡N

The triple bond between carbon and nitrogen forms a highly polar bond which imparts a large dipole moment to the compound. Consequently, benzonitrile has a correspondingly much higher boiling point than could be predicted on the basis of its molecular weight.

The first reported preparation of benzonitrile is that by Fehling, in 1844, in which he obtained it from the dry distillation of ammonium benzoate. Many different methods of preparation have been reported since that time, but the three most successful are: (1) the oxidation of toluene in the presence of ammonia at elevated temperatures over a dehydration catalyst, (2) the reaction of toluene with ammonia in the vapor phase and in the presence of a dehydrogenation catalyst, and (3) the catalytic liquid phase reaction of benzoic acid and ammonia with subsequent dehydration.

Physical Properties

Molecular W	103.12
Boiling point, °C	190.7
Freezing point, °C	−12.75
Specific gravity (60/60°F)	1.008

Solubility. Benzonitrile is completely miscible with common organic solvents and immiscible with water. It is soluble in water to the extent of 1% at 100°C. It is considered a good solvent for many common resins and polymers of which a few are: cellulose acetate butyrate, chlorinated rubber, gum arabic, nitrocellulose, polymethylmethacrylate, polystyrene, polyvinyl acetate, polyvinylchloride, shellac and wood rosin. Benzonitrile is most unusual in its solvent characteristics in that it is also a solvent for many anhydrous metallic salts that may behave as reaction catalysts, as well as being a good solvent for organic materials. To mention a few, these are: aluminum chloride, arsenic trichloride, bismuth trichloride, ferric chloride, zinc chloride, silver nitrate, and dibutyl tin dilaurate. This property, coupled with relatively low vapor pressure, heat stability and high polarity, suggests the use of benzonitrile as a solvent for liquid phase reactions and polymerizations.

Uses and Applications

Resin Products. Benzonitrile is condensed with dicyandiamide to form benzoguanamine, from which a variety of resins are made. The properties of these resins are of interest for use in domestic utensils, electrical materials, phonograph records, lacquer formulations and molding industry.

Solvent Applications. Benzonitrile is a polar aromatic mobile liquid which is immiscible with water. Its evaporation rate is low enough (only 10% as high as that for *n*-butyl acetate) to warrant interest in high quality specialty lacquers. It is a very powerful solvent for many commercially important gums and resins, and has been reported to be a strong solvent for nitrile rubber.

Handling Precautions. The physiological properties of benzonitrile have not been completely established, and it may be toxic to some persons. Symptoms are headache, nausea, weakness, increased heart beat, and dizziness. There has been no indication of chronic toxic effects in handling and use where the normal precautions for such have been observed. The following precautions are offered as suggestions

(1) Use good ventilation.

(2) Avoid contact with skin or eyes. In case of contact with skin, wash with water and mild soap. In case of contact with eyes, immediately flush with large volumes of water and get medical attention.

(3) Check exposed personnel for chronic toxic effects.

(4) Follow rules of good personal hygiene, such as a shower and change of clothes each day after work.

Bulk Handling and Storage Facilities

Benzonitrile, while inflammable, is not a difficult material to handle or store. To prevent discoloration, stainless steel, glass, "Teflon" or polyethylene can be used. Ordinary tanks, pumps, and fittings of these materials may be used. Storages should be adequately vented and so arranged that personnel are not exposed to the fumes.

R. W. INGWALSON

BENZYL ALCOHOL

Benzyl alcohol ($C_6H_5CH_2OH$) finds its largest use in the development of color motion picture film negative. However, in the plastics industry, benzyl alcohol is also used for dyeing filament nylons with fast-acid dyestuffs in synthetic-fiber textiles, an application which requires a high-quality inhibited grade of the product. Its solvent properties are utilized in the heat-sealing of linear polyethylene terephthalate films. Benzyl alcohol readily dissolves casein and gelatine at elevated temperatures, and also cellulose acetate and shellac. Its boiling point is 205.8°C; solubility, 1 part in about 30 parts of water, 1 part in 1.5 parts of 50% ethyl alcohol; it is miscible with alcohol, ether, and chloroform, and readily forms esters with acetic, benzoic, and sebacic acids; although, to a lesser extent, with formic, propionic, butyric, valeric, cinnamic, and salicylic acids.

Specifications and Standards. There are at least six grades of benzyl alcohol available on the market: technical, NF (National Formulary), photo, reagent, textile, and commercial.

The *technical grade* is a colorless-to-pale-yellow liquid, 98% minimum purity; ASTM distillation, 5–95% between 202–208°C; d_{25}^{25}, 1.040–1.050; n_D^{20}, 1.5385–1.5404; chlorine (as benzyl chloride), 0.15% maximum; acidity (as benzoic acid), 0.15% maximum; aldehyde (as benzaldehyde), 0.70% maximum.

The *NF grade* must be colorless; 94% must distill between 202.5–206.5°C; acidity, neutral to litmus; aldehyde, no yellow color produced by addition of a 5% NaOH solution; chlorine, none by Beilstein copper wire test.

The *photo grade* must be colorless; 1 g must dissolve complete in 30 ml of water; ASTM distillation, 5–95% between 203–206°C; acidity, negligible; benzaldehyde, 0.04% maximum; and chlorine, 0.005% maximum. In addition, customer specifications require the addition of 0.01–0.02% of a hydroquinone monomethyl or benzyl ether to prevent the oxidation of the alcohol to benzaldehyde.

The *reagent grade* is the highest grade of benzyl alcohol manufactured. It must meet all of the requirements of the photo grade with the exception of the addition of an antioxidant, and the further requirement of a maximum benzaldehyde content of 0.03%.

The *textile grade* is also an inhibited grade requiring a water solubility of 1 g in 25 ml of water at 50°C.

The *commercial grade* consists of a mixture of 80–85% benzyl alcohol, 10–15% dibenzyl ether and 5% water, maximum, and is used in dyeing textiles and sheet plastics. There are no special hazards in the handling of benzyl alcohol. It is manufactured on a commercial scale by the hydrolysis of benzyl chloride with sodium carbonate, the benzyl chloride being obtained by the chlorination of toluene.

WILLIAM F. RINGK

BLOWING AGENTS

The cellular structures of many types of foamed or expanded plastics are formed by the release of gas into the liquid polymer during the polymerization or molding process. The materials used as the source of gas are called "blowing agents" or "foaming agents." These are classified according to the three functional methods by which they operate: (1) chemical compounds which decompose to yield gaseous products, (2) liquids which volatilize without undergoing chemical change, and (3) mechanical foaming. Table 1 lists the properties required of a blowing agent.

TABLE 1. PROPERTIES OF AN IDEAL BLOWING AGENT.

(1) Gas must be released over a definite and short temperature range.
(2) The rate of gas release should be rapid, but controllable.
(3) Preferably, the gas should be neither corrosive (e.g., NO_2) or explosive, but CO_2 is acceptable in some cases.
(4) The blowing agent should disperse readily in the mix, and preferably should dissolve.
(5) The compound must be stable during storage.
(6) Residue, after decomposition, should not have an unpleasant odor.
(7) Residue should be colorless and non-staining.
(8) The compound and residue must be nontoxic.
(9) The compound should not produce a large amount of exothermic heat during decomposition.
(10) The blowing agent, and its residues, should not affect the rate of cure of the plastic.
(11) The blowing agent should function equally well in open and closed molds.
(12) The residue should have no effect on physical and chemical properties of the finished product.
(13) The blowing agent should be inexpensive in the proportions used.

Decomposition of Chemical Compounds

The use of water in the formation of urethane foam is an example illustrating the decomposition of a compound to effect the expansion of a rapidly polymerizing polymer. This reaction is illustrated as follows:

(1) An isocyanate reacts with water to produce an unstable carbamic acid.

$$R{-}N{=}C{=}O + H{-}O{-}H \rightarrow R{-}\overset{H}{\underset{}{N}}{-}\overset{OH}{\underset{}{C}}{=}O$$

Isocyanate *Water* *Carbamic acid*

(2) The carbamic acid decomposes to form an amine and carbon dioxide.

$$R{-}\overset{H}{\underset{}{N}}{-}\overset{OH}{\underset{}{C}}{=}O \rightarrow R{-}N{-}NH_2 + CO_2$$

Carbamic acid *Amine* *Carbon dioxide*

The sodium, potassium, ammonium, calcium, and magnesium carbonate salts, which liberate carbon dioxide upon reaction with water in the presence of an acid catalyst, have been used as blowing agents in the production of phenolic foams. Phenolic foams have also been prepared utilizing metal powders, such as aluminum, zinc, and magnesium which were reacted with acdic or alkaline catalysts to produce hydrogen gas as the foaming agent.

Organic gas liberating agents provide somewhat better control of foaming, materials such as *p,p*′-oxybis(benzene-sulfonylhydrazide), dinitroso pentamethylenetetramine, and diazonium salts such as benzene diazonium sulfate are among the most common blowing agents used in the commercial production of phenolic foams. Table 2 presents the properties and structures of widely accepted blowing agents which decompose to release gaseous products.

Liquids Which Volatilize Without Undergoing Chemical Change

It is now common practice to employ fluorocarbon gases, such as trichlorofluoromethane, as blowing agents in the production of rigid urethane foams. The fluorocarbon blowing agent, although relatively soluble in the liquid polymer, is very impermeable in the resultant foam. Thus, gas retention and thermal conductivity are excellent.

The fluorocarbon is blended into the polyol containing component in "quasi-prepolymer" systems or injected directly into the mixing chamber when using "one-shot" systems. The boiling point for fluorocarbon-11 (trichlorofluoromethane) is 74.8°F, thus the blowing agent is volatilized by the exotherm of the reaction which exceeds this temperature. Care must be exercised when designing a foam system to ensure sufficient growth of the polymer to prevent excessive loss of the blowing agent during foaming.

The processing of expanded polystyrene is accomplished by incorporating a volatile liquid such as methylene chloride, propylene, and butylene, or fluorocarbons into the polymer melt which is being forced through an extruder. As the mixture of blowing agent and polystyrene emerge from the orifice of the extruder, the melt expands upon release of pressure and cools quickly to produce a low density cellular product.

Expandable polystyrene beads containing an entrapped blowing agent may be prepared by polymerizing polystyrene in the presence of pentane, neopentane, or petroleum ether. These beads may be pre-expanded by use of infrared energy, steam, or other heat sources. The final molded products are produced by charging an excess of pre-expanded beads to a molding chamber and introducing heat (steam, autoclave, etc.). The volatile blowing agent expands the softened polystyrene beads causing them to fuse together, hus producing a low density expanded product.

TABLE 2. STRUCTURES AND DECOMPOSITION DATA ON COMMERCIAL ORGANIC FOAMING AGENTS.

Chemical description	Structure	Decomposition temp, in air, °C	Decomposition range in plastics, °C	Gas yield, ml(STP)/g	Literature reference
(A) Azo-compounds					
1. Azobisformamide (azodicarbonamide)	H_2N—CO—N=N—CO—NH_2	195–200	160–200	220	German Patent 871,835
2. Azobisisobutyronitrile	(see structure)	115	90–115	130	German Patent 899,414
3. Diazoaminobenzene	(see structure)	103	95–100	115	US Patent 2,299,593
(B) N-Nitroso-compounds					
4. N,N′-Dimethyl-N,N′-dinitroso-terephthalamide	(see structure)	105	90–105	126[a]	US Patent
5. N,N′-Dinitrosopentamethylene-tetramine	(see structure)	195	130–190	100[b] 200[c]	US Patent 2,491,709
(C) Sulfonyl hydrazides					
6. Benzenesulfonylhydrazide	(see structure)	103	95–100	130	German Patent 821,423 and US Patent 2,626,933
7. Benzene-1,3-disulfonylhydrazide	(see structure)	146	115–130	170	German Patent 821,423
8. Diphenylsulfon-3,3′-disulfonyl hydrazide	(see structure)	148	120–130	110	German Patent 829,423
9. 4,4′Oxybis (benzenesulfonyl hydrazide)	(see structure)	150	120–140	125	German Patent 829,423, and US Patent 2,552,065

[a] 70% active [b] 40% active [c] 80% active

Mechanical Foaming

Polyvinyl chloride foams may be prepared by a solvated gas process which depends upon the high pressure dissolution of gases in liquids such as plasticizers and solvents. The plasticizers are necessary to make flexible the rigid polyvinyl chloride homopolymer or vinyl acetate copolymer. Thus, the absorption of gases by the plasticizer under pressure is the basis for the mechanical foaming process.

A slurry or paste is prepared by blending the powdered polyvinyl chloride resin, stabilizers, plasticizers, and a solvent. This slurry is charged to a pressure vessel and the gas employed as a blowing agent is added under pressure. The fused material is cooled, removed from the mold as a partially expanded product. Final processing involves additional heating to produce maximum expansion of the low density polyvinyl chloride foam product.

Factors Affecting the Thermal Conductivity of Cellular Plastics

The use of blowing agents having a molecular weight in excess of 100 is desirable. Figure 1 shows

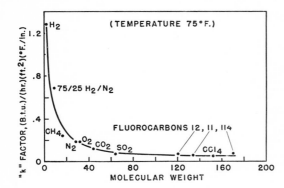

FIG. 1. Thermal conductivity of gases as a function of molecular weight.

the relationship that exists between the molecular weight of a gaseous blowing agent and its thermal conductivity.

Heat transfer through cellular materials, thermal conductivity, k, is defined by the Fourier equation for conduction through homogeneous materials. This k value is dependent upon the mean temperature, temperature difference, and sample thickness. The units for k, thermal conductivity, are Btu/°F sq ft per hr/in. of thickness. McIntire and Kennedy separated the total thermal conductivity, k, into component parts:

$$k = k_s + k_g + k_r + k_c$$

where k_s, k_g, k_r, and k_c are the contributors due to conduction through solid, conduction through

gas, radiation, and convection in gas. Skochdopole studied the factors affecting the thermal conductivity of polystyrene and urethane foams. His results, presented in Table 3, indicated that

TABLE 3. ANALYSIS OF THERMAL CONDUCTIVITY THROUGH VARIOUS FOAMED PLASTICS OF 2 LB/CU FT DENSITY.

Property	Polystyrene		Polyurethane		
Cell size, mm	1.0	0.1	Fresh	Equil.	Ult.
Gas	Air	Air	CCl$_3$F	CCl$_3$F Air	Air
k_g	0.17	0.17	0.05	0.10	0.17
k_s	0.02	0.02	0.04	0.04	0.04
k_r	0.11	0.05	0.03	0.03	0.03
k_c	0	0	0	0	0
k (total)	0.30	0.24	0.12	0.17	0.24
Aging character	nc	nc	Large	Small to nc	nc
Temp. dependence	A	A	A	B	A

nc = No change.
A = Slow decrease in k with decrease in T from room T.
B = Initial rise and then decrease in k with decrease in T from room T.

cell size and gas composition were the major factors affecting the thermal conductivity of cellular plastics. If the cell size of polystyrene foam was reduced from 1.0 mm–0.1 mm, the k_g, k_s, and k_c were unaffected, but the k_r was halved, resulting in a decrease in total k from 0.30 to 0.24. Review of Table 3 shows that the major difference in thermal conductivity characteristics between polystyrene and urethane foams is due to k_g (conduction in gas). As the urethane foam ages and the fluorocarbon blowing agent gradually migrates out of the sample, the k_g increases until the ultimate k_g of 0.17 (that of still air) is reached. At this time, projected to be approximately 20 years under standard conditions, 70°F and 50% RH, the total k of polystyrene foam and polyurethane foam should be equal.

I. N. EINHORN

BORIC ACID ESTERS

Epoxy resins have the ability to change readily from the thermoplastic or liquid state to the thermoset or "hard" state without the application of heat or pressure. This change is accomplished by the use of chemically active reagents called "curing agents," variously known as "hardeners," "activators," or "catalysts." The reason for this variety of names is that some curing agents cause the transformation by catalytic action, while others participate directly in the reaction and are incorporated into the resulting resin molecular chain. While most curing is accomplished at room temperature (the heat being produced by exothermic reaction), some hardening reactions may require the application of external heat. This article deals with only two special types of boron-containing epoxy-resin curing agents.

Boric Acid Ester Curing Agents

The US Borax Research Corporation of Anaheim, California, has been conducting extensive research and testing on boron-containing epoxy-resin curing agents—specifically aromatic borates (boric acid esters derived from phenols) or dioxaborinanes derived from both an alkylene glycol and a β-dialkyl-substituted aminoethanol.

"Borester 8." This is a registered trademark for $C_{21}H_{21}BO_3$, or tri-*m*, *p*-cresyl borate, a boric acid ester marketed by the US Borax Research Corporation. It is the aromatic borate prepared from commercially available *meta-para*-cresol mixtures, and has a molecular weight of 332.2, a boron content of 3.26%, a boiling point of 385–395°F at 760 mm, and a density of 1.065 at 25°C. Its structural formula is shown below.

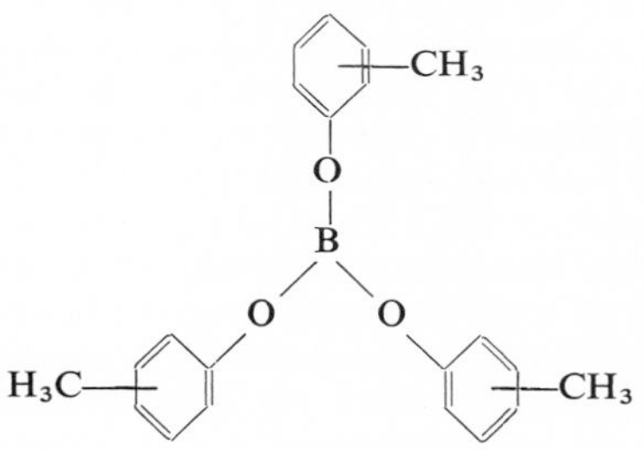

"Borester 8"

"Borester 8" is a mobile, pale amber liquid with a cresylic odor, and is said to be an excellent curing agent for (1) epoxidized cyclic polyolefins, such as Carbide "Unox 201," Carbide "Unox 206," Ciba X8200-104, etc.; (2) epoxidized linear polyolefins, such as FMC's "Oxirons"; (3) epoxidized unsaturated glycerides, such as Swift's "Epoxol 7-4," and "Epoxol 9-5," Carbide's "Flexol EPO," etc., and (4) varying mixtures and combinations of these.

As a mixture of aromatic borates, "Borester 8" is a nonvolatile, mobile, organic liquid, a characteristic that permits convenient and ready miscibility and compatibility with epoxy resins. It requires no external heat for initial rapid reaction with the epoxide groups of the various epoxy resins. The curing reaction is thus exothermic; maximum mechanical properties of the cured resin are obtained with a short postcure period at an elevated temperature. Peracid-derived epoxy

resins cured with "Borester 8" are said to have excellent values for heat-distortion temperatures, the actual value depending on the resin used. Thus Carbide "Unox 201" hardens with 35 phr "Borester 8," followed by treatment at 120°C for 4.5 hr, producing a cured resin with an HDT value of 153°C. In addition, rigid epoxy foams can be prepared by taking advantage of the exothermic reaction which results when "Borester 8" is mixed with a peracid-derived epoxy resin. The incorporation of varying amounts of a chlorofluorocarbon blowing agent and a silicone bubble-control agent into a Carbide "Unox 201-Borester 8" mixture gives a reproducible rigid epoxy foam with densities ranging from 0.5–4.0 lb/ft³. Foam properties can be varied by the use of different combinations and mixtures of the various epoxies. The curing reaction between "Borester 8" and peracid-derived epoxy resins is unaffected by the incorporation of metal powders, fillers, pigments, or flame-retardants.

"USB-110." Another epoxy-resin curing agent developed by US Borax Research Corporation is "USB-110," claimed to be a good curing agent for commercial glycidyl-ether type epoxy resins derived from epichlorohydrin and particularly for use in casting, encapsulation, glass-cloth impregnation, and filament-winding techniques. "USB-110" is a member of a new class of boric-acid esters derived from both an alkylene glycol and a β-dialkyl-substituted aminoethanol; specifically, it is 2-(β-dimethylaminoethoxy)-4-methyl-1,3,2-dioxaborinane, with structural formula:

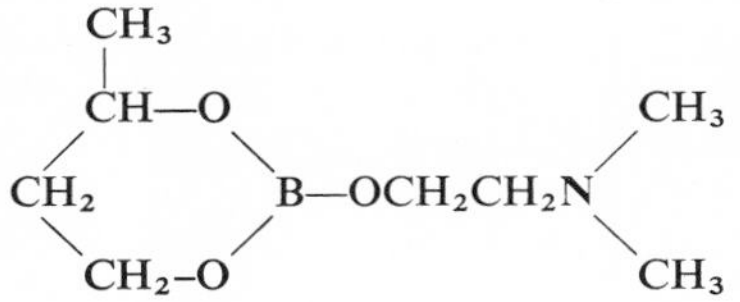

and molecular formula $C_8H_{18}BNO_3$. Its molecular weight is 187.05, specific gravity 0.9901, and refractive index (20C°) 1.4385. "USB-110" combines the well known epoxy-curing ability of the *tert*-dimethylamino group with the desirable retarding modification of the boron atom to give a smooth-acting, controllable, extended-life epoxy-resin curing agent. It is a mobile liquid with a faint amine odor, readily miscible and compatible with glycidyl-ether type epoxy resins.

Among the advantages claimed for "USB-110" as an epoxy curing agent are (1) high-heat distortion temperature (HDT) for a tertiary-amine curing agent—values as high as 170°C (338°F) can be obtained; (2) long-time usability after mixing with epoxy resin—for castings, glass-cloth impregnations, glass-fiber windings—curing to tough, hard shapes with high heat distortion temperatures; (3) more controllable curing reaction brought about by borate modification of the amino alcohol—the less violent cures of "USB-110," as compared to β-dimethylamino-ethanol, producing transparent castings of excellent clarity. In addition, the epoxy-resin curing ability of "USB-110" is not impaired by the incorporation of fillers, pigments, or flame-retardants, etc. As a strongly alkaline material, it can cause damage to skin and mucous membrane tissues, so that it should be handled with considerable caution, and the same precautions as are taken with any strong caustic agent.

IRVING S. BENGELSDORF

Cross-references: CURING AGENTS; EPOXY HARDENERS.

BORON FIBERS

Glass fibers have long been used as reinforcing for plastics. However, the Air Force Materials Laboratory, in seeking a reinforcing fiber having a modulus of elasticity-to-density ratio greater than that of glass, has found success with boron fiber reinforced plastics. The boron fibers used are made by the chemical vapor deposition process, in which boron is deposited from a boron trichloride-hydrogen reaction mixture onto a heated $\frac{1}{2}$ mil diameter tungsten wire substrate. The fibers thus made have a circular cross section and contain a tungsten boride core approximately the same diameter as the original tungsten wire substrate. observations of filament cross sections usually show radial cracks extending from the core, part of the way to the surface; yet in spite of these flaws, the fibers have high strength, are nonductile, and the surface layer, being water soluble, could be removed prior to fabrication.

A brief summary of the physical and mechanical properties of boron fibers compared to a high structural performance glass fiber, is given in Table 1. The more significant aspects of these data are that:

(1) Boron fibers have a modulus of elasticity about five times that of glass fibers.

(2) The strength of bare boron fibers (containing the tungsten boride core), after winding on a take-up spool and unwinding to obtain test specimens, is about 30% less than that of virgin glass fibers, but is about equal to the usable strength of glass fibers in composites. The net result is that the usable strength of boron fibers and glass fibers in reinforced plastics is about the same. The true strength of the "pure" boron part of the boron fiber is much higher than that of the overall fiber.

(3) The diameter of this type of boron fiber is usually in the 3–5 mil diameter range, which is about ten times that of glass fiber reinforcements. The reason for having this large diameter is based on the presence of the 0.5 mil diameter tungsten substrate. Since tungsten has a density of about 19.3 g/cc compared to 2.35 g/cc for amorphous boron, the final filament must have a large enough diameter to give a high volume percent of boron, thereby giving an attractively low density.

(4) Experiments were performed to determine weight loss and loss in strength of uncoated boron filaments exposed to air at 500°F, 600°F, and 700°F, for as long as 1000 hr.

(5) Aging at 500°F for as long as 1000 hr causes no further reduction in strength. In contrast, at both 600°F and 700°F there is a continued reduction in strength with increased exposure time. After 1000 hr at 600°F, the strength is half the initial room temperature value, and at 700°F after

TABLE 1. COMPARISON OF PROPERTIES OF BORON FIBERS WITH THOSE OF GLASS FIBERS.

Property	Boron fibers	AF-994 Glass fibers
Density, g/cc	2.5–2.8[a]	2.49
Diameter, mils	3–5	0.38
Single filament ultimate tensile strength at room temperature, psi	300,000–500,000	665,000 (virgin fiber) 500,000 (usable strength in composite)
Modulus of Elasticity at room temperature, psi	55×10^6	12.4×10^6
Modulus of rigidity, psi	26×10^6	—
Modulus of Rupture in shear, psi	500,000	—

[a] The densities of 2.5 g/cc and 2.8 g/cc correspond to 5-mil diameter and 3-mil diameter boron fibers, respectively having 0.5-mil diameter tungsten substrate.

1000 hr, it is about 10% of the initial value. It should be remembered that these results are for bare filaments, and that much less severe degradation is expected to occur when the filaments are incorporated into composites.

(6) Boron fibers by themselves, regardless of their attractive mechanical properties, are not a structural engineering material. In order for them to be exploited in aerospace vehicle structures, they must be incorporated into composites such as reinforced plastics.

R. T. SCHWARTZ and H. S. SCHWARTZ

Cross-references: REINFORCEMENTS; REINFORCEMENTS: CERAMIC WHISKERS.

C

CARBONS

Carbon materials are used in plastics in either particulate or in fibrous form. Particulate carbon has been used as an additive for many years while carbonaceous fibers have been developed only recently. Neither form of the carbons are naturally occurring but are created by pyrolysis of cellulose, petroleum products or natural gas. The pyrolysis is controlled to the extent that the noncarbonaceous portion of the hydrocarbon is removed with a minimal loss of carbon through incomplete combustion. In the particulate material also called carbon black, volatile contents may range between 0.5 and 15%. In fibrous forms, volatile contents may range between 0.1 and 4%.

The pyrolysis process on a gross basis is relatively simple but from a practical standpoint is complex because end product properties encompass many more characteristics than just carbon content. Consider for example, the production of carbon fibers for reinforcement. Most current forms are produced from cellulose in the form of rayon fibers and the theoretical reaction is:

$$(C_6H_{10}O_5)_n \rightarrow 6nC + 5nH_2O$$

with the cellulose having the following structural formula:

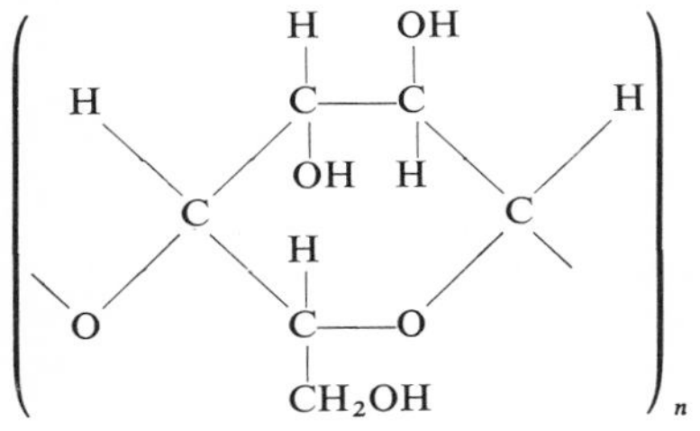

where n has a value on the order of 300–500 with the molecular weight being 50,000–80,000 for regenerated cellulose or rayon.

The pyrolysis of rayon is generally accomplished in the temperature range of 150–3000°F, with heat treating sometimes continuing on to 5000°F. As the rayon is heated above 150°F, the surface moisture is removed and decomposition starts as ring hydroxyl groups are evolved as water. At 500°F the dehydration is complete and the cellulosic structure is lost as the ring opens and aromatization occurs. As higher temperatures are experienced further carbon atom rearrangement occurs and the ring begins to stabilize. By 1300°F the major portion of the nonuniform shrinkage has occurred. Additional heating produces further outgassing of CO, CO_2, H_2 and complex tars. If heating is continued to about 2000°F, substantial stability is reached as carbon content approximates 97 w % and the surface area of individual filaments declines from a maximum of 400–500 sq m per g, to less than 100. Continued heating to above 4500°F removes the remaining volatiles consisting of hydrocarbon fragments and cations, leaving a carbon content of at least 99.0%.

Two types of fibers are "graphite" fibers, and carbon fibers. Graphite fibers are generally referred to as being crystalline, while carbon fibers are amorphous. However, all carbonaceous fibers have a low degree of crystallization as compared to the highly crystalline structure of pure graphite. The so-called graphite fibers are 5–15% crystalline. The significant difference results from temperature experienced by the two types of materials during manufacture. Table 1 lists the significant properties of the two types of materials. In the composite form still another significant difference exists

TABLE 1. COMPARATIVE PROPERTIES OF CARBONACEOUS FIBERS.

Property	Carbon	Graphite
Carbon content, %	97	99.0+
Surface area, m²/g	60+	5–10
pH	8.5–10	7–9
Ash content, %	<1	<.2
Crystallinity, %	None	5–15
Specific gravity	1.85	1.5

All values are nominal.

which is thermal conductivity. For phenolic resin composites made under similar conditions graphite composites have a thermal conductivity of approximately 8–9 Btu/in./Hr/Ft²/°F, as opposed to carbon composites which are 4.5–5.5 Btu/in./Hr/Ft²/°F. This difference is major because the carbonaceous fiber composites are used almost exclusively in thermal protection applications where "heat" flow through a protective layer of composite is minimal.

At the current time the total carbonaceous fiber usage approximate 300,000 to 400,000 lb annually at a market value of 7.5–11.0 million dollars. It has been estimated that the total usage of carbonaceous fibers is equally divided between the carbon and graphite fibers with carbon fibers becoming more prominent as time goes on. Fibrous carbon is sold for $20–$25 per lb in bulk fiber or fabric form, and fibrous graphite is $25–$30 per lb in similar forms. Approximately 90% of these fibers are used in ablative plastics. The function of carbonaceous fibers in an ablative plastic is complex because several phenomena occur in use, but can perhaps best be summarized as a reinforcement for the resin to provide load carrying capability, thermal stability, and low mass ablation rate.

Graphite fibers were developed first and found broad acceptance in solid rocket motor ablative liners as aft closures, blast tubes, throats and exit cones replacing other ablative plastics such as silica phenolics and some of the homogeneous refractories. Subsequently carbon fibers were introduced and because of lower thermal conductivity and cost they (in composites) became competitive for use in similar applications and components. In some cases it is felt the graphite-phenolics show a lower mass ablation rate but in most cases truly comparative rate tests have not been conducted. Both types of material are now being seriously considered for use in reentry body ablative plastics. Carbonaceous fibers have been used in limited quantities in nonplastic applications such as resistance heating elements, hot gas filtration, thermal insulation and corrosion resistant gaskets.

Carbonaceous fibers are produced in fabrics and several nonwoven forms such as yarn, cordage, bulk fibers (chopped yarn or macerated fabric) and felt. Figure 1 shows some of the current forms of carbonaceous fibers. In all cases the precursor rayon is used in the form desired, in the end application. For example, if carbon fabric is required, rayon fabric of the same construction (plus a shrinkage allowance) is used. Some suppliers have recently proposed supplying carbon fiber yarn in several forms that are adaptable to conventional weaving equipment and techniques. The advantage of this approach is the wide latitude then available in woven material

FIG. 1. Current forms of carbonaceous fibers.

thereby maximizing the adaptability of the reinforcement to the shape and fabrication process used in the end component. Carbonaceous yarn, cordage or roving are also readily adaptable to current methods used in filament winding design and processes.

Carbonaceous fiber resin systems and fabrication methods in current use are quite similar to those described in the section on silica fibers except that problems of uniformity are much greater. These problems have arisen because the carbonaceous fibers in some cases have a high surface area, considerable internal porosity and a high pH thereby making them highly responsive to even subtle variations in manufacture, resin impregnation or component fabrication.

Carbonaceous fibers are marketed by three companies: Carbon Products Division of Union Carbide Corporation, Basic Carbon of Carborundum Company, and HITCO, formerly H. I. Thompson Fiber Glass Company. Several other companies have marketed small quantities probably because of a presumed market potential and a similarity to existing products.

When carbonaceous fibers are used in plastics (primarily ablatives) the important properties are:
(1) Carbon content.
(2) Type and quantity of impurities.
(3) Specific gravity.
(4) Mechanical properties.
(5) Resin compatibility (especially phenolics).
(6) Uniformity of properties.
(7) Surface area and porosity.

These characteristics are important both in bare form and in composites and therefore must be considered because in some cases, properties of the "bare" fibers are not carried over into the composites.

Table 2 shows some of the composite properties of typical carbonaceous plastic using phenolic resins.

TABLE 2. TYPICAL PROPERTIES OF CARBONACEOUS FIBER FILLED PHENOLICS.

Property	Carbon	Graphite
Tensile strength	22,200	20,700
Tensile modulus, $\times 10^6$	2.7	1.5
Flexural strength	37,900	33,500
Flexural modulus, $\times 10^6$	2.3	1.8
Edgewise compressive strength	48,900	18,500
Edgewise modulus, $\times 10^6$	2.2	2.2

All values are in psi and using fabric reinforcement with nominally 34 % mil R-9299 unfilled phenolic resins.

As the aerospace industry searches for new fiber systems for composite materials, carbonaceous fibers indicate tremendous growth potential because current "research" carbon fibers show tensile strengths of 365,000 psi, elastic modulus of 55×10^6 psi, with a density of 0.060 lb/in.³ as compared to structural glass fibers with a tensile strength of 300,000–400,000 psi, elastic modulus of 12×10^6 psi, and a density of 0.090 lb/in.³. Graphite whiskers are reported to have a tensile strength of 2,850,000 psi with an elastic modulus of 102×10^6 psi, and a density of 0.060 lb/in.³ Even if only a portion of these values can be achieved in production composites carbonaceous fibers offer considerable potential and are consequently the subject of extensive study. The possible aerospace uses for carbonaceous fibers in the future will be in composite materials used in rocket motor and reentry ablatives, and high efficiency structural composites such as aircraft structures and pressure vessels such as underwater structures.

Carbon blacks, which are semigraphitic materials, are produced as numerous fine particle grades averaging in size at various areas in the 5–500mμ range. The total annual production exceeds 2500 million lb, being sold at prices ranging from 6–80¢ per lb, producing a total market of 150 + million dollars. The principal consumption of carbon black is in the rubber tire industry where the carbon strengthens and reinforces the elastomer.

Carbon black is used in many types of plastics including polyethylenes, phenolics, epoxies, polyurethanes, nylons, polycarbonates, ABS, vinyls, polystyrenes and polypropylenes for product improvement, process facilitation and cost reduction. The total amount of blacks used in plastics represents a small but growing percentage of the total annual consumption. Loadings are used anywhere from 1–200 parts per hundred of resin. Use is based upon the functioning of the carbon blacks as reinforcing agents, fillers, colorants, opacifiers, process aids (lubricants) barriers for ultra violet light and for lowering surface resistivity, altering electrical conductivity, enhancing physical properties and improving thermal stability.

The principal types of carbon blacks used in plastics are channel blacks, thermal blacks, and furnace blacks. Channel blacks are manufactured by impinging "smoky" natural gas flames upon cool metal surfaces. The metal surfaces are steel channel irons that are oscillated over the flames. The carbon is then removed by scrapping devices. The product is manufactured in various particle sizes averaging from 5–30mμ. It has a maximum color and jetness increases inversely to particle size. The volatile content ranges from 4–15%, pH from 3.0–5.0, nitrogen surface area from 100–1000 m²/g, and bulk density ranges from 0.1–0.2 g/cc.

Thermal blacks are produced by a thermal cracking process in which natural gas is heated to 2500–3000°F by passing through checker brick furnaces. The gas decomposes into carbon and hydrogen. The furnace is then cooled and a stoichiometric air-gas mixture is introduced and heated to temperature. Additional feed gas diluted with hydrogen and carbon monoxide is introduced and the cycle is repeated. The exit gas containing carbon particles is then filtered and the carbon black is separated and collected. The particle size of the product averages either 475 or 220mμ, and has a pH of 8.0–9.0 and a volatile content of less than 1%. It is grey in color with a nitrogen surface area of less than 20 m²/g, and a bulk density of 0.5–0.8 g/cc.

Furnace blacks are produced by injecting and firing alternating layers of natural gas and air into closed combustion chambers (furnaces or retorts) where partial combustion occurs at 2400–2700°F. Carbon then suspended in the gas is removed by successive processing through water spray towers, electrical precipitators and the cyclone separators. This process has been modified so that liquid hydrocarbons or oil can be used instead of natural gas. The furnace blacks are in the 20–80mμ particle size range with a pH of 8.0–10.0 having a volatile content of less than 2%. The nitrogen surface area is 20–220 m²/g, and a bulk density of 0.3 to 0.5 g/cc. The larger particle size material is semi-reinforcing and the small particle size material is called reinforcing black.

Other blacks such as acetylene black, made by thermal decomposition, are used for special applications such as lowering surface resistivity and inducing electrical conductivity. It has an average particle size of 40mμ, a pH of 5.0–5.0, and a nitrogen surface area of 60 m²/g.

As stated above, several modifications in plastics can be achieved by adding carbon blacks. These changes are property modifications, improved processability, and reduced costs. Normally the finer particle size blacks provide maximum product improvement such as better weather resistance, lower surface resistivity, and improved electrical conductivity. However, the same fine particle size materials create more problems in dispersion and greater water absorption. The high surface area materials (fine particle size) are also generally more expensive. Obviously, the user must be prepared to make trade-off's between properties, cost and processability.

It is recommended that the carbon black suppliers be consulted for their recommendations on the type of black to be used and the methods for compounding and processing it.

J. L. RENDALL

Cross-reference: FILLERS.

CASEIN

Historical

Casein granules when wetted are moldable under heat and pressure. The molded piece is hard and tough, and can be made relatively water-resistant when suffused with formaldehyde. Casein plastic had its origin as "Galalith," a well-recognized trademark in the early years of this century. The subtitle was "Artificial Horn," casein being an animal protein, as is natural horn. Other brands of casein plastic were produced and marketed under the names of "Erinoid," "Ameroid," etc. The world production of casein plastic reached a peak just before World War II with some 5000 tons being produced. During this period advances were made in the product and processes and machines for producing it, but synthetic molding compounds, with their great versatility starting with "Bakelite" in 1909, soon gained precedence over casein, restricted as it is to only protein and formaldehyde as raw materials.

Nevertheless, casein plastic has lived a long life as a specialized article of commerce, enjoying currently a steady production rate of 1000–2000 tons in the United States, which does not appear to be in danger of fading in the foreseeable future. The earlier end uses were quite diversified in view of little competititon. Currently casein plastic is almost entirely turned into button stock, and there, as will be related, it holds a favored and durable position.

Closely related uses of casein, include adhesives and coatings, of greater economic importance as far as the consumption of casein is concerned; these will also be briefly discussed.

Origin and Manufacture of Casein

The only source of casein is in milk. Other industrial proteins have at times improperly been referred to as "vegetable casein." True industrial casein, with milk as its single source, is fortunately very clearly defined, the grades differing slightly with respect to purity and viscosity. However, there are two types of casein, determined by the agent used in curding, and this is a significant differentiation. The raw material source of casein is skim milk, which is the fat-free portion of whole milk after separation of the cream. Skim milk may be processed to yield either rennet casein, or acid casein.

Rennet Casein. Chymase-like enzymes, of which there are many types in both the animal and vegetable kingdoms, cause curding of casein from milk. Of these, the enzyme rennin has been highly developed to the position of the pre-eminent agent for the curding of milk as an early step in the cheese-making process. Rennin is likewise the agent for separating casein from skim milk to yield rennet casein. Rennin is obtained commercially from the stomach of either the hog or of the new born calf, and is marketed as "Casein Rennet," a liquid of carefully controlled enzyme strength. So powerful is this catalyst that only 2 oz are required to completely precipitate the casein from 1000 lb of sweet skim milk. Rennet casein is prepared from skim milk by the process shown in Fig. 1.

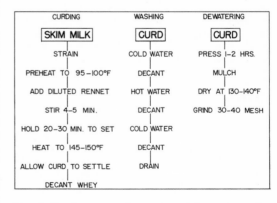

FIG. 1. Batch process for commercial rennet casein.

Ten thousand lb of skim milk yields 300 lb of dried casein granules in a typical batch. The more critical factors to be controlled in obtaining high quality product are: sweet milk, curding temperature and time, and washing of the curd.

Acid Casein. Casein curded from skim milk by the addition of acid, although not suitable for casein plastics, finds wide application in industry,

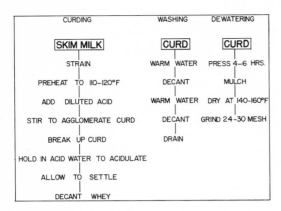

Fig. 2. Batch process for mineral acid casein.

TABLE 1. AMINO ACIDS IN CASEIN.

Ash-free basis, %, approximate

Glutamic acid	23	Phenylalanine	6
Leucine	10	Alanine	3
Valine	8	Aspartic acid	7
Proline	13	Tryptophane	1.3
Tyrosine	6	Cystine	0.4
Lysine	8	Glycine	2.1
Arginine	4.2	Serine	7
Isoleucine	7	Methionine	3.5
Histidine	3.2	Threonine	4.5

with some applications related to plastics. The process by which this type of casein is produced is shown in Fig. 2. The significant factors determining quality of this type of casein are: attainment of the isoelectric point of pH 4.5 on acidifying the milk, "acidulation" of the curd during a steeping period, and washing of the curd in finely divided state. Acid casein is subjected to a somewhat different set of tests for quality control than is rennet casein. Analytical procedures are applied for the determination of particle size, moisture, ash, fat, and nitrogen, as for rennet casein.

Acid casein differs significantly in analysis from rennet casein in having a lower pH (5.0–5.5) and a lower ash content (0.5–5.5%), and therefore a higher nitrogen content (15%, dry basis). As a consequence of the lower ash content, acid casein is readily dissolved with alkalies to pH 6 and higher, whereas rennet casein is readily soluble only with calcium-precipitating or calcium-sequestering alkalies, such as oxalates, pyrophosphates, and metaphosphates.

Casein Chemistry

The composition of casein is basically that of a protein with certain special characteristics relating to its origin. In common with all proteins its molecular structure is that of a long linear chain of amide linkages known as the "polypeptide chain." More specifically the amides result from the co-condensation of a number of different alpha-mino acids, which occurs through subtle and profound reactions occurring continuously and progressively in the living animal. Some of the amino acids are supplied directly from proteins ingested in the feed, which are joined by others, synthesized in vivo, to form the complete casein molecule.

The amino acid composition of casein with approximate proportions is shown in Table 1. The resulting elementary composition is: carbon 53.0%, hydrogen 7.0%, oxygen 22.85%, total nitrogen 15.6%, phosphorus 0.85%, and sulfur 0.7%, ash-free and dry basis. The ash is a mixture of the salts of many elements, mainly calcium, magnesium, sodium, and potassium, with some of the above phosphorus and sulfur in the ash also.

The condensation of amino acids with one another results in amide linkages between the amine group of one and an acid group of another, thus accounting for the charged molecule:

$$^+NH_3 \cdot CHR'CONHCHR''CONH....$$
$$CHR''COO^-$$

where the R groups are of several types, superfluous to the amide linkage. That some are acid, —COOH, and others basic amino —NH_2, imino =NH, or imidazolyl

$$\begin{array}{c} -C-N \\ \parallel \quad \parallel \\ CH \quad CH \\ \diagdown \; \diagup \\ N \\ | \\ H \end{array}$$

accounts for the amphoteric nature of casein, that is, its reactivity as either an acid or a base. Salts of casein with acids are formed below its isoelectric point of pH 4.5, and with alkalies in solutions of pH above this point. Other R groups are hydroxyl —OH, methylol—CH_2OH, phenoxy —C_6H_4OH, phosphate —H_2PO_4, and indolyl

$$\begin{array}{c} -C- \\ \parallel \\ CH \\ N \\ | \\ H \end{array}$$

representing polar groups in such profusion as to make the whole molecule reactive to a multiplicity of chemical agents.

Since, as will be shown, rennet casein is converted to plastic in the presence of water or aqueous solutions, end-group reactions are possible as modifications of the final plastic. It is upon the reactivity of the basic groups of casein with formaldehyde in post-treatment that most of the technology of casein plastic is based. Plastic of improved properties is possible through reaction of polar groups, by acylating the formalized product with fatty acid chlorides or by reaction with potassium cyanate. Direct molding of casein with chemicals reactive with polar sites has also been considered, among them dicyanidiamide, hexamethylenetetramine, furfural, and metallic salts.

Manufacture of Casein Plastic

The raw material for the manufacture of casein plastic, rennet casein, is received in bags varying in weight from about 60 to 140 lb, depending on the country of origin. Generally the casein is in a coarse unground state and to be suitable for making plastic must be milled down. It is desirable that the amount of "fines," that is, material passing 80 mesh, be at a minimum, for best processing properties.

The ground casein is stored in appropriate containers and, after passing laboratory tests for color, odor, ash, pH, mesh fineness, cleanliness, moisture and processing properties, is ready for production.

The first step in the making of casein plastic is mixing. The dry ground casein is weighed out into a suitable mixing vessel, and the required water, dyes, pigments and other additives are incorporated. Moisture must be maintained to a very close tolerance, and each batch tested carefully. Because color standards must be exact, the dyes are weighed with great accuracy. During the mixing cycle other ingredients to give transparency, pearliness, depth, etc. as desired are added, and after a short maturing period the batch is ready for extrusion.

TABLE 2. CASEIN MOLDING COMPOUND—CONSTANTS.

Compression molding temperature 200–225°F
Compression molding pressure 2000–2500 psi
Specific gravity 1.35 g/cc
Specific volume 20.5 cu in./lb
Tensile strength 10,000 psi
Elongation 2.5%
Modulus of elasticity in tension $5.1 - 5.7 \times 10^5$ psi
Compression strength $27,000 - 53,000$ psi
Flexural strength 10,000–18,000 psi
Impact strength 1.0 ft lb/sq in.
Hardness, Rockwell M70–M100
Hardness, Brinell 23
Thermal expansion $4.1–6.8 \times 10^{-5}$ per °C
Resistance to continuous heat 275°F
Heat distortion temp. 300°F
Dielectric strength $400–700 \times 10^{-4}$
Dielectric constant, 10^6 cycles 6.1–6.8
Power factor, 10^6 cyc 0.052
Water absorption, 24-hr, 1/8-in. 7–14%

The casein mix ready for extrusion is slightly damp, although it appears dry, and is fed by means of hoppers to the extruder. The machine consists of a barrel containing a screw with facilities for heating or cooling as required. The powder is fed into the back end of the screw, and passes along the barrel under great pressure, during which it becomes plastic. The plastic mass leaves the front end of the screw by means of various dies and appears as a rod, tube or other desired shape, depending on the type of die used.

The soft, warm plastic shape from the extruder can be processed in several different ways. The rods can be cooled and sliced into discs of any thickness or left as rods which can be placed in a mold and flattened and formed into a sheet of the desired thickness. These sheets can then be punched into discs, or retained as sheets.

After the operations described above, the discs, rods or sheets are ready for curing in dilute formaldehyde for a period of time governed by the thickness of the casein article. This period of time varies from several days for thin sections to as long as several months for thicker material.

After a proper cure time has elapsed, the casein plastic is dried down to a controlled moisture content in circulating hot air.

The resulting casein plastic is now ready for finishing operations such as grinding, drilling, shaping, cutting and polishing to form finished articles of commerce. The principal end use is in the manufacture of buttons where the material enjoys considerable use because of the variety of artistic effects possible and the ease with which it can be dyed.

TABLE 3. PROPERTIES OF CASEIN COMPOUND AS COMPARED TO THERMOPLASTICS IN GENERAL.

	Exposure Effect		
Sunlight	Colors may fade	Machining qualities	Good
Weak acids	Resistance	Clarity	Opaque
Strong acids	Decomposition		
Alkalies	Decomposition		
Organic solvents	Resistance		

Casein as Modifier of Other Plastics

In the ever-diversifying world of modern plastics, casein has often been considered as a modifying component in the molding or extrusion of the more important commercial plastics. It is not surprising that the long known attributes of extruded casein itself should have inspired many attempts to incorporate them in some way in the formulas of the rapidly developing types. Numerous patents attest to interest frequently shown in casein, particularly during the era of early development of the thermosetting phenolic and amino resins.

The improvements observed by the inclusion of casein as a minor component in molded thermosetting resins were: reduced brittleness, greater toughness, improved luster, and increased resistance to oils, to high temperatures, and to electric arcing. Casein is soluble in both phenol and urea, and thus can be incorporated before beginning the condensation with formaldehyde.

As new materials and chemicals were explored for plastics manufacture, casein appears to have been inevitably included in test formulas that, however, seldom reached a stage beyond that of patent issuing. Thus an extensive prior art in the modification of plastics with casein exists, including casein in cellulosic plastics, in vinyl polymers, in alkyd, epoxy, melamine, and polyamide resins, and in foamed plastics.

In the molded aggregates such as wood flour, cellulose pulp, cork granules, and leather scrap, casein may be the glue component. It therefore is incorporated in these materials as an alkaline solution, often with glycerin or glycol as plasticizer.

Related Products and Uses

Casein Fiber and Films. The polypeptide chain structure of casein lends itself to filament formation by extrusion through a spinneret. The procedures were developed step-wise through research efforts in the 1930's, notably in Italy by Ferretti, and Whittier in the United States. The technique by which the globular micelle of casein is converted to a strong filament is essentially that of extrusion of an alkaline "dope" into a strongly acid solution of formaldehyde and salts. The wet tow is taken up and stretched through a series of pulleys, is then steeped in formaldehyde solution and sometimes in solutions of metallic salts, acetylated to adjust its dyeing qualities, and lightly lubricated. The filament may be stapled to find use in unions with wool or fur or with synthetic fibers.

Casein films, cast from alkaline solution, are of glass transparency, but brittle and even friable at thicknesses of less than about 0.001 in. Flexibility of film is attained by the inclusion of a plasticizer such as glycerin. Casein films are hydrophilic, losing their brittleness in an atmosphere of high humidity, and are water-soluble unless cast from solutions containing a "hardener," such as formaldehyde or a heavy metal salt.

Unsupported casein films are not currently of commercial importance because of the difficulties of plasticizing them and because of their susceptibility to attack by microorganisms. On the other hand, their importance is substantial and continuing as coatings on paper, leather, and wood.

Adhesives. Casein finds its greatest use and most stable employment as an adhesive for wood, paper, and other porous materials, and as an adhesive for pigments in the coating of paper and in water-base paints. Casein glue is not adaptable to the assembly of plastic components and is not ordinarily included as a component of adhesives for plastics.*

Identification of Casein

Casein plastic can be identified with certainty by sacrificing a few grams to a burning test, in which the unmistakable odor of burning hair is experienced. The flame is smoky and the cinder does not glow upon removal of the flame, as do other nitrogenous plastics. The identification of sulfur and phosphorus by elementary analysis are also indicative of casein as the material of an unknown plastic.

The biuret reaction is a chemical test for positively identifying a protein. Copper sulfate is added to a solution of the sample in aqueous sodium hydroxide solution. Upon heating, a pink-to-violet color develops in the presence of casein or other protein.

Economic Aspects

Some 5 million lb of rennet casein is converted to plastic material in the United States annually, primarily as large buttons of truly beautiful coloring. The overriding factor of raw material cost in the commerce of plastics places casein in an unfavorable position, because of both unsteady pricing, characteristic of commodities of natural origin, and the relatively high price range of 30–40c per lb, prevalent for a long time. Full realization of the supreme value of casein as a food puts a premium on the value of skim milk in all countries, and although there will always be a surplus of skim milk exceeding that needed for conversion to food, its value is not expected to permit a return to the low pricing of casein which prevailed during the first half of this century.

H. K. SALZBERG
W. B. KINNEY

CASTOR OIL

Castor oil is one of the oldest ingredients in the compounding of plastics, having served as the plasticizer for nitrocellulose in the earliest days of that plastic, a use which is still continuing. However, subsequent use of castor oil in plastics, even in the case of nitrocellulose, has trended nearly

---

* See the Skeist book "Handbook of Adhesives," Reinhold Publ. Corp., Chapter 9, for a discussion on casein adhesives.

completely in the direction of the oil being used in the form of one or more of its many derivatives.

The composition of castor oil is unique among vegetable oils in that the fatty acids comprising the triglyceride are 90% ricinoleic acid (12-hydroxy oleic acid), making this triglyceride the purest of any vegetable oil available in commercial volume. This relative purity of the fatty acid composition combined with the fact that the 18 carbon ricinoleic acid has a hydroxyl group on the 12th carbon makes possible a variety of chemical conversions of castor oil which have resulted in specialty raw materials for the plastics industry. These derivatives are commonly called "ricinoleates." The following chemical reactions have been applied individually and in combinations of two or even three to produce the derivatives of value to the plastics industry which will be discussed later in this article.

Acetylation	Esterification
Alkoxylation	Hydrogenation
Amination	Oxidative Poly-
Caustic Fusion	merization
Chemical Dehydration	Pyrolysis
Epoxidation	Saponification

Most of these processes yield products which are primarily compounding ingredients for plastics such as plasticizers, lubricants, stabilizers, emulsifiers and anti-static additives. However, two reactions have the very interesting result of yielding products which themselves can be converted to plastics. By caustic fusion of castor oil, sebacic acid is formed and upon reaction of this dicarboxylic acid with a selected diamine, nylon-10 results. This particular nylon differs from the standard type of nylon in that it has higher resilience, less sensitivity to humidity and better molding and extrusion properties. In addition to being a raw material for the manufacture of nylon, the sebacic acid can be esterified to make high quality polymeric plasticizers and also superior special performance plasticizers such as dibutyl sebacate for use in the plastic interleaf of safety glass.

Another type of nylon based on castor oil is made by pyrolyzing the castor oil to form undecylenic acid, a vinyl/carboxylic compound, which can be converted to a polyamide identified as nylon-11. This is somewhat similar to nylon-10 except it has still better resistance to humidity along with improved electrical properties.

Plasticizers

The principal function of castor oil derivatives in plastics compounding is as plasticizers. None of these derivatives are primary plasticizers, so for the most part they are used as supplements for the special performance they impart such as lubricity, drape, improve pigment dispersion, etc. Among the plastics where these ricinoleates have demonstrated value are nitrocellulose, ethyl cellulose, polyvinyl acetate, polyvinyl butyral, cellulose acetate butyrate and epoxy resins.

The first improvement in the use of castor oil itself in plastics was its conversion by oxidative polymerization to an improved plasticizer for nitrocellulose. This treatment increases the compatibility with this plastic, resulting in a plastic with better flexibility and higher spew point. Such polymerized castor oils are commercially available with a considerable range of viscosity up to an ultimate form where the castor oil is actually gelled.

Most of these plasticizing derivatives are esters of castor oil and the following discussion characterizes their over-all performance. The alkyl esters, particularly those in which the hydroxyl has been replaced by an acetoxy group, are plasticizers for many synthetic resins and elastomers, including polyvinyl chloride, nitrocellulose and ethyl cellulose. Used in vinyls, the acetyl ricinoleates serve as lubricant/plasticizers of low volatility and excellent dielectric properties. They impart flexibility and drape to vinyl film at low temperatures and enhance hand and body at room temperature. Their high lubrication efficiency provides faster processing in calendering and especially in vinyl extrusions where very low amounts of such additives are desirable. Because of this lubricity they are used in strippable coatings. They contribute to low initial and retained viscosities in plastisols by inhibiting excess swelling of the vinyl resin by primary plasticizers. Their strong wetting action makes them highly effective in dispersing colors, pigments and fillers. In nitrocellulose and vinyl lacquers, their plasticizing properties are characterized by excellent cold check performance and contribution to gloss and depth. Saturation of the double bond in these esters yields hydroxy- and acetoxy-stearates which are equally effective plasticizers but have improved stability to oxidation and resistance to ultraviolet light. The following is a listing of the ricinoleate plasticizers currently being used by the plastics industry.

Ricinoleate Esters and Uses

Methyl ricinoleate	Lubricant/plasticizer in phenolic molding resins. Plasticizer for epoxy resins.
Butyl ricinoleate	Outstanding plasticizer for polyvinyl butyral and cellulose acetate butyrate. General purpose plasticizer for nitrocellulose and ethyl cellulose.
Methyl acetyl ricinoleate	General-purpose plasticizer for cellulosics and vinyls, facilitates processing and imparts excellent low temperature properties.
Butyl acetyl ricinoleate	Highly efficient plasticizer in cellulosics, imparting excellent plate release, cold-crack resistance and high gloss. Also, a good secondary

	plasticizer for vinyls, facilitating processing and extrusion.
Glyceryl tri–(acetyl ricinoleate)	As a plasticizer in vinyls and other plastics, this ester features very low volatility, excellent electrical properties, extrusion lubricity and heat stability. It is particularly good in vinyl wire jacketing and semi-rigid vinyls.
Butyl acetoxystearate	Oxidation-stable plasticizer for vinyls; used in plastisols for non-exudation, easy de-aeration and maintenance of low viscosity.
Glyceryl (acet–oxystearate)	Lubricant/plasticizer for vinyls. Excellent grinding medium and pigment disperser for vinyls. Plasticizer for nitrocellulose, conferring flex-life retention and minimal color development. Lubricant/plasticizer for high temperature vinyl wire jacketing, with outstanding electrical properties and extrusion lubricity. Heat and oxidation stable.
Glyceryl mono–ricinoleate	Processing aid for a number of plastics. In epoxy potting compounds, improves low temperature thermal shock.

Lubricants

The derivatives of castor oil which have proved useful as lubricants for plastics are special liquid forms of the castor oil triglyceride and other derivatives in the form of waxes. At the level of use normally required to impart lubricity and improved processing, these castor oil derivatives have permanent compatibility and little or no effect on physical properties of the finished product. For example, acetylation of castor oil converts it to an excellent medium for pigment dispersions for vinyls. This is one more demonstration of the established ability of ricinoleates to "wet out" pigments and fillers, thus aiding their dispersion. At the same time, it imparts good lubricity with some plasticizing action to the resulting compound. The castor derivatives which have found commercial acceptance in this application are listed below, with brief statements where applicable to any special properties they may have.

Castor Derivatives and Uses

12-hydroxystearin	Processing aid for cellulosics and polyvinyl butyral. Imparts anti-blocking and mold release plus improved grease and solvent resistance.
Ethylene diamide of hydroxy-stearic acid	In polystyrene, improves pigment dispersion to assure excellent color development.
Glyceryl tri-(octadeca-dienoate)	Processing aid and internal lubricant for vinyls. Imparts outstanding lubrication action during extrusion and molding of rigid and semi-rigid polyvinyl chloride.

Antistatic Agents

One of the more recently developed uses for derivatives of castor oil is as antistatic agents in vinyl resins. Two such products are known to be currently available: an ethylene oxide adduct of castor oil and the ethylene diamide of hydroxystearic acid. The latter is especially effective in polystyrene.

Emulsion Systems

Castor oil derivatives can also be used by the plastics industry during the manufacture of the plastic itself in that some are useful ingredients in the emulsion-polymerization process. Here the ethylene oxide adducts of castor oil are effective both as emulsifiers and anti-foaming agents. Similar performance can be obtained from sodium ricinoleate with the added advantage that this agent yields polymer units of more uniform size.

Stabilizers

Calcium ricinoleate is an interesting specialty stabilizer for PVC in that it has F.D.A. approval for use in vinyl films coming in contact with foods. Acetylated epoxidized castor oil is a very effective vinyl stabilizer with the added feature of imparting plasticizing action.

Miscellaneous

"Thixcin R' and Thixatrol ST," proprietary products of The Baker Castor Oil Company and presumably derivatives of castor oil, are very effective for developing viscosity, pigment suspension and flow control of solutions of plastics. "Thixcin R" imparts thixotropic body, sag and slump control, pigment suspension and controlled penetration to vinyl plastisols and organisols. "Thixatrol ST" is the preferred product to use for obtaining similar performance in epoxies, either solventless or solvent-containing.

On the other hand, polyethylene glycol 200 mono-ricinoleate has shown exceptional ability as a PVC plastisol viscosity depressant. Contrasting this action with that of "Thixcin R" certainly emphasizes the versatility of castor oil derivatives as useful ingredients in the compounding of plastics.

M. K. SMITH

Cross-reference: ANTI-STATIC AGENTS.

CATALYSTS, POLYMERIZATION

In most polymerization processes one uses certain accelerating, regulating or modifying ingredients effectively, even though these materials are present only in very small quantities. As long as there did not exist a clear understanding of the mechanism of polymerization the action of these additives resembled the effects of normal catalysis, and hence the name *catalysts* was used for them.

Today it has become evident that the actions of these substances during the formation of macromolecules does not obey the classical definition of the words catalysis and catalyst.

But the misnomer is established, and such correct expressions as initiator, transfer agent, terminator, telomer and cross-linking agent are interchangeably used with the general term *catalyst*. This article gives a brief review of accelerating, regulating and modifying actions which exist and of ingredients which are used in the polymerization of various systems.

Addition Polymerization

During such processes the initiation and propagation of a chain reaction which leads to linear macromolecules is effected by the opening of a double bond between carbon and carbon, carbon and oxygen, carbon and nitrogen, or carbon and sulphur or by the opening of a ring which consists of three or more singly bonded atoms of boron,

carbon, nitrogen, oxygen, silicon, and sulphur. In these cases the ingredients which *start* the process should not be called catalysts in the classical sense of the word since they are used up in the course of the reaction and are, in many instances, chemically bonded to the final product.

Free Radical Initiated Addition Polymerization. Most vinyl polymers and copolymers are made with ingredients which provide for the initiation and propagation of the growing chains through a free radical mechanism. They are molecules (usually organic molecules of molecular weights between 100 and 300) which, under the conditions of the reaction, slowly decompose and produce fragments which carry with them an unpaired electron. This unbonded orbital reacts with the pi-electrons of a colliding monomer under the formation of a covalent sigma bond and the reproduction of a new unpaired electron, capable of repeating this process and propagating a chain.

TABLE 1. A FEW IMPORTANT PEROXIDE-TYPE INITIATORS FOR FREE RADICAL ADDITION POLYMERIZATION.

Name	Formula	Solvent	Temperature range, °C
Benzoyl peroxide	C6H5—C(=O)—O—O—C(=O)—C6H5	Organic	80–100
Acetoylperoxide	CH_3—C(=O)—O—O—C(=O)—CH_3	Organic	70–90
para-Bromobenzoyl peroxide	Br—C6H4—C(=O)—O—O—C(=O)—C6H4—Br	Organic	60–80
Di-*tert*-butyl peroxide	$(CH_3)_3$C—O—O—C$(CH_3)_3$	Organic	80–100
tert-Butyl hydroperoxide	HO—O—C$(CH_3)_3$	Aqueous	60–80
Dicumyl peroxide	C6H5—C$(CH_3)_2$—O—O—C$(CH_3)_2$—C6H5	Organic	120–140
Cumene hydroperoxide	C6H5—C$(CH_3)_2$—O—O—H	Aqueous	80–10
para-Dimethoxy-benzoylperoxide	CH_3O—C6H4—C(=O)—O—O—C(=O)—C6H4—OCH_3	Organic	60–80

Peroxide Type Free Radical Formers. It is known that organic peroxides decompose by the breaking of the peroxydic R—O—O—R′ bond and form reactive species RO· and R′O· which can be considered free radicals. Table 1 gives a few representatives with their names and chemical constitution together with the commonly used temperatures and solvents.

Azo Catalysts. Organic peroxides are convenient initiators but, in some cases, their oxidizing character causes corrosive action or undesirable by-products. It is, therefore, important that certain aliphatic azo compounds R—N=N—R′ decompose smoothly under the evolution of nitrogen and the formation of free radicals of the type R· and R′· which initiate vinyl type addition polymerization.

Table 2 contains some of these azo catalysts together with favorable conditions for their application.

There exist other organic compounds which produce free radical fragments on decomposition such as diazo compounds, aromatically substituted lower paraffins, disulfides and diazothioethers which have not found larger scale application but which show that, in principle, any unpaired electron attached to an appropriate organic residue can initiate vinyl type polymerization.

Redox Systems. In all above cases certain bonds were broken and the reactive species were produced through the decomposition of one specific molecule.

It has been found that during many simple chemical processes, free radical species appear as transient intermediates but do not show up in the net result. For instance, the oxydation of ferrous ion Fe^{++} to ferric ion Fe^{+++} with hydrogen peroxide can be represented by the over-all equation

$$2Fe^{++} + H_2O_2 = 2Fe^{+++} + 2OH^- \qquad (1)$$

A kinetic study revealed that the reaction occurs in two steps:

(1) the donation of an electron from one Fe^{++}

TABLE 2. A FEW AZO-TYPE INITIATORS FOR FREE RADICAL INITIATED ADDITION POLYMERIZATION.

Name	Formula	Temperature range
Azobis isobutyronitrile		50–70
Azobis methyl butyronitrile		—
Azobis cyclopropyl butyronitrile		—

TABLE 3. SOME IMPORTANT REDOX SYSTEMS FOR EMULSION POLYMERIZATION.

Oxidizing agent	Reducing agent	Monomer	Conditions
K-persulfate	Na-bisulfite	Acrylonitrile	Emulsion at 35°C
Benzoyl peroxide	Fe-(NH₄)-sulfate	Vinylacetate	Emulsion at 40°C
Hydrogen peroxide	Fe-(NH₄)-sulfate	Styrene	Emulsion at 65°C
Potassium persulfate	Dodecylmercaptan	Butadiene/Styrene	Emulsion at 50°C
Hydrogenperoxide	Dodecylmercaptan	Butadiene/Acrylonitrile	Emulsion at 50°C

to the H_2O_2 molecule which is convered into a hydroxyl radical and a hydroxyl ion:

$$Fe^{++} \rightarrow Fe^{+++} + HO \cdot + HO^-_{\overline{}} \quad \text{and,} \quad (2)$$

(2) the donation of an electron from another Fe^{++} to the $HO \cdot$ radical to give another hydroxyl ion:

$$HO \cdot + Fe^{++} \rightarrow Fe^{+++} + HO^-_{\overline{}} \quad (3)$$

The radical $HO \cdot$ is present only as a transient species the existence of which was proved by the fact that the process (1) is capable to initiate addition polymerization of vinyl type monomers.

There are many reduction-oxidation reactions of a more general character than (1) in the course of which free radical fragments are produced; some are very efficient in the initiation of addition polymerization particularly in aqueous systems and at relatively low temperatures. As a consequence, redox systems of many compositions are used as efficient initiators particularly for suspension and emulsion polymerizations in aqueous environment. Table 3 contains a list of selected combinations of reducing and oxydizing agents as they are applied in the large scale production of plastics and elastomers in suspension and emulsion.

Initiation Through Radiation. Free radicals are also produced by the photo-dissociation of molecules through UV light, X-rays or ionizing radiation. No special chemical ingredient is needed except of sensitizers which are added to increase the absorptivity of a given system for a certain radiation.

Ionic Initiation of Addition Polymerization. Not only free radicals can start the growth of a vinyl type chain but also certain ionic species which exist in organic solvents, attach themselves to the double bond of a monomer through an electron pair displacement process and reproduce the active site at the end of the resulting adduct.

For cationic initiators this process can be represented by:

$$\text{cation } K^+ + \text{double bond } H_2C \overset{\cdot}{\div} \overset{H}{\underset{X}{C}} \rightarrow K-CH_2-\overset{H}{\underset{X}{C}}{}^+$$

where the carbonium ion C^+ propagates the chain reaction. For anionic iniation there is:

$$\text{anion } A^-_{\overline{}} + \text{double bond } H_2C \overset{\cdot}{\div} \overset{H}{\underset{X}{C}} \rightarrow A-CH_2-\overset{H}{\underset{X}{C}}{}^-_{\overline{}}$$

where the carbanion $C^-_{\overline{}}$ propagates the chain. In both cases a counter ion neutralizes the system electrically and always maintains itself in the immediate neighborhood of the growing chain end.

Cationic Catalysts. An important representative of this group is borontrifluoride BF_3, which complexes with water and other hydrogens containing molecules in organic solvents and dissociates into a proton H^+ and a negative counter ion $[BF_3OH]^-$ or $[BF_3X]^-$. The proton attaches itself to the double bond of the monomer and

TABLE 4. A FEW CATALYSTS FOR CATIONIC VINYL POLYMERIZATION.

Name	Formula	Cocatalyst	Monomer	Temperature, °C
Boron trifluoride	BF_3	Water	Isobutylene	−80
Aluminum chloride	$Al\,Cl_3$	Ethylchloride	Methylstyrene	−130
Boron trifluoride	BF_3	Ethylether	Vinylcarbazole	−60
Boron trifluoride	BF_3	Ethylether	Vinylbutylether	−70

TABLE 5. SOME ANIONIC CATALYSTS FOR VINYL- AND DIENE POLYMERIZATION.

Name	Formula	Cocatalyst	Monomer	Temperature, °C
Potassium	K	—	Methylstyrene	15
Sodium	Na	Liquid NH_3	Methacrylonitrile	−75
Sodium cyanide	NaCN	Dimethylformamide	Acrylonitrile	−50
Alfin catalyst	Amyl-Na	Isopropanol	Butadiene	ordinary
Sodium	Na	—	Butadiene	50

initiates the chain which is propagated by the terminal carbonium ion; the water or XH molecule which complexes with the BF_3 is called the cationic cocatalyst. Many combinations of Friedel-Crafts type catalysts with organic or in organic cocatalysts initiate vinyl type polymerization over a wide temperature range in a very effective manner. A list of them is given in Table 4 with the conditions under which they are applied.

Anionic Catalysts. Equally important are the anionic initiators of which butyl-lithium is a particularly simple representative. It dissociates in organic liquids into Li^+ and Bu^-. The butyl anion attaches itself to the double bond of the monomer and produces a terminal carbonium which propagates the chain. Table 5 contains a few anionic catalysts together with the conditions under which they work. To this class also belong the famous Ziegler catalysts which are prepared by the interaction of a transition metal compound and a light metal alkyl. Usually they are obtained in the form of a colloidal or semicolloidal slurry which carries the positively charged counterions whereas soluble anionic fragments X^- initiate the chains at the surface of the catalyst and provide for their growth through an ion pair, formed by the firmly complexed positive counter ion and the adsorbed anionic chain end of the growing macromolecule. Natta has shown in a series of brilliant contributions that certain ion pairs of this type are capable of exerting effective control on the mode of entry of each individual monomer into the growing chain which leads to stereoregulation, a phenomenon which is extremely interesting scientifically and, at the same time, of eminent practical importance. Table 6 lists a few Ziegler type catalysts which are already successfully used in commercial production.

Addition Polymerization Through Ring Opening. It is known that the epoxy-ring,

is a vehicle for addition polymerization during which linear polyethers of the form:

$$-CH_2-CHX-O-CH_2-CHX-O-$$
$$-CH_2-CHX-O-$$

TABLE 6. SOME TYPICAL ZIEGLER CATALYSTS FOR THE POLYMERIZATION OF OLEFINS.

Name	Formula	Cocatalyst	Monomer	Temperature
Titanium tetrachloride	$TiCl_4$	$AlEt_3$	Ethylene	Ordinary
Titanium trichloride	$TiCl_3$	$AlEt_3$	Propylene	Ordinary
Titanium tetrachloride	$TiCl_4$	$LiAl(C_{10}H_{21})_4$	Styrene	Ordinary
Vanadium oxychloride	$VOCl_3$	$Al(Hexyl)_3$	Ethylene Propylene	Ordinary
Titanium tetrachloride	$TiCl_4$	$Al(iso\text{-}butyl)_3$	Isoprene	Ordinary

TABLE 7. SOME CATALYSTS FOR EPOXY POLYMERIZATION AND FOR THE CURING OF EPOXY RESINS.

Name	Formula	Monomer	Temperature, °C
Sodium hydroxide	$NaOH$	Bisphenol	80–100
Triethylamine for curing	$N(C_2H_5)_3$	Epoxy monomer	Ordinary
Phthalic anhydride for curing		Epoxy monomer	120
Oxalic acid for curing	$HOOC-COOH$	Epoxy monomer	150
Strontium carbonate	$SrCO_3$	Propylene oxide	50
Ferric chloride	$FeCl_3$	Propylene oxide	80

are produced. This process can be initiated by certain functional groups such as—OH,—NH$_2$ or —COOH without any accelerating ingredients, but in practice one works with catalysts which either open one of the C—O bonds directly, or form a complex with the epoxysystem and facilitate the opening of the ring by the functional group of the initiator. Both cationic and anionic systems are applicable; the selection of a specific system depends on the preferred chosen reaction conditions such as character of the monomer, initiator, solvent and temperature and of the desired nature of the polymer such as molecular weight and degree of tacticity. Table 7 contains common catalysts for the formation of epoxy-polymers.

Cyclic oxygen containing compounds with four and five atoms, such as butoxydervatives and tetrahydrofurans, can also be converted into linear, polyether type macromolecules with the aid of ionic catalysts through a ring opening reaction. Table 8 contains a few particularly interesting cases.

Even more important are catalytically accelerated ring opening reactions of lactones and lactams with four to seven ring atoms which lead to linear polyesters and polyamides. Cationic and anionic systems have been used with success and Table 9 gives data on a few well investigated cases.

It also should be added that the polymerization of formaldehyde and acetaldehyde is a ring-chain transformation since, in most cases, the process is not started with the monomer but with the cyclic trimers which open up under the influence of certain catalysts and produce linear polyacetal-chains. Table 10 lists a number of catalysts which are used in these ring-chain transformation processes.

Polycondensation Reactions

Important macromolecules are formed by the polycondensation of bifunctional or multifunctional monomeric units such as dicarboxylic acids, dihydric alcohols, diamines, dihalides, phenols,

TABLE 8. CATALYSTS FOR THE RING-CHAIN TRANSFORMATION OF CYCLIC ETHERS.

Name	Formula	Monomer	Temperature, °C
Phosphorous pentafluoride	PF$_5$	CH_2—$\overset{\overset{\textstyle CH_2Cl}{\textstyle \vert}}{\underset{\underset{\textstyle O——CH_2}{}}{C}}$—$CH_2Cl$	−25
Phosphorous pentafluoride	PF$_5$	Tetrahydrofuran	30

TABLE 9. SOME CATALYSTS FOR THE POLYMERIZATION OF LACTONES AND LACTAMS.

Name	Formula	Monomer	Temperature, °C
Zinc chloride	ZnCl$_2$	δ-Valerolactone	85
Potassium carbonate	K$_2$CO$_3$	Lactone	85
Potassium carbonate	K$_2$CO$_3$	ε-Caprolactone	150
Sodium metal	Na	ε-Caprolactam	255
Potassium metal	K	γ-Butyrolactam	50

TABLE 10. SOME CATALYSTS FOR THE POLYMERIZATION OF ALDEHYDES.

Name	Formula	Monomer	Temperature, °C
Antimonytrifluoride	SbF$_3$	$(CH_2O)_3$	120–180
Triphenyl phosphine	P(C$_6$H$_5$)$_3$	CH$_2$O	25
Tributylamine	N(C$_4$H$_9$)$_3$	CH$_2$O	25

urea-type compounds formaldehyde and others. In all these cases, a part of the reacting units is split off and removed from the polymerizing system, either in the form of water, or of some other small molecule. The bonds between the individual monomers in such macromolecules are of the type of ester-, amide-, ether-, or methylene bonds. The removal of the condensing fragment and the formation of the bonds can be catalytically influenced and, in fact, most polycondensation reactions are run in the presence of one or more catalytically active ingredients.

Polyester Formation. The reaction of multifunctional alcohols and the corresponding carboxylic acids leads to linear or three-dimensional polyesters. Simple esterification catalysts such as acids and bases are used together with ester interchange catalysts of the organometallic type. Some typical polyesterifications and their catalysts are given in Table 11.

Polyamide Formation. Because of the intrinsically higher reactivity of carboxylic acids with amines it is common not to use any special catalysts in the synthesis of polyamides. However, in certain cases such as in the formation of copolymers of different character amide interchange catalysts are used such as simple amides of carboxylic, sulfuric, and phosphoric acids.

Phenol-formaldehyde Condensation. The junction of two phenolic units through methylol groups can either be effected by methylene bridges:

$$\text{(1)}$$

or by methylenic ether bonds:

$$+ H_2O \quad (2)$$

Acid and bases are used as catalysts; they do not only increase the rate of the polycondensation but also influence profoundly the type of bonding between the individual phenolic units.

If one uses alkali metal hydroxides, ($Ca(OH)_2$, NH_3 or quaternary ammonium bases), the primary reaction products are methylol phenols which are called *resoles* and which eventually polymerize to a three-dimensional network of the type 2 (resitols and resites). On the other hand, if acid catalysts are used such as HCl, H_2SO_4, toluenesulfonic acid or phosphoric acids, one obtains polymers of the type 1 in which the phenolic rings are bonded to each other by methylene bridges; they have been called *novolacs* and eventually also form insoluble and infusible three-dimensional networks.

HERMAN MARK

CATALYST, PROMOTER

A promoter is a substance which accelerates a reaction. In the field of polymers, when promoter catalysts are used, they decrease the activation energy required for the desired reaction to take place. This allows the reaction to proceed more rapidly in the desired direction. Many of the promoters act as part of an oxidation-reduction system resulting in the release of free radicals. The catalyst is the source which initiates polymerization, curing, or cross-linking while the promoter speeds the rate of reaction. Polymerization reactions may often proceed slowly; if no promoter is used, no reactions will occur.

Types of Reactions

The field of plastics utilizes a wide range of materials as accelerators for many different polymerizations or cures. The types of promoted systems widely used in the field of plastics are:

(1) Redox promoter systems for emulsion polymerization.

(2) Redox promoters for polyester, acrylics and other vinyl solvent or bulk polymerizations.

TABLE 11. SOME CATALYSTS FOR THE FORMATION OF POLYESTERS.

Name	Formula	Monomer	Temperature, °C
Antimony trioxide and calcium acetate	Sb_2O_3 $Ca(OCOCH_3)_2$	Dimethyl terephthalate	200–280
Tetraisopropyl titanate	$Ti(OC_3H_7)_4$	1,4-cyclohexan dicarbinol and dimethyl terephthalate	200–290
Antimony trioxide	Sb_2O_3	Glycolic acid	200–220

(3) Accelerators used in rubber compounding to speed the rate of curing or vulcanization.

(4) Accelerators used in drying oils and coatings to increase the rate of conversion of liquid coating to the dry film. These are also called driers.

(5) Co-catalysts can be considered as promoter systems for ionic polymerization.

There are many different reactions involved in each of the promoter uses listed above. Each use can utilize different promoter systems with completely different mechanisms of reaction.

Redox Promoter Systems for Emulsion Polymerization. A very large number of redox systems have been devised for use in emulsion polymerization. Since the chemical formation of free radicals requires electron transfer, one of the most versatile methods is a reduction of one component and the oxidation of the other, usually an oxygen containing catalyst. It is often possible for this catalyst to become self-activated and dissociate into free radicals. However, the energy requirements of this dissociation makes it more practical to use a redox promoted catalytic system. Many emulsion systems give better products and are easier to handle at low temperatures, which can only be used at a reasonable rate when redox promoted systems are employed.

A large number of redox systems tend to be quite specific in catalyst-promoter-monomer and emulsifier systems as far as reactivity is concerned. Metallic ions have been used extensively with hydrogen peroxide, cumene hydroperoxide and persulfates. Iron, copper and silver ions are utilized as active promoters in many large volume recipes. Amines and mercapto groups are also widely used, either as part of the redox promoter systems or as additional accelerators. Mercaptans may have an acceleration in addition to the chain transfer effect of the mercaptan.

Promoters for Polyesters. Very seldom are polyesters cured with peroxide catalysts alone. Too much peroxide may result in a very rapid cure, with a resulting law molecular weight and poor properties. Too little peroxide gives too long cure times unless the termperature is raised, which results in bubbles and cracks. The best practical solution to this problem involves the use of accelerator or promoter systems which activate the catalyst. The most common polyester systems utilize styrene which reacts or copolymerizes preferentially with the already polymerized polyester. Many other reactive diluents have been used such as diallyl phthalate or methyl methacrylate. Each system behaves somewhat differently, and a particular catalyst-promoter is often specific to the particular system.

Among the promoters which appear to be particularly suited to polyester cure systems care cobalt napthenate and other metallic salts, tertiary amines, and polyamines. Amine salts have also been suggested.

Promoters (or Acrylics). Promoter systems have been utilized in curing acrylic powder-liquid mixtures in dental plastics.

For use with methacrylate systems, dimethyl-p-toluidine appears to be particularly useful when minimum color is desired. Dimethylaniline gives a rapid cure with benzoyl peroxide where color is not a major factor. A number of peroxides or sulfinic acids can be used as catalysts.

Promoter-catalyst systems can suffer from a number of deficiencies, among them:

(1) Lack of color stability and initial color change.

(2) Too slow or too rapid rate of cure (too rapid rate may limit pot life).

(3) Inhibition on surfaces, i.e., a soft or tacky surface.

(4) Incomplete polymerization due to type and balance of the catalyst-promoter-monomer system.

Accelerators Used in Rubber Compounding. Rubber compounding accelerators comprise a separate science or art. The problem in rubber compounding is to obtain a fine balance which will allow a rubber compound to be compounded in a Banbury mixer or two-roll mill without scorching (or beginning to cure), while giving a fast rate of cure in the mold which may be as little as 20°F higher in temperature. This is generally accomplished by a judicious choice of accelerators in combination with all the components of the compound.

In the absence of an accelerator, the cure of a rubber compound containing sulfur as the usual vulcanizing agent may take hours, or even days. The use of accelerators can reduce this to minutes or seconds. In addition to this primary effect, accelerators will affect the final physical properties of the vulcanization such as improved tensile strength, set, and hysteresis on aging.

Although some steps have been taken towards the classification of rubber accelerators for compounding, no useful proposals have been published. Chemical classifications include organic gases such as amines, aldehyde-amines, guanidines, thiocarbanilide, thiazoles, dithiocarbamates and thuiram sulfides.

Other vulcanizing systems without a sulfur base are being used, particularly with newer rubbers such as acrylics or ethylene-propylene, which often utilize quite different promoter systems.

Accelerators Used in Drying Oils and Coatings. One major function of accelerators in coatings is to aid the rate of oxidizing of air dried coatings to produce a hard, dry film. These compounds, driers, are heavy metal soaps of organic acids such as lead, cobalt, magnesium or zinc salts of napthenates, octoates, linoleates, resinates or tallates.

Other metal ions may also be used. Often two or more metals which have different specific actions on the drying mechanism are used.

In many coatings, such as baked coatings, other cross-linking mechanisms not involving oxidation are used. Some such reactions involve use of hydroxyl groups or epoxy groups. These will also often assist use promoters such as amines or anhydrides to speed a hardening of the coating.

JOHN CORNELL

CATALYSTS, URETHANE FOAM

Urethane catalysts comprise a very small but highly important portion of the urethane foam formulation. The type and amount of catalyst in a given foam formulation will have a direct bearing upon the foam initiation time, the actual foaming time, the tack-free time, the density, tensile strength, elongation, compression/deflection, the K factor, heat distortion, and dimensional stability as well as the structure and type of cells.

It is obvious, therefore, that the specific catalyst system for a given compound will be dependent upon the desired foam properties and curing rates. Although the foregoing will be the primary factors governing the selection of a specific catalyst system, the system will also be dependent upon whether a prepolymer or a one-shot foam system is being used. The catalyst system should be balanced to produce the type of overall reactivity desired. For instance, there are some catalysts such as triethylenediamine, which produce a very high initial exotherm, followed by a gradual decrease of temperature, while others such as dibutyltin dilaurate, start off much more slowly but may wind up having a higher overall average foaming and curing rate.

Essentially, there are two basic types of catalysts used in the urethane foam industry: those which catalyze the reaction of the isocyanate group with water, and those which catalyze the resin forming (or gelling) reaction. Examples of the former type of catalysts would be amines such as triethylene diamine. The second type of compound would be metallo-organic such as stannous octoate, while the dibutyltins are intermediate in reactivity type.

The majority of foam formulations utilize combinations of the two types of catalysts to achieve an optimum balance between the rate of cure and the development of the foam. An unbalanced catalyst system containing an excess of amine can produce a foaming system which blows too fast and then collapses before the cell walls are gelled.

An imbalance at the other end of the system (an excess of tin) produces a foaming system which gels prematurely, consequently, when the blowing agent is released there is nowhere for the cells to expand and an overly dense foam is the result.

The properly balanced catalyst system will produce a foaming compound in which the development of foam cells and the rigidification of the cell walls proceed hand-in-hand.

Dibutyltin salts such as dibutyltin dilaurate are vigorous catalysts and withstand both hydrolysis and oxidation better than the stannous salts. Unfortunately, however, foams catalyzed with dibutyltins degrade badly upon humid and high temperature aging. This degradation severely limits the applications in which these catalysts may be used, although they are being used in some molding applications where not only is their better stability a virtue, but where their delayed acceleration of the gelling reaction and simultaneous rapid catalysis of gasification is an added bonus.

Among the materials which have been tried with varying success as oxidative degradation inhibitors for the dibutyltins are antioxidants (such as organic phosphites), substituted phenols and chelators.

As a result of the problems encountered with the dibutyltin compounds, stannous octoate became entrenched as the leading catalyst early in the development of the urethane product. It has survived the onslaught of all other organometallic materials until quite recently when it has been replaced in some instances with stannous oleate.

The early versions of stannous octoate were highly unstable with the result that no success was met in the field until means of stablilizing the stannous tin content was found. This has long been an accomplished fact so that stabilized stannous octoate is now the leading metallic catalyst in the flexible urethane foam field. Stannous octoate produces open celled foams having a good balance between the curing rate and the physical properties of the foam.

Stannous oleate has, in recent months, begun to supplant stannous octoate in some applications. Stannous oleate offers the advantage of a lower price per lb. but is actually more expensive to use on an equivalent weight of actual tin, often requiring as much as triple the concentration of the octoate. Stannous oleate is claimed by some to permit the inclusion of a higher amount of total tin in a flexible foam formulation than is possible through the use of stannous octoate. This is made possible by the fact that stannous oleate apparently shows a lower reactivity than does stannous octoate so that more may be incorporated into the foam without causing premature gelling. Those who use stannous oleate state that this added amount of tin gives them better physical properties in the final foam. It has been theorized that this is due to the oleate's promotion of a more linear type, higher molecular weight, polymer.

Other metallo-organic materials which have been investigated from time to time during the development of the urethane foam industry include those based upon lead and zinc. Organic compounds of lead such as lead octoate or lead naphthenate are extremely reactive catalysts. They start the urethane reaction vigorously but then taper off rapidly. Their use has not been widespread in flexible urethane foams because of their tendency to promote closed cell structure with subsequent shrinkage of the foam. Then, too, the toxicity of these lead compounds has also been a deterrent.

Zinc compounds have not shown themselves to be particularly reactive as catalysts so have been used primarily as a blending agent in exotic mixes, none of which has apparently met with any commercial success.

Ferrous iron present in even trace amounts contributes a secondary exotherm severe enough to cause core scorching in many cases.

When organo-tin catalysts are used in urethane foams, it is important that the organo-tin catalyst not be prematurely mixed with certain of the other foam ingredients. The wrong choice of materials can result in a degraded catalyst giving a long foam time with consequent increase in density or poor cell structure. In one-shot foam systems, the carrier for the organo-tin catalyst is generally the polyol itself.

Whether the amine can be preblended with the organo-tin catalyst depends upon the type of organo-tin being used. There is evidence, for example, to show that dibutyltin dilaurate is relatively stable in the presence of some amine catalysts whereas stannous octoate is much less so but normally, it is recommended that the metallo-tin catalyst not be preblended with the amine(s). It is also generally recommended that the silicone oil stabilizer not be preblended with the organo-tin.

Of course it is extremely important that no water be introduced into any blend containing the organo-tin catalyst because of the probability of hydrolysis with resultant degradation of the catalyst. The stannous tin catalysts are also susceptible to air and are supplied blanketed with nitrogen. For optimum storage life, the container should be blanketed with dry nitrogen after each use.

Amines, as previously mentioned, are primary catalysts for the foam reaction. As a general rule of thumb, the higher the amine/tin ratio in the compound, the lower the resultant density of the foam. Of course, the other properties of the foam will generally determine the upper limit for the ratio although there are many rigid foam formulations in which the amines are the only catalysts present. These are generally foams based upon polyesters.

Examples of amine catalysts used in urethane foams are given in Table 1. These amines differ from each other in their rate of reactivity and are listed in order of their general reactivity with the most reactive amine being at the head of the list and the least reactive being at the bottom.

TABLE 1. AMINE CATALYSTS.

Triethylenediamine
N, N, N′, N′ -tetramethyl-1, 3-butane diamine
Triethylamine
N-methyl morpholine
N-ethyl morpholine

Flexible foams, being mainly open celled and based upon polyethers, are generally produced by combinations of metallic and amine catalysts whereas rigid foams, still dominantly polyester based, are commonly of the prepolymer type and utilize, in many cases, only amine catalysts.

It should be pointed out that there is one problem which may be encountered in one-shot foams which must be controlled by the catalyst system. This is the problem of burning encountered in the core of the foam because of excessive exotherm due to a "too hot" catalyst system. The prepolymer system is one method of getting away from this because the exotherm is partially expended in the original formation of the prepolymer. Another way around it is to design a slower catalyst system. This is not necessarily an easy solution since the slower catalyst must still produce a foam having the desired finished qualities and be capable of curing within the desire production time.

Many of the common production problems encountered with urethane foam may be traced to the catalyst system which is being used. Difficulties which may be caused by having too high a content of organometallic catalysts are splits, foam shrinkage, closed cells, high density, burned core, loose skin, harsh hand, and blow holes. These difficulties, although not necessarily due to the catalyst system in each case, can often be corrected by either reducing the amount of organometallic catalyst in the system while maintaining the amine content or conversely by increasing the amine content while maintaining the organometallic level.

Problems which may be due to an excess of amine are foam collapse, coarse cells, excessively low density and excessive odor. Aside from the odor problem which may be alleviated only by an actual reduction of the amine content, these problems may often be corrected either by increasing the tin content while maintaining the amine content or by lowering the amine while maintaining the tin level.

If the foam is tacky at the end of the normal curing cycle, this is indicative of too low a metallo-organic catalyst content and may generally be corrected by increasing same.

R. W. VAIL

Cross-references: CATALYSTS, POLYMERIZATION.

CELLULOSE AND DERIVATIVES

Cellulose is the major constituent of the cell wall of the higher forms of plant life, where its function is that of a strengthening agent to make possible the support of large structures such as the trunks of trees. Because of this fact, it is the most abundant organic chemical in the world, and will probably continue this supremacy as long as conditions which favor plant life endure. Its abundance, and the fact that the supply is virtually inexhaustible (assuming proper conservation of natural resources), combine to make it one of the cheapest raw materials from which man can fashion shelter, clothing and various other articles to make his life more comfortable and varied.

The variety of uses to which cellulose is put in the form of wood and paper alone is sufficient to illustrate the vast potential of this chemical. In addition, it is used in cotton textiles, in the manufacture of man-made fibers, e.g., rayon and cellulose acetate, in films, and coatings and as a major raw material for cellulosic plastics of many types. The basic reason for this applicability is the fact that cellulose is a high polymer. The polymeric nature of the material gives it strength and durability and enables it to be fashioned into many different shapes.

Plastics Made from Cellulose

In general, the plastics made from cellulose derivatives are characterized by toughness, high impact strength, good weatherability and heat resistance, and low price. In 1964, over 160 million lb of cellulosic plastics were produced in the United States. The following is a list of the most important cellulose derivatives used in the plastics industry. Many of them, of course, are also used in the fiber, film, and lacquer industries.

Cellulose acetate is made by the acetylation of cellulose, with a mixture of acetic acid and acetic anhydride using sulfuric acid as the catalyst. Molding grade cellulose acetate contains about 39% acetyl (D.S. of 2.4). The higher acetyle derivatives, e.g., the triacetate, are not suitable for molding because of their high softening point.

Cellulose acetate butyrate is made the same way as cellulose acetate, except that butyric acid is also used, as well as acetic acid and anhydride. The butyryl content will vary from 17.5–48%, and the acetyl content from 29.5–6.0%, depending on the properties desired in the final product.

Cellulose acetate propionate, also called simply cellulose propionate, is made the same as the acetate, with the addition of propionic acid in place of acetic anyhydride. Propionyl content varies from 42–47%, and acetyl content from 2.5–9% depending on end use.

Cellulose nitrate is the oldest of the cellulose plastics and the toughest of all thermoplastics. It is made by the nitration of alpha cellulose with a mixture of nitric and sulfuric acids. Molding grade contains about 11% nitrogen. Higher nitrogen content esters are used in lacquers (12%) and explosives (13%).

Ethylcellulose is made by the alkylation of alkali cellulose with ethyl chloride. Alkali cellulose is the name given to cellulose which has been reacted with caustic soda and then dried. Ethoxy content, 46–49.5%, is suitable for molding grade ethylcellulose.

Hydroxyethylcellulose is made from alkali cellulose and ethylene oxide. If the degree of substitution is greater than 2.5, the material is water-soluble. Lower degrees of substitution are water insoluble, but often alkali soluble.

Carboxymethylcellulose is made from alkali cellulose and sodium chloroacetate. This material is watersoluble and used more as a sizing, gum, or water soluble colloid than as a plastic.

In addition to these materials there are a great many other esters and ethers derived from cellulose which have been used and are still being used in small quantities by the plastics industry. The materials listed above, of course, are seldom used in the pure state for the manufacture of plastic articles. They are usually compounded with large quantities of plasticizers, stabilizers, pigments, inhibitors, and lubricants before being extruded or molded.

Chemical Properties

Cellulose would be defined by an organic chemist as a carbohydrate, because of its empirical formula $C_6H_{10}O_5$, as a polysaccharide because it is a polymer whose monomer units are a simple sugar, glucose, and finally and most specifically as poly(1,4-glucose-β-glucoside) to distinguish it from other polysaccharides such as starch [poly(1,4-glucose-α-glucoside)].

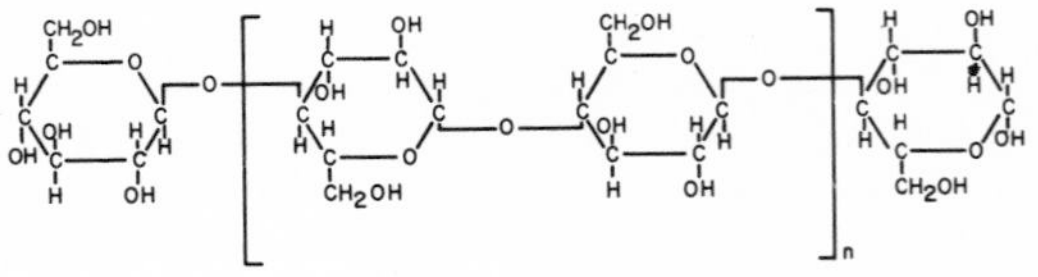

FIG. 1

The structural formula is shown in Fig. 1. The basic repeating unit is in reality cellobiose, as shown in the bracket, rather than glucose, but the degree of polymerization (DP) is usually calculated on the basis of the glucose content, i.e., DP would be $2n + 2$, with n defined as in Fig. 1. It is of interest to note that cellulose is a stereospecific polymer, i.e., that glucose or cellobiose units are all linked at the 1 and 4 carbons and are arranged in a regular spatial configuration as indicated by the β ether linkage. This fact accounts for the high crystallinity of the material, since randomly linked monomers would not possess the symmetry required for packing in a crystalline lattice.

It will be noted from Fig. 1 that cellulose is a polyhydric alcohol containing three hydroxyl groups per glucose unit. These hydroxyl groups are subject to all of the chemical reactions of simple alcohols, e.g., oxidation, reduction, esterification, etherification, alkoxide formation, etc., and it is this reactivity which makes possible the variety of cellulose plastics in use today. Of the three hydroxyls, the one on the 6-carbon atom is a primary hydroxyl, while the two on the 2- and 3-carbon atoms are secondary hydroxyls. In accordance with our knowledge of the chemistry of simple alcohols, it may be expected that the two different types of alcohols will have different reactivities and react at different rates, and this is indeed the case.

The degree of substitution (DS) of a cellulose derivative is usually given as a number between 0 and 3, representing the number of hydroxyl groups substituted *on the average* per glucose unit. Thus a DS of 3 represents a tri-substituted cellulose derivative as in cellulose triacetate, while the so-called "secondary" cellulose acetate used in fiber and plastic manufacture has a DS of about 2.4, meaning that 24 out of every 30 hydroxyl groups has been substituted. A tri-substituted cellulose retains the symmetry and stereospecificity of the original molecule, providing that all three substituents are identical. Such a derivative is therefore also a crystalline or crystallizable substance (for example cellulose triacetate). On the other hand, substitution of the hydroxyls to any degree less than 3 will introduce a random character to the chain molecule. Such a material will show little tendency to crystallize (for example secondary cellulose acetate).

In addition to the hydroxyl groups, cellulose can also undergo reaction at the ether linkage between the glucose units. In particular, hydrolytic cleavage of the bond in the presence of water and acid, and oxidation of the bond by oxygen or oxidizing agents are common reactions. Both of these reactions lead to loss in DP and this in turn decreases the strength and affects the other physical properties of the material.

The ether bonds are quite reactive, with the result that in practically all chemical modifications of cellulose, degradation of the polymer is a concomitant effect with resultant loss of DP. Of course, the loss of DP is also beneficial in most cases, since the DP of native celluloses such as cotton or wood pulp is too high for practical manufacturing purposes.

Other reactive groups in cellulose are the hemiacetal reducing groups at the ends of the chain (right side in Figure 1), and carboxyl groups which presumably arise from oxidation of the primary hydroxyl on the number 6 carbon. However, these groups are usually in very low concentration and have little effect on the chemical behavior of the cellulose.

Physical Properties

Cellulose is a white solid, obtainable in the form of fibers or powder. Even the powdered material will however be revealed to be fibrous in nature under strong magnification, reflecting the polymeric and "linear" nature of the molecules. X-ray diffraction patterns of almost all celluloses reveal the presence of crystalline regions which are presumed to be connected by regions of lower order often called the "amorphous" regions. The degree of crystallinity will vary with the previous history of the sample, being highest for the relatively pure, high DP, native fibers such as cotton and ramie and lowest for regenerated celluloses such as rayon and cellophane. The degree of crystallinity will affect the physical properties of the material as well as its chemical reactivity, but not the nature of the chemical reactions the material will undergo. For example, all cellulose samples will absorb moisture from the atmosphere, but the less crystalline materials will contain a higher equilibrium moisture content than the more highly crystalline materials. Thus, the equilibrium moisture content at 65% R.H. and 75°F of cotton is 6.7%, while ordinary rayon will absorb twice as much water (12–13%).

Table 1 is a list of some of the more useful physical properties of cellulose. As shown, a range of values is given for each property since the properties will vary in accordance with the crystallinity and such chemical factors as the ash, DP, and end-groups and carboxyl groups of the cellulose. In addition, cellulose in the form of fibers or films is anisotropic because the long-fiber like molecules are deliberately oriented in a preferred direction or directions. The degree of this orientation will also affect the value of certain physical properties, e.g., tensile strength, extension at break, and refractive index.

TABLE 1. PHYSICAL PROPERTIES OF CELLULOSE.

Specific gravity	1.50–1.56
Refractive index	1.555–1.563
Specific heat	0.32–0.35 B/lb/°F
Effect of temperature	Decomposes at 250–300°C without melting
Dielectric constant	7 (dry cotton)
Tensile strength	50–90 kg/sq mm (65% R.H.)
Extension at break	6–30% (65% R.H.)

High molecular weight cellulose is completely insoluble in all known solvents, although many polar liquids such as water, dimethylsulfoxide, dimethylformamide, and organic acids will swell the material to a greater or lesser degree. Swelling may be regarded as a limited form of solution and is due to the attraction of the hydroxyl groups in the amorphous regions of the cellulose for the polar molecules of the solvent. However, the crystalline regions of the cellulose are penetrated only with difficulty and tend to prevent the molecules from breaking free and entering the body of the liquid to form a solution.

Cellulose is soluble in solutions of certain inorganic salts where it is believed that the hydroxyl groups can take part in the coordination complexes of the cations. Examples are solutions of copper ammonium hydroxide (cuam) copper ethylenediamine hydroxide (cuene) and cadmium ethylenediamine hydroxide (cadoxene). The solution of cellulose in cuam is the spinning solution used in the production of Bemberg or cuprammonium rayon.

Organic and inorganic esters of cellulose such as the acetate, triacetate and nitrate are soluble in various organic solvents such as acetone, chloroform, and ethyl acetate. Such solutions are used commercially to make fibers, films, and lacquers.

Sources of Cellulose

The two major sources of cellulose for industrial purposes are wood and cotton. Wood is processed by various chemical methods to separate the cellulose from lignin and other wood contaminants, thus producing pulp of varying degrees of purity. The purest pulps are called the "dissolving" or "chemical" pulps, and these are the basic raw materials for the plastics, fiber and film industries.

The largest part of the cellulose produced by the cotton plant is used for textile purposes and represents a very pure form of high molecular weight, highly crystalline cellulose. However, a by-product of the textile cotton industry is cotton "linters," which represent fibers too short for textile purposes and which tend to cling to the cotton seed. These fibers are reclaimed and, after purification to remove wax, dirt and other contamination, are formed into linters pulp which is the second major source of industrial cellulose.

Cellulose pulps are characterized for quality according to their alpha-cellulose content. The alpha-cellulose content is that portion of the cellulose which is insoluble in 17.5% sodium hydroxide at 20°C. It represents in general the higher molecular weight cellulose present in the material. Beta-cellulose is the fraction of the cellulose which dissolves in 17.5% caustic at 20°C but which reprecipitates on neutralization; gamma-cellulose is that fraction which remains in solution after neutralization. The latter two fractions are low molecular weight cellulose and polysaccharides other than cellulose. Most indus-

trial dissolving or chemical pulp contain better than 90% and in some cases as high as 97% alpha-cellulose on a dry basis. The remaining contaminants consist of non-cellulosic carbohydrates, organic resins and inorganic impurities.

In general, cotton linters pulp is purer than wood pulps and for this reason was originally used almost exclusively in the manufacture of fibers, films and plastics. However, extensive research on the part of pulping companies and fiber and plastic manufacturers has led to the increasing use of wood pulp, to the extent that it is the major cellulosic raw material in use today. Cotton linters pulp is generally more expensive than wood pulp and suffers from severe price fluctuation due to annual variations in the cotton crop.

J. P. DUX

CITRIC ACID AND ESTERS

Citric acid, $HOOCCH_2C(OH)(COOH) — CH_2COOH$, is a monohydroxy tricarboxylic acid, best known for its application in food and pharmaceutical products for human consumption. Its polyfunctional structure, however, also establishes it as an appropriate raw material in the field of synthetic resins, for the preparation of plasticizers and polycondensation products.

Manufacture

Citric acid is produced by fermentation with certain strains of mold such as *Aspergillus niger*, and limited quantities are also recovered from lemon juice and pineapple wastes.

Properties

Anhydrous citric acid USP ($C_6H_8O_7$), formula weight 192.12, occurs in the form of colorless, translucent, monoclinic crystals, mp 153°C, sp. gr 1.665. The dissociation constants of the three hydrogen atoms at 18°C are 8.2×10^{-4}, 1.77×10^{-5}, and 3.9×10^{-6}, respectively. A saturated water solution at 20°C contains 59.2% citric acid by weight. The acid is moderately soluble in alcohol, sparingly soluble in ether

Although the anhydrous form is usually preferred for condensation reactions, citric acid is also available as a monohydrate, Citric Acid USP ($C_6H_8O_7 \cdot H_2O$), containing 8.58% water. The hydrate occurs in the form of colorless, translucent, orthorhombic crystals, sp. gr. 1.542, which soften on gentle heating at 70–75°C with loss of water and melt at 135–152°C. Upon rapid heating, the crystals melt at 100°C with loss of water, resolidify as they become anhydrous, and finally melt sharply at 153°C.

The commercially available trialkyl esters of citric acid, including those in which the hydroxyl group has been acetylated, are clear, colorless, high-boiling liquids, miscible with most organic solvents. The tricyclohexyl ester differs from the open-chain esters in being a solid, melting at 56°C. Physical properties are given in Table 1, and commercial specifications in Table 2. Boiling point and flash point rise with increasing molecular weight of the esterifying alcohol, and also with acetyla-tion of the hydroxyl group. Water resistance follows the same trend, and triethyl citrate is unique among the listed esters as being slightly water-soluble and relatively insoluble in oils and greases. Triethyl citrate is miscible with mineral oil to the extent of only 0.8 ml per 100 ml, versus a value of 90 ml per 100 ml for tributyl citrate. The

TABLE 1. PHYSICAL PROPERTIES OF CITRIC ACID ESTERS.

	Tri-ethyl citrate	Acetyl tri-ethyl citrate	Tri-n-butyl citrate	Acetyl tri-n-butyl citrate	Tri-cyclo-hexyl citrate	Acetyl tri(2-ethyl-hexyl) citrate	Acetyl tri(n-octyl, n-decyl) citrate	Triallyl citrate
Formula weight	276.3	318.3	360.4	402.5	438.5	570.8	—	312.3
Sp. gr. 25°/25°C	1.136	1.135^{23}	1.042	1.048	1.7	0.983	0.971	1.144^{20}_{4}
Bp at 1 mm, °C	126–7	131–2	169–70	172–4	(mp 57°)	225	—	$143^{0.4}$
n^{25}_{D}	1.440	1.438	1.443	1.441	—	1.441	1.449	1.469
H_2O soln at 25°C, g/100 ml	6.50	0.72	<0.002	<0.002	—	insol.	insol.	—
Viscosity at 25°C, cp	35.2	53.7	31.9	42.7	—	80.0	51.0	—
Pour point, °F	−50	−45	−80	−75	—	−67	−75	—
Flash point, °C (Cleveland open cup)	155	188	185	204	—	224	249	—

TABLE 2. COMMERCIAL SPECIFICATIONS OF CITRIC ACID ESTERS.

	Triethyl citrate	Acetyl triethyl citrate	Tri-n-butyl citrate	Acetyl tri-n-butyl citrate	Tricyclo-hexyl citrate	Acetyl tri(2-ethylhexyl) citrate	Acetyl tri(n-octyl, n-decyl) citrate
Assay, min., %	99.0	99.0	99.0	99.0	99.0	99.0	99.0
Acidity, max., % citric acid	0.02	0.02	0.02	0.02	0.1	0.02	0.01
Color, max., APHA	50	50	50	50	100	50	75
% water, max.	0.25	0.30	0.30	0.25	0.25	0.30	0.25

TABLE 3. COMPATIBILITY OF CITRIC ACID ESTERS WITH RESINS.

	Triethyl citrate	Acetyl triethyl citrate	Tri-n-butyl citrate	Acetyl tri-n-butyl citrate	Tricyclo-hexyl citrate	Acetyl tri(2-ethylhexyl) citrate
Cellulose acetate	C	C	P	P	I	P
Cellulose acetate butyrate	C	C	P	P	—	P
Cellulose nitrate	C	C	C	C	C	C
Ethylcellulose	C	C	C	C	C	P
Polyvinyl chloride	C	C	C	C	C	C
Polyvinyl chloride-acetate	C	C	C	C	—	C
Polyvinyl-vinylidene chloride	C	C	C	C	—	C
Polyvinyl acetate	C	C	C	C	C	I
Polyvinyl butyral	C	C	C	C	C	I
Chlorinated rubber	C	C	C	C	C	I

C = compatible, P = partially compatible, I = incompatible.

stability of the acetylated esters is exemplified by the fact that acetyl triethyl and acetyl tributyl citrates fail to hydrolyze after 6 hr in boiling water. Triethyl and tributyl citrates do not support fungus growth.

The compatibility of commercial citrates with resins is summarized in Table 3. In general, these esters are compatible with vinyl and cellulosic resins, although complete compatibility with cellulose acetate resins is confined to the ethyl citrates.

Toxicity. An outstanding property of the citrates is their low toxicity. Tributyl and acetyl tributyl citrates are nontoxic by the oral route in the cat and the rat. They have been reported to produce no local irritation or systemic effect at single doses as high as 30–50 cc per kg. Rats showed no toxic symptoms after two years on a diet containing 20,000 ppm acetyl tributyl citrate, and dogs receiving 140 mg of this ester daily for a like period were also free of adverse effect. The LD_{50} of the two corresponding ethyl esters has been reported to be 7 cc per kg in the rat. When mixed in the diet, the ethyl esters have been fed to rats at daily doses up to 4 cc per kg for 6 weeks without toxic effect.

Applications of Citric Acid Esters

Triethyl citrate and *acetyl triethyl citrate* are solvent plasticizers for cellulose acetate and cellulose acetate-butyrate (Tables 4 and 5), and both have been accepted for use in plastic food wraps

TABLE 4. PROPERTIES OF PLASTICIZED CELLULOSE ACETATE FILMS.

Plasticizer	Triethyl citrate	Acetyl triethyl citrate
Conc. based on resin, %	33.3	33.3
Tensile strength, psi	6500	6300
Elongation, %	21.9	23
Adhesion to metal, after 7 days' water immersion	fair	fair

TABLE 5. PROPERTIES OF PLASTICIZED CELLULOSE ACETATE MOLDINGS.

Plasticizer	Acetyl triethyl citrate	Dimethyl phthalate
Conc. based on resin, %	35	35
Rockwell hardness	M43	M34
Impact strength (Charpy), ft lb/in.	5.6	5.6
Volatile loss, 48 hr at 130°C, %	20.0	21.1
Warp (ASTM D741 modified), in.	1/32	7/8
Water absorption, 48 hr, %	1.60	1.06

by F.D.A., and the Keuringsdienst van Waren of the Netherlands. Triethyl citrate is especially

TABLE 6. PROPERTIES OF PLASTICIZED CELLULOSE NITRATE FILMS.

Plasticizer	Triethyl citrate	Acetyl triethyl citrate	Tri-*n*-butyl citrate	Acetyl tri-*n*-butyl citrate	Dibutyl phthalate
Volatile loss[a], 100–105°C					
24 hr, %	30.0	25.0	12.0	8.0	32.5
48 hr, %	33.5	26.0	14.5	11.5	34.0
172 hr, %	35.	32.0	24.0	23.5	36.0
Adhesion to metal, after 7 weeks' water immersion	lifted badly	very good	lifted	very good	lifted slightly
Tensile strength					
10% ester, kg/cm²	647	618	538	670	696
25% ester, kg/cm²	575	595	561	615	610
33.3% ester, kg/cm²	500	582	455	556	522
Elongation					
10% ester, %	3	5	3	8	5
25% ester, %	6	10	5	8	7
33.3% ester, %	6	15	5	8	7
Ultraviolet yellowing[b]					
10% ester, color units	1.2	1.9	1.3	1.8	6.0
25% ester, color units	0.8	1.8	1.1	0.9	7.3
33.3% ester, color units	1.3	2.2	1.1	1.1	7.2
Water permeability[c], g	3.80	—	3.13	—	3.24

[a]Plasticizer conc., 37.5%.
[b]Hunt reflectometer, 5 hr (unexposed control: 1.1 color unit).
[c]Plasticizer conc., 25%.

useful in formulations where high grease resistance is needed. Acetyl triethyl citrate has also been accepted by the Meat Inspection Branch of the US Department of Agriculture, and is likewise approved as a plasticizer in aerosol hair sprays and bandages by the F.D.A. The ethyl esters are also plasticizers for cellulose nitrate (Table 6), and the light stability they confer is advantageous in lacquer formulations. The ethyl citrates are also efficient plasticizers for vinyl chloride resins, but volatility precludes their use as primary plasticizers in this application.

Triethyl citrate has been reported to be a useful plasticizer for polyvinyl butyral and for natural resins such as dammar and ester gum, as well as a reactive plasticizer for phenol-formaldehyde resins. Acetyl triethyl citrate has been recommended as a plasticizer for ethyl cellulose and as a stabilizer for polyvinylidene chloride.

Tributyl citrate and *acetyl tributyl citrate* are effective plasticizers for vinyl chloride polymers and copolymers. Though somewhat more volatile than dioctyl phthalate, these esters impart a softer "hand" and may be used as partial or complete replacements for dioctyl phthalate in many formulations. Because of their freedom from toxicity, the butyl citrates find significant use in formulations intended for food packaging, beverage tubing, children's toys and products which come in contact with the human body. Vinyl films containing acetyl tributyl citrate are notable for good water- and oil-resistance (Table 7), as well as heat- and light-stability of a high order. The odor-free nature of this ester particularly recommends it for dairy product cartons, soft drink bottle caps and preserve jar cap seals. Acetyl tributyl citrate has been accepted for use in plastic

food wraps for both fatty and non-fatty foods by the F.D.A., and the Keuringsdienst van Waren of the Netherlands. It has also been accepted for use in plastic meat wraps by the Bureau of Animal Industry of the US Department of Agriculture and by the Office of the Quartermaster General; and for use as a plasticizer in aerosol hair spray and bandages by the F.D.A.

The butyl citrates are appropriate plasticizers for cellulose-based lacquers employed in food packaging. Cellulose nitrate films containing these esters exhibit lower volatile loss and are less susceptible to yellowing on exposure to ultraviolet light than films plasticized with dibutyl phthalate. Cellulose nitrate films containing acetyl tributyl citrate also exhibit better adhesion to metals (Table 6).

Tributyl citrate has been recommended as a plasticizer for polyvinyl acetal resins and as an antifoam agent in casein solutions. Acetyl tributyl citrate is useful in polyvinyl acetate adhesives, and as a stabilizer in polyvinylidene chloride.

The higher alkyl esters, *tri(2-ethylhexyl) citrate*, *acetyl tri(2-ethylhexyl) citrate* and *acetyl tri(n-octyl, n-decyl) citrate* find application in polyvinyl chloride resins where low volatility and good low temperature flexibility are required (Table 7). Volatile loss with acetyl tri-(2-ethylhexyl) citrate is approximately one-fourth of that encountered with the same level of dioctyl phthalate; brittle temperatures are comparable. This ester has also been described as a useful stabilizer for polyvinylidene chloride. *Tricyclohexyl citrate*, as a low-melting solid, is an appropriate plasticizer for heat-sealing compositions.

Triallyl citrate (Table 1) and *acetyl triallyl citrate* polymerize in the presence of peroxide

TABLE 7. PROPERTIES OF PLASTICIZED VINYL CHLORIDE POLYMERS.

Plasticizer	Tri-*n*-butyl citrate	Acetyl tri-*n*-butyl citrate	Acetyl tri-*n*-butyl citrate	Tri(2-ethyl-hexyl) citrate	Acetyl tri(2-ethyl-hexyl) citrate	Acetyl tri(*n*-octyl, *n*-decyl) citrate
Conc., PHR	50	50	70	P70	70	50
Resin	PVC-A	PVC-A	PVC-A	PVC-A	PVC-A	PVC
100% modulus[a], psi	1200	1400	700	925	1065	1680
Tensile strength[a], psi	2600	2600	2025	2035	2200	2320
Elongation[a], %	350	340	340	325	320	260
Brittle temp.[b], °C	−30	−25	−39	−46	−38	−35
Water absorption[c], %	0.31	0.24	0.21	0.17	0.11	—
Oil extraction[d], %	1.48	0.60	1.60	1.71	2.71	0.8

[a]ASTM D412,
[b]ASTM D746.
[c]ASTM D570.
[d]ASTM D543, No. 3 oil.
PVC = polyvinyl chloride.
PVC-A = 95% vinyl chloride—5% vinyl acetate copolymer.

catalysts to hard, brittle polymers of high heat distortion temperature.

Applications of Citric Acid

As a polyfunctional compound, citric acid is a useful raw material for condensation polymers. Heating with an excess of glycerol yields a triester which may be baked at 160°C to provide water-resistant finishes. Glyceryl citrates have also been employed in adhesives and cloth-coating. Other polyesters useful in varnishes have been prepared by condensation of citric acid with castor oil, with pentaerythritol, and with various glycols. Unsaturated resins which may be copolymerized with acrylate monomers for casting and laminating are obtained by mixed esterification of citric acid with allyl alcohol and glycols.

Low concentrations of citric acid prevent premature gelation of certain lacquers, and enhance heat- and light-stability of ethyl cellulose molding compounds. Metal salts of citric acid partial esters have promise as resin stabilizers. The dialkyl tin derivatives of citric acid monoesters are useful for this purpose in polyvinyl chloride resins.

Commercial

Citric acid is marketed as USP Anhydrous and USP Hydrous (monohydrate) in powder, granular and fine granular forms, in bags and drums. Esters are available in drums and tank cars. Approximate prices (1965) are given in Table 8. In

TABLE 8. APPROXIMATE PRICES OF CITRIC ACID AND ESTERS.

Citric acid USP, anhydrous (C/L)	$0.30
Citric acid USP, monohydrate (C/L)	0.30
Triethyl citrate (tank cars)	0.43
Acetyl triethyl citrate (tank cars)	0.355
Tri-*n*-butyl citrate (tank cars)	0.385
Acetyl tri-*n*-butyl citrate (tank cars)	0.315
Tricyclohexyl citrate (drums)	0.485
Tri(*n*-octyl, *n*-decyl) citrate (tank cars)	0.50

addition to the listed esters, tri(2-ethylhexyl) and acetyl tri(2-ethylhexyl) citrates are available in development quantities.

CHARLES J. KNUTH

COLD MOLDING MATERIALS

Cold molded plastics were introduced into the United States by Emile Hemming, Sr., around 1900. They differ considerably from the more common plastics molding materials in that they are neither thermoplastic nor thermosetting. The parts, when removed from the steel die, must be baked in an oven which hardens them because of oxidation and polymerization of the constituent oils and binder materials.

Cold molded plastics fall into two main categories based on the types of binders employed: organic and inorganic, or the refractory type. The organic materials are divided into two types: bituminous and synthetic resins. Asbestos is a common filler for both types. Each cold-molding compound is a proprietary product and specific formulas vary with the applications.

TABLE 1. BASIC TYPES OF COLD-MOLDING MATERIALS.

Class	Type of binder	Type of filler
Organic (bituminous)	asphaltic	asbestos
Organic (synthetic resin)	phenolic	asbestos
Inorganic (refractory)	silica-lime cements	asbestos

Non-refractory (Bituminous) Binder. This compound basically consists of an organic binder such as asphalt, gilsonite, stearine pitch blended with oils such as linseed, castor and tung to form a varnish-like resin. This resin is thinned to the desired consistency with solvents and mixed with asbestos fiber in a mixing or kneading machine resembling a doughmixer. The compound is allowed to age after which it is ground, then screened, and is ready for molding.

Organic Binder-Synthetic Resin-Phenolic Binder. A phenolic resin is treated with a solvent to produce a solution of the proper viscosity; it is then mixed with asbestos fiber, ground and screened to the proper size for molding.

Both of the above types of materials are used to produce switch bases, attachment plugs and caps, sockets, outlet covers, handles and knobs on heating appliances. The molded parts have excellent heat and weather resistance properties.

Inorganic Binder or Refractory. This type consists of asbestos as a filler and cement-water binder. The compound is composed mostly of calcium hydrate, fine silica, cement and asbestos fiber. The lime and silica combine, after molding by treatment under steam pressure, to a silica-lime cement. The asbestos furnishes the mechanical strengthening structure. The silica-lime cement is better for plastics than the cement mixture, but it does not have the ability to stand temperatures as high as the cement type.

The material is usually white or grayish in color; the molded parts are dried in an oven to remove moisture and then treated under steamed pressure, after which they are dried again. Moisture absorption of this material can be reduced by impregnating with oils or waxes. Parts produced from this material has superior heat and arc-resistance properties, and does not track or carbonize.

All of these compounds are pressed into shape with pressure alone using hardened tool steel dies. Production is rapid as high as 4000-5000 pieces per day. The molds are usually of single cavity design and operated at room temperature.

TABLE 2. ADVANTAGES OF COLD-MOLDING MATERIALS

1. Rapid molding cycle (500–800 pieces per hr from a single-cavity mold)
2. Low mold cost
3. Abundant raw materials
4. High heat-resistance
5. High arc-resistance

After the pieces have been molded, baking is required to harden the parts containing the organic binders. The molds wear rapidly because of the abrasive content of the molding compounds. All of these cold-molded articles can be produced with metal inserts molded into place.

The molding presses used to produce the parts are usually hydraulically operated, and it is customary to apply 4000 psi pressure over the projected area of the piece. Cold-molded articles usually lack the surface smoothness and appearance characteristic of many of the thermosetting and thermoplastic molded parts. However, it is possible in some cases to improve the appearance of the parts by polishing or a tumbling operation.

TABLE 3. PROPERTIES OF TYPICAL COLD-MOLDING COMPOUNDS.

Property or constituent	Organic type	Inorganic type
Binder	Asphalt or phenolic	Cement
Filler	Asbestos	Asbestos
Color	Black or brown	Gray-white
Finish	Good	Poor
Specific gravity	2.0	2.3
Tensile strength, psi	1500–2000	500–600
Compressive strength, psi	6000–15,000	16,000
Flexural strength, psi	3700–9300	1400–4700
Transverse strength, psi	3700–4000	5000–8000
Impact strength, ft lb per in. of notch, $1/2 \times 1/2$ in., notched bar—Izod test	0.4	0.4
Dielectric strength, vpm	50–100–140	40–80
Water absorption, % per 24 hr	0.6–7.5	0.5–2.6
Heat resistance, °F	500–600	1000

Source: American Insulator Corp. Data on organic types are based on properties of this company's Aico No. 1 (asphalt binder) and Aico No. 6 (phenolic binder); on the inorganic on Aico No. 5 (cement binder).

Machining of the molded parts is possible but not recommended because of the high percentage of asbestos in the material which soon dulls the cutting edge of the tool. Drilling of holes is possible, but tapping is never recommended. When machining is required, the cutting edges of the tools are usually tipped with carboloy or a diamond.

Because of the shrinkage factor, it is generally impossible to hold pieces within the close tolerance specified for thermosetting materials. The color of these molded parts are usually black or gray in the inorganic type of material. Generally, the phenolic-type molding compound produces a molded part with superior mechanical and electrical properties, also possessing an improved surface finish. Both types of materials can stand high operating temperatures—organic 600°F, and inorganic 1000°F. They resist most alkalies and solvents and are nontoxic. Because of the high production rates obtainable and low material costs, the molded parts are relatively low in cost. Research in cold-molding plastics is continuous, and there is every expectation that the field of applications will grow as the materials continue to be improved both in quality and appearance. An interesting trend, still in the developmental stage, is the use of other than phenolic-formaldehyde resins for binders in the synthetic resin class, and the use of newer types of pigments to improve the appearance.

B. FRANK HANTZ

COLORATION OF PLASTICS

In coloring plastics, pigments are the materials used chiefly. Dyes are used to a considerably less extent because of limitations in heat resistance, lightfastness, and solubility. Whether pigments or dyes are used, the choice of colorant must be made with careful consideration of its physical and chemical characteristics, making certain the colorant properties are compatible with (1) the method of processing, and (2) the characteristics desired in the final product. Among the most important factors to be considered are:
(1) Heat stability.
(2) Dispersibility.
(3) Lightfastness.
(4) Chemical inertness.
(5) Solubility.
(6) Opacity or transparency.
(7) Tinctorial properties.
(8) Electrical characteristics.

Heat stability is an important, and sometimes limiting factor in colorant selections. Thermoplastic resins are processed at temperatures ranging from 300–700°F. Thermosetting resins although processed at low temperatures, may be used continuously at high temperatures.

Dispersibility considerations are related to the method of incorporating the color in the plastic. Dry coloring (in which colorant and resin are tumble-mixed before extruding or molding), while a simple method, sometimes fails to bring out optimum color quality and uniformity. In such cases, more vigorous means of dispersion are required; where conditions permit, predispersion in plasticizer is very effective.

Lightfastness requirements are dictated by the end-use requirements. While pigments usually are superior to dyes in this characteristic, they vary widely and must be selected with care.

Chemical inertness is important, not only from end-use considerations (ability to withstand alkalies, detergents, acids, etc.) but also from considerations of reactivity with the polymer being colored. Reactions that might take place between the colorant and the plastic or the anti-oxidants, catalysts or other additives making up the composition, should be known. As examples, certain iron and manganese-containing pigments can accelerate degradation of polyvinyl chloride while zinc and manganese are detrimental to polyethylene. On the other hand, basic lead pigments have a stabilizing effect on the vinyls.

If the colorant is soluble in the polymer composition, the possibility of migration, i.e., the appearance on the polymer surface of a loosely adherent dry powder exists. This phenomenon, also described as crocking, is objectionable in many end-use applications.

Terminology

A pigment is a material insoluble (or essentially so) in the medium in which it is dispersed, added to the medium to give color and/or opacity. A pigment which is completely insoluble is said to be "non-bleeding," whereas one that has some solubility under conditions of practical use is said to "bleed." Bleeding pigments tend to migrate and crock in plastic systems; non-bleeding types do not.

Colors of any particular chemical type are frequently marketed in a number of physical forms, namely:

(1) Full strength.
(2) Resinated.
(3) Extended ("Lakes").
(4) Dispersions:
  (a) Aqueous,
  (b) Nonaqueous.

Full strength organic colors are known as "toners." Resinated colors are organic toners to which metallic resinates have been added to improve certain properties, chiefly texture.

Extended colors are those in which about 50%–90% is an inorganic base such as alumina hydrate, blanc fixe, whiting, and clay. With the exception of the cadmium pigments, very few extended inorganic colors are marketed at the present time since they are relatively uneconomical. Most of the extended colors are organic, and in this case, are frequently termed "lakes." Classically, the term "laking" involved chemical interaction or sorption of dyes on inorganic substrates. Today, the trade refers to most extended organic colors as "lakes," regardless of whether the substrate is present in physical admixture or in chemical combination.

Aqueous dispersions are smooth, fluid dispersions of pigments in water containing surface active agents. They are used in pigmenting aqueous systems such as plastic emulsions and elastomer latices. Nonaqueous dispersions are pigment dispersions in organic media compatible in the plastic systems for which they are intended to be used. Flushed color, i.e., colors transferred directly from presscake form to a vehicle, fall in this category.

Regardless of the physical form in which a color is used, the chemical aspects of its behavior remain a function of chemical constitution of the coloring matter itself. Accordingly, the following discussion of the chemical types given in Table I relates each type to its suitability as a colorant of for plastics.

Pigments

In considering colors, systematic classification is of real value. Classification by hue is one possibility; more helpful classifications, from a technical viewpoint, are those based on chemical structure. Table 1 shows such a classification for pigment colors of particular interest to the plastics industry.

TABLE 1. CLASSIFICATION OF PIGMENT COLORS.

(A) *Inorganic*
  (1) Chromate
  (2) Ferrocyanides
  (3) Sulfides and Selenides
  (4) Oxides
  (5) Silicates, Aluminates and Titanates
(B) *Organic*
  (1) Azo
  (2) Phthalocyanines
  (3) Quinacridones

Certain broad generalizations can be made on the basis of a classification such as this. First, the inorganic pigments are completely insoluble in organic vehicles, whereas many of the organics (but not all) are very slightly soluble. Inorganic pigments are generally higher in specific gravity. The organic pigments are usually more costly on a weight basis, but sometimes economically competitive by virtue of their higher strength. Inorganic colors tend to be more opaque, organics more transparent. Except for the earth colors, Van Dyke brown and a few others, all pigment colors of commerce are synthetic.

Chromate Pigments. Chrome yellows can be used satisfactorily in plastics at moderate processing temperatures (approx. 400°F); in fact, they help to stabilize vinyl to heat. They are available in a variety of bright, non-bleeding shades, have good hiding and low cost; and the light and medium shades have moderately good lightfastness. They are alkali-sensitive, however, and are subject to discoloration from sulfides. Because of the lead content, toxicity may limit their use. The medium chrome yellows are essentially normal lead chromate, whereas the lighter shades contain lead sulfate coprecipitated with the lead chromate. A special shade known as "greening" or "shading" yellow is used for making greens by blending with blue.

Chrome oranges are basic lead chromates, and find little use in plastics since they are weak and lack brilliance. Molybdate orange, a coprecipitation of lead chromate, molybdate, and sulfate, is a very strong and brilliant orange with properties similar to the chrome yellows. It is widely used not only as a self-color, but in blends with chrome yellows to give light oranges, and with quinacridone violet to give reds.

Ferrocyanides. The major pigment type in the ferrocyanide class is iron blue. Iron blues have limited acceptance in plastics because of only moderate heat stability, high sensitivity to alkali, and tendency to accelerate degradation of vinyl and polyolefins on exposure. Blends of irion blue with chrome yellow, marketed as chrome greens, also have limited acceptance.

Sulfides and Selenides. The sulfide-selenide pigments, or the so-called "cadmium" or "mercury-cadmium" colors consist of cadmium sulfide alone, or coprecipitated with selenium, zinc, or mercury. They range in hue from pale yellow thru orange and red shades, to maroon. They are available as "pure," i.e., 100% color, or as lithopones, i.e., coprecipitated with approximately 70% barium sulfate. Depth of hue is obtained through increasing amounts of selenium or mercury; lightness is obtained with zinc.

Cadmium yellows, oranges, and reds are used extensively in plastics because of their excellent heat resistance, their variety of bright, non-bleeding shades, and good lightfastness, except in acid atmospheres. Chief disadvantages are their high cost, low strength and sensitivity to acidic materials.

Oxides. Iron oxide provides a gamut of hues ranging from dull yellow thru red, brown, and black. Synthetic yellow iron oxides find wide use in plastics because of their low cost, good lightfastness, and resistance to chemicals and solvents. At sufficiently high temperatures (300–400°F), or

long periods at lower temperatures, they lose their water of hydration and revert to the red iron oxide color. Other limitations are their low color intensity and possible degradative effect on some vinyl resins that have not been properly stabilized.

Synthetic red iron oxides are also used extensively because of excellent heat and light stability and inertness to most chemicals and solvents. They are low cost, high hiding pigments, but are dull in shade. Like the yellow oxides, their use in vinyl may require special stabilizing considerations.

Chromium oxide provides a green of excellent heat stability, lightfastness, and chemical stability. However, its lower color intensity and relatively high cost, compared to phthalocyanine green, limits its use.

Silicates, Aluminates and Titanates. The silicate-aluminate-titanate group contains a variety of colors of limited but nevertheless important use. Ultramarine blue, an alumino-silicate pigment, is a very intense and red shade blue and is used in plastics because of its excellent heat resistance. Main disadvantages are its low strength-high cost relationship, sensitivity to acids, and hard grinding characteristics.

Cobalt blue, a calcined cobalt aluminate, is a bright blue of high transparency and exceptional heat resistance and lightfastness. Its low tinting strength and relatively high price limtit its use.

The titanium dioxide-treated silicate flake pigments, identified by the name "Afflair,"* are lightfast, chemical, and heat resistant nacreous types, ranging from pearl to deep gold in shade. They are used to give novel pearlescent effects.

Nickel titanates are yellows of excellent heat resistance and lightfastness and very resistant to chemical attack. Their usefulness is limited, however, by their low strength and low chroma.

Azo Pigments

Of the organic pigments the azo pigments, i.e., those in which the chromophore is the azo group ($-N=N-$), are used most widely in the plastics industry, particularly in formulating reds. They are found in two classes: (1) the so-called pigment dye type which contain no metal, and (2) the metallized types in which a precipitating metal such as calcium, barium, or nickel is used for insolubilizing the pigment.

The latter group is most widely used in the plastics industry; "Permanent Red 2B" (6-chlor, 4-toluidine, 3-sulfonic acid → 3-hydroxy, 2-naphthoic acid)†, the one most widely used since it is

---

* Du Pont registered trademark.

† The description given in parentheses describes the amine derivative coupled to the naphthol derivative to form the azo compound. This is a simple way of describing azo pigment composition. Of course, in metallized types the free acid groups react with the metal used for precipitation.

available in a variety of shades, is strong and bright in color, relatively low in cost, and has acceptable heat stability under many conditions of use. "Red 2B" is resistant to bleeding and crocking. However, its metal component is subject to substitution or stripping under certain conditions of stabilization (stabilizers containing other metals) and heat, with the result that color, heat stability, and bleed resistance might be affected. This pigment group is also prone to "plate-out" from vinyl formulations onto the surfaces of processing equipment; this condition can usually be minimized by adjustment in stabilizers or lubricants. The "Red 2B" pigments have fair lightfastness in high concentration masstone shades, but poor lightfastness in extensions. Shades range from a light yellow-toned red (barium precipitation), through dark red and maroon (calcium-strontium precipitates).

The BON reds are manganese precipitated "Permanent Red 2B" pigments, comparable to the calcium types in heat stability; however, these are of less intense color and more lightfast in masstone shade and tint. Because of the manganese content, BONs tend to accelerate degradation of polyolefins and may cause rancidity in vinyl if used in company with an oxidizable component (plasticizer, stabilizer, lubricant).

Other precipitated azo reds of importance to the plastics industry are lithol rubine (4-aminotoluene, 3-sulfonic acid → 3-hydroxy, 2-naphthoic acid-Ca) and pigment scarlet (anthranilic acid → R-salt). Lithol rubine is similar to the darker "Permanent Red 2B-Ca" pigments, but poorer in heat and light stability. Pigment scarlet is laked on a zinc oxide-aluminum base; the zinc may accelerate degradation of vinyls and polyolefins under some conditions. Tinctorially it is similar to "Permanent Red 2B-Ca."

Use of azo organic yellows in plastics is restricted chiefly by heat and bleed limitations. The benzidine yellows are the most popular because of their very high strength, intense color, and resistance to acids and alkali. However, they tend to crock and migrate in many systems and have poor lightfastness except in dark shades. The principal types of interest are the OT and OA varieties.* The latter has better light and heat stability in some systems (e.g., polyethylene), but is higher in cost. Benzidine yellows have good electrical properties and are widely used in extruded wire coatings.

Green-Gold (p-choraniline → 2,4-dihydroxyquinoline-Ni) is a greenish yellow of interest because of its good tint lightfastness. Depending on formulation and processing, however, it may

* "Benzidine Yellow OT" (Dichlorobenzidine → acetoacet-o-anisidide). "Benzidine Yellow OA" (Dichlorobenzidine → acetoacet-o-toluidide).

show some crocking and migration tendencies, and the possibility of chemical attack and demetallization of the Green-Gold with resultant bad bleed and poor lightfastness.

Phthalocyanines. Phthalocyanine pigments are available as blues (copper phthalocyanine) and greens (halogenated copper phthalocyanines), both the most important types in their respective hue categories. They are lightfast and sufficiently heat stable for most applications, although the blue may burn out in low concentrations at high temperatures. The blue is available in a red tone (alpha-type) and a greenish toner (beta).

The most widely used phthalocyanine green is the chlorinated type.

Quinacridones. The quinacridone pigments cover a range of scarlets, reds, violets, and maroons, which, by virtue of their brilliance, lightfastness, chemical resistance, and heat stability, are assuming a position comparable to that of the phthalocyanines in the industry. The violet serves as an excellent blending color with molybdate orange to produce bright, low cost reds of good quality.

Dyes

Dyes are used to a limited extent in coloring plastics since most of them migrate in vinyls and polyolefins. Furthermore, the processing temperatures of many thermoplastics are usually too high to permit the use of many dyes. As in the case of pigments, when dyes are used they must be carefully selected on the basis of end-use and processing requirements.

Rigid thermoplastics can be colored with dyes when good transparency and brilliance are required. Polystyrene and acrylic resins are typical examples. As little as 0.05% will provide good depth of coloration to polystyrene, thereby affording significant economy over pigments. The dye is incorporated by tumbling with crystal polystyrene cubes, followed by compounding in an extruder, and subsequent injection molding. The use of a screw-type injection molding machine will circumvent the extruding operation. Titanium dioxide and aluminum powder may also be used in conjunction with the dye, to obtain opacity when desired. The dyes employed are a selected group of oil dyes and disperse dyes. Lightfastness ratings vary with the individual dyes; anthraquinone types which darken (rather than fade) on extended exposure are usually favored.

Dyes are used in acrylic lenses, such as automobile taillights, and for coloration of transparent or translucent acrylic panels. In the latter instance, the dye (about 0.1%) may be dissolved in partially polymerized syrup together with the catalyst, poured into a mold, and cured. Since most dyes are deleteriously affected by peroxide catalysts, the use of a milder polymerization catalyst such as azobisisobutyronitrile (e.g., Du Pont's "VAZO"*) is required.

Polyester and epoxy resins are also candidates for coloration with dyes, where transparency and economy are desired. In the case of polyesters, a mild catalyst such as "VAZO" is suggested in place of methyl ethyl ketone peroxide. For epoxy resin, the dye may be dissolved in the polyamine hardener and thereby achieve a colored resin with a minimum of cost and processing.

Dyes are useful in the coloration of cellulosics, where compounding is usually effected with a heavy-duty roller mill. A typical example of this application is the tinting of automobile windshield interlamination.

Dyes may also be used for surface coloration of many thermoplastic and thermosetting resins. For example, molded nylon parts may be dyed by dipping for approximately 5 min at 180° F in dilute acetic acid solution containing an acid dye. Dyeing time may be reduced to a few seconds by inclusion of about 3% benzyl alcohol. Such a technique is employed for continuous dyeing of nylon-coated wire. Disperse dyes are useful for surface coloration of most resins in an aqueous bath at 180–200° F in the presence of a small amount of ethanol and a surfactant.

In brief, where maximum transparency, brilliance, and economy are desired, dyes are used provided there are no problems of migration, lightfastness, and heat stability.

W. F. SPENGEMAN

Cross-references: DYES AND PIGMENTS; ORGANIC COLORANTS

CRAMBE VEGETABLE OIL

The new oilseed crambe is an agricultural commodity that provides a vegetable oil rich in esterified erucic acid. The purpose here is to indicate the versatility of uses in the plastics industry for this type of raw material, which has only recently become available from domestic sources.

Background

Crambe abyssinica, or crambe, is an annual plant of the mustard family which originated in the Mediterranean area. Recently it has been found adapted to growth in several regions of the United States, particularly the northwestern and northern and central midwestern parts of the country. Crambe also has potential as a winter crop in Texas. Its attractiveness as a new farm crop derives from ready growth without serious insect or disease problems, high yielding poten-

* Du Pont registered trademark.

tial, amenability to mechanical harvest with conventional small grain combines and, of course, marketability of derived products. Crambe was first grown in the US commercially in 1965.

Crambe is useful because of its oil-rich seed. The seed as harvested occurs in a loosely adherent pericarp (hull) (Fig. 1). Seed plus pericarp contains about 31% oil and 23% protein. The seed

FIG. 1. Dark green crambe seed in a thin, light tan hull.

with pericarp removed has about 45% oil and 30% protein. Conventional equipment used for other oilseeds is applicable for processing crambe seed into oil and a protein-rich meal (Fig. 2).

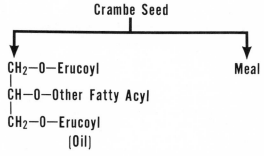

FIG. 2. Crambe seed when processed yields a glyceride oil and a high-protein meal.

Nature of Crambe Oil

Like other vegetable oils, crambe seed oil is mainly a triester of glycerol with long-chain fatty acids. However, crambe is chemically unlike other vegetable oils commercially produced in the United States. Between 55 and 60% of the acids in crambe glycerides is the 22-carbon straight-chain monounsaturated acid, erucic acid (cis-13-docosenoic acid); none of this component is contained in soybean, linseed, cottonseed, corn, or peanut oils. Unique uses for crambe oil stem from this difference in chemical composition. Crambe oil resembles rapeseed oil in composition, but contains more erucic acid than oil from rape.

The esterified erucic acid in crambe oil has been shown to occur primarily on the 1- and 3-carbon atoms of glycerol. Thus, the most frequently occurring molecular species in crambe oil may be represented diagrammatically as shown in Fig. 2. The typical fatty acid analysis of crambe oil, and some selected properties, are listed in Table 1.

TABLE 1. TYPICAL COMPOSITION[a] AND PROPERTIES OF CRAMBE SEED OIL.

Fatty acid	
Myristic %	0.1
Palmitic %	2
Palmitoleic %	0.3
Stearic %	0.7
Oleic %	16
Linoleic %	9
Linolenic %	6
Arachidic %	0.7
Eicosenoic %	3
Behenic %	3
Erucic %	57
Docosadienoic %	0.2
Tetracosenoic %	1
Iodine value	92
Sp. gr. 25°/4°C	0.939
Melting point, °C	~6
Viscosity, cps	85

[a] By gas-liquid chromatography of mixed methyl esters from the oil. Expressed as area percent of the individual ester in the total esters.

The iodine value, a conventionally used measure of unsaturation in vegetable oils, is consistent with the fatty acid composition found. Because of its relatively low extent of unsaturation, crambe oil has good oxidative stability. The viscosity of crambe oil is higher than that of other domestic oils, a property expected because of its large erucic acid content.

Uses for Crambe Oil

Crambe oil has threefold utility as a raw material: In the form of glyceride oil, as a source of erucic acid for the production of derivatives important as plastics additives, and as a source of 13-carbon compounds derived by chemical cleavage of erucic acid for use in preparing either ester plasticizers or polymerizable monomers for polyamides or polyesters.

Glyceride Oil. Crambe oil appears to be a preferred mold lubricant for the continuous casting of steel. The oil, when cross-linked with sulfur or sulfur monochloride, forms a factice useful as a rubber additive. Hydrogenation of the oil converts it to a white, solid wax.

Erucic Acid. Erucic acid may be obtained from crambe oil by any of the common commercial hydrolytic and fractionation techniques. The acid may be purified, or the mixed acids from crambe oil may be used as such if a higher erucic content is not required for the intended purpose. Recently, erucic acid amide has been reported to be a preferred additive for polyolefin films. Used at a level of 0.05–0.3%, the amide imparts good slip and antiblock characteristics to the film. Substituted amides of erucic acid or of fatty acid mixtures rich in erucic acid are primary plasticizers for vinyl resins, and show high efficiency, good compatibility, and low-temperature characteristics in the range of aliphatic diesters but with lesser volatility-loss.

13-Carbon Compounds. Since erucic acid is unsaturated between carbon atoms 13 and 14, it can be cleaved to provide a 13-carbon and a 9-carbon compound. Analogous to current commercial procedures for deriving azelaic and pelargonic acid from oleic acid, oxidative ozonolysis of erucic acid or of crambe oil acids provides brassylic acid or mixtures rich in this compound. Dialkyl brassylates are excellent low-temperature plasticizers for poly(vinyl chloride). Also, brassylic acid can form condensation polymers with diamines to provide a new family of nylons. Through other chemical routes starting with erucic acid, ω-aminotridecanoic acid can be produced and then polymerized to nylon-13. Preparation and evaluation of nylons-13, 13-13, and 13-9, plastic products expected to show toughness and low moisture regain, are under investigation.

Pelargonic acid obtained as a coproduct upon oxidation of erucic acid or mixed crambe acids has a wide spectrum of industrial uses.

IVAN A. WOLFF

D

DECORATION OF PLASTICS

Plastics have found their way into many diversified fields, and with every new introduction, the demand for decoration of some nature is universally heard. The method of decoration depends on several things, among them, the shape of the container, the equipment the customer has available, the design requested, the colors selected, and the product being packaged. An odd-shaped bottle, for instance, would not lend itself very well to offset or letterpress application. Silk screen, hot stamp or decal transfer would have to be used, unless foil colors or process art work is involved. By foil colors is meant bright metallic silver and gold, transparent blues, and transparent reds. For these, the hot stamp method of application is the best way to get the proper effects. Process work would have to be done with preprinted decals and then heat transferred to the substrate.

A most frustrating problem in the decorating field concerns the colors involved. The artist may choose specific shades which he thinks might be appealing, or it may be the customer's trademark color used for years. However, such may involve packaging a new detergent or shampoo, and the applied decoration must resist the product being packaged. Some of the shades chosen by the artist may limit the ink or label supplier to specific pigments. These pigments in turn may prove to be very poor for certain types of products. That is, they may not be resistant to such materials as alkalies, alcohols, essential oils and other items that might be generally found in the new household ingredients being used today. It is most important that every printed item be examined carefully to make sure that the product being packaged does not cause the ink to bleed or the film to leave the substrate. The final decoration may appear a bit dirtier or greener or redder, depending on the shades involved, if the product being packaged should affect the decoration. The big advantage of silk screen printing on any type of bottle is the thickness of film that can be applied. This result gives an excellent appearance and also aids resistance to scuff, rub and wear. The one disadvantage is the relatively slow speed in applying the decoration. Also, drying between colors is necessary, and therefore time consuming and costly.

Hot stamp limits the artist to line work, but the brightness of application cannot be obtained in any other manner.

Decals or heat transfer coatings are used where process work is required. This is an expensive method of decoration and requires expensive equipment. Small runs prohibit this method of decoration.

The plastic polyethylene tube is gradually replacing the metal collapsible tube for the packaging of many items. The dry offset method is used almost 100%, and this type of decoration can supply the trade with four colors and a topcoat at a relatively low cost. The method of application is usually made using mandrel presses with a varnishing unit attached. The most popular presses are Wifag (Switzerland), Montoli (Italy), Herland (Germany), and Rutherford (USA). The final design on the tube is effected by exact registration of colors. There is no overlapping unless it is on the seam or a wrap around label print.

Here again pigments are chosen which are resistant to most of the product packaged in a squeeze tube of this nature. There is one basic problem which can be taken care of with a special lacquer or barrier coat. As is known, polyethylene is somewhat permeable, and when used to package perfumes, shampoos, hair dressings, toothpaste, shaving cream and similar items, it is necessary to lacquer coat the polyethylene surface in order to completely seal it, otherwise some of the essential ingredients that are present in the product may be lost. The industry has overcome this by applying a barrier coat. Usually, this is a very inert epoxy coating which resists most any material.

This type of plastic tube is occasionally hot stamped or silk screened, but this amounts to a very small percentage of the decorations that are applied.

When are a letterpress and wet offset used to decorate plastics? Usually they are chosen for items such as polyethylene-coated stock, rigid vinyl, styrene, cellulose acetate, and mylar.

Polyethylene-coated stock is presented being used in the milk container field and the carton packaging field. Letterpress or offset can be applied and generally speaking, a good hard binding type of oxidizing ink will adhere well. Other systems have been used with moderate success, but where high gloss is required, an oxidizing oil ink system serves best.

Rigid vinyl has several end uses, and the method of ink application depends quite appreciably on this.

In the credit card and charge card field, which is growing in large strides, there are two schools of thought, depending on the art work. If only identification and line work are involved, letterpress is the best approach. This type of ink usually contains a vinyl resin, a carrier and pigment. The dried sheet is then subjected to a planishing or press polishing operation. This consists of sandwiching the printed specimen between nickel plates under heat and pressure to produce an almost "indestructible unit." What actually happens is that under the heat and pressure and with the acceptable pigments, the vinyl ink, which is very compatible with the vinyl sheet, becomes "married" due to the extreme compatibility.

When process design is involved, this effect cannot be accomplished ecnomically via letterpress, and henceforth, wet offset is required. This is now limited to inks that will adhere reasonably to vinyl sheeting and can be lithographed. Sometimes a good oil type oxidizing ink will work well here. However, oil ink films are very difficult to press polish due to incompatibility—therefore, most items printed in this manner are laminated. To obtain satisfactory adhesion, it is imperative that no printed material be run to a "bleed." In this way the overlay sheet will obtain no interference at the sheet edge during the laminating procedure.

Styrene, cellulose acetate and Mylar behave similarly with regard to types of printing inks which are recommended.

Modifications of oxidizing inks, whether they are letterpress or offset, are made to insure good adhesion. The requirements for product resistance, gloss and press stability continue to hold true. There is one exception to the above and this pertains to printing via letterpress on styrene display signs, pen and pencil barrels and similar items. Such products require inks that actually "bite" into the substrate and become part of it. The one disadvantage is the resulting finish. It is flat in nature but the adhesion is excellent and will pass a scotch tape test, scratch or rub resistance test.

In the case of polyethylene, the surface of the stock must be flame or corona treated first. In the case of vinyl plastics, the covering is applied to rigid vinyl only.

It is quite clear that the consumer or printer requires the following properties in inks for decorating plastics, regardless of the type:
(1) Adhesion.
(2) Product Resistance.
(3) Flexibility.
(4) Gloss.
(5) Permanency.

M. A. SPINA

Cross-reference: COLORATION OF PLASTICS.

DECORATIVE COATINGS

Coatings for plastics are usually solutions of resins in relatively fast evaporating solvents, so that after drying or curing, a film is left on the surface. Transparent solutions containing only resins are used to apply high-gloss clear finishes. Dull clear coatings usually consist of clear resins and a transparent dulling agent such as certain grades of silica. Colored coatings include either dispersions of pigments or solutions of dyestuffs dissolved in appropriate resins.

The function of coatings on plastics may be decorative and/or protective. This article will cover both types of coatings for molded, extruded and formed plastics, as well as for plastics films, The term film is meant to include both light and heavy gauge webs in unsupported form as well as supported by fabric or paper.

Decorative Coatings

In the decorative area, the most important reason for applying a coating to a plastic part, or to a film, is to change the color or gloss of either the entire surface or of a selected area.

The use of a pigmented finish, as compared to internal coloring, depends on a number of factors.

(1) Economics. In a thick molded part, the use of an expensive pigment may turn out to be more costly than the application of a coating to the surface. In addition, if the number of units of a particular color required is relatively small, coating would be more economical than internal coloring. This occurs at a level at which it is not worthwhile to obtain specifically colored molding powders, break into a smooth production flow, and change colors in the machine. The use of paint, instead of internal coloring, makes it possible to produce a wide variety of colors with no down-time on the molding, fabricating or forming equipment.

(2) Selected Areas. When only selected areas of formed parts are to be painted, the color is usually applied through masks. This includes surface painted areas as well as coloring of recessed portions of molded panels. When the register or

accuracy of color distribution is not important, an air brush may be used.

(3) Special Effects. Parts coming out of a mold may be either inadequate or nonuniform in gloss. A dull or gloss clear coating over the finished part is usually the only answer to this problem. In other instances, the temperatures and pressures of molding or fabrication may have a deleterious effect on the pigment to be used. The color may change or the brightness may be lost. Metallic and fluorescent colors are good examples of materials that show up to better advantage when painted on the surface instead of being added to the molding compound. Aluminum powder can be combined with transparent colors, thus producing a wide variety of colored metallic effects.

Protective Coatings

(1) Wear Resistance. Plastic items, which have been either printed or painted, may need a clear coating to protect the decoration or print from wear, and in the case of containers, from "spillage" of the contents.

(2) Barrier Coating. A barrier coating may be necessary to prevent migration of materials through permeable plastic containers and films. This will be explained more fully in the section on Plastics in Packaging.

(3) Light Resistance. Protective coatings are also used to provide resistance to yellowing from sunlight exposure.

Methods of Application

In view of the variety of plastic items and shapes that might be coated, a wide selection of application methods must be considered.

The usual method of coating irregularly shaped parts is spraying. This may be a small air brush for very light coatings and where a limited area is to be painted, conventional spray equipment including automatic spraying where the parts can be mounted on a continuous conveyor, and electrostatic coating, where, with some refinements and added installations, a substantial saving in spray costs can be effected. The spraying may be overall spraying or through masks.

On cylindrical objects, roller coating may be the most suitable method. On sheet stock, roller coating, off-set gravure coating, and flow coating are popular methods. Other methods are dip coating and tumbling.

Methods of Drying. The most desirable coatings from an application standpoint are those requiring only air drying. Many lacquers which dry at a rate sufficiently rapid so that the part sprayed can be packed at the end of the line are offered. However, in most instances where superior properties are required, additional drying is necessary. This may be forced drying, which evaporates slower boiling solvents and allows for better flow-out, as

well as some "bite" into the substrata. Beyond that, catalyzed drying is used. In this case a two-package system is usually necessary to keep the curing temperature below the softening point of the plastic. Only a few plastics can withstand the temperatures necessary to cure single-package thermosetting coatings.

Raw Materials

The surface coatings industry has a wide variety of raw materials to choose from in designing coating materials.

Film Formers. Among the factors that go into their selection are:

(1) Properties of films deposited.
        (a) Light resistance,
        (b) Heat resistance,
        (c) Water resistance, and
        (d) Barrier to permeating liquids and gases.

(2) Adhesion to specific surfaces.

(3) Economics of film former and of solvents required.

(4) Time-temperature cycle required for development of ultimate properties.

The oldest and perhaps still most common film former is nitrocellulose. It lends itself to a wide variety of modifications and can be offered in fast drying and low cost solvent combinations. Compounded with pigments and various resins and plasticizers, it is widely used where general decorative effects are required without rigorous resistance requirements.

Other cellulose derivatives, such as cellulose acetate butyrate and ethyl cellulose, have similar properties but are used to a lesser extent because of their higher price. They are also included as minor additives to improve block resistance as well as speed of touch-dry.

In addition to the cellulosic resins, a number of vinyl copolymer resins as well as acrylic copolymers are widely used in decorating plastics.

Vinyl resins demonstrate good resistance to oils, greases, acids, alkalis and aliphatic hydrocarbons, as well as to abrasion. They also have little, if any, residual odor or taste.

Acrylic resins are particularly suitable for their clarity and weather resistance, and for resistance to plasticizer migration from compounded plastics and films.

The above materials are all in the category of thermoplastics. They dry solely by evaporation of solvent, and retain their original composition.

There are other groups of resins which change after application. The first group of these may be called oxidizable materials, which cure to a hard surface by combining with oxygen from the air. The rate of curing is of course accelerated by the application of heat. These materials are suited primarily for thermosetting plastics such as phenolics, where high heat will have no effect on the plastic. They include a wide variety of oil modified alkyd-type resins.

The newer resins, such as epoxies and polyurethanes, can be formulated into coatings which will cure at relatively low temperatures and provide a film with superior properties. This makes it possible to finish thermoplastic surfaces with a coating which is hard, glossy and flexible, as well as chemical and abrasion resistant.

Solvents. The factors on which selection of solvents are based are:

(1) Solvency for resins required.
(2) Effect on the plastic to be coated.
(3) Economics.
(4) Balancing of drying rates.

Ketones and esters are usually the most active solvents, required for most cellulosic materials and certain other resins including vinyls. Hydrocarbons and alcohols are usually the lowest in cost. Most families of solvents have lower and higher boiling members.

Pigments. The choice of pigments is based on end-use requirements. For further details see article on Dyes and Pigments, p. 153, and Organic Colorants, p. 306.

Coated Plastics in Packaging

As in many other industries, the use of coatings on plastics has broadened their usefulness and value to the packaging industry. Going down the list of packaging structures, it can be seen that the tin can and the glass jar are now accompanied by the plastic container. The lead or aluminum tube shares shelf space with the polyethylene tube. Metal closures, or screw caps, have in many instances been displaced by phenolic, urea, polystyrene and polyolefin closures. Lastly, waxpaper, vulcanized fiber paper, and even cellophane have been supplemented, if not displaced, by polyolefin films, polyvinylidene chloride films and in some cases, polystyrene films

Coatings are broadening the use of these modern replacements. Polyethylene has been a particularly versatile plastic in the packaging industry, finding use in bottles, tubes, films and closures. For many applications, low price and ease of molding have made it an ideal material. However, its limitations are dull surface finish, relatively poor resistance to the permeation of oxygen and other gases and essential oils used in perfumes, flavoring materials, and volatile solvents. Therefore, there are, many materials, such as cosmetics, foods, pharmaceuticals and some industrial products, which cannot be packaged in polyolefin bottles, tubes, or film.

In order to overcome these problems, barrier coatings such as Interchem's "Barafene" are used. For rigorous conditions, the coating is applied as a lining in the container. Barrier coatings developed to date are usually either epoxy systems or copolymers of polyvinylidene chloride. Epoxy barrier coatings, applied to the outside, simultaneously impart high gloss. They must be furnished as two-package systems because of their short pot life and low temperature-curing requirements. Single package, high temperature curing cycles are not practical because of the low softening point of low density polyethylene.

Another very interesting use of coatings on polyethylene containers is the combination of a container and a toy. In such cases, containers have been blow-molded into the shape of popular comic figures. Lacquers or fast drying synthetics are used for decorating flame- or electronically treated polyethylene surfaces. Several proprietary products, such as Interchem's "Plethcote UT," have also been developed for application to untreated surfaces. Selected areas are sprayed with contrasting colors, using masks to block off the areas which will not be painted. The amusing appearance of the container helps sell the product and then serves as a toy after the product is used.

Other plastics gaining stature in the packaging industry are, vinyl, copolymers of polystyrene, acetal and polycarbonate resins. All of these plastic containers require coatings to retard moisture-vapor permeability.

Closures use coatings in metalizing as well as in the preparation of specially colored units.

Although plastics are usually considered where dealing with rigid objects, a large quantity of plastic materials is used to produce continuous films, both supported and unsupported. These include vinyl, polyethylene, polystyrene, and many other materials which are also available in molded form.

Films are usually coated, by gravure application, to enhance resistance to, (1) loss of essential oils which affect odor and taste stability, (2) permeation of greases, fats, and oils, and (3) permeation or attack of acids and alkalis.

In addition, coatings provide improved heat sealing, block resistance, visual appeal (gloss or clarity), durability (scuff resistance), and release properties.

Automotive and Household Applications, Molded and Formed

The use of plastics in automobiles increases almost every year. Most interiors now have, in addition to plastic buttons and knobs, molded parts such as arm rests, dashboard frames, instrument panels and dome lights. There is a great deal of development work with plastics such as ABS, polypropylene, and acetal on car bodies, fenders, emblems, and other exterior parts. Many of these require painting. Since metal and plastic are to be used side by side, paints, which will perform equally well on both substrates, are required.

Painting of molded or formed plastics finds application in household appliance parts also.

Requirements for these products are not as severe and the quantities used not nearly as great as compared to other products.

Automotive and Household Vinyl Film, Sheeting and Coated Fabrics

Of the 2 billion lb of vinyl resin manufactured in 1966, about 1/2 billion lb were used in the production of vinyl film (up to about 8 mils thick), vinyl sheeting (over 8 mils thick), and vinyl-coated fabric. Although industrial usage requires no further decoration, other uses such as automotive upholstery, door panels, furniture upholstery, leatherette jackets, handbags, shower curtains, tablecloths, and a variety of other consumer goods require inks and coatings. The coatings are primarily for the sheeting and coated fabric. They are used to:

(1) Protect the print.
(2) Correct or modify the color of the base sheet.
(3) Produce a uniform degree of dullness.
(4) Improve the gloss.
(5) Impart dielectric sealing properties.

A small amount of vinyl, used mainly by the handbag trade, is coated by either spraying or "hand souping," a process by which the clear topcoat is actually rubbed over the vinyl surface. The vast majority of vinyl sheeting and coated fabric is coated by gravure printing. The materials used are generally a combination of vinyl and acrylic resins, modified with additives for the purpose of imparting block-resistance, slip, heat sealability, etc. The vinyl resin imparts adhesion and the acrylic resin is used primarily to prevent the migration of plasticizer from the base vinyl sheet.

The clear vehicle is used by itself to impart high gloss, and may be modified with dulling agents to vary the sheen. It is blended with pigments— organic and inorganic, opaque and transparent— thus producing a variety of overall colors. Metallic effects may also be produced by adding aluminum powders. These in turn may be modified by the inclusion of a variety of transparent colors so that metallic pastels and simulated golds, without employing bronze powder, are produced.

The formulation of topcoatings for the automotive industry is very critical. Upholstery and door panels for automotive use must withstand stringent abrasion tests, low-temperature flexibility tests and, in many instances, dielectric sealing requirements. This is, of course, particularly true when aluminum powders are included.

The careful selection of pigments for vinyl topcoatings is also very important. Such properties as resistance to fading, resistance to bleeding in plasticizer, and in some instances, resistance to arcing, are all very vital. High hiding pigments must also be used because topcoating thicknesses on vinyl are generally in a range of only a few tenths of a mil.

Toys — Molded

Although toys have been made out of plastics for many years, the application of color by spraying has been most widespread on just two plastics, namely, vinyl and polyethylene. Other plastics have been coated in the metalizing process.

Vinyl. Vinyl plastisols were readily adaptable to the processes of rotational and slush molding in production of dolls and hobbyhorses. These items need decorative color in selected areas. Formulations, free of toxic heavy metal pigments in vinyl and acrylic solutions, are available for spraying such areas. These materials conform to state and federal regulations covering nontoxicity of coatings for children's toys. Freehand or art brush spraying has generally been adequate in spraying the cheeks and hair of dolls, as well as the harnesses, heads and limbs of hobbyhorses. Coatings of this type must dry by the time the particular object painted reaches the point of packaging.

Polyethylene. Due to the low price and ease of molding of polyethylene, a place has readily been made for it in the toy industry. Many objects, formerly made of vinyl, are now rotationally molded polyethylene. In addition, for many parts, the process of blow-molding has proven to be more economical and has served to produce a large number of toys. The resulting parts require decoration.

Painting polyethylene has proven to be a serious problem because of its waxy surface, impervious to most solvents. However, for the toy industry, coatings such as Interchem's Plethcote UT have been developed, which will adhere to many grades of untreated polyethylene. Where adhesion requirements are very critical as in higher priced toys and in the container industry, the polyethylene surface must first be treated, either electronically or by a flame process. Both of these processes are covered by patents. For these polyethylene end uses, coatings are available with optimum adhesion characteristics for treated polyolefin surfaces.

Conclusion

The wide variety of plastics available for industrial and domestic uses has resulted in the development of a broad plastic coating technology.

As the uses of plastic materials increase, there will be greater inroads in the use of metals and other conventional materials. This will, in turn, make greater the need for decorative and protective coatings on plastics.

GABRIEL F. GOLDSTEIN

DIALLYL PHTHALATE MONOMER

Diallyl phthalate (DAP) is a highly versatile monomer principally notable for low volatility, long shelf life, and efficacy in imparting heat resistance, good electrical properties, and mechanical strength to thermosetting resins. These exceptional attributes are largely responsible for its steadily increasing use as a cross-linking agent in a variety of resin systems. DAP also exhibits many latent possibilities for application that are attracting close attention among polymer scientists and plastic manufacturers. As a co-monomer, for example, it may be used in plastisols, urethane foams, epoxy formulations, and rubber compounds.

Properties

Diallyl phthalate is a colorless, high boiling liquid of low viscosity which has the ability to react with many types of unsaturated monomers and resins. Its vapor pressure (only 2.4 mm of mercury at 150°C) is considerably lower than that of styrene (944 mm of mercury at 150°C).

FIG. 1. DAP/Polyester Premix Molding Compounds. A long glass diallyl phthalate (DAP) polyester compound is preformed by hand. The compound has a putty-like consistency, and the glass fibers can be handled without irritation to the hands. The compound can be exposed without fear of monomer volatilization and subsequent hardening of the material.

This low volatility and long shelf life are responsible for its adoption in the production of stable thermosetting compositions which have excellent handling characteristics and which can be stored for extended periods of time.

Shrinkage of DAP during polymerization, only 11.8% by volume, is quite low compared to other commercial monomers. For example, shrinkage of styrene during polymerization is about 30% higher, namely, 17%.

Neither the monomer nor its prepolymer evolve water or other volatile by-products during polymerization or cure since these are addition-type polymerizations. This characteristic gives the prepolymer an advantage over condensation thermosetting resins in that curing may be effected at lower pressures, eliminating problems of blistering and gassing.

DAP is soluble in methanol, acetone, and most common polar organic solvents. It is insoluble or has limited solubility in water, gasoline, mineral oil, glycols, glycerol, and some amines. Other typical properties are listed in Table 1.

TABLE 1. PROPERTIES OF DIALLYL PHTHALATE MONOMER.

Molecular weight	246.35
Density, 25°C, g/ml	1.132
Refractive index, 25°C	1.518
Viscosity, 25°C, cP	12
Boiling point, 760 mm, °C	300[a]
Boiling range, 4 mm, °C	157 to 165
Mid-boiling point, 4 mm, °C	161
Freezing point, °C	−70[b]
Vapor pressure, 150°C, mm Hg	2.4
Vapor pressure, 200°C, mm Hg	27.0
Flash point, °F (°C)	330 (166)
Fire point, °F (°C)	359 (182)
Surface tension, 25°C, dynes/cm	34.4
Specific heat 50–150°C, cal/g/°C	0.50[c]
GE gel time, min (1% Benzoyl peroxide)	41.0
Thermal expansion, 10–40°C, in./in./°C	0.00076
Weight per gal, 25°C, lb	9.33

[a] Extrapolated value.
[b] Viscous liquid.
[c] Average value.

Reactions and Uses

DAP contains two allyl (vinyl-type) groups that enable it to form a thermosetting homopolymer. It also functions as a cross-linking co-monomer to form tightly knit thermosets with polyesters or other unsaturated polymers, or by polymerization with other vinyl monomers. The allyl groups have little or no tendency to polymerize at ordinary temperatures in the absence of initiators. Even in the presence of initiators the monomer remains unpolymerized at temperatures of 75–100°F for unusually long periods. This is one of its distinct advantages as a cross-linker in polyester formulations.

The ability of DAP to cross-link, plus its ease of handling, permit manufacture of end-products possessing good mechanical, chemical, thermal,

FIG. 2. DAP/Polyester Reinforced Plastics

These fiberglass structures include chemical-resistant tanks and containers, doff boxes, and truck and conditioning boxes. Such reinforced plastics offer high strength, exceptional weatherability, and light-weight advantages.

and electrical properties. Some of the principal commercial uses of this multifunctional material, which are described more fully in the following sections, include:

(1) Prepolymer molding and laminating compounds.

(2) Cross-linking agent for polyesters.

(3) Carrier for adding catalysts and pigments to polyesters.

(4) Modifier in vinyl plastisols.

(5) Impregnating and bonding agent.

(6) Plasticizer.

Other applications for which DAP is recommended include:

(1) Cross-linker in polyurethane foams.

(2) In epoxy formulations.

(3) In rubber compounds.

(4) As a co-monomer to upgrade the quality of other monomers and polymers.

Prepolymers

When DAP is homopolymerized under carefully controlled conditions, it yields a free-flowing, white, powdery prepolymer. In this form the material is essentially a linear thermoplastic material. It is soluble in solvents and under catalysis it can be further polymerized to a thermoset. The prepolymer is produced commercially by FMC Corporation under the trademark "Dapon."

Most shrinkage which accompanies vinyl polymerizations occurs during the formation of the prepolymer. Consequently, when the resin is cured during molding, the shrinkage is less than one per cent by volume. Another important attribute of this prepolymer is that it cures very rapidly because very little additional polymerization is needed for conversion into a compact cross-linked thermoset.

Typical properties of completely polymerized DAP monomer (or cured prepolymer) are listed in Table 2. Particularly outstanding among these are thermal stress resistance (deflection temperature is 155°C), electrical properties, and hardness. Cured prepolymer is further characterized by excellent dimensional stability, retention of good electrical properties on exposure to high temperature and high humidity, and outstanding chemical resistance.

The prepolymer resin is used chiefly in molding compounds (particularly for electronic and electrical parts), decorative laminates, and industrial laminates.

DIALLYL PHTHALATE MONOMER

TABLE 2. TYPICAL PROPERTIES OF PIECES MOLDED FROM DIALLYL PHTHALATE PREPOLYMER.[a]

Rockwell hardness (M Scale) ASTM D785-51	114–116
Barcol hardness	42–43
Density, 25°C gm/ml	1.270
Izod impact (ASTM D256-56), ft lb/in. notch	0.3
Deflection temperature, 10 mils deflection (ASTM D648-56 Formerly known as heat distortion)	
264 psi, °C	155
66 psi, °C	160
Compressive strength (ASTM D695-54), psi	22,000–24,000
Flexural strength (ASTM D790-59T), psi	7,000–9,000
Refractive index, 25°C (ASTM D542-50)	1.571
Water absorption, 24 hr, 25°C (ASTM D570-59aT), %	0.0–0.2
Tangent modulus of elasticity in bending (ASTM D790-59T), psi	0.05×10^6
Dielectric constant (ASTM D150-S4T): 60 cycles	3.5
10^3 cycles	3.6
10^6 (megacycles)	3.4
Volume resistivity, 25°C (ASTM D257-58)	1.8×10^{16}
Surface resistivity, 25°C (ASTM D257-58) ohm	9.7×10^{15}
Dielectric strength, 25°C, step-by-step, volts/mil (ASTM D149-59)	450
Arc resistance (ASTM D495-58T), sec	118
Dissipation factor, 25°C (ASTM D150-54T): 60 cycles	0.010
10 cycles	0.009
10^6 (megacycles)	0.011
Gardner color (unit)	7

[a] "Dapon" resin produced by FMC Corporation.

Cross-linking Agent for Polyesters

A major commercial application of DAP monomer is as a cross-linking agent for unsaturated polyester resins. Numerous commercial applications are reported for these diallyl phthalate-polyester blends. Most unsaturated polyesters containing monomer are not very stable during storage, particularly at high temperatures and in the presence of air. Their tendency to gel or cross-link is much greater when the cross-linking monomer is styrene instead of diallyl phthalate. The curing and handling characteristics of DAP monomer are advantages which permit production of finished parts of consistent quality. It is frequently used in preference to styrene in polyesters used for pre-impregnated fabrics, premix molding compounds, and catalyst carriers in which its very low volatility, high flash point, good storage stability

and viscosity offer processing and end-property advantages.

DAP-polyester blends are also used in industrial laminates prepared by the wet-layup method, impregnation of metal castings, banding tapes, and mat or preform binders. DAP monomer is used as a reactive vehicle or solvent to introduce catalysts or pigments into polyester resin compositions.

The amount of DAP used in polyesters varies from about 20–50 w %. Since DAP copolymerizes quite rapidly with maleate or fumarate double bonds, highly unsaturated polyesters may be used when fast cure rates are required.

Reinforced Plastics. The nonvolatility of the DAP-polyester blends makes them ideal for fabricating large glass-reinforced parts, such as radomes, by the hand-layup method since there is essentially no loss of monomer during cure. The relatively low exotherm (compared to styrene-polyester systems) of these DAP-containing resins results in strain-free and bubble-free cured parts. DAP-polyester glass cloth laminates qualify under Military Specifications Mil-R-7575B, Types 1 and 2.

Impregnation of Metal Castings. DAP and DAP-polyester blends are used to impregnate metal castings of all types. This is frequently necessary to seal the pores when the castings are to be used in applications involving pressure or vacuum, to prevent bubble formation in protective coatings resulting from gases trapped in the pores, or to prevent contamination of the pores and subsequent internal corrosion by metal bath salts.

Premixes. DAP, in concentrations of 20–40 w %, improves polyester premixes. The high viscosity of this monomer means better tack than that of the styrene-polyester premixes. Wet-out of fiber and filler is improved and resin squeeze-out is minimized.

Cured premix parts have good chemical resistance as well as good mechanical and electrical properties. They also have high flexural strength, good impact resistance, and good strength at high temperatures. Surface finishes are excellent and highly weather resistant. Use of DAP eliminates gassing and blistering during molding since vaporization of monomer is negligible.

Banding Tapes. DAP-polyester resins also are used to impregnate banding tapes designed for motor armature wrappings. These uncured preimpregnated tapes have the desired amount of parallel strand bonding with little or no interlaminar tack so that blocking poses no problem.

Catalyst and Pigment Carrier. DAP is finding favor with boat builders who employ it as a vehicle for adding catalyst and pigment to polyester resins. It is more suitable than other carriers such as inert, volatile solvents, because in addition

138

to its basic properties it is not polymerized by the catalyst at ambient temperatures. Since the DAP carrier becomes an integral part of the cured resin through copolymerization, it does not cause the problems of solvent removal or dilution encountered when conventional inert carriers are employed. From 2–10 w% of DAP monomer containing catalyst can be added to styrene-containing polyesters without significantly increasing the gel times or cure times. Ultimate mechanical properties are thereby maintained or, in many instances, improved.

Copolymerization of Diallyl Phthalate

The double bonds of DAP tend to copolymerize rapidly with a number of other monomers and unsaturated polymers. By proper selection of co-monomers the copolymerization of diallyl phthalate can be made to proceed many times faster than homopolymerization.

Diallyl phthalate has particularly strong copolymerization tendencies with monomers that have electron withdrawing groups attached directly to the carbon-carbon double bond. These co-monomers include maleic anhydride, maleates and fumarates (monomers and polyesters), acrylates, methacrylates, acrylonitrile and acrylamide. Diallyl phthalate also copolymerizes with monomers such as styrene and others whose carbon-carbon double bonds have a relatively high electron density.

Advantage can be taken of the copolymerizability of diallyl phthalate to improve properties of vinyl polymers. For example, the intrinsic good properties of cured DAP, such as resistance to thermal stress, resistance to solvents, high rigidity, etc. (shown in Table 2), can be imparted to styrene copolymers.

Other Uses for Diallyl Phthalate

Diallyl phthalate can be used in thixotropic coatings designed for applications where drainage is objectionable. The formula consists of approximately equal parts of diallyl phthalate, diethylene glycol maleate and clay. The clay maintains the composition in a firm state even at 100°C, while mechanical agitation converts it to a fluid. A possible application of these coatings is on high voltage equipment where unequal thermal conductivity, which would arise if the coating thickness was uneven, would lead to corona discharge.

DAP (diallyl phthalate) is used in a bonding resin for abrasive grinding wheels requiring resilience, high bonding strength, and good heat resistance in special applications where phenolic resins are inadequate.

A copolymer of diallyl phthalate with allyl laurate has been claimed as a viscosity index improver for lube oils. Copolymers of DAP with a number of other monoallyl esters have been reported. These copolymers may be useful as pour point improvers, corrosion reducers, and color stabilizers.

Diallyl phthalate has been copolymerized with vinylidene chloride to prepare moldable products having exceptional solvent resistance.

Dyes for cellulose acetate fabric are protected from fading by addition of diallyl phthalate monomer.

By incorporating DAP into vinyl chloride-vinyl acetate copolymers, their stability against deterioration by light is improved.

When DAP is used as a cross-linking agent during the polymerization of methyl methacrylate, it produces a resin which has better surface hardness and better elasticity than the unmodified polymethyl methacrylate. DAP-acrylonitrile copolymers have higher resistance to organic solvents than do acrylonitrile homopolymers. The use of diallyl phthalate copolymers in combination with melamine or urea-formaldehyde results in thermosetting compositions that have improved adhesion to glass fibers.

Diallyl phthalate has been used to form rigid polyurethane foams with diisocyantes and castor oil. These compositions are outstanding in energy absorption, dimensional stability, low moisture absorption, and compressive strength compared to conventional polyurethanes of equivalent density. Such foams can be made continuously in commercial machines or foamed-in-place by spray devices.

Summary

The low volatility, innate stability at ambient temperatures, low shrinkage during polymerization, and good handling characteristics of diallyl phthalate make it a versatile formulating ingredient in the plastics industry. It is effective in many cases, in imparting heat resistance, chemical and solvent resistance, good electrical properties, and mechanical strength to thermosetting resins. It is used to advantage as a cross-linking monomer in polyesters in applications such as preimpregnated laminates, wet lay-up laminates, and premixes, where long shelf life, low volatility and high flash points are desirable. It is also employed as a carrier for catalysts and pigments, as a bonding and impregnating agent, in banding tapes, as a modifier in plastisols, and as a cross-linking agent in the preparation of rigid polyurethane foams.

The monomer as a prepolymer, finds application in molding compounds, decorative laminates and industrial laminates because in the cured state, it has excellent dimensional stability, outstanding electrical properties even after exposure to high humidity and high temperature, good resistance to thermal stress and good chemical resistance.

CLINTON J. STARKE

DICYANDIAMIDE

Although known for over 100 years, this high nitrogen compound (66% N) first achieved major commercial significance in the late 1930's when satisfactory industrial methods for converting it to melamine (2,4,6-triamino-s-triazine) were developed. The compound is known in the trade as "dicy": its chemical nature is much more accurately described by the name cyanoguanidine—its structure is represented by: $(NH_2)_2C=N-C\equiv N$, and it is regarded as the dimer of cyanamide, H_2NCN.

Physical Properties

Dicy is a white, crystalline (monoclinic) solid which melts exothermically and with decomposition at 209°C. It is moderately soluble in water and polar solvents particularly at elevated temperature; its remarkably high solubility in liquid NH_3 (72 g per 100 g at $-33°C$) is utilized in some processes for the production of melamine.

Chemical Properties

The ease with which dicyandiamide may be converted to symmetrical triazines is the basis for its principal commercial use. By far the most important of these cyclization reactions is its transformation to melamine (q.v. page 276), which is readily accomplished by heat. The overall stoichiometry of this reaction is:

$$3(H_2N)_2CNCN \rightarrow 2H_2N \underset{\underset{NH_2}{\overset{N\quad N}{\bigcirc}}}{\overset{N}{}} NH_2$$

The reaction is highly exothermic and must be carefully controlled to provide high yields of pure product.

Another important reaction of dicy is its base catalyzed condensation with nitriles to form guanamines:

$$RCN + (H_2N)_2CNCN \longrightarrow H_2N \underset{N}{\overset{R}{\underset{N\quad N}{\bigcirc}}} NH_2$$

Benzoguanamine, an important component of surface coating resins, is made commercially by this reaction.

The pyrimidine nucleus is readily formed by reacting dicy with β-diketones, malonic esters, or acetoacetic esters:

$$(H_2N)_2CNCN + \underset{\underset{Y}{\overset{|}{C=O}}}{\overset{\overset{Y}{|}}{C=O}} \longrightarrow O= \underset{\underset{O}{Z_2}}{\overset{H}{\underset{}{\overset{N}{\bigcirc}}}} \overset{=NH}{NCN}$$

Y = alkyl, aryl, OR.
Z = H, alkyl, aryl.

A variety of open-chain molecules are readily synthesized from dicy and simple, readily available reagents. The most commonly employed synthesis of this type is represented by the preparation of guanidine salts from ammonium salts.

$$(H_2N_2)_2CNCN + 2NH_4X \rightarrow 2H_2NC(NH)NH_2 \cdot HX$$

The reaction is generally carried out in an anhydrous medium at 100–180°C. Guanidine nitrate is produced commercially in this fashion. N-alkyl substituted guanidines are formed from alkyl amine salts. Aromatic amines yield biguanides when reacted with dicy:

$$ArNH_2 + (H_2N)_2CNCN \rightarrow H_2N\overset{\overset{NH}{\|}}{C}-NH\overset{\overset{NH}{\|}}{C}-NHAr$$

Hydration in aqueous acid provides a route to guanylurea:

$$(H_2N)_2CNCN + H_2O \xrightarrow{HX} H_2N\overset{\overset{NH}{\|}}{C}NH\overset{\overset{O}{\|}}{C}NH_2 \cdot HX$$

Guanidine salts are available by the hydrolysis of guanylureas:

$$H_2N\overset{\overset{NH}{\|}}{C}NH\overset{\overset{O}{\|}}{C}NH_2 + H_2O \xrightarrow{HX}$$
$$H_2N\overset{\overset{NH}{\|}}{C}NH_2 \cdot HX + NH_3 + CO_2$$

Treatment of dicyandiamide with H_2S results in the formation of guanylthiourea or dithiobiuret, depending upon conditions:

$$(H_2N)_2CNCN + H_2S \rightarrow H_2N\overset{\overset{NH}{\|}}{C}NH\overset{\overset{S}{\|}}{C}NH_2$$

$$(H_2N)_2CNCN + 2H_2S \rightarrow H_2N\overset{\overset{S}{\|}}{C}NH\overset{\overset{S}{\|}}{C}NH_2 + NH_3$$

Manufacture

Dicyandiamide is a product of the electrochemical industry and is derived from limestone, coal and air. Its immediate precursor is cyanamide,

H_2NCN, which is liberated from calcium cyanamide (lime nitrogen) by acid treatment. The sequence of reactions involved is:

$$3C + CaO \xrightarrow[\text{arc}]{\text{electric}} CaC_2 + CO$$

$$CaC_2 + N_2 \rightarrow CaNCN + C$$

$$CaNCN \xrightarrow[\substack{\text{acidification} \\ \text{extraction} \\ \text{filtration}}]{H^+} H_2NCN \xrightarrow[\substack{\text{polymerization} \\ \text{crystallization} \\ \text{filtration}}]{OH^-}$$

$$(H_2N)_2CNCN$$

Dicy is widely available throughout the world, particularly in those areas (e.g., North America, Germany, Japan) where calcium cyanamide has been manufactured for decades as a source of nitrogeneous fertilizers.

Health and Safety Factors

Since dicyandiamide is essentially nontoxic, its use requires no unusual precautions. Excessive skin contact may produce dermatitis in sensitive individuals.

Analytical Determination

Dicy may be determined as silver dicyandiamide picrate or as nickel guanylurea sulfate. For routine quality control analysis, total nitrogen may be employed.

L. C. LANE

Cross-reference: MELAMINE.

DIISOCYANATES

Organic isocyanates are highly reactive chemicals which combine readily with water, alcohols, amines, acids, and practically all other compounds containing active hydrogens. Most important of the organic isocyanate compounds are the polyisocyanates, those containing two or more isocyanate ($-N=C=O$) groups in the molecule. Polyisocyanates are of significant commercial importance in the manufacture of flexible and rigid cellular urethane plastics and are becoming of increasing importance in the elastomer, coatings and adhesive fields. As a class, the aromatic polyisocyanates, because of their greater reactivity toward active hydrogen containing compounds, are preferred in most applications.

Types and Properties

Toluene diisocyanate (TDI) has reached the highest degree of commercialization with 1965 United States capacity rated at 283 million lb. The available grades of toluene diisocyanate are designated as to their isomer ratios. The TDI most commonly used is the 80/20 mixture of the 2,4 and 2,6 isomers. Table 1 shows the typical properties and characteristics of commercial toluene diisocyanates. Different grades of TDI may also be specified according to acidity. Material with

TABLE 1. COMMERCIAL TOLUENE DIISOCYANATES*, TYPICAL PROPERTIES AND CHARACTERISTICS.

ISOMER RATIOS

	100% 2,4	80% 2,4; 20% 4,6	65% 2,4; 35% 2,6
Physical state	Liquid	Liquid	Liquid
Color	Water White to pale yellow		
Boiling point at 760 mm	251°C	251°C	251°C.
Approx. flash point (open cup)	132°C	132°C	132°C
Melting point	19.5–21.5°C	11.5–13.5°C	3.5–5.5°C.
Heat of evaporation	144.9 Btu/lb (120–180°C)		
Hygroscopicity	Reacts with water with evolution of carbon dioxide		
Odor	Sharp, Pungent		
Specific gravity (25°C/15.5°C)	1.22	1.22	1.22
Specific heat (77–167°F)	0.375 Btu/lb/°F		
Vapor density (Air=1)	6.0	6.0	6.0
Vapor pressure at 20°C	Approx. 0.01 mm	Approx. 0.01 mm	Approx. 0.01 mm
Viscosity at 50°C	1.45 centistokes		

* Specifications for the various commercial toluene diisocyanates may be found in ASTM D-1786-60T.

TABLE 2. TYPICAL PROPERTIES OF COMMERCIAL AND DEVELOPMENTAL ISOCYANATES OTHER THAN TOLUENE DIISOCYANATE.

Compound	Melting point °C	Boiling point °C	Specific gravity	Isocyanate equivalent
4,4′-Diphenylmethane diisocyanate	37–38	194/199/5 mm	1.19^{50}	125
4,4-Di-o-toluene diisocyanate	69–71	—	1.174_8^{80}	132
Polymethylene polyphenyl isocyanate	Viscous liquid 250 cps at 25°C		1.2	133.5
Hexamethylene diisocyanate		140/142/21 mm	$1.04_{15.5}^{25}$	84

TABLE 3. PREPARATION OF TOLUENE DIISOCYANATE ISOMERS.

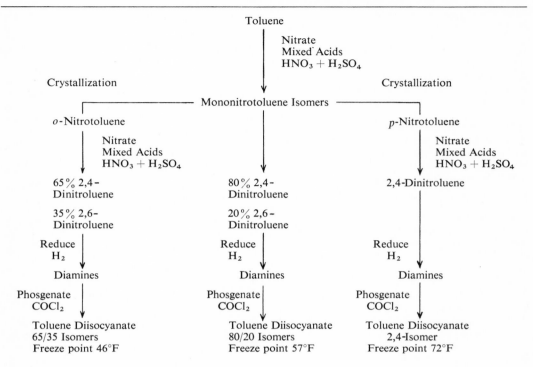

low acidity is usually used for the so-called "one-shot" flexible urethane foams, while a higher acidity product is more commonly used in preparation of prepolymers.

While currently available at much lower volumes than toluene diisocyanate, the other diisocyanates listed in Table 2 offer promise of greater importance in the future.

Manufacture

Numerous methods for the preparations of organic diisocyanates are available, including the Curtius, Hofmann and Lossen rearrangement reactions. However, based on critical economic evaluation, all current manufacturing routes are based on the method of Hentschel, which involves the phosgenation of an amine or its salt. The conventional process for manufacture of the various isomer combinations of TDI are illustrated in Table 3.

Chemical Properties of Diisocyanates

Each of the isocyanate groups in the various polyisocyanates exhibit the normal reactions of an isocyanate; however, their rates of reaction are different. For example, both groups in 4,4'-diphenylmethane diisocyanate are equally reactive, while in 2,4-toluene diisocyanate, the isocyanate group *para* to the methyl group is approximately 10 times as reactive toward *n*-butanol as the *ortho*-isocyanate group, when

used at room temperature. However, the relative activity of the *ortho* NCO group increases with increased temperature; for example, at 90°C the para NCO group is only 7 times more active than the ortho group. In reactions involving both isocyanate groups on the molecule, 2,4-toluene diisocyanate will usually react more slowly than 4,4'-diphenylmethane diisocyanate.

The reactions of a diisocyanate with primary and secondary amines yield ureas. Reaction with an alcohol gives urethane compounds. Both the urea and the urethane still contain active hydrogens and they, in turn, can, under proper conditions, react further with isocyanate groups to give, respectively, substituted biuret and allophanate structures. By these mechanisms, complex polymeric materials can be formed.

The reaction rate of isocyanates with groups containing active hydrogen is quite rapid but will vary with different compounds. Reaction with normal aliphatic amines is about 10 times as fast as with ammonia, which, in turn reacts twice as fast as aniline. Among the alcohols, primary alcohols react most rapidly, secondary alcohols about one-third as fast, and tertiary alcohols very slowly. The urethane formed from a tertiary alcohol is readily decomposable with heat to form an olefin. It has been found that water has a reaction rate close to that of a short chain secondary alcohol.

Catalysts markedly affect the reaction rates of isocyanates with compounds containing active hydrogens. Moderately basic materials such as tertiary amines effect desirable increases in reaction rates at room temperature. Very basic catalysts such as fixed alkalies cause exceedingly fast reaction rates and should be used cautiously lest they so increase the reaction rates as to be definitely hazardous. In this connection it should be noted, also, that some reactants, themselves, could be so inherently basic as to cause unsafe reaction rates with isocyanates. Friedel-Crafts catalysts and various organo-metal compounds are also effective catalysts in reactions of isocyanates with active hydrogen containing compounds.

Diisocyanates as a class, because of their difunctionality, undergo reactions with polyfunctional active hydrogen containing materials which lead to the formation of polymeric substances. In this respect they differ from monoisocyanates, which form only simple chemical entities with active hydrogen containing compounds. However, knowledge of the chemical properties of the isocyanate group itself, whether derived from studies of either monoisocyanates or diisocyanates, can, to a qualitative extent, be expected to be applicable to both classes.

Reaction with Primary Amines. Primary amines commonly react with diisocyanates to give the substituted ureas and biurets. Aliphatic amines are usually more reactive than ammonia, which in turn is more reactive than the aromatic amines. Apparently, one of the factors influencing the reactivity of these compounds is the basicity of the nitrogen atoms to which the active hydrogens are attached.

Reaction with water. Diisocyanates react very readily with water. They are usually fairly hygroscopic and thus require careful handling to avoid combining with moisture. This is especially true of many of the aromatic diisocyanates.

The initial reaction products with water are a primary diamine and carbon dioxide. It is probable that an intermediate dicarbamic acid is formed first, and that it decomposes as follows:

$$R' \begin{matrix} NCO \\ \\ NCO \end{matrix} + 2H_2O \rightarrow R' \begin{matrix} NHCOOH \\ \\ NHCOOH \end{matrix} \rightarrow$$

$$R' \begin{matrix} NH_2 \\ \\ NH_2 \end{matrix} + 2CO_2$$

This is an important reaction in the manufacture of foamed polyurethane products. The carbon dioxide is utilized as the foaming agent, and is controlled by the quantity of water added to the reaction mixture.

Reaction with Polyhydric Alcohols. With polyhydric hydroxy compounds, diisocyanates usually give only polymers, unless the diisocyanate is used in excess. Under the latter conditions, mobile, liquid adducts called prepolymers are obtained with dihydric alcohols. These contain both active hydrogens and reactive isocyanate groups. Extensive use has been made of these reactions in the preparation of various polyurethane products.

Reaction with Carboxylic Acids. Diisocyanates readily react with compounds containing carboxyl groups, to give, initially, what are probably mixed anhydrides (a) of the dicarbamic acid and the carboxylic acid. These mixed anhydrides can decompose in two ways; either by loss of carbon dioxide to yield the diamide (b), or by disproportionation into the anhydrides of the two acids followed by loss of carbon dioxide from the polycarbamic anhydride to produce a polyurea (c).

Polymerization. A common characteristic of isocyanates, including diisocyanates, is their tendency to form dimers and trimers. The aromatic isocyanates are most prone to give the former, while the aliphatic derivatives tend to yield the latter. Such polymerization reactions are readily brought about under the influence of heat or by the presence of such substances as iron, peroxides, phenolates, pyridine, calcium carbonate, triethylamine, oxalic acid, Grignard reagents and triethylphosphine. Some diisocyanates even dimerize upon standing at room temperatures.

The following structures are usually given for these polymers:

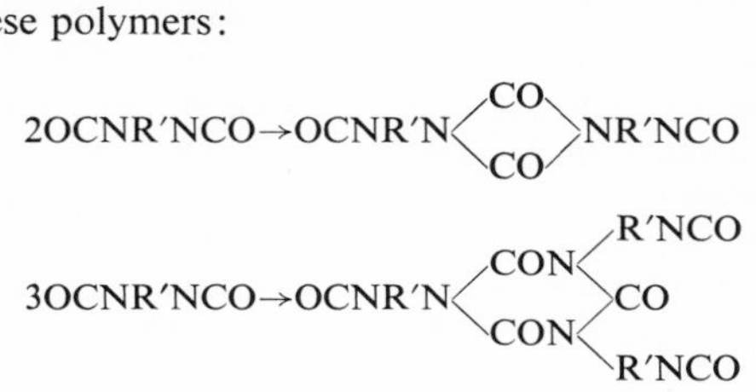

$$2OCNR'NCO \rightarrow OCNR'N \begin{matrix} CO \\ \\ CO \end{matrix} NR'NCO$$

$$3OCNR'NCO \rightarrow OCNR'N \begin{matrix} CON \begin{matrix} R'NCO \\ CO \end{matrix} \\ CON \begin{matrix} \\ R'NCO \end{matrix} \end{matrix}$$

The dimer may be regarded as a 1,3-disubstituted 2,4-uretidinedione and the trimer, as a trisubstituted isocyanuric acid. Rigid cellular products utilizing the trimerization reaction have been prepared.

Phosphorus chlorides and acyl chlorides have been recommended as inhibitors for these polymerization reactions.

Pyrolysis. Two molecules of phenyl isocyanate condense with a loss of carbon dioxide, upon heating, to give diphenylcarbodiimide:

$$2C_6H_5NCO \rightarrow C_6H_5N{=}C{=}NC_6H_5 + CO_2$$

Mono- and diisocyanates have been more easily converted to their respective carbodimides using phospholine oxide and other catalysts at temperatures below 100°C.

Polymerization of Monoisocyanates. More recently monoisocyanates (aliphatic and aromatic) have been polymerized at low temperatures

(-20 to $-100°C$) by anionic catalysts to give linear high molecular weight polyamides. These polymers are classified as l-nylons.

Diisocyanate Handling Precautions

The two major sources of difficulty in handling and using diisocyanates are contamination with water and exposure to temperature extremes.

Storage Temperatures

Toluene diisocyanates should be stored in the temperature range above their freeze point, and not in excess of 100°F. Exposure to heat above this temperature range may result in discoloration of the product. Temperatures below this range can result in freezing of the product and stratification of the isomers. Below 57°F, e.g., the 2,4-isomer and the 2,6-isomer of the 80/20 mixture, will both begin to solidify, but at different rates. In thawing, any partially melted material will have a higher content of the 2,6-isomer. Since this isomer reacts more slowly than the 2,4-isomer, the use of partially melted product will result in a slower reaction rate than what can be expected of the liquid 80/20 TDI. Mixing of any thawed isomer mixture of toluene diisocyanate is recommended before use.

Provisions must be made to heat bulk storage tanks, tank cars and tank trucks in order to maintain the proper storage temperatures.

TDI reacts with any available moisture to form carbon dioxide gas and insoluble ureas. The humidity in the air is the most common source of contamination. In order to protect toluene diisocyanate from this contamination, it should be stored under a blanket of a dry, inert gas, such as dry nitrogen or dry air having a $-40°$ maximum dewpoint. Moisture should also be kept away from TDI pipelines and other transfer equipment, since the resulting ureas may result in plugging of the pipelines, valves, etc.

The most satisfactory results are obtained when all handling equipment is constructed of one, or a combination, of the following materials:

(1) Stainless steel (types 302, 304, 316 and 410).
(2) Aluminum (types 1100, 3003, 5052 and 5154).
(3) Glass lined steel (e.g., "Heresite," "Synthetasine 100," or "Unichrome B-125-17").
(4) Nickel.

Pipelines may be constructed of stainless steel, aluminum or nickel. Pumps, fittings, and valves may be constructed of the same materials used in pipelines or of "Durichlor," "Durimet 20," or "Duriron". Carbon steel tanks are not recommended.

Health and Safety Precautions

While toluene diisocyanate is considered a prime irritant rather than an extremely toxic chemical, its irritant properties must not be underrated as a hazard. It is used by many industrial concerns without problems, but the proper protective devices and working area conditions must be observed for safety.

Safety precautions are briefly discussed below. However, persons coming in contact with TDI should become thoroughly familiar with the bulletin published by the Manufacturing Chemists' Association, Inc., titled "Properties and Essential Information for Safe Handling and Use of Tolylene Diisocyanate," Chemical Safety Data Sheet SD-73.

Low molecular weight isocyanates are highly lachrymatory. This effect appears to be proportional to the molecular weight of the isocyanate. Thus TDI is relatively mild in such activity while diphenylmethane diisocyanate has little, if any, effect as an eye irritant.

Isocyanate vapors are also extremely irritating to the respiratory tract. Efficient ventilation systems should be provided in any work areas. With TDI, recommended maximum allowable concentration limits are 0.1 ppm vapor in air for extended exposure.

Liquid isocyanates are especially irritating to the skin and proper precautions should be taken to protect individuals working with these materials. Their oral toxicity is rather mild as observed in animal feeding tests.

Analytical Methods for Diisocyanates

The most common method for the analysis of the NCO group is the amine equivalent method which involves the rapid reaction of the isocyanate with an amine. The isocyanate or polymer with unreacted isocyanate groups, is dissolved in an appropriate solvent and allowed to react with an excess of a standard amine solution, such as 1 N dibutylamine solution. The unreacted amine is then titrated with a standard hydrochloric acid solution. The amine reacted with the —NCO— of the isocyanate can then be readily calculated to provide the per cent purity or its equivalent weight. This method is described more fully in ASTM Method D-1638-59T.

Applications for the Various Diisocyanates

The reaction of a polyisocyanate with the hydrogen of a hydroxyl group to form urethane linkages is the basis for a series of urethane products. The proper selection and manner of combining the polyisocyanates and polyols creates a number of commercial urethane products, such as flexible and rigid foams, elastomers, coatings, spandex fibers and adhesives. The typical polyols that are reacted with polyisocyanates are hydroxyl terminated polyethers and polyesters.

Urethane cellular foam products are based on toluene diisocyanate (TDI), produced as an

80/20 mixture of the 2,4- and 2,6-isomers. A crude grade of TDI is commercially available for use in the rigid urethane foams. The crude product is composed of pure TDI and treated still bottoms containing dimers and trimers of TDI. In general, the crude TDI is an 85 to 90 % active diisocyanate raw material.

Flexible Urethane Foams. One-shot flexible polyether slab foams at various densities and load bearing characteristics may be manufactured by reacting TDI with polyether and water in the presence of catalysts. The flexible foams obtained have outstanding cushioning characteristics, good chemical resistance and aging properties, light weight and thermal insulating properties. The foams are non-allergenic, nontoxic, and withstand moisture or body odors. Major market outlet for flexible foams is in cushioning for furniture, automotive seating and mattresses.

Another market for TDI is in the production of cellular polyester foams. The polyester foam is manufactured by the one-shot method by reacting TDI with polyester adipate resin in the presence of catalysts. The major outlet for this foam is to the textile trade for the heat lamination of thin gauge foam sheeting to a wide variety of cloth fabrics. This laminated interlining gives good wearing and dry cleaning properties so necessary in outer garments.

Rigid Urethane Foams. The general purpose rigid urethane foam may be produced by the one-shot or prepolymer method by reacting the intermediate TDI with polyhydroxyl polyethers while blown with monofluorotrichloromethane. The slab, foam-in-place or spray-up techniques may be used for the manufacture of the rigid foam. Since the rigid foams are more cross-linked and are composed essentially of closed cells, they exhibit excellent insulating characteristics. The K factor for polyether fluorocarbon-blown rigid foam falls in the range of 0.11–0.16 Btu/hr/ft^2/°F/in. for foams of about 2.0 lb/cu ft density. Other outstanding properties for the rigid urethane foams are compressive strength, resistance to moisture absorption, chemical resistance, dimensional stability and heat resistance.

Most insulation applications use the foam-in-place techniques such as for refrigerators (household appliances and commercial units), panels for home construction, transportation equipment (trailer trucks and railroad cars), and industrial application. Additional rigid foam markets are being developed in the marine field for adding buoyancy, military applications, automotive and packaging.

The polyisocyanate may be varied in the foam formulation in order to impart special physical properties or to improve processing of the rigid foam. For example, MDI (4,4′-diphenylmethane diisocyanate) claims far better dimensional stability. Also, an added advantage for the MDI is low vapor pressure with reduced toxicity, in particular when used in spray-up applications. Another isocyanate, PAPI (polymethylene polyphenylisocyanate) imparts high temperature resistance to the rigid foam.

Lower reactive isocyanates, such as crude TDI and MDI of about 85–90 % active diisocyanates have found use in one-shot rigid foams. Because of the high exotherm level in one-shot systems, the crude isocyanates have contributed to a better rigid foam by minimizing the tendency for internal scorching.

Urethane Coatings. A urethane coating system contains TDI reacted with polyols in such a way as to yield polymers containing any ratio, proportion or combination of urethane linkages, active isocyanate groups or polyisocyanate monomer. The reaction products may contain excess isocyanate groups available for further reaction at the time of application or may contain essentially no free isocyanate as supplied. In general, some of the principal advantages of a formulated urethane coating are fast drying characteristics, hard surface, deep gloss, and abrasion and chemical resistance.

The urethane coatings on the market are classified by ASTM under five principal types. These coatings are either one- or two-component systems. The coatings are also classified as to type of cure and type of modifier.

Urethane Elastomers. These elastomeric materials are produced through the reaction of certain polyisocyanates (TDI, MDI) and polyhydroxy compounds (polyether diol or OH-terminated polyester) to form a long linear polyurethane which is then chain extended and crosslinked to complete the reaction.

The urethane elastomers are especially noted for extreme toughness and abrasion resistance, along with hydrocarbon fluid resistance.

Urethane Fibers. Versatile synthetic fibers can be manufactured from polyurethanes. One such man-made fiber is the spandex type (a generic name approved by the F.T.C. to cover fibers containing at least 85 % segmented urethane). Advantages of the spandex fiber are light weight and fine denier; also good dyeing properties, good restraining power, flex life and durability.

The current usage of spandex elastic fibers is in foundation garments, swimsuits, hosiery and related products. In general, the spandex is covered with a double wrapping of other material or a cover is spun around a filament core. Blends of spandex staple with conventional fibers are under test to extend the use of spandex to conventional woven and knitted fabrics.

GEORGE T. GMITTER

Cross-references: POLYURETHANES; URETHANES.

DIMETHYL TEREPHTHALATE AND TEREPHTHALIC ACID

In the 1940's, J. R. Whinfield and J. T. Dickson of the British firm of Calico Printers discovered poly(ethylene terephthalate), (PET) which has proven to be a most successful polymer for film and fiber.

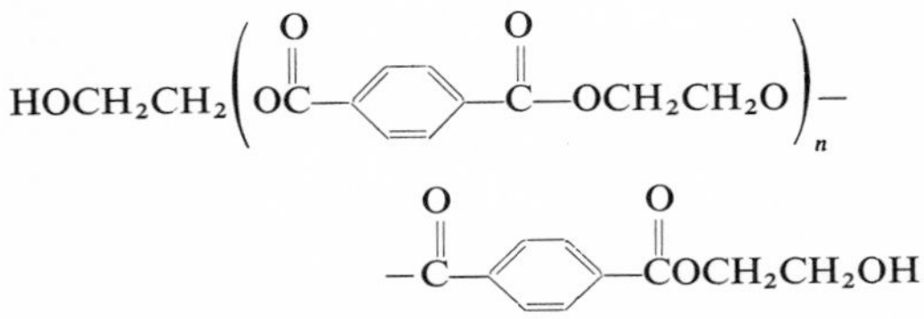

Poly(ethylene terephthalate)

Until recently the principal raw materials for PET have been dimethyl terephthalate (DMT) and ethylene glycol. The use of terephthalic acid (TPA) in place of DMT has recently become possible because of technological advances in the purification of TPA to give a polymer-grade acid. The growth of DMT and TPA as commercial chemicals has paralleled the enormous expansion of the PET market. In the United States this market was 40 million lb in 1955, and 450 million lb in 1965; it is forecasted to reach 1.6 billion lb by 1975. Markets outside the United States appear to be growing at a similar rate.

Chemistry and Methods of Manufacture

DMT is a white, crystalline solid, melting at 141°C, quite insoluble in water, but soluble in ether, hot hydrocarbons and alcohols. The carbomethoxy groups of DMT are typical of those attached to a benzene ring, and their ready participation in alcoholysis reactions is the basis for most of the utility of DMT.

The principal method for attainment of DMT is oxidation of p-xylene. Until 1955 this oxidation was done with nitric acid, but since then, oxidation with air has become the dominant means. In Germany and Japan, some DMT is produced by a process involving rearrangement of potassium benzoate or potassium phthalate to potassium terephthalate.

The nitric acid oxidation of p-xylene to TPA, according to the basic patent.* is carried out with 25–40% nitric acid at 150–250°C and 200–400 psig; a yield of 85% is attainable and the xylene to toluic acid step controls the yield. The terephthalic acid is esterified with methanol to give DMT.

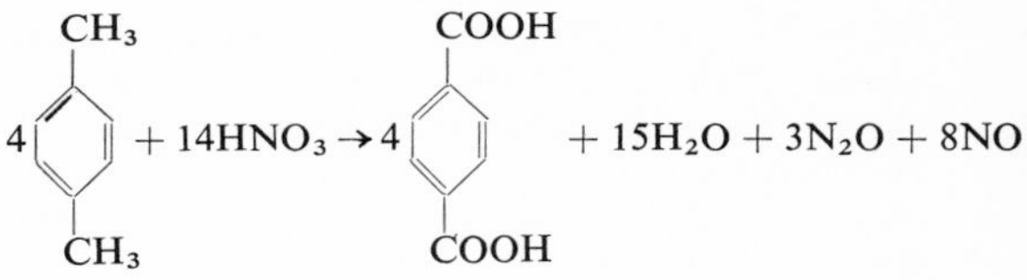

* [L. A. Burrows, R. M. Cavanaugh, and W. M. Nagle (to E. I. du Pont de Nemours & Co.) U.S. 2,636,899. April 28, 1953].

$$4 \; \text{p-Xylene} + 14\text{HNO}_3 \rightarrow 4 \; \text{Terephthalic acid} + 15\text{H}_2\text{O} + 3\text{N}_2\text{O} + 8\text{NO}$$

One of the principal commercial air oxidation processes consists of four chemical steps, as seen below:

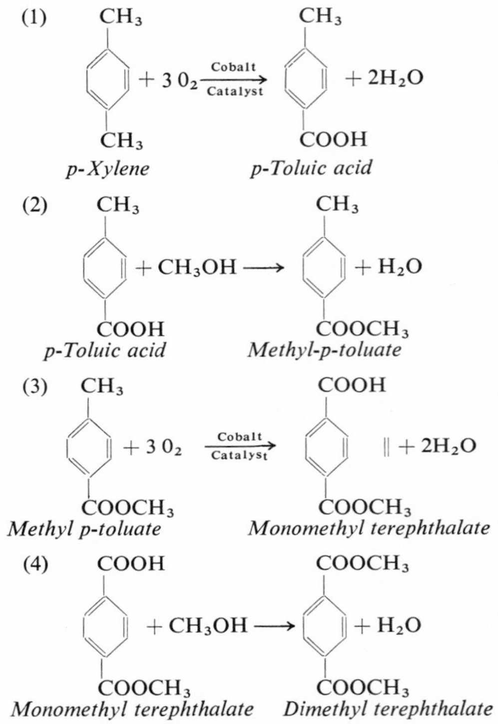

(1) p-Xylene $+ 3\text{O}_2 \xrightarrow[\text{Catalyst}]{\text{Cobalt}}$ p-Toluic acid $+ 2\text{H}_2\text{O}$

(2) p-Toluic acid $+ \text{CH}_3\text{OH} \longrightarrow$ Methyl-p-toluate $+ \text{H}_2\text{O}$

(3) Methyl p-toluate $+ 3\text{O}_2 \xrightarrow[\text{Catalyst}]{\text{Cobalt}}$ Monomethyl terephthalate $+ 2\text{H}_2\text{O}$

(4) Monomethyl terephthalate $+ \text{CH}_3\text{OH} \longrightarrow$ Dimethyl terephthalate $+ \text{H}_2\text{O}$

The oxidation of p-xylene to p-toluic acid is a facile reaction. The oxidation of p-toluic acid to TPA, however, is extremely sluggish under conventional air-oxidation conditions. Thus, the important feature in the success of this process was the discovery that methyl p-toluate is readily oxidized by air to monomethyl terephthalate. In practice, the methyl p-toluate and xylene are oxidized together in the same reactor; following esterification of the oxidate, methyl toluate is separated and recycled to the oxidizer. DMT is the direct product of this process; there is no necessity to handle the rather intractable terephthalic acid. The basis for this process is covered by numerous patents.†

†[I. E. Levine (to California Research Corp.), U.S. 2,653,165, September 22, 1953, and I. E. Levine and W. G. Toland, Jr. (to California Research Corp.) U.S. 2,772,305, November 27, 1956].

More recently, methods of oxidizing *p*-xylene directly to TPA with air have been developed and two commercial processes are now in operation. The first uses bromide promotion of a heavy metal-catalyzed oxidation, preferably in acetic acid as solvent, to give high yields of terephthalic acid under relatively mild conditions. The basic process is described in a patent.*

p-Xylene   *Acetic acid solvent*   *Terephthalic acid*

Special attention must be given to materials of construction in this process. The crude acid can be esterified with methanol to give DMT that can be purified to the required quality. Alternatively, the crude acid can be converted to fiber-grade TPA by a purification process which probably includes a hydrogenation step.

The second commercial direct process for TPA uses a co-oxidant such as methyl ethyl ketone to promote the cobalt-catalyzed air-oxidation of *p*-xylene; acetic acid is a by-product. The basis for the process is described in a patent [W. F. Brill (to Mathieson Chemical Corp.), U.S. 2,853,514, September 23, 1958].

The only commercial routes to TPA and DMT not based on *p*-xylene are based on the thermal rearrangement of potassium salts of aromatic acids to potassium terephthalate [cf. B. Raeche, *Angew Chem.*, 70, 1 (1958)]. These rearrangements are carried out at temperatures near 450°C and often under high pressure. Several catalysts for the rearrangement are known, of which cadmium salts appear to be the best.

* A. Saffer and R. S. Barber (Mid-Century Corp.), U.S. 2,833,816, May 6, 1958.

Potassium benzoate   *Potassium benzene terephthalate*

Potassium phthalate   *Potassium terephthalate*

Variations on the basic process such as addition of potassium carbonate, carbon monoxide, etc., reportedly improve the ratio of potassium terephthalate to benzene in the benzoate process. The principle problems encountered with this process are due to solids handling and the need to recycle the potassium effectively.

Many other routes to DMT and TPA have been reported. A TPA process, based on the nitric acid oxidation of chloromethylated toluene, has reached the plant stage in Japan. None of the other known processes, such as air-oxidation of *p*-diisopropylbenzene, or oxidation of *p*-xylene with sulfur and ammonia, have reached commercial operation.

One of the critical aspects for commercial success of a DMT or TPA process is the ability to produce a product of the extremely high purity required for polyester production. DMT is one of the purest commercial-grade chemicals ever sold; the minimum freezing point specification for commercial DMT is 140.62°C, which is only 0.03°C lower than the freezing point of the pure material. The purification processes for DMT are all based on combinations of crystallization and distillation. The purification processes for TPA are more complex and less well documented, but fiber-grade TPA must approach DMT in quality to be acceptable.

DMT is available commercially as almond-shaped pellets, as flake, or in the molten form, with pellets being the preferred form for shipment. Some typical properties of commercial DMT are:

Freezing point, °C	140.64
Color (molten) ASTM Pt-Co	10
Color stability, 4 hr at 175°C	10
Acid number	0.01
Aldehyde ester, ppm	20
Assay as DMT, %	99.97
Saponification number	578
Vapor pressure, mm Hg	
at 150°C	13
at 200°C	84
at 250°C	360
at 300°C	760
Bulk density (pellets), lb/cu ft	47

TPA is usually sold as a powder. Some typical properties of commercial TPA are:

Acid number	675
Aldehyde ester, ppm	<15
Assay as TPA, %	<99.95
Total significant metals, ppm	2
Moisture, wt %	0.02
DMF color, 5% solution, ASTM Pt-Co	<5
Benzoic acid, ppm	20
Toluic acid, ppm	80
Isophthalic acid, ppm	<25
Methyl dibasic acids, ppm	30
Dimethyl benzoic acids, ppm	ND
Tribasic acids	ND

Uses

By far the major use for DMT and TPA is the manufacture of PET. This is a two-step process in which DMT or TPA is first reacted with ethylene glycol to form a glycol terephthalate prepolymer with the elimination of methanol or water, and then the glycol terephthalate prepolymer is converted to high molecular weight polymer by heating (270–290°C) under reduced pressure (< 1.0 Torr) to eliminate ethylene glycol.

Many catalysts for these reactions are known, but the catalyst for the first step is usually a metal oxide or acetate, and for the second step an antimony or titanium compound. Since high molecular weight and good color are key properties of PET, extreme purity in the raw materials is essential. DMT and TPA will probably compete on a nearly equal footing as raw materials for PET manufacture.

PET crystallizes readily above about 75°C and is an extremely brittle polymer unless oriented. Thus, the major outlets for PET are as a fiber which is oriented by drawing, or a film which is oriented by tentering. As a fiber, PET is well established and growing rapidly in the textile market. Use of PET or modified PET as a tire cord is a more recent development which should open up another large market for the fiber. PET is well known as a general purpose film and is also used extensively for photographic film and magnetic tape.

Recently, modifications have been made to the poly(ethylene terephthalate) molecule by preparing copolyesters in which part of the terephthalic portion of the polymer is replaced by other dibasic acids such as isophthalic, azelaic, and cyclohexanedicarboxylic. These polyesters show utility in the unoriented state and some markets have been developed for them as adhesives, coatings, and plastics. Derivatives of DMT are used in wire enamels for high temperature insulation of electric motors, in dyeing aids for polyethylene terephthalate, and in high temperature-resistant oil additives. None of these uses is a large consumer of DMT or TPA.

JOHN F. WALKER

DISPERSING AGENTS

As used in liquid or solid suspensions, dispersing agents are substances that increase or promote the separation of colloidal particles and thus prevent agglomeration, flocculation, or settling out. Dispersing agents are generally polymeric electrolytes such as condensed sodium silicate, but they may also be various types of polyphosphates and certain derivatives of lignin. Although the action of dispersing agents is not completely understood, it is generally agreed that they function by imparting an electric charge on the surface of the solid particles in a suspension or colloid, making them mutually repellent and thus reverse their tendency to agglomerate. Another type of reaction is the creation of a polymolecular layer or film which acts as a physical barrier to direct contact between particles or with the surrounding aqueous media.

Dispersing agents have many industrial and agricultural applications, including use as stabilizers in agricultural chemical formulations such as DDT, BHC, sulfur, copper sulfate, aldrin, dieldrin, toxaphene, and other pesticides or insecticides; applications involving the impregnation of materials with emulsions for lubricating or waterproofing; dust and dirt removal in industrial cleaners, paint strippers, electrocleaners, and polishing compounds; dispersion of pigments in water-based paints; as dispersants and stabilizers in dyeing processes, involving the use of acetate and vat anthraquinone paste colors which otherwise would deposit unevenly; as dispersants of gypsum stucco in the manufacture of gypsum board; as humectants and re-dispersants in the manufacture of dyestuff pastes and in the dispersing of carbon black in the production of GRS rubber; as clay deflocculants in the brick, tile, refractory, pottery, and porcelain industry; and in the plastics industry for numerous applications such as control of polymerization, dispersal of pigments, reinforcements, and additives, and in various waterproofing and flame-retarding processes applied to plastics and laminates of many types.

Lignosulfonates

Lignosulfonates such as "Marasperse" (American Can Company's Marathon Division) are hetero-disperse polymers whose molecular weights vary between 1000 and 20,000. The "Marasperses" are manufactured from the higher molecular weight fractions produced in the Marathon process for the purification of crude lignosulfonates. The organic structure of lignosulfonate compounds has not been completely determined, but it is known that the basic lignin monomer unit is a substituted phenyl propane. A section of the polymeric lignosulfonic acid could have the following structure:

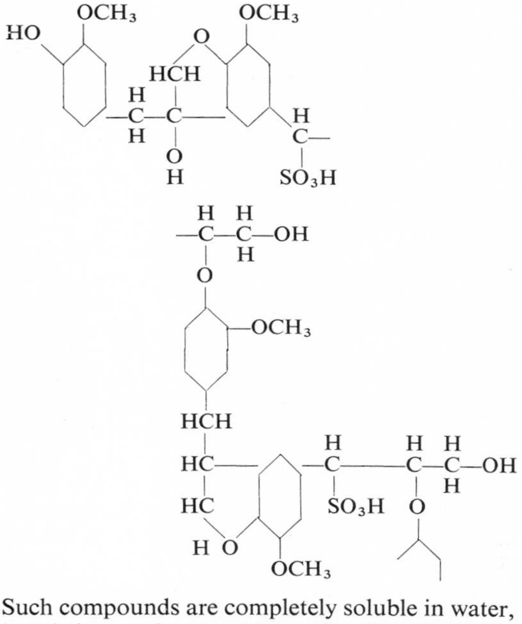

Such compounds are completely soluble in water, but their complex structure makes them insoluble in oils and most organic solvents. Aqueous solutions of the "Marasperses" containing 35–40% "Marasperse" by weight are available.

Action of Lignosulfonates. The action of "Marasperse" lignosolfonate dispersants is largely electrokinetic in nature. As they are absorbed by the particles of solids in suspension, they impart negative charges to the particles, causing them to repel one another. Adsorption on a suspended particle may also create a polymolecular layer or film barrier, as noted above. The lignosulfonates will also act as sequestrants under certain conditions. As is well known, the tendency for suspended solids to settle depends largely on their particle size and specific gravity. If small enough, the particles will remain in suspension because of Brownian movement. Larger particles, which are subject to greater gravitational forces, will settle. Dispersing agents prevent or minimize the formation of agglomerates and thus retard or prevent settling. Moreover, when aggregates are formed they impede the movement of a liquid and impart a high viscosity to the suspension. To reduce the viscosity, dispersants are often added during mechanical mixing, thereby increasing the fluid-flow characteristics of the liquid. Still another effect of dispersants is the inhibition of crystal growth by the process of sequestering ions in solution, holding their concentrations below the point where they form insoluble precipitates.

Emulsion Stabilization. Lignosulfonates (and similar dispersants) are used to stabilize oil-in-water emulsions in much the same manner as they disperse solids. Since they do not appreciably lower interfacial tension, mechanical shearing action such as that provided by a colloid mill or homogenizer is required to form the small droplets of the oil phase. The dispersants will then stabilize minute droplets of any type of immiscible liquid in water to give an oil-in-water emulsion, which is highly resistant to breaking ordinarily caused by wide variations in pH, temperature, mechanical handling, or the action of electrolytes.

Concentrations Required. The correct amount of lignosulfonate dispersant needed to obtain best results will vary with the material being dispersed. Even with the same material, variations in particle size or shape, or in the amount and kind of impurities, will affect the quantity required. Accordingly, trials should be made with the particular material to be dispersed under the proper conditions of usage. The following ranges of "Marasperse" concentration have been found suitable in tests:

Material	Amount of Marasperse (Based on Weight of Solids)	
	Minimum	Maximum
Kaolin-type clay	0.05%	1.0%
DDT-clay mixture	0.2	2.0
Phenyl-beta-naphthylamine	0.2	2.0
Ball-type clay	0.5	1.0
Calcium carbonate	0.5	3.0
Sulfur	0.5	2.0
Iron oxide	1.0	3.0
Titanium dioxide	1.0	3.0
Zinc oxide	1.0	3.0
Carbon black	2.0	3.0

Properties of Lignosulfonates

Lignosulfonates are derived from lignin by sulfite pumping of wood. Lignin, the "natural plastic" that binds cellulose fibers together in wood and woody plants, is a polymer—a giant molecule built up from smaller molecular units which in lignin vary somewhat in chemical make-up. Although it is fairly certain that the smaller units or monomers are substituted phenyl propane molecules, the exact manner in which they combine to form lignin is not known. Indications are, however, that the monomers build in more than one way. Thus lignosulfonate obtained from lignin constitutes a *group* of closely related compounds rather than comprising a distinct chemical entity. Because of the variation in chemical structure and composition, the lignosulfonates vary in toxicological properties, and the manufacturer should be consulted before engaging in any protrated or commercial-scale use so that adequate precautions can be taken. However, it may be said that most of these substances are relatively nontoxic in ordinary applications, and the Department of Agriculture has certified many of the lignosulfonates for use in pesticide sprays or dips for preharvest or post-harvest application to bananas and other perishables, as well as in the coating and sizing of paper and paperboard used in food packaging.

Other Dispersing Agents

In addition to the sulfonates of lignin, other typical dispersing agents include sodium silicate (for clays, slips, glazes); sodium tripolyphosphate (oil-well muds, clays); sodium hexametaphosphate (dyes, pigments); calcium lignin sulfonate (sulfur dispersions); and stearic acid (carbon black, zinc oxide, and similar pigments). In nonaqueous media, nonionic dispersing agents such as sterols, lecithin, and fatty acids can be employed.

DAVID W. STUTZ

DIVINYLBENZENE

Divinylbenzene is a clear, colorless, mobile liquid possessing an aromatic odor similar to that of styrene, to which it is structurally related. Empirically, divinylbenzene has the formula $C_{10}H_{10}$; its molecular weight is 130.18.

Divinylbenzene occurs in three isomeric forms: *ortho-*, *meta-*, and *para*-divinylbenzene. The structure of the *meta* isomer (or 1,3-divinylbenzene) is given below:

$$CH{=}CH_2$$

$$CH{=}CH_2$$

The divinylbenzenes belong to a class of organic compounds known as monomers. These materials readily undergo addition polymerization under the influence of heat and/or catalytic initiation. Addition polymerization is a unique type of chemical reaction wherein monomers like divinylbenzene react rapidly with themselves and with other molecules containing one or more vinyl ($CH_2{=}CH{-}$) groupings to produce very high molecular weight addition compounds called polymers. These derivatives are either thermally plastic or thermally setting (i.e., permanently rigid), depending on the amount of divinylbenzene contained.

Manufacture

Divinylbenzene is prepared commercially by the catalytic dehydrogenation of diethylbenzenes. For this reason, commercial grades of divinylbenzene contain the three isomeric forms, together with the isomeric ethylvinylbenzenes and trace amounts of unreacted diethylbenzenes. It is not commercially feasible to separate further the components of this mixture because of the closeness of their boiling points.

Specifications and Analysis

Two grades of divinylbenzene are obtainable commercially; mixtures containing 20–25% and 50–60% divinylbenzene. Typical specifications are given in Table 1.

TABLE 1. SPECIFICATIONS.

	20–25	50–60
Purity, %		
Total polymerizable material, %, min	55	90
Color, Hellige varnish scale, max	14	3
Bromine number, min	100	170
Inhibitor (*tert*-butylcatechol), ppm	400–600	900–1100
Boiling point (760 mm Hg), °C	180	195
Flash point, °F, Tag open cup	125	170
Specific gravity, 60°F/60°F	0.900	0.915
Weight, lb per gal	7.55	7.62

A typical detailed analysis of the 50–60% commercial divinylbenzene mixture is given in Table 2.

It will be noted in Table 2 that the *meta-/para-*divinylbenzene ratio in the mixture shown is about 2.5 : 1. This ratio may vary somewhat, depending upon manufacturing conditions. Commercial mixtures contain, at most, only a few per cent of *ortho*-divinylbenzene. Since the *ortho* isomer does not polymerize as readily as the *meta* and *para* isomers, it is relatively unimportant, industrially.

The physical constants of the three isomeric forms are summarized in Table 3.

TABLE 2. TYPICAL CHEMICAL ANALYSIS OF 50–60%
DIVINYLBENZENE.

Component	Amount
By vapor phase chromatography:	
meta-Divinylbenzene	42.5%
para-Divinylbenzene[a]	16.7
Ethylvinylbenzenes	39.3
Diethylbenzenes	Trace
Styrene and *ortho*-xylene	0.9
Ethylbenzene	Trace
Naphthalene	0.7
Total sulfur	10 ppm
Polymer content	12 ppm
tert-Butylcatechol	1098 ppm

[a] May include a very small amount of *ortho*-divinyl-benzene.

TABLE 3. PHYSICAL CONSTANTS OF THE DIVINYLBEN-ZENE ISOMERS.

	ortho	*meta*	*para*
Boiling point, °C/mm Hg	78.5/11	52/3 210.55/760	46–9/1–2 52/4 85–6/16
Melting point, °C		−52.25	31
Density, g/cc/°C	0.934/21	0.926/22	0.913/40
Refractive index, η_D/°C	1.5760/21	1.5746/22	1.5835/25 1.5820/40

Hazards

Divinylbenzenes are flammable and may form explosive mixtures with air. For these reasons, adequate ventilation should be provided when these materials are being handled. Precautions must also be taken to assure that adequate protection against fire and static electric discharge is available.

Like benzene, styrene, and other related aromatic hydrocarbons, divinylbenzenes are toxic. Inhalation of vapors and liquid contact with the skin should be avoided.

Reactivity

Pure divinylbenzenes and the commercial mixtures are extremely reactive and will autopolymerize slowly, even at 0°C. These materials should therefore be stored in a cool place and are ordinarily protected against spontaneous reaction by the addition of *tert*-butylcatechol or other polymerization inhibitors. Higher levels of inhibitor are required than for styrene and related monomers because of the much greater reactivity of the divinylbenzenes.

In many commercial applications, the inhibitor is not removed prior to utilization of divinylbenzene in chemical reactions because divinylbenzene is usually a minor ingredient, constituting less than 25% of the total polymerizable monomers. Moreover, the effect of the inhibitor is easily overcome by the action of heat and the usual polymerization initiators. When, for reasons of color improvement or product purity, removal of the *tert*-butylcatechol inhibitor is desired, it can easily be done by washing with a 5% aqueous caustic solution. Inhibitor-free divinylbenzene should be used immediately or reinhibited.

Applications

General. Divinylbenzene is utilized commercially almost exclusively as a monomer for polymerization. Because of the difunctionality conferred on the molecule by the presence of two vinyl groups, divinylbenzene is commonly employed to introduce cross-linking into polymer structures. The two vinyl groups exhibit almost equal reactivities and therefore tend to undergo polymerization independently.

Styrene and other monovinyl monomers undergo addition polymerization to produce predominantly linear macromolecules:

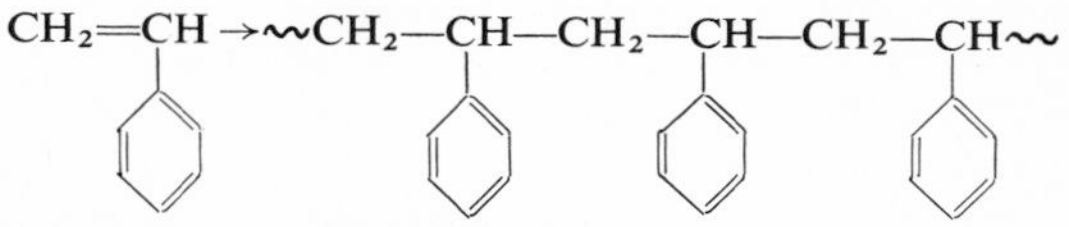

Introduction of divinylbenzene into a styrene polymerization makes possible the creation of branches and cross-links as follows:

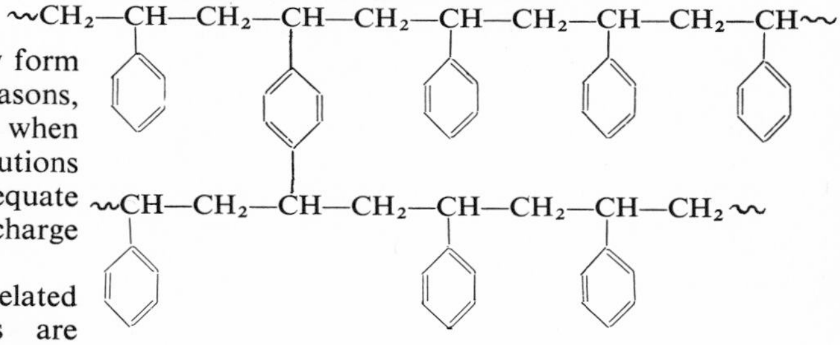

It is easy to see that a very small amount (less than 0.05%) of divinylbenzene, properly spaced throughout the polymeric system, may serve merely to increase the spread of molecular weights by occasionally linking together two other (primary) growing chains to produce a mixture of products as follows:

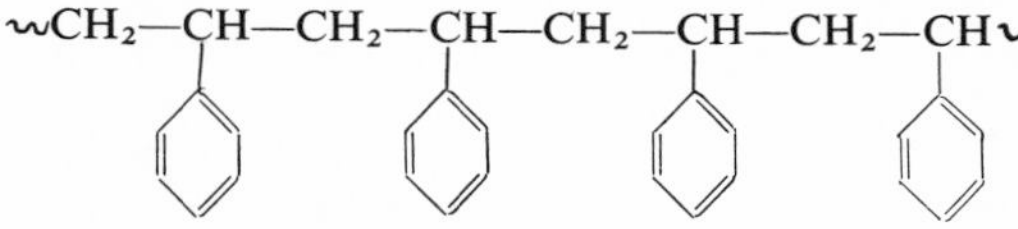

linear polystyrene

~CH$_2$—CH—CH$_2$—CH—CH$_2$—CH—CH$_2$—CH~

~CH—CH$_2$—CH—CH$_2$—CH—CH$_2$—CH—CH$_2$~

cross-linked polystyrene

while, at the same time, introducing some chain branching.

It is erroneous to infer from the foregoing that detailed control of the placement of divinylbenzene units (or any other type of monomer units) is normally possible in the common free-radial types of polymerization under discussion, for the molecular architecture is usually a random structure determined primarily by the composition of the co-monomeric feed and the relative reactivities of the monomers employed. As little as 0.1% divinylbenzene in a copolymer system will normally give rise to some structures containing more than one cross-link, resulting in some insoluble products. The frequency of occurrence of cross-links increases as the divinylbenzene content of the copolymer increases.

At higher contents of divinylbenzene (several per cent), the cross-linking becomes tighter, i.e., more closely spaced, and the tendency becomes more pronounced for cross-linking to occur between more than two primary polymeric chains. Thus the complex molecules so generated assume a three-dimensional aspect, and the molecular weight approaches infinity. In effect, copolymeric systems containing as little as 5% divinylbenzene consist of only a few giant molecules because essentially all primary chains are attached to at least one other chain by at least one cross-link. Under these circumstances, the polymer is no longer soluble but merely swells when placed in contact with an organic medium, which would dissolve an uncross-linked polymer of the same approximate composition. The degree of swelling and the amount of "solvent" imbibed by the polymeric gel are inversely proportional to the number of cross-links present and, therefore, also to the divinylbenzene content of the copolymer. Polymers containing small amounts ($< 0.10\%$) of divinylbenzene may swell as much as 20–40 times their original volumes. Swelling of polymers containing more than 10% divinylbenzene is practically nil.

The ultimate in cross-linking is achieved in a polymer composed exclusively of divinylbenzene. This composition has little practical importance since, as stated earlier, no commercial source of pure divinylbenzene exists. Pure homopolymers of

divinylbenzene have been prepared and studied to a limited extent.

Copolymers produced from the styrene/*ortho*-divinylbenzene copolymerization do not show any indication of cross-linking as far as solubility is concerned. In this, the *ortho*-isomer differs from the *meta*- and *para*-isomers. Absence of cross-linking by *ortho*-divinylbenzene is attributed to steric shielding of the second vinyl group by the main polymer chain.

As indicated previously, the relative reactivities of the comonomers in any copolymeric system control in part the ultimate placing (i.e., the sequential distribution) of the monomeric units in the copolymer. This phenomenon gives rise to rather complicated reaction kinetics since divinylbenzene is usually copolymerized with at least one other monomer, and the commercial divinylbenzene mixtures are composed of the two isomeric forms of divinylbenzene, plus other polymerizable monomers such as the *meta* and *para*-ethylvinylbenzenes, all of which exhibit different chemical reactivities with each other and with styrene. From a practical point of view, however, the limitations imposed by these complexities are not important in most commercial applications since the final balancing of polymer properties can usually be achieved by empirical adjustments in the comonomeric feed and/or in the polymerization process conditions.

Ion-Exchange Resins. Currently, the most important commercial application of divinylbenzene is in the manufacture of ion-exchange resins. While most other cross-linking applications employ from 0.5% to a few per cent of divinylbenzene, the divinylbenzene contents of ion-exchange resins vary from about 8% to about 15%. The amounts of ion-exchange resins produced in this country are in the multi-million pound range. The most common application is in the manufacture of resins for water softeners.

Styrene-based polymers are the most prevalent among ion-exchange resins. Spheres (called beads) composed of styrene and divinylbenzene copolymers in the 20–50 mesh range of sizes, are first prepared by a suspension polymerization technique. Cation-exchange resins are produced from these by swelling the beads in perchloroethylene followed by reaction with sulfonating agents. The result is a system of solid, spherical beads of insoluble, aromatic polysulfonic acids. These ion-exchange resins are highly effective in the removal of specific cations from solutions such as are encountered in commercial and household water conditioning, demineralizing of aqueous and nonaqueous liquids, recovering of metals from waste liquids, and purifying of sugar solutions, antibiotics and organic chemicals.

Divinylbenzene can also be reacted with acrylic acids and their esters, with or without the inclusion of styrene monomer, to produce other types of cation-exchange resins. If the acrylic or methacrylic acid esters are used, the product is hydrolyzed to form the free carboxylic acids. Resins containing both the carboxylic and the sulfonic acid groupings can be prepared by including a sulfonating step since the sulfonation usually occurs on the aromatic nuclei provided by the styrene units.

Halomethylation (mainly chloromethylation) of a styrene-divinylbenzene copolymer, followed by treatment with a phosphorous ester such as triethylphosphite, gives rise to a phosphonic acid-type cation-exchange resin. Chloromethylation followed by amination converts a styrene-divinylbenzene copolymer to an anion-exchange resin. The product is a quaternary ammonium compound. Anion-exchange resins are useful in removing mineral acids from organic acid solutions, in concentrating weak alkali solutions and in preparing salts from bases. Mixed cation/anion-exchange resin beds are used in the deionization of water for industrial processes.

Molding Resins. Inclusion of a small amount of divinylbenzene in a styrene polymerization recipe causes an increase in the heat distortion temperature of about 3°C for each per cent of divinylbenzene used. Small amounts ($<5\%$) of divinylbenzene also increase the tensile and impact strengths of polystyrene. Higher amounts reduce the strength and increase the brittleness, however. The hardness of polystyrene increases continuously with increasing divinylbenzene concentration.

Rubbers and Adhesives. Divinylbenzene in amounts up to about 0.5% improves the processing characteristics (i.e., milling, molding, calendering and extrusion) of many butadiene-styrene synthetic rubbers. Elastomers containing divinylbenzene may be converted to adhesives for floor and wall coverings by the addition of tackifier resins and solvents.

Cold flow in polybutadiene and butyl rubbers can be markedly reduced by copolymerization of small amounts of divinylbenzene.

Partial Polymers. Some applications for divinylbenzene have been reported wherein only one of the two vinyl groups has apparently been polymerized. These partial polymers are useful intermediates in the preparation of casting and laminating resins and other thermosetting vinyl resins. Final curing after molding or casting is achieved by polymerization of the residual vinyl groups.

Miscellaneous. Divinylbenzene can be incorporated with styrene, or other monomers, which are copolymerized with unsaturated polyesters to produce coating, laminating, potting and adhesive resins. Divinylbenzene can be added alone or with styrene to drying oils and coreacted to produce

coating vehicles of higher molecular weight and solvent resistance.

Controlled carbonization of polydivinylbenzene beads yields polymeric carbon spheres which are claimed to be useful for bearings and semiconductors.

Chelating (i.e., metal-complexing) resins have been prepared by carboxymethylation of polymers containing divinylbenzene and vinylbenzylamino monomers. Polyacrylonitrile fibers have been cross-linked by divinylbenzene to improve their tensile strength. Sulfonated styrene-divinylbenzene copolymers have been reported to be useful as thickening agents for butyl rubber latexes. Binders for carbon (graphite) molds for heat-resistant metals and polymeric binders for rocket propellants constitute other areas of utilization for divinylbenzene copolymers.

Divinylbenzene has been copolymerized with a wide variety of other monomers including acrylonitrile, substituted styrenes, vinyl pyridine, vinyl acetate, isoprene, cyclopentadiene, ethylene, and vinyl chloride to produce high molecular weight products suitable for fabrication into many useful items of commerce. A number of copolymers containing divinylbenzene are used as chemical catalysts. Applications cited in the patent literature include the polymerization of olefins and the production of hydrogen peroxide from peracetic acid and water.

In addition to the aforementioned applications of divinylbenzene which involve copolymers prepared by free-radical mechanisms, there are instances wherein useful products are reported as emanating from the ionic copolymerization of divinylbenzene with titanium, aluminum and vanadium metal coordination catalysts. Ethylene, butadiene and isobutene copolymers with divinylbenzene appear to be prominent among those cases cited in the patent literature.

The methods of utilization of divinylbenzene which do not involve some type of polymerization reaction appear to be quite limited. One reported application is in the defoliation of cotton. In addition, divinylbenzene can be regarded to be a chemical intermediate for a very few nonpolymer type organic reactions.

W. N. MACLAY

Cross-reference: STYRENE.

DYES AND PIGMENTS

The two basic colorant classifications are pigments and dyes; the essential difference between the two is particle size. Dye particles are submicroscopic (molecular size), and thus form true solutions which are absorbed to impart color. They are of both synthetic and natural origin, and are soluble in most common solvents to yield bright, strong, transparent colors of almost limitless range. However, high process heats required in the processing of most plastics limit their use to the certain families of dyes offering the highest heat resistance.

Dyes also tend to migrate in polyolefins and vinyls. Post-dyeing of finished plastic parts is a very economical way of coloring items such as buttons, which can be molded in large numbers and colored later to any shade and in any quantity. Dyes are classified according to their origin and mode of application.

Pigments are rarely available in less than micron size, and are inherently insoluble. However, they will form suspensions. Pigments are further classified as organic and inorganic, not only due to their chemical structure, but also due to their inherent differences in application. Organic pigments possess certain features in common with dyes. Translucent and nearly transparent colors can be obtained, although their tinctorial power is considerably less (basic hue plus white). They resist migration better than dyes, and are characterized by low specific gravity.

Inorganic pigments offer the best economics of the basic types of plastic colorants. With few exceptions, they produce opaque colors. Tinctorial power is weaker and less clean than the organic pigments and, of course, than the dyes.

There are two basic characteristics for evaluating dyes and pigments:

(1) Performance, which includes brightness, hiding power, tinctorial strength, transparency, etc.

(2) Resistance to heat, light, weather, migration, chemicals, etc.

Incorporation of Dyes and Pigments

There are several methods of incorporating color into plastics, the choice being based on such factors as cost, quality, type of operation, quantity involved, and the physical characteristics of the plastic itself. Basically, they are: compounding with Banbury mills, roll mills and extruders, color concentrates, dry colorants and the aforementioned *post-dyeing*.

Dry Coloring. This is the simplest and generally the least expensive method of coloring plastic materials. Dry-colorant powder is tumbled (mixed) with basic or compounded plastic resin. In the case of thermoplastics, this tumbled mix is then passed through an injection machine, blow molder or extruder. The only real drawback to this method is the difficulty in obtaining complete dispersion of the colorant particles throughout the mix. Finished parts often present a streaked, or mottled appearance, partly due to the natural tendency of finely ground particles to form

agglomerates, and partly to the effect of resin flow characteristics on color dispersion.

Resins with low melt index values are fairly easy to disperse, but others require special dispersion aids and molding techniques. Product shape, too, can affect dispersion. Flat, thin, symmetric parts pose the greatest difficulty, since dispersion *must* be uniform in all directions. Another problem encountered in dry coloring is contamination, and special care and equipment is required which may counterbalance the initial financial saving.

The prime advantage of dry coloring is the wide range of color possibilities available to the processor from a relatively small inventory of natural or colorless molding compounds. Resin is colored only as needed and, if perfect matching or difficult color effects are not specified, dry coloring is the most practical method.

Dry coloring of thermosetting resins requires special equipment. Ball milling is preferred for quality mixing, but is only practical when large quantities are required (up to 1 ton per batch). Attrition grinding is preferred for the smaller batches, but does not afford the same efficiency. In either case, care must be exercised to prevent overheating which could prematurely cure the resin.

Dye and Pigments. These concentrates involve the use of up to 100 times the amount of color required for the finished part into the resin formulation. If supplied as pellets, chips, or powders, these concentrates are often referred to as "masterbatches." The actual amount of color incorporated into the formulation will depend on the colorant itself, the fabrication method, and the end use.

Extruders and screw-injection machines (but not conversion units) offer excellent mixing of concentrate with uncolored resin, so that large concentrations of color may be incorporated in the masterbatch (except with film as mentioned earlier). This means a smaller amount of concentrate is needed, which cuts the cost of concentrates as well as the inventory. Ram injection machines and the converted units do not provide the same shear in mixing.

Dry color concentrates (or masterbatches) are generally preferred with the following thermoplastics: polystrene and ABS materials, polyethylene, polypropylene, acrylics, and vinyl powders. Although it is theoretically possible to concentrate color in other thermoplastics, the quantities involved have not yet been sufficient to warrant the initial expense involved for the compounder.

Color concentrates offer a number of advantages for the small to medium-size molder. Color fidelity is assured, and no special equipment is required at the processing level. Guess work is eliminated, and so are the large inventories of colored materials which might otherwise be required.

Color concentration requires considerable skill on the part of the concentrate manufacturer as well as special extrusion equipment, roll mills and Banbury mixers. Precise metering of dry solids is a must, as well as a closed conveyor system with pneumatic controls.

Liquid and paste concentrates are used primarily with vinyls (plastisols and organosols) and with the liquid and paste thermosetting resins. Liquid thermosets cannot be colored with dry powders unless resin, filler, and colorant can be blended in a sigma blade mixer or ribbon blender.

The liquid carrier or paste vehicle must be compatible with either the resin or another compounding ingredient such as a plasticizer or stabilizer. The liquid or paste is mixed with powdered or paste colorants and milled to produce a paste of predetermined consistency and composition. Usually, a final blending on a ribbon blender is required. Three-roll mills, ball mills, and other wet grinders are also used. Concentrate manufacturers use vehicles of the same chemical type as the resin to be colored, so as not to affect the physical properties of the molded part.

Pastes will vary in viscosity from pourable to thick, depending on solids content and other factors. Pastes pose almost insurmountable problems when used with dry resins. This *had* been required with pearlescent pigments, for example, until the recent development of shear-resistant pearl powders. Especially with vinyls, the presence of volatiles (vehicle) has a corrosive effect on thermoplastic processing equipment.

Gel coats bear a certain kinship to the paste concentrates, and are a popular method of coloring glass-reinforced polyesters and some phenolics. Designed to resemble a top-quality paint finish, gel coats consist of pigmented resin which is brushed or sprayed on the thermosetting structure before cure.

The gel coat reacts with the outer layer of resin during cure to form an integral part of the finished product. Depending on the mold surface, special decorative and textured effects can be obtained as well as a high-gloss surfacing. In addition, the gel coat masks the glass fiber patterns, where present, a persistent deterrent in the past to consumer acceptance of reinforced plastics.

Color Compounding. This method is a further refinement of dry coloring, involving an additional step or two—either extruding the dry blended mixture through a special die as continuous, spaghetti-like strands or, if special coloring refinements are required, running the dry blend through a Banbury or roll mill and then through the compounding extruder. This latter process gives the ultimate in color dispersion, and works very well with the difficult to color materials.

Hot cutting gives spherical pellets; cool cutting, the conventional rod-like pellets. The extrudate can be ground to give colored, granular molding powders.

This technique is restricted to thermoplastics, and is impractical unless large quantities of a given color are required. Color dispersion is far better than with straight dry blending, but the large compounding extruders required are of a special type and require special dies. Extrusion coloring is largely restricted to the material suppliers, compounders, and the large processors who are equipped to do their own color matching.

Selection of Dye or Pigment

The two prime factors affecting choice of coloring methods are quality and cost. Dry coloring is the least expensive method, but entails some sacrifice of quality. Far more consistent color fidelity is obtained with color concentrates at a somewhat higher cost.

Color compounding or concentrates plus an added compounding step on a Banbury or a roll mill furnish the ultimate in color dispersion. Costs are proportionately higher than any of the other methods.

These two factors, quality and cost, must be weighed one against the other, along with such other considerations as inventory, delivery delays, knowledge of the physical properties of colorants, colorant limitations, compatibility, color matching skills, available equipment, and plant house-keeping.

It is generally impossible to match a color using only one colorant. Frequently, colorants from different families are blended since they behave differently in different media (resins). Clarity and opacity are factors, since few resins are absolutely colorless and clear. Some plastics, particularly the alkaline materials, will develop color during or after processing. Others will react chemically with the colorant. The most effective means, therefore, is to consider each plastic classification separately and discuss its requirements and limitations.

Acetals. Currently, there are two acetal resins on the market—a homopolymer and a copolymer, both offering high clarity and softening points (347°F). Both accept dyes readily, but the high processing temperatures limits the use of dyes to those few having high heat resistance. In addition, dyes tend to fade when used with acetals.

Metallic effects are out, also those pigments which cause gas evolution that will generate high pressures during molding. The copolymer is said to perform better in this latter respect. Inorganic pigments are preferred for their heat stability, but the success of dry blending will depend on the shape of the part, wall thickness, and design of the mold (short gates and thick sections best suited).

Extrusion coloring is the recommended method, as the quantities involved are not yet sufficient to warrant color concentrate manufacture. In addition, high pigment loading causes scorching in the homopolymer, poor color distribution in the copolymer. Recommended loadings are limited to 0.1% in dry blends, 0.2–0.3% with the extrusion coloring step. Test runs are highly recommended.

ABS Resins. These materials contain the three basic monomers of acrylonitrile, butadiene and styrene in tailored proportions. There is only one transparent grade which is intended for blending, not extrusion or injection molding, but there is a wide range of color possibilities. The resins require intensive mixing, usually a Banbury, which pretty much eliminates the possibility of dry coloring. In addition, they must be *absolutely* dry. Extrusion coloring, which is essentially the method employed by the material suppliers, is recommended—or the use of color concentrates. In general, ABS materials handle and color much the same as polystyrene except for clarity.

Acrylics. These include straight and modified acrylics; the latter being copolymers of acrylic or methacrylic esters with styrene, alpha-methyl styrene, acrylonitrile, or butadiene. They are catalyzed with peroxide or other free radical-forming materials.

Crystal clarity and outstanding weather resistance are their prime features, and a full range of colors in any clarity can be obtained. The modified acrylics, however, are limited somewhat in colorant possibilities due to additives.

If dyes are used, they must not be bleached by or react with the peroxide catalysts. Heat resistance is a must with the modified acrylics. In either case, they must be light-fast for most applications. Colorants must not require stabilization, and color concentrations must be kept low to prevent migration due to the presence of solvents. Dry coloring is perfectly satisfactory with acrylics, assuming the usual care.

Alkyds. These thermosetting materials are formulated from polyesters crosslinked to monomers. Problems involved in coloring them are the same as polyesters (see *Polyesters*).

Amino Resins. The two best known amino resins are melamine and urea formaldehyde. Both are thermosetting resins, and almost any color effect can be obtained by dry ball milling or attrition grinding equipment. Colorants must not cause premature cure, and must be heat resistant and light fast. Production requirements and uses make it more profitable, except in very short runs, to obtain the material in colored form from the basic material supplier.

Allyls. Allyls, like alkyds, are used primarily in industrial applications where color is used more for coding than decoration. Here, too, the problems involved are similar to those for the larger classification, the polyesters.

Cellulosics. There are five cellulosic resin types, all derived from cotton linters or wood pulp: cellulose acetate, cellulose acetate butyrate, cellulose propionate, cellulose nitrate, and ethyl cellulose, Colorants must be light fast and heat resistant. Some pigments cause odor problems, and migration is a frequently occurring problem with dyes. Organic pigment toners tend to crock. Best dispersion is obtained with a hot roll mill, and best done at the material supplier level. In fact, colored cellulosic compounds are *cheaper* than the natural.

Epoxies. Epoxy resins require colorants which will neither catalyze nor inhibit polymerization (cure). Pigments are difficult to disperse in liquid epoxies, even with conventional paste grinding equipment. The material tends to chalk and powder outdoors, and colorants for that type use need not be lightfast nor weather resistant. They also tend to yellow on exposure, which means that the colorant should mask this effect— also that of the glass reinforcements, if used. Low temperature molding virtually eliminates heat resistance requirements, although some exothermic heat is given off during cure.

Fluorocarbons. These materials are chemical analogs of polyolefins with some of the hydrogen atoms replaced by fluorine to impart chemical, heat and moisture resistance. They also have a low coefficient of friction and resistance to oxidation and weathering. There are four basic types, one of which is also chlorinated. All require very high processing heats, which eliminates all but certain inorganic pigments, Coloring is best done by those specially qualified, i.e., material supplier or compounder.

Most fluorocarbons are expected to have high electric properties, which eliminates metallic pigments. Some high temperature pigments lower the degradation temperature of the resins and must be ruled out. Colorants must be of extremely fine particle size to yield high mask tones in low concentrations, and must not react with the chlorinated material.

Nylons. The several nylon types all require processing temperatures above 400°F, which rules out most of the dyes and organic pigments. Where chemical resistance is a problem, natural nylon is usually used—in fact, it is used for many of the industrial applications.

Carbon black and titanium dioxide will protect nylons from the effects of weathering, but require a high degree of dispersion beyond the usual capabilities of extrusion blending. In these situations, color concentrates are usually used.

Dry coloring is employed rarely; in those situations where very small batches are required. Colorants in general applications must be light- and color-fast, and fluorescent effects cannot be obtained due to lack of heat stability of these pigments.

Phenolics. These materials take on color (darken) shortly after processing, which limits the color choice to very dark reds, greens, browns, and blacks. In addition, most applications require the use of carbon black, fillers, and the use of inorganic pigments.

It is imperative to use nonconductive colorants in most applications except for closures where the reverse is true. Process heats up to 400°F are required, and high opacity is required in any pigment used.

Polycarbonates. These are the most difficult plastics to color. Colorants must resist temperatures up to 600°F, chemicals, migration, must not degrade the resin and must also be completely free of moisture. In fact, re-drying of the resin/colorant blend is required in all cases.

Dispersion is difficult, and best left to the material supplier. Screw injection works well, but not ram injection machines. Resistance to shear is also, then, a factor. Volume demands are still too small to warrant the use of color concentrates.

Polyethylenes. Basic requirements for coloring polyethylenes are lightfastness, compatibility with stabilizers, resistance to migration and, with the high density materials, considerable heat resistance. High pigment concentrations are desirable in improving light stability. Color concentrates work extremely well for this reason, preventing migration with the low density materials.

Inorganic pigments are preferred to mask the natural opacity of the resins. All dyes migrate, but some organic pigments can be used if partly soluble. Pigments must not cause resin degradation, which rules out zinc and manganese. Warpage and thermal cracking can be induced by colorants, especially the phthalocyanine blues.

Polypropylene. The same problems encountered with polyethylene occur with the polypropylenes, but heat resistance is more of a factor. Polypropylene is more translucent than polyethylene, therefore many more color effects can be obtained.

Polyesters. The high percentage of outdoor applications dictates lightfastness and weatherability for most colorant systems used with polyesters. Inorganic pigments, which will neither acclerate nor inhibit cure are usually selected. Molding temperatures are not excessive, making heat resistance less of a problem.

Dispersing dry pigments usually requires the added grinding of pigment before incorporation into liquid systems. Paste concentrates are effective, and are available in a large range of viscosities. The grinding carrier must be compatible with the resin, and should react with it to prevent subsequent softening. Dry colorants can be used with premixes, but these require extremely high shear.

As mentioned earlier, gel coats are very popular since they mask fillers and reinforcements. All special effects can be obtained, including pearl, tinsel, metallics, etc., as long as they do not affect the cure cycle.

Polystyrene. General purpose polystyrene is crystal clear, which permits a full range of colors and transparencies. The impact materials are translucent to opaque, and light in color to colorless. Lightfastness is not really a factor, since most applications are done indoors. Pigments should pass through a 325-mesh screen to assure proper dispersion.

Polystyrene tends to built up a static charge which adds to the dispersion problem. Liquid wetting and dispersion agents are employed, and color concentrates are very effective. Heat resistance is also a factor.

Polyurethanes. Colorants used must be inert to alkaline conditions and catalysts. They must disperse well, but need not be heat resistant or lightfast. Colorant systems must not accelerate or inhibit cure, and concentrations should be kept under 1% so as not to affect the tensile and tear strength of these elastomers.

One problem with inert pigments is that they tend to promote open cell formation, as well as increase the gas and nucleation rate at the beginning of the reaction. When reaction is completed, the cell membranes may break more readily.

Silicones. Finished parts are often subjected to heats up to 1000°F, making high heat resistance a must. Processing heats are also high. The inorganic pigments used must also be lightfast and resistant to weathering. Lead, tin, and zinc will affect polymerization.

Vinyls. Vinyls should be considered as being of two groups from the points of view of processing and coloring: plasticized, and rigid (unplasticized). Flexible vinyls are processed at lower temperatures than most thermoplastics, but tend to become acidic. Pigments also tend to agglomerate. Being plasticized, migration is a problem and the colorant must not migrate with the plasticizer. Rigid vinyls require high process heats and are far more difficult to color.

Color requirements in either case will also depend on the end use for the vinyl product. Stabilizers must be used to achieve lightfastness, and care must be taken to avoid plate-out and chemical reactions with resin, stabilizer, and plasticizer. Electrical properties are very important with the flexible material, since electrical insulation is one of the biggest applications.

Vinyls are supplied already colored, but dry coloring seems preferred since much of the compounding is done at the processor level. Plastisols, however, usually require the use of color concentrates. Since vinyl can be obtained completely transparent, any color effect is theoretically possible.

GUY A. MARTINELLI

Cross-references: COLORATION OF PLASTICS; ORGANIC COLORANTS.

E

EPOXY CURING AGENTS

Epoxy resins are converted from liquids or brittle low melting solids to useful thermoset materials by reacting with a variety of catalysts and copolymerizing agents. These reactants, referred to generally as curing agents, may be acidic or basic, organic or inorganic. They are used in ratios varying from 1 part to greater than 100 pph of epoxy. While some of the copolymerizing agents may constitute the greater part of the cured resin, the catalysts do not form an essential part of the cured material at all. Thus it is impossible to consider the properties of an epoxy without giving equal consideration to the curing agent used. Furthermore, the time and temperature of cure affect the final properties to the extent that they also must be defined for each system.

Epoxy resins are cured by four types of mechanisms: (1) reaction of epoxy groups with crosslinking agents containing active hydrogens; (2) self polymerization of the epoxy catalyzed by acidic or basic groups; (3) reaction of the hydroxyl groups with polyfunctional organic acid or anhydride crosslinking agents; (4) acid catalyzed cross-linking of epoxy with hydroxyl groups that are present in most epoxy resins.

The most commonly used catalysts are tertiary amines and borontrifluoride complexes such as borontrifluoride monoethylamine. Polyfunctional primary and secondary amines, polybasic organic acids and anhydrides and polysulfides are the most common cross-linking agents. A variety of materials that are not curing agents themselves are used to accelerate various curing reactions. Two examples are phenol and triphenylphosphite.

The choice of curing agent is determined by handling characteristics such as working life, cure time, and temperature; by properties desired, and by cost. Very often it is necessary to compromise between handling characteristics and properties desired or between mutually conflicting properties. For example, the best heat and chemical resistance can be obtained only by using a high temperature cure with its concomitant difficulties.

The general range of properties of a standard bisephenol A-epichlorohydrin-based epoxy cured with the various types of curing agents is given in Table 1. The gross differences between the various classes can be understood by studying the chemical composition of the curing agents. While the details of the various polymerization reactions are complex, even a superficial understanding of the chemistry involved can be of great assistance in gaining an appreciation of the properties that will be obtained.

Aliphatic Primary and Secondary Amines

By far the most important class of room temperature curing agents is the aliphatic polyamines. These are true crosslinking agents which combine with the epoxy to form a part of the cured resin molecule. The basic reactions involved in the cure are:

(1) a primary amine reacts with an epoxy:

(2) the secondary amine so formed then reacts with another epoxy group.

Since both the epoxy and the amine are polyfunctional, a highly cross-linked structure is formed. The epoxy-hydroxyl reaction does not occur to any great extent in this type of cure.

The first used amines were those that were commercially available such as diethylenetriamine

TABLE 1. TYPICAL PROPERTIES OF A LIQUID BISPHENOL A-EPICHLOROHYDRIN BASED EPOXY CURED WITH VARIOUS TYPES OF CURING AGENTS.

Hardener type	PHR[a]	Pot life[b]	Cure conditions	Physical properties				Electrical properties		
				Tensile strength psi	Tensile mod. psi	Elongation, %	HDT,[e] °F	Dissipation factor 10^3cps	Dielectric constant	Volume resistivity
Aliphatic amine	12	30 min	Overnight @ rm temp.[c] (3–7 days full cure)	10,000	0.49×10^6	2.5	220^d	0.026	3.91	1.2×10^{16}
Aliphatic amine epoxy adduct	25	30 min	Overnight @ rm temp.[c] (3–7 days full cure)	10,500	0.51×10^6	2.4	216^d	—	3.50	1.0×10^{15}
Aliphatic amine-monofunctional carboxylic acid adduct	50	90 min	Overnight @ rm temp.[c] (3–7 days full cure)	8300	0.17×10^6	6.4	153^d	0.021	3.57	3.1×10^{15}
Polyamide	82	2 hr	Overnight @ rm temp.[c] (3–7 days full cure)	5700	0.23×10^6	9.3	150^d	0.028	3.14	1.5×10^{14}
Polysulfide	100 (+10DMP –30)	35 min	Overnight @ rm temp.[c] (3–7 days full cure)	2800		30.0	less than rm temp.	0.012	5.50	6.0×10^{14}
Aromatic amine	26	7 hr	1 hr @ 130°F + 2 hr @ 225°F	8150	0.36×10^6	3.8	314	0.016	3.90	8.9×10^{15}
Tertiary amine salt	12	2 hr	2 hr @ 350°F	11,000	0.50×10^6	4.7	154	0.004	3.80	8.7×10^{14}
Polyazelaic polyanhydride	70 (+1DMP –10)	2 hr @ 165°F	4 hr @ 140° + 4 hr @ 246°F	5150		74.0	less than rm temp.	0.005	4.41	1.3×10^{16}
Hexahydrophthalic anhydride	80 (+1DMP –30)	2 hr @200°F	16 hr @ 300°F + 2 hr @ 200°F	8100	0.40×10^6	6.0	273	0.01 (@10^6cps)	3.52 (@10^6cps)	1.2×10^{16}
Methyl Nadic anhydride	80 (+2DMP –30)	2 1/2 hr	2 hr @ 400°F + 2 hr @ 212°F + 2 hr @ 302°F	11,600	0.76×10^6	2.7	280	0.005	3.07	5.8×10^{15}
Pyromellitic dianhydride	60 (+0.25 di-ethyl amino ethanol)		2 hr @ 392°F + 1 hr @ 350°F + 2 hr @ 400°F	3900	0.42×10^6	0.8	530	0.008	3.47	1.3×10^{16}
Borontrifluoride complex	3	6 months	3 hr @ 250°F + 1 hr @ 390°F	6200	0.39×10^6	3.0	345	0.006	3.35	9.6×10^{15}

[a] Parts by weight of hardener per 100 parts epoxy.
[b] Useful working life after mixing. At room temperature unless otherwise indicated.
[c] Achieves about 80% full strength after overnight cure.
[d] Obtained with 200°F postcure.
[e] Heat deflection temperature.

(DETA) H_2N—CH_2—CH_2—NH—CH_2—CH_2 —NH_2; triethylenetetramine (TETA) H_2N— CH_2—CH_2—NH—CH_2—CH_2—NH—CH_2—— CH_2—NH_2; diethylaminopropylamine (DEAPA)

$$CH_3—CH_2$$
$$\diagdown$$
$$N—CH_2—CH_2—CH_2—NH_2.$$
$$\diagup$$
$$CH_3—CH_2$$

They give cures at temperatures as low as 60°F to yield resins with good tensile, compressive and flexural strengths, but low flexibility and comparatively poor impact resistance. Their chemical and electrical properties are good. They are generally useful at temperatures as high as 200–250°F.

The aliphatic amines present some rather difficult handling problems. They are used in small, critical mixing ratios, have short working lives, exhibit high exothermic temperature during cure and are skin irritants. In addition, under some conditions they do not give good surface cures in thin sections exposed to the air. Since epoxies have been introduced, a number of amine curing agents that do not have at least some of these shortcomings have been developed.

Modified Aliphatic Amines

The curing agents generally referred to as modified aliphatic amines or amine adducts are those that have been modified to eliminate the handling and curing problems encountered with the unmodified amines while retaining the good physical, electrical, and chemical properties they yield.

One type of amine adduct is the reaction product of an excess aliphatic amine with an epoxy resin. These are viscous liquids that contain an excess of unreacted amine. Because they contain a certain amount of epoxy resin their mixing ratios are higher. One such adduct of diethylene triamine is used at 25 pph of epoxy, as opposed to 10 pph for DETA. The higher viscosity and lower vapor pressure of these curing agents result in a reduced handling hazard. The properties of resins cured with these adducts are pretty close to those of the unmodified amine used.

A number of proprietary amine adducts are available that give mixtures with longer working lives. For example a group of adducts can be formed by combining amines with acrylonitrile in a reaction involving saturation of the acrylonitrile double bond.

$$NH_2—R—NH_2 + CH_2{=}CH—CN \rightarrow$$
$$\overset{H}{\underset{|}{}}$$
$$NH_2—R—N—CH_2—CH_2—CN$$

Obviously, this reaction can proceed further and the more acrylonitrile added, the less active will be the resulting amine.

The complex formed by adding one mol of diacetone alcohol to 0.33 mole of DETA has been suggested for use in solution coatings as it gives mixtures with improved viscosity stability. The following viscosity changes of 60% solids solutions of solid epoxy resins cured with DETA and the DETA/DAA complex are reported:

Viscosity, cps, at 100°F	DETA	DETA/DAA
After 5 hrs	1450	150
Initial	350	400

A modified polyamine that yields cured resins with somewhat different properties, besides having improved handling characteristics is the reaction product of a monofunctional carboxylic acid with an alkylene polyamine.

$$H_2N—R—(H)N—R—NH_2 + HOOC—R' \longrightarrow$$
$$\overset{H}{\underset{|}{}} \overset{O}{\underset{\|}{}}$$
$$H_2N—R—NH—R—N—C—R'$$

An excess of amine is used to leave active hydrogens to react with the epoxy. The hydrogen of the amide group does not react at room temperature. One such curing agent is used in ratios of 40–100 phr and has a comparatively low irritation potential. The carboxylic acids used are long chain fatty acids, so the cured resins are not as tightly crosslinked as those cured with something like TETA. As a result the resins are softer, have lower tensile strength, greater elongation, and better impact strength than corresponding TETA cured products. A comparison with TETA is given in Table 2.

In this example, a long aliphatic side chain has been introduced into the curing agent to provide

TABLE 2. COMPARISON OF DIFFERENT AMINE CURING AGENTS.

Material	Parts by wt	Hardness, shore D	Tensile strength psi	Tensile elongation, %	Izod impact (ft-lb/in notch)
Epoxy (eq. w 190)	100	88	9900	2.1	0.30
TETA	12				
Epoxy (eq. w 190)	100	82	8350	6.0	0.48
Acid amine adduct	50				

a certain amount of flexibility and impact resistance. If the long chains are incorporated into the cured resin network, even greater flexibility is achieved. Two curing agents that accomplish this are the polyamides and polysulfides.

Polyamides

The amido-amines generally referred to as polyamides are a class of room temperature curing agents that provide properties significantly different from the simple amines. They are condensation polymers of dimerized and trimerized unsaturated fatty acids and polyamines. A simple example is the reaction product of the linoleic acid dimer and ethylene diamine.

$$COOH$$
$$|$$
$$(CH_2)_7$$
$$|$$
$$CH$$

HC⟍   ⟍CH—(CH_2)_7—COOH

HC⟋   ⟋CH—CH_2—CH=CH—(CH_2)_4—CH_3

$$CH$$
$$|$$
$$(CH_2)_5$$
$$|$$
$$CH_3$$

Linoleic acid dimer

$$+ 2H_2N—CH_2—CH_2—NH_2 \rightarrow$$

Ethylene diamine

$$O \quad H$$
$$\| \quad |$$
$$C—N—CH_2—CH_2—NH_2$$
$$|$$
$$(CH_2)_7$$
$$|$$
$$CH$$

HC⟍   ⟍CH—(CH_2)_7C—N—CH_2—CH_2—NH_2

HC⟋   ⟋CH—CH_2—CH=CH—(CH_2)_4CH_3

$$CH$$
$$|$$
$$(CH_2)_5 \quad\quad Acid\ amide$$
$$|$$
$$CH_3$$

Two things are noteworthy about this molecule. The first is that it contains two free primary amines capable of further condensing with acid groups. Thus a range of polymers can be produced by controlling the degree of reaction. If acid trimers or amines of higher functionality than two are used, further ramifications are possible. In most cases, the polyamines used contain more than two amine groups to provide greater reactivity. The second point is that there are twenty-four atoms in the chain connecting the two primary amine groups. This chain will be introduced directly into the cured resin when the two amines

react with epoxies. Therefore, one of the outstanding properties of the polyamide curing agents is greater flexibility and impact strength. Furthermore, since these curing agents have a high equivalent weight, a high curing agent to epoxy ratio can be used. The ratio can be varied over a wide range. The more hardener used, the softer and more flexible the cured product will be. The effect of resin ratio on hardness of a typical epoxy/polyamide blend is shown:

Ratio of Polyamide/Epoxy

40 : 60	50 : 50	60 : 40	65 : 35	70 : 30	75 : 25
60–65[a]	20–25[a]	90[b]	85[b]	50[b]	30[b]

Hardness   [a] Barcol Impressor Model GYZJ-935.
           [b] Shore Durometer A.

In addition to convenient mixing ratios and good impact resistance, the polyamides give good adhesion and are virtually nontoxic. This combination of properties makes them most useful in formulating adhesives, floor and road surfacing compounds, two component paints, and caulking materials. The outstanding properties are gained at the expense of heat and chemical resistance. It is possible to blend polyamides with shorter chain aliphatic amines to get properties intermediate between the two.

Polysulfides

A second type of polymer used to impart flexibility and impact resistance by the incorporation of long aliphatic chains is the mercaptan terminated polysulfide. As is the case with the polyamides, these are available in different molecular weights. Their idealized structure is:

$$H—S—CH_2—CH_2—O—CH_2—O—CH_2—CH_2—$$
$$(S—S—CH_2—CH_2—O—CH_2—O—CH_2—CH_2)_n—$$
$$S—H$$

"n" can vary from 4–26. The hydrogen atom on the —SH group is not active enough to combine with an epoxy unless a catalyst is present. Amines are the most common catalysts, particularly tridimethyl amino methyl phenol (DMP-30, Rohm & Haas or EH 330, Thiokol). The curing mechanism may be pictured as follows:

1. The polysulfide forms a mercaptide ion in the presence of the tertiary amine:

$$HS—R—SH + 2R'_3N : \rightarrow {}^-S—R—S^- + 2R'_3N : H^+$$

2. The mercaptide ion can then link with two molecules of epoxy resin:

$$\overset{O}{\overset{\diagup\diagdown}{}}$$
$${}^-S—R—S^- + 2C\!\!-\!\!-\!\!-\!\!-C—R'' \rightarrow$$

$$\quad\quad\quad\quad O^- \quad\quad\quad\quad\quad\quad O^-$$
$$\quad\quad\quad\quad | \quad\quad\quad\quad\quad\quad\quad |$$
$$R''C—C—S—R—S—C—C—R''$$

3. and the amine base is regenerated:

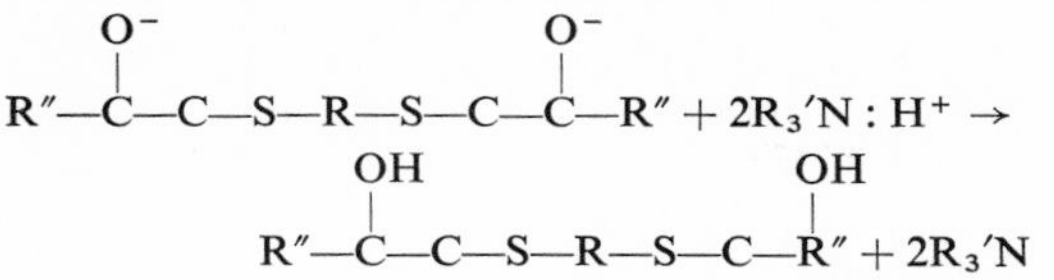

$$R''—\overset{\overset{O^-}{|}}{C}—C—S—R—S—C—\overset{\overset{O^-}{|}}{C}—R'' + 2R_3'N : H^+ \rightarrow$$

$$R''—\overset{\overset{OH}{|}}{C}—C—S—R—S—C—\overset{\overset{OH}{|}}{C}—R'' + 2R_3'N$$

Like the polyamides, the polysulfides can be used in increasing ratios to give increasing flexibility and impact strength. The variation of properties of a common polysulfide-epoxy system is shown below:

Epoxy resin	100	100	100
Polysulfide	—	50	100
EH 330	10	10	10
Tensile strength, psi	3500	6900	2800
Elongation, %	0	10	30
Shore D hardness	80	78	63
Impact strength, ft-lb	0.5	2.8	60

Note: The data reported in this article are taken from different sources using different test methods. Exact comparisons cannot be made between different curing agents by comparing properties listed in different charts.

The polysulfides are generally used in applications requiring toughness and flexibility. The more important examples are: flexible castings, floor and road toppings, adhesives, caulking compounds, and electrical sealing compounds.

Aromatic Amines

The aliphatic polyamines discussed above are generally rigid and useful for temperatures as high as 200–250°F. A curing agent that provides greater flexibility is obtained by introducing long chain aliphatic groups in the cases of the polyamides and polysulfides. These are somewhat less heat resistant than the polyamines. There upper useful temperature range is 150–200°F. It is reasonable to assume that a polyfunctional amine containing more compact and rigid groups would provide greater heat resistance. This is indeed the case, for the aromatic amines are the best to use in higher temperature applications. Three commonly employed aromatic amines are, *meta*-phenylenediamine

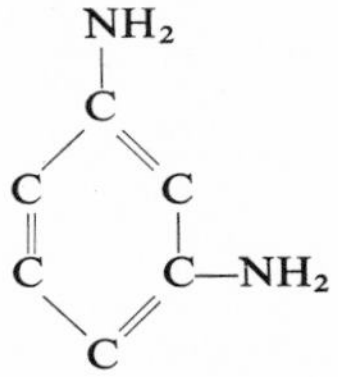

(MPDA), 4,4′- methylenedianiline (4,4′MDA)

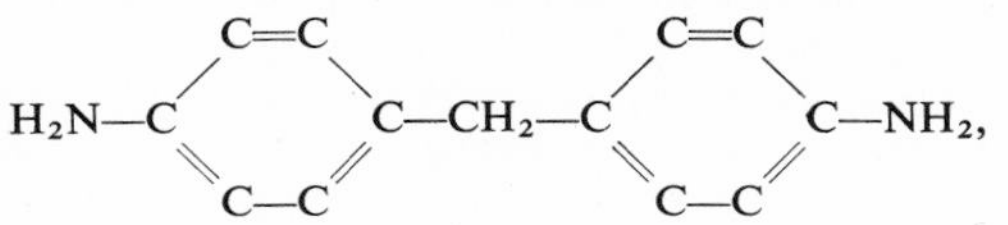

and diaminodiphenyl sulfone (DADPS)

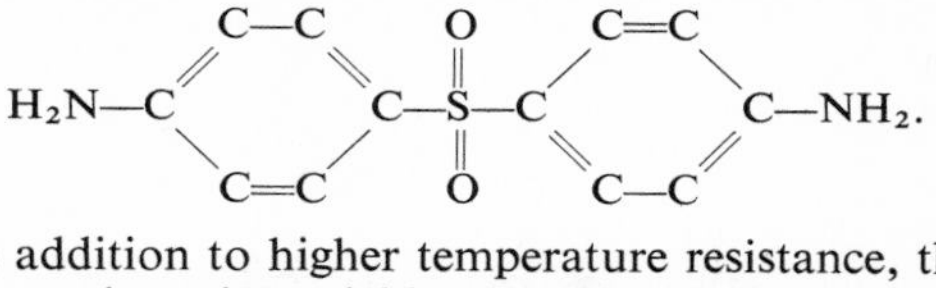

In addition to higher temperature resistance, the aromatic amines yield somewhat better chemical resistance than the aliphatics. Thus a common bisphenol based epoxy cured with TETA and MPDA have the following deflection temperatures and chemical resistance:

	TETA	MPDA
Deflection temperature, °F	220	302
% Retention of flexual strength after absorption in:		
25% HCl, 130°F	58	82
25% Acetic acid, 130°F	failed	93
100% Trichloroethylene, 130°F	81	77
6% Sodium hypochlorite, 130°F	88	99
Distilled water, 130°F	82	94

The three curing agents mentioned are solids. They are incorporated by mixing with the resins at temperatures of 150–200°F. The systems have pot lives of several hours at room temperature and require cures of 1–6 hr at 200–400°F to obtain useful properties. If allowed to gel at room temperature, they will reach a "B" stage in which the resin has set to a semipolymerized solid that is soluble in strong solvents and capable of flow on the application of heat. This characteristic is used in dry lay up laminating and in casting to avoid the high exotherm that can result from heat curing the system immediately after mixing.

The handling difficulties caused by the fact that the aromatic amines are solids can be overcome by blending two amines to form eutectic mixtures that are liquid at room temperature. One example of a low melting mixture is:

MPDA	60 parts by weight
MDA	40 parts by weight
Bisphenol A	6 parts by weight

These mixtures give cured properties similar to the unmodified aromatics. A number of proprietary compounds of this type are available.

Tertiary Amines and Amine Salts

Tertiary amines catalyze curing of epoxy resins by first causing the epoxy ring to open, then react with a second epoxy group as indicated.

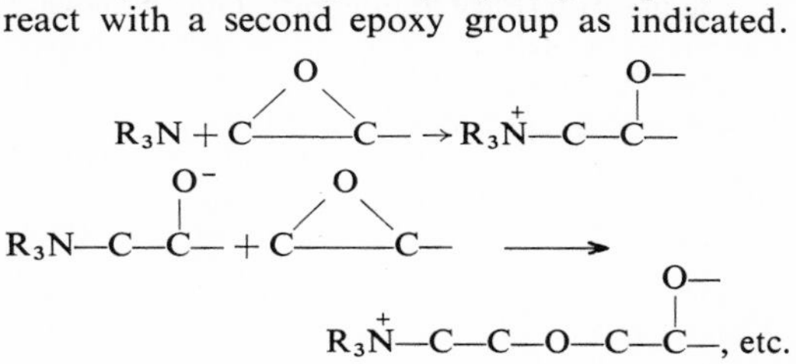

Most frequently used as accelerators with other curing agents, they have found some use as the sole curing agent in adhesive, coating and casting applications. Three typical amine catalysts are:

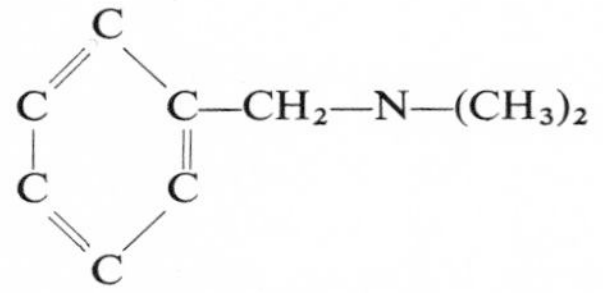

Benzyldimethylamine

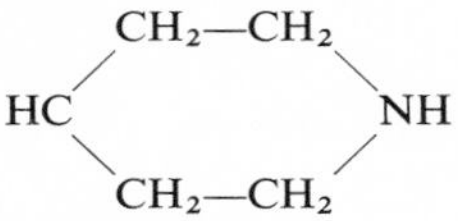

Piperidine

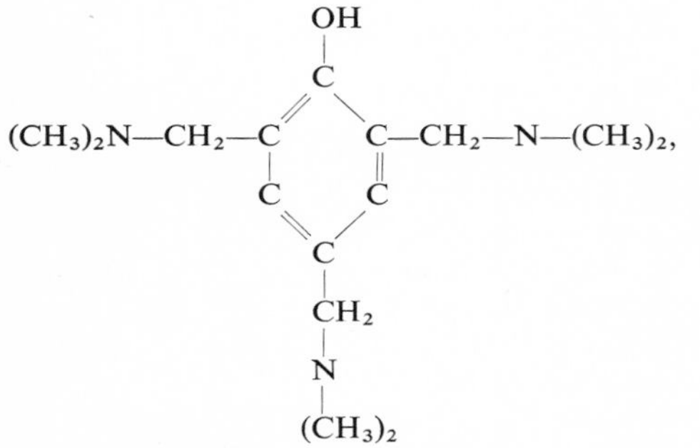

Tridimethyl amino methyl phenol

These are all low viscosity liquids that provide easily pourable mixtures with liquid epoxy resins. They give useful cures at room remperature although a mild elevated temperature cure is necessary for ultimate strength. Some such as piperidine provide pot lives on the order of eight hours with mild elevated temperature cures. The more reactive, such as tridimethyl amino methyl phenol, have short working lives and cure with a high exotherm. Properties of the cured resins are similar to those of the aliphatic amines. The tertiary amines share with the unmodified aliphatic amines the disadvantages of small mixing ratios and a tendency to cause skin irritation.

The problems of critical mixing ratios, short working lives and high exotherms of the more active tertiary amines are lessened to some extent by the use of tertiary amine salts. One is the tri-2-ethylhexoate salt of tridimethyl amino methyl phenol. This has the following properties as compared with the amine:

	Mixing ratio, pph of epoxy	Useful pot life, 1 pint	Exotherm, °F 1 pint
Amine	5–6	30 min	280
Amine salt	10.5–13.5	120 min	150

Because of its longer cure and lower exotherm, the amine salt requires a short post cure at 150–190°F. This curing agent is most frequently used in formulations for potting and encapsulation.

Anhydrides

The second important class of curing agents is the acid anhydrides. These react by combining with both the epoxy groups and the hydroxyl groups present in most resins. The reaction is initiated by the joining of an anhydride with a hydroxyl group to provide the half ester:

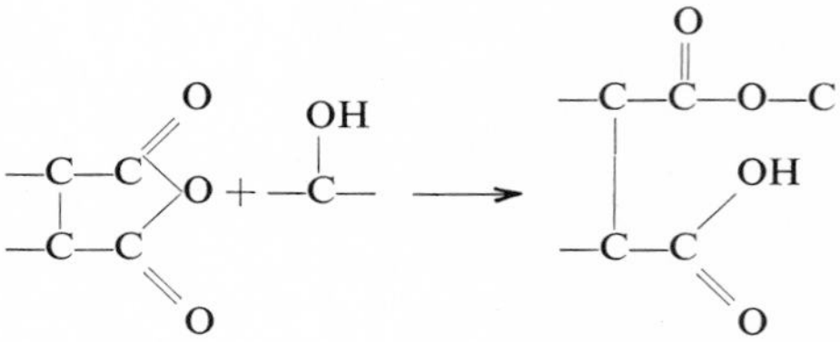

(1)

The remaining acid group then reacts with an epoxy group:

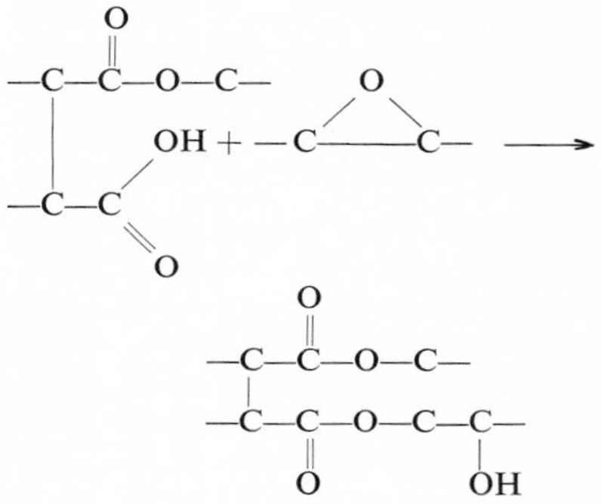

(2)

In addition, self polymerization of the epoxy through the epoxy-hydroxyl reaction is possible:

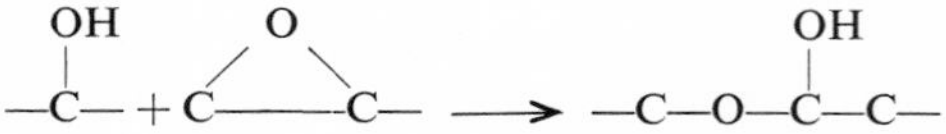

(3)

The first two reactions yield ester linkages, the third an ether.

Cure with the anhydrides is sluggish and is generally catalyzed by 0.1–5% of a tertiary amine or less frequently a borontrifluoride complex. The type of catalyst used affects the relative rates of the three curing reactions. The basic tertiary amines promote the anhydride-hydroxyl reactions (reaction 1) while the acidic BF_3 accelerates the epoxy-hydroxyl self-polymerization (reaction 3). Thus a one to one equivalent ratio of anhydride to epoxy is found best with amine catalysis, while 0.55–1 is suggested as optimum when a Lewis acid catalyst is used. If no catalyst is present, a ratio of 0.85 : 1 is suggested.

Even when a promoter is used, the anhydride curing agents generally permit long working lives and require an elevated temperature cure. These two handling characteristics influence the uses to which the anhydrides are put. The long pot lives and resultant low exotherms are an advantage in a number of casting and laminating uses, particularly in production line applications. The necessity of a heat cure, on the other hand, prohibits their use in many instances. Other handling properties that enhance the utility of the anhydrides are their low skin irritation potential, and high mixing ratios.

Properties of anhydride cured epoxies are generally similar to the amine cured. Excellent temperature resistance and retention of physical and electrical properties at elevated temperatures can be obtained with some systems. Chemical resistance is quite good except for alkalies which attack the ester linkages.

As is true with the amines, the properties imparted to cured epoxies by the different anhydride curing agents depend on the structure of the anhydride. Those containing long aliphatic chains impart flexibility and good low temperature properties, while the aromatic anhydrides and dianhydrides yield rigid products with high heat distortion temperatures. Four typical anhydrides are polyazelaic polyanhydride (PAPA), hexahydrophthalic anhydride (HHPA), methyl NADIC anhydride (MNA) and pyromellitic dianhydride (PMDA).

Polyazelaic polyanhydride (PAPA) has the structure

$$HO—(—\overset{O}{\overset{\|}{C}}—(CH_2)_7\overset{O}{\overset{\|}{C}}—O—)_nH$$

Its average molecular weight is 2300. Like many of the commonly used anhydrides, it is a low melting solid incorporated into the epoxy at 160–180°F. It yields comparatively soft, flexible resins that are tough and resistant to low temperature cracking. An interesting property that is not always shown by other flexible curing agents is retention of flexibility for long periods at temperatures as high as 300°F.

PAPA can be blended with other anhydrides to yield more rigid materials. It is also possible to obatin low melting mixtures that are liquid at room temperature. For example 40/60 PAPA/MNA and PAPA/HHPA mixtures melt at about 68°F.

Hexahydrophthalic anhydride (HHPA) is a good general purpose aliphatic anhydride. As its structure

would indicate, it provides more rigid cures than does PAPA. It tends to add resilience to the cured products without any appreciable loss of strength. For example, the same epoxy cured with HHPA and MNA shows the following room temperature tensile properties:

	HHPA	MNA
Tensile strength, psi	11,200	11,600
Modulus, psi	0.40×10^6	0.50×10^6
Elongation, %	7.0	3.0

HHPA cured resins share with PAPA and other anhydrides the property of retaining their original resilience after exposure to elevated temperatures. The HHPA-epoxy system above after 200 hr at 302°F showed a modulus of 0.40×10^6 and an elongation of 6%. The HHAP-epoxy hardened castings tend to be more stable electrically than amine cured types.

HHPA is a low melting solid that can be handled as a liquid by warming it to 122–140°F. 50/50 mixtures of HHPA/MNA are liquid at room temperatures. The generally good electrical and physical properties obtainable from HHPA make it useful for laminating, casting and encapsulating.

Methyl "Nadic" anhydride is the trade name for methylbicyclo (2.2.1.) heptene, 2,3-dicarboxylic anhydride.

It is a liquid that is compatible at room temperature with most liquid and low melting epoxies, and gives pourable mixtures with long pot life. The physical and electrical properties are close to those of HHPA with the exception of resilience noted above. Heat of deflection temperatures are generally about 25°F higher. The combination of ease of handling and good properties makes MNA one of the more popular anhydrides. It is used for encapsulating, laminating and filament

TABLE 3. EFFECT OF TEMPERATURE ON FLEXURAL PROPERTIES OF EPOXY-PMDA CURED RESIN.

	Test temperature, °F				
	77	200	300	400	500
Ultimate strength, psi	6000	5800	4200	1500	1250
Initial modulus, psi	0.42×10^6	0.32×10^6	0.22×10^6	0.14×10^6	0.15×10^6
Deflection, in.	0.08	0.10	0.10	0.06	0.04

winding applications. Both MNA and HHPA cured resins have short term heat resistance similar to the aromatic amine cured, and somewhat better resistance to prolonged exposure at elevated temperatures. The following table compares the change of tensile strength and elongation with temperature of the same resin cured with MNA and metaphenylene diamine.

	MNA	MPDA
Tested at 77°F		
Ultimate strength, psi	10,150	10,630
Elongation, %	2.9	4.6
Tested at 200°F		
Ultimate strength, psi	8100	7940
Elongation, %	4.8	6.2
Tested at 300°F		
Ultimate strength, psi	1580	2800
Elongation, %	31.0	16.7

The best heat resistance is obtained with the dianhydrides, of which pyromellitic dianhydride (PMDA)* is an example.

PMDA is a sparingly soluble, high melting solid supplied in the form of a fine powder. It is best incorporated into the liquid resins by dispersing with something like a three roll mill or high speed disperser. Short cure schedules on the order of three hours at 400°F are used.

The presence of two anhydride groups joined by a benzene ring provides highly crosslinked rigid resins having heat deflection temperatures close to 600°F. The flexural properties of a highly refined diglycidyl ether of bisphenol A cured with 60 parts per hundred of PMDA and 0.25 part of diethylaminoethanol are given in Table 3. PMDA is useful in laminates where high temperature resistance is necessary.

One Package Systems

All the curing agents discussed so far have been used in two component systems that are gelled

(* See article on Pyromellitic Dianhydride, p. 401)

and cured within a few hours of mixing. From the time epoxies were first introduced, efforts have been made to develop one package formulations. Some useful systems that are stable for 6 months or more at room temperature and cure in a few hours at 250–400°F are feasible. These can be used for adhesives, caulking compounds, potting formulations, preimpregnated fiber glass laminates, coatings and molding compositions.

The boron trifluoride-monoethylamine complex can be dissolved in liquid epoxy resins. At room temperature, solutions of BF_3—MEA in liquid bisphenol A based epoxies have useful shelf lives of about 6 months. When heated above 200°F the complex disassociates to form the reactive BF_3 catalyst:

$$\begin{matrix} F & H & & F & H \\ F:B:N:C_2H_5 & \xrightarrow{heat} & F:B + :N:C_2H_5 \\ F & H & & F & H \end{matrix}$$

A typical cure schedule is 2-1/2 hr at 200°F plus 1 hr at 300°F and 1 hr at 350°F. The cured resins are rigid solids with low impact strength and high heat distortion temperatures.

Dicyandiamide H_2N—$\overset{\overset{NH}{\|}}{C}$—$NH$—$CN$ is a latent curing agent that is essentially unreactive at room temperature. It is insoluble in liquid epoxies but can be milled to form mixtures with more than a year's stability. It is particularly useful for laminates and adhesives. Cure schedules on the order of one hour at 350°F are used.

The aromatic amines discussed previously cure to a B stage that is stable for some time. These B staged mixtures have found application in prepregs. 4,4′-diaminodiphenyl sulfone, which yields compositions with several months shelf life is the most stable. However, it requires cures of several hours. The other commonly used solid aromatics yield more easily cured but less stable systems.

In addition to the products generally thought of as curing agents epoxies coreact with certain thermosetting resins: phenolics, ureas, melamine and triazine resins for example. These reactions form the basis of one package solvent based, heat cured coatings with outstanding resistance to solvents, chemicals and physical abuse.

H. JAMES WHITE

Cross-reference: BORIC ACID ESTER.

"EPOXY INTERMEDIATES"

The epoxies are one of the most versatile of all the polymers created in our current revolution of plastics, even though their use is limited almost entirely to industrial applications. Epoxy resins are being utilized in metal forming dies, adhesives, chemical resistant coatings, electrical insulations, electronic packaging, and rocket cases to name only a few. Their outstanding performance in such widely differing applications is a result of epoxy's unique combination of many desirable properties.

What is Epoxy?

There exists within the plastics industry a certain amount of freedom concerning the use of the word "epoxy." Therefore, in order, to logically develop a discussion of "raw materials for epoxies" one must first draw a distinction between the four different classes of materials which are commonly referred to in the plastics industry as "epoxies."

Epoxy Compounds. From a strictly chemical standpoint, there is little ambiguity over exactly what constitutes an epoxy, since the chemical term has long been assigned to a particular molecular group, namely $>\!C\!-\!C\!<$. The

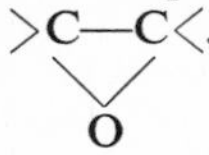

$$>\!C\!-\!C\!<$$
$$\diagdown O \diagup$$

epoxy group exists in materials such as epichlorohydrin ($Cl\!-\!CH_2\!-\!CH\!-\!CH_2$), phenyl glycidyl ether, and styrene oxide, along with many others. Because there is only one epoxy ($C\!-\!C$) group per molecule, in the above

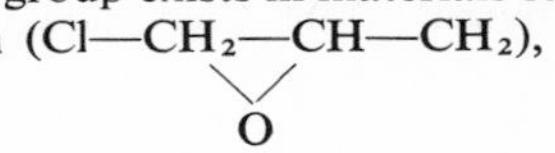

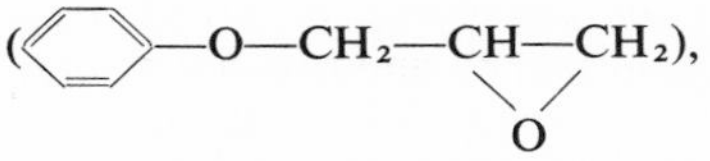

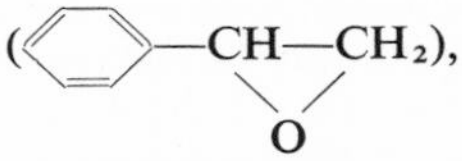

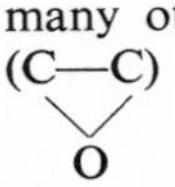

chemicals, they are properly described as monoepoxides. The plastic industry uses monoepoxides as raw materials for further reacting into more complex epoxides, and also as reactive diluents for reducing the viscosity of other more viscous epoxides. Diepoxides, or those having two epoxy groups per molecule, are typified by the diglycidyl ether of bisphenol A:

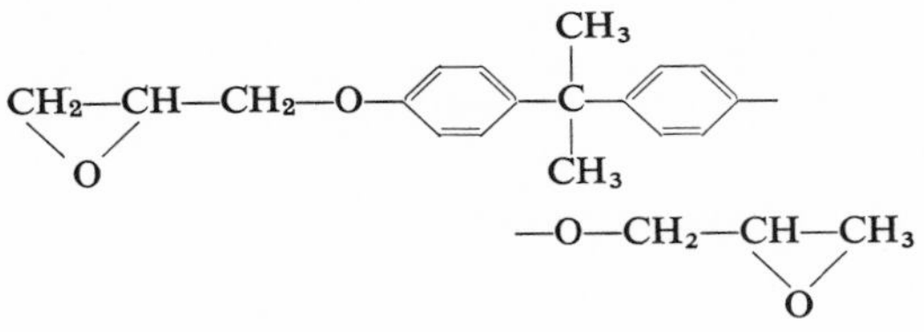

Of all the epoxies, this particular diepoxide is the one most widely used in the plastics industry and the most commonly referred to as "epoxy." More will be said about this in later sections. A proper descriptive term for these epoxy chemicals is "raw epoxy," due to the fact it usually must be further processed to be useful to the plastics industry.

Although there exists triepoxides, tetraepoxides and even epoxides of higher functionality, only a few of these are of any appreciable significance to the epoxy industry at the present time and because of their specialized nature will not be discussed in detail here.

Formulated Epoxy Resins. The basic epoxy compound can be reacted into a cured, thermoset resin by the reaction with certain curing agents or hardeners. For example, the diglycidylether of bisphenol A when reacted with diethylene triamine cures into a hard, glassy, polymeric material of limited usefulness. Therefore it is generally necessary to modify the properties of this cured polymer quite extensively by adding inert fillers such as aluminum or silicon dioxide, or by adding liquid modifiers such as reactive monomers, or by partially reacting a portion of the resin and curing agent together forming a reactive adduct, or by other modification techniques. Only by proper formulation can a plastic material be created which satisfies the precise requirements of a particular application. Although the unreacted compound consists of a mixture of raw epoxy, fillers, modifiers and other reactants, some in the plastic industry still refer to the entire mixture as "epoxy" rather than the more accurate description "formulated epoxy" which would avoid much confusion.

Cured Epoxy Resins. Upon mixing raw or formulated epoxy resin with a suitable curing agent, a reaction takes place which eventually cures the ingredients into thermoset resin. From a chemical standpoint, the epoxy groups are no longer present, having reacted with the curing agent into a completely new polymeric material. Nevertheless the resin product resulting from the reaction is sometimes called an "epoxy." In this article the more common and more descriptive term "epoxy resins" will be used.

Epoxy Esters. A widely used raw material in the manufacture of high quality industrial coatings is the reaction product between an epoxy of high molecular weight and a fatty acid such as the acid of linseed oil. Although the reaction product is an ester and has no epoxy groups remaining, many call it an epoxy because of the use of an epoxy compound as the starting material. Chemically speaking, it is no longer an epoxy, and so it is increasingly being referred to as an "epoxy ester."

Plasticizers and Stabilizers. Epoxy plasticizers

and stabilizers are employed in such a way as to set them in a different class from the normal raw epoxies. Examples include oils, such as soybean oil, which have been epoxidized, resulting in a long chain, flexible structure containing one or more reactive epoxy groups. Their main usage is in polyvinylchloride plastics where the long oil chain contributes flexibility and the reactive epoxy groups act as acid scavengers, preventing degradation of the vinyl or long-term aging. These are referred to more generally as "epoxy plasticizers."

Monoepoxides

Epichlorohydrin, represented by the structure, $Cl—CH_2—CH—CH_2$ is a typical mono-

epoxide, widely used in the plastics industry as the basic starting raw material for the manufacture of more complex epoxides. It is usually manufactured as follows: Propylene is chlorinated, yielding allylchloride and hydrochloric acid. Allylchloride is further reacted with hypochlorous acid, producing glyceryl dichlorohydrin. The monoepoxide, epichlorohydrin, is then formed by removing one chlorine atom and one hydrogen atom by dehydrochlorination with sodium hydroxide.

Several other monoepoxides which are of interest to the plastics industry are: Ethylene oxide, $(CH_2—CH_2)$ which can be obtained by heating

a solution of ethylene chlorohydrin with a base and distilling off the ethylene oxides or by direct oxidation of ethylene with oxygen of the air; Propylene oxide $(CH_3—CH—CH_2)$, is obtained

from propylene chlorohydrin in a similar manner and phenyl glycidyl ether

is obtained from epichlorohydrin and phenol.

Although monoepoxides are extensively used as a basic material for further reacting into more useful monomers and polymers, they are, in addition, used as reactive diluents for the more viscous diepoxides since they are low in viscosity and contain are active epoxy group which will tie into the cured structure. The single reactive epoxy group however stops the polymer chain formation at that point and so prevents the high degree of cross-linking necessary for maximum chemical stability. Table 1 shows the more common monoepoxides used in epoxy plastic chemistry.

Diepoxides

Diepoxides are, as a class, the most useful of the raw epoxies to the plastics industry. Since they contain two reactive epoxy groups, one usually at each end of the molecule, a long chain polymer can be easily formed. In practice, most epoxies also contain one or more reactive hydroxyl groups within the molecule permitting cross linking at several points, thereby forming a three-dimensional polymer network of unusual strength and stability.

The most common of the diepoxides in the plastics industry is the diglycidyl ether of bisphenol A, which can be obtained from the reaction of epichlorohydrin and bisphenol A (made from phenol and acetone) in the presence of caustic. Theoretically, 2 moles of epichlorohydrin to 1 mole of bisphenol A will give the pure diglycidyl ether, but in fact, using the stoichemetric ratio results in yields of less than 10%. The tendency for this reaction to result in higher weight condensation products and polymers leads to the use in practice of an excess of epichlorohydrin. Ratios as high as 20:1 are employed to obtain yields of 70% pure diglycidyl ether.

The theoretical reaction is as follows:

Epichlorohydrin   *Bisphenol A*

TABLE 1. TYPICAL MONOEPOXIDES.

Monoepoxide	Formula	Mol. w	Boiling point atm./°C
Ethylene oxide	$CH_2\!-\!CH_2$ $\diagdown O \diagup$	44	12°
Propylene oxide	$CH_3\!-\!CH\!-\!CH_2$ $\diagdown O \diagup$	58	35
Styrene oxide	⟨⟩$-CH\!-\!CH_2$ $\diagdown O \diagup$	120	191
Epichlorohydrin	$CH_2\!-\!CH\!-\!CH_2\!-\!Cl$ $\diagdown O \diagup$	92.5	117°
Butyl glycidyl ether	$CH_2\!-\!CH_2\!-\!O\!-\!C_4H_9$ $\diagdown O \diagup$	130	175°
Allyl glycidyl ether	$CH_2\!-\!CH\!-\!CH_2\!-\!O\!-\!CH_2CH\!=\!CH_2$ $\diagdown O \diagup$	114	—
Phenyl glycidyl ether	⟨⟩$-O\!-\!CH_2\!-\!CH\!-\!CH_2$ $\diagdown O \diagup$	150	245

TABLE 2. REACTANTS FOR BASIC EPOXY RESINS.

Reactant	Formula	Mol. w	Melting/Boiling point, °C
Bisphenol A	CH_3 HO—⟨⟩—C—⟨⟩—OH CH_3	228	153/—
Bisphenol F	HO—⟨⟩—CH_2—⟨⟩—OH	220	158/
Butadiene dioxide	$CH_2\!-\!CH\!-\!CH\!-\!CH_2$ $\diagdown O \diagup \quad \diagdown O \diagup$	86	—
Butanediol	$CH_3\!-\!CH\!-\!CH\!-\!CH_3$ $\quad OH \quad OH$	90	/182
Catechol	OH ⟨⟩OH	110	105/247
Diglycidyl ether	$CH_2\!-\!CH\!-\!CH_2\!-\!O\!-\!CH_2\!-\!CH\!-\!CH_2$ $\diagdown O \diagup \qquad\qquad \diagdown O \diagup$	130	—
Dihydroxydiphenyl	HO—⟨⟩—⟨⟩—OH	186	280/—
Epichlorohydrin	$CH_2\!-\!CH\!-\!CH_2\!-\!Cl$ $\diagdown O \diagup$	92.5	—57/117

169

TABLE 2 (*continued*). REACTANTS FOR BASIC EPOXY RESINS.

Reactant	Formula	Mol. w	Melting/Boiling point, °C
Ethylene glycol	$CH_2{-}CH_2$ $\quad OH \quad OH$	62	/198
Glycerol	$CH_2{-}CH{-}CH_2$ $\quad OH \quad OH \quad OH$	92	/290
Glycerol dichlorohydrin	OH $Cl{-}CH_2{-}CH{-}CH_2{-}Cl$	129	−23/174
Hydroquinone	 OH / OH (benzene ring)	110	172/286
Novalac phenolic	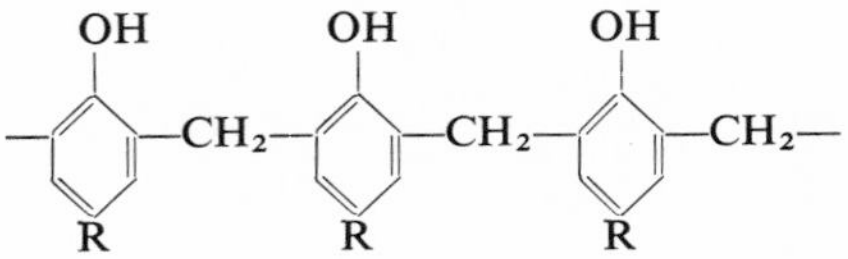 ${-}$—CH$_2$—...—CH$_2$—...—CH$_2$— (OH, R substituted rings)	N.S.	—
Phloroglucinol	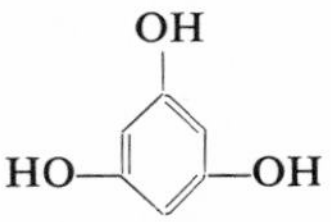 OH, HO—ring—OH	126	215/
Resorcinol	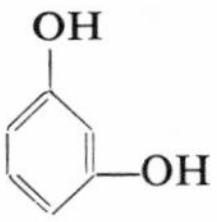 OH, ring—OH	110	110/275

Since pure diglycidyl ether is quite costly and is also prone to crystalize easily, the usual industrial grade of raw epoxy contains an average of only 1.8–1.9 epoxy groups per molecule, and has an average mol. wt. of 380.

Higher molecular weight resins can be easily made by reducing the amount of epichlorohydrin to bisphenol A. An excess of bisphenol A will react with the epoxy terminal groups to lengthen the chain and will form side hydroxyl groups which are also useful as reactive sites. Such an epoxy would be represented by the structure:

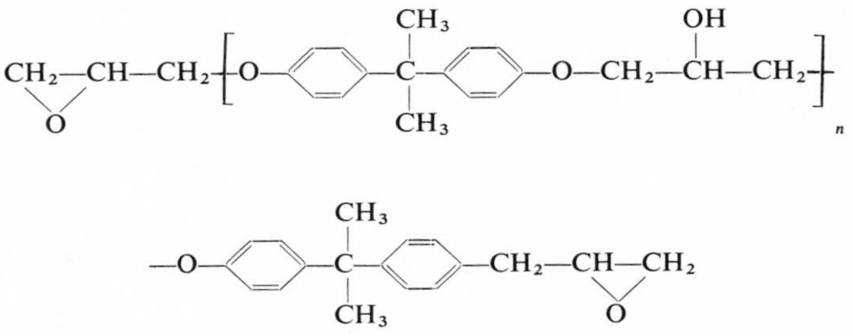

The value of n can be varied from 0 (mol. w 340) = 10 mol. w 3000) or even higher if required. These higher molecular weight raw epoxies are solids at room temperatures.

Although the vast majority of commercial diepoxides are manufactured from epichlorodrin and bisphenol A, there are many other raw materials that are used in limited quantities to manufacture raw epoxies for special uses. Included among these are bisphenol F (greater toughness), phenol-formaldehyde novolaks (high heat resistance) cashew biphenol (flexible),

$$CH_2{-}CH{-}CH_2{-}\left[O{-}\bigcirc{-}\underset{CH_3}{\overset{CH_3}{C}}{-}\bigcirc{-}O{-}CH_2{-}\underset{}{\overset{OH}{CH}}{-}CH_2{-}\right]_n$$

$$-O{-}\bigcirc{-}\underset{CH_3}{\overset{CH_3}{C}}{-}\bigcirc{-}CH_2{-}CH{-}CH_2$$

tetrabromobisphenol A (flame retardance), glycerols and other aliphatic diols or triols (low viscosity and flexible). Table 2 lists the most common, reactants for manufacturing diepoxides of interest to the plastics industry.

CHARLES E. CHASTAIN

Cross-reference: EPOXY CURING AGENTS.

EPOXY RESIN INGREDIENTS

As usually defined, an epoxy resin is a fully cured, thermoset polymer which has resulted from reacting a basic epoxy resin with a suitable curing agent. The formulated epoxy resin will be chemically modified and may contain extenders of fillers to achieve a particular combination of properties in the end product. Several hundred different ingredients are commonly used in formulating epoxy plastics and the formulator must choose the optimum percentage of each component carefully since as little as 1% of some ingredients can alter the characteristics of the epoxy significantly. The following few sections will summarize these ingredients and their uses.

Basic Epoxy Resins

Although the most common type of basic epoxy resin used to formulate epoxy plastics is the diepoxide from epichlorohydrin and bisphenol A; Within this type, there are several epoxies resins which differ markedly in their reactivity, viscosity, and molecular weight. Such difference will greatly influence the properties of the epoxy plastic created from them. A representative group of the most important of the basic epoxies used in formulating epoxy plastics are shown in Table 1.

The choice as to which raw epoxy to use for a particular formulation is largely a matter of experience and knowledge of the properties available from each different raw epoxy. In addition, the choice is always influenced by the choice of modifiers, fillers and curing agent since the final cured plastic will exhibit the composite properties of all of its individual ingredients. Raw epoxies are almost always modified in some way in the manufacture of epoxy plastics.

Curing Agents

To produce the cured epoxy compound, a curing agent is necessary to open the molecular bonds within the epoxy molecule and cause it to cross-link into the three dimensional network of a thermoset plastic. Since there are virtually hundreds of different curing agents available, each one creating a different epoxy plastic, the choice of which curing agent to use is even more difficult than choosing between the various epoxies resins. Each curing agent has certain advantages in a particular application, and also corresponding limitations which make it a poor choice for other applications. Curing agents will greatly affect the physical properties of the end product, along with its electrical and chemical resistance; it will affect processing characteristics such as viscosity, pot life and cure time; and it can affect the economics of the formulated epoxy quite substantially. Epoxy curing agents may be grouped into three types: amines, anhydrides, and miscellaneous.

Amine Curing Agents. Probably the most commonly used of the curing agents are the amines. Primary amines (RNH_2) and secondary amines (R_2NH) will co-react with the epoxy by direct opening of the epoxy ring, forming two dimensional and three dimensional polymers. The degree of cross-linkage depends in theory upon the number of active hydrogens available from the amine molecule and the number of epoxy groups on the epoxy molecule. In practice, the reaction is more complex because of the presence of hydroxyl groups in most raw epoxies which can, under suitable conditions, eventually link directly with other epoxy groups. In general however, with primary and secondary amines, the amine-epoxy reaction proceeds preferentially over the hydroxyl-epoxy reaction. Table 2 lists a variety of amine curing agents. Tertiary amines (R_3N), on the other hand, behave quite differently in curing epoxy resins, since they exert a strong catalytic effect upon the epoxy group permitting it to react directly with another epoxy group, resulting in an epoxy-to-epoxy polymeric linkage. Again, due to the presence of hydroxyl groups the reaction may also proceed under catalytic influence through the hydroxyl group as an intermediate step to achieving direct cross linking between epoxy molecules.

Amine adducts are a special class of amine curing agents. They can be obtained by a partial reaction between an amine in great excess and an epoxy. Amine adducts are useful, primarily because of their more convenient mixing ratios, their lower skin irritation potential and better thin section cure.

Anhydrides. Acid anhydrides, such as methyl Nadic anhydride, will cure raw epoxies under certain controlled conditions. The precise step-by-step reaction is quite complex and will not be detailed here* except to say that it is cross-linking in nature rather than catalytic and the final cured polymer contains both polyether and polyester configurations. Heat is normally required in the reaction. Epoxy resins which have been cured by acid anhydrides are widely used in electrical insulating and in filament winding applications.

Miscellaneous Curing Agents. Polyamides are basically thermoplastic polymers which are

---

* For a more detailed discussion, see *Epoxy Hardeners*.

prepared by the condensation of polymerized linoleic acid with a polyamine. The long fatty acid chain and the presence of active amine hydrogens on certain of the polyamides enables these materials to be utilized as flexibilizing curing agents for epoxies.

Boron trifloride complexes (i.e., BF_3MEA) have been described as latent catalysts, since they can be mixed into the basic epoxy and will remain unreacted for months. Free BF_3 is a highly corrosive gas which will catalyze basic epoxy resins in seconds unless its reactivity is blocked by

TABLE 1. COMMERCIAL BASIC EPOXY RESINS.

Average Epoxide Equiv.[a]	Viscosity cps or Melt Point, C°	Typical Trade Marks[b]
Bisphenol A-Epichlorohydrin Types		
172–176	4000–6400	DER. 332, EPI-REZ 508, Araldite 6004
182–189	7000–10,000	Araldite 6005, EPI-REZ 509, EPON 826, ERL 2772, DER 330.
185–196	12000–16000	EPI-REZ 510, EPON 828, ERL 2774 DER 331, Araldite 6010
172–185 (modified)	500–700	EPON 815, DER 334, EPI-REZ 504 Araldite 506, 507 and 509
180–195 (modified)	4000–9000	DER 336, EPI-REZ 5091, EPON 820
196–208	16000–20,000	Araldite 6020, EPON 830, DER 2633.17
232–278	m.p. 30–45°C	EPI-REZ 515, DER 337, Araldite 6040, EPON 834
385–510	m.p. 60–75°C	EPON 836, Araldite 6060, DER 2633.12
425–550	m.p. 65–75°C	DER 661, Araldite 6071 and 7071, EPI-REZ 520, EPON 1001
550–700	m.p. 75–85°C	Araldite 7072, EPON 1002
875–1025	m.p. 95–105°C.	Araldite 6084, EPI-REZ 530C, EPON 1004, DER 664
1650–2000	m.p. 113–123°C	Araldite 7097, DER 667, EPI-REZ 540C
2000–2500	m.p. 125–135°C	EPON 1007, Araldite 6097
2500–4000	m.p. 145–155°C	EPON 1009, DER 669, Araldite 6099, EPI-REZ 550
Diol-Triol Types		
90–200	30–350°C	DER 736, EPI-REZ 5042, EPON 812
300–350	50–100°C	EPI-REZ 502, DER 732
400–455	2000–5000	Araldite 508
Fatty Acid Types		
400–420	450–600	EPON 871
700–750	m.p. 30°C	EPON 872
Higher Functionality Types		
172–179	1400–2000 52°C	Ciba EPN 1139
175–182	50,000(52°C)	Ciba EPN 1138, DEN 438, EPI-REZ 5155
190–220	m.p. 70–90°C	EPON 1031, DER 2638.7
1000–1400		ERL 2131
200	35°C m.p.	Ciba ECN 1235
225	73°C m.p.	Ciba ECN 1273
230	78–81°C m.p.	Ciba ECN 1280
235	99°C m.p.	Ciba ECN 1299
Halogenated Types		
300–400	m.p. 60–65°C	EPI-REZ 5161, DER 542
455–500	m.p. 70–80°C	Araldite 8011
450–550	m.p. 75–85°C	DER 511, EPI-REZ 5163
Cycloaliphatic Epoxy Resin Types		
74–78	20 cps	UNOX 206, Araldite RD-4
140	350 cps	UNOX 221, Araldite CY 179
213	900 cps	Araldite CY 178

Notes:
   [a] Epoxide equivalent = Grams of resin containing 1 gram equivalent of epoxy.
   [b] Trade marks are identified as being registered by the following Companies: "Araldite," CIBA Products Co., "DER," Dow Chemical Co., "EPI-REZ," Jones Dabney Co.,; "EPON," Shell Chemical Co.; and "ERL," Union Carbide Plastics Co., "UNOX," Union Carbide Chemicals Co.
Other Symbols
   ECN = Epoxy cresol novalak.   EPN = Epoxy phenol novalak.
    CY = Cycloaliphatic epoxy resin.   RD = Reactive diluent.

TABLE 2. AMINE CURING AGENTS FOR EPOXY RESINS.

Amine	Formula	Mol. WT.	Boiling Point, °C
Ethylene diamine	$H_2N-CH_2-CH_2-NH_2$	60	116
Diethylene triamine	$H_2N-CH_2-CH_2-\overset{H}{\underset{\|}{N}}-CH_2-CH_2-NH_2$	103	206
Triethylene tetramine	$H_2N-CH_2-CH_2-\left(\overset{H}{\underset{N-CH_2-CH_2}{\|}}\right)_2-NH_2$	146	277
Tetraethylene pentamine	$H_2N-CH_2-CH_2-(\overset{H}{\underset{\|}{N}}-CH_2-CH_2)_3-NH_2$	189	134
Dimethylamino propylamine	$\overset{CH_3}{\underset{CH_3}{N}}-CH_2-CH_2-CH_2-NH_2$	102	134
Diethylamino propylamine	$\overset{CH_3-CH_2}{\underset{CH_3-CH_2}{N}}-CH_2-CH_2-CH_2-NH_2$	130	169
Monoethanolamine	$HO-CH_2-CH_2-NH_2$	61	170
p, p'-Methylene dianiline	[structure]	198.3	265 (25 mm)
Aminoethylpiperazine	[structure]	129	217
Diaminodiphenylsulfone	$NH_2-\bigcirc-SO_2-\bigcirc-NH_2$	248	170 (m.p.)
Menthane diamine	[structure]	170	115
meta- Xylene diamine	$H_2N-CH_2-\bigcirc-CH_2-NH_2$	136	250
Dicyandiamide	$H_2N-\overset{NH}{\underset{\|}{C}}-NH-CN$	84.08	210°C (m.p.)
Propylene oxide-amine adducts (typical)	$H_2N-CH_2-CH_2-\overset{H}{\underset{\|}{N}}-CH_2-\overset{OH}{\underset{\|}{CH}}-CH_3$	N.S.	N.S.
Acrylonitrile-amine adducts (typical)	$NC-CH_2-CH_2-\overset{H}{\underset{\|}{N}}-R-\overset{H}{\underset{\|}{N}}-CH_2-CH_2-CN$	N.S.	N.S.
Diethanolamine	$(HO-CH_2-CH_2)_2-NH$	105.14	268
Piperidine	[structure]	85.15	106

173

TABLE 2 (*continued*). CURING AGENTS FOR EPOXY RESINS.

Amine	Formula	Mol. Wt.	Boiling Point, °C
Pyridine		79.10	115
Benzyldimethylamine		135	181
Dimethylaminomethyl phenol		151	100 (2 mm)
Imeta- Phenylenediamine		108	60°C (m.p.)

complexing it with other molecules such as monoethylamine. Upon the application of heat above 150°C, the complex will disassociate, freeing BF_3 to accomplish a rapid catalytic cure. Both the anhydride and miscellaneous type curing agents are shown in Table 3.

Blends of Curing Agents. Mixtures, blends and partially reacted mixtures of curing agents constitute one of the most important commercial uses for curing basic or formulated epoxies. The possible mixtures are almost infinite and so the potential for varying properties, pot life, cure time, viscosity, etc. is tremendous. Most commercial formulations contain therefore a precise blend of several agents in order to achieve a better combination of superior properties and convenient processing conditions than is possible with any single curing agent.

Fillers

The purpose of adding a filler to the epoxy resin is for one or more of the following reasons: Reduce cost, reduce shrinkage, reduce thermal coefficient of expansion, reduce peak exotherm, alter viscosity, alter electrical properties, improve adhesion, improve abrasion resistance, alter physical strengths, and improve thermal conductivity.

A careful choice of fillers is required to obtain the desired end properties of the epoxy plastic. A particular filler such as silica will improve the electrical resistance while another such as silver will make it electrically conductive. Using an aluminum filler improves the machinability while another filler such as silicon carbide makes

it almost impossible to machine. Fillers will also change an epoxy's viscosity, color, shrinkage, pot life, cure time, flexibility, wear resistance, hardness and tensile strength. A number of types of fillers are shown in Table 4, indicating their usefulness.

The particle size of a filler, its specific gravity and its oil absorption value play an important part in the choice of a suitable filler, particularly from an economic point of view. Heavier loadings, which will reduce costs, are possible as the particle size increases and the oil absorption value decreases. In pastes, however, small particle size and high oil absorption fillers are commonly employed to achieve thixotropy or a gel-like consistency.

Fillers must be oven dried to prevent incorporation of moisture into the epoxy formulation since moisture will react with most epoxy curing agents, preventing a thorough cure. Fillers almost always contain some moisture absorbed or adsorbed on the particle which must be removed.

As the size and specific gravity of a filler particle increases, so does its tendency to settle out. However, small or light particles which do not settle out usually increase the viscosity of the resin rapidly, so the normal approach is to use the largest particle size consistent with the application and keep it suspended by either of two methods: (1) include a certain amount of smaller or lighter particles, or (2) treat the surface of the large particles with various methods which will alter the charge on each particle helping it to repel other particles.

The second method is far superior, since if

TABLE 3. ANHYDRIDES AND MISCELLANEOUS CURING AGENTS.

Curing Agent Anhydrides	Structure	Mol. Wt.	Melting Point, °C
Phthalic		148.11	132
Maleic		98.06	52
Tetrahydrophthalic		154.2	35
Methyl Nadic		178.2	12
Dodecenyl succinic		266.4	12
Nonyl succinic		226	206 (16 mm)

TABLE 3 (*continued*). ANHYDRIDES AND MISCELLANEOUS CURING AGENTS.

Curing Agent Anhydrides	Structure	Mol. Wt.	Melting Point, °C
Dichloromaleic		167	118 (m.p.)
Chlorendic		371	240 (m.p.)
Pyromellitic		218	285 (m.p.)
Miscellaneous Boron triflorine- monoethylamine complex	$BF_3 \cdot NH_2-CH_2-CH_3$	113	89 (m.p.)
Polyamides (typical)		N.S.	N.S.

$$H_2N-CH_2-CH_2 \cdot \underset{\underset{H}{|}}{N}-CH_2-CH_2-$$

$$\underset{\underset{H}{|}}{N}(-\underset{\underset{H}{|}}{C}-R-\overset{\overset{O}{\|}}{C} \cdot \underset{\underset{H}{|}}{N}-CH_2-CH_2-\underset{\underset{H}{|}}{N}-CH_2-CH_2-\underset{\underset{H}{|}}{N}-)N$$

$$\overset{\overset{O}{\|}}{C}-R-\overset{\overset{O}{\|}}{C}-\underset{\underset{H}{|}}{N}-CH_2-CH_2-\underset{\underset{H}{|}}{N}-CH_2-CH_2-NH_2$$

settling does occur it is usually a soft, gel-like settling which is very easily dispersed. Failure to prevent settling in epoxy formulations can lead to serious errors in mix ratios when the formulation is finally used.

Because of this and other reasons, where fillers are used in formulated epoxies, the filler will almost always consist of several different fillers, several different sizes and even different surface treatments.

Fillers must be non-reactive with both the resin and the curing agent; so only neutral or slightly basic fillers are normally used in epoxy formulations. There are however special cases where a reactive filler can be employed to advantage but in general they should be avoided.

Diluents and Liquid Modifiers

In addition to the use of solid fillers, liquid fillers and modifiers are extensively employed to further alter the properties of the basic epoxy resins such as improving flexibility, toughness,

TABLE 4. FILLERS FOR EPOXIES.

Filler	Specific gravity	Improvement in Epoxy Plastic
Aluminium	2.7	Machinability, impact
Aluminum oxide	4.0	Abrasion resistance, electrical
Aluminum silicate	3.2	Extender
Antimony trioxide	5.7	Flame retardant
Asbestos fibers	3.0	Reinforcement
Barium sulfate	4.5	Extender
Calcium carbonate	2.7	Extender
Calcium sulfate	2.3	Extender
Carbon black	1.8	Color, and reinforcement
Copper	8.9	Machinability
Glass fibers	2.6	Reinforcement
Graphite	2.2	Lubricity
Iron	7.0	Abrasion resistance
Iron oxide	2.9	Color, magnetic
Lead	11.3	Radiation shielding
Kaolin clay	2.5	Extender
Mica	2.8	Electrical resistance
Silica sand	2.2	Abrasion, electricals
Silicon carbide	2.4	Abrasion resistance
Silver	10.5	Electrical conductivity
Titanium dioxide	4.0	Color
Zinc	7.1	Adhesion and corrosion resistance

adhesion and working characteristics. But probably the most important single function of liquid modification is to reduce the viscosity of the base raw epoxy.

Since the standard liquid epichlorohydrin-bisphenol A epoxy resin is a thick, honey-like liquid with a viscosity of about 12,000 cps, it becomes apparent that its viscosity must be materially reduced with liquid diluents if fillers are to be added or if easily pourable compounds are to be achieved. Liquid diluents and modifiers are of two types, reactive or nonreactive.

Reactive Diluents and Modifiers. Reactive liquids are those containing chemical groups capable of reacting with either the basic epoxy or the curing agent. The chief advantage in using a reactive liquid over a nonreactive liquid is that the cured plastic polymer is completely interracted into one homogeneous product. Reactive liquids therefore do not degrade the properties of raw epoxies nearly as much as nonreactive liquids. Several such reactive compounds are shown in Table 5.

Nonreactive Diluents and Modifiers. Nonreactive diluents and modifiers, even though they are not chemically reacted with either the raw epoxy or the curing agent, still serve many useful purposes in the modification of epoxy plastics. Low boiling diluents such as methyl ethyl ketone are used extensively as carriers and viscosity reducers for the solid epoxy resins in coating formulations, and simply evaporate out of the coating film after application. If the solvent is not allowed to evaporate it will be encapsulated by the cured epoxy,

and remain as a plasticizer yielding soft end products. Thus, a high-boiling liquid such as dibutyl phthalate will function as an effective plasticizer for epoxy with good long term stability because of its low volatility. However, nonreactive diluents and modifiers will degrade most physical, electrical and chemical properties if left in the cured epoxy, and so their use is largely limited to very cheap compounds where low cost is essential and low strengths are acceptable. Several examples of nonreactive diluents are shown in Table 6.

"Epoxidized Oil" Plasticizers and Stabilizers

An epoxidized oil usually is referred to as an "epoxy plasticizer," and is used both as a plasticizer and acid scavenger in PVC compounds to improve the resistance to aging embrittlement.

One of the first epoxy plasticizers was the triglyceride of unsaturated soy bean oil, which, although of limited compatibility, found acceptance in many applications. Other unsaturated fatty acids were epoxidized by many methods and several found commercial interest. Currently the most promising method is via the peracetic acid process, where the unsaturated oil is epoxidized by peracetic acid as it is formed (*in situ*) from glacial acetic acid and hydrogen peroxide. Epoxy plasticizers, thus formed, have greater compatibility with PVC and less tendency to volatilize on aging. Although some interest has developed in using some of the epoxidized oils for flexibilizers in formulating epoxy plastics (since they do have reactive epoxy groups), this

TABLE 5. REACTIVE DILUENTS AND MODIFIERS.

Name	Formula	Viscosity, cps @ 25°C	Boiling Point, °C
Allyl glycidyl ether	$CH_2\!=\!CH\!-\!CH_2\!-\!O\!-\!CH_2\!-\!CH\!-\!CH_2$ with epoxide O	1	154
Butyl glycidyl ether	$CH_3\!-\!CH_2\!-\!CH_2\!-\!CH_2\!-\!O\!-\!CH_2\!-\!CH\!-\!CH_2$ with epoxide O	3	170
Phenyl glycidyl ether	$C_6H_5\!-\!O\!-\!CH_2\!-\!CH\!-\!CH_2$ with epoxide O	6	245
Cresyl glycidyl ether	$CH_3C_6H_4\!-\!O\!-\!CH_2\!-\!CH\!-\!CH_2$ with epoxide O	25	265
Furfural alcohol	HC——CH / HC C—CH₂—OH / O (furan ring)	5	170
Butyrolactone	CH₂ CH₂ CH₂ C=O with O ring	—	—
Triphenyl phosphate	$(C_6H_5)_3PO_4$	—	—
Butanediol diglycidyl ether	$CH_2\!-\!CHCH_2O(CH_2)_4OCH_2\!-\!CH\!-\!CH_2$ with two epoxide O	15	260
Vinyl cyclohexene dioxide	O-cyclohexane ring—CH—CH₂ with epoxide O	20	227
Aliphatic (C₈ to C₁₀) glycidol ethers	$C_8H_{17}OCH_2CH\!-\!CH_2$ with epoxide O	4	—

use is small compared to the volume currently used in PVC processing. Some of the fatty acids used in manufacturing epoxy plasticizers are those contained in linseed, soybean and tall oils.

Epoxy Esters

In the paint or protective-coating industry, basic epoxies are commonly esterified with various oil derived fatty acids, and the resultant ester is referred to as an epoxy even though no epoxy groups remain. It is more truthfully an epoxy ester. Manufacture of epoxy esters is normally accomplished by reacting a solid diepoxide such as the higher molecular weight resins based upon bisphenol A, with certain oil derived fatty acids such as linseed fatty acid to the degree of esterification as required

Properties of Epoxy Resins

Physical Strength. Epoxy resins have high tensile, compressive and flexural strengths along with a low specific gravity, resulting in a strength-to-weight ratio four times that of steel. By choos-

ing correct modifiers, fillers and curing agents, the physical strength of epoxy can be varied from hard and wear resistant, to soft and easily machinable as desired. Many industries are now using epoxy to replace steel or other metals in such high strength requirements as forming dies, molds, patterns, jigs and fixtures for plastic or metal fabrication.

Electrical Strength. Epoxy resins are among the best of the insulating materials. Their high electrical resistance, low dielectric constant and low power loss have been widely utilized in the protection of transformers, coils, printed circuits, resistors, condensers and motors for all types of civilian and military equipment.

Chemical Resistance. Epoxy resins cure to a dense, thermoset product which, because of its very stable ether linkages and aromatic rings, is unusually resistant to a wide range of acids, alkalis and solvents. Protective coatings of epoxy resins are being widely used to protect tanks, equipment, floors and parts from corrosive environmental attack.

TABLE 6. NONREACTIVE DILUENTS AND MODIFIERS.

Name	Formula	Boiling Point, °C
Dibutyl phthalate	$C_6H_4(CO_2C_4H_9)_2$	340
Dibutyl sebacate	$(CH_2)_8(CO_2C_4H_9)_2$	345
Dioctyl phthalate	$C_6H_4(CO_2C_8H_{17})_2$	386
Chlorinated biphenyl	$(C_6Cl_4H)_2$	390
Polyethylene glycol	$HO(CH_2CH_2O)_n CH_2CH_2OH$	>300
Coal tar	(mixture of Aromatic and Heterocyclic Hydrocarbons)	N.S.
Pine oil	(Mixture of Terpene Alcohols)	215
Petroleum oils	(Mixture of Aromatic, Aliphatic and Cycloaliphatic Hydrocarbons)	290
Methyl ethyl ketone	$CH_3—CO—C_2H_5$	79
Toluene	$C_6H_5CH_3$	110
Xylene	$C_6H_4(CH_3)_2$	144
2-Nitropropane	$(CH_3)_2CH—NO_2$	120
Dimethyl formamide	$(CH_3)_2NCHO$	153
Butyl alcohol	$C_4H_9 OH$	99

Adhesive Strength. The epoxy molecule is highly polar and thus is capable of producing adhesive bonds of high strength. Epoxy resins, as a result, are the strongest general purpose adhesives used in industry, and come closest to that "miracle" glue that bonds anything to anything. Epoxy adhesives are being regularly used to bond most metals, rubbers, woods, glass and plastic, to themselves or each other, replacing welding, mechanical fasteners and many other adhesives.

Low Shrinkage. Because epoxy resins will cure (solidify) with little or no shrinkage compared to other plastics or metals, it can be molded to accurate shapes and dimensions without requiring expensive machining or finishing. Thus, industrial dies can be cast directly to size; delicate electrical parts can be encapsulated without fear of crushing due to encapsulant shrinkage; and adhesive bonds are enhanced, due to lack of shrinkage stresses in the adhesive.

Ease of Use. Many of the epoxies used in industry are pourable liquids and can be used without solvents or heating. Their handling characteristics can be regulated over a wide range to suit processing requirements and no expensive equipment is normally required. Cure time can be regulated from a few minutes to many hours.

As can be already observed from the foregoing, epoxy plastic has a very useful combination of properties and characteristics not found in any other material, which accounts for its acceptance and utilization in such a wide range of applications. Virtually unknown commercially in the U.S.A. until about 20 years ago, sales of epoxy resins in 1965 were over 110 million lb yearly, with a steady increase of about 15% per year projected for the future.

CHARLES E. CHASTAIN

EPOXY RESINS, NOVOLAK

Novolak epoxy resins are, in many ways quite similar to the more familiar and conventional bisphenol A based epoxy resins. The main differences are in the higher functionality, which gives them much more rigidity, heat resistance and chemical resistance, and in their greater rate of reactivity. The melting point is generally higher than for a bisphenol A resin.

The idealized structure shown below for the two types of resins illustrates this difference. In the case of the novolak epoxy, each repeating unit contains an epoxy group; in the case of the bisphenol A based resins, each repeating unit in the interior of the molecule contains only an hydroxyl group:

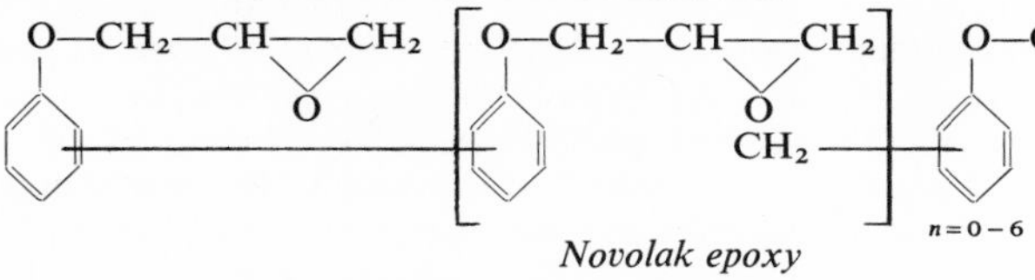

Novolak epoxy

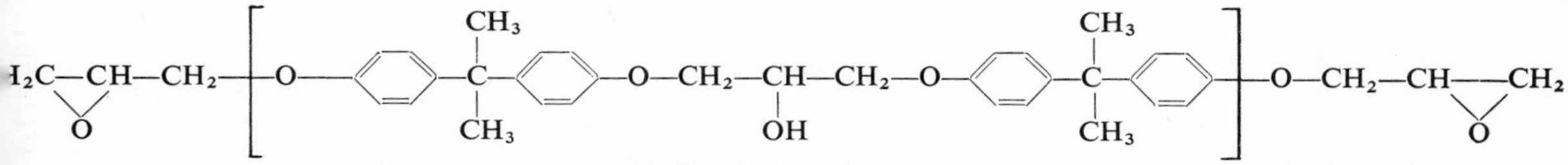

Bisphenol A based epoxy

Typical novolak epoxy resins have a degree of polymerization n from 0–6, and melting points from approximately 20–100°C. They can be cross-linked with the same cross-linking agents used for bisphenol A epoxides. These include aliphatic and aromatic amines, orgnic acids and their anhydrides, and Lewis type acids, such as boron trifluoride complexes.

The novolak epoxy-type resins are manufactured as typical novolak phenolic resins to start; that is, they use an excess of phenol with formaldehyde, with acid catalyst. Typical amounts would be:

Phenol	1 mole
Formaldehyde	0.8 mole

with a catalyst such as hydrochloric, oxalic, or sulfuric acid.

The reaction will proceed along the lines of the scheme as shown below:

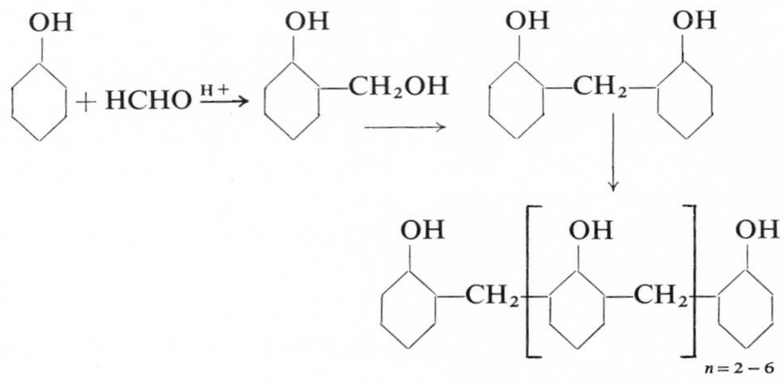

and with good short-term thermal resistance. Long-term thermal resistance will not be as good as when cured with aromatic acid anhydrides such as hexahydrophthalic anhydride or methylnadic anhydride. A typical formulation evaluated was:

Epoxy novolak (W.P.E. 180)	100	Parts
Methyl Nadic anhydride	13.3	Parts
Hexahydrophthalic anhydride	75.2	Parts
Lithium aluminum silicate	282	Parts

Cure cycle used was 16 hr at 125°C, and 4 hr at 232°C. Tests on this cured formulation shows a weight loss of 7.2% after 500 hr at 232°C; a shrinkage of 2.8% after 500 hr, and a heat distortion temperature of 160°C. The cured resin exhibited good thermal shock resistance.

Transfer molding compounds can be made by several methods. One of earliest methods used consisted of melting an aromatic diamine such as

It will readily be seen in the above that a wide variety of raw materials can be used. *ortho*-Creosol as well as phenol is commonly used. The proportions of starting materials, catalyst, and reaction conditions may be varied to form a variety of widely differing resins.

The novolak obtained above is then treated further with epichlorohydrin and a base to form the epoxy novolak. The resulting products are amber colored, highly viscous liquids or solids.

The epoxy novolaks are presently used in several applications which employ their unique properties to best advantage. The largest volume of usage at present is probably in transfer molding for encapsulation of electrical and electronic components. This takes advantage of the fast cure speed of the resins and of the excellent electrical and thermal properties of the cured product. Other significant applications include liquid potting and casting, laminating systems, adhesives and coatings.

Liquid potting and casting systems are usually cured with aromatic amines or anhydrides. Aromatic amines, when used with the novolak epoxy resins, will produce castings with excellent solvent resistance, good electrical properties,

metaphenylenediamine with a liquid epoxy resin, pouring into shallow pans and letting the mass harden to a so-called "B" stage polymer. This is a brittle, partially polymerized resin. This is then ground up, pulverized, and either used almost immediately or cooled and kept under refrigeration until used.

Transfer molding compounds may be filled or unfilled. They usually have an aromatic amine or anhydride curing agent with accelerator and flow-control agent. Other methods of production include the extrusion method where the resin and curing agent are processed through a plastic extrusion machine, thoroughly mixed and reacted in a very short time so that the reaction of the resin and curing agent is not allowed to progress beyond a very limited stage. This type of production usually uses solid resin and a solid curing agent. A solid resin and curing agent may also be used in a dry-blend production in which the pulverized solid resin and solid curing agent are merely dry-blended in bulk or in a mechanical mixer.

Adhesives based on novolak epoxies are used principally where their good thermal stability is important. The high viscosity of the liquid novolak epoxy resins is a definite disadvantage in adhesive applications. Usually, a low viscosity modifier or resin will be used with the novolak to bring the viscosity to a workable level. This compromise will usually reduce the thermal stability to some extent. When used as adhesives with the typical aliphatic polyamines, the pot life will be approximately one-half that of the usual bisphenol A based epoxy resins.

Additionally, the adhesive strength found with the novolak epoxies is generally lower than that found with the bisphenol A based epoxies. This is probably due to a combination of factors—namely, that once they are cured, they are much more rigid, and thus more brittle; and, in the usual tests run in the adhesives industry, a brittle material will not perform nearly as well as a slightly more flexible or resilient material. They also do not have the hydroxyl groups in the polymer chain which are on the bisphenol A based resin molecule, which impart considerable polarity and aid in obtaining adhesion with this type resin.

Novolak epoxy resins have also been quite successful in laminating applications, which include filament winding. Here, of course, their excellent thermal and chemical resistances are used to great advantage to produce systems with marked superiority over the conventional bisphenol A based epoxies. Some of the curing agents used with the novolak epoxies and their peculiarities are noted: Aromatic amines, which include metaphenylenediamine, diaminodiphenyl sulfone and methylenedianiline, give very good strengths at elevated temperatures, are fairly easy to handle, and have good cure cycles; however, their strength on long-term exposure to high temperature is poor. Lewis acids, which include boron trifluoride complexes and various borate compounds, are useful in high-temperature applications. Their properties, in many cases, fall between those of the aromatic amines and the aromatic anhydrides. The aromatic anhydrides, as a rule, impart the best combination of physical strengths and long-term strengths after heat exposure. These include hexahydrophyhalic, phthalic anhydride, methyl Nadic anhydride, dodecenylsuccinic anhydride, and pyromellitic dianhydride.

Pyromellitic dianhydride would probably give the best combination of properties of the anhydrides; however, its reactivity and cost are so high that it is of little practical use.

Coatings made with the novolak epoxy resins have not found a very wide market as yet. The unmodified resins, when cross-linked with the usual aliphatic amines or polyamide resins, do not show sufficient advantage over the conventional bisphenol A based epoxies to warrant their usage in any great quantities. Some coatings have

been made from the solid novolak epoxies by dry-blend processes similar to those used for transfer molding compounds. To date, this application has been limited because of their extreme brittleness when applied in this manner.

In summary, for the plastics engineer or chemist, the novolak epoxy resins are a class of epoxy resins with superior properties for many applications, but with certain application limitations which restrict their usage to those areas where their superiorities outweigh their other less desirable properties.

A. J. GOOD

ESSENTIAL OILS

A small amount of an essential oil imparts a pleasing odor or flavor to many materials. They are especially useful in masking unpleasant odors which may occur in synthetic plastics, elastomers, fibers, latices, and leather-substitute products. Materials otherwise objectionable may be transformed into a marketable product with odor appeal by the inclusion of a small amount of an appropriate essential oil.

Essential oils are usually volatile oils obtained from plants. Their group name comes from the fact that they are essences. The word "quintessence" (fifth essence) in alchemical writings refers to the odorous or otherwise active principle extracted from natural sources.

Production

Essential oils are produced by means suitable to the particular oil being obtained. For many oils the operation is seasonal, small scale, and in crude apparatus. For a few oils, the conditions of production are carefully controlled. As is general in working with natural source materials, the products are subject to variation. Essential oils may come from any part of a plant.

(1) *Crushing* the material is the simplest method of extraction of an essential oil. Citrus oils are obtained this way. The oil is found in little sacs in the rind. The expressed oil is floated on water and separated by decanting.

(2) *Distillation* is a more general method of obtaining essential oils. The process has several variations—(a) dry distillation or destructive distillation, (b) distillation in contact with boiling water, (c) water and saturated steam distillation, usually with low-pressure steam (d) distillation with dry steam, sometimes at increased temperature and pressure. Each method has its applications.

(3) *Extraction* using a solvent. Solvents used include low-boiling hydrocarbons such as petroleum ether, benzene, alcohols, and even hot fat. The solvent dissolves the oil, without dissolving much other plant matter. Recovery of the essential oil is then accomplished by evaporation of the

solvent. In the case of using fat as a solvent, the fat is chilled and removed after it hardens.

(4) *Enfleurage.* Glass plates in trays are covered with a layer of fat. Petals, such as rose petals, are sprinkled on the fat. After a while the plates are washed with alcohol which dissolves the fat containing the delicate essential oil from the petals. The fat is removed by chilling, and the extract may be available as a concentrated alcoholic extract.

(5) Ultrasonic or supersonic waves in the presence of a solvent claim many advantages for agitating the plant material. The oil is removed rapidly and without damage to heat-sensitive materials. There are approximately 520 types of essential oils*. Often several subvarieties are included in a single type, and a definitive classification is extremely difficult.

The total world production (1959) of the important natural perfume and flavor materials includes 200,000 metric tons of turpentine oil of all types. Pine oil is about 1/2 that of turpentine oil. These two items together constitute 80% of the combined total production of all essential oils. Java-type citronella is about 1/20 that of pine oil production. Other essential oils range downward in amounts, some being produced only in insignificant quantities. The total value of these essential oils exceeded one-quarter billion dollars.

An average use level is 0.30–0.80 mg % based on fine natural oil, while the minimum perceptible is 0.05–0.10 mg %. When "ordinary commercial grades" are used, probably adulterated with less expensive substances of synthetic origin, the average use-level is 1.50–2.50 mg %, and the minimum perceptible is 0.60–0.90 mg %.

Composition

Terpenes are commonly present in essential oils. While some oils may be 85 or even 98% one component, other components are present, sometimes as many as 30 of them. While most essential oils are hydrocarbons, some may contain nitrogen as organic isothiocyanates, and sulfur as organic sulfides, for example garlic and onion oils.

Turpentine oil, American, contains 25–35% beta-pinene, and 50% alpha-pinene. Turpentine oil from other sources is much lower in the beta-pinene. Alpha-pinene ($C_{10}H_{16}$) is a bridge hydrocarbon which is auto-oxidizable.

Oil of sweet birch is 98% methyl salicylate ($C_6H_4(OH)COOCH_3$), and clove oil contains about 95% eugenol.

Attempts to reconstitute natural essential oils by a combination of synthetic products are generally non-productive. The oils themselves contain a great variety of compounds.

* Steffen Arctander *Perfume and Flavor Materials of Natural Origin*, Rutgers Univ., 1960.

Assay

Because of the great assortment of compounds present, variations among sources from different countries and other influencing factors, assay of essential oils is difficult.

Measurements used include boiling-point ranges, specific gravity, refractive index, optical rotation, spectrometry, and in some cases chromatography. Chemical analyses may be applied to evaluate acids, and to detect definite types of functional groups and their amount in a sample. Adulterations are generally difficult to detect. The best evaluations of essential oils are made by reliable specialists in that field.

ELBERT C. WEAVER

ETHYLENE

Ethylene (C_2H_4) is classified as a hydrocarbon because it is composed of carbon and hydrogen only. Unlike ethane (C_2H_6) which is saturated, ethylene is unsaturated because its molecule can combine with additional hydrogen atoms.

Ethylene was mistaken for a base in 1828 by Jean B. A. Dumas (1800–1884), who recognized that ethyl chloride could be considered equivalent to ethylene and hydrogen chloride:

$$C_2H_5Cl \rightleftharpoons C_2H_4 + HCl$$

Similarly,

$$C_2H_5OH \rightleftharpoons C_2H_4 + H_2O$$
$$C_2H_5HSO_4 \rightleftharpoons C_2H_4 + H_2SO_4$$
$$(C_2H_5)_2O \rightleftharpoons 2C_2H_4 + H_2O$$

Three important hydrocarbon series are the alkane (C_nH_{2n+2}), alkene (C_nH_{2n}), and alkyne (C_nH_{2n-2}). The 2-carbon members of these series are respectively, C_2H_6 ethane, C_2H_4 ethylene, and C_2H_2 acetylene. Ethylene is the simplest member of the alkene series of hydrocarbons, each of which contains one double bond.

ALKENE SERIES, C_nH_{2n}

$n=2$	ethylene	C_2H_4	$CH_2{=}CH_2$
$n=3$	propylene	C_3H_6	$CH_2{=}CH{-}CH_3$
$n=4$	butene-1	C_4H_8	$CH_2{=}CH{-}CH_2{-}CH_3$
	butene-2	C_4H_8	$CH_3{-}CH{=}CH{-}CH_3$
	isobutylene	C_4H_8	$CH_3{-}\underset{\underset{CH_3}{\vert}}{C}{=}CH_2$

Ethylene, a colorless gas at room temperature, has a somewhat sweet odor. It dissolves to the extent of about 1/4 liter of the gas in 1 liter of water, and 3.5 liters of the gas in 1 liter of alcohol.

Some of its physical properties may be shown comparatively with other 2-carbon hydrocarbons:

		Molecular Weight	Density g/liter, 0°C	Melting Point, °C	Boiling Point, °C
Ethane	(C_2H_6)	30.07	1.357	−172	−88.3
Ethylene	(C_2H_4)	28.05	1.2604	−169.4	−103.9
Acetylene	(C_2H_2)	26.04	1.173	−81.8	−83.6 subl.

The refractive index of ethylene at $-100°C$ is reported to be 1.363. The double bond in ethylene accounts for the greater chemical activity of this unsaturated hydrocarbon than for ethane. Ethylene burns readily with a sooty flame, and when mixed with air and ignited it explodes violently. The explosive limits are from 3–34% by volume of the gas with air at ordinary temperatures.

Preparation of Ethylene

Ethylene is available in great quantities from petroleum refinery gases where it is a product of thermal cracking. When a saturated hydrocarbon "cracks" (decomposes by heating, usually in the presence of a catalyst), at least one unsaturated hydrocarbon results. The following equation illustrates the point, although it may not represent an actual reaction:

$$C_{16}H_{34} \rightarrow 2C_7H_{16} + C_2H_2$$

Cetane	Heptane	Ethylene
(saturated)	(saturated)	(unsaturated)

While ethylene is obtained chiefly from petroleum and natural gas refineries, other manufacturing methods are interesting.

Dehydration of ethyl alcohol, using kaolin or aluminum oxide (Al_2O_3) as a catalyst, and a temperature of 350–400°C, and sometimes at reduced pressure, promotes the reaction:

$$C_2H_5OH \rightarrow C_2H_4 + H_2O$$

Similar dehydration has been effected by using acids, such as hydrochloric (HCl), orthophosphoric (H_3PO_4), potassium hydrogen sulfate ($KHSO_4$), and oxalic acid [$(COOH)_2$]. With sulfuric acid, the reaction may be expressed as:

$$2C_2H_5OH + H_2SO_4 \xrightarrow{170°C} H_2SO_4 \cdot H_2O + 2C_2H_4\uparrow$$

(concentrated)

other reactions between these reactants predominate at different temperatures.

Additional methods of making ethylene are illustrated by the equations which follow.

Eliminating a hydrogen halide from an alkyl halide by means of a strong base:

$$CH_3-CH_2Cl + NaOH \rightarrow NaCl + H_2O + C_2H_4\uparrow$$

Ethyl chloride

Removal of halogen from adjacent carbon atoms by means of zinc or similar reducing agent is shown by:

$$CH_2Cl \cdot CH_2Cl + Zn \rightarrow ZnCl_2 + C_2H_4\uparrow$$

Reactions of Ethylene

While paraffin hydrocarbons do not react with halogens as a rule, olefins react readily. For example, ethylene reacts with chlorine or bromine to form ethylene dichloride.

$$C_2H_4 + Cl_2 \rightarrow C_2H_4Cl_2$$

Similar reaction takes place with halogen acids such as HBr:

$$C_2H_4 + HBr \rightarrow CH_3CH_2Br$$

Ethyl bromide

Hydrogenation of alkenes may be accomplished with a catalyst:

$$C_2H_4 + H_2 \rightarrow C_2H_6$$

Finely divided platinum or palladium catalyze this reaction as does nickel at higher temperatures and pressures. Raney nickel is also an efficient catalyst and at a lower temperature.

Alkylation of aromatic hydrocarbons can take place with ethylene in the presence of aluminum chloride as a catalyst. For example, the ethylation of benzene:

$$C_6H_6 + C_2H_4 \xrightarrow{AlCl3} C_6H_5 \cdot CH_2CH_3$$

benzene   ethyl benzene

Complete burning of ethylene occurs as follows:

$$C_2H_4 + 3 O_2 \rightarrow 2CO_2 + 2H_2O$$

Partial burning may occur if the amount of oxygen in the ethylene and air mixture is limited, as seen by the equation:

$$C_2H_4 + 2 O_2 \rightarrow 2CO + 2H_2O$$

or, $$C_2H_4 + O_2 \rightarrow 2C + 2H_2O$$

The presence of glowing carbon particles in the flame from this partial oxidation accounts for the luminous character of a flame from burning ethylene.

Catalytic oxidation of ethylene yields ethylene oxide, a colorless gas which boils at 10.7°C, and is soluble in all proportions in water and in alcohol.

$$2C_2H_4 + O_2 \rightarrow 2(H_2C\underset{O}{\overset{}{\diagdown\diagup}}CH_2)$$

Ethylene oxide

When chlorine water is reacted with ethylene the hypochlorous acid adds to the double bond, forming ethylene chlorohydrin. This compound, as well as the ethylene oxide above, is used in the production of ethylene glycol, a well known antifreeze liquid and coolant medium.

$$H_2C{=}CH_2 + HOCl \rightarrow CH_2OH \cdot CH_2Cl$$

Ethylene   Ethylene chlorohydrin

$$CH_2OH \cdot CH_2Cl + NaHCO_3 \rightarrow$$
$$NaCl + CO_2\uparrow + HOCH_2CH_2OH$$

$$CH_2\underset{O}{\overset{}{\diagdown\diagup}}CH_2 + H_2O \rightarrow HOCH_2CH_2OH$$

Ethylene glycol

Isobutane similarly can be alkylated by ethylene:

$$(CH_3)_3CH + C_2H_4 \xrightarrow[500°C]{AlCl_3}$$

Isobutane Ethylene

```
        H   CH3   CH3  H
        |    |     |   |
   H — C —— C ———— C — C — H
        |    |     |   |
        H    H     H   H
```

2,3-Dimethylbutane
(diisopropyl)

Since isobutane boils at 10.2°C, the reaction occurs in the gaseous phase.

Another important reaction of ethylene is its polymerization to polyethylene, as seen in the equation:

$$nC_2H_4 \rightarrow (C_2H_4)_n$$

Polymerization of liquid ethylene is carried out at a temperature of 200–300°C, under a pressure of over 1200 atm, to form the conventional low density polyethylene. A peroxide catalyst is generally employed.

With Ziegler catalysts (titanium tetrachloride, $TiCl_4$ and aluminum alkyls), low pressure polymerization results in a different type of polymer, known as high density or linear polyethylene.

The resulting polymer can be made into a film or sheet of plastic, inactive chemically, and with high resistance to electricity. Some of the low molecular weight polymers may be used as lubricating oils. The high molecular weight material (above 6000) is a white, tough, leathery resin.

Properties of Ethylene

Low density polyethylene (0.915–0.925 g/ml), and high density polyethylene (0.941–0.965 g/ml) exhibit the following properties.

		Low Density	High Density
Tensile strength, 23°C	psi	1750	3,300
Tensile strength, 70°C	psi	850	1,100
Elongation, 23°C	%	600	600
Elongation, 70°C	%	600	600
Modulus of elasticity, 23°C	psi	35,000	120,000
Impact strength, 23°C	ft/lb/in.	no break	2
Stiffness, 23°C	psi	27,000	90,000
Coefficient of linear expansion, /°F	in./in.	9×10^{-5}	9×10^{-5}
Thermal conductivity	Btu/hr/ft²/ °F/in.	1.8	1.8
Specific heat, 20°C		0.55	0.55
Dielectric strength		Excellent	Excellent
Dielectric constant, 60 cycles		2.3	2.3
Index of refraction		1.51	1.54
Water absorption, 24 hr	%	0.01	0.01
Flammability	in./min	1	1

Polyethylene can be manufactured and fabricated by extrusion, rolling, molding, and other methods. It resists attack by water, acids, alkalies, grease, oil, and most of the organic solvents. Xylene at 200°F, however, does dissolve it appreciably. It is readily heat-sealed. It can be made to burn, but its flammability is not great.

It is used extensively for making transparent sheeting, rope, opaque sheeting used in building construction and packaging lumber. As an opaque product it is used for bottles, pails, cans, and other sorts of containers. A huge demand for polyethylene non-returnable milk bottles is anticipated.

Copolymerization of ethylene is a reality. Copolymers with polypropylene give varied properties and useful products are foreseen. Ethylene-methyl acrylate, ethylene-ethyl acrylate, ethylene-methyl methacrylate, and ethylene-vinyl acetate copolymers may also be formed. Ethylene is today's largest volume organic chemical. The demand is ever-increasing. Consumption in 1964 was 2.9 billion lb, with predictions of 4 billion lb in 1966; 12 billion lb has been the estimated capacity for 1970. In 1964 and early 1965 the production of polyethylene hovered around 220 million lb per month, according to the US Tariff Commission.

New processes for making ethylene are coming, including one using naphtha as starting material and cracking it under high severity conditions. Propane from natural gas is another source of starting material for making ethylene. While substantial increase in demand is anticipated, use of ethylene runs about 80% of full-capacity production.

The reason for the steady increase in demand for ethylene is based on a steady and sharply rising demand for polyethylene. Ethylene oxide, the second largest outlet for ethylene, is also expected to increase but at a slower rate than that estimated for polyethylene.

Ethylene now finds its way into synthetic rubber. This outlet, although small has a promising future and a steady increase in demand is anticipated.

Ethyl alcohol and other straight-chain alcohols are made from ethylene and are steadily increasing in demand. Ethanol has been used for the production of acetaldehyde, but recently a direct method for the production of acetaldehyde from ethylene has taken its place.

Halogenation of ethylene produces ethyl chloride, dichloroethylene, perchloroethylene, and trichloroethylene (such as 1,1,1-trichloroethylene), and brings ethylene into the market as a source of useful chlorinated solvents.

Other important products based on ethylene include styrene ($C_6H_5CH=CH_2$), about one-half of which is made into polystyrene.

Transporation of ethylene by pipeline is supplemented by trailertruck hauling of the compound in liquid form at a temperature of about $-150°F$.

ELBERT C. WEAVER

ETHYLENE GLYCOL DIMETHACRYLATE

Ethylene glycol dimethacrylate is a high boiling, low viscosity, monomeric liquid having a mild, pleasant odor and with a clear water white color. It is a highly active crosslinking agent suitable for crosslinking vinyl type bonds. This monomer has polymerizing characteristics similar to methyl methacrylate. It is usually inhibited with hydroquinone. Ethylene glycol dimethacrylate is prepared either by esterification with methacrylic acid and ethylene glycol or ester interchange with methyl methacrylate and ethylene glycol.

$$CH_2{=}C{-}C{-}O{-}CH_2{-}CH_2{-}O{-}C{-}C{=}CH_2$$

with CH_3 groups on the C and C and O double bonds below.

Physical Constants of Ethylene Glycol Dimethacrylate

Molecular weight	198
Molecular formula	$C_{10}H_{14}O_4$
Appearance	Clear, water white liquid
Odor	Mild
Boiling point	83°C @ 1 mm (260°C @ 760 mm)
Density	1.051 ± 0.002
Refractive index N_D^{25}	1.4530 ± 0.0005
Flash point	235°F
Viscosity, cps	3.4
Solubility	Soluble in alcohol, ether, ketones, esters, aromatic and aliphatic hydrocarbons. Insoluble in water.

Polymerization

The two methacrylate groups in the molecule give ethylene glycol dimethacrylate bifunctionality in a peroxide catalyzed polymerization. Using 0.5% benzoyl peroxide the ethylene glycol dimethacrylate gels within 15 min at 80°C and polymerization is essentially complete in 1–1.5 hr. The gel contains a large fraction of unreacted methacrylate groups.

Copolymerization

Ethylene glycol dimethacrylate will copolymerize with vinyl monomers such as styrene, substituted styrenes, vinyl chloride acrylic and methacrylic esters, diallyl esters, vinyl carbazoles, acrylonitrile, butadiene and many other monomers. A common reaction is that with methyl methacrylate, using small amounts of the ethylene glycol dimethacrylate.

Properties of the commercially important polymers of methyl methacrylate cross-linked with ethylene glycol dimethacrylate are:
(1) Improvement in solvent resistance.
(2) Increased heat resistance.
(3) Improved hardness of methyl methacrylate castings.

The polymer obtained with 0.5% ethylene glycol dimethacrylate is practically insoluble, but swells to some extent in acetone, benzene and chloroform. When the amount of ethylene glycol dimethacrylate is increased above 5% the polymer is insoluble in these solvents and does not soften up to 200°C.

Suggested Applications

The properties above suggest the use of ethylene glycol dimethacrylate for methyl methacrylate castings with improved craze resistance, heat resistance and hardness. It is used in the button and watch crystal industries because of this improvement in hardness and heat resistance.

Polyvinyl chloride slurries with added ethylene glycol dimethacrylate in a plastisol process result in a more rigid material which is desirable in many applications. Ethylene glycol dimethacrylate is being used as a co-agent with peroxides by rubber compounders.

Some of the objectionable qualities of an acrylic denture material such as crazing can be overcome by the use of small quantities of ethylene glycol dimethacrylate which hold together adjacent molecules of acrylic polymer in a lattice form. This is quite superior to ordinary methyl methacrylate in many respects. Ethylene glycol dimethacrylate is being used in some systems being irradiated with gamma and beta rays because it tends to allow a reduction in the required dosage, thereby reducing the radiation cost.

In any experimental work with ethylene glycol dimethacrylate as a cross-linking agent or copolymer amounts in the range of 0.1–5% by weight based on the weight of the total monomers are suggested as a starting point. Other suggested uses for ethylene glycol dimethacrylate are with fiber glass reinforced polyesters and ion-exchange resins.

Handling and Storage

Ethylene glycol dimethacrylate is supplied with 60 ppm hydroquinone as inhibitor to prevent premature polymerization. It is not generally necessary to remove this small amount of inhibitor for use of the monomer. Ethylene glycol dimethacrylate should be stored at temperatures not exceeding 100°F, and should be stored preferably at 70° or lower. Containers should be kept away from any source of heat, since otherwise polymerization may occur. It is not necessary to refrigerate, but it is advisable to keep the monomer away from direct sources of sunlight.

As with any chemical, prolonged contact of the monomer with the skin should be avoided. Wash with soap and water to remove from the skin.

ROBERT P. DEL VECCHIO

ETHYLENIMINE

Ethylenimine, all but unknown before World War II, and a specialty chemical in the years intervening, is now on the verge of becoming a commodity chemical. This growth will certainly be marked by a rapid increase in the number of applications to which both the monomer and polymer will be put, despite the large number of uses already revealed in the patent and scientific literature. It may, likewise, be expected that numerous new and surprising uses for the closely related substituted alkylenimines, e.g., 2-methyl, 2-ethyl, N-methyl, N-ethyl, N-phenyl-ethylenimine, etc., and their polymers will be found.

It is possibly a bit surprising that both a monomer and its polymer would considered as basic materials for use in the plastics industry, yet such is the case for this highly interesting and reactive family of chemicals.

Ethylenimine Monomer and its Derivatives

Chemistry. The interest in ethylenimine is intimately bound up with the structure which may be represented as:

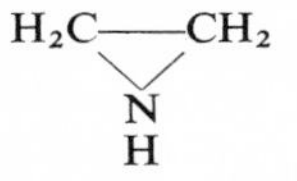

$$H_2C\text{----}CH_2$$
$$\diagdown \diagup$$
$$N$$
$$H$$

Thus, the two main facets of its reactivity are shown, i.e., the presence of a secondary amine which can undergo most of the common amine reactions and a labile, readily-opened three-membered ring.

Physical Properties

Ethylenimine is a highly reactive, volatile, flammable, toxic and corrosive substance, with the physical properties seen below.

Appearance	Clear, colorless liquid.
Odor	Pungent, ammoniacal.
Specific gravity 25/25°C	0.8326.
Index of refraction $n_D{}^{25}$°C	1.4123.
Boiling point 756 mm, °C	56–57°C
Freezing point, °C	−78.
Flash point, °C	−11.1.

The major physical properties of ethylenimine are its relatively low boiling point, permitting vapor transfer or vapor phase reaction, and its infinite solubility in water and most of the common organic solvents.

The chemical reactivity of ethylenimine, is related to two major types of reactions: (1) derivative formation via reaction with the secondary amine and, (2) ring-opening. The ease with which the latter reaction occurs under acidic conditions imposes some limitations on the processes which may be utilized to achieve derivatives. Maintenance of neutral-alkaline conditions, however, permits the preparation of many derivatives.

Acidic conditions will permit one or another of two possible reactions to occur: simple ring opening or polymerization. Of these, the ring opening reaction is of interest with regard to the use and application of the derivatives. Ring-opening may be depicted as:

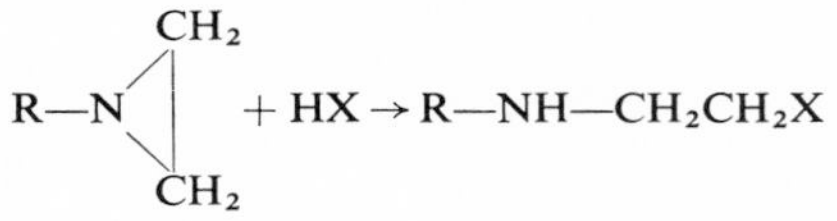

$$R\text{---}N \diagup^{CH_2}_{\diagdown CH_2} + HX \rightarrow R\text{---}NH\text{---}CH_2CH_2X$$

If the HX reactant is HCl, for example, the product will simply be $R\text{---}NH\text{---}CH_2CH_2Cl$, but if a more complex material, such as adipoyl chloride is used then the initial product would be:

$$\rightarrow Cl\text{---}\overset{O}{\overset{\|}{C}}\text{---}(CH_2)_4\overset{O}{\overset{\|}{C}}\text{---}\underset{R}{N}\text{---}CH_2CH_2Cl$$

or, with an excess of the ethylenimine

$$\rightarrow ClCH_2CH_2\underset{R}{N}\text{---}CO(CH_2)_4CO\underset{R}{N}CH_2CH_2Cl$$

Applications. *Amino Alkylation.* This reaction, the step of adding a group of the form $\text{---}CH_2CH_2NH_2$ to a substrate is best known, to date, for its use on cotton, in order to improve dyeing properties. However, it holds potential for the modification of both surface character, when used on a finished fiber or article, or basic characteristics if a polymer is treated prior to spinning, casting, molding, etc.

Copolymerization. Although no true addition copolymers of ethylenimine, other than those with other ethylenimines are known to date, there exists the possibility of forming two types of polymers in which ethylenimine or its residue appears throughout the chain. The first of these is by graft or block polymerization so that shorter or longer ethylenimine polymer segments are bound to or in another polymer. Such a procedure would, in all probability, be somewhat complicated, but the possibility of including highly reactive amino groups within a polymeric structure may well make it worth while.

The second is the pre-reaction of ethylenimine with a monomer which can then be polymerized to form a useful resin. Such a reaction might be of the type:

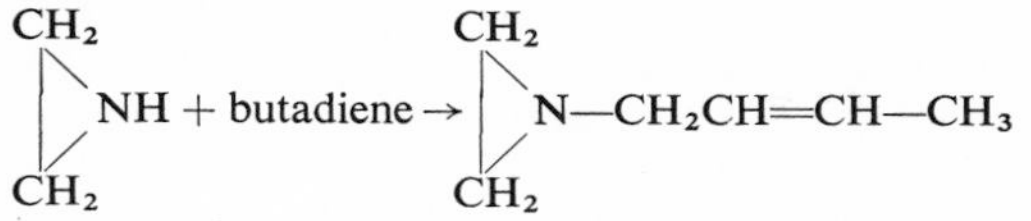

$$
\begin{array}{c}
CH_2 \\
\diagdown \\
\quad NH + \text{butadiene} \rightarrow \\
\diagup \\
CH_2
\end{array}
\qquad
\begin{array}{c}
CH_2 \\
\diagdown \\
\quad N—CH_2CH{=}CH—CH_3 \\
\diagup \\
CH_2
\end{array}
$$

or,

$$
\begin{array}{c}
CH_2 \\
\diagdown \\
\quad NH + \text{divinylbenzene} \rightarrow \\
\diagup \\
CH_2
\end{array}
$$

$$
\begin{array}{c}
CH_2 \\
\diagdown \\
\quad N—CH_2CH_2—\bigcirc—CH{=}CH_2 \\
\diagup \\
CH_2
\end{array}
$$

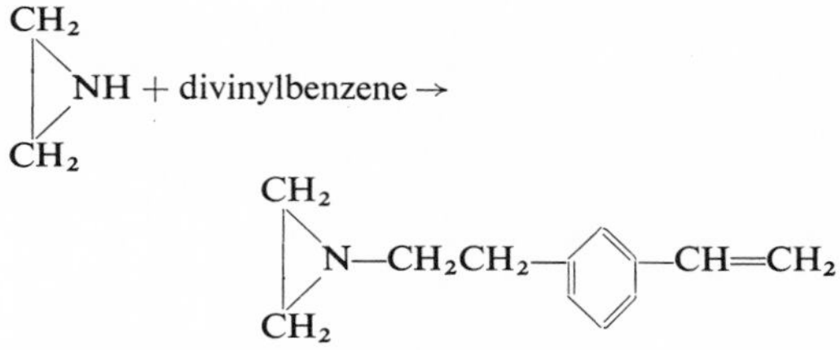

A resin which showed some promise in the crease-proofing of cotton was formed by the reaction of acrolein with ethylenimine.

Cross-linking. The area of cross-linking of polymers has received, of course, much attention in recent years. Included in these studies has been the possibility of utilizing the controllable reactivity of ethylenimine and alkylenimine derivatives as cross-linking agents. By proper adjustment of conditions, these cross-linking reactions have been found to be capable of modifying a natural or synthetic polymer or of curing it to an insoluble condition.

Polycarboxylic acids present probably the best case in point since they are readily reacted with ethylenimine derivatives and have been so used in several applications. Printing ink binders, for example, are regularly cured through the use of APO or the analogous product formed from 2-methyl-ethylenimine (2-methyl APO; MAPO). Similarly, specialty lacquers are subjected to the same treatment, as are the higher molecular weight acrylic acid—butadiene copolymers used as binders, potting resins, etc.

Carboxy modified polymers used as adhesives, coatings and binders have, likewise, been cured by the use of APO, dibasic aziridino-amides and dibasic aziridino-carbamides.

Some of the other uses for this cross-linking reaction include the hardening of photographic gelatin, crease-proofing of rayon, curing of epoxide resins, and improving dyeing properties of textiles.

Polyethylenimine

Chemistry. Polyethylenimine (PEI) is usually represented as:

$$\cdots\!—CH_2CH_2NH—(CH_2CH_2NH)_n—$$
$$—CH_2CH_2NH—\cdots$$

However, this representation fails to take into account the possibility of chain-branching and cross-linking reactions which occur with great frequency in the usual course of polymerization of ethylenimine. The degree of chain-branching has been estimated at a rate as high as one branch point for every two back-bone units. Therefore, the resulting polymer possesses a large percentage of both primary and tertiary amine groups, in addition to the expected secondary amine functions.

Polymerization can be catalyzed by a wide variety of acidic or acid-acting materials, e.g., carbon dioxide, zinc chloride, sulfuric acid, butyl chloride, etc.

PEI, unlike the monomer, is nontoxic and can be handled with ease and in complete safety. It has been approved by the F.D.A. for use in paper, paperboard, adhesives and laminates destined for use in food packaging.

The common forms of PEI are completely soluble in water and lower alcohols, but insoluble in nonpolar solvents. The properties of a typical form of commercially available PEI are seen below.

Properties

Polyethylenimine content, %	50
Water content, %	50
Nitrogen, %	16
Color	Water-white
Viscosity, centistokes, 25°C	10,000
„ 1% aq. solution, centistokes	1.24
pH, 25°C	12.2
Density, sp. gr. 25°C	1.07

The interest in PEI as a potential raw material for other polymers lies in its inherent reactivity. This reactivity, due to the multiple amine groups present in the polymer, can be used as the means by which PEI can be attached to some other macromolecule; such attachment occuring either before or after the second polymer is formed. Examples of these processes would be:

(1) Treatment of a fiber or tow with PEI so as to enhance its ability to accept dyes or coatings.

(2) The formation of a resin in the presence of PEI so that the growing polymer chains will start from or link to amine groups of the PEI.

In either case, the result will be a polymer containing, as an essential element, some PEI. This treatment will serve to modify its properties.

Applications. *Cellulosics.* The best known applications of PEI are concerned with the treatment of cellulose, both as paper pulp and as cotton. PEI displays a rapid reaction with these materials and is strongly adsorbed, forming a complex having new properties.

In the case of paper pulp. these properties include easier removal of water, and a retention effect for fillers, pigments, and dyes.

A very common use of PEI with paper and cellophane, as well as with many other substrates, is its application as a priming or anchoring agent to yield a modified surface which will more readily accept an extruded or laminated coating of polyethylene.

PEI, both in its free form and as a quaternary derivative, is known to be a dye-anchoring agent for use on cotton and rayon.

Synthetic Fibers. Polyethylenimine has been combined with polyamides to yield a fiber having good dyeing properties. The same benefit is claimed when it is incorporated into polypropylene, as well as its assistance in preparing a bulked yarn from this polymer.

Polyvinyl alcohol fibers, treated with various ethylenimine derivatives, are also claimed to exhibit water-resistance and improved dyeing properties.

PEI has been used with acrylonitrile to yield a new fiber. A similar use with a natural polymer is the shrink-proofing of proteins, i.e., wool.

Adhesives and Resins. In addition to the use of PEI as a surface modifier for improved lamination of polyolefins, nitrocellulose lacquers, polyvinylidene chloride and vinyl resins to such substrates as paper, cellophane, rayon, and aluminum, it has also been used in the formulation of adhesives. One such is a reaction product of an epoxy resin, butyl phthalate and PEI. Aldehyde-PEI reaction products have also been reported as adhesives, and in a related area, PEI serves as a bonding agent for tire cords to rubber.

PEI has been used as a hardener for epoxy resins, and in its quaternized form, as an antistatic agent for PVC, polyamides, polyacrylonitrile and polyesters. This antistatic effect is also claimed for both PEI and its quaternary derivative when used on textiles.

Halogenated polyolefins are claimed to have been stabilized by the incorporation of PEI. It is also known that PEI will react with PVC and vinyl chloride copolymers to produce insoluble, thermoset systems.

Anion Exchange Resins. There have been a number of publications and patents in the field of ion exchange resins wherein PEI is cited as the basic constituent. In general, these are characterized by a treatment which results in an insoluble, cross-linked polymer. The reagents which have been used for this purpose include epichlorohydrin, chloromethylated polystyrene, ethylene dibromide and sodium cellulose xanthate.

ALBERT GOLDSTEIN
HANS OSBORG

F

FABRICS FOR VINYL COATING AND LAMINATING

Many applications are today being found for vinyl coated and laminated synthetic fabrics. Vinyl *coated* fabrics are usually knife-coated with low viscosity polyvinyl chloride or polyvinyl chloride copolymer plastisols which are cured upon application. Vinyl *laminated* fabrics generally consist of fabric bonded to a vinyl film on one or both sides by application of heat and pressure.

Vinyl coating and laminating compounds are flexible, tough and highly resistant to severe abrasion and continued flexing, and when applied to synthetic fabric, produce materials which outperform traditional cloth, wood, metal, and plastics for many purposes, and in addition, can do many jobs which could not be done at all with standard materials. Vinyl compounds and synthetic fabrics are both inert to mildew and other microbiological attack.

Coated and laminated fabrics can be looked upon as basic engineering materials, the characteristics of which can be modified to suit the given end use, the same as wood, metal and plastic.

The principal synthetic fabrics used for both coating and laminating are nylon and polyester, though acrylics and polypropylene are also used in small amounts. Coating fabrics have sufficiently high thread count to prevent excess from passing through the fabric during the coating operation.

Vinyl scrims have more open weaves since vinyl is applied as a solid film by calendering and the problem of flow through is nonexistent. These fabrics are also sold with a water repellent finish without coating. Their close weave yields high hydrostatic resistance. When extremely high hydrostatic resistance is required, the fabric is coated.

Since fabrics used for coating have more threads per square inch than fabrics used for laminating, they are generally stronger than fabric used for laminating, and coated fabric is generally recommended for heavier duty applications such as swimming pools, grain storage bins, and inflated structures. This is not a hard and fast rule, for tear strength, which is often the marginal property, with tensile often being excessive, is related to yarn size rather than count, and often judicious selection of a low count, high denier laminating fabric can produce an end product which will meet overall requirements at lower cost than coated fabric. Since fabric for laminated products has less yarn and a lower count than fabric for coated products, it is the less expensive of the two.

A "rip-stop" weave produces coating fabrics of increased tear strength without increasing fabric weight. Rip-stop fabric incorporates a grid work of yarns heavier than those which make up the main body of the fabric. For example, by doubling the denier of the yarn in the grid in comparison with that of the main body of the fabric, tear strength is nearly doubled with virtually no increase in weight.

Flat yarn fabrics provide a means of increasing yarn denier and fabric tear strength without increasing weight. They are used in coating in lieu of high-count fine-denier fabric to prevent the compound from going through the fabric. Flat yarn fabrics use either zero-twist or "producers twist" yarns which flatten into ribbons during the weaving process, yielding a thin low-weight fabric with good cover permitting knife coating. A 15×15, 1260-denier flat yarn fabric has recently been successfully substituted for a widely used 22×22, 840 denier nylon fabric, maintaining the same weight but increasing tear resistance by 50%. Laminating fabrics are referred to as "scrims," and since open spaces exist between yarns making up the cloth, scrims must be resin treated at the mill to bond the yarns at the intersections so they do not shift at any stage prior to laminating. Polyvinyl acetate, polyvinyl chloride, and other resins are used in finishing scrim, depending on the compound to be used in the laminating process. Coating fabric also often is finished with a polymeric tie-coat to assure proper bonding of plastic to cloth.

Du Pont is now in pilot production of "Nomex" nylon, and recommends considerations of this fiber for continuous exposure to temperatures up to 400°F. The fiber has a tenacity on the order of magnitude of that for nylon. It has low elongation, good dimensional stability, and high modulus.

All of the above fibers are available in many variations. There are, for example, several different polymers available in the polyesters. Nylon, of course, is available in nylon 66 and nylon 6, with the major variation being melting point. Some polymers are available in staple fiber form, some in multifilament form, some in both. Individual fiber denier or filament denier can be varied; total denier, of course, is variable. Nylon, being the synthetic fiber with the largest use, has the largest number of types. It is available in regular tenacity and high tenacity, bright, semi-dull and full dull. It is available in sunlight-resistant yarn and sunlight-and-heat-resistant yarn. All of this makes a wider spectrum of properties available to suit individual needs. However, the increased number of variables adds to the complexity of the choice of the right material.

Producers of synthetic fibers used in vinyl coating and laminating are paying increasing attention to this market as it continues to grow. Du Pont reports that it has improved the uniformity of its yarns used by coaters and laminators to help weavers make better fabric and reduce production problems encountered by the coater and laminator.

Chemstrand has developed a new nylon yarn in 840 and 210 deniers which is more uniform than yarn presently available. Designated as "A04," it is designed to minimize shrinkage and puckers, and to handle better and reduce rejects for the coater and laminator.

Allied Chemical has modified its 840 denier nylon tire cord for use in auto seat belts and is now promoting its use for coating and laminating applications. The gold color of tire cord nylon has been eliminated, and the white filament can now readily be dyed. The modified fiber also has added abrasion resistance, a property needed for seat belts but not so much for tire cord, and of value to the industrial market. Of course, abrasion resistance of the fiber is not important in a fabric used for coating or laminating, since the vinyl resin protects it.

Celanese, while relatively new in the market with polyester, states that the application technology of this fiber is catching up with that of longer-established nylon.

GEORGE W. EWALD

FABRICS, LEAD COATED

Lead metal in extremely fine powdered form is compounded with a PVC resin system and coated onto various fabrics such as woven glass, cotton, nylon, asbestos, paper, etc. with the resulting lead coated vinyl fabric finding application in many areas of the aircraft, marine, ground transportation, military, institutional and industrial fields. In the form of high density, limp, easily handled flexible sheets of continuous length and width, they provide for optimum noise-control as well as control of vibrating or resonating panels. They are available in weights from 0.15–1.5 lb/sq ft, with thickness (0.02 to 0.10 in.) varying according to weight. Special grade unsupported lead-vinyl sheets find use as soft X-ray barrier materials.

Leaded vinyl septums or barriers, alone or in combination with highly absorptive materials (glass or mineral wool insulations, or certain types or grades of plastics foams) are highly efficient in confining or reducing high noise-levels. At high noise-levels, the visco-elastic characteristics of these leaded vinyl fabrics provide or exhibit strong attenuation in the medium-low to high-frequency noise spectrum; the higher weight-levels of lead-vinyl (i.e. 0.87 lb/sq ft) also give good attenuation in the lower frequencies of about 125 cps upward.

In controlling vibrating or resonating metal panels, lead coated vinyl fabrics do an outstanding job because of their limpness or acoustical "lossiness" characteristics, plus the added mass.

Applications include: confining noise radiating from apartment piping, and gas-transmission pipelines; heating and ventilating equipment; room-walls of portable folding traveling exhibits, floating noise-barrier septums in wall panels and doors; cross-talk barriers over suspended ceilings; as a suspended blanket in low cost apartment wall-systems; aircraft and marine sound control-blanket treatment; controlling high-pitched whine of stand-by turbine-driven electric-generator sets. A large volume application is that controlling resonance of components of, or housing panels of business machines, etc.

F. M. HALL

F.D.A. REGULATIONS FOR PLASTICS

The introduction of cellulose acetate plastics in 1927 and subsequent developments in thermoplastic materials have had, and will continue to have, a significant impact on the administration of the Federal Food, Drug, and Cosmetic Act. New legislation has to some extent been inspired by use of plastics in the regulated industries. Their greatest impact under the Act involves use as packaging materials for foods, drugs, and cosmetics. However, bio-mechanical use of plastics in prosthetic devices for tissue implants is achieving a significant degree of importance in the advancement of modern reparatory processes in surgery.

The importance of plastics used for food packaging and processing is understandable when one considers that the ingestion of a chemical as a part of food may continue over the entire life of the individual during periods of good health, disease, and malnutrition. Thus, the problem common to all plastic materials intended for use in a manner that involves food contact, whether rigid molded utensils, films, or piping, usually concerns the use of plasticizers, stabilizers, resins, colorants, and adhesives or release agents. These must not contribute a harmful substance to foods wrapped, packaged, conveyed, or stored in plastic containers, since the contamination of foods, animal and human, with harmful substances is a violation of the Federal Food, Drug, and Cosmetic Act, whether such substance results from indirect addition during processing, from contact with the container or wrapper, or from deliberate incorporation in the food.

Regulation of plastics for use in food containers or in other materials which may come in contact with food is under the Food Additives Amendment of 1958 to the Federal Food, Drug, and Cosmetic Act. The term "food additive" or, as someone may suggest, "chemical additive," may be defined broadly to include any substance, the intended use of which results or may result directly or indirectly in its becoming a component of or otherwise affecting the characteristics of any food. The Amendment requires that a new additive be proven safe before it may be used under any condition. It also provides a system for the establishment of safe tolerances for substances that may be harmful in larger quantities.

When safety has not been previously determined to authorize use of plastic food containers, this can be secured under the aforementioned Amendment where the facts demonstrate safety. Where there is no reasonable expectation of migration and the characteristics of the food in the container are not otherwise affected, there would be no need to petition for approval from the F.D.A. However, when migration does occur, or may reasonably be expected to occur, then the identity and safety of the migrant should be established according to the provisions of the Amendment.

An impressive set of regulations has been promulgated since passage of the Food Additives Amendment. These provide a guide for compliance. They do not yet include all items priorly sanctioned or generally recognized as safe and thus exempt from the Amendment.

Appropriate tests are required to establish the safety of a food additive and to determine tolerance levels that will be safe. Such tests include acute toxicity studies, allergic responses of the product, subacute and chronic toxicity studies, the adsorption and metalbolic fate and excretion of the substance, and pathology of the animals in which the tests are made. The scientists of the

F.D.A. discuss with industry scientists the design of such tests, and offer their services in the evaluation of data obtained when these include, in addition to test results, (1) complete composition of the plastic involved, (2) the constancy of composition that can be controlled, (3) the extractability by each food type for which the container is used, (4) sensitive analytical tests for each component of the plastic except those known to be nontoxic, (5) analysis of a representative number of individual package samples, and (6) several blanks and recoveries on each food or solvent.

The existence of a regulation establishing safe conditions of use for a plastic in contact with food does not relieve the user of the need to comply with other provisions of the Act. For example, tinted film to improve color of inferior packaged foods, the use of film printed with lines or checks of the same color on an inferior packaged food to improve its appearance, the use of film with opaque areas to conceal damage or inferiority, or a use which may impart an unacceptable odor or taste to a food would result in misbranding or adulteration under other sections of the Act.

Developments in the plastic industry have also had a major impact on the manufacture and distribution of drugs and therapeutic devices. Today, practically all drugs reach the pharmacist in the final dosage form packaged in a manner which should be suitable for storage in the pharmacy or for passing on to the final consumer. Since there is a possibility that hazard may result from chemicals leached out of plastic materials used for drug packaging, F.D.A. requires those firms marketing drugs intended for administration by injection or administered in substantial volume by clysis to clear such products through the new drug procedures provided for by the Food, Drug, and Cosmetic Act. These require proof before marketing concerning the safety and effectiveness when used for the purposes intended in accordance with the directions in their labeling. The sponsor of new drugs marketed in plastic containers must therefore submit new-drug applications containing convincing evidence of safety and efficacy before the drugs may be placed on the market in this country.

Some of the hazards which may arise from the medicinal use of plastics include the possibility that a foreign substance will be injected into the patient or that the patient will not get the drug in the form or amount intended. These effects may be caused by (1) the leaching of a component of the plastic into the drug; (2) chemical reaction between a constituent of the plastic and an active or inactive ingredient of the drug; (3) degradation, oxidation, or precipitation in the drug product resulting from the transmisson of oxygen, carbon dioxide, or other gases from the plastic into the drug; system (4) migration of a component of the drug through the walls of the plastic container, or (5) binding of certain ingredients of the pharmaceutical preparation into the plastic (i.e., nylon tends to bind a number of products such as the parabens and phenols containing an acidic hydrogen). The extent of these will be dependent on such factors as contact time, temperature, concentration, etc.

The F.D.A. is unable to specify a plastic container that may under all conditions be used with all drugs or biologicals without question of its safety or possible toxicity. The only certain approach to determine the safety of a plastic substance for use as a suitable drug or biological serum container is to conduct appropriate tests. It is therefore incumbent upon the manufacturer and distributor of drugs or biologicals packaged in plastic containers to conduct adequate tests to insure that the plastic material does not in any way contaminate or otherwise change the drug packaged therein.

It is also of utmost importance that drugs packaged in plastics be tested for stability under normal conditions of storage and use. Some plastic materials possess distinctive disadvantages such as: lack of full retention of aromatic flavors, permeability to certain greases, oils, nitrogen, oxygen, and moisture, acceleration of the phase separation of emulsions, and formations of complexes with drugs having acidic hydrogen in the molecule. Also, since drugs in plastic containers do not lend themselves to sterilization by heat, other satisfactory sterilizing procedures must be developed and adopted for this purpose.

Use of plastic in the cosmetic industry is in general limited to their suitability for packaging; not all plastic containers are acceptable for cosmetic use. Most cosmetic creams and many lotions contain mineral oil or other organic substances which slowly attack the container, and, for this reason, a high degree of selectivity must be employed when determining which container may be used for a specific product. Generally speaking, when a firm desires to use a plastic container for a cosmetic, the particular product involved is formulated with this viewpoint in mind.

A wide range of mechanical properties available in synthetic high polymers has made them attractive candidates for bio-mechanical applications for such purposes as external and internal body prosthesis. These include preparation of artificial limbs to be worn over amputee stumps, preparation of artificial arteries, veins, bile ducts, etc. They are also employed successfully in dentistry for making artificial teeth, complete dentures, impressions, etc. These objects may, depending upon the circumstances under which they are used, be regarded as either drugs or

therapeutic devices under the Federal Food, Drug, and Cosmetic Act.

While there are no new device requirements in the law similar to those for new drugs, and firms may proceed to market therapeutic devices without any prior approval or discussions with the F.D.A., in the public interest of safety and efficacy, the F.D.A. will discuss any proposed use of a plastic which may involve the Food, Drug, and Cosmetic Act. The Administration will evaluate the facts in any set of circumstances and advise whether the proposed usage of a plastic is or is not likely to run afoul of the statute.

HAROLD F. O'KEEFE

FILAMENT WINDING MATERIALS

Filament wound structures have been developed, having the highest strength-to-weight ratio of any known structural material, as shown in Table 1. Design parameters have been developed based on experimental and production units. The design criterion is concerned with fiber orientation. The basic design method is to orient the fibers in the direction of the principal stresses and proportion the number of fibers with respect to the size of the principal stresses.

In structures, where it is geometrically impossible to orient the fibers precisely in the direction of the principal stress, orientation at some angle may be done. A balanced structure can be achieved by proportionately locating fibers at two basically different winding angles—namely, low helicals and circumferentials. The balanced structure is one in which the fibers oriented in any direction have equal stress applied to them under load.

The use of circumferential wrappings to increase the bursting strength of certain structures is not new. Historically, wire wrappings have been used to prevent bursting of cannon barrels and to wrap wooden pipes, both to increase the bursting strength and to hold the two parts together so that a leak-proof cylinder is formed. However, the use of filamentary structures for applications requiring ultimate structural performance is recent and unique. Filament winding is a fabrication for forming reinforced plastic parts of high strength and light weight. It is made possible by exploiting the remarkable strength properties of their continuous fibers or filaments encased in a matrix of a resinous material, either organic or inorganic.

For this process, the reinforcement consists of filamentous nonmetallic or metallic materials processed either in fibrous or tape forms. Most frequently used at the present time is some form of glass as continuous filament, roving, yarn, or tape. The glass filaments, in whatever form, are

TABLE 1. PROPERTIES OF INTERNAL PRESSURE VESSEL MATERIALS.

Material	Ultimate hoop (tensile) strength, psi	Density, lb/cu in.	Specific strength[a], 10^6 inch	Thermal conductivity[b]	Tensile modulus of elasticity, 10^6 psi	Compressive strength, psi
Glass-resin[c] (Unidirectional)	130,000 to 170,000	0.077	1.6–2.1	2.0–5.0	6.0–9.0	70,000 to 175,000
Glass-resin (Bidirectional)	60,000	0.072	0.7	2.0–5.0	2.0–3.5	40,000 to 60,000
Steel wire-resin (Bidirectional)	150,000	0.166	1.0	—	12	—
Titanium (Homogeneous)	50,000	0.163	0.9	—	16.5	135,000
Steel (Homogeneous)	280,000	0.280	0.9	314	30.0	—
Aluminum (Homogeneous)	80,000	0.097	0.8	1,416	10.0	40,000
Magnesium (Homogeneous)	32,000	0.064	0.5	—	—	—

[a] Specific strength equals ultimate tensile strength/density (approx.).
[b] Btu/hour/°F/square foot/inch.
[c] Interlaminar shear strength = 6000 to 8000 psi (parallel to laminations); 20,000 psi (perpendicular to laminations)
   Axial bearing strength = 20,000 to 40,000 psi
   Compression strength = 50,000 to 70,000 psi

encased in a resin matrix, either wetted out immediately before winding (wet process), or impregnated ahead of time (preimpregnated process). The resin fundamentally contains the reinforcement, holding it in place, sealing it from mechanical damage, and protecting it from enviromental deterioration. The reinforcement-matrix combination is wound continuously on a form or mandrel whose shape corresponds to the inner structure of the part being fabricated. After curing of the matrix, the form may either be discarded or used as an integral part of the structural item.

Filament winding is carried out on specially designed automatic machines. Precise control of the winding pattern and direction of the filaments are required for maximum strength, which can be achieved only with controlled machine operation. The equipment in use permits the fabrication of parts in accordance with properly designed parameters so that the reinforced filamentous wetting system is in complete balance and optimal strength is obtained. The maximum strength is achieved when all major stresses are carried by filaments in tension. Under proper design and controlled fabrication, hoop tensile strengths of filament wound items can be achieved of over 500,000 psi, although a strength of 210,000 psi is more frequently achieved.

Since this fabrication technique allows production of strong, light weight parts, it has proved particularly useful for components of aerospace, hydrospace, and military applications (Table 2), and for structures of commercial and industrial usefulness (Table 3). Both the reinforcement and the matrix can be tailor-made to satisfy almost

TABLE 2. FILAMENT-WOUND STRUCTURES FOR AEROSPACE, HYDROSPACE, AND MILITARY APPLICATIONS.

Rocket motor cases	Rocket exit cones
Rocket motor insulators	Chemical rockets
Solid propellant motor liners	Chemical tanks
Nose cones for space fairings	Sounding rocket tubes
Rocket nose cones	Tactical bombardment rockets
Rocket nozzle liners	Tent poles
Jato motor	Heat shields
APU turbine cases	Artillery shell shipping grommet
High-pressure bottles (gas or liquid)	Artillery round-protective cones
Vacuum cylinders	Submarine fluid pipes
Torpedo launching tubes	Submarine tanks and containers
Rocket launcher tubes	Submarine ventilation pipes
Flame thrower tubes	Submarine hulls
Missile landing spikes	Underwater buoys
Deep space satellite structures	Cryogenic vessels
Radomes	Electronic packages
Igniter baskets	Submarine fairwaters
Wing dip tanks	Sonar domes
Helicopter rotor blades	Engine cowlings
Thermistors	Fuse cases
Missile shipping cylinders	Torpedo cases and launchers
Boat ventilator cowlings	
Liquid rocket thrust chamber	

any property demand. This aids in widening the applicability of filament winding to the production of almost any military or commercial item wherein the strength to weight ratio is important. Filament winding recently has also been used to produce rectangular shapes.

Railway tank cars	Irrigation pipes
Storage tanks: acids, alkalies, water, oil, salts, etc.	Salt water disposal pipes
	Underground water pipe
High-voltage switch gears	Oil well tubes
Electrical containers	Ladders
Propellers	Extension arms for telephone trucks
High-pressure bottles	
Decorative building supports	Textile bobbins
	Weather rockets
Containers for engines, batteries, etc.	Gas bottle-mines
	Structural tubing
Buoys	Insulating tubes
Valves	Electrical conduit
Aircraft tanks	Chemical pipe
Aircraft under-carriage	Pulp and paper mill pipe
Aircraft structures	Water heating tanks
Fishing rods	Pipe fittings and elbows
Round nose boat	Truck-mounted booms
Boat masts	Highway stanchions
Lamp poles	Capacitor jackets and spacers
Golf clubs	
Race track railing	Coil forms
Auto bodies	Electronic waveguides
Drive shafts	Printed circuit forms
Air brake cylinder	Electric motor rotors, binding bands
Heating ducts	
Acid filters	Circuit breaker housing
Recoil-less rifle barrel	High-voltage insulators
Pontoons	Rectifier spacers
Motor housing	Antenna/dishes
Computer housings	Rotating armatures—DC motors
Marker buoys	
Laundry tubs	DC commutator
Ventilator housings	Fan housing
Rifle barrel	High voltage fuse tubes
Dairy cases	Floating ducts
Auto and truck springs	Automotive parts
Circuit breaker rupture pots	Tank trucks
	Light poles
Cartop boats	Brassiere supports
Electroplating jigs	Looms

The high strength-to-weight ratio in filament-wound structures can be attributed largely to the reinforcement. The matrix material (or resin), though not in itself providing strength capability, can be a very important factor in limiting performance of the composite. The matrix material is essential, for it serves to bond the reinforcements together and transmits the loads to the fibers so that optimum fiber stresses can be developed before failure. Efficient strength-weight structures can exist only if the fibers of the composite have an efficient strength-weight relationship in the monfilament form. Glass fibers presently provide the most efficient filament structure.

Glass fiber is one of the strongest materials now available in large quantities. It is also comparatively low in density, inexpensive, stiff, chemically resistant, relatively submissive to textile manu-

facturing techniques, and capable of extensive modification in composition. The glass reinforcements applicable to winding operations are principally continuous-fiber filament, roving, yarn, and undirectional woven tape. These forms are applied by the resin preimpregnated method or the wet method.

The general process used for manufacturing glass textiles is that of melting glass through a platinum bushing. Glass marbles, approximately 3/4 in. in diameter, are prepared for the bushing. However, various forms of chipped glass are sometimes used in place of the glass marbles. The bushings hold approximately 5 lb of molten glass. The electrical heat applied to the bushing is approximately 2400°F. This temperature is very closely controlled in order to obtain the proper viscosity of the liquid glass.

Fiber glass reinforcements are supplied in several basic forms. These forms allow for flexibility in cost, strength, and choice of process. Many variations of the basic forms have been developed to meet performance and economic needs, which vary considerably.

Glasses are prepared by melting together oxides and oxide-producing materials. The melt is then cooled rapidly enough to prevent devitrification. Most fibers are produced by the mechanical drawing process. Other commercial processes involve steam or air blowing and flame blowing. These latter processes produce wool and staple or short fibers. Only the mechanical drawing process produces continuous fibers which are specifically used in filament-winding operations.

From small orifices in the bushing, continuous glass filaments are drawn. It is estimated that a filament is pulled at a speed of 2 miles per min. in order to form a continuous filament having a controlled diameter. The commercial practice is to draw a large number of filaments in one operation, e.g., groupings of 51, 102, or 204 continuous filaments. The most common practice is to pull 204 filaments, which in turn form a strand. This strand is then gathered around a winding tube.

Continuous glass strand is ordinarily supplied in the form of yarn and roving. Continuous glass filaments, usually amounting to the 204 individual filaments, make up the glass strand immediately after the mechanical drawing operation. Production of glass roving only requires plying together the desired number of (untwisted) glass strands. If twisted yarns are to be produced, the 204 filament strand is put through a twist machine.

In turn, twisted yarns can be plied together in order to meet any configuration desired. Untwisted multi-strands are also made available in the form of "spun roving." A continuous single strand is looped many times upon itself, and holds the roving together with a slight twist.

While the terms "rovings" and "yarn" are sometimes used interchangeably, they definitely have different meanings. Yarns and rovings are used to fabricate the majority of filament-wound vessels. The nomenclature of glass fiber yarns differs from that used for other types of textile fibers, because there are many different glass fiber varieties of nearly identical characteristics.

It is apparent that the materials used and the winding process constitute the most important steps in the fabrication of efficient wound vessels. However, packaging of the fibers is another important aspect. Regardless of reinforcement strengths, improved surface treatments of reinforcements, improved matrix materials employed, and controlled fabrication processes, the ultimate capabilities of the vessel are also directly related to the manner in which glass fibers are packaged. A package should be constructed to reduce the possibilities of twist to a minimum. Twisting of the glass during winding causes abrasion of the filaments, and unequal fiber tension, resulting in a lowering of the composite strength.

Up until type "S"-glass was recently produced, the type "E"-glass was predominately used. Virgin single fiber strength of "S" fibers is approximately 700,000 psi, as compared to 500,000 psi fiber stress for "E"-glass. This significant increase in fiber strength has put the strength of the glass-epoxy filament-wound composites higher than structural metals on a volume basis. Before the development of these fibers, glass-filament-wound plastics were no stronger than metals on a volume basis, but instead on a specific or weight basis. The strength-to-weight ratio of "S"-fiber composites is further enhanced by the slightly lower density of 0.090 lb per in., as compared to a density of 0.092 lb per cu in. for "E"-glass.

Another improvement over "E"-glass fibers offered by "S"-glass is the higher strengths retained at elevated temperatures. At 1400°F, "E"-glass yields and loses its fiber stength, whereas "S" still retains a strength of 180,000 psi and does not yield until a temperature of 1600°F is reached.

Other fibers are now being developed for use in filament winding and reinforced plastics. Table 4 lists properties of some of these fibers, including

TABLE 4. COMPARISON OF FIBROUS AND WIRE REINFORCEMENTS.

Fiber/Wire	Density, lb/cu in.	Specific gravity	Melting point of	Tensile			
				Strength		Mod. of elasticity	
				Ultimate $\times 10^3$ psi	Ratio to density $\times 10^5$	$\times 10^6$ psi	Ratio to density $\times 10^7$
Aluminum	.097	2.70	1,220	90	9	10.6	11
Aluminum oxide	.144	3.97	3,780	100	7	76	53
Aluminum silica	.140	3.90	3,300	600	43	15	11
Asbestos	.090	2.50	2,770	200	22	25	28
Beryllium	.067	1.84	2,343	250	37	44	66
Beryllium carbide	.088	2.44	3,800	150	17	45	51
Beryllium oxide	.109	3.03	4,650	75	7	51	47
Boron	.093	2.59	3,812	500	54	60	65
Carbon	.051	1.40	6,700	250	49	27	53
Glass							
E—Glass	.092	2.55	2,400	500	54	10.5	11
S—Glass	.090	2.49	3,000	700	78	12.5	14
R & D Target	.090	2.49	3,000	1,000	111	16.0	18
Graphite	.051	1.40	6,600	250	49	37	72
Molybdenum	.367	10.20	4,370	200	5	52	14
Polyamide	.041	1.14	480	120	29	0.4	1
Polyester	.050	1.40	480	100	20	0.6	1
Quartz (fused silica)	.079	2.20	3,500	1,000	127	10	13
Steel	.282	7.87	2,920	600	21	30	11
Tantalum	.598	16.60	5,425	90	2	28	5
Titanium	.170	4.72	3,035	280	16	16.7	10
Tungsten	.695	19.30	6,170	620	9	58	8
Tungsten monocarbide	.565	15.70	5,200	106	2	104	20

1. Sources-Filament Winding, J. Wiley & Sons, Inc., NYC; *Plastics World* and *Reinforced Plastics*, Cahners Corp., Boston; etc.
2. Boron fiber contains tungsten boride core.
3. Also of interest are whiskers with extreme high E and strength; examples—
   Aluminum oxide: 1.8×10^6 psi tensile strength.
   Graphite   : 3.0×10^6 psi tensile strength.
   Iron   : 2.0×10^6 psi tensile strength.

the new glass fibers. Higher strengths are being developed but more important are the higher modulus of elasticity values which are above 50×10^6 psi.

Filament Winding Process

The tape-winding process consists of winding a resin-impregnated woven or nonwoven tape onto a mandrel of the desired configuration. In the application for reentry space vehicles, the tape is wound on a mandrel under tension in a continuous operation from the stagnation region to the conical base of the reentry body; the laminations are parallel to the longitudinal axis. Tape winding is also easily adapted to cylindrical shapes. Cost probably contributes more to the motivation of the development of tape-winding processes than any other factor. Where tape winding can be applied, it is generally expected that costs will be reduced and strength properties will be increased when compared to filament winding or other techniques.

The tape-winding process is similar to the convolute tube-winding process, presently being used to make insulators and coil forms for the electrical industry. A hot roll is used to melt the resin on the impregnated reinforcing material or the adhesive for metal tapes just before it is wound on a mandrel. Pressure is applied to this mandrel, as it contacts the mandrel by the hot roll, which is connected in turn to a pressure cylinder. Tension, applied to the impregnated material as it is being wound, is close by a tension device such as a friction brake.

The rolling or winding speeds that apply for convolutely wound tubing apply to the tape-winding process as well. The curing takes place on a mandrel, in either an air-circulating oven or other suitable compartment. Curing problems can be more complicated for certain shapes. For example, in a conical reentry vehicle, curing lap-wound parts is somewhat more involved because the compressive forces created during the cure tend to push the part from the mandrel.

The overall mechanical strength of a reinforced plastic depends on the amount of reinforcement and its arrangement in the finished article. The chemical, electrical and thermal performances result from the choice and formulation of the resinous matrix materials. The materials selection, along with design and production requirements, determine which process of fabrication is most desirable. Finally, the economical cost and quality of performance result from good design and proper choice of reinforcement and matrix.

The major resins used in a filament-wound structure vary in resistance to corrosion and heat. Performance of a given resin can be changed by formulation of ingredients, such as filler, pigment, and catalyst systems. For general reinforced plastics, polyesters comprise a large percentage of the total because they are economical. Other resins in use are epoxies, phenolics, silicones, melamines, acrylics, and polyesters modified with acrylics. For filament-wound structures, heavy emphasis has been placed on the epoxies.

In developing maximum strength properties, the aim is to apply a minimum amount of resin. The amount is dependent on the space available between the fibers. When fibers are closely netted, the available volume to be filled by the resin can be predetermined. In addition to having the resin occupy this volume, an extremely thin layer of resin is required between mating or adjoining fibers. The thickness of this separating film is usually less than 0.0001 in. When the proper finish is applied to the reinforcement, resin completely covers the fiber surfaces. The resin

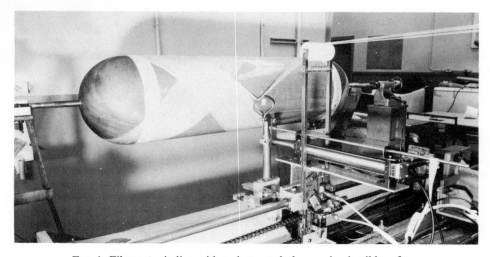

FIG. 1. Filament winding with resin treated glass roving in ribbon form.

matrices used are designed specifically for filament-wound composites. The resin provides strong bonds to the reinforcement, produces high shear strength and has an elongation of approximately 1–2% so that it can match the glass reinforcements.

When the concept of glass-resin filament winding was initiated approximately a decade ago, polyester-resin systems were used. At that time, polyesters accounted for about 85% of all resins consumed by the glass-reinforced plastics industry. During the interim period, epoxy resins have almost completely displaced polyesters for filament winding. It is estimated that over 90% of the resin used presently in filament winding is the commercially available bisphenol A-epichlorohydrin epoxies.

When polyesters are compared to epoxies, they are found to be more brittle and to provide a lower-strength bond to the glass fiber. Phenolic resins have also been introduced into filament winding since they basically exhibit higher temperature resistance and are lower in cost. The latter structures are not as strong at room temperature. In selecting a resin matrix for filament winding, processing characteristics of the system are very critical. Much production today is by the wet-winding technique. The resin is liquid at room temperature with a low viscosity ranging from 500–1000 cp. The desired pot life (before resin gels or hardens) has to be long enough in order to complete the winding operation. In general, an 8 hr working life is desired. Another important characteristic for the resin is that it contains 100% solids.

When heat-resistant structures are required, the phenolic and silicone resins are used. New resins are now available which permit developing high strength and stiffness properties at temperatures ranging from 500°–1200°F. These new resins include the polyimides and polybenzimidazole(PBI).

Basic filament reinforcement is essentially continuous and is drawn from a spool for pretreating before winding around a mandrel. Two basic methods for pretreating or impregnating the filament resin are used. The first basic method, commonly referred to as "wet" system, involves the impregnation of the filaments with liquid resin prior to winding around the mandrel. A second method uses preimpregnated (wet or dry) filaments which have been wetted and dried with partially cured resin.

One of the earliest so-called wet systems was to wind the glass filaments dry onto the mandrel and then impregnate it on the mandrel. Impregnation was performed either by applying resin directly on the mandrel as it rotated or by taking the wrapped resin-dried mandrel and immersing it in the liquid resin. Vacuum, autoclave, and dip tank methods were used to apply the resin. This method of impregnation was abandoned by most fabricators very early. The method did not permit reproducibility or sufficiently satisfactory properties in applications where efficient structures were being fabricated. However, it is still used to develop special handling or property characteristics, such as the construction of gun barrels, by filament winding. In the past the wet system was used almost exclusively. At present the major usage is the preimpregnated system. The trend for the future is that the preimpregnated system will be used exclusively as major production programs are developed.

As the term implies, the wet method applies a liquid resin to the filament before winding, while still wet, around the mandrel. Selection of the resin is limited to resins which are adaptable to liquid application, that is, epoxies and polyesters.

Another disadvantage of this method is the low rate of speed at which the filaments can be impregnated with liquid resin. If a filament is drawn through the resin bath too rapidly, little if any resin will cling to its surface. Since the filaments may not be wound around the mandrel any faster than they can be thoroughly penetrated by the resin, the winding process is slow. One way to shorten the "wetting" time is to pass the filaments between two very soft resin-impregnated rubber sponges after they emerge from the resin bath. The soft "stroking" of the filaments by the sponges tends to force resin between adjacent fibers and distribute the liquid uniformly through a band of parallel fibers. It is apparent that resin viscosity plays an important role in the wetting speed of the filament. The more viscous the resin, the slower the process.

In this method large quantities of resins are usually wasted either by being left in the tank at the end of a run or by being scrapped off the part itself. In addition, it is impossible to be sure that the resin content of the part will be accurately reproduced from part to part. A further disadvantage is the fact that the resin content increases with larger-diameter parts when constant winding tension is used. This increase in resin content is very undesirable when high strength to weight ratio parts are required. In order to reduce the content, the winding tension must be increased. This can only be accomplished within defined limits because of the danger of breaking the filaments.

A further problem with wet winding lies in inability to use a large number of resin systems because of the high viscosity. In some cases, high-viscosity systems can be used if they are heated to reduce the viscosity, but this also reduces the pot life and requires additional equipment. Still other systems cannot be used even when heated, but can only be used by thinning with solvents.

Solvent systems, however, cannot be used in wet filament winding, since there is no practical way to remove the solvent before the filaments are applied to the mandrel.

The biggest advantage of the wet system is economy. An epoxy-"E"-glass system averages about 92¢ per lb for applications to military specifications and 57–60¢ per lb for commercial products. This is compared with a cost of $1.45 per lb for a preimpregnated system of the same resin and glass. Technically, a wet system provides a less permeable vessel, since the excess liquid forces entrapped air bubbles to the surfaces. This is accomplished by simple bubble-exudation and by the pulsing-squeezing action as each additional taut filament is laid onto the surface.

For a compound-curvature surface, an even-coverage pattern produces an open "net" structure. Previously, it was believed that the resulting interstices should be filled or "potted" with resin to distribute stress and prevent chain-reaction ripping at failure. This philosophy is currently open to question. If these interstices need not be filled, it is then possible to remove all excess resin, for example, by centrifugal spinning.

Although it is believed that a wet system provides better impregnation of the reinforcing fibers compared to a solvent-assisted preimpregnation, either will be affected by the care and consistency of the operation. The physical geometry of the impregnated fibers is easier to predict and control in a wet system. The optimum configuration of the strand at the point of winding is a flat band of parallel fibers.

In a wet system, this is accomplished by drawing the band of filaments over a rounded surface, the "eye", immediately before contact with the mandrel. This causes the filaments to rearrange themselves to assume uniform tension and lay into a flat ribbon as they pass over the curved surface. Redesign of the "eye", from a cylindrical to a slightly crowned surface, allows precise rearrangement of parallel fibers into a flat band which approaches a theoretical optimum. This is best accomplished with a wet system, since a liquid will not interfere with the rearrangement of the fibers and, in fact, provides the necessary lubrication to facilitate the adjustment and prevent fiber damage.

Preimpregnated wet system is a modified system, which is more efficient than winding immediately after the resin bath. It has been in use for the shortest period of time in the field of filament wrapping. Here the filaments are pre-impregnated with resin and partially cured before being used for winding. This method of impregnation has been widely used for other reinforced plastic work.

Several important advantages follow. A higher production rate is available. Because the resin is preapplied to the filament elements, winding speed is not limited to the speed of adequate wetting and therefore may be increased to the physical limits of the winding machinery. Easier impregnation techniques are used. A rig to unwind, impregnate, and rewind the filaments which optimizes the impregnating operation can be assembled. Thus it is possible to treat the filaments with care and to minimize handling damage. The rig can be a simple installation requiring very little surveillance; therefore, the operation will be unhurried. The liquid resin can be treated as necessary to provide better wetting, including heating it to reduce viscosity or to "hot melt" a normally solid resin, agitating it to maintain a balanced compound, etc. None of these features can be economically included in a winding machine. Better impregnation is developed. After "wet-impregnation," a spool of impregnated filaments must be protected from heat, to avoid advancing the cure or increasing viscosity, until the winding operation. This is accomplished by placing the wet-impregnated spool in a plastic bag and storing in a cool refrigerator. During the hours of storage the resin migrates throughout the mass, seeking a natural balance and infiltrating areas that were not reached during impregnation. Air that has been entrapped deep in the filament cord is displaced by infiltrating resin. A vacuum tube may be inserted in the storage bag to assist in removing air or volatiles. Control of resin content is easily accomplished. The amount of resin picked up in the "wet" system is difficult, if not impossible, to control. It is obvious that a bench-top impregnating device provides a better opportunity for control of net resin percentage. Before and after weighing is usually sufficient, assuming that the job of "in-line" impregnation has been reasonably consistent. Of even greater significance, the "wet-spool" weights afford an accurate prediction of the weight of impregnated material used in a winding operation. The ability to better control and predict the resin-to-glass ratio minimizes the possibility of overweight rejects. A hidden advantage of using preimpregnated roving for winding lies in the fact that a greater variety of shapes can be wound. Because of the possible high tack of the material, the roving will not slide off of steep slopes as will roving that is used in the wet stage. To a great extent, the use of preimpregnated material also reduces the dermatitis problem to a minimum.

D. V. ROSATO

FILLERS, CALCIUM CARBONATE

Calcium carbonate fillers can be divided roughly into two major categories—natural ground limestone, and precipitated grades of calcium carbonate. Ground limestones range from a minimum of $1/2\mu$ in particle size, to 44μ, the latter being the upper practical limit for a pigment grade. The ground limestones can be subdivided into two types, dry and wet ground. Dry ground types are usually over 20μ, wet ground less than 20μ in particle size. In addition, the more efficient wet grinding narrows particle size range, rounds off particles, and lowers salt content.

Chemically, the ground limestones range from 100% calcium carbonate content to less than 90%, the latter being primarily dolomitic types relatively high in magnesium carbonate. Depending on geographical area, the ground limestones range from trace amounts of metals to high levels. High levels of iron usually contribute to brown and grey grades. Most domestic limestones are calcitic in crystal formation; amorphous grades are more common in England.

Ground limestones, especially the dry ground types, are usually lower in moisture than either wet ground or precipitated types. Ground limestones, as a group, are also lower in water soluble salts.

The precipitated calcium carbonates are manufactured by several processes, the most common being soda ash-calcium chloride, ammonium carbonate-calcium chloride, and carbonated milk of lime reactions. Other sources of precipitated calcium carbonate are treatment of hard water with soda, and treatment of cauticized waste in paper plants. The first three reactions are most important in the US, and depending on concentration, time, and temperature of the reaction, various particle sizes and shapes are obtained. The soda ash-calcium chloride and ammonium carbonate-soda ash reactions produce particles ranging from 0.05μ (ultra-fine) grades, up to 10μ. The particle shapes are usually cubical, typical of the calcite crystal (see Figure 1). Carbonated milk of lime types are distinguished by a needle-like (aragonite) type of crystal, the particles usually average about $1/2\mu$. Purity of the carbonated milk of lime types range from U.S.P. conforming grades to grades relatively high in magnesium and alkali salts.

The precipitated grades of calcium carbonate also are available, with several types of organic coating agents, the most common coating agents being resins and fatty acids. Coatings agents can be introduced either during precipitation or in the dry processing stage.

Selection of Calcium Carbonates for Plastics

Most plastic compounders are using selected precipitated grades of calcium carbonate or wet ground limestone. The precipitated grades are usually surface treated types with low oil-plasticizer absorptions, or uncoated larger particle grades (up to 10μ). Wet ground limestones in the less than 20μ particle size range are also popular,

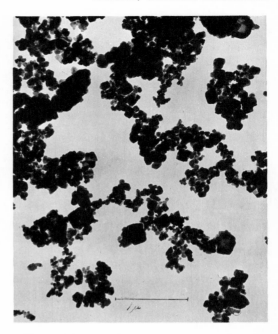

FIG. 1. Electron microscope magnification 54,000 times, precipitated calcium carbonate, 0.06 micron, average particle size. Calcite crystal.

again selection being those with low oil-plasticizer absorption.

Due to the low oil-plasticizer absorption and particle size uniformity, both types offer easy processing, little or no abrasion on equipment, and possibility of employing high levels of filler. These types also have little or no effect on the physicals of thermoset resins except at extremely high loadings. In thermoplastic resins, they reduce physicals in proportion to amounts used, but to a lesser degree than the coarser dry ground limestones.

Organic surface coatings contribute to poorer heat stability (color degradation) than the uncoated grades of precipitated calcium carbonate. In most cases these types are relegated to darker colored plastics. Trace metals such as iron also contribute to poorer heat stability, as do water soluble salts.

Discoloration can also be contributed to wear on processing equipment caused by irregular and over-sized particles. Precipitated grades are usually preferred for low abrasion, with wet and dry ground types usually poorer in this respect.

The ultra-fine, submicron grades of precipitated calcium carbonates are the only types that improve the physicals of thermoset and thermoplastic resins when used in specified amounts and adequately dispersed.

The calcium carbonates major limitation as fillers for plastics are sensitivity to acid media. Calcium carbonate reacts with both inorganic and organic acids and consequently should not be used in plastic compounds subjected to acids. On the other hand, calcium carbonates are not affected by alkaline environment.

Calcium Carbonates in PVC Compounds

The most popular filler used in PVC compounds is calcium carbonate. Favorable raw material cost, ready availability and a wide range of particle shapes and sizes are major considerations.

Precipitated grades in the $5-10\mu$ range and wet ground types are the most popular. These grades have relatively low oil-plasticizer absorptions which permit high filler loading levels without excessive use of plasticizers. Extruder die and roller wear is at a minimum when these grades are employed. In addition, these are pure chemically with resulting good heat stability during processing. Homogeneous PVC floor tile, extruded and calendered products are areas for these precipitated and wet ground grades. Following PVC extruded compound illustrates effect of a precipitated calcium carbonate in the range of $0.2-6\mu$ on physical properties when used from 20–140 parts on 100 parts PVC resin:

Intermediate particle size precipitated calcium carbonates in the range of $0.10-0.25\mu$ impart considerably more brightness and hiding than the larger particle types or sub-micron precipitated grades. Because of their brightness and hiding, they are used in white PVC compounds to supplement the more expensive titanium dioxide pigment. The high hiding of these grades also contributes to more efficient UV screening action.

The ultra-fine precipitated grades in the area of $0.05-0.07\mu$ are used sparingly in PVC compounds. Their large surface area contributes to excessive plasticizer absorption with increased raw material cost and processing problems. Outstanding characteristics imparted by these ultra-fine types are mar resistance plus low whitening on flexing; higher surface gloss is also possible with ultra-fines. Homogeneous high grade PVC floor tile is a major end use for ultra-fine grades.

PVC plastisols demand easy mix-in types calcium carbonate. Micronized coated and uncoated precipitated grades in the $0.5-10\mu$ range are preferred. To a more limited extent, wet ground limestones are employed. Larger particles (over 10μ) constitute a greater problem in plastisols because of settling possibilities and oversizes that could create an irregular surface. Small amounts of ultra-fine, both coated and uncoated, are used to develop thixotropic bodied plastisols.

TABLE 1. PVC EXTRUSION COMPOUND.

	1	2	3	4	5	6	7	8
PVC 450[a]	100.00	100.00	100.00	100.00	100.00	100.00	100.00	100.00
Stearic acid	1.00	1.00	1.00	1.00	1.00	1.00	1.00	1.00
Ferro 1212 A[b]	2.00	2.00	2.00	2.00	2.00	2.00	2.00	2.00
DOP	45.00	45.00	45.00	45.00	45.00	45.00	45.00	45.00
Precipitated calcium carbonate ($0.2-6\mu$)	—	20.00	40.00	60.00	80.00	100.00	120.00	140.00
	148.00	168.00	188.00	208.00	228.00	248.00	268.00	288.00
100% modulus, psi	1660	1620	1490	1390	1270	1230	1150	1075
Ultimate tensile, psi	2760	2530	2320	2030	1760	1660	1550	1420
Elongation, %	300	300	270	230	210	190	170	170
Tear (Graves) pit	425	385	360	320	285	250	220	205
Shore "A", 10 sec.	83	84	85	87	89	90	91	94

[a] Diamond Alkali Co.
[b] Ferro Chemical Co.

Dry ground limestones generally over 20 microns are preferred in vinyl asbestos floor tile. Due to the larger particle size, they have extremely low oil-plasticizer absorption and permit high filler loading levels. The larger particle of calcium carbonate, plus irregular shaped asbestos, develops a compacted hard surface generally desirable in vinyl asbestos floor tile.

These finer grades must be properly dispersed in order to develop required body. The three-roller mill, sand grinder, ball mill, and Morehouse mill are preferred.

The following chart indicates viscosity characteristics of vinyl plastisol with 50 parts calcium carbonate type filler on 100 parts PVC resin:

TABLE 2. CALCIUM CARBONATE IN VINYL PLASTISOLS.

	Control	1	2	3	4	5	6
PVC 71[a]	100.00	100.00	100.00	100.00	100.00	100.00	100.00
DOP	70.00	70.00	70.00	70.00	70.00	70.00	70.00
G-62[b]	5.00	5.00	5.00	5.00	5.00	5.00	5.00
Mark M[c]	2.00	2.00	2.00	2.00	2.00	2.00	2.00
Mark PL[c]	1.00	1.00	1.00	1.00	1.00	1.00	1.00
Precipitated calcium carbonate (0.5μ)		50.00					
Precipitated calcium carbonate (0.1μ)			50.00				
Resin coated precipitated calcium carbonate (0.1μ)				50.00			
Wet ground limestone					50.00		
Precipitated calcium carbonate (Ultra-fine .06μ)						50.00	
Double coated precipitated calcium carbonate (ultra-fine .05μ)							50.00
Viscosity (72 h) Brookfield, cp	2,500	7,600	15,400	130,000	13,800	170,000	340,000

Procedure:

Ingredients blended for 5 min in Hobart Mixer, and given two passes over three-roll mill.
Viscosities were taken on a Brookfield viscosimeter, Model RVT, using spindle No. 3 at 10 rpm.

[a] Diamond Alkali Co.
[b] Rohm & Haas Co.
[c] Argus Chemical Co.

Calcium Carbonates in Polyester Compounds

Polyester compounding has now become a large end use area for calcium carbonate fillers. As in PVC compounding, calcium carbonates offer favorable raw material cost, availability, various particle sizes and shapes, plus good color characteristics.

The easy mix-in or micronized types of precipitated calcium carbonate and wet ground limestone are most preferred grades. Low oil-plasticizer absorption types permit higher filler loading levels. Resin-coated precipitated calcium carbonate is extremely popular due to excellent dispersibility plus affinity for polyester resin, resulting in improved suspension and physical properties. The resin-coated grade imparts considerably smoother laminate surfaces than uncoated grades. Filler loading levels in compression molded laminates average about 35% total weight of mix. Physicals, such as impact and flexural strength, increase with the use of calcium carbonate up to 50% of total weight of mix, and then start to drop off rapidly. Besides increasing impact and flexural strengths, mix-in types lower pound-volume cost, improve surface smoothness and hardness, and heat resistance, and reduce mold shrinkage.

A typical polyester compression molding formulation with resin coated precipitated calcium carbonate, from 28.5% to 60% loading levels is shown in Table 3.

To a more limited extent, fillers are used in hand lay-up operations. Resin coated precipitated calcium carbonates and wet ground limestones of the easy mix-in type are used. In this application, calcium carbonate is usually less than 30% weight of mix. Excessive use of filler prevents adequate penetration of the fiberglass causing resin starved areas and weak laminates.

The intermediate precipitated grades in the 0.10–0.25μ range impart hiding and brightness and permit lower amounts of opacifying pigment such as titanium dioxide.

Premix polyester molding employs higher levels of filler in order to develop necessary stiffness or body. Low oil-plasticizer absorption precipitated calcium carbonates and wet ground limestones are usually employed. Sometimes these are modified with finer particle size precipitated grades in the intermediate and ultra-fine particle range.

Polyester gel coats contain calcium carbonate

TABLE 3. FILLED POLYESTER COMPOUNDS.

	Loading		Level	
Formulation:	28.5%	40%	50%	60%
Polyester resin[a]	100.00	100.00	100.00	100.00
Styrene	11.00	11.00	11.00	11.00
Benzoyl peroxide	.88	.88	.88	.88
Resin coated precipitated Calcium carbonate (0.1μ)	44.43	74.00	111.08	166.00
	156.31	185.88	222.96	277.88

Owens-Corning Fiberglas mat No. 219, 1–1/2 and 2–1/2 oz was used. Panels cured 3 min at 235°F.

[a] Selectron 5158—Pittsburgh Plate Glass Co.

TABLE 4. PHYSICAL PROPERTIES OF LAMINATE MADE WITH FILLED POLYESTER COMPOUNDS.

		Loading Level		
	28.5%	40%	50%	60%
Specific gravity	1.76	1.80	1.87	1.95
Izod Impact, ft lb/in. notch	14.40	16.20	17.30	16.507
Tensile strength, psi	20,300	21,300	20,100	19,300
%, Elongation	1.89	1.92	1.94	1.87
Modulus of elasticity in tension, psi $\times 10^6$	1.15	1.36	1.45	1.85
Flexural strength, psi	33,150	33,600	37,800	37,000
Modulus of elasticity in flexure, psi $\times 10^6$	1.08	1.18	1.44	1.20
Barcol hardness (10 sec. reading)	55	57	62	66
Initial viscosity of mix	1,200	2,100	3,200	5,000
Glass mat, % by weight	40	40	33.3	33.3

up to 25% of the total mix. In most cases easy mix-in types of low oil-plasticizer precipitated calcium carbonates and wet ground limestones are employed as good dispersibility and low spraying viscosities are mandatory. Outstanding properties calcium carbonates contribute to gel coats are brightness and whiteness, hiding, smoothness, better adhesion to substrate and improved spraying characteristics. Limited amounts of ultra-fine precipitated calcium carbonates are used in gel coats as suspension agents and for control of sag.

Calcium Carbonates in Epoxy Compounds

The lower oil-plasticizer absorption grades of precipitated calcium carbonate and wet ground types of ground limestone are preferred in epoxy molding compounds. Resin coated grades of precipitated calcium carbonate are especially desirable because of greater affinity for epoxy resins permitting higher levels of filler and easy mix-in.

Encapsulating and potting compounds contain high loadings of these fillers, generally consistent with pourability. High loadings of filler reduce compound shrinkage to a minimum. Other advantages of filler are increased impact strength, greater resistance to heat, and lower co-efficient of thermal expansion. Fillers in encapsulating and potting compounds will usually total 50% or more of the resin mix.

Epoxy adhesives are another major use area for calcium carbonates of the easy mix-in type. Resin coated precipitated calcium carbonate and low oil-plasticizer absorption types of wet ground limestone are most commonly used in epoxy adhesives. Total level of calcium carbonate in epoxy adhesives range from as low as 5–50%, with average about 20% total weight of mix. Most important contributions of filler in adhesives are increase in tensile and shear strength, minimum loss of adhesive in porous substrates and increase in modulus. Secondary considerations are control of shrinkage, increased resistance to heat and thermal expansion. Table 5 indicates an epoxy-polyamide resin adhesive with various fillers at 20 parts on 100 parts resin:

TABLE 5.

EFFECT OF FILLERS ON POLYAMIDE/EPOXY ADHESIVES (ASTM D1002–49T)
Standard Composition:
Versamid 115[a]
ERL 2759[b]
Filler 50 : 50 : 20

	Tensile shear, psi	
Filler	RT	–104°F
Tabular alumia	3200	3400
AFD filler	3420	3030
Metronite	2760	—
Resin coated precipitated calcium carbonate (.05–1μ)	2730	—
Uncoated precipitated calcium carbonate (.05–1μ)	2900	2840
Nylon powder	2940	2150
Unfilled	2000	—

[a] General Mills, Chemical Div.
[b] Union Carbide Plastics Co.

Epoxy resin laminates are compounded along the lines of polyester resin laminates, usually averaging about 30% calcium carbonate on total weight of mix. Resin coated easy mix-in grade of precipitated calcium carbonate is preferred although some of the finer grades of wet ground limestone are employed. Low oil-plasticizer absorption of these grades permits higher loadings with good flow properties.

Calcium Carbonates in Polyolefin Compounding

Limited amounts of calcium carbonate are being used in polyethylene and polypropylene compounds. Fillers impart hardness, stiffness and opacity as well as cost reduction. Filler preference is generally ultra-fine precipitated calcium carbonate, larger particle precipitated grades, and wet ground limestone.

Ultra-fine grades of precipitated calcium carbonate are used up to 30% of the total weight mix. The effect of various loading levels of ultra-fine precipitated calcium carbonate on low density polyethylene is shown in Table 6.

TABLE 6. FILLED POLYETHYLENE PLASTICS.

	1	2	3	4	5	6
Polyethylene (low density)	100.00	100.00	100.00	100.00	100.00	100.00
Ultra-fine precipitated calcium carbonate (.06μ)[a]	—	10.00	20.00	30.00	40.00	50.00
	100.00	110.00	120.00	130.00	140.00	150.00
Specific gravity	0.92	0.98		1.08	1.13	1.18
Tensile strength, psi	1300	1350	1450	1430	1500	1500
Ultimate elongation	640	340	100	100	70	40
Shore "D" hardness	47	48	50	51	52	53
Graves tear, pit	446	453	418	352	317	290
Tensile strength, psi[b]	1685	1695	2040	2120	2080	1710

[a] All filled compounds were Banbury mixed.
[b] Injection molded specimens.

Calcium Carbonates in Phenolic Molding Compounds

Beside increasing volume and lowering compound cost, calcium carbonate fillers improve the physical properties of the molded article. Impact strength and heat resistance are improved and mold shrinkage decreased. Resin coated precipitated calcium carbonate is used because of its affinity for phenolic resins and consequent improvement in physicals and surface smoothness. Wet and dry ground limestones are also employed in phenolic molding powders.

The amount of calcium carbonate used in phenolic compounds is usually over 50% of the total mix and often as high as 70%.

Calcium Carbonates in Polyurethane Foams

Calcium carbonates are being used in rigid and flexible polyurethane foams in order to decrease cost. They also lower compressibility and contribute to a more uniform cell structure. Easy mix-in types of resin coated precipitated calcium and wet ground limestones are preferred in both rigid and flexible foam. Low moisture content types are most popular. Amounts range from 10–50% on the total weight of compound.

PHILIP F. WOERNER

FILLERS, CONDUCTIVE, FOR EPOXY RESINS

Epoxy resins are compatible with a wide range of filler materials. Because of their polar structure, the resins adhere tenaciously to substrates and exhibit good wetting properties.

Thus fillers may be added to the resins and upon curing to a thermoset state, the filler becomes an intimate and homogeneous part of the resin system. It does not easily separate or flake from the resin.

Most filler materials, when added to epoxy resins, increase the thermal conductivity of the system. However some special types will make the epoxy electrically conductive.

Thermal Conductivity

Epoxy resins are widely used because of their excellent insulating properties. However, it is desirable to improve the thermal conductivity, in many instances, while still maintaining the insulating properties.

In the potting of electronic components, the dissipation of heat will present local overheating and increase power ratings. For example, an electric radiator control, when sealed in an aluminum case, had an operating temperature of 260–270°F. The same unit potted with a silica filled epoxy exhibited an operating temperature of 220–230°F, or 40° lower. This reduced the danger of burnout.

In casting large tools and dies, the exothermic heat during cure must be dissipated to prevent charring and cracking. Dies used for vacuum forming must retain uniform heating throughout the surface. Fillers are used extensively to provide the increased thermal conductivity to make this possible.

Fillers

Fillers are inert solids generally in powdered form but occasionally in fiber form. When added to epoxy resins, they contribute their value by a simple bulk volume effect. Generally, there is no chemical reaction between the fillers and the resin. The fillers usually have a higher thermal conductivity than the resin and therefore increase the conductivity of the system.

Types

The types of fillers used to improve conductivity are metals, metal oxides, glasses and minerals. These may vary in size and shape. The sizes range from fine powders of 200 mesh–0.1μ, to course particles of 30–100 mesh. Fibers of 1 in. or smaller are also used. These fibers are known as reinforcing fillers because they contribute their high mechanical strength. The effect is similar to steel bars in concrete.

Long continuous filaments and woven metal and glass cloth are also used with epoxy resins to increase thermal conductivity as well as strength. Metal screens have been used on the upper surface of table top laminates to conduct heat away and thus prevent charring.

Selecting Fillers

In selecting fillers, the shape, particle size and absorption characteristics must be considered in addition to the chemical structure. The oil absorption is a property of the filler which influences the viscosity effect of the filler-resin system. By rubbing a given volume of filler with resin, the viscosity increases. Each filler will behave differently. The lower the oil absorption number, the lower the viscosity effect. Thus, more filler of a low oil absorption value could be added than of a high oil absorption filler. Fillers such as silica, talc and aluminum powder may be used up to 200 phr (part per hundred of resin). Heavier or denser fillers, such as copper powder, may be incorporated in concentrations up to 900 phr.

Effect of Filler Concentration

The volume loading as opposed to weight loading is more significant on thermal conductivity. This is also true on the thermal expansion characteristics of the system. As increased amount of filler is added, the viscosity increases until the mixture becomes too thick to be pourable and workable.

Figure 1 shows a graph on thermal conductivity of powdered silica in an epoxy resin. The per cent volume and per cent weight of filler are plotted against the thermal conductivity. The units are in cal/sec/cm²/°C/cm.

The weight percent filler at 40 per cent shows a thermal conductivity of 12×10^{-4}, as opposed to a volume percent loading of 20×10^{-4} cal/sec/cm²/°C/cm.

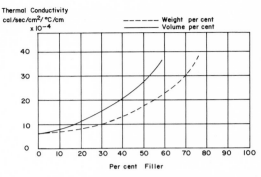

FIG. 1. Effect of filler concentration on thermal conductivity.

Effect of Filler Type and Shape

The filler type whether metal, metal oxide or mineral has some effect on thermal conductivity. However, the conductivity of the system is far lower than the filler alone. Table 1 compares various epoxy filler systems.

The maximum amount of filler was added to the limit of workable viscosity in the above table. As can be observed, the aluminum metal is more than 100 times as conductive as the aluminum filled epoxy.

Fibrous Fillers. Metal fibers have been found to provide the highest thermal conductivity particularly when pressure is applied during cure. O'Connor and White studied the thermal conductivity effect of copper-aluminum fibers and aluminum powder combinations on epoxy resins. With pressure, more fibrous filler could be incorporated than casting in an open mold.

In one method (slurry casting), the specimens were prepared by mixing the resin, fibers and aluminum powder and casting in an open mold. In the pressure cast method, the specimens were gelled under heat and pressure. The mold was vented and excess resin escaped when pressure was applied. The results which followed are seen in Table 2:

TABLE 1. THERMAL CONDUCTIVITY OF EPOXY COMPOUNDS COMPARING VARIOUS FILLERS.

Filler	phr	Weight, %	Volume, %	Thermal Conductivity Btu/hr/ft²/°F/ft
None				0.13
Aluminum oxide	325	73	48	0.82
Atomized aluminum	200	63	45	0.94
Iron powder	300	72	30	0.52
Copper powder	1200	91	60	0.94
Silica (325 mesh)	150	56	39	0.44
For comparison			Steel	26.0
			Aluminum	116.0
			Copper	224.0

TABLE 2. THERMAL CONDUCTIVITY OF METAL FIBER FILLED EPOXY COMPOUNDS.

Method	Resin, %	Aluminum powder, %	Fiber, %	Thermal conductivity, cal/sec/cm²/°C/cm
Slurry cast	100			3.3×10^{-4}
Slurry cast	20	80		13.9×10^{-4}
Slurry cast	16	64	20	16.6×10^{-4}
Slurry cast	13.6	54.4	32	37.4×10^{-4}
Pressure	45		55	23.0×10^{-3}
Pressure	12.4	49.6	38	49.3×10^{-3}

Thermal Conductivity Measurements

The literature on thermal conductivity of epoxies may be somewhat confusing because various units are used. The thermal conductivity unit is expressed as:

$$\frac{\text{Heat energy transfer in unit time per unit area}}{\text{Temperature difference per unit length}}$$

The following table may be used to convert from one unit to another. A thermal conductivity expressed in any of the units designated in the left column can be converted into any units in the headings of the column by multiplying by the number which is common to the row and column. An example may be seen below:

0.1 btu/hr/ft²/°F/ft = 0.1 × 0.004134

= 0.0004134 cal/sec/cm²/°C/cm

The method of testing thermal conductivity of epoxies most widely used is the Cenco-Fitch method. This is described in Mil-1-16923E (Military Specification, Insulating Compound, Electrical, Embedding), as well as by the Central Scientific Company.

Three specimens, 3 × 3 in. by 1/8 in. thick are tested. The apparatus consists of a source of heat and a receiver. The source is a copper vessel, heat insulated on the sides. The receiver consists of a thermally insulated cylindrical block of known thermal capacity. Thermocouples and a galvanometer are used to indicate temperature differences. The source of heat is boiling water in the source vessel.

The test specimen is placed between the source vessel kept at constant temperature, (100°C), and the receiver. The heat conducted through the specimen raises the temperature of the copper receiver by a measured amount. From the rate at which the heat is conducted through the material, and the area, thickness and temperature difference of the faces of the specimen, its thermal conductivity can be calculated.

The galvanometer deflection is measured at regular interval of 1, 2, and 3 min, depending on the rate of change of deflection until approximately 24 readings are taken.

The data is plotted on semilog paper, with time plotted as the ordinate on the straight scale, and the deflection readings on the log scale. The slope of the curve is determined. The coefficient of thermal conductivity is then calculated as follows:

$$K = \frac{2.303 \, LMC}{Am}$$

where:

K = coefficient of thermal conductivity
L = thickness of specimen in centimeters
M = mass of copper plug
C = specific heat of copper
A = area of copper plug in centimeters
m = slope of curve.

The average coefficient determined on three specimens are reported, expressed in cal/sec/cm²/°C/cm.

Electrically Conductive Epoxy Compounds

Electrically conductive epoxy adhesives and coatings have been extremely useful for attaching lead wires to electronic components, repairing or making electrical contacts and printed circuits, shielding, grounding and in wave guide applications.

Epoxy resins which are inherently excellent insulators can be made electrically conductive

TABLE 3. CONVERSION FACTORS FOR THERMAL CONDUCTIVITY UNITS.

	Cal/sec/cm²/°C/cm	W/cm²/°C/cm	Btu/hr/ft²/°F/ft
cal/sec/cm²/°C/cm	1	4.186	241.9
W/cm²/°C/cm	0.2389	1	57.79
Btu/hr/ft²/°F/ft	0.004134	0.01730	1

FILLERS, CONDUCTIVE, FOR EPOXY RESINS

by incorporating conductive fillers such as carbon and metals.

Theory

The hypothesis of why and how the filled epoxies conduct is not fully understood.

One theory is that the conductive filler actually makes particle-to-particle contact. This permits an electric current to flow through the plastic composition.

Another theory is that although a thin film of epoxy completely surrounds the filler particles, when a potential is applied, the insulating layer breaks down and this permits the current to flow.

Unfortunately, neither theory will adequately predict the electrical behavior of any given epoxy filler system, so that at the present state of the formulating art, any meaningful information about electrical conductivity in epoxy-metal or epoxy-carbon mixtures must be derived from experimental data.

Properties

In general, an epoxy-metal or epoxy carbon system may be considered to have properties which are somewhere between those of a pure epoxy polymer and a pure sample of filler. Many of the desirable qualities of epoxies are retained, such as the high adhesive strength, low cure, shrinkage, excellent resistance to unfavorable environments, and good mechanical strength. These composite systems, like the more conventional epoxy resin systems, may be cured at room temperature or slightly elevated temperature to a tough, infusible, thermoset mass.

Unlike the usual epoxies, these metal or carbon filled systems exhibit the phenomenon of electrical conductivity. Table 4 shows some typical values obtained with both conductive and nonconductive epoxy resin systems.

Volume resistivities of 10^{-5}–10^4 ohm-cm are available in filled conductive epoxy systems, depending on the filler used. While, at best, these specific resistivities are considerably higher than those of metals, they are nevertheless low enough for conductive epoxies to be used effectively in

applications where properties such as adhesion to a variety of substrates and low temperature curing, make their use desirable. Table 5 compares the specific resistivities of commonly used materials.

TABLE 5. RESISTIVITIES OF VARIOUS MATERIALS.

10^4	Carbon-epoxy
10^2	Conductive rubber
1	Boron carbide
10^{-2}	Graphite
	Silver-epoxy
10^{-4}	Mercury
10^{-6}	Aluminum
	Copper, silver

Resistivity (ohm-cm)

Conductive Fillers

Carbon. Both graphite and acetylene black have been used successfully as fillers for electrically conductive epoxies. They have the advantage of being inexpensive and lower in specific gravity than metals. The volume resistivities are limited to a minimum of 1 ohm-cm. The addition of carbon to epoxy resins increase the viscosity considerably, without lowering the resistivity below 1 ohm-cm. By varying the per cent carbon, resistivities can be varied up to 100,000 ohms and greater.

Metal Fillers. Metallic fillers may be formulated with epoxy resins to achieve finished compositions with volume resistivities as low as 10^{-4} ohm-cm. While many metals have been used including silver, copper, aluminum, tin, lead, stainless steel, cadmium, gold, platinum and nickel, the most satisfactory results to date have been obtained with silver powder. Some success with copper powder has been reported, but apparently it is quite difficult to prepare the resin-copper composite without at least partially oxidizing the surface of the copper. This lowers the conductivity considerably. The same problem occurs with aluminum.

TABLE 4. COMPARISON OF PROPERTIES OF FILLED EPOXY RESINS*.

	Silver filled 3021	Silver filled 3012	Aluminum filled 2220
Type of system	2 part	1 part	2 part
Cure temperature	77°F	300°F	77°F
Cure time	24 hr	1 hr	24 hr
Lap shear-steel-steel	2000 psi	2500 psi	2400 psi
Specific gravity	2.2	2.2	1.5
Volume resistivity	0.005 ohm-cm	0.001 ohm-cm	10^{15} ohm-cm

* Epoxy Products, Inc.

206

Silver satisfies most of the requirements of a conductive filler. It is highly conductive, low in chemical reactivity, and its oxide and sulfide are conductive. Other noble metals, such as gold and platinum, have given satisfactory results, but their high cost has limited their use.

An approach which has met with success recently has been to use a base metal powder plated with a noble metal. Since it has been hypothesized that conductivity in plastic-metal composites is a surface effect of the fillers, the plated powders are an attempt to circumvent the high cost of silver powder. Both gold and silver plated copper powders have been used successfully.

Considerable work has been done in determining the optimum size and shape of the conductive filler particles. Most of this work is proprietary in nature. However, some published results indicate that a platelet or flake form is superior to spheres and this superiority lies in the possibility of increased surface contact area between the filler particles. These conclusions, however, are not universally accepted and formulators working with spheroids point out that higher filler loadings are possible with spherical particles than with flakes. The flakes tend to increase viscosity rapidly.

While most fillers used in conductive epoxies are quite fine (through 200 mesh), at least one formulator has taken a radically different approach, using spheroids ranging from 0.001–0.030 in. in diameter at high filler loadings. This approach has been taken in order to obtain high unit contact pressure between filler particles and therefore squeeze out the layer of insulating binder between the particles. This approach has been fairly successful using a resilient binder such as in gasketing materials.

Resistivity Measurements on Electrically Conductive Epoxy Resins

The introduction of electrically conductive epoxies has necessitated the development of new test procedures for product evaluation and quality control. While the principles behind these measurements are the same as those employed for resistivity measurements of other materials, the nature of these conductive cements make some modifications of techniques necessary.

Volume resistivity is defined as the ratio of the potential gradient parallel to current in the material, to the current density. In the metric system, volume resistivity is expressed in ohm-centimeters, and is numerically equal to the volume resistance between opposite faces of a centimeter cube of the material under consideration. By a simple application of Ohm's Law, volume resistivity may be calculated from the measured resistance if the sample has a regular cross section and known dimensions.

$$\text{Volume resistivity } (P) = \frac{A}{L} \times R \qquad (1)$$

where:

A = Cross-sectional area (in.cm^3)
L = Distance between electrodes (cm)
R = Resistance of sample.

One method of making the resistivity measurements uses a glass silicone sheet of 1/2 in. × 1 in. × 1/8 in. thick. Three slots of 0.025 in. wide × 0.025 in. deep × 1 in. long are milled into the sheet. The conductive epoxy is trowelled into the slots and cured. Excess material is sanded off flush with the top surface of the block.

Resistance measurements are made with a Wheatstone Bridge by applying test probes to end of each slot. The volume resistivity can then be calculated from Equation (1).

$$\frac{A}{L} = \frac{0.025 + 0.025 + 2.54}{1} = 0.00159 \text{ cm}$$

where:

R is the measured resistance (ohms).

Then P(volume resistivity) = 0.00159 R (ohm-cm)

Another test method uses brass cylinders of 1.29 in. diameter by 1 in. long. The conductive adhesive is used to bond the two cylinders with a controlled glue line of 0.010–0.020 in. thick. A Kelvin Bridge must be used to measure the resistance since the adhesive resistance is of a very low order of magnitude in this shape.

The volume resistivity is then calculated as in Equation(1). The cylinders are also used to measure the bond strength by pulling them apart.

VINCENT SUSSMAN

Cross-references: EPOXY INGREDIENTS, EPOXY INTERMEDIATES.

FILLERS, HOLLOW GLASS SPHERES

Hollow glass spheres[a] are tiny bubbles of glass, ranging in size from to 10–250μ in diameter. The typical average particle size is approximately 65μ. The bulk density is approximately 14 lb/cu ft, with a true density of each particle (measured by liquid displacement) of 0.30–0.35 g/cc. As a lightweight filler, the material can be used in many resin systems, maintaining its low density and imparting this property to the end product. The high melting (1400°F) glass composition, along with the low thermal conductivity (0.38 Btu/hr/°F/sq ft/in. at a 6°F mean temperature) of the particle resulting from its hollow structure,

[a] Trade mark "Microballoons."

gives the glass sphere very interesting and unique properties.

Physicial properties of these glass spheres are shown in Table 1.

It is important to recognize that this new material cannot be considered as a simple replacement for inorganic fillers in use today in resin systems. The unique properties of these glass spheres will not only be reflected in handling and processing techniques, but also in the physical properties of the final product.

These spheres can be used in resin systems to lower the density, extend the resin, increase flame resistance, reduce costs, or for many other specific purposes. As a primary structural material held together by many possible binder systems, both organic or inorganic, it is possible to create physical foams with high melting points that have high strength-weight ratios, are nonflammable, and have low thermal conductivity, as well as other unique properties. In low volume loadings the liquid system is still pourable; in high loading applications the system can be handled as a damp sand-like mixture. The material can be used along with other fillers or fibers, or as a low-density, high-strength core material in laminated structures.

Some resins that have been used with this new material are epoxies, silicones, polyesters, phenolics, and acrylics. Physical foams prepared by this technique will not replace chemical foams in many applications. Chemical foams will usually have a lower density than will the physical or "syntactic" foams prepared with glass spheres. The physical foams, however, are very uniform and are entirely unicellular with nonconnecting cells. The result is good physical strength and an excellent strength-to-weight ratio. In general, the physical foams will exhibit higher strength characteristics than do the chemical foams. The density can be controlled much more closely in a physical foam with more predictable end properties merely by controlling the amounts of hollow spheres and binder. The physical foams are much more

thermally stable than any of the chemical foams as yet developed. However, physical foams prepared with glass particles are density limited. The lowest possible density that can result is the density of the hollow particles themselves.

Hollow filler particles exhibit some weakness in high shear mixing operations, but they can be mixed successfully in mixers exhibiting low shear action. In using this product in resin systems it should be recognized that mixing techniques, resin viscosity, curing times, as well as weight-volume relationships can all be affected by this low density material. Such physical changes should be expected and understood so that system adjustments can be made.

One important point to be considered in resin formulations is the effect of the filler on the viscosity of the resin. In comparison with other types of fillers this low density bulk material will affect the viscosity of a resin, such as an epoxide, much less than do widely used high density material fillers. It is interesting to note that the viscosity of a highly loaded hollow glass sphere-resin system can be lowered by some substantial degree by the addition of small amounts of filler material sized in the one and under micron size range. In such a system, the volume of small sized filler finds its way into the voids between the glass spheres. This in essence liberates an euqal volume of resin required to fill the voids in the structure; thus, the resin becomes available to lower the viscosity of the over-all system. The application of such a technique results in a higher loading than would normally be anticipated with such a formulation.

The use of these glass spheres will affect the curing exotherm of resin systems because of their insulating properties. This effect should be noted in preparing large castings in which this material is used.

Glass spheres can be used in both thermoplastic and thermosetting systems where processing pressures up to 500 psi are employed. The thin-walled spheres are sensitive to both point-to-point contact and high shear. Applications and processing techniques employing high shear operations such as injection molding, extrusion, compression, and transfer molding, etc., should be approached with caution.

Resistance of the spheres to hydrostatic or pneumatic pressures is good. This is particularly true when the material is held together with a resin matrix. Taking advantage of this property, the material is being used in syntactic or physical foams specially designed for high hydrostatic pressures as found in deep water buoyancy applications. Resin-glass microsphere systems have been developed that have 20 lb of positive buoyancy per cubic foot, and can withstand over 20,000 psi of hydrostatic pressure.

TABLE 1. PROPERTIES OF HOLLOW GLASS PARTICLES.

Color	White
Density	
Bulk g/cc	0.19–0.24
lb/cu ft	12 – 15
True g/cc	0.30–0.35
lb/cu ft	19 – 22
Particle size range, μ	10 – 250
Average particle size, μ	65
Softening point, °F	1200
Melting point, °F	1400
Thermal conductivity,	0.38
Btu/hr/sq ft/°F/in.	

Such particles have been successfully used in a formulation developed specifically for the encapsulation of the complex electronic circuitry designed to withstand extremely severe environments. Their use in a filled epoxide as compared with mica-filled epoxide shows a considerable weight saving, particularly where the weight of the encapsulating material is an appreciable part of the total weight of the package. In addition, the composition shows both excellent mechanical and thermal shock resistance.

Other epoxy systems in which hollow glass spheres have been used include the electrical potting or encapsulation of surface and aircraft components, low density adhesives, tooling, and as structural fillers for honeycomb sections. Of considerable importance is the straight resin extension value obtained by the inclusion of a high bulking material in high cost resin systems. In many instances the material has straight economic value, which alone will justify its use.

Hollow glass spheres have been demonstrated to be unique in polyester systems, both straight and reinforced. It is possible to produce synthetic tile and marble with this light material having only one-third the weight of the normal mineral filled synthetics. It is also possible to produce thicker sections of these synthetics utilizing the structural advantage that comes from the lighter weight material.

Normal physical properties of filled polyester do not depreciate as rapidly without glass spheres as with the common fillers. These include compressive, tensile, and flexural strengths. The strength-weight ratio is increased, as is the rigidity of the filled material, using the hollow spheres. In chopped glass fiber systems it has been found that the flexural strength of polyester resin containing the hollow glass spheres is considerably higher than that containing the mineral filler, particularly at higher concentrations of chopped glass fiber. In similar fashion, these spheres can be used in polyester glass-mat laminate or as a high strength core material in sandwich-type structures.

Other systems in which this material has been utilized include PVC plastisols and organisols, phenolics, silicones among the organic binders, and sodium silicate and portland cement among the inorganic binder systems.

The hollow glass particle holds promise of widespread use in many diverse applications. However, it should be remembered that this is a new material and not a straight replacement for currently available materials. In working with it, it may be that old handling and fabricating techniques based on currently available materials will not work satisfactorily, and it may be necessary to devise new techniques to handle this novel product. It is felt that this is a unique material that will find widespread usage in the plastics and ceramic industries.

JOHN M. DEMPSTER

FILLERS, INORGANIC

The principal inorganic natural fillers include kaolin clay (aluminum silicate), talc (magnesium silicate), silica, wollastonite (calcium silicate) and Barytes (barium sulfate). While most of these are available from deposits in many parts of the world, only those mined and processed in the United States are included here.

In general, these fillers are used to improve such properties as impact resistance, chemical resistance, heat resistance, dimensional stability, and strength. They affect electrical properties, water absorption, and help control shrinkage. At a cost ranging from perhaps 1/2¢ to, at the most, 9 or 10¢ per lb, these natural inorganic fillers will obviously contribute to reduced cost in almost any plastic composition in which they are used, compared with the identical unfilled material.

While fillers vary widely in cost within the limits mentioned above, their choice should be influenced far more by the properties desired in the end product than by filler cost, since a saving 1 or 2¢/per lb in the cost of the filler will normally have a very minor effect on the cost of the finished composition.

Natural inorganic fillers differ greatly in particle size, particle shape, oil absorption and color. The choice of a filler is often determined by its effect on viscosity. If a high filler content is desired, a filler with relatively low oil absorption must be chosen. If viscosity control is desired with a small amount of filler, a high oil absorption filler is indicated.

Before making a final choice of filler for any particular application, a thorough check of its compatibility with the resin system should be made. Slight variations in processing from one supplier to another, in either the filler, the resin or other components of a system which appear to be identical when only the specifications of the material are considered, can result in unforeseen problems.

The chemical analyses and physical properties tabulated on the following pages were obtained from the producers of the various materials described.

Kaolin Clays

Washed Georgia Clay. Most domestic kaolin clays originate in the Southeast. Chemical composition and physical properties vary somewhat with the location of the deposit and the method of processing. The most versatile of these is

209

probably *water washed Georgia clay*, whose typical chemical analysis is as follows:

Silicon (SiO₂)	45.4%
Aluminum (Al₂O₃)	38.8%
Iron (Fe₂O₃)	0.3%
Titanium (TiO₂)	1.5%
Calcium (CaO)	0.1%
Sodium (Na₂O)	0.1%
Potassium (K₂O)	Trace
Loss on ignition	13.8%
	100.0%

The major components shown in the above analysis are combined as complex aluminum silicate and do not exist as free oxides. This analysis is on a moisture free basis.

Typical properties of water washed Georgia clays are as follows:

Particle Shape: Platey under 3μ, mixture of plates and stacks (laminated plates) over 3μ.

Average Particle Size: Available in grades ranging from less than 0.5μ to more than 5μ.

Maximum Particle Size: About 30μ, with maximum residue on 325 mesh of 0.15% for the coarsest grades.

Oil Absorption: From 25 for large particle, surface-treated grades (see below), to 41 for fine particle size grades without surface treatment. (ASTM D281-31)

Color: From 80.5–88.0% G.E. brightness, depending on grade. 90–92% for fine grade produced by ultraflotation process.

Refractive Index: 1.56.

Specific Gravity: 2.58.

pH: 3.8–5.0 for grades without surface treatment. Surface-treated grades available up to pH 8.0 (TAPPI Tent. Std. T 645 M-54).

Free Moisture: 1.0 max., as produced.

It can be seen from the above properties that there is a wide range of grades of water washed Georgia clay available, fitting many different filler requirements. It is therefore obvious that any formulation calling simply for "clay" calls for thorough study to make sure that the grade of clay with the properties called for in the particular application is chosen.

As mentioned previously, among the many different grades of water washed Georgia clays which are commercially available there are several surface-treated variations. Both surfactant-treated and resin-coated grades are available. Surface treatment generally results in lower oil absorption values. This means that higher filler loadings are possible without sacrificing properties inherent in fine particle size clays. Lower water absorption of filled resin is another benefit of this type of surface treatment.

Table 1 shows results of a test comparing water absorption of a polyester laminate using various fillers.

TABLE 1.

Filler	Weight gain, % (24 hr immersion)	Weight loss, % on reconditioning	ASTM water absorption, %
Unfilled resin	.30	0	.30
Surface-treated clay, 0.55μ	.17	0	.17
0.55μ Clay; no surface treatment	.23	0	.23
Fine particle talc	.38	0.1	.39

The effect of surface treatment of clay on viscosity is demonstrated by Table 2:

TABLE 2. BROOKFIELD VISCOSITY OF VARIOUS WATER WASHED GEORGIA CLAYS IN GENERAL-PURPOSE POLYESTER RESIN.

	35% Loading			
Spindle speed, rpm	10	20	50	100
0.55μ Clay, surface-treated	4000	3800	3300	3100
0.55μ Clay, untreated	12,000	8200	6600	5400
4.8μ Clay, surface-treated	4000	3800	3600	3500
4.8μ Clay, untreated	5200	4400	4000	3600
	40% Loading			
Spindle Speed, rpm	10	20	50	100
0.55μ Clay, surface-treated	28,000	22,000	16,000	14,000
0.55μ Clay, untreated	180,000	110,000	56,000	36,000
4.8μ Clay, surface-treated	6000	6000	5000	—
4.8μ Clay, untreated	10000	8000	6000	—
	45% Loading			
Spindle Speed, rpm	10	20	50	100
4.8μ Clay, surface-treated	13,000	12,000	10,800	6300
4.8μ Clay, untreated	27,000	19,200	13,400	—

When working with surface modified fillers, the possibility of some sort of effect of the surface treatment on the resin must be kept in mind. For example, some of the surface modifications used may have a catalytic effect in certain resins, which might necessitate some adjustment in catalyst content.

Water washed Georgia clays are characterized by the following properties:

(1) Wide variety of viscosity characteristics, depending on particle size and surface treatment. Due to the relatively fine particle size of even the coarsest grades commercially available, their use is limited where extremely high filler loadings are desired. Fine particle size grades without surface treatment are rather thixotropic.

(2) Easily dispersed in most resins.

(3) Good suspension properties.

(4) Specific gravity is relatively low.

(5) Good electrical properties, including high dielectric strength, high arc resistance, and low power factor.

(6) Water absorption is low.

(7) Minimum effect on the strength of laminates.

(8) Non-abrasive, results in minimal damage to reinforcing fibers, dies and molds.

(9) Excellent surface characteristics.

(10) Some opacity, depending on particle size.

Typical Applications. Applications of water washed Georgia clays includes their use in various types of reinforced plastics, including alkyds, polyesters and epoxies; premix molding compounds, molded laminates, and gel coats; phenolic molding powders; vinyl plastisols, vinyl insulation.

Hard Clays. Kaolin in clays originating in South Carolina, or normally processed by dry grinding or air flotation, are generally classified as "hard clays," because their fine particle size and high oil absorption results in high hardness rubber compounds.

Hard clays have the following typical chemical composition:

Al_2O_3	$39.5 \pm 1\%$
SiO_2	$44.5 \pm 1\%$
TiO_2	$0.5 \pm .25\%$
Fe_2O_3	$0.4 \pm .25\%$
CaO	$0.25 \pm .25\%$
Cu	None
Mn	None
Moisture	1.0%
Loss on ignition	$14 \pm .5\%$

By definition, hard clays are available in only one particle size range; typical particle size distribution of a hard clay is shown below:

99.85% finer than 44μ
96% finer than 10μ
83% finer than 2μ
75% finer than 1μ

Other typical physical constants of hard clays:

Dry pigment brightness, green filter	$83.0 \pm 2\% - 87.0 \pm 1\%$
Screen fineness, min. through 325 mesh	99.5%
pH	6.0 ± 0.5
Bulking value (gal/lb)	.0465
Oil absorption	45

While hard clays have a high proportion of fine particles, they also retain a fair amount of large particles, and tend to be somewhat more abrasive than water washed Georgia clays. They are also lower in price. Their high oil absorption limits their use to applications calling for low filler loadings.

Typical applications for hard clays include their use in vinyl flooring and in polyester "gunks."

Calcined Clays. Still another group of clays are the *calcined clays*. These are normally produced by calcining Georgia clays. This process results in a harder textured, whiter clay of higher oil absorption and greater opacity than most hydrous i.e., uncalcined clays.

Calcined clays show the following typical chemical analysis:

Ignition loss	0.5 or 0.9 % (depending on grade)
Silica	52.1–52.3 %
Alumina	44.6–44.4 %
Iron oxide	Trace
Titanium dioxide	2%
Manganese	None

TABLE 3. TYPICAL PHYSICAL CHARACTERISTICS OF CALCINED CLAYS.

Sp. Gr.	2.50 or 2.63 (depending on grade)
Moisture max.	1.0%
Screen residue, % wet 325 mesh	0.5
Average particle size	Available in 1.0, 2.0 and 4.5μ grades
G.E. brightness	90–92 (80–85 for the 4.5μ grade)
pH	5.8–6.3
Oil absorption	56–58 for 1μ grade, 44–47 for the others.

Calcined clays have excellent electrical properties and impart a minimum of water absorption properties in vinyl compositions. They are widely used in vinyl insulation. Other applications include polyvinyl chloride calendered goods, and vinyl organosols and plastisols, particularly where their whiteness and opacity are of value.

Talc

Talc is actually a mixture of several minerals, including pure talc (hydrated magnesium silicate, both platy and fibrous), serpentine or antigorite, which has the same chemical composition, and tremolite, which is hydrated magnesium-calcium silicate consisting of platy and nodular particles.

Talc is mined domestically mainly in New York State and California.

Talcs are available with excellent color. They are generally oleophyllic, therefore disperse easily in resins and do not tend to agglomerate. Their

FILLERS, INORGANIC

particle size is normally considerably larger than that of even the coarser clays. This is true even of the "micronized" or "superfine" grades of talc.

Typical New York State talcs show the following properties:

Specific gravity	2.85
pH (ASTM D 1208–52T(4a)	9.5
Dry brightness	90
Plus 325 mesh, max. %	Trace to 2%, depending on grade
Oil absorption (ASTM rub-out, D28–31)	22–40, depending on grade
Particle shape	Mixture of nodular and platy or fibrous, nodular and platy

Table 4 shows particle size distributions of four different grades of New York State talcs:

TABLE 4. PARTICLE SIZE OF NEW YORK STATE TALCS (BY SEDIMENTATION).

	Extra coarse	Coarse	Medium	Fine
W% finer than:				
20μ	82	86	95	—
10μ	56	62	73	93
7μ	44	49	58	81
5μ	35	39	46	66
3μ	26	29	32	46
2μ	24	25	25	35
1μ	—	—	—	24

The average chemical composition of New York State talc is as follows:

MgO	29%
SiO_2	57%
CaO	8%
Al_2O_3, Fe_2O_3	2%
Ignition loss	4%
	100%

Typical applications for talcs include their use in vinyl compounding, automobile body putties where they contribute desired working properties and viscosity control, and epoxies where good machinability is desired.

Silica

Natural silica occurs in both amorphous and crystalline forms, and as Diatomaceous Silica.

Amorphous silicas are available in average particle sizes ranging from $2–15\mu$, with maximum particle size from $10–100\mu$. In spite of this large variation in particle sizes, oil absorption is generally between 39 and 47.

Crystalline silicas are available in a similar range of particle sizes, but show much lower oil absorptions than the amorphous grades. Oil absorptions of crystalline silicas range from 14 to 34.

Both crystalline and amorphous silicas have a specific gravity of 2.65. Amorphous silicas are generally 99% SiO_2, crystalline silicas are even purer, at 99.7% SiO_2.

These materials are most widely used as general purpose fillers for epoxies, where they permit moderately high filler loading without excessive viscosity increase.

Diatomaceous silicas differ from the other natural silicas by their intricate particle structures, which result in much higher oil absorptions, ranging from 125–175. They also show much lower specific gravity (2.10 to 2.30), and a lower SiO_2 content, ranging from 86.7–92.8% for typical commercial grades, with 3.3% Al_2O_3, 1.2% Fe_2O_3, and smaller amounts of P_2O_5, TiO_2, CaO, MgO, Na_2O and K_2O, as well as ignition losses from 0.2–3.6%.

The use of diatomaceous silicas in plastics is limited by their high oil absorption, which may, of course, be used to advantage in certain applications. Typical applications include their use in phenol-formaldehyde molding powders, where they improve surface properties, and their use in plastic film where they contribute anti-blocking properties.

Calcium Silicate

Calcium silicate occurs naturally as wollastonite. It is mined commercially in New York State.

Wollastonite has an acicular particle shape. Its outstanding properties include its brilliant whiteness and its low oil absorption. It also shows good electrical properties.

Wollastonite is commercially available in particle sizes ranging from 3.0–8.2 (average), and oil absorptions from 22.5–25. Specific gravity is 2.9, and pH is 9.9.

A typical chemical analysis of wollastonite shows the following:

SiO_2	50.90%
CaO	46.90
FeO	.55
Al_2O_3	.25
MnO	.10
MgO	.10
TiO_2	.05
Ignition loss	.90
	99.75%

Typical applications of wollastonite includes vinyl compounding, polyester and epoxy resin compositions.

Barytes

Probably the outstanding properties of Barytes (naturally occurring barium sulfate) are high specific gravity and extremely low oil absorption.

Both dry ground and wet ground barytes are commercially available. Typical physical constants of commercial grades are as follows:

	Wet Ground Barytes	Dry Ground Barytes
Particle size, max.	20μ	60μ
Particle size, av.	3μ	12μ
Min. through 325 mesh	99.99%	99.5%
Oil absorption (rub-out)	8–9	5–6
pH	6.5–7.0	65–7.0.
Ohms resistance	50,000	50,000
Specific gravity	4.3	4.3

The following is a typical chemical composition.

$BaSO_4$	94%
Fe_2O_3	0.9%
Al_2O_3	1.2%
SiO_2	2.5%
MnO	0.15%
Copper	0.005%
Ignition loss	0.15%

Barytes is used where its high specific gravity and low oil absorption are advantageous, as in vinyl cold solders where a high specific gravity compound is desired.

FREDERICK M. KAFKA

FILLERS, PROPERTIES AND USES

Fillers are defined as comminuted solid materials which occupy a volumetric proportion of a plastics composition as a discontinuous phase. Extenders serve a distinctly different purpose, being monomeric or polymeric diluents for the primary polymer and a part of the continuous phase of the composition. The terms "filler" and "extender" are, to a certain degree, synonymous in the popularly held connotation as materials which reduce the costs and properties of the polymer forming the basis of the composition. This, however, is not necessarily the case.

Many fillers provide beneficial effects beside reducing costs. The general functions of fillers will be described below, emphasizing the reasons for their use and their particular limitations. Certain highly specialized types of inorganic materials which are more properly described as modifiers, such as pyrogenic silica, which is used as a consistency modifier, flatting agents, suspension agents, etc. have been excluded since replacing polymer is not their principal function.

Properties of Fillers

A great range of properties are available from a large number of different type fillers as will be noted in Table 1. Properties may vary considerably within a class, depending upon the purity or source of the filler and the method of processing. A predominant influence is exerted by particle-size distribution, the coarseness parameter being a more important consideration than average particle size since it is the coarseness which determines the thickness of the plastics section in which the filler can be incorporated without particles protruding through the surface.

Many properties are self-evident from the chemical composition of the material, but some treatments radically alter properties. Calcining, acid washing, alkali washing, bleaching, surface-treating, etc., are often used to extend the applicability of a particular type of filler or to enable it to provide a desirable function.

Within a class of fillers, surface area and oil absorption are directly related to particle-size distribution. Difference in particle shape limits direct comparison between classes of fillers; for example, platy or fibrous fillers will have much higher surface areas than the same average particle-size non-platy or nonfibrous filler.

Many properties of fillers do not reflect the properties obtained when they are dispersed and completely wet in plastics. A low concentration of calcium carbonate in a relatively impervious polymer will not produce a severe loss in acid-resistance, as may be expected from the nature of the calcium carbonate. However, scratches or breaks in the surface of the part or permeable plastics will evidence the inherent properties of the filler.

The pH of a filler is of primary importance in certain applications where peroxides, stabilizers dispersants and other additives are used in the plastics composition. Acidic fillers may be regarded as very weak acids, however, their effects upon acid sensitive agents and polymers (polyvinyl chloride, epoxy resins) requires the use of neutralizing agents. Basic fillers also require particular formulating considerations.

Functions of Fillers

Some fillers are used primarily for reducing the cost of the plastic. Here the fillers replace a volume of the more expensive resin in the plastic composition.

Physical properties of filled plastics are generally affected by the type and amount of filler they contain. Tensile strengths, impact resistance and elongation are reduced in proportion to the filler concentration. Modulus (stiffness) is usually increased by fillers since they function as rigid additives and reduce the mobility of the polymer when strained. Flexural strength effects depend upon the nature of the polymer; thermoplastics are generally embrittled and their flexurals strengths decline, whereas thermosets, which are rigid systems, are generally improved to a certain degree depending upon the filler concentration. Particular types of very fine particle-size fillers frequently exert a physical strength improvement at very low concentrations, but these effects are specific for certain types of

TABLE 1. PROPERTIES OF FILLERS.

Filler type	CaCO$_3$[a]	Precip. CaCO$_3$[b]	Silica[c]	Feldspar[d]	Talc[e]	BaSO$_4$[f]	Kaolin[g]
Property							
Density, g/cc	2.71	2.65	2.65	2.61–2.64	2.69–2.97	4.18–4.46	2.58
pH, 10% in water	9–10	9–10	3–4	7.0–10.0	9–10	2.0–4.0	3.0–6.0
Color[o]	White	White	White	White	White	White	White to Tan
Hardness, Mohs	3.	3.	7.0	6.0–6.5	1–2	2.5–3.5	1–2
Solubility, water	Low	Low	V. Low	Low	Low–V. Low	V. Low	V. Low
Acid resistance	Poor	V. Poor	Exc.	V. Good	Poor–Exc.	Exc.	Exc.
Alkali resistance	Good	Fair	Fair	Exc.	Fair–Exc.	Exc.	V. Good
Elect. props.	Poor	Poor	V. Good	Good	Poor–Good	Fair	Good
Refractive index, average	1.49–1.66	1.49	1.54	1.53	1.57	1.64	1.56
Surface area	V. Low–Low	High	Low	V. Low–Low	Med.	Low	High
Particle shape[p]	NUF	R;P	NUF	NUF	Platy, Acicular	NUF	Plates and stacks
Particle size, average, μ[q]	Coarse to 1.3	1.–0.03	Coarse to 1.0	Coarse to 7.0	Coarse to 0.5	Coarse to 0.5	8.–0.3
Oil absorption[r]	V. Low–Low	Med.– V. High	V. Low–Low	Low- Med.	Med.– High	Low	Med.– High
Temperature resistance	Good	Good	Exc.	Exc.	Exc.	Exc.	Exc.

[a] Wet or dry ground marble or limestone.
[b] Some fatty acid and resin coated varieties provide large improvements in dispersibility, flow, etc.
[c] Amorphous or crystalline (quartz) including sand, SiO$_2$.
[d] Many different types depending upon source and processing. Mixed anhydrous alkali aluminum silicates.
[e] Generic name for magnesium silicates. Varieties differ substantially depending upon impurities.
[f] Natural (barytes) or precipitated (blanc fixe) barium sulfate.
[g] Many grades, depending upon source and processing, but generically Al$_2$O$_3 \cdot$ 2SiO$_2 \cdot$ 2H$_2$O.
[h] Dry or water ground muscovite (white) mica.
[i] Properties depend upon temperature of processing.

systems, especially the more distensible thermoplastics. Improvements in physical properties of filled versus unfilled systems generally reflect interaction or reinforcing between the polymer and filler having surface treatments to provide a high degree of interaction through electrostatic or chemical bonding.

Modulus improvement by the use of fillers is also reflected in the improvements occurring in heat distortion temperature and resistance to creep in thermoplastics. Cold flexing temperatures are also increased. In the curing of thermosets compensation must be made for the filler content since the filler interferes with the completeness of the cure simply by diluting the reacting mass. When the conditions of polymerization are not properly adjusted filled thermosets may develop thermal properties opposite those described above

Optical properties vary widely, depending upon the filler used. The colors of plastics are frequently indicative of the filler present. Gloss is a function of particle-size distribution, the volume of filler present and the particle shape. Large, blocky particles or aggregates of particles effectively reduce gloss at a concentration which is peculiar to the type of plastics and the shrinkage occurring

during processing. Platy particles tend to align in the plane of the surface and have considerably different effects frequently increasing the gloss by providing a smoother surface due to reduced shrinkage. The opacity of both thermoplastics and thermosets is influenced by several properties of fillers; index of refraction, color, particle-size distribution, particle shape, porosity, relative completeness of dispersion or wetting by the plastics and others. Certain fillers, such as feldspar, have indices of refraction which are very nearly equal to those of many plastics and, since they are glassy, transparent, nonporous and are very readily wet and dispersed, provide an exceedingly high degree of optical clarity even at concentrations of 40% by volume. The greater the difference between the index of refraction of the filler and the plastics in which it is dispersed, the greater will be the opacifying effect. Infrared and ultraviolet are not as well characterized in the literature, but appear to be of the same nature as the luminous properties related above.

A very important attribute of fillers is their ability to alter the rheological properties of a system. This aspect is essentially related to liquid systems, but also applies to rheologically plastic

TABLE 1 (continued).

Mica[h]	Calcined kaolin[i]	Alumina[j]	Alumina hydrate[k]	$CaSO_4$[l]	Asbestos[m]	Wood flour[n]	Coal dust
2.73–2.83	2.60	3.97	2.05–2.55	2.7–3.0	2.2–2.3	0.35–0.5	1.4–1.8
7–8	5.8–6.3	3–6	3–6	3–5	7–9	5–7	4–6
Pearly gray	Pink to White	White	White	White	Gray	Tan	Black
2–3	7.	9.0	1–3	3.0–3.5	3.0–3.5	V. Low	2–3
V. Low	V. Low	V. Low	V. Low	High	Low	High	Low
Good	Good	Good	Exc.	Poor	Poor–Exc.	Poor	V. Good
V. Good	Good	Good	V. Good	Good	Exc.	Poor	V. Good
Exc.	Exc.	Exc.	Exc.	Poor	Good–Exc.	V. Poor	Poor
1.56–1.59	—	1.76	1.58	1.57–1.61	1.75–1.83	—	—
High	High	Low–High	Low–High	Low	Med.	High	Low
Platy	Plates and stacks	Nodules	Plates and stacks	NUF	Fibrous	Needle	NUF
Coarse to fine	5.0–1.0	Coarse to fine	Coarse to 0.1	Coarse to fine	Long to short	Coarse to fine	Coarse
Low–Med.	High	Low–Med.	Low–Med.	Low	High	V. High	Low
Exc.	Exc.	Exc.	Exc.	Poor	Exc.	Burns	Burns

[j] Calcined, high purity Al_2O_3.
[k] Partially hydrated types $Al_2O_3 \cdot nH_2O$.
[l] Anhydrite, anhydrous gypsum, roasted and dry ground.
[m] Type depends upon fiber length and processing.
[n] Usually pine, defiberated bundles, short fiber.
[o] Relative; colors change appreciably when in plastics media.
[p] NUF, nonuniform fractures; R, rhombic; P, prismatic.
[q] Particle-size distributions vary widely; average particle-size by weight as specific surface diameter.
[r] Lb oil/100 lb filler; low = 10, med. = 30, high = 50.

systems. Filler particles act as non-mobile agents, interfering with liquid flow and therefore introduce varying degrees of thixotropy to a system. Depending upon their physical characteristics and the nature of interaction between the filler and the liquid, a wide range of consistencies is obtainable.

Electrical properties of filled plastics are directly related to the chemical compositions and structures of the fillers. Trace quantities of ionizable compounds exert a pronounced influence upon electrical conductivity. Accordingly, specific processing conditions of the fillers govern their electrical properties. The classifications given in the table are broad generalities which in some instances, as for example, calcined kaolin, apply to specifically processed varieties.

The chemical resistance of filled plastics is a cooperative function of both the filler and matrix; the character of the matrix being dominant, providing that the plastics represents a volume sufficient to coat all of the particles of the filler. When the filler is exposed on the surface of a composite, it is obvious that the resistance of the filler to the particular corrosive environment will have an overriding influence.

Weather resistance is probably the result of all the properties of fillers listed in the table and more. Certain physical factors, such as the volume of filler present, are highly influential but, as a general rule, fillers reduce the ability of the plastics matrix to expand and contract with ambient conditions and accordingly accelerate the effects of weathering. Although this rule may be generally applied to thermoplastics, thermosets having low orders of flexibility are affected to a lesser degree. In the latter case, hydrogas permeance, surface smoothness and other properties of the composite are controlling factors.

Many specialty fillers are also used for specific purposes; iron filings or magnetic iron oxide for magnetic properties, powdered metals for heat and electrical conductivity, walnut shell flour and hollow glass spheroids for low density and a host of others.

Thomas H. Ferrigno

FILLERS, AND REINFORCEMENTS

Plastics, like many other engineering materials, have limitations, some of which may be overcome by proper design. However, a large number of properties may be enhanced by the addition of properly selected fillers to the resin system. The properties of the filled composite differ from those of the resin since the filler rather than the resin becomes the load bearing member and the resin functions primarily as a binder. Thus, the properties of a filled resin are essentially related to the adhesion between the filler and the resin.

In many instances, fillers such as calcium carbonate, calcium sulfate, talc and silica cost less than the resin, and are called extenders. In contrast, some of the more sophisticated fillers cost many times that of the resin. Fillers contribute to the temperature resistance, moisture resistance, fire retardancy, electrical resistance, specific gravity, shrinkage, and coefficient of expansion of plastics. Actually the use of appropriate fillers permits the design of plastics to meet a wide variety of physical requirements.

The choice of fillers, of course, is governed largely by the end use application. Dark colored fillers, such as carbon black, and opaque materials like wood flour, cannot be used when pastel or transparent products are required.

The amount of filler may vary from a few per cent, when its function is the improvement of surface properties, to over 90% in resin-sand mixtures for shell molding composites. Since most properties of the composite are a function of the filler, the optimum resin content is that required to coat the surface of the filler and bond it firmly together.

Most reinforcing fillers are fibrous in physical structure. The fiber length may be reduced to aid processing as in the case of wood flour. However, the physical properties of wood flour-filled phenolic molding compounds are related to the fiber length. The length of fiber may be varied, as in the case of "Orlon," "Nylon," "Dacron," rayon, glass fiber and sisal, or it may be inherent, as in the natural product. The long filaments are usually chopped for convenience in processing. Cotton flock, alpha cellulose and asbestos have characteristic short fiber lengths.

The ultimate properties of the fiber in the composite are seldom obtained because of inadequate adhesion to the resin. Fillers, such as aluminum silicate and glass, are treated before use in order to improve the bond with the resin. Glass fibers are treated with silane and chrome finishes. Other fillers are sometimes coated with resins.

Glass Fibers. These fibers are available with high strength, low dielectric or low density properties. The last property is obtained by using hollow glass fibers in which voids account for 40% of the filler. Glass flakes require a minimum amount of resin and produce a composite with multidirectional rather than uni or bidirectional properties. The ultimate reinforcement is obtained when a continuous glass filament is used.

Asbestos Fibers. Occurring naturally in several different forms, the use of asbestos in composites contributes to high temperature, rot, mildew, weather and corrosion resistance. This additive serves as a thermal, electrical and acoustical insulating filler. Chrysolite, a fibrous serpentine type asbestos, is the most widely used form. It is available in several ranges of fiber length. It provides superior thermal and electrical properties but only moderate corrosion resistance.

The amphibole varieties viz., anthophyllite and crocidolite provide better resistance to corrosives. All asbestos-resin composites exhibit good resistance to dimensional changes in presence of high humidity.

Cotton Flock. Cotton flock usually obtained by the caustic purification of cotton linters yields molded phenolic composites with moderate impact resistance and a higher degree of water absorption than when wood flour is used.

Alpha Cellulose. Produced by a caustic treatment of wood pulp, alpha cellulose is used as a filler for urea and melamine resins when light colored moldings are required. Chopped paper, macerated fabric, and chopped cotton cord are used as fillers to provide controlled impact resistance in phenolic molding compounds.

Calcium Carbonate. This is available as natural ground limestone and as precipitated calcium carbonate in a wide range of particle sizes. The small-sized product imparts opacity, whiteness and excellent surface characteristics to the finished composite.

Aluminum Silicate. China clay fillers, another name for aluminum silicate, are produced by air flotation or water fractionation of "Kaolin" clays. Calcined "Kaolin" is also used as a filler for epoxy, polyester and polyvinyl chloride resins. Improved water resistance is observed when the aluminum silicate is treated with resin before use. Naturally occurring calcium silicate (Wollastonite) is also used as a filler for resins.

Carbon Black. Carbon black is widely used for reinforcing rubber and for providing weather resistance for polyethylene. Carbon based fibers produced by charring cellulosic fibers have particularly useful ablative properties. They retain most of their original strength at temperatures as high as 3000°F.

Quartz. This substance also contributes to extreme temperature resistance essential for space-age applications. Silica and diatomaceous earth serve as inexpensive inert fillers. Pyrogenic silica obtained by thermal oxidation of silicon tetrachloride is an effective thixotropic agent for liquid resins. It also serves as an anti-caking agent for resin powders.

Barium Ferrite. When used as a filler, yields composites with potential magnetic properties. The finished product must be placed in a strong magnetic field to produce a permanent magnetic article. Barium sulfate-filled plastics are opaque to x-rays.

Powdered Metals. These provide conductivity but little reinforcement. Fibrous metals reinforce resins. Composites of resin and fibrous copper are machinable and have good resistance to abrasion.

The toughness of polyfluorocarbons is increased by the addition of powered boehmite. Conversely, the addition of powdered polyfluorocarbons as a filler to other resins provides readily moldable products with inherent lubricity.

Single Crystal Filaments. Aluminum oxide filaments with diameters as low as 1μ, these may be produced by vapor condensation, electrodeposition or solution growing techniques. These crystals called "whiskers" have tensile strengths as high as 2,800,000 psi, and have considerable potential as fillers for high strength temperature-resistant plastics.

Properly selected fillers when used with either thermoplastic or thermosetting resins produce composites with unique properties. These properties are characteristic of the fillers but are seldom obtainable without the resin adhesive. Plastics often serve as functional materials whose properties can usually be developed by use of appropriate fillers and resins. Since in most instances, the additive is not simply an extender, these functional materials should be called fortifying or reinforcing agents rather than fillers.

TYPES OF FILLERS

Organic Materials

I. Cellulosics
   A. Wood products
      (1) Chips
      (2) Coarse flour
      (3) Ground flour
         (a) Softwood flour
         (b) Hardwood flour
         (c) Shell flour
   B. Fibers
      (1) Rayon
      (2) Cotton flock
      (3) Alpha cellulose
      (4) Sisal
   C. Miscellaneous
      (1) Chopped paper
      (2) Diced resin board
      (3) Crepe paper
      (4) Pulp preforms
      (5) Textile by-products
II. Ligneous
   A. Ground bark
   B. Processed lignin
III. Proteinaceous
   A. Soybean meal
   B. Ground feathers
IV. Synthetics
   A. Nylon
   B. Dacron
   C. Orlon

V. Carbon
   A. Fibers
   B. Carbon black
   C. Graphite

Mineral Fillers

I. Asbestos
   A. Chrysolite
   B. Anthophyllite
   C. Crocidolite
II. Siliceous
   A. Diatomaceous earth
   B. Quartz
      (1) Fibrous
      (2) Pulverized
   C. Ground silica
   D. Pyrogenic silica
III. Glass
   A. Fibrous glass
      (1) Filament
      (2) Roving
      (3) Mat
      (4) Milled
      (5) Yarn
      (6) Fabric
      (7) Hollow
   B. Glass flake
IV. Silicates
   A. Mica
   B. Clay
      (1) Air fractionated
      (2) Water fractionated
      (3) Calcined clay
   C. Calcium Silicate
      (1) Wollastonite
V. Metallic Oxides
   A. Sapphire ("whiskers")
VI. Miscellaneous
   A. Calcium carbonate
      (1) Ground chalk
      (2) Precipitated chalk
      (3) Barium ferrite
      (4) Barium sulfate
      (5) Boehmite
      (6) Perlite
      (7) Carborundum
      (8) Metals
         (a) Powdered metals
         (b) Fibrous metals

Cross–reference: REINFORCEMENTS.

RAYMOND B. SEYMOUR

FILLERS FOR THERMOSETTING PLASTICS

Fillers for thermosetting compounds and prepregs may be classified into either organic or inorganic types. Often, combinations of both are included in a reinforced plastic composition. Fillers may enhance surfaces, reduce crazing, alter shrinkage, improve electrical properties, increase heat resistance, etc. A listing of the more frequently used fillers for both thermosetting compounds and prepregs, with the main purpose for each, is in Table 1.

Inorganic fillers are used in all resin systems. A host of fillers other than mentioned above may be

FILLERS FOR THERMOSETTING PLASTICS

TABLE 1. INORGANIC (MINERAL) FILLERS.

Filler	Main purposes
Glass	
Milled	Heat resistance, stability, electrical resistance.
Powdered	Heat resistance, surface, electrical resistance.
Flake	Heat resistance, higher modulus, electrical resistance.
Asbestos	
Shorts	Some electrical resistance, heat resistant, toughness, chemical resistance.
Floats	Some electrical resistance, heat resistance, chemical resistance.
Clays	Surface hardness, electrical resistance, heat resistance, cost reduction.
Calcium carbonates	Cost reduction, shrinkage, surface hardness, crack resistance, wet strength, predictability.
Mica	Electrical properties, dimensional stability, heat resistance, thermal conductivity.
Talc	Putty materials, inertness, electrical properties, cost reduction.
Graphite	Lubricity, heat resistance, thermal conductivity.
Aluminum oxides	Electrical properties, thermal conductivity, chemical resistance.
Silica (flour)	Inertness, stability, heat resistance, chemical resistance, mechanical strength.

Note: Chrysolite asbestos are most commonly used—others include crocidilite and amosite.

TABLE 2. ORGANIC FILLERS (NATURAL OR SYNTHESIZED).

Filler	Main purposes
Wood	
Alpha-cellulose	Whiteners, cleanliness, mechanicals, electrical resistance.
Flour	Cost reduction, impregnability, uniformity, electrical resistance.
Flock	Improved mechanical strengths.
Particles	Cost reduction, boards, stability.
Textile	
Flock	Impregnability, uniformity, electrical and mechanical properties.
Short fiber	As flock, better mechanical strength.
Shell flour	Cost reduction, some wear resistance.
Nylon	Wear resistance, low modulus, mechanical strengths.
Fluorocarbons	Wear resistance, electrical resistance.

employed for special effects. Chemical and mechanical handbooks list the properties in great detail. Important characteristics to be considered when selecting an inorganic filler are particle sizes, bulk factor, natural color, effect of other ingredients on the filler, opacity, dispersability, behavior under physical conditions, geological form, and cost. Inorganic fillers may be found in nature (minerals) or may be chemically processed.

Organic fillers do not have the good stability of the inorganics. They are used more in condensation type resin systems. Due to the greater effect of humidity, organic fillers exhibit a reduction in electrical properties. Specific gravities are much lower than the inorganic fillers. There is less tendency of anisotropy, less segregation, more reliability, less brittleness, and very little cracking and crazing when using organic fillers.

TABLE 3. METAL POWDER FILLERS.

Filler	Main purposes
Aluminum	Thermal conductivity, electrical conductance, dissipation of heat.
Steel	Increase wear resistance, stability, lower thermal expansion.
Copper	Electrical conductance, heat dissipation.

In general, metal fillers counteract the insulation properties of plastics. Metal fillers are heat dissipators, showing high thermal diffusivity. Electrical conductivity requirements can be achieved if the metal filler content is high enough.

TABLE 4. SPECIAL TYPE FILLERS.

Filler	Main purposes
Pyrolytic graphite	High temperature resistance, ablative.
Microballoons	
Ceramic	Low density, high temperature, insulation, low thermal conductivity.
Phenolic	Low density, high compressives, electrical and heat resistance.
Glass	Low density, high compressives, electrical and heat resistance.
Aggregates	Low cost, bulk filler.
High silicas	High temperatures, ablative, stability, inertness.
Quartz	High heat resistance, ablative, inertness.
Ceramics	High heat resistance, stability, inertness, electrical and heat resistance.

Plastics research laboratories are in constant search for unusual properties. Lightweight materials such as microballoons are in demand by the aerospace industries. High ablation resistance is needed in rockets and missiles for reentry systems, internal combustion chambers, nozzles, and external portions. Whisker or monocrystalline fibers are needed not only as reinforcement but as fillers for specialized effects. Oxidation resistance, high modulus, chemical inertness, non-outgassing, ceramitizing, increased insulation, are among the special or exotic properties in demand. New developments are requested by military, electrical industry, and other industries.

Reinforcements

Reinforcements for thermosets come in many forms. The forms may be fibrous, filament, roving, fabric, paper, matte, yarns, papers and felts. The reinforcements may be used in a continuous form, cut or chopped before or after impregnation. The molding techniques dictate the form of the compound or prepreg. The ultimate properties depend upon the molding or fabrication technique used. The size of the part, the configuration, the cross sections involved, the composite form, the required direction of strength (isotropic, orthotropic, anisotropic) are the factors which determine the curing process or molding technique used. The form of the reinforcement usually establishes the appearance of the thermoset material.

The main purposes of reinforcements are for improvement in chemical, mechanical, thermal, and electrical properties. The major benefit is in mechanical strength improvement. The mechanical properties are increased multifold in most cases. The inherent bonding properties of the resin system to the reinforcement determines the ultimate properties.

An important consideration for many reinforcements is the finishes, coupling agents, or sizings used to improve the bond. These are important for better wetting of the reinforcements, especially glass by the resins.

Composites are not necessarily new to plastics but have a renewed interest. A composition of more than one material type bonded or molded together into a heterogenous mass is termed a composite. The main purposes of composites are to derive combined properties of more than one material, to obtain alternate properties, or to utilize the singular properties of one material to enhance the singular properties of another. Familiar forms of composites are laminate rim gears, honeycomb panels, decorative laminates, filament wound structures, particle board construction, rocket nozzles, radomes, heat shields for re-entry (Gemini), airframe structures, mold-

TABLE 5. FORMS AVAILABLE.

Reinforcements	
Asbestos	Fibers, yarn, felts, paper, woven goods, cord.
Glass	Fiber, paper, roving, matte, woven roving, broadgoods or fabrics, tapes, honeycombs.
Wood (cellulose) products	Kraft paper, wood particles, alpha-cellulose, lignin fibers, jute, sisal, alpha-cellulose paper, crepes, vulcanized fiber, honeycombs.
Cotton	Fibers, linters, duck, cords, threads, broadgoods.
Synthetic fibers and fabrics[a]	Nylon, polyester ("Dacron"), acrylic ("Orlon"), polypropylene, cellulose acetate, rayon and polyfluoroethylene.
Metallic[b]	Steel wire, copper wire, tungsten wire, aluminum wire, matted or wool-like metal fibers, metal felts, metal fibers, metal cloths, honeycombs.
Inorganic	Ceramic fibers, graphite fibers and fabrics, high silica (quartz, refrasil, siltemp) fibers and fabrics, boron filament, carbon (amorphous) fibers and fabrics, carbonized rayon, carbon-silica fibers, oxide treated carbons, pyrolytic coated silica and carbon fibers, metallic carbides, pyrolytic nitrides, monocrystalline metallic whiskers, zirconia fibers.
Composites	Unidirectional tapes, bimoldings, honeycomb and fabrics, filament windings, alternate layers of various fabrics (laminates) tape wrapped parts, multi-layer circuitry, copper clad laminates, fiber mixes in resin matrices, sandwich structures, cores and overlays.

(*Note*: There are many variations of fabric structure. Also there are grades of electrical, mechanical, high tensile, and high modulus glass fibers.)

[a] Synthetic reinforcements are derived from man-made fibers. These fibers are formed into cords, yarns, or woven into broadgoods.

[b] Metallic fibers or wires are used for the same general purposes as metallic fillers—strength is in addition. Special finishes are needed for the metals to obtain bond strengths. Metallic reinforcements are used in conjunction with other fibers to form composites.

ings where more than one type of reinforcement is used, etc.

As pointed out previously, some reinforcements such as glass have a need for treating the fiber surfaces to either protect the fiber or develop a better chemical bond between resin and the fiber. Coupling agents are employed to improve the bond between the fiber and the resin. A coupling agent may consist of two different chemicals. These finishes may be different with the type of fiber or the type of resin. The use of finish may imply that a coating has been supplied and also may refer to any form of surface treatment as de-sizing, heat cleaning, and/or coating or coupling agent. Finishes are particularly important to smooth filament type fiber as fiber glass. Finishes are used with fiber type reinforcements to improve the bond between the fiber and the resin.

FLAME RETARDANTS

Long before the appearance of synthetic polymers, natural polymeric materials such as wood and cotton had been flame retarded by treatment with inorganic salts like zinc chloride, ammonium sulfate, ammonium phosphates and borax. Large markets requiring varying degrees of flame resistance are now opening up for synthetic polymers. A few of these, such as polyvinyl chloride or the polyfluorocarbons, do not support combustion, but many of the more common large volume polymers burn. This has prompted the development of modifiers to render these polymers flame retardant.

Chemistry of Flame Retardance

The mechanism of action of flame retardants is not understood in detail, but a general picture of a burning piece of plastic gives some insight into the various possibilities. Pyrolysis occurs in the solid phase to generate gaseous decombustion products. When these mix with the surrounding air, ignition occurs at certain combinations of temperature and fuel-air composition. Heat from the resulting combustion is fed back to the solid phase to sustain pyrolysis, thus completing the cycle. Modifying any or all of the four basic steps—pyrolysis, ignition, combustion and heat transfer—will change the flammability characteristics.

Empirically, it has been found that compounds containing certain elements retard or inhibit combustion. Most important of these are chlorine, bromine, phosphorus, antimony and nitrogen (in the amine or ammonium form). Some variation in efficiency exists according to the type of structure in which the flame retarding element occurs, e.g., aliphatic halogen is sometimes more efficient than aromatic halogen, but in general, structure has surprisingly little influence, and the degree of flame retardancy depends mainly on the amount of the flame-retarding elements in the composition. This amount is often distinctly different for different polymers; the relative efficiency of chlorine and phosphorus, for example, varies widely with the types of polymers.

It has been observed that phosphorus compounds generally promote heavy charring, presumably through formation of phosphoric acids which catalyze carbonification through dehydration or related mechanisms, as has been proven for α-cellulose. This holds for inorganic salts like ammonium phosphates, as well as for organic compounds. For maximum efficiency the phosphorus must remain in the solid phase, with the charred layer acting as an effective barrier to reduce heat transfer from the combustion to the pyrolysis zone. Reduction of heat transfer is also an important factor in intumescent paints for the protection of wood. In addition to influencing the heat transfer through char formation, phosphorus changes the pyrolysis mechanism so that less fuel is generated. The changes in pyrolysis and heat transfer cause secondary changes in the combustion zone.

Halogen compounds, on the other hand, are believed to act primarily in the combustion zone through the formation of hydrogen halides. These terminate the free radical chain reactions involved in oxidation of the fuel. Some increase in charring often occurs also with these compounds. The action of halogenated flame retardants has also been attributed to a "blanketing" effect of volatile halogenated combustion products.

Synergism between halogen containing flame retardants and phosphorus or antimony has been observed in many cases and a number of commercial organic flame retardants actually are combinations of two or more active flame retarding elements.

Reactive and Additive Type Flame Retardants

The two types of flame retardants in use are inert additives, and materials that react to become part of the polymer structure. There are no significant differences in efficiency between the two types; in both cases the dominant factor is the content of flame-retarding elements. Convenience, availability, cost and influence on physical properties other than flame retardancy have to be weighed to decide in each individual case which type is to be used most advantageously.

Additives include inorganic materials and low and high molecular weight organics such as phosphate esters, chlorinated hydrocarbons and polyvinyl chloride. They are convenient to use since no reformulation of the basic polymer is required, the flame retardant is simply blended with the polymer, the prepolymer or the monomers, in proportions depending on the desired degree of flame retardancy. Difficulties with additive materials arise from the large amounts needed to flame retard certain polymers. Physical properties may change significantly as a result of dilution and plasticization of the polymer. Furthermore, lower molecular weight materials, particularly when incompatible, may migrate to the surface and be lost during long term exposure.

TABLE 1. ORGANIC POLYMER FLAME RETARDANTS.

Chemical description or formula	Active elements	Manufacturer	Recommended use	Trademark
Chlorinated paraffins	Cl	Diamond Alkali	Polyolefins, polystyrene	Chlorowax—Series
		Hooker Chemical	Polyolefins, polystyrene	CP-40
		Hercules Powder	Polyolefins, polystyrene	
		Dover Chemical	Polyolefins, polystyrene	
		Keil Chemical	Polyolefins, polystyrene	
		Neville Chemical	Polyolefins, polystyrene	
		McGean Chemical	Polyolefins, polystyrene	
Chlorinated di- and polyphenyls	Cl	Monsanto Co.	Polyolefins, PVC, rubber	Aroclor—Series
Chlorinated naphthalenes	Cl	Koppers Co.	Polyolefins, PVC, rubber	Halowax—Series
Perchloropentacyclodecane	Cl	Hooker Chemical	Polyolefins, polystyrene	Dechlorane
Tetrachlorophthalic anhydride	Cl	Hooker Chemical	Polyester resins	Niagathal
		Monsanto Chemical	Polyester resins	Tetrahal
1,4,5,6,7,7-Hexachloro-5-norbornene-2,3-dicarboxylic acid	Cl	Hooker Chemical	Polyester resins, alkyds, polyurethanes	HET—acid
1,4,5,6,7,7-Hexachloro-5-norbornene-2,3-dicarboxylic anhydride	Cl	Hooker Chemical	Polyester and epoxy resins, alkyds, polyurethanes	HET-anhydride
		Velsicol Chemical	Polyester and epoxy resins, alkyds, polyurethanes	
ortho- and/or para-Chloro-styrene	Cl	Dow Chemical	Polyester resins	
Bis-β-chloroethyl-vinyl phosphonate	P	Stauffer Chemical	Comonomer	
Phosphate polyol	P	Dow Chemical	Rigid polyurethane foam	
		Union Carbide	Rigid polyurethane foam	
		Jefferson Chemical	Rigid polyurethane foam	
		Wyandotte Chemical	Rigid polyurethane foam	
		Pittsburgh Plate Glass	Rigid polyurethane foam	
		Virginia Carolina	Rigid polyurethane foam	Vircol-82
		Richardson Co.	Rigid polyurethane foam	PXU-110
Tetrabromophthalic anhydride	Br	Michigan Chemical	Polyester resins	Firemaster PHT 4
Tetrabromo-bisphenol A	Br	Dow Chemical	Epoxy resins	
		Michigan Chemical	Epoxy resins	Firemaster BP 4A
Vinyl bromide	Br	Dow Chemical	Comonomer	

TABLE 1 (*continued*). ORGANIC POLYMER FLAME RETARDANTS.

Chemical description or formula	Active elements	Manufacturer	Recommended use	Trademark
Pentabromochlorocyclohexane	Br	Dow Chemical	Polyurethane foam, polyvinyl acetate, PVC	Celluflex CEF
Tris-2-chloroethylphosphate	P,Cl	Stauffer Chemical	Nitrocellulose, polyesters, cellulose acetate	
Tris-dichloropropylphosphate	P,Cl	Stauffer Chemical	Polyurethane foam, PVC, epoxy resins	Celluflex FR-2
			Polyurethane foam, polymethylmethacrylate,	Phosgard C-22-R
Polyphosphonate	P,Cl	Monsanto Co.	Phenolic resins, synergist in chlorinated and brominated polyester and epoxy resins, Cellulosics	
Phosphate polyol	P,Cl	Richardson Co.	Rigid polyurethane foam	PXU-112
		Richardson Co.	Epoxy resins	Pyrostop E-100
$(HOC_2H_5)_2NCH_2P(O)(OC_2H_5)_2$	P,N	Stauffer Chemical	Rigid polyurethane foam	Fyrol 6
Tris-2,3-dibromopropylphosphate	P,Br	Michigan Chemical	Polyurethane foam, PVC, polystyrene, polyester, epoxy nitrocellulose, polymethyl methacrylate	Firemaster T-23-P
PVC/antimony oxide	Cl,Sb	Union Carbide	Polyurethane foam	Niax-A

Reactive flame retardants are used mainly in thermosetting resins. Generally, they replace part or all of one of the components of the resin formulation, thus becoming an integral part of the polymer. With proper selection of the reactive material, high loadings with flame retardant can be achieved without significant change in physical properties and no possibility for migration exists. In the selection of a reactive flame retardant, particular attention must be given to potential hydrolytic or thermal instability of the flame retardant. Bond fission in the flame retardant is of much more serious consequence when it is part of the polymer chain because of the resulting sharp loss of strength of the composition.

Commercial Formulations

Table 1 gives a compilation of the more commonly used, commmercially available organic polymer flame retardants. Not included in this list are the phosphate plasticizers since although they are commonly used to formulate flame retardant flexible PVC formulations, their primary purpose is to plasticize an already flame retardant polymer. In addition to organic flame retardants, inorganics are used frequently. By far the most common of these is antimony oxide which is used extensively, particularly as synergist in combination with chlorinated hydrocarbons. Ammonium-, urea-, and melamine-phosphates are finding increasing use as intumescing agents for fire retardant paints; ammonium bromide, ammonium chloride, ammonium sulfate and many others have been reported to be active.

In the following a few of the more common flame retardant resin systems are briefly discussed.

Polyester Resins. Most flame retardant unsaturated polyester resins are internally flame retarded by incorporating halogenated dibasic acids like tetrachlorophthalic, tetrabromophthalic or 1,4,5,6,7,7 - hexachloro - 5 - norbornene - 2,3 - dicarboxylic acid (chlorendic acid). Generally, 15-30% chlorine or 8–15% bromine are used and antimony oxide or organic phosphorus compounds (for clear formulations) are frequently used as synergists. Some resin is flame retarded with a combination of halogenated hydrocarbons and antimony oxide. More recently, ring substituted monochlorostyrene has been suggested as partial or complete replacement of the normally used styrene cross-linker.

Epoxy Resins. Phosphorus-based flame retardants are relatively ineffective in epoxy resins. Attention has therefore centered on halogen-containing materials. The reactive approach has usually been taken either by using halogenated dicarboxylic anhydrides as curing agents with conventional epoxy resins or by using epoxy resins that are based on halogenated ring structures such as the diglycidylether of tetrabromobisphenol A.

Polyurethane Foam. Flexible and particularly rigid polyurethane foams represent a major and fast growing market for flame retardants. Both additive and chemically reactive types are used. The amount of flame retardant required to achieve a specific degree of flame retardance depends considerably on the type of polyol and isocyanate, generally about 1–2% phosphorus, 4–8% bromine, or 8–12% chlorine are used.

Polymethyl Methacrylate. Both phosphorus and halogen compounds are effective as flame retardants for polymethyl methacrylate and the two types show synergism. A combination of about 5.5% chlorine and 3% phosphorus is claimed to give good self-extinguishing properties. The flame retardants used are generally added to the monomer or syrup when casting sheets.

Polyolefins. Phosphorus-based flame retardants show poor efficiency in polyolefins; as a rule they are also incompatible. The most widely used materials are chlorinated hydrocarbons, often in combination with antimony oxide. Loadings of 30% of the flame retardant blend are often required to meet specifications. At these loadings,

some loss in physical properties and heat resistance is experienced.

Polystyrene. Phosphorus-based flame retardants show poor efficiency in polystyrene and present compatibility problems. Some molding compounds are flame retarded with chlorinated hydrocarbons, bromine containing materials are used and flame retarded polystyrene is sold in form of self-expanding pellets for the manufacture of rigid foam containing proprietary flame retardant systems. Bromine based flame retardants appear to be most effective; their addition level can be substantially reduced while maintaining the same degree of flame retardancy if small amounts of free radical generators are added as synergists.

Flammability Tests

Flammability depends on many aspects other than chemical composition. Size and shape of the test specimen, its position with regard to the ignition source, draft, nature of ignition source, length of exposure to ignition source, and many other factors are equally important. Furthermore, flammability itself is not a clearly defined property; it can be viewed as resistance to ignition, fuel contribution, weight loss as a function of time, velocity of flame spread over a surface,

TABLE 2. MEDIUM AND SMALL-SCALE FLAMMABILITY TESTS.

Designation	Description	Data obtained[a]
ASTM D-568-61	Flammability of plastic film and sheeting	BR, SEX or NB
D-635-56T	Flammability of rigid plastics over 0.05 in. thick	BR, SEX or NB
D-757-49	Flammability of self-extinguishing plastics (Glow-bar)	BR
D-1360-58	Test for fire-retardancy of paints (Cabinet method)	Weight loss and char volume on painted wood surface
D-1361-58	Test for fire-retardancy of paints (Stick and Wick Method)	
D-1433-58	Flammability of flexible thin plastic sheeting	BR, SEX or NB
D-1692-59T	Flammability of plastic foams and sheeting	BR, SEX or NB
D-229 (Sect. 45–50)	Flammability of rigid sheet and plate insulation	Time to ignition
D-1929-62T	Ignition properties of plastics	Flash ignition temp. Self ignition temp.
E-162	Surface flammability of materials using a radiant heat source (Radiant Panel)	Flame spread, fuel contribution, smoke weight and density
US Bureau of Mines Test[b]	Penetration of torch flame through plastic material	Burn-through time
Fed. Test Method Std. No. 406 Method 2021	Flammability of plastics over 0.050 in. thick (analogous to ASTM D-635)	BR, SEX or NB
2022	Flammability of plastics under 0.050 in. thick	Burning time, burned area
2023	Flame resistance (Ignition of vapors from heated sample by spark plugs)	Time to ignition, flame spread, burning time.

[a] BR = burning rate.
SEX = "self-extinguishing".
NB = "nonburning".
[b] See USBM Report of Investigations #6366.

length of burn, resistance to flame penetration, etc. There is often little or no correlation between relative ratings of materials by these criteria. Considering the multitude of end use applications, it is not surprising that a large number of flammability tests are in use.

In code-regulated applications or where approval by insurance agencies is sought, the end-product generally must pass large scale flammability tests approximating actual use conditions. These are costly and few laboratories are equipped to run them. For development purposes, the bench scale tests listed in Table 2 are used most frequently.

E. Peter Benzing

FLUOROCARBON MONOMERS

Fluorine-containing compounds today find their widest use in the form of polymeric materials. This is because the fluorocarbon polymers possess in varying degree the chemical inertness, thermal stability, and other unique properties characteristic of the fluorocarbon family; these features are of outstanding practical utility when manifested in a rubber, oil, or resin.

General Properties of the Fluorocarbons

The simple aliphatic fluorocarbons, in comparison to their hydrocarbon analogs are extremely resistant to thermal decomposition. Perfluoroethane (CF_3CF_3), for example, is stable to 840°C. The absence of hydrogen in perfluorinated compounds renders them extremely resistant to oxidative attack. Considering their highly oxidized state, they are also surprisingly inert to reducing agents, being attacked only by hot alkali metals, metal alkyls, and similar substances. The high C—F bond energy (120 kcal/mole in CF_4) and the shielding effect of the bulky fluorine atom accounts for the thermal stability and chemical inertness of the saturated aliphatic fluorocarbons. Also contributing to this inertness is the physical immiscibility of fluorocarbons with most chemical reagents and solvents.

Fluorocarbon derivatives having functional groups are, on the other hand, often more reactive than the analogous hydrocarbon derivatives. Trifluoroacetic acid (CF_3COOH), for example, resembles the halogen acids rather than acetic acid in its ionic strength because of the powerful electron withdrawing effect of the CF_3 group.

The fluorocarbons are, as would be expected, much more dense than hydrocarbons, having densities in the region of 2. They exhibit very low viscosities and high vapor pressures in relation to their molecular weights. The fluorocarbons have the lowest refractive indices of any chemical class, e.g., heptane $n_D^{20} = 1.375$, perfluoroheptane $n_D^{20} = 1.2618$, and are highly transmissive to visible and near infrared light.

Perfluorinated versus Partially Fluorinated Species

The term "fluorocarbon," strictly defined as used above refers to compounds containing only carbon and fluorine. In common parlance, however, "fluorocarbon" and "fluorocarbon polymer" are used in reference to materials whose properties reflect the presence of a significant fluorine content. Of course, these "fluorocarbon-like" properties are progressively diluted and lost as one replaces F atoms with, e.g., H or Cl in any typical fluorocarbon structure. The weaker C—H and C—Cl bonds provide points more vulnerable to chemical attack or initiation of thermal decomposition.

Fluorocarbon Monomer and Polymer Types

Many monomeric fluorocarbon compounds and derivatives have been converted into polymers by polymerization reactions analogous to those familiar to the polymer chemist. Typical of these are the fluorocarbon acrylates such as heptafluorobutyl acrylate:

$$CH_2{=}CHC{-}OCH_2C_3F_7 \quad \overset{O}{\overset{\|}{}}$$

Here the perfluoroalkyl group does not appreciably affect the polymerization behavior characteristic of the acrylate esters but is strategically placed so as to confer solvent-resistant properties upon the elastomer that results:

$$\left(\begin{array}{c} CH_2{-}CH \\ | \\ C{=}O \\ | \\ O{-}CH_2C_3F_7 \end{array}\right)_n$$

Polyamides and polyesters can be synthesized by polycondensation of fluorocarbon dicarboxylic acid chlorides with diamines or diols, as seen below:

$$ClC(CF_2)_n{-}CCl + H_2N(CH_2)_6NH_2 \xrightarrow{-HCl}$$

$$(CH_2)_6HN{-}C(CF_2)_n{-}C{-}NH)_n$$

Depending upon the choice of monomers, such polycondensations can give rise to physically strong thermoplastics or elastomers. However, because of their high cost and their inherent lack of resistance to hydrolytic attack, particularly in the polyesters, they are not commercially available at present.

Fluorocarbon silanes have been successfully polymerized to fluorine-containing silicones:

$$\begin{array}{c} R_f \\ | \\ CH_2 \\ | \\ CH_2 \\ | \\ Cl-Si-Cl \xrightarrow[\text{multi-step}]{H_2O} \\ | \\ CH_3 \end{array} \quad \left(\begin{array}{cc} R_f & R_f \\ | & | \\ CH_2 & CH_2 \\ | & | \\ CH_2 & CH_2 \\ | & | \\ -Si-O-Si- \\ | & | \\ CH_3 & CH_3 \end{array} \right)_n$$

It is necessary to introduce methylene groups between the R_f (perfluoroalkyl) and the silicon to provide stability. Fluorocarbon silicones are commercially available as "LS-Silastics."*

The fluorocarbon expoxides can be ring-opened to give rise to liquid polymeric ethers which are particularly useful as lubricants at high temperature:

$$R_fCF\!\!-\!\!CF_2 \xrightarrow{\text{carbon black}} \left(CF\!\!-\!\!CF_2\!\!-\!\!O \right)_n$$
$$\overset{O}{\overset{\diagup\diagdown}{}} \qquad\qquad \underset{R_f}{|}$$

These materials are produced by the DuPont Company.

Fluorocarbon polyethers have also been prepared by workers at the Montecantini Company by an unusual reaction between perfluoroolefins and oxygen in the presence of ultraviolet light.

In addition to the reactions which bear a *prima facie* similarity to those of conventional organic polymer chemistry, certain fluorocarbon derivatives form polymers by reactions which have no parallel. For example, trifluoronitrosomethane will copolymerize spontaneously with fluorocarbon olefins at very low temperatures,

$$CF_3NO + C_2F_4 \xrightarrow{-40°C} \left(N\!\!-\!\!O\!\!-\!\!CF_2\!\!-\!\!CF_2 \right)_n$$
$$\underset{CF_3}{|}$$

to yield elastomeric, high molecular weight polymers. This reaction proceeds by a free radical mechanism in which CF_3NO is its own initiator. These polymers are useful because they remain rubbery at low temperatures ($T_g = -60°F$) and resist chemical and solvent attack.

The foregoing is intended merely to show the diversity of fluorine-containing monomer and polymer types. Many more could have been cited. Although the fluorine-containing monomers and polymers synthesized and evaluated in the laboratory number many hundreds only a few of these have attained significant commercial volume.

Fluorocarbon Olefins and Their Polymers

From the standpoint of volume usage, by far the most important fluorine-containing polymers

* Dow Corning Corp.

are those derived from the addition homopolymerization of partially and wholly fluorinated olefins. The resulting high polymers can range from amorphous elastomers to polycrystalline thermoplastics depending on choice and/or ratio of monomers employed.

The olefins are simple and, for fluorocarbons, inexpensive compounds which originally were outgrowths of the refrigerant industry, being derived from chlorofluorocarbons which were originally developed and introduced as refrigerants in the 1930's. This versatility and availability have been the principal factors leading to the preeminence of the polyfluorocarbon olefins, of which more than 21 million lb were consumed in 1965.

The fluoroolefins of principal commercial importance are:

Tetrafluoroethylene	$CF_2{=}CF_2$
Chlorotrifluoroethylene	$CF_2{=}CFCl$
Vinylidene fluoride	$CH_2{=}CF_2$
Vinyl fluoride	$CH_2{=}CHF$
Hexafluoropropene	$CF_3CF{=}CF_2$

Tetrafluoroethylene accounts for ca. 90% of the fluorocarbon polymer manufactured and sold in 1965. The physical properties and synthetic routes to these monomers are summarized in Table 1.

Manufacture of Fluorocarbon Monomers

Tetrafluoroethylene ($CF_2{=}CF_2$) the first completely fluorinated olefin to be synthesized, was isolated by O. Ruff, an early worker in the fluorocarbon field. Ruff found that $CF_2{=}CF_2$ was formed, along with other fluorocarbons, when carbon tetrafluoride was passed through an electric arc. This method is not used today for the manufacture of tetrafluoroethylene because of the economics of the process. Instead chlorodifluoromethane is dehydrohalogenated thermally with operating conditions set to optimize the yield of the C_2 olefin:

$$2CF_2ClH \xrightarrow{\Delta} CF_2{=}CF_2(\text{b.p.},-76.3°) + 2HCl$$

Chlorotrifluoroethylene ($CF_2{=}CFCl$) was first prepared by fluorinating hexachloroethane and then dehalogenating the product with zinc metal in alcohol:

$$CCl_3\!\!-\!\!CCl_3 + SbF_3/SbCl_5 \rightarrow CF_2Cl\!\!-\!\!CFCl_2 \xrightarrow[\text{alc.}]{Zn}$$
$$CF_2{=}CFCl + ZnCl_2$$

Dechlorination of $CF_2ClCFCl_2$ with zinc is still employed as the principal industrial route to this monomer.

Vinylidene Fluoride ($CH_2{=}CF_2$). The earliest preparation of this monomer was accomplished by Swarts, another pioneer in early organic fluorine chemistry. Fluorination catalysts of antimony chlorides and fluorides are often

TABLE 1. SUMMARY OF PHYSICAL PROPERTIES AND SYNTHETIC ROUTES TO FLUOROCARBON OLEFINS.

Monomer	Boiling point, °C	Melting point, °C	Density	Method of preparation
$CF_2{=}CF_2$	-76.3	-142	1.58 ($-78°C$)	$2CF_2ClH \xrightarrow{pyrol.} CF_2{=}CF_2 + 2HCl$
$CF_2{=}CFCl$	-27.9	-157	1.61 ($-78°C$)	$CF_2Cl{-}CFCl_2 \xrightarrow{Zn/alc.} CF_2{=}CFCl + ZnCl_2$
$CH_2{=}CF_2$	-82		1.39 ($77°K$)	$CH_3CClF_2 \xrightarrow{500-1700°} CH_2{=}CF_2 + HCl$
$CH_2{=}CHF$	-72.2	-160.5	0.998 ($-149°C$)	$CH{\equiv}CH + HF \xrightarrow{cat.} CH_2{=}CHF$
$CF_3CF{=}CF_2$	-29	-156.2	1.71 ($-78°C$)	$CF_2{=}CF_2 \xrightarrow{pyrol.} CF_3CF{=}CF_2 +$ other products

referred to as "Swarts catalysts" and were utilized by him to synthesize CH_2BrCHF_2 which was subsequently dehalogenated with sodium amylate to give vinylidene fluoride. For laboratory preparation, the above route is convenient, however, more economical methods have been developed for industrial purposes. As an example, chlorodifluoroethane can be dehydrohalogenated thermally:

$$CH_3CClF_2 \xrightarrow{500-1700°C} CH_2{=}CF_2$$
$$\text{(b.p., } -82°C) + HCl$$

Vinyl Fluoride ($CH_2{=}CHF$) Vinyl fluoride, has been prepared by addition of hydrogen fluoride to acetylene:

$$HC{\equiv}CH + HF \xrightarrow{cat.} H_2C{=}CHF \text{ (b.p., } -72°)$$

This reaction was probably first studied in detail in Germany during the 1930's employing mercury salts as catalysts. However, catalysts such as boron trifluoride, fluorosulfonic acid and hydrogen chloride are also claimed to be promoters for the addition.

Hexafluoropropylene ($CF_3CF{=}CF_2$). This monomer was originally isolated from pyrolysis products of tetrafluoroethylene. Laboratory scale quantities of this monomer are readily obtained in good yield by thermal decarboxylation of sodium perfluorobutyrate

$$C_3F_7CO_2Na \xrightarrow{\Delta} C_3F_6 + CO_2 + NaF$$

Commercial methods have been developed which utilize the relatively cheap starting materials, CF_2HCl and tetrafluoroethylene. These processes are believed to involve the formation of difluorocarbene radicals which then react with tetrafluoroethylene:

$$C_2F_4 \xrightarrow{\Delta} 2CF_2 : \xrightarrow{C_2F_4} CF_3CF{=}CF_2 \text{ (b.p., } -33°)$$

Other Fluorocarbon Monomers

Esters, Amides, Acid Chlorides, and Alcohols. The starting materials for these derivatives,

namely the fluorinated acids, can be prepared by an electrochemical fluorination process, telomerization reactions or by the Swarts fluorination reaction discussed earlier. The derivatives are prepared by conventional methods.

Silane Monomers. The most important example of this class of monomer is methyl 3,3,3-trifluoropropyl dichlorosilane. This compound is prepared by the addition of methyl dichlorosilane to 3,3,3-trifluoropropene:

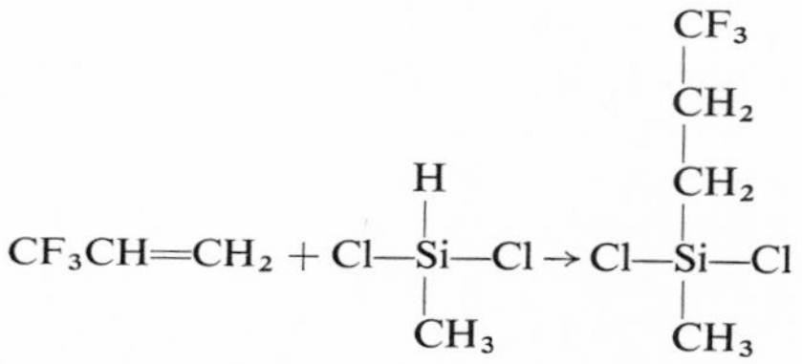

Epoxides. These compounds can be prepared by the dehydrohalogenation of bromoalcohols, e.g., $CF_3CH(OH)CH_2Br$ with sodium or potassium hydroxide, or by epoxidizing fluorocarbon olefins.

Nitroso Derivatives. These unusual fluorocarbon monomers can be synthesized by reacting nitric oxide with perfluoroalkyl iodide or more conveniently by the decarboxylation of nitrosyl fluoro acylates, e.g.,:

$$(R_fCO)_2O + N_2O_3 \rightarrow R_f\overset{O}{\overset{\|}{C}}ONO$$

$$R_f\overset{O}{\overset{\|}{C}}ONO \xrightarrow{\Delta} R_fNO + CO_2$$

Polymerization of Fluoroolefins

Because of the powerful electron withdrawing effect of fluorine, the π-bond in a fluoroolefin is electron poor, the "e" value being positive and proportional to the halogen content, e.g.,

$e = +1.5$ for $CF_2=CFCl$, while $e = +0.2$ for $CH_2=CHCl$. Highly fluorinated olefins are, therefore, polymerized by anionic and free-radical techniques with the latter being by far the most widely used.

Generally, commercial-scale polymerizations of fluoroolefins are carried out at elevated pressures and temperatures in aqueous systems either with or without an emulsifier in the presence of an organic or inorganic peroxide catalyst. In contrast to the fluorine-containing ethylenes which readily lend themselves to homopolymerization by such techniques, the higher perfluoro-1-olefins are difficult to *homo*polymerize by typical free radical means. Olefins such as perfluoropropene can, however, readily be homopolymerized in anionic systems using, e.g., CsF as the initiator.

On the other hand, higher perfluoro-1-olefins readily enter into free-radical copolymerization reactions with the fluorine-containing ethylenes and are chiefly used in this way. Here their role is to modify the properties of the parent homopolymer through disruption of crystallinity. This can result in merely improving the processing characteristics (low content of incorporated 1-olefin), or with the proper parent monomer, conversion of a crystalline thermoplastic into an elastomer (higher content of incorporated 1-olefin).

The polymerization of the fluoroolefins listed above and the inherent characteristics of the resultant commercially-important polymers are now considered individually.

Tetrafluoroethylene (TFE). TFE is commonly polymerized in aqueous systems using free-radical initiators at high pressures. Redox initiator systems such as persulfate-bisulfite-copper sulfate have been employed as well as organic peroxides. Dibasic acid peroxides in aqueous media yield stable suspensoids.

TFE is a highly crystalline, waxy polymer which cannot, because of its very high "melt" viscosity, be processed by conventional techniques. Various sintering methods have been developed for processing the solid polymer into useful shapes. The coagulated suspensoid can be cold-formed with an oil processing aid, then fused. Films can be cast from dispersions of the polymer.

Hexafluoropropene (HFP). The homopolymer of hexafluoropropene has been prepared using anionic initiators such as CsF and "Ziegler"-type catalysts.

Copolymerizations with fluorine-containing ethylenes are conducted in emulsion free-radical systems at elevated pressures and it is herein that the commercial utility of HFP lies. When TFE is copolymerized with a small amount of HFP the crystal structure of the parent polymer is partially disrupted and the polymer becomes processible.

When HFP is copolymerized with vinylidene flouride

$$CH_2=CF_2$$

it similarly disrupts the crystallinity of that parent polymer, and because of the inherently low glass transition temperature of poly VF_2 ($-39°C$) an elastomer results. This highly stable solvent resistant rubber is sold commercially as "Viton"* or "Fluorel"**.

Chlorotrifluoroethylene (CTFE). This was first polymerized commercially in bulk using a peroxide initiator at low temperatures. It has been polymerized in the presence of "Ziegler"-type catalysts. Commercial processes utilize aqueous emulsion and suspension techniques.

Poly CTFE is a very hard, transparent, partially crystalline thermoplastic which can be melt processed by conventional techniques.

The properties of the polymer can be modified by copolymerization with VF_2 and other comonomers such as TFE to give rise to products ranging from somewhat crystalline insoluble thermoplastics to essentially amorphous soluble thermoplastics from which coating laquers can be prepared. Incorporation of about 50–80 mole % of VF_2 yields tough, thermally stable, solvent resistant elastomers with handling characteristics and ultimate properties depending upon the amount of VF_2 co-monomer introduced. These rubbers are known as "Kel-F"** elastomers.

Vinylidene Fluoride (VF_2). The homopolymer prepared in aqueous free-radical polymerization systems at elevated pressure is characterized by alternating CH_2 and CF_2 groups in its backbone and is an extremely tough, transparent thermoplastic which can be melt processed. The polar character introduced by the alternating groups contributes significantly to this toughness. The introduced hydrogen results in some sacrifice in thermal properties (Table 2).

Vinyl Fluoride (VF). This monomer contains the least fluorine and consequently most resembles the conventional vinyls in its general reactions and polymerization characteristics. It can be polymerized in aqueous recipes in the presence of free radical catalysts such as potassium persulfate. The polymer is a transparent thermoplastic with excellent film-forming properties.

In Table 2 are summarized the commercially important polyfluorocarbon olefins, showing their representative formulae and the monomers and monomer combinations from which they are derived.

Typical properties of the commercially available fluorocarbon resins are summarized and compared in Table 3.

* DuPont.
** 3M Company.

TABLE 2. ROUTES TO FLUOROCARBON POLYMERS.

Monomer	Co-monomer	Polymer or copolymer	Nature of polymer	Selected trademarks
Tetrafluoroethylene (TFE)		Poly TFE	Opaque, waxy crystalline polymer	Teflon (duPont) Halon (Allied Chemical) Tetran (Pennsalt)
$CF_2{=}CF_2$		$-(CF_2{-}CF_2)_n$		
	$CF_3CF{=}CF_2$ hexafluoro propene (HFP)	$-(CF_2{-}CF_2{-}CF{-}CF_2)_n$ CF_3	Transparent thermoplastic	Teflon FEP (duPont)
Chlorotrifluoro-ethylene (CTFE)		Poly CTFE	Tough, transparent thermoplastic	Kel-F (3M)
$CF_2{=}CFCl$		$-(CF_2CFCl)_n$		
	$CH_2{=}CF_2$ vinylidine fluoride (VF$_2$) and/or other monomer	$-(CF_2CFClCF_2CH_2)_n$	Modified thermoplastic or elastomer	Kel-F (3M) Plaskon (Allied Chemical) Kel-F Elastomer (3M)
Vinylidene fluoride (VF$_2$)		Poly VF$_2$	Tough transparent thermoplastic	Kynar (Pennsalt)
$CH_2{=}CF_2$		$-(CF_2CF_2)_n$		
	$CF_3CF{=}CF_2$ hexafluoro propene (HFP)	$-(CH_2{-}CF_2{-}CF{-}CF_2)_n$ CF_3	Elastomer	Viton (duPont) Fluorel (3M)
Vinyl fluoride (VF) $CH_2{=}CHF$		Poly VF $-(CH_2CHF)_n$	Transparent thermoplastic	Tedlar (duPont) Dalvor (Diamond Alkali)

Fluorocarbon Elastomers

The fluorocarbon elastomers share in many of the properties of the fluorocarbons but generally have sacrificed some of the chemical stability of the perhalogenated resins. This is a direct consequence of introducing $-CH_2-$ links to provide the backbone flexibility necessary for elastomeric properties.

The $CH_2{=}CF_2/CF{=}CF_2$ elastomers are CF_3 superior to the $CH_2{=}CF_2/CFCl{=}CF_2$ elastomers from the standpoint of thermochemical stability and processing ease. Both tend to be quite tough, but can be handled on conventional compounding and molding equipment.

Since these elastomers are completely saturated and lack any other formal cross-linking site, special vulcanization techniques are necessary. Hexamethylene diamine is commonly employed as a curative. It is believed to function by abstraction of the elements of HF from the chain backbone, although the exact chemical nature of the established cross-link is not entirely understood. Conventional carbon black and silica reinforcing fillers can be employed with fluorocarbon elastomers

Applications for Fluorocarbon Polymers

The chemical and thermal inertness of these polymers combined with excellent electrical, low friction and anti-stick properties permit them to be used for applications where no other polymer type is suited. Poly TFE, the first fluorocarbon polymer to be exploited commercially, is being produced at a rate of about 16–17 million lb per year. The total annual consumption of fluorocarbon polymers is approximately 22 million lb per year, with annual sales of about 85 million dollars. Poly TFE at the present time enjoys the largest share of this market and has been utilized for a greater variety of applications than the other fluorocarbon resins. Poly TFE is available in the form of molding powders, extruded rods, sheets, and other shapes, thin films and emulsions. The chemical inertness of this material has gained it

TABLE 3. COMPARISON OF TYPICAL PROPERTIES OF FLUOROCARBON RESINS.

Property	Polyvinylidene fluoride (VF$_2$)	Polychlorotri-fluoroethylene (CTFE)	Polytetra-fluoroethylene (TFE)	Polyperfluoro-ethylenepropylene (FEP)
Specific gravity	1.76	2.12 (77°F)	2.15	2.15
Refractive index, n_D^{25}	1.42	1.435 (77°F)	1.35	1.341–1.347
Tensile strength, psi	7000 (77°F)	4630 (77°F)	2500–3500	2500–3500 (73°F)
Elongation, %	300 (77°F)	120 (77°F)	200–300	300
Coefficient of linear thermal expansion, in./in./°F	8.5×10^{-5}	4.8×10^{-5} (below Tg)	5.5×10^{-5} (73° to 140°F)	4.6–5.9×10^{-5} ($-100°$ to $+160°$F)
Coefficient of friction to steel	0.14–0.17		0.04	0.09
Max. continuous service temp., °F	300	390	500	$+400$
Min. service temp., °F	< -80	-320 to -400	-275 to -450	-120 to -425
Water absorption, %—24 hr	<0.04	0.00	0.00	<0.01
Dielectric constant				
60 cycles	8.40	2.63 (100 cps)	2.0–2.2	2.0
10^6 cycles	6.43	2.40 (10^5 cps)	2.0–2.2	2.1
Dissipation factor				
60 cycles/sec	0.049	0.062 (100 cps)	0.0002	0.0002
10^6 cycles/sec	0.159	0.014 (10^5 cps)	0.0002	0.0007
Dielectric strength, volts/mil	1280 (0.008″)	3700 (0.001″)	3200 (0.001″)	6500 (0.001″)
Volume resistivity, ohm/cm	2×10^{14}	2.5×10^{16}	$>10^{15}$	$>10^{17}$
Chemical resistance				
Acids	C—Fum. H$_2$SO$_4$, ClSO$_3$H	E	E	E
Bases	D—n-BuNH$_2$ and other primary amines, otherwise E	E	E	E
Solvents	S—by certain strongly polar solvents, otherwise E	S—certain halo-genated and aromatic solvents, otherwise E	E	E
Other chemicals	All are attacked by ClF$_3$, F$_2$ at elevated temperatures and by molt enalkali metals.			

Symbols: C = chemical attack; D = degraded; E = excellent; S = solvent attack.

wide acceptance in chemical processing equipment. Various forms are used for lining reaction vessels, chemical hose and liners for pipe, gaskets, "o"-rings, pump blades, valve diaphragms, expansion joints, etc.

The excellent electrical insulating and low dissipation factors makes these polymers suitable for wire and cable insulation, feed-through insulators, stand-offs, connectors, coaxial wire spacers, and many other electrical and electronic applications.

Fluorocarbon resins, particularly those based on poly TFE, have low-friction and antistick properties and are used for pistons, bearings, and bushings, and chute liners. The largest single factor in the growth of poly TFE resin in recent years has been its utilization as an antistick surface in frying pans and other cookware.

Poly CTFE and FEP copolymers are also used for many of the applications cited above. CTFE films are widely used in specialty packaging and electronics industries. They are remarkable for

their retention of useful physical properties at extremely low temperatures (to $-400°$F) and for their extremely low permeability by gases and water vapor.

Polyvinylidene fluoride and polyvinyl fluoride resins, like poly CTFE and FEP, are heat sealable and are therefore adaptable to many packaging applications. They do not possess the same degree of chemical and thermal inertness as poly TFE resins but nevertheless they find applications in similar areas where thermal requirements are not so rigorous. Both poly VF$_2$ and poly VF can be expected to find wide application in the form of films and coatings because of their unusual toughness, abrasion resistance, optical properties and particularly, resistance to outdoor weathering. The latter makes possible their use in permanent outdoor installations, e.g., coatings for aluminum siding and roofs.

The fluorocarbon elastomers are employed where corrosive chemical and solvent resistance in combination with thermal stability is required in a rubber. Elastomers based on VF_2 are quite tough and strong but tend to stiffen below 0°C. Where elastomeric properties are needed at lower temperatures, the fluorine-containing silicones can be employed advantageously.

G. H. Crawford
H. A. Brown

FOAM INGREDIENTS

Plastic foams (cellular plastics, foam plastics or expanded plastics) generally consist of two phases, a dispersion of a gaseous phase (blowing agent and/or a gas derived from it), in a solid phase (plastic). While the chemical composition of the solid plastic phase is the dominant factor in determining the properties of the resulting foams, some properties, such as thermal insulation, are dependent on the composition of the gaseous phase. The density of the foam and the cell geometry are also important factors in determining foam properties.

Foams may be organic, inorganic or metal-organic in nature, and thermoplastic or thermosetting. The cellular materials may be derived from natural products such as latex rubber, or synthetic products, as polystyrene foams. The degree of cross-linking in the polymer structure will determine if the foam is flexible or rigid, although the dividing line between these two forms is not readily distinct. In normal use, rigid foams can also be defined as having a glass transition (second order) temperature above room temperature. Flexible foams have second order transition points below room temperature.

Foams may be either closed-cell cellular plastics, in which the individual cells are completely surrounded by a thin membrane of polymeric material, or open-celled foams, in which the individual cells are interconnected, or intercommunicating similar to a natural sponge. Regulating the amount of blowing agent with respect to the solid polymer will permit the preparation of a wide range of densities in the foam.

Polymeric materials can be fabricated into foams by either mechanical, physical, or chemical means. The mechanical whipping of gases into a polymer system as it hardens, thus entrapping the gas bubbles in a matrix, will yield a cellular plastic. The expansion of a dissolved gas or of small thermoplastic resin beads as well as the volatilization of low boiling liquids will produce similar results. Expanded plastics can also be prepared by chemical techniques, such as the thermal decomposition of a blowing agent or by the formation of a volatile reaction product during polymerization. These former groups of blowing agents encompass such materials as the inorganic carbonates, bicarbonates, nitrates and borohydrides. Examples of organic compounds which thermally decompose to liberate gases are the azo compounds, hydrazides, azides, nitroso compounds, etc. Blowing agents may also be generated by the interaction of two reactive groups, such as the formation of carbon dioxide by the reaction of water with an isocyanate.

Many cellular plastics may be produced *in situ* by spraying or foaming-in-place. Plastic foams are available in many forms such as blocks, boards, slabs, sheets, molded shapes or in composite forms as laminates with metals, fabrics, paper, wood, etc.

The properties of plastic foams can be widely varied depending on the raw materials and foaming techniques employed. While it may be impossible to include all types of plastic foams in this article, some of the more important types of commercial foams will be discussed and have been listed below:

(1) Thermosetting Foams:
    Polyurethane
    Epoxy
    Phenol-formaldehyde
    Urea-formaldehyde
    Silicone
(2) Thermoplastic Foams:
    Polystyrene
    Styrene copolymers
    Polyethylene
    Polypropylene
    Polyvinyl chloride
    Cellulose acetate

A comparison of properties of the more common of several commercial cellular plastics is shown in Table 1.

Polyurethane Foams

Polyurethane foams, commercially known as urethane foams, are prepared by the reaction of di- or polyisocyanates with di- or higher functional hydroxyl compounds in the presence of a blowing agent, surfactant(s) and catalyst(s). Special additives such as flame retardants, fillers, pigments, etc. may be incorporated into the formulation where special properties are desired. Depending upon their composition, the foams can be made either flexible, semi-rigid or rigid. Since there exist some notable differences in the composition of flexible and rigid foams, the raw materials for the manufacture of these foams are treated separately.

Raw Materials for Flexible Foams. The most common hydroxyl components of flexible foams are hydroxyl-terminated polyesters or polyether diols or polyols. The polyesters are usually adipate esters of glycols such as ethylene-, diethylene-, propylene- and dipropylene glycols or combinations thereof. Dimer acids (dimer of linoleic

TABLE 1. COMPARISON OF PROPERTIES OF PLASTIC FOAMS.

Material	Types	Density, lb/ft³	Thermal conductivity, Btu/ft²/hr/ °F/in.	Tensile strength, psi	Compressive strength, psi	Water absorption, % at 50% relative humidity
Polyurethane	Flexible	1.5–20.0	0.12–0.25	13–150	0.2–1.5 (at 25%)	0.5–4.0
	Rigid	1.5–30.0		15–800	7–1500	
Polyvinyl chloride	Flexible	3.0–45.0	0.27	10–200		1.0–5.0
	Rigid					
Cellulose acetate	Rigid	6.0–8.0	0.31	150–180	125	1.9–2.5
Phenolic	Rigid	0.3–25.0	0.18–0.28	4–200	1–1100	1.0–5.0
Polystyrene	Rigid	1.0–5.0	0.24–0.26	33–180	14–150	Nil
Polyethylene	Semi-rigid	3.0		670		Nil
	Rigid	15.0				Nil
Silicone	Flexible	12.0–16.0	0.3	15		1.0
	Rigid	3.5–18.0	0.3		100–325	1.0
Epoxy	Rigid	4.0–40.0	0.25–0.30	100–1000	10–900	

acid) can be substituted for adipic acid. Caprolactone-derived polyesters have also been employed. By far the most important hydroxyl components are poly(oxypropylene) derivatives of glycols or glycerine or trimethylolpropane. Frequently combinations of polyether diols and triols are used. In order to achieve greater reactivity of the terminal hydroxyl groups, the polyethers are frequently "capped" with oxyethylene groups to provide the more reactive primary alcohol groups. Poly(oxypropylene) poly(oxyethylene) derivatives of ethylene diamine ("Tetronic" polyols, Wyandotte Chemicals Corp.) are also being used for the production of flexible foams, usually in combination with poly(oxypropylene) glycols. An 80/20 mixture of 2,4- and 2,6-tolylene diisocyanate (TDI) is for all practical purposes the sole isocyanate component in the flexible foam manufacture in the United States. In Europe, other isomer blends such as 65/35 TDI mixtures are also being used.

Carbon dioxide is the most common blowing agent in flexible foams and is generated *in situ* by the reaction of water with excess isocyanate. Low boiling solvents such as fluorocarbons (e.g., trichlorofluoromethane), methylene chloride and others are used as auxiliary blowing agents, especially for very low density foams.

Tertiary amines are commonly used as catalysts for polyester-based foams while polyether-based foams employ either tertiary amines or a combination of metal catalysts and tertiary amines, particularly for use in one-shot foams. Tertiary amines are catalysts for the isocyanate-hydroxyl reaction as well as isocyanate-water reaction while metal catalysts such as stannous octoate, dibutyltin dilaurate, lead naphthenate, etc. are extremely effective catalysts for the isocyanate-hydroxyl reaction. The most common tertiary amines are 1,4-diaza(2,2,2)bicyclooctane ("Dabco," Houdry Process & Chemical Company), N,N,N', N'-tetramethyl-1,3-butane diamine, 1,2,4-trimethylpiperazine, N,N'-dimethylethanolamine, N-ethylmorpholine, N-cocomorpholine, and triethylamine. It should be noted that a synergistic effect exists between metal catalysts, such as stannous octoate, and tertiary amines.

Surfactants are being used to promote better mixing of the foam components, to stabilize the foam and to act as a controlling factor in determining cell size, shape and uniformity. In the case of polyesters, surfactants such as long chain fatty acid partial esters of hexitol anhydrides ("Spans," Atlas Chemical Industries), poly(oxyalkylene) derivatives of hexitol anhydride, partial long chain fatty acid esters ("Tweens," Atlas Chemical Industries) and proprietary surfactants such as "Emulphor EL-719" (Antara Chemical Co.), and "Witco 77–86" (Witco Chemical Co.) may be used. Silicones are usually employed for polyether-based foams. These may consist of polydimethylsiloxanes for foams made by the prepolymer route while poly(oxyalkylene) polydimethylsiloxane block copolymers and, more recently, polymers containing the silicon-carbon bond (which are hydrolytically more stable) have been employed for foams made by the one-shot process.

A special type of flexible urethane foam is also referred to as "urethane sponges." These are most often used for high density foams requiring a high degree of abrasion resistance, and are usually made by foaming urethane-urea elastomers (generally prepared from polyethers, diisocyanates and aromatic diamines). Water (carbon dioxide), fluorocarbons, nitrogen-generating compounds such as N,N'-dinitrosopentamethylene tetramine ("Nitrosan," E. I. DuPont de Nemours & Co., Inc.) or air may be used as blowing agents. Silicone surfactants are normally employed as cell regulating agents and other additives may be included in the foaming formulation to meet special end use requirements.

Raw Materials for Rigid Foams. As is the case for flexible foams, hydroxyl-terminated polyesters and polyether polyols are used as hydroxyl components for rigid foams, though with greatly increased functionality. Castor oil or castor oil-based polyols are also being utilized for the preparation of rigid and semi-rigid foams. The trend is toward using polyols with functionality of four or greater in the case of polyether-based foams. These include poly(oxypropylene) derivatives of pentaerythritol, α-methyl glucoside, sorbitol and sucrose.

In addition to TDI, 4,4′-diphenylmethane diisocyanate (MDI) is being utilized in the manufacture of rigid foams. More recently "crude" isocyanates, either of TDI or MDI, are being employed, particularly in the production of one-shot foams. These latter are polyisocyanates derived from aniline-formaldehyde condensates. The functionality of the crude isocyanates may vary between two and three (most frequently about 2.6–2.8).

Water may be used in rigid foam formulations to generate carbon dioxide as a blowing agent. However, the most common blowing agent for low density foams is trichlorofluoromethane (Fluorocarbon 11). The use of this blowing agent results not only in reduced foam costs (less isocyanate is required because of the absence of the water-isocyanate reaction) but also yields foams with greatly improved thermal insulation properties as measured by the "K-factor" (expressed in Btu/in./hr/sq ft/°F, 0.10–0.14 versus 0.24 for CO_2-blown foams). Dichlorodifluoromethane (Fluorocarbon 12) is used in conjunction with trichlorofluoromethane in the manufacture of rigid foams where the frothing technique is applied.

Tertiary amines and metal catalysts, used in flexible foams, are also utilized in the production of rigid foams. Likewise, surfactants similar to those used for flexible foams are applied for rigid foams. Since most rigid foam applications require a maximum of closed cell content, surfactants such as silicone block copolymers are utilized to meet these requirements. Flame resistance can be imparted to rigid foams by three methods:

(1) The incorporation of flame-retarding, unreactive additives such as tris(chloroethyl)phosphate, tris(dibromopropyl) phosphate, diammonium phosphate, antimony oxide, etc,.

(2) The coating of the foam with a flame-retardant, e.g., 60–60N (Benjamin Foster), and

(3) The addition of flame-retardant compounds containing functional groups such as hydroxyl or isocyanate, which become chemically bound in the polymer. Typical examples are phosphorus-containing polyols and halogenated di- or poly-isocyanates.

Methods of Manufacture. Urethane foams may be prepared by three principal methods. These are (1) prepolymer, (2) semi- or quasi-prepolymer, and (3) one-shot.

The prepolymer method consists of the reaction of a polyester or polyether with an excess of di- or polyisocyanate to form isocyanate-terminated adducts which are called prepolymers. The latter are then foamed in the presence of water and (or) other blowing agents, catalysts and surfactant.

The semi- or quasi-prepolymer method involves the reaction of part of the polyols with the isocyanate component thus forming a low viscosity, low molecular weight adduct dissolved in a large excess of isocyanate. The semi-prepolymer is then foamed by addition of the remainder of the polyol component in the presence of blowing agent, catalysts and surfactant.

In the one-shot method the foam components are admixed simultaneously at the time of foaming; two or more foam components may be blended prior to foaming in order to reduce the number of streams which are metered into the mixing head of the foam machine and to provide for more efficient mixing.

Flexible foams are usually produced by continuous slabstock formation or molding operations. In addition, foams may be sprayed using either external or internal mix spray guns.

Other specialized manufacturing methods for urethane foam include foam laminating to various substrates, e.g., textiles, paper, etc., and frothing. The latter method is increasingly being used, particularly for rigid foam applications.

Epoxy Foams

Epoxy foams are produced by expansion and curing of suitable epoxy resins. Typical epoxy resins which are used for this purpose are condensation products of bisphenol-A and epichlorohydrin. Depending upon the mole ratio of bisphenol-A to epichlorohydrin, the resulting resins vary from low molecular weight, liquid condensation products such as the diglycidyl ether of bisphenol-A to higher molecular weight, solid products containing both epoxy and hydroxyl groups.

The most prominent curing agents are polyamines such as diethylene triamine and triethylene tetramine. Adducts of polyamines with diepoxides or mono-functional epoxy compounds such as phenyl or butyl glycidyl ether are also used, resulting in faster reactions than occur with the use of polyamines. Adducts of this type are used in concentrations of about 20–25 parts per hundred parts of epoxy resin. Aliphatic polyamines and their adducts result in more exothermic reactions than do aromatic polyamines and their adducts, and, hence, are particularly useful in the production of one-shot foams, where the heat of reaction volatilizes the blowing agent, e.g., halogenated hydrocarbons, etc.

Other curing agents, such as cyclic amines, ethoxylated amines, cyanoethylated amines, and polyamides containing terminal amino groups are used to obtain special properties. These curing agents yield cross-linked epoxy resins due to the reaction between the epoxide and amine groups. The use of acid anhydrides as curing agents likewise yields cross-linked polymers. Tertiary amines and boron trifluoride-monoethylamine complexes are curing agents promoting the reaction between epoxide groups.

The presence of alcohol groups or phenolic hydroxyls has an accelerating effect on the curing reaction and is of importance in the preparation of one-shot foams.

The selection of the blowing agent(s) depends upon whether a high or low density foam is desired. In addition to the liquid resin, high density foams utilize blowing agents such as p,p′-oxy-bis(benzenesulfonyl hydrazide) ("Celogen," Naugatuck Chemical Company, Division of U. S. Rubber Company) or ammonium carbonate, an emulsifier such as "Tween 20" (Atlas Chemical Industries), a solvent such as toluene (to moderate the exothermic reaction), and a polyamine curing agent, e.g., diethylenetriamine. The foam is produced by heating the resin to 110°C and adding, with vigorous mixing, the other components, with the exception of the curing agent. The polyamine is added at the onset of foaming. A typical foaming formulation yielding a foam of about 7 lb/ft^3 is given below:

Epoxy resin 450 mol wt.	100 parts by wt.
"Celogen"[a]	2
"Tween" 20[b]	0.1
Toluene	5
Diethylenetriamine	6

[a] Naugatuck Chemical Co., Div. U.S. Rubber Co.
[b] Atlas Chemical Industries.

Epoxy foams may be produced from powdered systems consisting of solid epoxy resins and blowing agents such as diaminodiphenylsulfone. The foams are generated by merely heating the powder in a mold at 300–400°F. These systems are used for the filling of intricate cavities and where high strength and resistance to high temperature are required.

Low density foams (about 2 lb/ft^3) with excellent thermal insulation properties are obtained by the use of fluorocarbon blowing agents, such as trichlorofluoromethane, silicone surfactants, a phenolic activator and a polyamine curing

agent, e.g., diethylene triamine or triethylene tetramine.

Epoxy resins can be formulated to be flame-retardant by the incorporation of phosphorus- and (or) chlorine-containing compounds (e.g., "Pryostop" E-100, Richardson Co.).

Foamed epoxides can be used in foam-in-place applications or as preformed slabs and blocks, with preponderantly intercommunicating or closed-cell structures. Foam machines, similar to those used for the manufacture of urethane foams, providing automatic mixing and dispensing, are used. Spray systems have also been developed using either external or internal mix spray guns. Epoxy foams have excellent dimensional stability over a wide temperature range, good adhesion and electrical properties and are characterized by low shrinkage.

Phenol-Formaldehyde Foams

Phenolic foams may be prepared by two basically different routes. The first method (reactive) is based on the vaporization of solvent and the small amount of water in the resin, due to the heat of reaction generated during the curing of the phenol-formaldehyde condensate. The second method (premixed cellular mortar or "syntactic foam") consists of curing a mixture of microscopically small, hollow spheres of phenolic resin and a resin binder such as a phenolic, epoxy or polyester resin.

The phenolic resins in the reactive-type of foam manufacture are generally low reactivity, casting type resins. They are prepared by condensing 1.3–3.0 moles of formaldehyde with 1.0 mole of phenol in the presence of an alkaline catalyst such as barium hydroxide. Base catalysis of this reaction leads initially to a reaction mixture consisting of methylol phenols as well as low molecular weight condensation products containing methylol groups. These alkaline reaction products are also referred to as "resoles." After neutralization with lactic or oxalic acids, water is removed under reduced pressure. Approximately 25% is left in the residual resin to assist in the foaming step.

Foaming of the resole is brought about by acid catalysis (in the presence of a blowing agent), which produces a highly exothermic condensation of the methylol groups to form methylene bridges between the benzene rings. Acid catalysts normally used in the foaming reaction include hydrochloric, sulfuric and phosphoric acid. However, because of the corrosive nature of these acids, other catalysts such as benzenesulfonic, toluenesulfonic and phenolsulfonic acids are widely used today. Catalyst systems consisting of blends of organo-phosphoric acids, mineral acids and polyhydric alcohols have also been utilized. Peroxide catalysts such as metallic peroxides, e.g., calcium peroxide, and urea peroxides, have been reported; they require heat to activate the foaming reaction. Diisocyanates as well as isocyanate-terminated prepolymers have been used as cross-linking agents. They undergo exothermic reactions with the residual water in the resole, resulting in foams with improved compressive strength and water resistance.

Various types of foaming agents have been described for the manufacture of phenolic foams. These include low boiling solvents, such as isopropyl ether and metal carbonates, e.g., sodium, potassium, ammonium or calcium carbonates. The use of an acid catalyst in the foaming formulation causes evolution of carbon dioxide. Another blowing agent is hydrogen, generated from metal powders such as aluminum, zinc and magnesium, used with acid or alkaline catalysts.

The use of air prior to the addition of catalyst in the frothing of resoles has been reported to give resilient foams but lower strength properties. A number of nitrogen-liberating blowing agents have been used such as dinitroso pentamethylenetetramine, p,p'-oxybis(benzenesulfonylhydrazide), benzene diazonium sulfate, etc.

Surfactants are used in the formulation of phenolic foams to aid in foam stability and to control cell size uniformity. Surfactants range from fatty acid esters to alkylene oxide adducts of phenols, lecithin, alkyl-aryl sulfonates and sulfates.

Fillers which may be used include wood flour, walnut shell flour, diatomaceous earth and mica.

A typical phenolic foam formulation yielding a foam with a density of 5 lb/ft³ is given below:

Components	Parts by wt.
Resole (78–85% solids)	100
Sodium bicarbonate	0.7
Phenol sulfonic acid (aqueous, 30% solids)	10.0
Surfactant	0.2

The density of phenolic foams can be regulated by means of the type and concentration of catalyst, the nature of the blowing agent, and the molecular weight of the resin, which to a large extent controls the amount of exothermic heat developed during the final condensation reaction.

The thermal stability, chemical and solvent resistance, low cost and ability to be foamed-in-place of phenolic foams have led to their use in structural panels and thermal and sound insulation. Due to the porosity of the foams, they have been used for vacuum forming dies. Although water resistance is excellent, because of their partly open cell structure, phenolic foams (3–6 lb/ft³ density) absorb about 10% water by volume after 14 days immersion.

Syntactic foams are made by mixing a thermosetting resin, e.g., epoxy, in a dough mixer with curing agents such as amines. The phenolic spheres are then added and mixing continued until a putty-like mass is obtained. This mass is then foamed in a suitable mold and allowed to cure at room temperature. Application of heat will accelerate the cure.

Due to their spherical cell shape, syntactic foams exhibit a high strength-to-weight ratio, as well as good insulating and high temperature properties. They have been utilized in sandwich core structures and as a reinforcing cellular mortar in such applications as boat hulls, airplane structures and for repairs on wood structures in homes or industry.

Urea-Formaldehyde Foams

The preparation and chemistry of urea-formaldehyde foams are similar to those from phenol-formaldehyde resins. The resins are prepared by condensing urea with formaldehyde at 80–110°C and adjusting the pH of the cooled solution to 7–9. The formaldehyde-urea ratio is usually between 1.6/1 and 2.0/1. The resulting product (60–90% resin solids) consists of a mixture of methylol and methylene ureas with low molecular weight condensation polymers.

Many methods have been employed for the preparation of urea-formaldehyde foams. Air or other gases can be dispersed in the liquid resin, with high speed agitation, followed by the addition of an acid curing agent.

Another procedure consists of mixing in a beater a solution of an acid, such as phosphoric acid, water, and a surfactant with a liquid resin, which has air blown into it, yielding a product having the consistency of whipped cream. The foam is discharged onto a conveyor belt and passed through a heating zone for an initial cure. The final cure is achieved, after cutting the foam, in an oven. Another method provides for solution of a gas in the liquid resin under pressure and allowing the mixture to foam upon release of the pressure, similar to the frothing process in the manufacture of urethane foams.

Foaming agents similar to those used in phenolic foams may be utilized by liberation of gases upon acidification of the urea-formaldehyde resin. All of the above procedures yield predominantly open-celled foams.

Emulsion procedures have recently been introduced for the manufacture of urea-formaldehyde foams. These consist of emulsifying low boiling solvents such as halogenated hydrocarbons, pentane, propane (under pressure), etc., in the liquid resin in the presence of an emulsifier, such as dibutyl phenylphenol sodium disulfonate. The addition of an acid catalyst, e.g., phosphoric acid, causes an exothermic reaction leading to vaporization of the solvent and subsequent foaming of the reaction mixture. This type of procedure yields foams with predominantly closed cells.

The unmodified urea-formaldehyde foams are brittle and generally lack toughness. This may be improved by adding about 10%–35% by weight of intermediate molecular weight polyethylene glycols (D.P. 5–25) in the foam formulation. In order to chemically bond these glycols into an integral part of the foam, the formaldehyde : urea ratio is increased to 5 : 1, enabling the excess formaldehyde to react with the glycol, resulting in plasticization and toughening of the cellular plastic.

Similar to the syntactic phenolic foams, hollow urea-formaldehyde spheres, 2–60μ in diameter, can be aggregated to low density foams with the aid of thermosetting binders, such as polyesters and epoxy resins. Low molecular weight polyethylene or paraffin may also be employed as a thermoplastic matrix for the beads.

Urea-formaldehyde foams are noncorrosive, nontoxic, and will not support combustion, thus making them suitable for insulation applications.

Silicone Foams

Silicone foams are made from standard polysiloxane resins in which a —Si—O—Si—backbone accounts for their outstanding thermal stability (they may withstand continuous exposure to 650°F). The silicone polymers, consisting essentially of copolymers of di- and trifunctional methyl- or phenyl silicone resins, containing free hydrogen or hydroxyl groups, are used either in solid or liquid form. Various modifications in the design of these resins may be achieved by the type of comonomers used in the preparation and by end-blocking of the polysiloxane chains. Flexible or rigid foams may be produced depending upon the amount of trifunctional component present in the polysiloxane chain. Foams are produced from solid silicone foaming powders by heating to 320°F in the presence of a blowing agent, catalyst and filler. During foaming, condensation of neighboring hydroxyl groups takes place with the formation of siloxane crosslinks, resulting in a cellular, thermoset product.

Compounds are used as blowing agents which decompose to give off nitrogen gas, such as N,N′-dinitrosopentamethylene tetramine ("Nitrosan," E. I. Du Pont de Nemours & Co., and p,p-oxybis(benzenesulfonylhydrazide) ("Celogen," Naugatuck Chemical Div., U. S. Rubber Co.). Sometimes mixed blowing agents such as "Nitrosan" and "Unicel ND" (40% N,N′-dinitrosopentamethylene tetramine and 60% inert filler) may be used. The nitrogen gas causes expansion of the silicone resins while the amines formed in the decomposition of the blowing agents act as a condensation catalyst for the hydroxyl groups.

A typical high temperature catalyst is tert-butyl perbenzoate, which acts as a primary curing agent for sponge formulations. Peroxide catalysts, e.g., dichlorobenzoyl peroxide, are also used, usually in conjunction with the perbenzoate catalyst. Suitable fillers which may be used in the foam formulations include diatomaceous earths such as "Celite Superfloss," (Johns-Manville) or certain silica fillers.

Typical silicone sponge formulations are shown below:

	A	B	C
Silicone resin	100	100	100
Unicel ND[a]	3	3	2
Nitrosan[a]	—	1.5	1
Dichlorobenzoyl peroxide	0.6	0.6	1.1
Celite Superfloss	3.0	3.0	3.0
tert-Butyl perbenzoate	1.5	1.5	1.5

[a] E. I. DuPont de Nemours & Co.

Formulations A and B are well suited for molding sheets or simple shapes, while formulation C is suitable for extrusion.

The catalysts and filler are usually added to the silicone gum stock by blending on a mill and are followed by the blowing agents. The uniform mixture is then allowed to stand for at least 24 hours prior to processing. Silicone sponges may be produced by a variety of manufacturing processes. They may be cured in a closed mold or, initially, in a mold for a sufficient length of time to develop a skin and then allowed to undergo further expansion and cure in an oven. Silicone sponges may be fabricated into flat sheets or extruded, making allowances in the design of the die to provide for expansion of the sponge compound. Post curing is normally required for silicone sponges to remove traces of catalyst and blowing agent residues.

Liquid systems have recently been developed which merely require mixing of the silicone resin with an alkaline catalyst for 30 sec. at room temperature to initiate foaming. The silicone resin contains 20% methylene chloride which, together with a small amount of hydrogen which is generated during the expansion, acts as blowing agent. Foaming is complete in about 15 min. The foam can be handled after 10 hr of room temperature curing. A 2-hr cure is required at 100°C.

Polystyrene Foams

Cellular polystyrene foam is currently available in (1) expanded form, a prefoamed type, produced in many different shapes such as boards, logs, planks, etc., (2) expandable form usually as free-flowing beads, and (3) self-expanding form, utilizing a combination of expandable beads and a thermosetting resin system.

Expanded Polystyrene Foams. This type of foam is prepared by forcing molten polystyrene, containing a blowing agent, through an extruder orifice at elevated temperature and pressure. The melt expands upon release of pressure and cools into a rigid, low density foam. Blowing agents include volatile liquids such as methyl chloride, which is injected into the polymer melt, or hexane, which can be mixed first with a finely divided pigment to form a dry powder, subsequently blended with the granular polystyrene. The hexane can also be added to the blend of polystyrene and pigment prior to extrusion. The foam is taken continuously from the extruder and cut into desired sizes, depending upon the application. The board stock is then subjected to a heat treatment which anneals, cures and stabilizes the foam prior to shipment. Internal stresses are thus relieved, resulting in greater dimensional stability. Expanded polystyrene has a unicellular structure and exhibits low thermal conductivity and good structural strength. It is widely used as a low temperature insulation material in many industries, and is extensively employed as a combination insulation and plaster base in residential masonry construction, as well as a solid insulated backup to gypsum wall board, wood paneling, ceramic tile and decorative wall board. Other uses include roof insulation board, core material for sandwich panel construction, refrigerated truck bodies and railroad cars, buoyancy and floral display applications.

Expandable Polystyrene Foams. Expandable polystyrene is produced in the form of free-flowing beads, containing a blowing agent, which expand on application of heat. A great number of foaming agents have been used, but the most common are saturated hydrocarbons such as pentane, hexane or heptane. For the extrusion of expandable beads special nucleating agents such as a mixture of citric acid and sodium bicarbonate are used. The additive system is employed to develop a very fine cell structure and to impart a smooth, satiny finish to the extruded foam. Conventional extruders with low compression screws and high ratios of length to diameter are suitable for foam extrusion. This process is being used for the production of sheet tubing and rods.

For molding of expandable polystyrene beads there are generally two separate steps:

(1) Pre-expansion of the beads, usually by means of steam heat.

(2) Further expansion and fusion of the prefoamed beads, by means of heat within the confines of a steam cavity mold.

The purpose of prefoaming is to obtain uniform low density, free-flowing beads having a smooth surface. The blowing agent within the bead condenses upon cooling to form a partial vacuum within each cell. An aging period, of approximately 20 hr is required between the prefoaming and molding step to allow the beads to come to pressure equilibrium.

Molding of the prefoamed beads is generally carried out using hot, dry steam. Other types of heating such as high frequency, dielectric heating have also been successfully employed. Before fabricating, the molded foam is allowed to age for short periods, permitting it to absorb air, to dry uniformly, and to become dimensionally stable.

Expandable polystyrene can also be injection molded for applications such as toys, flower pots and decorative boxes.

Blow molding of expandable polystyrene beads has led to the production of many hollow objects at exceptionally high rates because of the fast cooling characteristics of the foam.

Flame-retardant polystyrene foams can be made by incorporation of various additives to the foamable beads such as a combination of chlorinated paraffin and antimony oxide. Other flame-retardant additives are combinations of bromine-containing compounds and organic peroxides; or phosphate derivatives of 2,3-dibromo-l-propanol, or other bromine compounds.

Coloring of polystyrene foam can be accomplished either by dry-coloring, which involves coating the unexpanded beads, or by dyeing the pre-expanded beads with the aid of a dye solution or emulsion. In the dry coloring methods the virgin beads are coated with a mixture of about 0.1% wetting agent and about 0.2% colorant, based on the weight of the beads. Tumbling of the mix for 5 min. is usually sufficient for uniform distribution.

Pre-expanded beads may be dyed by an emulsion technique in which the dye is carried in agents such as o-phenylphenol, methylsalicylate, biphenyl and trichlorobenzene. Solution dyeing is carried out by dissolving oil-soluble dyes in highly volatile solvents such as petroleum ether, Stoddard's solvent, or V.M. & P. naphtha, in conjunction with 10% carbon tetrachloride, acetone or perchloroethylene, thus providing more complete penetration of the dye into the beads. Soaking of the beads in the dye solution for 30–60 min is followed by a solvent wash to remove the excess dye. Drying of the beads is then carried out at room temperature.

Currently the largest uses for molded polystyrene foam are insulation board, packaging, coolers, drinking cups, toys, novelties and flotation items such as small boats, life preservers and surfboards.

Self-expanding Polystyrene Foams. Self-expanding polystyrene foams have recently been developed. A combination of expandable polystyrene beads, a thermosetting resin, curing agent and modifier is used. The heat developed during the exothermic curing reaction of the resin is utilized for the expansion of the thermoplastic polystyrene beads. This type of foam can be used in sandwich construction for structural panels, refrigerator doors, surfboards, etc.

The properties of polystyrene foam can be summarized as follows:

(1) Low thermal conductivity.
(2) High strength-to-weight ratio.
(3) Low water absorption.
(4) Low water transmission.
(5) Closed cell structure.
(6) Controllable density (in general, mechanical strength properties vary directly with the density).
(7) Excellent energy absorption.
(8) Good chemical resistance.
(9) No toxicological effects.

Polystyrene-Copolymer Foams

Foams based on styrene-acrylonitrile have recently been developed. Styrene copolymer foams have been prepared from expandable beads of various acrylonitrile contents for applications requiring gasoline resistance. In order to make the foams resistant to premium gasoline, an acrylonitrile content of at least 28.5% is necessary whereas foams containing 18.5% acrylonitrile resist regular grade gasoline.

Foams based on styrene-butadiene-acrylonitrile terpolymers (ABS) have also been developed.

Polyethylene Foams

Polyethylene foams have been produced by either physical or chemical foaming processes. Some of the physical foaming methods consist of admixing or dissolving a gas such as nitrogen in the molten resin under high pressure, and expanding the reaction mass under reduced or atmospheric pressure with simultaneous cooling. While these processes did not reach commercial significance, similar methods employing volatile liquids such as fluorocarbons (e.g., 1,2-dichloro-tetrafluoroethane) led to the introduction of commercial foams. In the latter, flowable gels are formed which are extruded into a zone of reduced pressure followed by cooling. The foam structure can be controlled by careful cooling or by partial cross-linking utilizing ionizing radiation. In general, the physical foaming processes are characterized by low raw material costs, but relatively high investment in specialized equipment is required to produce a particular type of polyethylene foam. Chemical foaming processes in which a gas is evolved during a chemical reaction (generally by decomposition of a blowing agent) are preferred for the commercial manufacture of polyethylene foam.

Both organic and inorganic blowing agents have been described in the literature but only a few have attained commercial significance. The most important are 4,4-oxybis(benzene sulfonyl hydrazide) ("Celogen"), dinitrosopentamethylenetetramine and 1,1'-azobis(formamide)[azodicarbonamide]. The decomposition temperature of the blowing agents is the most critical factor in their applicability with resins. "Celogen," for instance, is suitable for use with branched but not linear polyethylene because its decomposition point (150°C in air) is below the mixing temperature necessary to obtain a uniform dispersion in the linear resin. Dinitrosopentamethylenetetramine is used preferentially for low density polyethylene. Azodicarbonamide can be utilized for foaming either low or high density polyethylene because its decomposition temperature in air is relatively high (195°C.)

Both extrusion and compression molding techniques can be applied to chemical foaming processes of polyethylene. In the extrusion process the resin pellets are coated with the foaming agent and the coated pellets fed into the extruder. The temperature of the extruder is regulated in such a way as to progressively heat the extruder barrel to or above the decomposition temperature of the foaming agent. The gas from the blowing agent is liberated near the head of the extruder and is dissolved in the molten resin as the latter moves through the head and the die. Foaming occurs as soon as the mass leaves the die. Important factors affecting the cell structures are type and concentration of the blowing agent, the particle size distribution of the foaming agent, and the melt index of the expanded resin.

For compression molding, the foaming agent is dispersed in the resin (e.g., by blending on a two-roll mill) and, after cooling, either granulated or cut into sheets. Molding is then carried out at temperatures which vary from about 345°–400°F, depending upon whether a low or high density polyethylene is being used. A one- or two-stage processing cycle may be used for full expansion of the foams. In the two-stage process the mold cavity is filled to capacity with the foaming compound and the first heating cycle carried to the decomposition of the foaming agent under pressure. After cooling, the preformed cellular mass is then expanded by heating to the softening point of the polyethylene. A typical formulation for the preparation of an open-celled linear polyethylene foam is as follows:

Linear polyethlene (melt index 1.2)	100.0
Azodicarbonamide	2.0

Molding of the resin-blowing agent blend (in granular form) is carried out in a hydraulic press at 400°F for 15 min, and the mold then cooled to room temperature in a 20 min cycle.

A typical formulation for a closed-celled, low density polyethylene foam is given below:

Low density polyethylene (melt index 1.7)	100.0
Azodicarbonamide	5.0

Sheets of the above blend are molded at 345°F for 15 min under a pressure of 3000 psi, followed by cooling of the mold. The preformed material is then removed from the mold and the expansion is carried out by heating in a hot air oven at 230°F for 30 min.

More recently, cross-linked polyethylene foams have been prepared utilizing organic peroxides as cross-linking agents. Suitable peroxides are dicumyl peroxide, 2,5-dimethyl-2,5-di(*tert*-butylperoxy) butane and 2,5-dimethyl-2,5-di(*tert*-butylperoxy) hexyne-3. The first two are recommended for use with branched polyethylene while the third may be employed with linear polyethylene. The physical properties and density of these foams are largely governed by the choice and amount of blowing agent used while the melt viscosity of the polyethylene does not appear to have a significant influence. "Celogen" and azodicarbonamide are generally preferred as blowing agents for cross-linked polyethylene foams.

Polyethylene foams, because of their outstanding electrical properties combined with excellent water resistance and toughness, are very suitable insulating materials for wire and cable applications, as well as for other uses.

Polypropylene Foams

Much the same techniques are employed in preparing cellular polypropylene as are required for expanded polyethylene foams. For foaming of polypropylene, blowing agents of higher decomposition temperatures are employed than are normally used for the expansion of polyethylene. Compounds which have been recommended for this use are 4,4′-oxybis(benzenesulfonyl semicarbazide), trihydrazino-sym. triazine, bis-(benzenesulfonyl hydrazide), and barium azodicarboxylate.

The blowing agent may also be masterbatched with a vehicle compatible with the base resin or it may be incorporated into a resin mixture having a lower fluxing temperature (e.g., a polypropylenepolyisobutylene blend) to enable more uniform dispersion. As would be expected, higher extrusion temperatures are necessary because of the higher softening temperature. In wire coating applications, special stabilization against aging and copper corrosion is required. Because of the good abrasion resistance, high service temperature, and potentially lower cost than polyethylene, cellular polypropylene materials are becoming increasingly important.

Polyvinyl Chloride Foams

Polyvinyl chloride foams may be prepared either in open- or closed-cell form; they may vary from very soft to rigid foams. Usually dispersiontype vinyl resins or low molecular weight, Type 1 resins are used for foaming. Copolymers of vinyl chloride with vinyl acetate (5%) are also often employed. Polyvinyl chloride homopolymers or vinyl acetate copolymers are rigid resins which require plasticizers to make them flexible. In the preparation of flexible polyvinyl chloride (PVC) foams a great variety of plasticizers may be used.

The selection of the plasticizer will depend upon the end use requirements of the vinyl foam. Major factors to consider are migration (volatility), toxicity, color, odor and cost. In many cases a combination of plasticizers will give the desired solvation characteristics.

Generally, the plasticizers are divided into monomeric and polymeric types. The former includes phthalate esters such as di-2-ethylhexyl, diisodecyl, butyl benzyl, etc; phosphate esters such as tricresyl, trioctyl, etc; benzoates such as dipropylene glycol dibenzoate; adipate esters, sebacate esters, etc. and are characterized by relatively low viscosity. Polymeric plasticizers are generally of the linear polyester type, and are used where resistance to migration and extraction are required. They usually are based on dibasic acids such as azelaic, adipic and sebacic acids. The glycols employed include propylene glycol, butylene glycol, neopentyl glycol and 2-ethyl-1,3-hexanediol. Pelargonic, myristic and coconut acids have been used as the monobasic acid chain stoppers. Because of the limited solvating power of this type of plasticizer, they are frequently used in combination with monomeric plasticizers. In addition, epoxy plasticizers such as epoxidized soya oil have been used extensively.

The plasticizers can be readily incorporated into the dispersion-type PVC resins by mixing in simple dough or paste mixers. If plasticizers are the sole liquid dispersion medium (no volatile solvents present), the dispersion is termed a "plastisol," while an "organosol" denotes a plastisol containing a volatile solvent.

Vinyl chloride polymers release hydrogen chloride on heating, resulting in double bonds and color formation in the resin. For this reason heat stabilizers are employed in PVC resins which act as scavengers for hydrogen chloride. The most common stabilizers are:

(1) Stabilizers based on lead.

(2) Stabilizers based on barium, cadmium, zinc and calcium. This group includes phosphites and epoxies as co-stabilizers.

(3) Stabilizers based on tin.

Lead stabilizers include white lead carbonate, dibasic lead phthalate, dibasic lead phosphite, and tribasic lead sulphate. Dibasic lead phosphite is a light stabilizer, and dibasic lead phthalate exhibits activity as a stabilizer "kicker" in PVC foams blown with azobisdicarbonamide.

Barium-cadmium soaps, usually stearates and laurates, are generally used with epoxy plasticizers and a phosphite chelator. Liquid complexes, which are based on barium-cadmium salts of phenols, and short chain fatty acids, are frequently used. They also usually contain organic phosphites.

Barium-cadmium zinc complexes used in combination with epoxy-chelator systems have also found widespread use. Other stabilizers include barium, zinc, and calcium-zinc salts.

The organotins are among the most effective stabilizers. These include compounds such as dibutyltin dilaurate, dibutyltin maleate, thiotin compounds, and octyltin compounds.

It should be pointed out that each type of stabilizer is specific with regard to the gelation characteristics of the plastisols, and has a considerable influence on the rate of gas evolution in the preparation of PVC foams using blowing agents.

The manufacture of PVC foams can be carried out by either mechanical or chemical blowing processes. The mechanical blowing processes involve dissolving an inert gas in a plastisol under pressure, and introducing the mixture onto a conveyor or into molds. The mechanical blowing processes produce primarily open-celled foams. In the Elastomer Corporation process, carbon dioxide gas is injected into the line feeding the plastisol from a pump to a mixer. The latter disperses the gas thoroughly throughout the plastisol under a pressure of 100 psi or more, and discharges the mixture onto a moving belt or into appropriate molds. The foam is then cured by oven heating, or the oven cure can be supplemented with radio frequency dielectric heating. The Elastomer Corporation process, and a similar process patented by Dennis Chemical Company, are used primarily for the manufacture of slab stock.

The Vanderbilt process employs air and a plastisol containing a foam stabilizer. This process is similar to the Dunlop process used in the manufacture of rubber latex foam.

Solvents such as methyl ethyl ketone, tetrahydrofuran, etc., have also been used in mechanical blowing processes. In these cases the solvent may be considered as fugitive plasticizers. However, high operating pressures are generally required and the solvent must be completely removed to avoid excessive latent shrinkage and to obtain satisfactory foam properties.

In the chemical blowing processes, foaming is achieved by the controlled decomposition of a specific blowing agent in a vinyl plastisol containing stabilizers and other additives, which may include surface active agents, lubricants, fillers and pigments. The blowing agents are either organic or inorganic materials which decompose under the influence of heat to generate at least one gaseous product. Organic blowing agents that release nitrogen dominate the field. The decomposition temperatures depend upon the chemical nature of the blowing agent. Catalysts may be used to reduce the decomposition temperature of the blowing agent; many of the conventional PVC stabilizers possess this property, and thus act in a dual capacity. Nitrosan (N,N'-dimethyl N,N'-dinitroso terephthalimide) has a decomposition temperature in vinyl resin of 100°F, below the gelation point (160–200°F) of a vinyl plastisol. This makes this blowing agent suitable for a process of atmospheric blowing of low density open-cell vinyl foam. Other important blowing agents are p,p'-oxybis(benzenesulfonyl hydrazide) ("Celogen," decomposition temperature in vinyl 310°F), which is extensively used in extrusion, azodicarbonamide or azobisformamide (ABFA), which is presently the most widely used foaming agent in the manufacture of expanded vinyl fabrics by both the plastisol coating and the calendering post-expansion techniques. It is also used in extrusion processes. Barium azodicarboxylate ("Expandex 177", decomposition temperature in vinyl 450°F) is used in rotocasting of vinyl foams.

A typical inorganic foaming agent is sodium borohydride which liberates hydrogen in the presence of water. This reaction is utilized to produce PVC foams at room temperatures or higher, which are then cured by heating to 340°F. Organic acids may be used to activate this reaction. The strength of the acid influences the foaming behavior. Thus, vinyl plastisol paste containing glycine foams rapidly only on heating, while acetic acid causes foaming at room temperature. The foam density is directly related to the type and amount of gas that is liberated by the decomposition of the foaming agent.

In certain plastisol formulations, particularly in the presence of monomeric plasticizers, surface active agents are included to lower the decomposition temperature of the blowing agent. These include compounds such as lauryl sulfate and neutral calcium petronate. Other compounds used to lower the decomposition temperature of the blowing agent are calcium oxide and dibasic lead phthalate.

For the production of low density PVC foams (both flexible and rigid), solvents may be added to enhance utilization of the blowing agent. Solvents which have been used include acetone, toluene, and various chlorinated solvents. However, the need for complete removal of the volatile solvents by a final heating process limits somewhat the commercial applicability of this method.

The chemical blowing processes encompass a variety of procedures. These include:
(1) Plastisol to open-celled foam.
(2) Plastisol to closed-celled foam.
(3) High density vinyl extrusion.
(4) Low density vinyl extrusion.

(5) Injection molded cellular vinyl.

(6) Calendered cellular vinyl.

(7) Rotational cast vinyl foam.

(1) *Plastisol to Open-celled Foam.* Chemically blown open-celled vinyl foam is made at atmospheric pressure. Less blowing agent is used than for the manufacture of closed celled foam, and polymeric plasticizers are used extensively. The mixture of the foam components is placed in a vented mold, and heated to the decomposition temperature of the blowing agent. Expansion and gelation take place followed by further heating to fuse the foam. Expansion of the foam can be carried out by a one-stage or two-stage process. In the latter the expansion and gelation are separated from the fusion step in order to control more effectively the heat transfer. The entire heating cycle may take from 10–60 min, depending upon the oven temperature, the nature of the plastisol, the dimensions of the foam, shape of mold, etc. Open-celled vinyl foam can also be produced by casting onto a moving conveyor belt. This procedure is also widely used for the manufacture of flexible vinyl foam-fabric laminates.

(2) *Plastisol to Closed-celled Foam.* In this process, the cold mixed formulation of resin, plasticizer, stabilizer and blowing agent is heated in a closed mold under a pressure of 4000–10,000 psi. After expansion and fusion are completed the mold is cooled to below 120°F, at which temperature the pressure is released and the partially expanded piece removed from the mold. It is then heated in a circulating air oven to complete expansion and annealing.

(3) *High Density Vinyl Extrusion.* High density cellular extruded vinyl foam ranges from about 40–75 lb/ft³. A small amount of blowing agent is introduced into the resin and the mixture is extruded at temperatures which allow decomposition of the blowing agent and fluxing of the mix. Blends of vinyl plastisol and butadiene-acrylonitrile rubber can also be used.

(4) *Low Density Vinyl Extrusion.* In this process about 3–5 parts of blowing agent to 100 parts of vinyl resin are used. Extrusion is accomplished below the decomposition temperature of the blowing agent, and the expansion is carried out by post heating the extruded material. The foam can be made almost entirely closed celled by extruding into a pressure chamber.

(5) *Injection Molded Cellular Vinyl.* High density cellular vinyl foam is produced by injection molding. The heating conditions are similar to those employed for injection molding of solid PVC. The mold closure time is a critical factor in this process, since too long a period will yield a solid product or only a slightly cellular material.

(6) *Calendered Cellular Vinyl.* All the foam components are milled together at a temperature below the decomposition point of the blowing agent. The fluxed material is sheeted off the mill and calendered on standard vinyl equipment (below the decomposition temperature of the blowing agent). The calendered sheet is then expanded by passing through an oven at temperatures above the decomposition point of the blowing agent. Calendered vinyl foam is generally closed celled. The calendered operation lends itself also to the lamination of vinyl foam to fabric or other materials.

(7) *Rotational Cast Vinyl Foam.* This process consists of rotating a fluid plastisol within a mold which is heated from the outside. A patent issued to Sun Rubber Company describes this process which is suitable for the preparation of flexible as well as semi rigid foams. Conventional plastisols and blowing agents are used. However, best results are achieved by utilizing blowing agents which are activated at relatively high temperatures (about 450°F). A typical example is "Expandex 177". (Barium azodicarboxylate, National Polychemical, Inc.) This type of blowing agent permits formation of a skin next to the mold prior to gas release of the blowing agent. This prevents gas pockets on the surface resulting in a smooth, even finish. Blow molding of vinyl foam has also been reported.

Cellulose Acetate Foams

Cellulose acetate foams are prepared by the flash volatilization of a pressured mass of molten cellulose acetate containing a mixture of acetone-ethyl alcohol. The solvent pair is not miscible with the polymer at room temperature, but is miscible above 160°F, and acts as a blowing agent as well as a plasticizer during the continuous extrusion process.

The uniformity of the cells is controlled by nucleating agents, finely dispersed inert materials, e.g., comminuted minerals, that are dispersed into the cellulose acetate dough. Since no chemical reactions are involved during the formation of cellulose acetate foams, the polymer must be sufficiently high in molecular weight to be self-supporting. To further improve the strength of these unicellular foams, fillers, such as chopped glass fibers, are incorporated into the formulation. Cellulose acetate foam has excellent strength properties as well as good low temperature properties, and is serviceable for extended periods at 350°F.

K. C. FRISCH
H. C. VOGT

FORMALDEHYDE

Formaldehyde is one of the most important of the raw materials for the plastics industry because it is used in a larger variety of plastics than any other single chemical. It is combined with phenol to make a variety of phenol-formaldehyde resins, with melamine in the various melamine-formaldehyde resins, with urea to produce UF resins, with ketones to make the ketone-aldehyde resins and, by itself, it is polymerized to the polyoxymethylene type plastics.

Most of the formaldehyde of commerce is sold as fluid water solutions containing from about 37% by weight of formaldehyde to approximately 52%. It is also available as solid paraformaldehyde which usually contains small amounts of water.

Manufacturing Processes

Formaldehyde is customarily manufactured from methanol, either by a dehydrogenation process over a silver catalyst in the presence of air, or by the newer method, which seems to be gaining in favor, of catalytic oxidation of methanol with air. While some formaldehyde is made commercially from hydrocarbons by catalytic partial oxidation processes, the simplicity of its manufacture from methanol causes this raw material to be the preferred source. A summary description of the major processes is as follows.

Silver Process. When methanol is passed over heated copper or silver, a dehydrogenation occurs, resulting in a mixture of hydrogen and formaldehyde. In commercial processes, enough air is usually mixed with the methanol to supply the heat necessary to maintain the reaction. This results in the formation of some water by burning the hydrogen. At the same time, formic acid and even carbon monoxide and additional water are formed as by-products.

Commercially, silver is the metal of choice and may be used in the form of gauze sheets, rolled gauze plugs or particles of silver. The burners may be as small as 2 in. or as large as 30 in. in diameter. The ratio of methanol to air fed to these burners depends on the heat losses and the throughput rate for the particular plant, but it usually falls in the range of 1 lb of methanol to 0.3–0.5 lb of oxygen. The ratio is often controlled by passing compressed air through a bath of methanol which is heated to a temperature such that the partial pressures of methanol vapor and air fall within the desired range.

Depending on the particular burner design, the temperature of reaction may be as low as 450°C to as high as 650°C. Many burners are operated at temperatures of about 550–600°C. It is desirable, once the formaldehyde has been formed at the high temperature, to cool it to below 350°C rapidly for prevention of further decomposition of the product to either formic acid or carbon monoxide and water. Cooling can be done by

radiation, by heat exchangers or by spraying the exit gases with water or formaldehyde.

Some manufacturers use steam or other inert gases along with the methanol and air, since, in their particular process, they have found that this gives them a better product. However, it should be pointed out that the exit gases from a silver plant contain, in addition to water and formaldehyde, nitrogen, oxygen, hydrogen, formic acid, carbon monoxide, small amounts of carbon dioxide and methyl formals, as well as unreacted methanol.

From the burner, the gases are passed through an absorption tower to wash out the desired formaldehyde, and the resultant liquid is then stripped of the excess methanol to produce the commercial grade formaldehyde solution.

Catalytic Oxidation. In this process, the air-methanol mixture is passed through a heated catalyst bed—the catalyst usually consists of oxides of metals, such as iron and molybdenum—and from catalyst bed through an absorber where the formaldehyde solution is concentrated. It is possible by the catalytic oxidation method to control the reaction so that very little methanol is present in the final product. However, there is a tendency towards a higher formic acid content, since iron oxide is an excellent catalyst for the continued oxidation of formaldehyde to formic acid and to carbon monoxide and to water. By controlling the conditions of manufacture, it is possible to achieve yields of 95–97% of theory by this process, whereas yields from the silver process are usually in the 87–92% range if the methanol is stripped and recycled.

Forms of Formaldehyde

Formaldehyde itself is a water soluble gas; however, in dilute aqueous solutions, it is hydrated to methylene glycol. As the solutions become more and more concentrated, the formaldehyde polymerizes to polyoxymethylene glycols. These materials are less soluble in water than formaldehyde itself and tend to precipitate from the solution, unless measures are taken to prevent it. Thus, data sheets specify a minimum recommended storage temperature for each grade. The presence of methanol in "inhibited" grades lowers the temperature at which precipitation occurs. In addition, most formaldehyde manufacturers now also supply "stabilized" grades which also can be stored at lower temperatures without precipitation, even though they contain very little methanol.

In addition to the foregoing "standard" grades, special grades are available from most manufacturers if the volume demand warrants the production.

SPECIFICATIONS FOR FORMALDEHYDE

Type	Uninhibited	Uninhibited	Inhibited	Inhibited	Inhibited
% by wt. HCHO min	37	44	37	37	44
% Methanol	1.0	1.0	6–7.5	12–15	5.5–6.5
Specific gravity 25°/25°C	1.110 – 1.114	1.137 – 1.133	1.080 – 1.100	1.070 – 1.085	1.118 – 1.119
Max % acidity as formic acid	0.02	0.02	0.02	0.02	0.02
Iron ppm max	0.5	0.5	0.5	0.5	0.5
Recommended storage temp., °F	80–100	120–140	70–90	60–80	110–115

Typical specifications for paraformaldehyde are as follows:

Type	Flake or Powder
% by w H_2CO min	91.0
Iron ppm % by wt., max	2.0
Max % acidity as formic acid	0.03
Max water, % by wt.	9.00

Formaldehyde is also available as solutions in some lower boiling alcohols. The formaldehyde content varies from 40–55%, depending on the alcohol, while the water content is between 8 and 12%.

For some purposes, concentrated formaldehyde solutions can also be obtained stabilized with urea. Such urea concentrates will contain as much as 60% formaldehyde by weight, 25% urea and only 15% of water, yet they are liquid under normal use conditions.

Another form in which formaldehyde is combined and used is as hexamethylenetetramine. Formaldehyde reacts with ammonia in the mole ratio of 3 : 2 to give the hexa compound, which is sold as a white solid chemical. At elevated temperatures and in the presence of a formaldehyde type of resin, the chemical releases its aldehyde and, at the same time, liberates the ammonia which acts as an alkaline catalyst for further polymerization or curing of the resin. It is widely used in the compounding of phenolic molding powder for this purpose.

Shipping and Storage

Formaldehyde solutions are shipped in bulk in stainless steel or specially lined tank cars or tank trucks which are usually insulated to permit maintenance of the proper temperatures, so that polymer precipitation does not occur. It is also available in specially lined steel drums. To prevent precipitation of the polymers, the proper minimum temperature for the particular grade must be maintained.

If precipitation does occur, the precipitate can usually be redissolved by agitation at an increased temperature. Unless this is done, the supernatant liquid is lower in strength than the prescribed grade designation would indicate and, of course, the solid precipitate is much higher in strength.

Bulk storage containers can be of stainless steel, aluminum or specially lined mild steel. Such tanks should be insulated and the proper temperature controlling devices installed to maintain the required storage temperatures.

Paraformaldehyde and hexamethylenetetramine, both solid materials, are normally shipped as dry chemicals in multi-wall paper bags or fiber drums. They should be stored in cool, dry areas which are well ventilated.

Safety Precautions

Formaldehyde gas forms explosive mixtures with dry air when the ratios are between 7–75% formaldehyde by volume. The closed-cup flash points of solutions change moderately with composition from a low of about 130°F when the higher amounts of methanol are present, to a high of 180°F when the 37% grade is uninhibited.

Since formaldehyde is a pungent, irritating chemical, the presence of which is readily detected before it reaches hazardous proportions, simple common sense precautions provide protection against the three main hazards attendant to its storage or handling: breathing of vapors, contact with skin and fire. Adequate ventilation, safety goggles, face shield, gas mask, ordinary care to prevent splashing and proper maintenance to preclude leaks in equipment are required.

Avoid direct contact with the skin. Use rubber gloves and protective cover gear if needed. Protective creams are helpful when applied correctly to exposed skin areas. Any spillage should be immediately flushed thoroughly with water.

H. L. WAMPNER

FUMARIC ACID AND ESTERS

Fumaric acid is a crystalline white powder, an organic dicarboxylic acid with the following schematic structure:

$$H-C-\overset{\overset{\displaystyle O}{\|}}{C}-OH$$
$$HO-\overset{\overset{\displaystyle}{}}{C}-C-H$$
$$\underset{O}{\|}$$

Fumaric acid is the *trans* isomer of maleic acid,

$$H-C-\overset{\overset{\displaystyle O}{\|}}{C}-OH$$
$$H-C-\overset{\displaystyle C}{}-OH$$
$$\underset{O}{\|}$$

which is normally supplied commercially in the form of its anhydride,

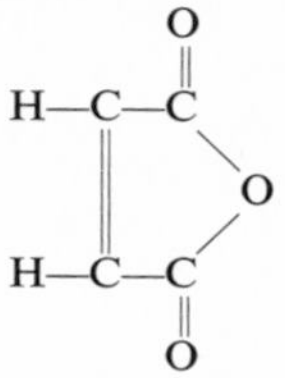

$$
\begin{array}{c}
\text{O} \\
\text{H—C—C} \\
\quad\quad\quad \text{O} \\
\text{H—C—C} \\
\text{O}
\end{array}
$$

Although the less important of the two isomers in terms of total volume consumption, fumaric acid (FA) is an important raw material and chemical intermediate in its own right. The largest single use of FA is in unsaturated polyesters, so widely used in fiber glass-reinforced plastics. It also finds important use in modifying alkyds, drying oils, and rosin esters (for coatings, inks, paper sizes), in PVA copolymers (in form of dibutyl fumarate), and as a food acidulent.

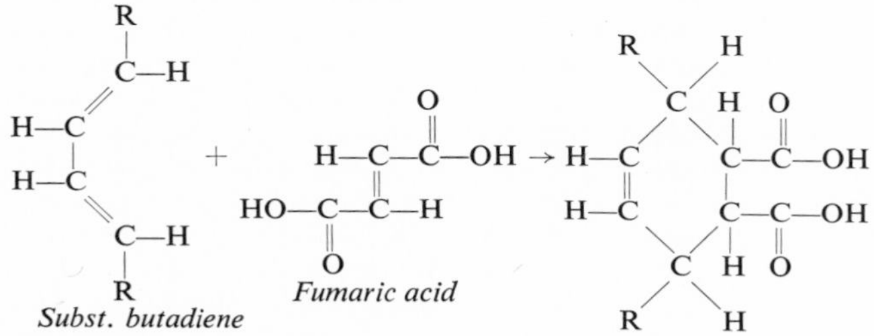

preparation of unsaturated polyesters, and with n-butanol in the preparation of dibutyl fumarate. (See Applications.) In both of these commercially important uses the double bond is also later utilized: In the polyester, by addition copolymerization with the vinyl monomer (e.g., styrene) during the resin "cure"; with dibutyl fumarate, by copolymerizing with vinyl acetate in the preparation of copolymers used widely in latex paints.

Addition reactions of both maleic anhydride and fumaric acid are described by L. H. Flett and W. H. Gardner in their book, "Maleic Anhydride Derivatives" (John Wiley & Sons, New York, 1952).

Fumaric acid will undergo the classical Diels-Alder addition to a conjugated unsaturated compound:

Subst. butadiene + Fumaric acid →

Physical Properties

Appearance	White crystalline powder
Odor	None
Empirical formula	$C_4H_4O_4$
Molecular weight	116.1
Melting point (sealed tube)	286–287°C
Boiling point (760 mm Hg)	290°C (sublimes)
Specific gravity (20°C/4°C)	1.635
Heat of combustion (kcal/mole)	320
Ionization constants (25°C)	$k_1 = 1 \times 10^{-3}$
	$k_2 = 3 \times 10^{-5}$

Solubilities (g/100 ml)	
Water at 25°C	0.7
at 100°C	9.8
Ethyl alcohol at 29.7°C	5.75
Ethyl ether at 25°C	0.72
Acetone at 29.7°C	1.72
Xylene at 29.7°C	0.027

Chemical Properties

Fumaric acid undergoes typical reactions of organic carboxylic acids, such as esterification, amidation, salt formation and acid chloride formation. It also contains a reactive double bond which can be copolymerized with other vinyl unsaturated compounds. Various chemical constituents can be added to fumaric acid at the double bond, providing considerable versatility for this material in chemical syntheses.

Fumaric acid is esterified with glycols in the

Other addition reactions include: hydrogenation to succinic acid; chlorination to dichlorosuccinic acid; hydrochlorination to chlorosuccinic acid; hydrolysis to malic acid (hydroxysuccinic acid); ammoniation to aspartic acid (aminosuccinic acid); amination to other alkylaminosuccinic acids.

Manufacture

Fumaric acid is usually prepared by isomerizing maleic acid or isomerizing a mixture of the two isomers while recovering the fumaric acid. Oxidation feedstock can therefore be benzene, orthoxylene (MA/FA by-product in making PA), or butenes. Oxidation catalysts are usually based on vanadium pentoxide (sometimes modified with Mo, K or P) on an inert carrier. Isomerization can be catalyzed by acid or certain sulfur compounds, or it may be thermally induced. Fumaric acid has also been produced commercially by fermentation of sugar (molasses). (See *Maleic Acid and Anhydride* for manufacturing details).

Applications

Unsaturated Polyesters. Like its isomer, maleic acid or anhydride, the greatest single use of fumaric acid is in unsaturated polyesters. These thermosetting polyesters are by far the largest volume class of resins used in reinforced plastics, and particularly fiberglass products. Polyester consumption has grown steadily in keeping pace with the growth in existing applications for fiber-glass-reinforced plastics (FRP), and the development of new applications. Unsaturated polyesters also have important non-fiber-reinforced uses, such as synthetic pearl shirt buttons, casting and impregnating resins, coatings, synthetic marble, and repair putties.

Maleic anhydride (MA) finds greater use in polyesters than fumaric acid because of its lower price. MA can also be handled in molten form, reacts more readily to the half-ester, and produces only half as much water as FA during complete esterification. However, MA is more toxic and irritating, with a tendency to sublime. Properties imparted to the resin are frequently somewhat different for the two isomers.

Much of the MA is isomerized to the fumaric (*trans*) structure during the course of normal preparation of the resin. The rate and degree of isomerization depends on the specific glycol or glycols used, the cooking temperature, the presence or absence of catalyst, etc.

Nevertheless, in certain resins prepared under controlled or even commercial conditions, significant differences are found. This is particularly true in more resilient or flexible resins where greater copolymerization reactivity, higher heat distortion temperature, and higher modulus and strengths are found in the fumaric version.

The preparation of a polyester based on fumaric acid (FA), phthalic anhydride (PA), and propylene glycol (PG), may be depicted as follows:

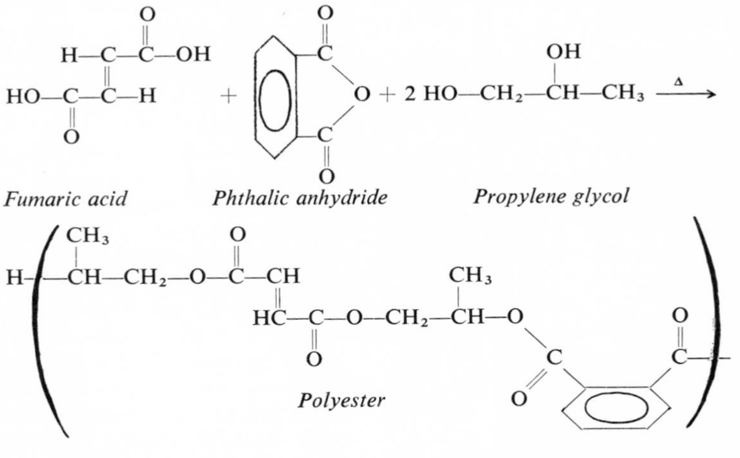

Polyvinyl Acetate Copolymer Emulsions

Dibutyl fumarate is the product of esterification of fumaric acid by *n*-butanol. This fumarate ester is copolymerized with vinyl acetate in the preparation of polyvinyl acetate (PVA) latex emulsions for water-based paints. These copolymers are softer and more flexible than straight vinyl acetate homopolymers and are thus more suitable for use as coatings. Furthermore, this internal plasticization is permanent.

Dibutyl maleate finds similar use in latex copolymers. However, the fumarate ester copolymerizes more readily with vinyl acetate, styrene, and vinyl chloride than the corresponding maleate.

In a comparison of dibutyl fumarate (DBF) and dibutyl maleate (DBM) in one-charge emulsion copolymerization with vinyl acetate, the same amount of the maleate ester was found to impart greater flexibilization. Also, continuous addition of ester comonomer and catalyst resulted in copolymers with greater elongation than when using the one-charge procedure. The faster rate of copolymerization of the fumarate ester with vinyl acetate was also demonstrated; this was stated as the primary reason for DBF is often preferred to DBM.

In a later study of the two isomeric esters in solution polymerization (by gradual addition) with vinyl acetate, the fumarate ester showed the greater plasticizing effect on the copolymer. It

Fumaric acid   *Phthalic anhydride*   *Propylene glycol*

Polyester

Such a hard to very viscous resin is prepared by thermal esterification. It is then partially cooled, stabilized, and diluted in a reactive vinyl monomer, most commonly styrene. At the time of use, organic peroxide initiation of the free radical copolymerization between styrene and fumaric unsaturation in the polyester backbone results in a highly cross-linked or three-dimensional "cured" product.

was also demonstrated in this work that a one-charge solution polymerization results in products with much lower flexibility than when adding the fumarate or maleate ester stepwise or continuously.

Alkyds. Either fumaric acid or maleic anhydride can be used in small quantities in alkyd formulations to increase the viscosity and provide a faster drying and generally lighter colored alkyd.

Typical would be a replacement of fumaric acid for 1–4% of the phthalic anhydride or isophthalic acid in the oil modified alkyd.

In this use the fumaric acid performs as a highly functional constituent because the carboxylic acid groups are esterified by polyols while the double bond adds to reactive double bonds present in the drying or semi-drying oil acids.

Drying Oils. The use of fumaric acid to upgrade drying oils and semi-drying oils is very similar to its use in alkyds. Up to 7 or 8% of fumaric acid, based on the weight of oil, is used in some cases. Processing time is decreased, viscosity is increased, and the color and speed of dry are improved. A small amount of polyol, such as pentacrythritol or glycerol, is often used to further increase molecular weight and viscosity and to control acid number. Drying oils upgraded with FA may be used in varnishes, inks, or paints.

Modified Rosin Esters. Rosin, which consists primarily of abietic acid and its isomers, can be heat-treated with fumaric acid. The fumaric adds through its double bond to isomerized rosin acids and thereby forms a tricarboxylic acid. This product is then esterified with polyols, such as glycerol or pentaerythritol, to form modified rosin esters, also referred to as modified ester gums. Molecular weights and melting points are higher. Hardness, color, and compatibility for nitrocellulose are improved.

Modified rosin esters are used in varnishes, lacquers and inks. Alkali salts of the fumaric acid-rosin adducts described above are also used in paper sizing.

Water-dispersible Vehicles. Drying oils and alkyds can be modified with fumaric acid to form a relatively high acid number vehicle which can be neutralized with either amine or alkali bases and either dissolved or dispersed in water. The Pan American Tung Research and Development League has developed and proposed water soluble vehicles of this type based on fumaric-modified tung oil.

Toxicity and Handling

Fumaric acid is essentially nontoxic. The F.D.A. has approved the use of fumaric acid and its calcium, magnesium, potassium, and sodium salts "in food at a level not in excess of the amount reasonably required to accomplish their intended effect."

Normal precautions for handling chemicals are usually sufficient. However, it should be kept in mind that fumaric acid can sublime into maleic anhydride at slightly elevated temperatures. Care should be taken in contacting fumaric acid or maleic anhydride with alkali and other bases. In addition to the normal exothermic reaction of neutralization, it has been found that alkali and certain alkaline compounds can initiate an auto-catalytic decomposition of maleic anhydride at elevated temperatures which can be of explosive proportions.

DONALD G. HUGGINS

FUNGICIDES

In the early part of World War II, it was found that plastics and plastic compositions exposed to service in the tropics were susceptible to attack by microorganisms to an extent so as to render the object useless or unsightly.

Programs were immediately set up by various military agencies to determine suitable antiseptic chemicals for incorporation in the various plastics to prevent both economic loss and military hazards caused by failure of equipment. It was not till about 1946, however, that significant reports appeared in the literature describing the work carried out by the government agencies as well as by industrial laboratories. Until fairly recently, work has centered about determination of fungus resistance of plastics and the development of compounds which would render the plastic resistant to fungal attack.

Because the chief component of the plastic is the polymer itself, studies were made of the fungal resistance of the pure resin (without plasticizer, or other components).

It was found that cellulose nitrate, polyvinyl acetate, melamine formaldehyde, and cellulose acetate were susceptible in varying degrees to fungal attack—by this it is meant that these resins could serve as a source of carbon for the growth of fungi.

Resins which do not support the growth of fungi include cellulose acetate butyrate, cellulose acetate and propionate, ethylcellulose, polyethylene, polymethyl methacrylate, polystyrene, polydichlorostyrene, nylon, polyvinyl butyral, polyvinyl chloride, urea formaldehyde, and phenol formaldehyde.

Despite the fact that a considerable number of pure plastics will not act as carbon sources for microorganisms, they will, nevertheless, not prevent the growth of fungi on their surfaces. The metabolic products of fungal growth can cause deterioration of the surface, and possible impairment of function, or the fungi can cause disfiguration.

Most resins are rarely used without considerable amounts of additives such as plasticizers, stabilizers, lubricants, fillers, etc., and their resistance to microbial attack, therefore, becomes no greater than the resistance of any of the components of the plastic composition.

Fungi have the ability to metabolize esters; in 1955, Reese, Cravetz and Mandels reported that

95% of 358 cultures grew on coconut oil, 90% of 309 cultures metabolized methyl acetyl ricinoleate, and 60% of 82 cultures grew on dihexyl sebacate. Brown (1945) summarized the work of a number of laboratories, which demonstrated that more than half of 144 plasticizers tested could serve as fungal nutrients.

In general, extremely susceptible plasticizers comprise all derivatives of lauric, oleic, ricinoleic, and stearic acids.

Resistant plasticizers include: esters of short chain aliphatic dicarboxylic acids, as succinic and adipic acids; esters of tricarboxylic acids, as citric, aconitic, tricarballylic; phthalic and phosphoric acid esters, derivatives of toluene sulfonic acid, and aromatic hydrocarbons.

The necessity of preventing the decay of the plastic composition or the disfigurement of the surface led to the testing of a wide variety of microbicides.

Microbicides for plastics must meet many requirements, including resistance to leaching, low volatility, negligible effect on appearance and on physical and electrical properties, low toxicity, durability, and ease of incorporation. Most important, however, is the compatibility with the plastic and plastic composition, which includes plasticizers, stabilizers, ultraviolet absorbers, and fillers.

The complete list of microbicides which have been recommended or used at one time or another for plastic compositions would undoubtedly number thousands, but it is indicative of the severity of the requirements for a successful product that there are probably less than a dozen compounds which are being used commercially with varying degrees of efficiency.

One of the first microbicides to be successfully utilized was salicylanilide, $C_6H_4(OH)CONHC_6H_5$.

The product, result of the condensation of salicylic acid and aniline, was found to be effective in phenolic and in melamine resins at levels of 2%. Chlorinated and brominated salicylanilides do not seem to be any more effective in plastics than the parent compound.

Phenyl mercury acetate, $C_6H_5Hg(CH_3COO)$, has proven to be a very potent microbicide, and functions at low levels, such as .01–0.5% by weight of the plastic. It is a toxic material, and one which cannot withstand prolonged heating cycles in excess of 300°F without serious decomposition. It is, therefore, somewhat limited in use. Other phenyl mercury compounds, such as phenyl mercury salicylate, phenylmercury borate, PM oleate, and di(phenyl-mercury)dodecenyl succinate behave similarly.

Zinc dimethyldithiocarbamate, $Zn[(CH_3)_2NCSS]_2$ has proven effective in polyvinyl chloride-acetate copolymers, but cannot be used in straight polyvinyl chloride plastics because of the harmful effects of zinc on the durability of the material. Sulfur compounds are also of limited utility in polyvinyl chloride because of the reaction of sulfur with the metallic soaps used as stabilizers.

Copper 8-quinolinolate is a very active fungicide, but its color, a dark green, has a high tinting strength, and it is difficult to render the product soluble in polyvinyl chloride or other plastics without eventual spewing or discoloration.

Dodecyldimethylbenzyl ammonium napthenate is an oil soluble compound that has been used successfully in various plastic compositions. 2,2'-thiobis (4,6-dichlorophenol), used at a level of 4%, is claimed to render polyethylene bacteriostatic (US Patent 2919200).

Chloronitrobenzoic acid esters are also suggested as fungicides (US Patent 284115221).

Chlorinated phenols, such as tetrachlorphenol, pentachlorphenol, parachlormetacresol, and metallic salts, such as zinc pentachlorphenate, have been suggested for use in plastics.

Dihydroxydichlorodiphenylmethane and tetrabromo-o-cresol have been used in phenolic resins, but have not yielded fungistatic surfaces.

Tributyltin oxide, triphenyltin chloride, and various fatty acid soaps of these compounds have been used as microbicides in plastics, but have proven more useful in anti-fouling compositions.

N-(trichloromethylthio)phthalimide has been used as a fungicide in plastics, but the active sulphur and chlorine groups tend to limit its usefulness because they may react with metal soaps used as stabilizers. It has also been found in certain instances, microbicides of this type cause the plastic to turn yellow or brown on exposure to ultraviolet light.

There seems to be no rule to predict the efficiency of a microbicide in various plastics. A compound that works well in polyvinyl chloride may be totally useless in polyethylene, or even in another polyvinyl chloride resin. In general, one can only postulate that certain microbicides have better chances of functioning in plastics than other compounds, and it is necessary to test each proposed composition to insure that the results are as desired. Changes in average molecular weight or distribution of molecular weight of the polymer, modification of the plasticizer, stabilizer, or method of processing—any of these could have a profound effect on the activity of a microbicide.

Numerous attempts have been made to render plastics immune to microbial attack by the chemical reaction of the polymer with groups or with compounds of known microbicidal activity. For example, phenolic polymers have been mercurated by reaction with mercuric acetate so as to form carbon-mercury bonds as in phenylmercury compounds. The resultant compositions have proven far less effective, on the basis of percent mercury contained, than a similar polymer into which is incorporated phenyl mercury acetate.

MILTON NOWAK

FURFURAL AND DERIVATIVES

Furfural was launched as an industrial chemical in 1922, and during that same year it was used in the production of phenolic resins. Since that time it has played an increasingly important role in the plastics industry.

Oat hulls, corn cobs, and other agricultural waste products are sources of furfural, which is formed by the acid hydrolysis of these raw materials.

The important chemical reactions of furfural in terms of its use in the plastics industry are outlined below:

Resins from furfuryl alcohol are characterized by: (1) the ability to cure under a wide variety of conditions, (2) availability over a broad viscosity range as high solids content resins without the need for nonreactive solvents or diluents, (3) resistance to attack by solvents, nonoxidizing acids, and alkali, and (4) a high carbon to hydrogen ratio, responsible for high carbon yields on pyrolysis.

The following examples illustrate how these properties are utilized in the plastics industry.

Corrosion-resistant mortars based on furfuryl alcohol resins are prepared by adding the resin to an acid-treated inert filler such as coke flour or silica. The acid level is controlled to allow a troweling time from 15–30 min, and a setting time from 36–48 hr.

The following list of chemicals to which

Furfural phenolic resins

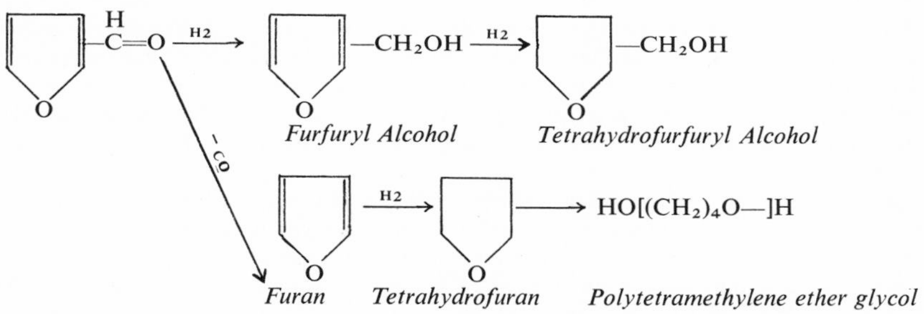

Furfuryl Alcohol   *Tetrahydrofurfuryl Alcohol*

Furan   *Tetrahydrofuran*   *Polytetramethylene ether glycol*

Although many significant uses of furfural in the plastics industry depend on its ready conversion to other resin formers and solvents, it is an important resin intermediate in its own right. Thus, the long flow contributed by furfural to phenolic molding compounds, which was first utilized in 1922, is still a useful property. Also, as a reactive solvent for phenolic resins, furfural is an important ingredient in resinoid grinding wheels and coated abrasive products.

Catalytic hydrogenation of furfural results in the formation of furfuryl alcohol, a much more versatile resin former than its precursor. In the presence of acid catalysts, furfuryl alcohol readily undergoes resinification. This reaction is highly exothermic, and requires close control of catalyst concentration and temperature. The reaction can be stopped at the desired viscosity simply by neutralizing the catalyst. The resins can be stored for prolonged periods at this stage, without significant change, but are converted to high yield thermoset solids when reactivated with an acidic catalyst. Formaldehyde or furfural is often used in making these resins to modify their curing characteristics.

furfuryl alcohol based mortars were exposed at 150°F without adverse effect provides good reason as to why such mortars are so widely used in brick lined reactors, tanks and industrial floors.

40% sodium hydroxide	Chlorinated solvents
35% hydrochloric acid	Alcohols
25% sulfuric acid	Esters
60% phosphoric acid	Ketones
Hydrofluoric acid	Mineral oils
50% acetic acid	Vegetable oils
Aliphatic hydrocarbons	Alkalies
Aromatic hydrocarbons	Food acids
	Soap and cleansers

This same chemical resistance is responsible for the use of reinforced furfuryl alcohol resins in cast molded equipment such as pipes, tanks and reaction vessels.

Furfuryl alcohol resins are also used in the production of foundry binders. When used in the no-bake process for making cores, the general practice is to first mix a catalyst, such as phosphoric acid with the sand, and then add about 2% furfuryl alcohol resin, based on sand weight. The entire mixing procedure is generally accomplished in less than 5 min. If the catalyst has been adjusted to allow for a working life of about 30 min, the core can generally be drawn from the box in about 90 min. Castings produced from such cores can be made to close dimensional tolerance and with a very low scrap rate. The no-bake process has been adapted successfully to production of steel, grey iron and nodular iron castings.

A striking example of the adaptability of furfuryl alcohol resins to a variety of curing conditions lies in comparing the above process to the use of these resins in the so-called hot box process for core production. This process calls for essentially the same amount of resin, and the mixing procedure is not significantly different than that for the no-bake process. However, the catalyst employed provides a working life for the mix of about 8 hr at room temperature, and yet the resin cures in a matter of seconds at temperatures in the 350–400°F range. Actually, the required residence time in the heated box will to a large extent depend upon the thickness and the shape of the core to be made; however, tensile strengths in excess of 500 psi can be achieved in 30 sec or less on 1–in. tensile specimens. At the time the core is removed from the box, only the outer shell is cured, but as the core cools to room temperature, the curing process continues and the soft center hardens to full strength.

Carbon and graphite products which utilize furfuryl alcohol resin binders offer the unique advantage of high bulk density and a minimum decrease in bulk density on baking when compared to other synthetic binders and coal tar pitch. Also, the relatively low electrical resistivity of such products is a significant advantage. These properties explain why furfuryl alcohol resin binders are used in relatively high cost specialty carbon and graphite products. However, these binders offer substantial process economies which extend their application beyond the realm of specialty products.

It is also possible to formulate binder systems using furfural and furfuryl alcohol monomers as reactive plasticizers for high melting pitch. This approach offers a means of utilizing the performance advantage of a high melting pitch binder and yet maintaining the relatively low processing temperatures normally used with tars. Generally, furfural and furfuryl alcohol are used in equal parts, but the optimum ratio depends upon the specific grade of pitch involved. The amount of pitch in the binder can also be varied, depending on the properties required.

Furfuryl alcohol's contribution to the plastics industry is not limited to its function as a resin former. When it is added to other resin compositions, such as phenolics, epoxies and ureas, it has the effect of substantially upgrading their properties.

Of greatest commercial significance are the properties contributed to urea formaldehyde resins. Some of these advantages, cited below, are:

(1) Longer working life without sacrifice in curing speed can be achieved with as little as 10% furfuryl alcohol.

(2) Higher solids content resins are possible with furfuryl alcohol.

(3) Improved toughness and craze resistance also result from the addition of furfuryl alcohol to urea resins. This probably results from the fact that, unlike butylated ureas which split out butanol during cure, furfuryl alcohol remains as part of the cured resin solids.

Other properties of furfuryl alcohol modified urea resins which are particularly useful in production of foundry cores are:

(1) Resistance to over-cure which permits maximum curing speed without degrading the resin through over-cure under production conditions.

(2) Reduced rate and amount of gas evolution at metal pouring temperatures, and

(3) Increased compressive strength at 2500°F which is a function of furfuryl alcohol content.

In general, resins containing 25% furfuryl alcohol are used on nonferrous castings such as aluminum and brass, whereas the greater hot strength required for grey iron castings necessitates the use of resins containing at least 35% furfuryl alcohol.

The craze resistance imparted to urea formaldehyde resins by furfuryl alcohol is utilized primarily in gap-filling wood adhesives. Such adhesives also have improved dimensional stability.

As a modifier for acid-cured epoxy resins, furfuryl alcohol offers the advantage of reduced viscosity and higher flexural strength. Also, as a solvent for hygroscopic Lewis acid complexes, such as boron trifluoride monoethyl amine, furfuryl alcohol offers a convenient method for introducing the catalyst into the resin.

The addition of furfuryl alcohol to phenolic resins results in vastly improved alkali resistance without adverse effect on the acid resistance normally associated with phenolics.

Tetrahydrofurfuryl alcohol is another hydrogenation product of furfural. Its utility in the plastics industry is twofold in that it is an excellent resin solvent and a useful plasticizer intermediate.

The conversion of furfural to tetrahydrofuran is of particular significance to the plastics industry because of the unique solvent action of this chemical on polyvinyl chloride, polyvinylidene chloride and polyurethane resins.

Polymerization of tetrahydrofuran results in the formation of polytetramethylene ether glycol, a useful intermediate in the preparation of polyurethane resins of superior hydrolytic stability, used in millable gums, liquid casting systems, thermoplastics and elastic fibers.

As a by-product of furfural production, a material consisting primarily of modified cellulose, lignin and resins is obtained. When processed further, this material is an excellent extender for phenolic glues, both for exterior and interior grade plywood.

ROBERT W. REARDON

G

GLASS FIBER MATS

There are two major types of glass fiber reinforcing mats available to reinforced plastics processors and to the plastics industry in general. These carry the designation "high solubility type" and "low solubility type". The designation "solubility" refers to the behavior of the mat in monomeric styrene, the reactive diluent for the major portion of polyester resins used today. "High solubility" refers to rapid or fast dissolution of the mat binder in the styrene-rich polyesters, and "low solubility" refers to slowness of or resistance to solution in styrene.

Hence, high-solubility mats find utilization in processes for fabricating hand lay-up structures, tooling, and corrugated architectural paneling, where rapid wet-out and impregnation of the mat by the resin are highly desirable. On the other hand, low solubility mats are used in pressure molding, where freedom from rapid solubility of the mat binder is necessary for prevention of "washing" or movement of the reinforcing fibers during molding.

Several parameters are common to each type of mat, i.e., fiber length and proportion, ignition loss (or binder content), weight per sq ft (mat uniformity), and tensile strength. These will be explained in greater detail as this discussion proceeds.

Two major documents provide specifications for selection and use of Chopped Strand Mats. These are ASTM D-1529 and MIL-M-43248. A third type, designated as "mechanically-bonded" mats, are also widely employed in the industry.

Manufacture

Chopped strand mats are fabricated by a three-step process that involves mat formation, binder deposition and curing, and roll up and packaging.

Glass strands are sheared off or broken using any of several types of high speed, continuous cutters. Some filamentation of the cut fiber ends is desirable to provide frictional contact which permits development of mat integrity and tensile strength, and also which allows the mat binder to be held and properly distributed. In fact, a type of fiber designated as "split filament" is used in both types of mats to provide a multi-fine strand which improves drapability and provides a minimum of surface fiber pattern in molded parts.

Binder types used are those which chemically provide the necessary compatibility with a resistance to solution by styrene as required by high and low solubility mats, respectively. For certain types of high solubility mat and most types of low solubility mat, a secondary surface binder treatment is desirable to prevent washing of the fibers during molding.

Uniform cure of mat binders is accomplished by both application of heat and circulation of the heated ambient air through the porous mat structure. Compaction of the mat after curing and prior to rollup is desirable to "set" the binder and provide maximum integrity for best surface properties and highest tensile strength.

Mechanically bonded mats are manufactured using a "needle-punching" process. No resinous binder is added.

The most important quality of chopped strand mat products, uniformity of fiber distribution, is established in this manufacturing stage. The importance of having each unit area of mat weigh the same as all other unit areas is obvious. Also, logically desirable are freedom from holes, clumped fibers, soft spots, hard spots, and discolored fibers and dirt.

Performance

Because of the difference in end use application, performance of the two types of mats are discussed individually:

High Solubility Type. Generally, the most desirable functional properties of chopped strand mats for hand or wet lay-up applications are:

(1) *Handleability and Drapability*. The mat must have sufficient tensile strength to resist tearing when being unrolled or cut to pattern size. Yet it must not be so stiff or "boardy" that it will not drape well into compound curvatures of the lay-up work. Mats with the softest hand or drape (generally, with lowest binder content) are more suitable for open lay-up work into curved shapes, while the materials with the additional surface

binder treatment are better adapted to flat lay-up such as for corrugated or flat architectural paneling.

(2) *Rate and Character of Wet Out.* Desirable qualities for chopped strand mat as regards making the actual combination with resin are: fast wet out with a minimum amount of resin picked up, and a minimum of entrained air voids.

Many tools and devices are available for spreading resin into mat which is in place on a mold. These include paint brushes and rollers of many different configurations, but all serrated to permit bubbles to rise to the surface during rolling.

A resin-spread test is available to evaluate wet out and select proper type of mat for a given application. This test can be done easily using a piece of mat approximately 18 in. sq, and a weighed amount of polyester resin to provide the glass-to-resin ratio normally used. Pour the resin in a spiral pattern from the center of the mat. Roll out in the normal manner. Compare the area wet-out for each type mat.

Usually, great care is required in wet-layup work to prevent movement of the fibers during initial wet out and subsequent working. Selection of the proper type mat will aid in avoiding this defect. Also, employment of auxiliary types of reinforcement such as cloth or woven roving is sometimes desirable.

(3) *Surface Properties.* The actual exposed surface of hand or wet layup structures constitutes a gel coat, or a smooth smooth surface defined by an appropriate container film. The exposed laminate surface after cure may contain sharp, protruding fibers. These may be removed by sanding, and the laminate surface protected by painting. However, the type mat selected should be the one which provided minimal laminate surface problems.

Low Solubility Mat. As with the high solubility mat, handleability, wet-out and surface problems are salient features and may be given the following consideration:

(1) *Handleability.* Mechanical dry tensile strength is equally important for low solubility mat, but the most important factor is the degree of drapability during molding. Flat mat is normally limited in the amount of compound curvature it will drape to without wrinkling. The requirements for a boardy finish (high binder content) to prevent washing have made drapability of chopped strand mats a problem, and have hastened the development of chopped strand mats with mixed lengths greater than 2 in. (up to 15 in.) and also continuous-strand swirl mats, which provide good drapability in matched die molding.

(2) *Wet-Out.* Wet-out in low solubility mats used for matched die molding is pretty well accomplished automatically due to the fact that the filled polyester molding resin becomes water-like in consistency and readily spreads to all parts of the glass reinforcement during molding.

Establishment of the optimum pour-pattern is of paramount importance in preventing dry spots and resin rich areas. The requirement of good uniformity of glass and binder distribution in mat construction is also obvious in this consideration, since diversion from standard on either of these requirements could result in poorly molded parts, or non-reinforced patches of cured resin.

(3) *Surface.* Polyester resin upon curing exhibits a thermal contraction which is dimensionally approximately ten times greater than that of the fiber glass. Hence, even though the filler material alleviates this condition to a degree, the molding resin shrinks around the fibers upon cooling and forces them to protrude out of the surface of the molded part. Split strand mats, use of surface veil, preimpregnation of glass fiber mats, surface-levelling primers and many other techniques have been devised. However, persisting need for surface conditioning, requiring sanding and filling after molding, remains the major deterrent to use of glass reinforced plastics in many additional areas.

J. GILBERT MOHR

GLASS FIBERS, MILLED

Milled fibers are short lengths of glass fiber. Occasionally these fibers will be $\frac{1}{4}$–$\frac{1}{2}$ in. in length, but commonly they are anywhere from $\frac{1}{16}$ in.–$\frac{1}{32}$ in. in length. They are manufactured from glass strands of any diameter. It is the short length of these fibers, and the fact that they are normally monofilaments that differentiates them from chopped fibers.

Milled fibers are manufactured by hammer-milling glass fibers from a variety of sources. Some manufacturers actually draw glass specifically for the manufacture of milled fibers, but the most common practice is to consider milled fibers a by-product, and make them out of short roving packages, edge trim from mat operations, or from other forms of manufacturing scrap.

The size designation, given in fractions of an inch, actually refers to the size of the openings in the hammermill screen. Fiber lengths for any screen size will range up to the screen size, with usually some fibers slightly longer.

In appearance, milled fibers are a light grey in color. The small fibers ($\frac{1}{32}$ in.) agglomerate into small pills or balls when packaged, while the longer fibers ($\frac{1}{4}$ in.) tend to remain more or less as discrete fibers.

The nodules of milled fiber of short length handle much like a coarse powder, and are pourable and can be handled with scoops and shovels. The longer strands are fluffier and are a bit more difficult to handle. (Pulverized fibers form an almost free-flowing powder, which offers no resistance to pouring or mixing.)

Milled fibers are available with virtually any binder, size, or finish desired. Cationic binders are the most common binders, but fibers are available with polyester, acrylic, urea, and starch binders, as well as with no binder at all.

Any of the sizes used in the industry can be applied to fiber prior to the milling operation, so milled fibers can, therefore, be obtained with any size desired.

Silane coupling agents and chrome complexes are also applied to milled fibers. Special silanes are used when the end use for the fiber is to be in polyester resins, and cationic sizings or heat cleaned fiber is used for maximum compatibility with epoxy resins.

Product specifications for milled fibers vary from manufacturer to manufacturer, but normally specifications will include ignition loss, binder type (if any), moisture content, and fiber diameter and length specifications.

Length measurements are most frequently made by optical methods, as it is practically impossible to run a dry seive analysis on milled fibers. The ignition loss and moisture checks are run using conventional techniques. For total loss on ignition, the fibers are ignited in a muffle oven at about 600°C for 20 min. A temperature of 100°C is usually sufficient for measurements of moisture content.

Milled fibers are packaged in cartons containing from 20–50 lb of fibers per carton. Fiber drums are also available.

The majority of milled fibers are used in casting and plotting compounds, although a large amount is used in plastics adhesives and in the preparation of a sealant for clay and concrete pipes.

In casting and potting compounds, milled fibers are used to increase the impact resistance of the casting, increase the heat distortion point of the casting, minimize the tendency of the resin to develop stress cracks, impart dimensional stability to the casting and to reduce the tendency of some thermoplastics to cold flow.

Glass is usually used in conjunction with mineral fillers in casting and potting compounds, because of the economies associated with mineral fillers; however, when practical, a system filled only with milled fibers is preferred because of the superior qualities of such a system. The chemical inertness of glass is an advantage in that milled fibers have no effect upon the curing characteristics of the resin, and glass filled parts are much more resistant to moisture absorption than are clay or carbonate-filled parts. Milled fiber castings

also show improved electrical properties, particularly when the fibers are dried before mixing.

Short length milled fibers($\frac{1}{32}$–$\frac{3}{32}$ in.) are used in potting and casting processes. The glass is mixed throughly into the resin (with other filler, if used) using a ribbon mixer or ball mill. For small charges or one-shot applications a small batch can be mixed by hand. The promoter is added to the resin at this point, and the catalyst at the time of use. Standard catalyst systems are used.

Because of the tendency of polyesters to form cracks and craze marks when cast, low-shrink resins are usually chosen for this type of application. Typically casting and potting compounds use polyesters of low exotherm and low viscosity. Flexible or resilient resins are also commonly used because of their inherent resistante to crazing.

Milled fibers increase the viscosity of resins much more than conventional fillers, and the longer the fiber length, the more rapid the viscosity build-up. For this reason, casting resins which are to contain more than 10–12% milled fibers should be formulated with resins of the lowest practical initial viscosity.

Milled fibers also find application in epoxy casting and encapsulating resins, in automotive body putties, and as an ingredient in putties used in the preparation of tools.

The addition of small amounts of milled fibers in resinous adhesives upgrades the adhesive and improves the strengths of the bond obtained. Specifically, the breaking strength is increased by the action of the fibers in spreading the stresses, and by decreasing the coefficient of expansion of the resin.

Milled fibers, incorporated into mat or cloth laminates of otherwise conventional construction, increase tensile and flexural strengths, until about 4% milled fibers are added. The fibers in this case are added to the resin, and act to increase the interlaminar bond between plies of the reinforcement.

Milled fibers are available from most manufacturers of glass fibers. The total market appears to be somewhere between $\frac{1}{2}$–1 million dollars of fibers per year. At the present time (1967) milled fibers sell for about 30–35¢ per lb.

GEORGE J. HEH

GLASS REINFORCEMENTS

Properties of Glass

Fibrous glass filaments used as reinforcements are formed from a lime-aluminum-borosilicate glass usually referred to as "E" glass. This glass has good electrical characteristics and is quite durable. "C" glass, or low-soda glass, is usually used for overlay and surfacing mats. It has good durability and is resistant to most strong acids.

"S" glass is a new type of glass which produces a higher modulus and tensile strength at elevated temperatures. This glass has a tensile strength of 665,000 psi, and a modulus of elasticity of 12.4×10^6 psi.

Fibrous glass filaments have many physical and chemical properties identical to those of bulk glass, such as low specific gravity, high electrical resistance, no flammability, and a high degree of chemical inertness. Tensile strength of fibrous glass is about 500,000 psi and, after handling and processing a strength of about 200,000 psi is realized. Fibrous glass has a modulus of elasticity quite similar to that of bulk glass— 10,500,000 psi. Fibrous "E" glass filaments have unusual elastic properties. They will stretch about $3\frac{1}{2}\%$ before breaking, and there is no measurable difference between their yield and ultimate strength.

Surface Treatment

Surface treatment specifications vary with performance requirements. A few industry terms are useful in understanding this point:

A size is a chemical surface treatment applied immediately after fibers are formed. It protects the strand and couples the strand to the plastic which is being reinforced.

A finish is a chemical coupling agent applied to fabric after it is woven and cleaned to make fabric compatible with molding resins.

A binder is a bonding resin to hold glass fiber strands together in a mat or preform during manufacture of the molded object.

Forms of Glass

Fibrous glass reinforcements are supplied in several basic forms. These forms allow for flexibility in cost, strength, and choice of process. Many variations of the basic forms have been developed over the years to meet performance and economic needs which vary over a wide range.

Most fibers are made by mechanically drawing a filament from a stream of molten glass. During the early stages of processing, a chemical treatment is applied to the surface of the glass fiber.

A number of fibers, or filaments, are formed simultaneously. These "filaments" are collected into a bundle known as a "strand" at a gathering device where the chemical surface treatment is usually applied. Below the gathering device, the strand is wound into a forming package. The forming package is a delicate intermediary product from which shippable forms of fibrous glass are produced as continuous strand, yarn, roving, chopped strands, fabric, reinforcing mat, surfacing mat, and woven roving.

Reinforcements

Fibrous glass manufacturers have developed reinforcements to suit a wide variety of processes and end uses, among which are the following.

Continuous Strand. This is supplied in the form of yarn and roving. Yarn is supplied as twisted single-end strand on tubes. Roving is supplied as untwisted multi-strands, wound together on a spool. It is also made in the form of "spun roving" by looping a continuous single strand many times upon itself and holding it together with a slight twist. Continuous rovings are used in high strength parts. Laminates of glass contents as high as 80% are possible.

Fabrics are woven from yarns of various twists and ply constructions into a wide range of types, weights and widths. Fabrics are selected by a number of factors, but primarily thickness and weight. Weights vary from $2\frac{1}{2}$–40 oz a sq yard. Thickness of fabrics varies from .003 in.–.045 in. These same yarns are also fabricated into non-woven fabrics similar to cloth. Both materials come close to duplicating strength properties achieved in the use of continuous parallel strands. Maximum glass content in a laminate is from 65–75% by weight.

TABLE 1. FORMS OF FIBROUS GLASS.

Glass form	Maximum glass content in FRP part, % of Wt.	Relative materials cost
Continuous roving	80	Low
Yarn	80	High
Spun roving	50	Low
Fabric (181 series)	75	High
Fabric (unidirectional)	75	High
Fabric (1000 series)	65	High
Woven roving	60	Medium
Woven spun roving	55	Medium
Double layer mat-chopped strand mat and woven roving	50	Medium
Continuous strand mat	50	Medium
Chopped strand mat	50	Medium
Mechanically needled mat	50	Medium
Chopped strands	50	Low
Chopped spun roving	50	Low
Surfacing and overlay mat	20	High
Milled fibers	15	Medium

Continuous or Spun Rovings. These are woven into coarse, heavy drapeable fabrics called "woven roving". They give high strengths to a part and are lower in cost than conventional facrics. The weight of woven roving varies from 15–27 oz a sq yard. Thickness varies from 0.035–0.048 in. Woven roving is used mainly in the manufacture of large structural objects such as boats and swimming pools, and to make plastics tooling for the metal stamping industry.

Chopped strand is normally supplied in $\frac{1}{4}$ $\frac{1}{2}$, 1 or 2 in. lengths. Spun roving is normally cut into $\frac{1}{4}$–$\frac{1}{2}$ in. lengths, although it is also used in 1 in. lengths. Milled fibers are *hammer-milled* into $\frac{1}{32}$–$\frac{1}{8}$ in. lengths and used for applications where less than the highest strengths are called for. Strands of 1–2 in. from either continuous or spun roving, are used to fabricate large medium strength parts of uniform cross section. Low to moderate strength parts, which require complex cross sectional walls, utilize chopped fibers of $\frac{1}{4}$ and $\frac{1}{2}$ in.

Reinforcing Mats. These are made of either chopped strands or continuous strands laid down in a swirl pattern. Strands are held together by adhesive resinous binders, or mechanically bound by "needling". Lower in cost than woven materials, mats are slightly more expensive than bulk chopped strands or roving. Chopped and continuous strand mats are available in weights from $\frac{3}{4}$–3 oz a sq ft. Mechanically bonded or needled mat weights are available from 2–10 oz a sq ft. Reinforcing mats are used for medium parts with uniform cross section.

Surfacing mat is often used (with other reinforcements) for appearance and weathering. It covers irregularities by drawing a slight excess of resin to the surface next to the mold. This resin-richness compensates for resin shrinkage and forms a smoother surface. The reinforcing value of a surfacing mat is lower than other forms because the glass filaments in this mat are not designed for strength.

Processes

The preparation and curing of glass-resin laminates may be accomplished by a number of different processes. Selection of the most economical method of production will depend on end use, resin, volume of production, and dimensional accuracy required.

Preforming. Preforming processes have been developed to more satisfactorily mold large, complex shapes. The preforming approach places the fibrous glass reinforcement in position, shaped closely to the contours of the final molded part. The resin is then combined with the preform prior to molding. Preforming is a unique process and helps assure a uniform distribution of reinforcement in very large, complex shaped parts.

Roving is cut into 1–2 in. lengths of chopped strand which are blown through a flexible hose onto a rotating preform screen. Suction holds them in place while a binder is sprayed on the preform and the preform cured in an oven. The operator controls both deposition of chopped strands and binder.

Chopped strands may be preimpregnated with pigmented polyester resin and blended with cellulosic fiber in a water slurry. Water is exhausted through a contoured, perforated screen, and glass fibers and cellulosic materials are deposited on the surface. The wet preform is transferred to an oven where hot air is sucked through the preform. When dry, the preform is sufficiently strong to be handled and molded.

Filament Winding. Filament winding uses continuous reinforcements to achieve efficient utilization of glass fiber strength. Roving or single strands are fed from a creel through a bath of resin and wound on suitably designed mandrel. Preimpregnated roving is also used. Special lathes lay down glass roving or strands in a predetermined pattern to give maximum strength in the directions required. When the right number of layers have been applied, the wound mandrel is cured at room temperature or in an oven.

End Uses. Rocket motor cases, chemical tanks, pipe, pressure bottles, high strength tubing, shotgun barrels, missile bodies.

Premix/Molding Compound. Prior to molding glass reinforcement, usually chopped spun roving, is thoroughly mixed with resin, pigment, filler, and catalyst. The premixed material can be extruded into a rope-like form for easy handling, or may be used in bulk form.

The premix is formed into accurately weighed charges and placed in the mold cavity under heat and pressure. Amount of pressure varies from 100–1500 psi. Length of cycle depends on cure temperatures, resin, and wall thickness. Cure temperatures range from 225°–300°F. Time varies from 30 sec–5 min.

Transfer molding is a high speed modification of compression molding utilizing premix/molding compounds. The premix is preheated in a chamber (called a pot), then forced into the hot mold cavity for curing. This process is used to mold small, complicated parts incorporating many delicate inserts.

End Uses. Electrical switchgear, laundry tubs, trays, housings, automotive and appliance components, impeller blades, pump housings.

Raw Materials. Resins, Polyester (general purpose, chemical resistant, flame resistant, high heat distortion, hot strength, low exotherm, extended pot life), epoxy.

Molding Compounds. Phenolic, polyester, silicone, melamine, alkyd, diallyl phthalates, epoxy.

Encapsulation. Milled fibers or short chopped

strands are combined with catalyzed resin and poured into open molds to cast terminal blocks, electrical casings, and electronic components and similar objects. The fibers decrease shrinkage and crazing, and increase useful temperature range of the resin system. Cure is at room temperature. A post-cure of 20 min at 200°F is normal.

End Uses. Embedding of coils, windings, transformers, chokes, resistors, transistors, diodes and other electrical parts.

Raw Materials. Resins, polyesters (low exotherm), epoxies.

Other molding processes employing glass fiber reinforcements are: Hand lay-up, spray-up, mat molding and centrifugal casting.

Major Products in these Markets

Transportation. Auto bodies, truck cabs and bodies, trailers, cooling system components, component parts in buses, trucks, autos, motor scooters, insulated tank trucks; special purpose vehicles, farm equipment.

Construction. Structional shapes, patio roofing, panelling, siding and curtain wall materials, glazing and skylighting panels, concrete pouring forms.

Marine. Boats, ships and submarine hulls for recreation, Navy, commercial and Coast Guard; shipboard applications such as fuel and water storage tanks, duct work, ventilation cowls, marker buoys, marinas, floating docks.

Materials Handling. Pharmaceutical trays, industrial tote trays and boxes, food processing and delivery trays, boxes, bins, piping and storage tanks.

Electrical. Application in transformers, motors, generators, switchgear, and electrical equipment.

Sporting Goods. Fishing rods, archery bows and arrows, golf carts, golf clubs, hockey sticks, vaulting poles, shot gun barrels, water and snow skis, protective helmets (racing and baseball), swimming pools, playground equipment.

Seating. Luxury office seating, bowling alley settees, school and auditorium furniture, occasional chairs, lawn furniture, subway and bus seating, benches and arena seating.

Corrosion Application. Fuel and chemical storage tanks, fertilizer, and chemical storage hoppers, tanks, pipe, fume carrying ductwork, ventilator housings, pumps, stacks, cooling tower frames and grids, scrubbers, chemical and photographic processing equipment.

Protective Covers and housings. Outboard engine and lawn mower housings, electrical equipment, computer and business equipment housings, photo equipment cases, machinery guards and mail boxes.

Appliance and Equipment. Consumer appliance components, dryer ducts, dishwasher lids, decorative panels, structural gussets, laundry tubs, water softener tanks and pipes, clothes washer tubs, gear housings, air conditioner components, fan housings and hand tool housings.

Aerospace and Military Market. Rocket motor cases, nozzles, nose cones, submarine fairwaters and pressure hulls, radomes, wing tip tanks,

TABLE 2. MAJOR MARKETS FOR "FIBERGLASS" REINFORCED PLASTICS.

FRP ADVANTAGES	Transportation	Construction	Marine	Materials Handling	Electrical	Sporting Goods	Seating	Corrosion Applications	Protective Covers and Housings	Appliance and Equipment	Aerospace and Military Uses
Non-corrosive	✓	✓	✓	✓	✓	✓	✓	✓	✓	✓	✓
Less Finishing		✓	✓	✓		✓	✓	✓		✓	
Electrical Properties					✓				✓	✓	✓
Accurate Detail	✓		✓	✓					✓	✓	✓
Molded-in Color		✓	✓	✓		✓	✓			✓	
Decorative	✓	✓				✓	✓		✓	✓	
Warmth		✓	✓	✓			✓			✓	
Translucent	✓	✓									
Good Surface Finish		✓	✓	✓		✓	✓			✓	
Molded-in Attachments		✓			✓			✓	✓	✓	✓
Molded in One Piece	✓		✓	✓	✓		✓	✓	✓	✓	✓
Strength	✓	✓	✓	✓	✓	✓	✓	✓	✓	✓	✓
Dimensional Stability	✓	✓			✓	✓				✓	✓
Temperature Resistance				✓	✓			✓	✓	✓	✓
Light Weight	✓	✓	✓			✓		✓			✓
Low Maintenance	✓	✓	✓	✓	✓	✓	✓	✓	✓	✓	✓

KEY   [✓] MOST IMPORTANT TO THESE MARKETS   ✓ ALSO IMPORTANT TO THESE MARKETS helicopter rotor blades, pressure bottles and spheres, assault boats, liquified gas storage vessels, rifle stocks, sonar domes, aircraft lounge seats, engine cowlings, duct work and complete aircraft fuselage surfaces.

CLARE E. BACON

GLYCERINE

History

In 1779, Scheele, a Swedish chemist, accidentally isolated glycerine while heating a mixture of olive oil and litharge. Scheele named the product "the sweet principle of fat" because of the very sweet taste of the isolated glycerine, and described

Methods of Production

Commercially, glycerine is produced primarily as a natural by-product from soap or fatty acid manufacturing, or by synthetic processes from petroleum raw materials or carbohydrates. More than half of the current consumption of glycerine in the United States is produced synthetically.

Natural Glycerine. Although most of the natural glycerine produced in this country is derived from the direct saponification of fats with caustic soda and recovered as a by-product from the resulting soap, a large part is made by hydrolyzing or "splitting" the fats to free fatty acids and glycerine. The resulting fatty acids are used mainly in soap making, although a considerable quantity is used for other purposes. The general reaction is shown below:

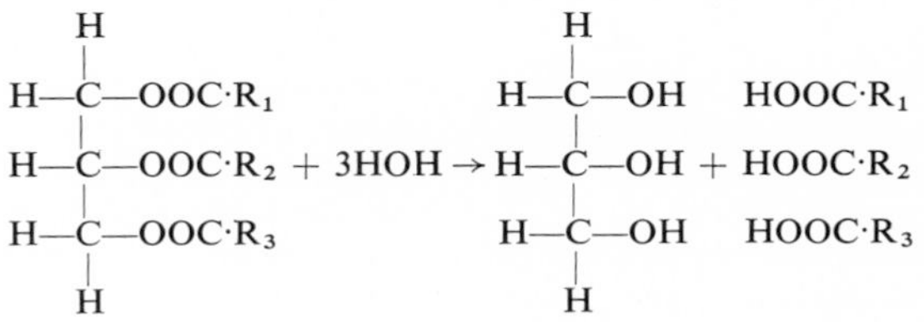

$$
\begin{array}{ccc}
\text{H} & \text{H} & \\
| & | & \\
\text{H–C–OOC·R}_1 & \text{H–C–OH} & \text{HOOC·R}_1 \\
| & | & \\
\text{H–C–OOC·R}_2 + 3\text{HOH} \rightarrow \text{H–C–OH} + \text{HOOC·R}_2 \\
| & | & \\
\text{H–C–OOC·R}_3 & \text{H–C–OH} & \text{HOOC·R}_3 \\
| & | & \\
\text{H} & \text{H} &
\end{array}
$$

Triglyceride   Water   Glycerine   Fatty acids

the method of preparation in the "Transactions of the Royal Academy of Sweden," in 1783. In 1811, Chevreul named the product "glycerol" from the Greek word meaning "sweet". In 1823 Chevreul obtained the first patent for the production of fatty acids by treating fats with an alkali, acidifying the resulting soap with sulfuric acid and recovering glycerine from the water. In 1836, Pelouze announced the empirical formula as $C_3H_8O_3$, and the accepted structure, $C_3H_5(OH)_3$, was established by Berthelot and Fucca in 1883.

Sobrero in 1846 reported the reaction of glycerine with nitric acid to form nitroglycerine. Twenty years later, Alfred Nobel succeeded in incorporating nitroglycerine in kieselguhr. This permitted safe handling and brought about the production of dynamite. Blasting gelatin was prepared by Nobel about ten years later, by mixing nitroglycerine with nitrocellulose. During this same period, Perkins' work with synthetic dyes led to the use of glycerine in the textile and printing industry and Berzelius reported a resinous product obtained by combining glycerine and tartaric acid. The products were forerunners of today's alkyd resins.

In 1948, Shell Chemical Company commenced the first large-scale production of synthetic glycerine from petroleum products.

From the standpoint of glycerine production, this method has the advantage that the glycerine may be obtained directly in a relatively concentrated solution without going through the numerous operations required to separate it from the soap formed simultaneously in direct saponification. The splitting of fats has been practiced on a commercial scale for about 100 years, and first attained considerable importance because of the demand for fatty acids by the candle industry.

Another process which can be used to derive glycerine from a natural product involves the hydrogenation and hydrogenolysis of carbohydrates.

Synthetic Glycerine. In the Shell Company plant at Houston, Texas, where the first successful commercial synthesis of glycerine has been in operation since August 1948, propylene obtained by distillation from a propanepropylene fraction is dried, preheated, and reacted with electrolytic chlorine in adiabatic reactors. Each reactor has its own product cooler, and pairs of reactors and coolers operate alternately to permit cleanout of carbon. Hydrogen chloride and unreacted propylene are removed from the chlorinator product; then the product, allyl chloride, is purified by distillation for further treatment.

Allyl chloride can be processed in two ways:

(1) hydrolyzed to allyl alcohol which is then treated with chlorine and water followed by hydrolysis to glycerine:

$$
\begin{array}{ccc}
\text{H—C—H} & & \text{H—C—H} \\
\| & \xrightarrow{\text{OH}^-} & \| \\
\text{C—H} & & \text{C—H} \\
| & & | \\
\text{H—C—H} & & \text{H—C—H} \\
| & & | \\
\text{Cl} & & \text{OH} \\
\textit{Allyl chloride} & & \textit{Allyl alcohol}
\end{array}
$$

$$
\begin{array}{ccccc}
 & \text{Cl} & \text{OH} & \text{Cl} & \text{H} \\
 & | & | & | & | \\
\text{H—C—H} & \text{H—C—H} & \text{H—C—H} & \text{H—C—H} & \text{H—C—OH} \\
\| \xrightarrow{\text{Cl}_2/\text{H}_2\text{O}} & | & | & | & | \\
\text{C—H} & \text{H—C—Cl} + & \text{H—C—Cl} + & \text{H—C—OH} \xrightarrow{\text{OH}^-} & \text{H—C—OH} \\
| & | & | & | & | \\
\text{H—C—H} & \text{H—C—H} & \text{H—C—H} & \text{H—C—H} & \text{H—C—OH} \\
| & | & | & | & | \\
\text{OH} & \text{OH} & \text{OH} & \text{OH} & \text{H} \\
\textit{Allyl alcohol} & \textit{Dichloro-} & \textit{Monochlorohydrins} & & \textit{Glycerine} \\
 & \textit{hydrin} & & &
\end{array}
$$

(2) Treated with chlorine and water to give glycerine-dichlorohydrins which are then hydrolyzed to glycerine:

$$
\begin{array}{cccc}
 & \text{OH} & \text{Cl} & \text{H} \\
 & | & | & | \\
\text{H—C—H} & \text{H—C—H} & \text{H—C—H} & \text{H—C—OH} \\
\| \xrightarrow{\text{Cl}_2/\text{H}_2\text{O}} & | & | & | \\
\text{C—H} & \text{H—C—Cl} + & \text{H—C—OH} \xrightarrow{\text{OH}^-} & \text{H—C—OH} \\
| & | & | & | \\
\text{H—C—H} & \text{H—C—H} & \text{H—C—H} & \text{H—C—OH} \\
| & | & | & | \\
\text{Cl} & \text{Cl} & \text{Cl} & \text{H} \\
\textit{Allyl chloride} & \textit{Dichlorohydrins} & & \textit{Glycerine}
\end{array}
$$

Each procedure has its advantages and disadvantages: In practice, (1) is shorter but involves more difficulties in the chlorohydrination steps than are encountered in (2). The desirability of securing various intermediates for their own sake is also a consideration in the choice of methods.

Two other routes to glycerine on a commercial scale are (1) a process discovered by Shell Development Company involving hydrogen peroxide and acrolein as reactants, and (2) the isomerization of propylene oxide to allyl alcohol which, when processed as indicated above yields glycerine.

Uses of Glycerine in Plastic Products

Alkyd Resins. The largest single outlet for glycerine is in the manufacture of alkyd resins. These resins have been known for over 100 years, but it was not until 1927 when Kienle filed a patent describing oil-modified polyesters that alkyds became commercially important. Since that time, alkyds have assumed a dominant position as plastic materials, and they are now produced at the rate of about 600 million lb per year. The bulk of this huge volume goes into surface coatings having a wide variety of enduses.

Alkyd resins can be defined as the resinous products derived from the esterification of polyhydric alcohols, e.g., glycerine with, a dibasic acid. The reaction of glycerine with phthalic anhydride leads to an insoluble, brittle resin having little or no commercial importance. However, if a fatty acid (or other monocarboxylic acid) is included as a co-reactant, a product is obtained which is soluble in common hydrocarbon solvents and is useful as a coating vehicle.

By varying the amount and type of fatty acid, i.e., saturated, unsaturated, a wide variety of alkyd resins can be produced from the basic glyceryl phthalate product. Additional variations in the final resin can be obtained by further treatment of the alkyd with materials such as styrene, vinyl toluene, acrylonitrile, phenol, phenol-formaldehyde resins, silicones, or the acrylics.

By and large, glycerine is the most useful of all the commercially available polyols since its ideal functionality and its liquid nature make it adaptable to all types of alkyd formulations and processing conditions.

The manufacture of alkyds is a batch operation and is carried out by either a fusion process or a solvent process. In fusion processing the reactants are charged to a kettle which may or may not be equipped with a condenser. The kettle is usually heated by a direct oil or gas fire, and the reactants are maintained at a specified temperature until essentially all of the acids are consumed. This method leaves much to be desired since large losses of reactants can be incurred.

The solvent process employs a closed system and a small amount of azeotroping solvent (usually xylene) in addition to the reactants. In solvent processing the solvent not only acts as an azeotroping agent to carry off water of reaction, but also aids in maintaining better color in the resin. Since the system is a closed one, better batch-to-batch uniformity is obtained as losses of reactants are not incurred.

Because of its low cost and the flexibility obtainable both in formulating and processing of glycerine alkyds, it is safe to assume that glycerine will continue to hold its dominant position in the alkyd industry.

Ester Gums. Rosin, a natural resin derived from pine trees or as a by-product of the Kraft paper industry, is essentially an unsaturated monobasic acid which finds wide use in the paint, paper, soap, and various other chemical industries. When rosin or its hydrogenated or dimerized derivatives are esterified with glycerine the products are known as ester gums. The ester gums enjoy considerable use in nitrocellulose lacquers and in varnishes. Certain variations can be made in ester gums to impart special properties. For example, ester gums having high acid numbers are preferred for use in tung oil varnishes in order to retard gelation. Modification of ester gum with maleic anhydride increases the melting point of the resin, and contributes to better solvent release in lacquers.

Urethanes. Urethanes and polyurethanes are prepared by the reaction of an isocyanate such as toluene diisocyanate with hydroxyl-bearing compounds. The urethanes have in recent years assumed considerable commercial significance especially in flexible and rigid foams and to a somewhat lesser extent in coatings.

Mono- and di-glycerides produced by the alcoholysis of vegetable oils with glycerine were among the first materials of practical use in urethane technology. The mono- and di-glycerides of oils such as linseed oil will react with toluene diisocyanate to yield useful coating vehicles which air dry by oxidative polymerization. By varying the mono- to di-glyceride ratio and/or the type of diisocyanate, vehicles of differing properties may be obtained.

Castor oil is a particularly versatile natural oil for the preparation of urethane oil vehicles. Castor oil is the triglyceride of 12-hydroxy-9,10-oleic acid (ricinoleic acid) and, thus, contains 3 hydroxyl groups. Because of its functionality, castor oil is usually only partially pre-reacted with a diisocyanate before use in order to avoid

gelation. At the time of application the vehicle is catalyzed with a tertiary amine or with a metallic drier.

Improved urethane intermediates can be obtained by alcoholysis of castor oil with glyceride or by blowing the oil with air. As with other vegetable oils the ratio of mono- to di-glycerides can profoundly affect the performance characteristics of castor oil urethane vehicles.

Polyesters based on glycerine-glycol mixtures also find use in high quality urethane surface coating vehicels. An example of such a polyester is the resin obtained by reacting adipic acid and the polyol blend in such a way that the final product contains a 4–8% hydroxyl excess. The free hydroxyls are available to react with a diisocyanate just prior to application to produce a coating of high molecular weight. It is important in making polyesters of this type to maintain a judicious ratio of glycol to triol in order to avoid gelation in processing, but at the same time the vehicle should have a high enough functionality for effective cross-linking with a diisocyanate.

Polyols are used also as initiators in the polymerization of propylene oxide to polyethers which are used in large quantities for the production of urethane foams. Although polyesters are used in urethane foams too, the polyethers have grown much more rapidly mainly because of their lower cost. Materials such as ethylene glycol, propylene glycol, and water are used to initiate the propylene oxide polymerization to produce long-chain diols. If glycerine is used as the initiator, triols result. The triple functionality limits the use of polyether triols to some extent in flexible foams since the crosslinking which occurs on reaction with diisocyanates reduces the flexibility of the foam. On the other hand, rigid foams require the use of a polyol having a functionality of more than three. In addition to the fact that the initiating polyol constitutes only about 2–4% of the polyether polymer, the two aforementioned limitations reduce large scale usage of glycerine in urethane foams.

Miscellaneous. Monoglycerides produced by esterification or alcoholysis find some use in the manufacture of alkyd resins. As an additive to alkyd resin paint formulations, the monoglycerides improve the solubility of high viscosity alkyds in aliphatic solvents.

Glycerine α-allyl ether and glyceryl phthalimide have found limited use in alkyd resins. The former has been used in conjunction with phthalic anhydride to form oil-free alkyds, and the latter is useful in promoting better hardness and resistance to water than is found in conventional alkyds. The allyl ethers of glycerine are also used as one of the major components in non-air inhibited, unsaturated polyester coatings.

Triacetin, or glyceryl triacetate, has become of

Physical Properties of Glycerine[a]

Molecular weight		92.094
Apparent specific gravity, in air, 20/20°C[b]		1.2639
Vapor pressure, mm Hg	50°C	0.0025
	100°C	0.195
	150°C	4.30
	200°C	46.0
Boiling point, at 760 mm Hg pressure, °C		290.00
Freezing point, °C		17
Flash point, Cleveland open cup, °F		350
Heat of vaporization, at 760 mm Hg pressure	195°C	18,170
in cal/mole	55°C	21,060
Specific heat, cal/g/°C	−27.7°C	0.2922
	9.2°C	0.5537
	26.4°C	0.5795
Coefficient of expansion, in/°C		
(sp. gr. 1.254 − 1.264 at 15.5/15.5°C)	15.5 − 25.0°C	0.000617
Viscosity, cps	20°C	1410
	100°C	14.8
Refractive index, n_D^{20}		1.47399
Surface tension, dynes/cm	20°C	63.4
	90°C	58.6
	150°C	51.9
Dielectric constant current at 0.57×10^6 cycles/sec	25°C	42.48
Heat of fusion, at 760 mm Hg pressure, cal/mole		4370

[a] Glycerol, Miner, C.S., and Dalton, N.N. Reinhold Publishing, N.Y., 1953.
[b] From data of Bodart and Snoddy (*Ind. Eng., Chem.*), **19 506** (1927). Corrected by the work of Timmerman (*J. Chem. Phys.*), **32 507** (1935).

considerable importance in the past few years as a plasticizer for cellulose acetate used in cigarette filters. Triacetin is an ideal plasticizer in this application since it is odorless and tasteless and has received approval from the Food and Drug Administration.

Glycerine itself is used widely as a plasticizer for glassine paper, cork, and cellophane because of its non-toxicity, permanency, and efficient humectancy as well as its effective plasticizing action.

STAFF MEMBERS
SHELL CHEMICAL CO.

I

IMIDAZOLES AND DERIVATIVES

Condensed imidazoles such as benzimidazoles are readily available chemicals and have been the basis of many new compounds of value in the plastics field. The non-condensed imidazoles, however, have only recently become commercially available for polymer applications through the development of new efficient manufacturing processes.

Imidazoles, also referred to as iminazoles, glyoxalines or 1,3-diazoles, are heterocyclic five-membered compounds containing two nitrogen atoms. The parent compound is imidazole:

$$
\begin{array}{ccc}
(4) & CH{=}CH & (5) \\
 & | \quad\quad | & \\
(3) & N \quad\quad NH & (1) \\
 & \diagdown\!\!\diagup & \\
 & CH & (2)
\end{array}
$$

Imidazole compounds are sufficiently basic to form salts with organic acids of intermediate acid strength; their amphoteric nature is shown by their ability to also form metallic salts. In addition, they have been found to undergo coordination-complex formation with certain metal salts. The complexing capacity is often found to be far greater than would be predicted from proton affinities. These unique properties are of industrial importance in polymer applications involving both urethane and epoxy catalysis, and in the preparation of versatile addition polymers.

The compounds 2-ethyl-4-methylimidazole and 2-methylimidazole are particularly useful for the catalysis of epoxy and polyurethane reactions. The 2-ethyl-4-methylimidazole possesses outstanding effectiveness both as the sole curing agent, in which homopolymerization predominates as the thermosetting mechanism, as well as an accelerator for epoxy-anhydride crosslinking. A supercooled liquid at room temperature, 2-ethyl-4-methylimidazole offers processing advantages: easy compounding; non-staining to the skin; and much lower order of toxicity than most other amine curatives.

As previously mentioned, imidazoles are highly associated at room temperature. 2-ethyl-4-methyl-imidazole therefore offers significant pot life advantages; yet, when heated above 70°C, ranks among the most active catalysts. Highly cross-linked epoxy castings are obtained having ASTM Heat Deflection Temperatures generally higher than the cure temperature employed. Alternatively, the high catalytic activity of 2-ethyl-4-methylimidazole has been used to achieve excellent physical properties with extremely short matched-die mold cycle times of 4–5 min employed in the manufacture of glass reinforced articles. Similarly, molding powders compounded with 2-methylimidazole, MP 144°C, cure rapidly and offer excellent mechanical and electrical properties.

Filament wound, glass-reinforced epoxy pipe cured with 2-ethyl-4-methylimidazole has excellent overall chemical resistance. Particularly outstanding performance is indicated on exposure to H_3PO_4, KOH and oxidants such as H_2SO_4 and H_2O_2. Homopolymerization of typical low cost, bisphenol A-glycidyl ether-derived epoxy resins with 2-ethyl-4-methylimidazole produces polymers having superior retention of properties on prolonged exposure to elevated temperatures.

The higher ultimate operating temperature of 550°F obtained with 2-ethyl-4-methylimidazole is of interest in epoxies for reinforced plastics and electrical performances, competing in high temperature performance with phenolic resins.

The high polar surface activity inherent in the imidazole nucleus is believed responsible for the dramatic increase in HDT found to occur with silica-filled epoxy resin when cured with 2-ethyl-4-methylimidazole; a resin-filler interaction is postulated. ASTM Heat Deflection Temperatures of >280°C are obtained with this system, as opposed to 150°C for the unfilled resin—a phenomenon not known to occur with other amine curing agents. Further evidence of the high order of imidazole surface activity is the superior strength reported for glass-reinforced polyester and phenolic resins containing about 10–25% of poly-N-vinylimidazole.

Alkyl substituted imidazoles are effective catalysts for the urethane reaction. Compounds such as 2-methylimidazole, in which the imino nitrogen is not substituted, again reflect a significant increase in activity at elevated temperatures. The high coefficient of thermal activation leads to moderate pot life systems which can be rapidly heat cured for urethane coating, adhesive, and encapsulation applications. 2-Methylimidazole has also been proposed as a co-catalyst with other amine catalysts to insure completeness of urethane cure. 2-Ethyl-4-methylimidazole has been proposed in continuous short-cycle casting production, where the delay in catalytic activity is exploited to prevent frequent equipment shutdowns for cleaning.

Imidazole-containing polymers are accessible through homo- and co-polymerization of both N- and C-vinyl substituted imidazoles using typical vinyl addition initiators. N-vinylimidazoles such as N-vinyl-2-methylimidazole are obtained by catalytic vinylation with acetylene. 2-Vinyl imidazole is prepared by the following sequence.

coatings, and wet strength resins for paper. Protective colloids and dispersing agents are obtained by the copolymerization of N-vinyl-2-alkylimidazoles with acrylic or methacrylic acids.

Flame-resistant polymers are obtained by copolymerization bis (2-chloroethyl) vinyl phosphonate and vinyl imidazole. The use of imidazoles as solvents for the wet spinning of polyesters has also been described.

H. A. GREEN

IRON OXIDE PIGMENTS

General Properties of Iron Oxides

The modes of occurrence of iron oxides are varied. Their compositions consist of Fe_2O_3, Fe_3O_4, $Fe_2O_3 \cdot H_2O$, and less common forms as $Fe(OH)_3$. The oxides exist in a range of colors—black, brown, orange, red and yellow, and are of

$$\underset{CH-N}{\overset{CH-N}{\big|}} CCH_3 + HCHO \rightarrow \underset{CH-N}{\overset{CH-N}{\big|}} CCH_2CH_2OH \xrightarrow{-H_2O} \underset{CH-N}{\overset{CH-N}{\big|}} CCH=CH_2$$

The N-vinyl monomers are generally liquids which are bulk or bead polymerized for use in a number of diverse applications. Weakly basic anion-exchange bead resins have been prepared by co-polymerization of an N-vinyl imidazole with divinylbenzene followed by treatment with bis(2-chloroethyl)ether. Poly(vinylimidazole)(PVI) either treated with NH_3 and epichlorohydrin or quaternized with dimethyl sulfate or methyl iodide also leads to anion exchange resins. Poly(vinylimidazole) membranes may be cast from organic solutions for this purpose.

The poly(vinylimidazolinium quaternary) polymers have also been proposed as effective as anti-static treatments for use in hydrophobic synthetic fiber production.

Several techniques developed for improving the dyeability of acrylic fibers depend on the cationic dye receptivity and fiber substantivity of imidazoles. One method involves the use of 2-methylimidazole or N-vinyl-2-methylimidazole as dye bath auxiliaries. Alternatively, vinylimidazoles may be copolymerized in minor amounts with acrylonitrile to produce fibers receptive to acid dyes. The unusual receptivity for both acid and base dyes demonstrates the amphoteric nature of imidazoles which contain nitrogen atoms having the characteristics of both acidic pyrrole and basic pyridine.

Terpolymers of butadiene-styrene, and a vinylimidazole have been proposed as components of latices effective for bonding nylon to rubber. Co-polymers of vinylimidazole with acrylamide are claimed as ingredients for effective binders,

several mineral classes, with varying particle shapes and sizes. They occur as natural oxides of many types in various parts of the world, and can be manufactured chemically by a number of processes, from a range of iron compounds such as the sulfate, nitrate and chloride. They are both magnetic and nonmagnetic.

The iron oxides are a hardy family, having existed for ages without change, attributable to their permanence and stability. With every civilization, from primitive man to the present, they have appeared as coloring materials in architecture and art. Other types of colors may possess cleaner, brighter shades, but iron oxides have the advantages of chemical stability, and reasonable cost. Through modern manufacturing techniques, they have been made brighter and finer in recent decades.

These synthetic oxides are now the most widely used of the iron oxides in the plastics field. They have the highest purity, best color, best tinting strength, and a very wide range of shades and tints.

Oxides possess the following characteristics:
(1) Lightfastness in masstone and tint—excellent.
(2) Heat resistance—good to excellent depending upon type.
(3) Weathering resistance—excellent.
(4) Alkali resistance—excellent.
(5) Acid resistance—excellent in plastic dispersions.
(6) Oxidation resistance—usually excellent, but depends upon type of oxide.

(7) Reduction resistance—excellent.

(8) Opacity—usually excellent, but a few grades are transparent and translucent.

(9) Tinting strength—on a dollar basis they have very high tinting strength.

(10) Brightness—relatively low.

(11) Color range—very wide.

(12) Solvent resistance—excellent.

(13) Bleeding and migration resistance—excellent.

Classification

A classification of the iron oxides, both natural [made from ores] and synthetic [made by chemical manufacturing processes], follows:

Color	Natural	Synthetic
Black Fe_3O_4	Magnetite	Pure black
Brown	Metallic brown Raw and burnt umber	Pure brown [Mixture oxides] Gamma magnetic oxides
Orange	None	Pure orange [mixture oxides of iron]
Red Fe_2O_3	Natural red [Spanish, Persian, etc.], Burnt sienna	Pure red
Yellow $Fe_2O_3 \cdot H_2O$	Ocher Raw sienna	Pure yellow

Natural Oxides. The natural oxides are made by processing selected ores such as hematite, limonite, siderite, magnetite, pyrites, etc., by operations of calcining, grinding and classifying. They range in iron oxide content from 20% for ochers, to as high as 97.5% for some of the newer metallic browns. Whereas a fineness of 2% retention on a 325 mesh (44μ) screen was acceptable 15 years ago, today some natural oxides are available with a top size of 15μ, and a 325 mesh retention of less than 0.01%.

Synthetic Reds. These are now made by four different chemical processes to produce pigments with very definite chemical and physical characteristics for specific applications. These processes follow, together with the range of basic properties of the particular oxide:

(1) Produced by calcination of ferrous sulfate, with washing and classification:

Fe_2O_3	99.5+ %
Mineral class	Hematite
Particle shape	Spherical
Specific gravity	5.15–5.20
Surface area	3.0–10.0 sq m/g
Oil absorption	13–24
pH	6.0–7.5
Particle size; top,	10–15μ
average	0.25–3.5μ

(2) Produced by direct precipitation from iron salts with no calcination:

Fe_2O_3	97.0–98.0%
Mineral class	Hematite
Particle shape	Rhombohedral
Specific gravity	4.90
Surface area	3.6–9.0 sq m/g
Oil absorption	20–25
pH	6.5–8.0
Particle size; top,	3μ
average	0.3–1μ

(3) Produced by calcination of iron hydrate and hydrated iron oxides:

Fe_2O_3	96.0–98.0%
Mineral class	Hematite
Particle shape	Acicular
Specific gravity	4.5–5.0
Surface area	3.0–20.0 sq m/g
Oil absorption	40–70
pH	5.5–7.5
Particle size; top,	5–20μ
average	0.3–1.5μ

(4) Produced by oxidation of precipitated magnetite (Fe_3O_4):

Fe_2O_3	99.0%
Mineral class	Hematite
Particle shape	Cubic
Specific gravity	5.15
Surface area	4.0–5.0 sq m/g
pH	7–8

In addition to the preceding four types, ferric oxides having a gamma crystal structure are produced for magnetic applications.

In the first three groups, a wide range of colors varying from light salmon to deep maroon is manufactured. All these oxides are extremely fine, averaging from 0.20–0.75μ in particle size, are essentially free from oversize, have controlled oil absorption, and are very low in impurities, especially soluble salts which are present in the range of only a few hundredths of a per cent.

Yellows. Pure yellow oxides cover a range from a chromy light yellow on the greenish side, to a deep yellow with an orange cast, and are made in various grades of chemical purity and physical properties.

Fe_2O_3	86–88%
$Fe_2O_3 \cdot H_2O$	99.0%
Mineral class	Goethite
Particle shape	Acicular
Specific gravity	4.03
Surface area	7–18 sq m/g
Oil absorption	28–55
pH	5.0–6.5
Particle size, top	3–5μ
average	0.2–1.2μ

General Applications

It is quite possible to use all of these described pigments in plastics and many of them are used in varying resins and polymers. Commercial practices and experiences have directed the majority usage to the pure synthetic iron oxide pigments. Reasons for this are the following:

(1) More uniformity in color and other physical properties.

(2) Greater brightness in masstone and tint.

(3) Better tinting strength.

(4) Higher dollar color value.

(5) Higher chemical purity.

Where extra richness of brown color is desired, the transparent burnt natural umbers are used. Where some transparency of color is desired, the natural siennas and umbers may be used. Special effects can be obtained by the inclusion of metal powders and flakes in combination with the transparent pigments. Where magnetic properties are desired in a plastic, the synthetic black and special synthetic brown gamma oxides are employed.

Specific Applications

Table 1 gives most of the significant properties of iron oxide pigments in their applications in the various plastics; Table 2 shows the use pattern of oxide pigments in various polymers.

Vinyls. Iron oxides are widely used in all the various vinyl types of polymers. Transparent, translucent, metallic and the usual opaque colors are found in products that are manufactured by all the established processing methods. Today's improved polymers and compounding techniques readily permit their un-questioned wide-spread use. They do not bronze, crock or migrate. The pigments are also used in latex coatings and in foam.

Suitable stabilization of all vinyl systems containing iron oxides is readily achieved. Four guides for stabilization are as follows: (1) Stabilizers may be selected from all major chemical classes, primarily on a trial and error basis, (2) use of calcium carbonate as a filler is very effective, (3) use of epoxy compounds is generally desirable, (4) polymeric plasticizers are also effective in imparting good heat stability.

Acrylics. Here again the iron oxides may be used. The applications are somewhat limited because the brighter types of colors are frequently specified by designers. Exposure testing of these compositions containing iron oxides has proven satisfactory.

Polyesters. Oxide pigments in the dry state may be stirred or ground into polyester resins prior to the addition of catalysts. Very often they are used in combination with filler pigments which modify not only the physical but also the chemical properties of the cured polyester. The addition of oxide pigments to polyester resin may cause increases or decreases in gel time and cure time and they also usually reduce cure temperature.

TABLE 1.

		Red iron oxides	Yellow iron oxides	Black iron oxides	Umbers and siennas
	Colorant cost	Low	Low	Low	Low
	Opacity	E	E	E	F–E
	Hiding power	E	E	E	F–E
	Tint	Salmon to lavender	Greenish yellow to reddish yellow	Bluish gray	Yellow, red, tan, green
	Brightness	F	F	F	F
	Transparency	Opaque	Opaque	Opaque	Transparent to translucent
Resistance in Plastic	Acid	G–E	G–E	G–E	G–E
	Aldehyde	G	G	G	G
	Alkali	E	E	E	E
	Heat	E	F–G	F–G	G–E
	Light (Masstones)	E	E	E	E
	Light (Tints)	E	E	E	E
	Migration	E	E	E	E
	Oxidation	E	E	G	G–E
	Reduction	E	E	E	E
	Weathering	E	E	E	E
	Bleeding	E	E	E	E

Key:

E – Excellent
G – Good
F – Fair
P – Poor

TABLE 2.

	Red	Yellow and orange	Black and brown	Umbers and siennas
Acetyls	1	1	1	1
Acrylics	2	2	2	2
Cellulosics	2	2	2	2
Nylons	2	1	1	2
Polyolefin	2	2	2	2
Polycarbonate	2	1	0	2
Fluorocarbons	2	1	0	1
Polystyrene	2	1	1	2
Vinyls	3	3	3	3
Mastics	3	3	3	2
Amino	2	2	2	2
Dialkyl phthalate	2	2	2	2
Epoxies	3	3	3	3
Phenolics	3	2	2	3
Polyesters	3	3	3	2
Polyurethane	3	3	3	3
Silicones	3	3	1	1

Widely used   – 3
Applicable   – 2
Limited   – 1
Not recommended – 0

These changes are small, except in the case of burnt umber which may significantly extend the cure time.

Polyolefins. Iron oxides are recommended for general usage in most polyolefins. Their properties of nonbleeding, nonexuding, good heat and light stability are valuable. It is interesting to note that different grades of pigments may create various processing and exposure effects which are associated with the built in stabilization of the polymers, and probably with the nature of the polymer itself.

Polystyrene. There is limited application of iron oxides here. Although iron oxides have been used, the demand is generally for the brighter colors. As with some other polymers, various grades may react differently with the oxide groups and thereby show varying degrees of stability in processing.

Fluorocarbons. In general for tetrafluoroethylene ("Teflon") the most successful and most widely used type of colorants—from a standpoint of stability and non-reactivity—are the intimately mixed and calcined inorganic pigments. These colors can be composed of such compounds as Fe, Cr, Zn, Cu, Cd, and many other oxides.

Polyurethanes. Iron oxides impart a wide range of pleasing shades to all types of rigid and flexible polyurethane systems. As iron oxides always contain traces of water of approximately 0.2%, dispersion of the pigments should be effected in the liquid components which are not sensitive to moisture. This is readily carried out and minor adjustments are made in compounding to compensate for the moisture.

Cellulosics. Oxides are recommended for use with excellent resistance to outdoor exposure. Application of the oxides are limited only by the demands for the shades obtained from them.

Phenolics. Most phenolic plastics use iron oxides for coloring. Although pure oxides are used, large quantities of burnt umbers, used to produce deep rich brown shades, are sometimes employed.

Mastics. These are a generic type of plastic used for flooring in which large quantities of red and yellow iron oxides are used for pigmentation. Shades from fairly light red to dark brown to yellow to similated cork are readily produced.

F.D.A. Applications. The F.D.A. clearly states that iron oxide pigments may be used *without restriction* in all types of materials in contact with food. This means that all food packagings may contain any desired quantity of iron oxide. The latter are generally recognized as harmless mineral pigments.

IR and UV Effects. Choosing colorants with respect to their spectral characteristics can frequently extend the life of plastics. Weathering may be improved if colorants are chosen that absorb uv light. Iron oxides absorb 95% of the uv rays at 350–375mμ. These pigments are comparable in this respect to zinc oxide, carbon black and chrome yellow.

Iron oxides absorb 78% of infrared rays at 800mμ, and 70% of the rays at 1000 mμ. There are applications where these heat absorbing qualities are beneficial.

ARTHUR K. WOERNLE

Cross-References: COLORANTS, PIGMENTS.

ITACONIC ACID

Methylenebutanedioic acid $CH_2=C(COOH)—CH_2(COOH)$ was first isolated in 1837. First obtained by pyrolysis of citric acid, it was called citricic acid. Decomposition of aconitic acid in 1840 produced the same product, referred to today as methylene succinic acid and sold commercially as itaconic acid. This unsaturated dicarboxylic acid is of significant importance as a monomer as the free acid and in the form of mono and diesters. Capable of both homopolymerization and copolymerization all three forms have been introduced to most of the polymer systems now used in adhesives, coatings, moldings, and some fibers.

Physical Properties

Itaconic acid has a formula weight of 130.10 and crystallizes from water into trimetric octahedra. The specific gravity is 1.632; melting point 167–168°C. The acid is soluble in 100 g of water in the following amounts: 8.3 g at 20°C, 29.2 g at 50°C, 45.9 g at 60°C, and 72.6 g at 70°C. The approximate solubility of itaconic in organic solvents is shown in Table 1. The ionization constants are $K_1 = 1.5 \times 10^{-4}$ and $K_2 = 2.2 \times 10^{-6}$ at 25°C. When 1, 2, 4 and 8 g of itaconic acid are added to 100 ml water at 25°C, the pH drops from 2.45 to 2.10, 1.83 and 1.60, respectively.

Manufacture

Itaconic acid by fermentation was first accomplished in 1931 by Kinoshita. *Aspergillus itaconicus* was used to ferment sugar in surface cultures. The acid was later prepared with *Aspergillus terreus*. Some reports state fermentation yields of 20–50% based on the weight of carbo-

hydrate introduced. Today itaconic is commercially produced by submerged fermentation.

Partial acidification and autoclaving at 140°C decarboxylates alkaline earth salts of aconitic acid $CH(COOH)=C(COOH)—CH_2(COOH)$, producing itaconic.

Chemical Properties

The uniqueness of itaconic acid is its ability to form the usual carboxylic acid derivatives and also act as a monomer with a reactive double bond. The two carboxyl groups readily form metal salts ranging from the water soluble ammonium salt to the silver salt which is water insoluble. Itaconic reacts with alcohols to form diesters. The sodium salt reacts with methyl halides and sulfates, and reactive halogenated aromatics to form diesters.

The double bond can be reduced by catalytic hydrogenation, producing methyl succinic acid. Halogens, hydrogen halides and thioacetic acid add to the double bond in the usual manner. Sodium bisulfite adds to the unsaturated sodium salt. Primary amines produce lactams whether the amines are alkyl, aryl or alicyclic.

Conversion to citraconic anhydride

$$C(CH_3):CH \cdot CO \cdot O \cdot CO$$

occurs above the melting point of itaconic. When heated to 180°C in a concentrated aqueous solution, the double bond shifts and mesaconic acid $CH_3(COOH)C:CH(COOH)$ is formed. Itaconic acid reacts with permanganate, yielding hydroxyparaconic acid which is converted to hydroxylactone

$$HOC(COOH)CH_2—C=O$$
$$CH_2——O$$

TABLE 1. APPROXIMATE SOLUBILITY OF ITACONIC ACID IN ORGANIC SOLVENTS.

Solvent	g/100 ml solvent @ 25°	Solvent	g/100 ml solvent @ 28°C
Butyl acetate	1.6	Acetic acid	7.0
Dioxane	16.6	Benzene	0.05
Ethyl "Cellosolve"	21.8	*n*-Butanol	8.0
Ethyl chloride	0.04	Chloroform	0.1
Ethyl ether	1.4	Ethanol	21.0
Ethylene glycol	25.2	Ethyl acetate	1.6
Isopropyl ether	0.3	Hexyl alcohol	6.0
Methyl "Cellosolve"	30.8	Isopropanol	13.0
n-Pentanol	5.1	Isopropyl acetate	2.0
2-Pentanol	6.5	Methanol	31.0
n-Propanol	10.7	Methyl acetate	4.0
Propylene glycol	7.2	Methyl ethyl ketone	5.0
		Methyl isobutyl ketone	2.0

Homopolymerization and Copolymerization

Molecular weights of polyitaconic acid reach approximately 30,000 when polymerized in an aqueous solution using potassium persulfate as the initiator. Homopolymerization continues even when the dissociation of one carboxyl group is complete; however, it stops on the further dissociation of the second carboxyl. Allylic hydrogen chain transfer prohibits extremely high molecular weights. The resulting polymer is more soluble in water than the original monomer. As expected, notably low viscosity solutions result. The polymer is soluble in methanol, but insoluble in ethanol. Polyitaconic acid can also be prepared by the hydrolysis of polymonoalkyl itaconate. This procedure can produce far higher molecular weight polymers than those formed from free acid.

Itaconic acid has been most widely used as a comonomer with acrylates, butadiene and vinyls. Its primary advantage is the addition of free carboxyl groups to the copolymer for increased polarity and cross-linking sites. For greater

TABLE 3. PHYSICAL PROPERTIES OF DIMETHYL AND DIBUTYL ITACONATE.

	Dimethyl itaconate	Dibutyl itaconate
Molecular weight	158.15	242.31
Appearance	Crystalline solid	Colorless liquid
Boiling point, °C (10 mm Hg)	91.5	145
Melting point, °C	36	
Specific gravity	1.27	0.9833
Refractive index	1.441	1.442
Solubility in water, 20°C	2.2 g/100 ml	Insoluble

itaconate distribution, monoesters may be used as comonomers.

Monoesters and Diesters

The monoesters formed from the reactions of itaconic acid with methyl, butyl, hexyl and octyl alcohols are available in commercial and development quantities. Chiefly recommended in copolymer systems where itaconic acid is needed, the monobutyl itaconate $CH_2\!=\!C(COOH)\!-\!CH_2\!-\!COOC_4H_9$ offers increased distribution in the polymer while supplying a free carboxyl group for cross-linking sites. The reactivity ratios in Table 2 are attributed to the greater attraction of the monoesters to the micelles in redox polymerizations. It is apparently more difficult to attract and initiate propagation of the more polar dibasic acid in the micelle structures. The monoesters of course also supply an ester group providing inherent plasticization of the copolymer. If additional inherent plasticization is desired then diesters are used.

TABLE 2. REACTIVITY RATIOS OF ITACONIC ACID AND MONOBUTYL ITACONATE.

M_1	M_2	r_1	r_2
MBI	Acrylonitrile	1.7	0.6
IA	Acrylonitrile	0.5	1.7
MBI	Butadiene	0.07	0.3
IA	Butadiene	0.04	1.7
MBI	Vinyl acetate	5.9	0.02
IA	Vinyl acetate	2.8	0.09

MBI = monobutyl itaconate. IA = itaconate acid.
Note: Reactivity ratios calculated from Q and e values.

TABLE 4. ITACONATE REACTIVITY RATIOS.

M_1	M_2	r_1	r_2	Q_1	e_1	Ref.
DMI[a]	DBI	1.1	1.1	—	—	17
DMI	Styrene	0.14	0.48	0.56	0.84	18
DMI	Styrene	0.12	0.59	—	—	19
DMI	Styrene	0.25	0.32	0.88	0.79	20
DMI	p-Chlorostyrene	0.15	0.69	—	—	18
DMI	Methyl methacrylate	0.3	1.3	0.67	1.13	17
DMI	Methyl methacrylate	0.3	1.2	—	—	18
DMI	Butyl acrylate	0.94	0.40	—	—	17
DMI	Acrylonitrile	0.68	0.26	—	—	19
DMI	Methacrylonitrile	0.28	1.26	—	—	18
DMI	Vinyl chloride	5.1	0.053	0.5	1.3	21
DBI[b]	Styrene	0.38	0.40	0.83	0.57	20
DBI	Methyl methacrylate	0.4	0.8	1.00	1.23	17
DBI	Vinyl acetate	6.3	0.02	0.86	1.13	17

[a] DMI = dimethyl itaconate.
[b] DBI = dibutyl itaconate.

Dimethyl itaconate $CH_2\!\!=\!\!C(COOCH_3)\!\!-\!\!CH_2\!\!-\!\!COOH_3$ and dibutyl itaconate $CH_2\!\!=\!\!C(COOC_4H_9)\!\!-\!\!CH_2(COOC_4H_9)$ are commercially available and many higher alkyl diesters are available in development quantities. In addition to their role as monomers these esters, like itaconic acid, are useful intermediates. They undergo the typical reactions of simple esters and also those typical of unsaturation. Table 3 lists the physical properties of the two commercial products.

The lower alkyl itaconates can be polymerized by bulk, solvent, emulsion and suspension methods. Homopolymers vary from hard and brittle with the methyl ester to soft and tough with the butyl ester. Poly(dibutyl itaconate) produces films with excellent light and heat stability and scrubbability resistance. The presence of dimethyl or dibutyl itaconate in copolymers improves such properties as light stability, hardness or internal plasticization, depending on the itaconate selected, and good specific adhesion to certain substrates. Table 4 lists the reactivity ratios and calculated Q_1 and e_1 values of these two itaconates with other typical monomers.

J. THURMAN FREEZE

J

JUTE

Although this fiber is not extensively used in the plastics field, it is still potentially important, for it is the cheapest textile fiber. Jute is a glossy fiber and comes almost exclusively from two East Indian plants. Being a coarse plant fiber like sisal, it requires retting for separation of the finer fibers before they can be prepared as a filler material for plastics.

Jute in the form of burlap cloth is used in lay-up work for large reinforced irregular plastics parts. The separate fibers as received at textile mills are fine but somewhat irregular in cross section, and are yellowish-white in color. They are soft, without much tensile strength. Nevertheless, in autoclave molding of the pressure-bag type, they prove satisfactory when proper care is taken. Jute burlap is impregnated with resin (usually phenolic) and curing is accomplished by catalyst. Before curing, the fibers are sensitive to water.

The resin has good penetration so that the overall strength is sufficient for a large portion of the bag molded products.

Formed into convenient mats or pads of resin impregnated fibers, jute and sisal are adaptable to many low pressure molding operations. By the proper predistribution of the fibers and resins, much of the work of molding is reduced. Resin-jute preforms, which approximate the dimensions of the mold, require lower molding pressures than do powders or granules.

HERBERT R. SIMONDS

K

KETONE PEROXIDES

Ketone peroxides are a class of commercially available organic peroxides, all of which, when used in conjunction with promoters or accelerators, initiate room-temperature polymerization* (curing) of unsaturated polyester resins.

Organic peroxides in general can be considered as analogs of hydrogen peroxide (H_2O_2), in which one or both of the hydrogen atoms are replaced by an organic radical. In the case of the ketone peroxide family, the base ketone, e.g., methyl ethyl ketone, cyclohexanone, is reacted with hydrogen peroxide in acidic media to form a mixture of peroxide and hydroperoxide structures. The number of structures as well as the relative proportion of each structure present governs the reactivity of the resulting product. Commercial processes require rigid control measures to insure reproducible performance from lot to lot for each product.

The major ketone peroxide usage category is in polyester-based reinforced plastics, ranging from hand lay-up and "spray-up" fabrication of boats, truck cabs, etc., to encapsulation of fine electronic parts.

Methyl Ethyl Ketone Peroxides (MEKP)

Perhaps the most widely used room temperature curing agents for polyesters are the peroxy derivatives of methyl ethyl ketone. These are generally available as 60% solutions containing 11% active oxygen. Although no two manufacturers of MEKP formulations make exactly identical products, similar formulations will give about the same results in a particular resin. The major producers offer three standard types which differ mainly in reactivity, thus allowing the polyester fabricator to select a particular curing agent pertinent to his particular requirements.

In recent years, fire-resistant grades of MEKP have been developed which are generally

* Although "polymerization initiators" or "curing agents" more correctly describes the chemical action of organic peroxides in free radical-initiated polymerization, usage of terms such as "catalyst" or "hardener" is common, particularly in the FRP industry.

the most reactive of this family of peroxides. Fire-resistant curing agents have found particular application where speed of cure is a critical factor, e.g., clear casting operations (buttons, novelties, etc.) and molding of polyester joints in clay sewer pipe. In most fabricating operations, fire-resistant grades can be substituted for conventional catalysts where increased reactivity and an added margin of safety are desirable. The self-extinguishing feature allows shipment without ICC Yellow cautionary labels affixed to containers. These added safety features may make possible lower plant insurance rates and fewer storage restrictions.

Special formulations of MEKP especially suited for spray-up operations are commercially available. These are the diallyl phthalate (DAP)-extended MEKP solutions, generally ranging from 15–30% active peroxide content. DAP dilution offers a number of advantages, among them: (a) significant increase of flash-point by lowering the overall volatility of the peroxidic mixture, (b) no potentially hazardous by-products formed in the resulting solution, (c) DAP cross-links or copolymerizes with the polyester resin, providing in most cases improved physical properties, (d) elimination of pin-holing and blistering caused by solvent volatilization, and, (e) facilitation of more accurate catalyst metering.

Where catalyst extension by the consumer is necessary, the use of diluents such as DAP, phthalate esters (e.g., dimethyl, dibutyl), and even isobutyl acetate are recommended wherever possible, not only from a safety standpoint, but also in view of physical catalyst losses incurred with rapid volatilization of low flash-point solvents during and after spray application.

In the event use of a volatile solvent is mandatory, diluents such as methyl ethyl ketone, ethyl acetate, butyl acetate or isobutyl acetate are recommended. Acetone should never be used to extend an MEKP, as hazardous peroxide derivatives can form, some of which are crystalline and sparingly soluble in acetone, and some which are extremely friction- and shock-sensitive. It should be noted that the choice of solvent will determine the flash-point of the MEKP solvent mixture.

All of the aforementioned liquid peroxides can be obtained in light colors at a nominal upcharge, cost dependent upon usage volume and the particular colorant. Colored solutions are especially suited for spray systems as a visual means of checking catalyst flow.

Cyclohexanone Peroxides

There are other commercially available ketone peroxides commonly used in room temperature applications with polyester resins, the best known member of this group being 1-hydroxy-1'-hydroperoxydicyclohexyl peroxide, available either as a 50% homogeneous paste with dibutyl phthalate, or as a fine granular powder with 15% dibutyl phthalate. This particular peroxide provides gel times in the MEKP range and a somewhat longer but slightly lower peak exotherm than MEK peroxides. The 85% active product is often used in applications where low plasticizer content is important.

Another cyclohexanone peroxide derivative widely used in room temperature operations is bis(1-hydroxycyclohexyl) peroxide (BHCHP). Available as a 95% crystalline solid, it decomposes with a characteristically low peak exotherm in solution, thus making this peroxy compound particularly applicable to thick-section cure, e.g., polyester-based bowling balls. To achieve optimum physical properties, use of an MEKP in conjunction with BHCHP or postcuring the finished product at elevated temperatures (e.g., 100°C) is necessary. BHCHP, being extremely sensitive to metallic soap promoters (cobalt naphthenate), will cause rapid gelation with little or no color development. This makes this catalyst especially suited to clear casting work (e.g., buttons).

There has recently been introduced a completely new ketone peroxide solution, designed also for the rapid room temperature curing of polyester resins. Characterized by outstanding pot life in unpromoted precatalyzed systems, it offers, in addition to fast gelation, rapid tack-free cures in singly promoted (cobalt) systems. The long pot life aspect makes this new catalyst of particular interest to fabricators utilizing split-phase spray equipment.

Promoter Systems for Ketone Peroxides

The choice of a catalyst-promoter system is governed, mainly by catalyst and/or resin reactivity and, in the case of clear, unfilled applications, color limitations in the finished product.

The most commonly used promoter or accelerator systems for the ketone peroxides are the metallic soaps, such as cobalt octoate, and cobalt naphthenate. At half the resin use level, cobalt octoate, 12% metal concentration, exhibits less discoloration while providing slightly faster acceleration of the cure than cobalt naphthenate, 6% metal content. Still faster gel and cure times are obtained with doubly promoted systems comprised of cobalt octoate and a tertiary amine such as dimethyl or diethyl aniline. However, such a resin-promoter system has the disadvantages of (a) poor resin stability or shelf life due to the amine promoter, and (b) discoloration (generally a pronounced yellow) in the finished product imparted by the tertiary amine.

The pinkish hue imparted to an MEKP-cured polyester resin by cobalt soaps can be effectively reduced by substituting a portion of the peroxide with BHCHP thus allowing use of lower cobalt levels.

Conclusion

With the numerous peroxygen catalysts available for the low or room temperature curing of polyester resins, the fabricator is faced with the problem of choosing the most effective peroxide. Because of the near-infinite number of possible resin-catalyst-promoter-inhibitor systems, it is extremely difficult to predict in every instance which combinations would be most effective in a given situation. Therefore, consideration must be given to all aspects of the operation, pot life, gel time, cure time, exotherm temperature, color development, hardness, etc. The fabricators' choice of catalyst should be determined by conditions peculiar to his sytem, actual experimentation, and/or recommendations of the resin and catalyst suppliers.

F. H. LAUCHERT, JR.
D. J. BOLTON

M

MALEIC ACID AND DERIVATIVES

The presence of two reactive carboxyl groups and a reactive double bond makes maleic anhydride and maleic acid ideally suited as an intermediate for the production of resins and plastics. The most important commercial use of maleic anhydride is in the manufacture of unsaturated polyester resins. Significant amounts are also used in the production of paints, coatings for textiles and paper, adhesives, rubber modifiers, alkyd resins, and epoxy curing agents. Formulas for maleic anhydride and maleic acid are shown below:

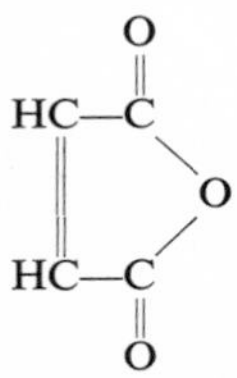

Maleic anhydride 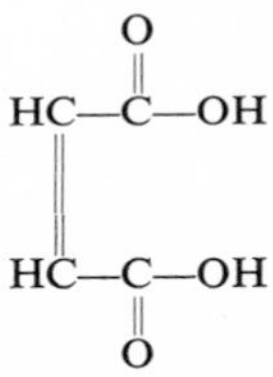   *Maleic acid*

Maleic anhydride is the more important, with approximately 117 million lb produced in the United States in 1964.

Physical Properties of Maleic Anhydride, Maleic Acid and Derivatives

TABLE 1. PHYSICAL PROPERTIES OF MALEIC ANHYDRIDE.

Molecular weight	98.06
Freezing point, °C	52–53
Boiling point, °C	200
Vapor pressure, mm Hg	
at 30°C	0.1
at 53°C	2.2
at 100°C	25
at 150°C	140
at 200°C	760
Specific gravity	
Solid	1.48
Liquid, at 50°C	1.32
Viscosity, liquid, mP	
at 60°C	16.1
at 70°C	15.3
at 80°C	13.1
at 100°C	9.9
at 150°C	6.0

Crystalline form	Orthorhombic needles
Heat of formation, solid, kcal/mole	112.2
Heat of combustion, solid, kcal/mole	333.9
Specific heat	
Solid	0.285
Liquid	0.396
Heat of fusion, kcal/mole	2.75
Heat of vaporization, kcal/mole	10.5
Heat of hydration to the acid, kcal/mole	8.33
Heat of neutralization, kcal/mole	30.32
Heat of solution of maleic acid, kcal/mole	−4.44
Solubility, at 25°C, g/100 ml solvent	
Water	Very soluble (hydrolyzes)
Benzene	43.7
Toluene	20.2
o-Xylene	16.99
Carbon tetrachloride	0.95
Chloroform	78.4
Ethyl alcohol	Very soluble (esterifies)
Ethyl acetate	100.2
Dioxane	Very soluble
Acetone	178.2
Kerosene (boiling range 190–250°C)	0.20
Flash point, Cleveland open cup, °F	212

TABLE 2. PHYSICAL PROPERTIES OF MALEIC ACID.

Molecular weight	116.07
Melting point, °C	130.5
Boiling point, °C	160 (forms anhydride)
Specific gravity, 20/4°C	1.590
Heat of combustion, kcal/mole	326.1
Dissociation constants, at 25°C	
K_1	1.17×10^{-2}
K_2	2.6×10^{-7}
Solubility, g/100 ml solvent	
Water, at 25°C	78.8
at 97.5°C	392.6
Ethanol, at 30°C	69.9
Ethyl ether, at 25°C	8.19
Acetone, at 30°C	35.8
Benzene, at 25°C	0.024
Xylene, at 30°C	0.0085
Carbon tetrachloride, at 25°C	0.002
Chloroform, at 25°C	0.011

Manufacture

The bulk of the maleic anhydride produced in the United States comes from the catalytic vapor phase oxidation of benzene. A minor amount is produced by the vapor phase oxidation of butenes.

The benzene oxidation is accomplished in a tubular reactor at 350–450°C, approximately atmospheric pressure, and over a vanadium pentoxide catalyst supported on alumina. A much higher ratio of air to benzene than the theoretical 106 cu ft air per lb of benzene is used in practice. The oxidation is exothermic producing 10,500–13,500 Btu per lb of benzene oxidized. Removal of the heat is accomplished by circulating a high-temperature heat transfer salt around the reactor tubes. The hot gases issuing from the reactor are cooled by producing steam and preheating the feed stream. Some maleic anhydride is recovered as such in a primary condenser. The remainder is removed as maleic acid in a water scrubbing condenser. The acid is converted to the anhydride by azeotropic distillation with xylene, and high purity maleic anhydride is obtained by vacuum distillation. The overall yield is in excess of 80 wt. %.

Maleic acid is produced by the hydrolysis of maleic anhydride.

Polymerization

Condensation Polymerization. Maleic acid and anhydride are readily esterified with glycols and other polyhydric alcohols to form polyesters. The polyesterification reaction is carried out at elevated temperatures and either under vacuum or by sparging with an inert gas to aid in the removal of the water. The reactants (acids and glycols) are generally charged to the reactor in approximately a 1 : 1 mole ratio. Catalysts are seldom used in the esterification since their removal would present a problem.

Addition Polymerization. Homopolymerization of maleic acid and its derivatives is difficult. It was not until 1961 that the first successful homopolymerization of maleic anhydride was demonstrated. Copolymerization however is readily accomplished. Maleic anhydride and maleic esters copolymerize with vinyl monomers such as the acrylates, butadiene, diallyl phthalate, ethylene, methyl vinyl ether, styrene, vinyl acetate, vinyl chloride, vinylidene chloride, etc., in the presence of free radical polymerization catalysts to yield a number of useful resins. These polymers generally contain equal amounts of both monomers.

Maleic derivatives are strong dienophiles, and will readily undergo the Diels-Alder reaction with conjugated dienes. The Diels-Alder reaction has been used to produce high molecular weight polymers from dienes and dimaleic compounds. The reaction of a thiophene-1,1-dioxide with a dimaleimide produces an adduct that loses sulfur dioxide on heating to yield a diene-dieneophilic monomer which polymerizes further to a high molecular weight polymer. A dimaleimide and an α-pyrone or a cyclopentadienone will undergo similar reactions with the evolution of carbon dioxide, and carbon monoxide respectively during polymerization. A didiene such as 2-vinyl butadiene can react with a dimaleimide and generate a new diene, and thus propagate the polymerization reaction.

These Diels-Alder polymers have high softening points (200 to 300°C), exhibit good electrical properties at elevated temperatures, are relatively inert to acids and bases, and possess high strength. Degradation takes place at temperatures above their softening points presumably by

TABLE 3. PHYSICAL PROPERTIES OF ESTERS OF MALEIC ACID.

Ester	Melting point °C	Boiling point °C	Refractive index, n_D^{20}	Specific gravity, d_4^{20}	Viscosity, at 25°C, cP	Flash point, °F	Solubility at 25°C, g/100 ml H_2O
Dimethyl	−19	202	1.4423	1.1502			7.0
Diethyl	−11.2	219	1.4401	1.0662			1.5
Di-n-propyl		126_{12}	1.4433	1.0245			
Di-n-butyl	−85	280.6 147.5_{12}	1.4454	0.9938	3.66 cst at 100°F	280	<0.05
Diisobutyl		126_5	1.4418	0.9820			
Di-n-amyl		161_{10}	1.4475	0.9741			
Diisoamyl		157_{13}	1.4459	0.914			
Diisohexyl	−80	164_5	1.4490^{25}	0.9590_{25}^{25}	9.11		
Diisooctyl	−75	200_5	1.4570^{25}	0.944	16.5		
Di-2-ethylhexyl	−60	209_{10}	1.4540^{25}	0.9436_{20}^{20}		360	<0.01

reversal of the Diels-Alder reaction. The polymers are neither crystalline nor orientable.

Maleic Polymers and Their Uses

A great variety of polymers and resins can be derived from maleic compounds by addition and condensation polymerization. Their ability to undergo the Diels-Alder reaction with conjugated diene systems also enables them to introduce additional functionality into the system. Subsequent sections will discuss the various polymers and resins produced from maleic compounds.

Polyesters. As mentioned earlier, maleic anhydride, when reacted with a glycol, forms a linear unsaturated polyester by the usual condensation polymerization route. The unsaturated linear polyester can be converted to a thermoset resin by admixing with a vinyl monomer such as styrene, and adding a free radical generating catalyst and an accelerator. Recent evidence has shown that the final configuration of the acid portion of the polyester is predominantly in the trans or fumaric form. Generally the glycol maleate styrene copolymer is brittle. However, both flexibility and toughness can be incorporated into the molecule by decreasing the number of double bonds, and/or by changing their spatial position. This is usually accomplished by substituting phthalic anhydride or a long chain aliphatic dibasic acid, i.e., adipic, for part of the maleic anhydride or fumaric acid, or by using a longer chain glycol. Variations in the amounts and type of acids or glycols used allow the resin manufacturer a wide latitude in the variety of resins he can produce. One of the outstanding characteristics of these resins is their fast rate of cure at low temperature and pressure. When cured, they are rigid, insoluble solids with good dielectric properties and high structural strength. The resins, when filled with glass fibers and other reinforcing materials, are used to produce large rigid moldings by low pressure lamination. These reinforced laminates are used in structural building panels, automobile bodies, molded boats, chemical storage tanks, luggage, furniture, light weight pipe, etc.

Maleic Anhydride Copolymers. A variety of polymers have been prepared by copolymerizing maleic anhydride with acrylates, methacrylates, ethylene, methyl vinyl ether, vinyl chlorides, styrene, butadiene, vinyl acetate, etc. The copolymers from styrene, vinyl acetate, vinyl chloride, methyl vinyl ether and ethylene along with their derivatives are commercially available. Maleic anhydride and styrene copolymerize rapidly in a 1 : 1 ratio at 50°C in the presence of benzoyl peroxide. The rate of polymerization can be controlled if a solvent, such as benzene or xylene, is used. Styrene-maleic anyhdride resins are brittle, incompatible with most other resins, and insoluble in most solvents. They undergo the reactions of most anhydrides; hydrolysis with water to form the acid, ammonolysis with ammonia and amines to the amide-ammonium salt with ammonia and amines, and esterification with alcohols to the mono and diesters. These polymers can also be cross-linked with glycols or diamines to thermoset resins. Styrene-maleic anhydride copolymers and their derivatives have found use in sizing textiles, and in floor polishes and latex paints where they are used as leveling agents and pigment dispersants.

A copolymer containing 85 parts vinyl chloride, 14 parts vinyl acetate, and 1 part maleic anhydride is widely used in the coatings trade. Presence of maleic anhydride improves the adhesion of the vinyl coating to the substrate. Good adhesion can be obtained when the coatings are air dried, but without maleic anhydride, the coatings require baking at elevated temperatures. Maleic anhydride copolymerizes in bulk or solution with methyl vinyl ether in a 1 : 1 ratio in the presence of lauroyl peroxide at 40–50°C. The polymer is soluble in water over the entire pH range, is stable in both acid and alkaline solution, and has wide compatibility with other substances. It functions as a dispersant, stabilizer, coupler, protective colloid, and as a thickener in either aqueous or organic solvent systems. These resins are intended for use in hair sprays, adhesives, shampoos, hand cleaners, detergents, textile sizes, paper additives, antistatic agents, and coating agents in photography. Ethylene and maleic anhydride are polymerized with a peroxide catalyst in an autoclave with or without a solvent, i.e., toluene, under a pressure of 860–950 atm and temperatures of 85–100°C. The copolymer is a white powder that undergoes reactions with water, ammonia, amines, alcohols and glycols. The ethylene-maleic anhydride resins and derivatives have been suggested for use as dispersants, adhesives, hair sprays, textile coatings, paper sizes, suspending agents, and core-binder resins.

Maleic Anhydride Commercial Copolymers—Methyl Vinyl Ether—Maleic Anhydride Copolymers. Commercial copolymers of methyl vinyl ether-maleic anhydride are available under the name "Gantrez" AN* resins. Table 4 lists the typical properties of these resins.

TABLE 4. TYPICAL PROPERTIES OF "GANTREZ" AN RESINS.

Appearance	White, fluffy powder
Softening point range, °C	200–225
Specific gravity of film	1.37
Bulk density of powder, lb/cu ft	20
Residual free maleic anhydride	0
pH, 5% aqueous solution (free acid)	2

Ethylene-Maleic Anhydride Copolymers. The "EMA"† resins are available in anhydride, acid, and salt forms. A description of their properties may be found in Table 5.

Styrene-Maleic Anhydride Copolymers. The "SMA"‡ resins are low molecular weight copo-

* Registered trademark of General Aniline & Film Corporation.

TABLE 5. PROPERTIES OF "EMA" RESINS.

Form	anhydride White powder	acid White powder	sodium salt White powder
Softening point, °C	170	155	–
Melting point, °C	235	217	–
Decomposition point, °C	247	250	–
pH, 1% aqueous solution	2.35[a]	2.35	6
Bulk density, lb/cu. ft.	20	37	ca 25

[a] Hydrolysis to free acid after 2–3 hr at 80°C, or 10–15 min at 95°C

TABLE 6. PROPERTIES OF "SMA" RESINS.

Form	White powder
Molecular weight, range	700–1900
Acid No., range	415–500
Melting range, °C	50–170
Viscosity range, cSt, at 30°C (10 g/100 ml acetone)	0.53–0.67
Bulk density range, lb/cu ft	35–38
Solubility 1 g/10 ml solvent (24 hr at 26°C)	
Petroleum ether	Insoluble
Acetone	Soluble
Carbon tetrachloride	Insoluble
Methanol	Soluble
Benzene	Slightly soluble to insoluble
Ethylene glycol	Insoluble
Alkali	Soluble

lymers. Typical properties are presented in Table 6.

The "Lytron"† resins are partially esterified styrene-maleic anhydride copolymers. These resins are insoluble in water, hexane, and toluene, but soluble in bases, i.e., sodium and potassium hydroxide, and ammonia, and in ketones, alcohols and esters. Typical properties of these "Lytron" resins may be found in Table 7.

"Stymer S"† resin is the sodium salt of a maleic anhydride-styrene copolymer. The properties of "Stymer S" are given in Table 8.

† Registered trademark of Monsanto Co.
‡ Registered trademark of Sinclair Petrochemicals.

TABLE 7. PROPERTIES OF "LYTRON" RESINS.

	Equivalent wt.	Acid no.	Softening point, °C	Average molecular wt.	Viscosity, cP, 10% NH₄ salt	Parts NH₃ for solubilization
"Lytron" 810	175	320	220	50,000	250	66
"Lytron" 812	180	300	120	1,500	3	40
"Lytron" 820	300	180	210	20,000	150	30

TABLE 8. PROPERTIES OF "STYMER S" RESINS.

Form	Free-flowing, fine powder
Odor	Faint aromatic
Solubility	Soluble in water
pH·	7.5–8.5
Specific gravity at 140°F	1.005
Surface tension, DuNoüy, at 86°F	57
Color, APHA	50
Clarity	Very slight haze
Water dilution	Uniformly dilutable
Stability	Excellent under normal conditions

Maleic Ester Copolymers. The copolymers of dialkyl maleates, particularly the dibutyl esters with vinyl acetate, have found extensive use in latex paint formulations. Poly (vinyl acetate) homopolymer latexes, plasticized with dibutyl phthalate, are suitable for interior paints, but their performance is poor when applied to exterior surfaces. When vinyl acetate is copolymerized with dibutyl maleate, a more permanent improvement in film properties results. The maleate ester is functioning as an internal plasticizer and, unlike an external plasticizer, cannot be removed by weathering from the paint film. In addition, these copolymers have lower flux temperatures, lower tensile strength, improved coalescence, and greater flexibility than do vinyl acetate homopolymers. Paints prepared from these latexes are suitable for both indoor and outdoor applications. The latexes can also be used in the preparation of adhesives, and for treating paper and textiles. Acrylate esters copolymerized with monomaleates produce polymers capable of being thermoset by reaction of the pendant carboxyl group with epoxy or amino resins. Thermoset acrylic resins with improved gloss and color retention, weatherability, chemical resistance and adhesion may be obtained by varying the composition of the acrylate copolymer and/or by the choice of cross-linking resin. Tin plate coatings that will resist forming operations are prepared from a vinyl chloride-maleic ester-phenol-formaldehyde resin. A hydrolyzed terpolymer of vinyl chloride, vinyl acetate and maleic anhydride that will thermoset upon heating is useful for coating glass and steel. A wide choice of formulation can be achieved by combining these resins with other heat-curing resins such as melamine-formaldehyde, phenol-formaldehyde, etc. Thermosetting resins suitable for coatings and casting and molding applications can be prepared by polymerizing allyl maleates. Excellent adhesives for polyethylene, "Saran", aluminum foil and wax paper can be prepared by internally plasticizing polyvinyl pyrrolidinone with dialkyl maleates or

fumarates. Cellulose acetate can be laminated to paper with an adhesive prepared by dissolving a vinyl acetate-dibutyl maleate copolymer in an alcohol or ester that does not dissolve cellulose acetate. Polyvinyl chloride sheets or films can be bonded to paper, cardboard, textiles, wood and concrete with an adhesive prepared from vinyl acetate-dibutyl maleate copolymer admixed with dibutyl maleate. A flexible adhesive recommended for binding books and magazines is based on a plasticized monoalkyl maleate-vinyl ester copolymer.

A terpolymer composed of monooctyl maleate, dodecyl methacrylate and styrene is a satisfactory size for acetate or viscose fibers. Nylon warp yarns are sized by immersing them in a solution of a sodium salt of a styrene monomaleate copolymer. The size is easily removed from the finished fabric by washing with warm water. Pigmented dibutyl maleate-vinyl acetate copolymer latexes have been used as such, and as a 50 : 50 starch-latex mix for coating tape. An adherent, glossy, water-resistant finish can be imparted to paper by a dispersion of maleic anhydride-vinyl acetate-vinyl chloride terpolymer. The sodium salt of a monoalkyl maleate-styrene copolymer is a suitable pigment and mineral finish binder for coated printing paper.

The half ester of maleic acid and ethoxylated dodecyl phenol when copolymerized with vinyl acetate produces a detergent suitable for lubricating oils. Synthetic lubricating oils having high viscosity indexes and low pour points have been prepared by polymerizing aliphatic diesters of maleic and fumaric acids. Plasticizers for phenolic and cellulosic resins are obtained by reacting monomaleates with epichlorohydrin. Thermosetting resins may be prepared by adding monobenzyl maleate to a solution of a polyepoxide in styrene and then curing with benzoyl peroxide. Enteric coatings for drugs may be prepared from a monobutyl maleate-acrylic acid-styrene copolymer.

Alkyd Resins. Maleic anhydride is often substituted for part of the phthalic anhydride in alkyd formulations in order to shorten the processing time. When about 2% of the phthalic anhydride is replaced with maleic anhydride, the processing time is reduced by approximately 30%. If shorter processing times are desired, then more maleic can be used. Alkyds containing maleic anhydride dry faster and possess better baking properties. The dried films from these modified alkyds are harder, more durable, more water- and alkali-resistant, and superior in color and color retention to alkyd films prepared without maleic anhydride. Suitable vehicles for alkyd resin emulsion paints may be prepared from a cook of rosin, glycerol and linseed oil, that has been adducted with maleic anhydride. The adduct is further formulated with ammonia or amines and sodium silicate. Paints prepared from these vehicles give comparatively hard, water-insoluble films.

Maleinized Oils. Maleic anhydride reacts with various unsaturated oils at elevated temperatures to produce maleinized oils. Maleinized soybean and linseed oils exhibit the same processing time with resins as conjugated oils do. The advantages these products have over ordinary oleoresinous varnishes are faster drying and greater hardness. They can also replace the harder drying tung and oiticica oils. The rapid gelling characteristics of tung and dehydrated castor oil are lost when they are modified with maleic anhydride.

Maleinization of drying oils may be accomplished in two ways: (1) Maleic anhydride is reacted with the oil for one hour at 235°C, then a polyhydric alcohol is added and the temperature increased to 270°C and held there until the acid number is less than 10. (2) The oil and a polyhydric alcohol are heated together at 230°C in the presence of 0.01% litharge and then cooled to 150°C; maleic anhydride is added and the mixture is cooked at 270°C until the acid number is less than 10. Both procedures are carried out under a blanket of inert gas, and the products are filtered to insure satisfactory clarity.

Diene Adducts. Maleic anhydride and conjugated dienes readily form Diels-Alder adducts which in turn may be used to produce a variety of resins. The adducts still contain unsaturation, and can undergo additional polymerization upon heating. The Diels-Alder adduct of maleic anhydride and butadiene, tetrahydrophthalic anhydride, may be used to replace phthalic anhydride in an air-drying, wax-free polyester coating system. Atmospheric oxygen retards the curing of the conventional polyester-styrene coating. One way this inhibition can be minimized is by the use of paraffin wax; another alternative is to use polyester resins based on tetrahydrophthalic anhydride which cure in the presence of oxygen. Another advantage of this system is its solubility in styrene at room temperature. Conventional resins are difficult to dissolve in styrene at ambient temperatures; however, they can be dissolved at elevated temperatures, but if too high a temperature is used the batch may gel. Coatings, based on the tetrahydrophthalic anhydride resin, air-dry tack-free in 2–4 hr at room temperature; at 150°C they air-dry in 15–30 min. With only one coat the coatings give a deep gloss on most substrates, with little or no buffing. These coatings have high impact strength and are mar resistant, moisture and stain resistant, and flexible.

Coating resins have also been prepared from the cyclopentadiene-maleic anhydride adduct.

In addition to their use as coatings resins, the Diels-Alder adducts of butadiene, cyclopentadiene, and methyl cyclopentadiene with maleic anhydride find extensive use as curing agents for epoxy resins. With these anhydrides the final cure is effected by heating at 80–150°C. Epoxy resins cured with anhydrides generally have high heat distortion temperatures, and are used primarily as potting and encapsulating resins for electrical applications.

Rosin Adducts. The ability of maleic anhydride to react with conjugated dienes to form Diels-Alder adducts makes it ideally suited for modifying rosins. Resins prepared from maleic modified rosins are referred to as maleic ester gums. They can be produced by one of several methods, all of which give the same type products. In one method, rosin and a polyhydric alcohol are reacted together first, followed by reaction with maleic anhydride. In another, the reverse is done —rosin and maleic anhydride are reacted together and are then esterified with a polyhydric alcohol. In a third method, all three are reacted together simultaneously. These ester gums, when processed with oxidizing oils, yield air-drying resins. In contrast to unmodified rosins, resins produced from these maleic modified rosins have increased melting points, increased hardness, decreased alcohol solubility, reduced crystallization tendency, increased viscosity and refractive index, and are non-tacky. Films from these modified rosins have excellent solvent release, lower color and better resistance to yellowing and aging than do the unmodified rosin esters. They find use in varnish and cellulose nitrate finishes.

Tall Oil Adducts. Tall oil, because it consists of rosin and unsaturated fatty acids, will react with maleic anhydride to produce resinous products suitable for the coatings industry. Preparation of these tall oil resins is accomplished by the following procedure. The tall oil is heated to 300°F with agitation under an inert gas. Maleic anhydride, 10–15% based on the rosin content, is added, and the temperature is then raised to 425°F and held there until the mixture becomes clear. This takes approximately 0.5 hr. Litharge and calcium hydroxide are then added and heating is continued for an additional 0.5 hr. Pentaerythritol is added and the mixture heated at 525°F until the resin develops body. Improvement in color can be accomplished by the addition of triphenylphosphite. The addition of soya, safflower, or linseed oil, along with the tall oil, will improve flexibility and weatherability of the dried films. These tall oil resins are used in general coatings applications, particularly in industrial dip coatings. They have also been used as binders for the sand in metal casting molds.

Terpene Adducts. Maleic anhydride will react with a variety of terpenes. Esterification of these adducts with polyhydric alcohols forms products ranging from brittle resins to elastomeric materials. Maleic anhydride reacts with practically all the $C_{10}H_{16}$ terpenes including the straight chain terpenes containing conjugated double bonds, some of the bicyclic terpenes with 3- or 4-membered rings, and most of the monocyclic terpenes, whether they contain conjugated double bonds or not. With conjugated terpenes, maleic anhydride forms the usual Diels-Alder adducts. Other products that may also form are chain copolymers that vary in the maleic anhydride-terpene ratio. Both the Diels-Alder adducts and the chain copolymers form polyesters.

The nonconjugated terpenes, dipentene, terpinolene, γ-terpinene react with maleic anhydride in more than one way. The presence of maleic or other acids isomerizes them to conjugated terpenes which undergo the Diels-Alder addition. In the absence of acid, no isomerization takes place and linear copolymers are formed. Maleic anhydride and terepinolene yield a product 50% of which is a pale, oily, yellow monomer that may be separated from the polymer by vacuum distillation. Neither the monomer nor the polymer are characteristic of a Diels-Alder adduct. Terpinolenyl succinic anhydride and ethylene glycol produce hard brittle resins suitable for high grade furniture lacquers where high gloss, light color, resistance to temperature and toughness are required. Softer resins suitable for calendered fabric coatings are obtainable when diethylene or triethylene glycol are used. The glycerol resins are harder and gel more readily than the glycol resins. They are infinitely soluble in alcohol, a property that makes them suitable as a shellac substitute in coatings formulations and aniline inks. Aqueous dispersions of some of these terpene-adduct resins find use as impregnants and binders for felt, as impregnants for paper used in the manufacture of artificial leather, as sizes, and coatings for paper, metal foil, cellulose films, and natural and synthetic fibers. They are also used as warp sizes for textile yarns, and as rubber compounding materials.

Specifications and Standards

Commercial maleic anhydride is uniform in quality and purity. It is generally supplied as solid dust-free briquettes or in molten form. Typical specifications are:

Color, molten, max	20 APHA
Assay as maleic anhydride, min	99.5%
Solidification point, min	52.5°C
Sediment	Sediment-free melt

It can be shipped in insulated tank trucks (40,000 lb), in fiber drums (250 lb net), or in multiwall bags (50 lb net).

TABLE 9. SPECIFICATIONS FOR MALEIC ESTERS.

	Dibutyl maleate	Di-2-ethyl-hexyl maleate
Color, APHA max	40	50
Assay as % ester, min	99.0	99.0
Specific gravity, 20/20°C	0.995	0.944
Acidity, meq KOH/100 g, max	0.2	0.2
Moisture, Karl Fischer in CH_3OH, % max	0.10	0.10
Odor	mild	mild

Toxicological Effects

Maleic Anhydride and Maleic Acid. Maleic anhydride fumes or dust are potent irritants to the skin and mucous membranes; inhalation of the fumes or dust causes burning of the eyes, irritation to the nose and throat, and coughing. Exposure to the fumes or dust may also cause temporary double vision, especially to individuals with hypersensitivity. This is presumed to be due to local irritation; no permanent damage to the eyes has been noted. Part of the effect of maleic anhydride is due to its dehydrating action and, in addition, maleic acid, the hydrolysis product, is also a potent acid. Maleic anhydride and maleic acid, taken internally, are as poisonous to the human system as oxalic acid.

Dibutyl Maleate. Dibutyl maleate is a mild skin irritant causing redness and slight swelling—however, the vapors do not constitute much of a hazard. Test animals survived exposure to a saturated atmosphere for six hr. Taken internally, dibutyl maleate is considered slightly toxic. The LD_{50} obtained on test rats fed single doses is 3.6 g/kg of body weight.

GEORGE L. BROWNELL

MELAMINE

Melamine, 2,4,6-triamino-s-triazine, has been an important ingredient in the preparation of amino resins since about 1940, although it was first prepared by Liebig in 1834 from potassium thiocyanate and ammonium chloride.

Physical Properties

Melamine is a white, crystalline (monoclinic) solid, melting at about 354°C with simultaneous decomposition and sublimation. It is sparingly soluble in most polar solvents and insoluble in non-polar solvents. Water is the most satisfactory solvent for recrystallization, particularly if the process is conducted in a closed system at a maximum temperature of about 130°C.

Chemical Properties

Melamine is a weakly basic trifunctional amine; many of its chemical reactions resemble

$$\text{H}_2\text{N}-\text{C} \quad \text{C}-\text{NH}_2 + 2\text{HCHO} \rightarrow \text{HOCH}_2\text{NH}-\text{C} \quad \text{C}-\text{NHCH}_2\text{OH}$$

(melamine triazine ring, with NH$_2$ at bottom) $\xrightarrow{+ 4\text{HCHO}}$

$$(\text{HOCH}_2)\text{N}-\text{C} \quad \text{C}-\text{N(CH}_2\text{OH})_2$$

$$\text{N(CH}_2\text{OH})_2$$

those of amides. Its commercial importance stems from its reactivity towards formaldehyde.

The di- and hexamethylolmelamines are important precursors of many amino resins. For some applications, e.g., surface coatings, the methylolmelamines are alkylated (esterified) to enhance their solubility in organic solvents.

Melamine forms salts with a wide variety of organic and inorganic acids; melamine picrate and particularly melamine cyanurate because of

tion of melamine from dicy is represented by:

$$3(\text{H}_2\text{N})_2\text{C}=\text{N}-\text{CN} \rightarrow 2\text{H}_2\text{N}-\text{C} \quad \text{C}-\text{NH}_2$$

(triazine ring with NH$_2$ at bottom)

The reaction is highly exothermic; both dicy and

$$\text{HOCH}_2\text{NH}-\text{C} \quad \text{C}-\text{NHCH}_2\text{OH} + \text{ROH} \rightarrow \text{ROCH}_2\text{NH}-\text{C} \quad \text{C}-\text{NHCH}_2\text{OR}$$

(triazine rings with NH$_2$ at bottom)

their extreme insolubility are used for the quantitative determination of melamine.

Melamine can be alkylated and arylated. The former reaction gives rise to isomelamines which are strong bases:

$$\text{H}_2\text{N}-\text{C} \quad \text{C}=\text{NH}$$

(triazine ring with NH$_2$ at bottom)

Except for the methylol derivatives, no melamine reaction products have found significant use in the formulation of plastics and resins.

Manufacture

Melamine is produced commercially by heating dicyandiamide (dicy) or urea, the latter being a relatively recently developed process. The forma-

melamine are solids. Melamine decomposes at a significant rate, at and above its melting point (354°C). Consequently, most of the very extensive patent literature dealing with melamine manufacture from dicy is concerned with processing schemes designed to obviate the aforementioned difficulties. Commercially operable processes usually employ anhydrous ammonia, alone or in combination with an inert solvent or diluent to act as a heat buffer. Both batch and continuous processes based on dicy have been patented, including some for the removal of melamine from the reactor as a vapor.

In recent years a large number of patents have been granted on processes for the conversion of urea to melamine. The extent to which these processes are utilized commercially is obscure. When urea is heated in a closed system to temperatures between 300 and 450°C, good yields of melamine are obtained, provided that sufficient minimum partial pressure of ammonia is maintained. The overall reaction occurring under these conditions is generally believed to be:

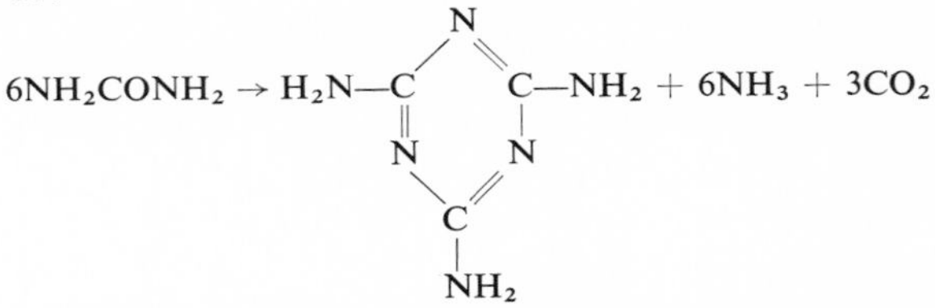

$$6NH_2CONH_2 \rightarrow H_2N-C \overset{\displaystyle N}{\underset{\displaystyle N}{\parallel}} C-NH_2 + 6NH_3 + 3CO_2$$

The exact mechanism of the reaction is not known. The patent literature discloses that the above reaction is quite endothermic and highly corrosive towards most commonly employed alloys. As is true in process employing dicy, much of the patent literature describes ingenious methods intended to provide operable processes.

In the presence of certain catalysts, e.g., silica gel, urea can be converted to melamine at or about atmospheric pressure; this method avoids the difficulties of high pressure operation typical of many melamine processes.

The stoichiometry of the urea to melamine conversion is such that a recovery and recycle system for the by-product NH_3 and CO_2 is essential for economic operation.

Handling and Safety Factors

Melamine is thermally stable and nontoxic; no extraordinary precautions are necessary in its utilization as an industrial chemical.

Analytical Determination

Melamine forms a number of insoluble salts which may be used for its assay; the picrate and especially the cyanurate are best suited for quantitative determinations.

L. C. LANE

METHYL CHLORIDE

Methyl chloride (chloromethane) was first known in about 1835 in Europe. It did not attain much commercial importance until used as a refrigerant in the early years of mechanical refrigeration in the United States. The beginning of World War II saw the demise of methyl chloride as a refrigerant and the start of several other commercial uses. Three wartime uses were as a raw material in the production of quaternaries and silicone resins, and as catalyst solvent for butyl rubber production. Following the war, methyl chloride found several uses as a low cost methylating agent for such products as methyl cellulose, methyl ethers, pharmaceuticals, arsenical herbicides and tetramethyl lead.

Physical Properties

Molecular weight	50.49
Boiling point, 760 mm	$-10.76°F$ $(-23.76°C)$
Freezing point	$-143.7°F$ $(-97.6°C)$
Liquid density at 32°F	59.92 lb/cu ft

Vapor density, 32°F and 760 mm	0.144 lb/cu ft
Vapor pressure, 68°F	56.3 psig
Specific heat	
Liquid, 68°F	0.381
Vapor, 77°F and 1 atm, C_p	0.199
Vapor, 77°F and 1 atm, C_r	0.155
Critical pressure	968.7 psi absolute
Critical temperature	289.4°F (143°C)
Thermal conductivity, Btu/ (hr)(sq ft)(°F/ft)	
Liquid, 68°F	0.093
Vapor, 32°F	0.00486
Color, vapor and liquid	Colorless, transparent
Flash point	Below 32°F

Solubility at 68°F and 1 atm

Solvent	wt% Methyl chloride
Water	0.7
Carbon tetrachloride	5.1
Ethanol	10.0
Benzene	10.5

Chemical Properties

Methyl chloride has the following structural formula:

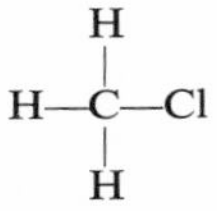

$$H-\underset{\displaystyle H}{\overset{\displaystyle H}{\underset{|}{\overset{|}{C}}}}-Cl$$

The hydrogen atoms are rather strongly bound, but the chlorine atom is not. Most of the chemical reactions of methyl chloride are connected with the replacement of the chlorine atom with other atoms or chemical groups.

At ordinary temperature, methyl chloride is stable to heat. It will decompose if heated to a temperature of 800°F or higher.

Methyl chloride reacts slowly with water at room temperature to form methyl alcohol and hydrochloric acid. The rate of reaction is increased with temperature. When water at 120°C is saturated with methyl chloride gas at a pressure of 75 psig, about 1 g of methyl chloride reacts per hr, per each 100 g of water. The hydrochloric acid produced in this reaction is highly corrosive to most metals. The addition of alkali metal hydroxides or carbonates reduces the corrosion, but increases the rate of reaction of methyl chloride with water.

Commercial grade liquid methyl chloride, as sold in steel cylinders, contains a water content below about 100 ppm. This extremely dry product is non-corrosive to metals such as steel, iron, copper, and brass, but not to galvanized iron, magnesium and aluminum. It reacts very readily with aluminum forming the highly reactive trimethyl aluminum.

Most of the chemical reactions of methyl chloride involve the displacement of a hydrogen or sodium atom in some other chemical with a methyl (CH$_3$) group, or a direct addition of the methyl group to a metal atom. The reaction of methyl chloride with ammonia to form methylamine is an example of a hydrogen displacement, and the reaction with sodium phenolate to form anisole is an example of sodium displacement. The reaction of methyl chloride with aluminum to form the trimethyl aluminum is an example of addition to a metal.

Specifications and Analysis

Typical specifications for liquid methyl chloride in steel containers are as follows:

Methyl chloride	99.5 (mole %) min
Boiling range (at 760 mm)	−23.6 to −24.6°C
Water	100 ppm max
Acidity (as HCl)	0.002 wt % max
Non-condensible gas (liquid phase)	0.5 vol % max
Dimethyl ether, methanol	Nil
Methylene chloride	0.1 wt% max
Residue or evaporation	0.01 wt% max

The analysis procedures for these specifications can be obtained from the manufacturer.

There are several tests, both qualitative and quantitative, that can be used to detect methyl chloride, but none are specific. About the best procedure is gas chromatography. This procedure can also be used to detect impurities in methyl chloride vapour. For details of these various methods, contact the manufacturer.

Handling

Methyl chloride is shipped in steel cylinders, drums and tankcars as a liquified gas under pressure. At 68°F, the pressure is 56.3 psig. These containers should be handled with the same procedures as are usually followed with a moderately flammable and toxic liquified gas. Detailed handling instructions are available from each manufacturer, and from the Manufacturing Chemists' Association.

Safety Devices. Liquid methyl chloride expands with temperature. The I.C.C. permits filling of containers with liquid methyl chloride up to 0.84 times the full water weight at 60°F. This permits some expansion with temperature. As a safety precaution to prevent overheating, with subsequent rupture of the container due to hydrostatic pressure, cylinders and drums are equipped with fusible metal plugs that melt when the temperature reaches 165°F. Tankcars are equipped with pressure relief valves. In transferring methyl chloride by pipe line, care must be taken that valves on both ends of the line are not shut off while full

of liquid, unless a pressure relief valve is installed. Heating of cylinders and drums, to facilitate transfer, should not be above about 120°F to avoid melting of the fusible plugs.

Small Containers. For the small user, methyl chloride is available in steel cylinders of 100 and 140 lb, net. If gas phase delivery is desired, these cylinders must be mounted upright and safely clamped in position. For liquid phase delivery, the cylinders must be inverted. Instructions are available from the manufacturer for construction of a special cylinder yoke and stand for inverting cylinders.

Drums. For the small or intermediate size user, methyl chloride is available in steel drums of 1300 lb, net. These drums must be handled with a derrick or monorail system. They are mounted on their side when in use, with the two end valves lined up vertically. The upper valve will deliver gas phase and the lower valve liquid phase methyl chloride. Instructions for heating these drums are available from the manufacturer.

Tankcars. For the large user, railroad tankcars and tank trucks are available in a variety of sizes. Tank delivery requires an intermediate storage tank at or near point of use. Transfer requires a pressure differential between tankcar and storage tank. This is accomplished by pumping methyl chloride vapor from storage tank to tankcar or by pressurizing the tankcar with an inert gas, such as carbon dioxide or nitrogen. Air must not be used. For detailed instructions on transfer, consult the manufacturer.

Using Methyl Chloride. Transfer of methyl chloride from container to point of use is best done by copper tubing or black iron pipe. Most large applications require liquid methyl chloride at point of use. The flow rate is determined by means of a tapered-tube flow meter. The amount used is determined by weight difference of the container or by means of a weigh tank, or by volume difference in a liquid level equipped intermediate container.

Use of methyl chloride in the gas phase requires a steam heated evaporating tank for large users. Small users can heat the container by means of thermostatically regulated heaters that keep the container temperature below about 120°F. Flow rate can be determined with a tapered-tube flow meter. Gas phase application is most practical for small laboratory uses, because of difficulty in regulating flow of small volumes of liquid methyl chloride.

Leak Detection. The toxicity and flammability of methyl chloride requires a constant check for leaks in piping, valves and containers. This is best done by placing the equipment under carbon dioxide or nitrogen pressure, and checking for suspected leaks with soap solution. Never use a flame type halide torch to detect leaks. All areas where methyl chloride is used should be well ventilated and checked periodically with a Bureau of Mines explosimeter.

Toxicity. The acute and chronic exposure of animals to methyl chloride vapor in air has shown that 6 hr of exposure for one week produced acute toxic symptoms in mice at 500 ppm, in guinea pigs and dogs at 1000 ppm, and in rats, goats and monkeys at 2000 ppm. Chronic toxic effects were observed in dogs and monkeys on prolonged exposure to 500 ppm. Based on these results a suggested maximum allowable concentration for short exposure to methyl chloride is 100 ppm. Because of the low level of odor of methyl chloride, there is not adequate warning of exposure. In addition, the toxic effects of methyl chloride are delayed for several hours. As a result, over-exposure to methyl chloride vapor in air is easily possible.

The symptoms of methyl chloride poisoning are drowsiness, weakness in the legs, blurred vision, salivation, vomiting, convulsions and paralysis. Death will occur from prolonged over-exposure.

If over-exposure to methyl chloride is suspected, a physician should be consulted immediately. The individual should be placed in a well ventilated room and given oxygen by trained personnel. If breathing has stopped, artificial respiration should be given. If conscious, hot tea or coffee can be given as a stimulant. Do *not* administer adrenaline in methyl chloride poisoning.

If skin has been exposed to liquid methyl chloride in any quantity, freezing will result. Treatment should be that for frost-bite or freezing.

Flammability. The flammability limits of methyl chloride vapor in air are between about 8.1 and 17.2% by volume. The limits vary somewhat with the source of ignition. Glowing cigars and cigarettes did not produce ignition within the above range, whereas igniting or burning matches, gas flames, hot wires and spark plugs were able to cause ignition, but the flammability limits varied a little with each ignition source. With a 15,000 volt spark ignition, the flammability limits were increased from 7.6–19.1% by volume.

Uses

Methyl chloride is being used as a refrigerant, solvent, rectifying agent for metal heat treating baths, and as a methylating agent. The major uses are in the preparation of silicones, quaternaries, butyl rubber, methylcellulose and tetramethyl lead. The uses related to the plastics industry are silicones, butyl rubber and methylcellulose.

Silicone Resins. Methyl chloride is used as a raw material in the preparation of silicone resins. The basic structure for the silicone resins is an alternating silicone oxygen arrangement called a siloxane network:

$$\begin{matrix} & R & & R & & R & \\ -Si & -O- & Si & -O- & Si & -O- \\ & R & & R & & R & \end{matrix}$$

The R's can be any organic group or hydrogen, but are usually methyl groups.

An intermediate for preparing these silicone resins is dimethyldichlorosilane.

$$\begin{matrix} & CH_3 & \\ & | & \\ Cl- & Si & -Cl \\ & | & \\ & CH_3 & \end{matrix}$$

This material is prepared by direct reaction of a copper-silicone alloy with methyl chloride. Other methylchlorosilanes are simultaneously produced and can be separated by fractional distillation.

Dimethyldichlorosilane reacts with water to form the dimethylsiloxy group:

$$\begin{matrix} & CH_3 & \\ & | & \\ - & Si & -O- \\ & | & \\ & CH_3 & \end{matrix}$$

which builds chains to form the dimethyl silicone oils or resins, depending on the degree of polymerization attained.

Butyl Rubber. Methyl chloride is used as a solvent for aluminum trichloride in the low temperature (-125 to $-150°F$) polymerization of a mixture of 98% isobutylene and 2% isoprene. Attempts have been made to find a better catalyst solvent, but the results have been largely unsuccessful. Many improvements have been made in reducing the losses of methyl chloride, which were quite high in the early stages of butyl rubber production. The specifications for methyl chloride have also been tightened, particularly with respect to dimethyl ether and low boiling alkyl halides such as ethyl chloride.

Methylcellulose. Methyl chloride is used as a raw material in making methylcellulose. The basic process consists in reacting methyl chloride with alkali cellulose in a pressure reaction at elevated temperatures and then processing the reaction mixture to separate methylcellulose of specific properties from unreacted products and by product sodium chloride.

The alkali cellulose for this reaction is prepared by reacting cellulose with strong aqueous sodium hydroxide solution. Either cotton or wood cellulose can be used. A high alpha cellulose content is desirable but not essential. Because the reaction is heterogeneous, the physical form of the cellulose is very important. Shredded or powdered cellulose gives the best results. A 50% sodium hydroxide solution is best for making water soluble methylcellulose.

The commercial grade of methylcellulose is a white powder, soluble in cold water, insoluble in hot. It is odorless and tasteless. It has a methoxyl content of about 29%, which is equivalent to 1.8 methyl groups per cellulose molecule. By varying the methoxyl content and the reaction conditions, methylcellulose preparations can be prepared which show viscosities, as a 2% solution in water, ranging from 5–25,000 centipoises. The various preparations have found uses in pharmaceutical preparations, paint removers, water-soluble paints, sizing agents for paper and a thickening agent in rubber products.

Other Uses. Attempts have been made to use methyl chloride as a foaming agent for foamed plastics. This market has now been largely captured by the fluorinated solvents.

Methyl chloride has found some applications as a solvent and propellant for aerosol paints, particularly in formulations where the excellent solvent properties of methyl chloride are an advantage.

P. J. Ehman

METHYL PYRROLIDONE

Certain solvents are becoming increasingly important in the chemical processing and plastics industries. This selected group of high cost–high performance solvents exhibits broad and unusual solvating properties. N-methyl-2-pyrrolidone, (referred to as NM2P) is fast becoming one of the more important members of this small group of special solvents which includes dimethyl-formamide, tetrahydrofuran, dimethylacetamide, sulfolane, dimethylsulfoxide and isophorone.

NM2P (N-methyl-2-pyrrolidone) is a stable high boiling chemically inert lactam exhibiting unique solvating properties. It is supplied as an essentially water white liquid possessing a characteristic amine-like odor. It is completely miscible with water, and most organic solvents including alcohol, esters, ethers, lactones, aromatic and chlorinated hydrocarbons, vegetable oils and other exotic solvents. Its physical properties are listed in Table 1.

Low toxicity, ability to dissolve a wide variety of resins, miscibility with water as well as common organic solvents, stability, high boiling point and moderate cost combine to make NM2P a very useful industrial solvent. It is used in solvent-welding, casting, stripping, spinning, surface coating, wire enameling, and cleaning operations.

Polymers soluble in NM2P include hydrocarbons as well as highly polar materials. Such diverse products as acrylics, polybutenes, epoxies, polyvinyl chlorides, polystyrene, polyurethanes and cellulosic derivatives can all be dissolved in this unusual solvent.

Solvent Welding

Plastic materials may be fused without the application of heat by using NM2P to etch and soften the surfaces which are then pressed together to form a durable bond without resorting to cements. This solvent gives a good "bite" into such polymeric materials as cellulose, esters, vinyls, polyamides and acrylics.

The same polymeric softening effect is of interest in compounding fiber-locking adhesives.

Casting, Extruding, Molding

In the production of sheets and films of polyvinyl chloride and its copolymers, NM2P is a useful solvent. Such solutions are adaptable to methods employing water soluble or inflatable supports.

NM2P is a latent solvent for polyvinyl fluoride. Hot solutions of this plastic may therefore be extruded to form self-supporting shaped structures when cooled.

Spinning of Synthetic Fibers

Since the introduction of NM2P as a spinning solvent for acrylic fibers, widespread recognition of its advantages have led to the use of this solvent with other synthetic fibers in both dry and wet-spinning operations. In wet-spinning it exhibits particularly good distribution characteristics between fiber and water.

TABLE 1. PHYSICAL PROPERTIES OF
N-METHYL-2-PYRROLIDONE (NM2P).

Physical form	Liquid with mild amine-like odor
Color (APHA)	50 max
Active ingredient content (melamine %)	97.0% max
Moisture content	0.2% max
Freezing point	24.4°C min
Boiling point	202°C (395°F)
Viscosity (25°C)	1.65 cps
Refractive index (n_D^{25})	1.469
Specific gravity (d_4^{25})	1.027
Flash point (open cup)	95°C (204°F)
Dipole moment	4.09 ± 0.04 debye
Heat of combustion	719 kcal/mole
Autogenous ignition temp. (ASTM Method D-286-58T)	346°C (655°F)
Miscibility with other solvents	Completely miscible with water and most organic solvents, including alcohols, ethers, ketones, aromatic and chlorinated hydrocarbons, and vegetable oils.

Wire Coating

Polyamides used to insulate wires for high temperature service are normally difficult to dissolve. However, solutions of these polycarboxylic acid aromatic amine based resins, having high aromatic content, may be made easily with NM2P. Among the types of polymers currently marketed and for which NM2P is the solvent of choice are pyromellitic anhydride, trimellitic acid and benzophenone acid dianhydride based resins.

Production and Purification of Polymers

The purification of polyamides is facilitated by the employment of NM2P. It aids in the removal of color bodies, as well as colorless impurities and unreacted monomers from, for example, polycaprolactam and its copolymers.

In the preparation of polyamides, NM2P may be added prior to the condensation reaction. The melt can then be spun directly into water, or the solvent removed by distillation before spinning.

A method for the manufacture of polyurethane foam sponges with improved hydrophylic properties has been developed through the use of N-methyl-2-pyrrolidone as catalyst. The prepolymer is converted to a foamed plastic by treatment with a wetting agent and approximately 4% NM2P, which is added with water.

Pigment Dispersions

In paints, lithographic inks, and other protective and decorative pigmented coatings, NM2P is an effective dispersing agent at a level of 1% or less (based on pigment) for both organic and inorganic pigments. It is easily used in conventional grinding techniques, such as 3-roll mill, ball-mill, or Hoover automatic muller.

Cleaning

Polymer solutions and latices often leave an undesirable deposit on surfaces above the liquid level of storage vessels, tank cars or trucks, and processing equipment. NM2P can be formulated with surfactants, caustic and diluents to provide cleaners for such areas.

MILTON FREIFELD
F. J. PRESCOTT

Cross-Reference: SOLVENTS, SPECIAL.

METHYLENE GLUTARONITRILE

Methylene glutaronitrile, a dimer of acrylonitrile produced catalytically rather than thermally, is a versatile new chemical. The dimer is expected to supplement acrylonitrile in ABS (acrylonitrile-butadiene-styrene) type copolymers. It can combine with butadiene to produce an oil-resistant rubber with good elasticity. The full name of this new vinyl polymer is methylene glutaronitrile, 2,4-dicyanobutene-1 (α-cyanoethyl acrylonitrile). Its structural formula is:

$$N\equiv C-CH_2-CH_2-\overset{\displaystyle CH_2}{\overset{\|}{C}}-C\equiv N$$

The dimer, MGN, is slightly soluble in water, insoluble in aliphatic and alicyclic hydrocarbons, and soluble in aromatic hydrocarbons and polar organic solvents. Physical properties are as follows:

Description	Colorless liquid
Molecular weight	106.13
Boiling point	103°C/5 mm
	142°C/20 mm
Freezing point	−8.6°C
n_D^{25}	1.4505
d_4^{25}	0.9756
Toxicity (Oral LD_{50})	0.147 ml/kg

The new intermediate can be considered as a vinyl monomer for polymerization and copolymerization using free radical or anionic catalysis. It has particular potential as a modifying comonomer in polyacrylonitrile, in polyacrylates, and in ABS polymers in order to effect changes in solubility, softening point, or molecular weight. MGN is useful in cyanoalkylation reactions analogous to those of acrylonitrile, e.g., addition to alcohols, aldehydes, amines, amides, HCN, etc. It can be used in the synthesis of a new series of chemical intermediates, including a 2-methyl-pentamethylenediamine, 2-methyl-5-amino valeronitrile, methylvalerolactam, 3-pipecoline, 2-methylene glutaramide, etc.

The development cost of MGN has been established at $1.50 per lb. Commercial pricing will depend largely upon the ultimate volume this product may reach and, to some extent, upon the future price of the acrylonitrile raw material. At 5–10 million lb per year, MGN is expected to sell in the range of 34–50¢ per lb. Higher volume sales could lower the price even more.

Potential Applications

A significant prospect for MGN lies in new types of modified acrylic fibers. For example, fibers modified with 2-methylglutaronitrile might be melt-spun rather than solution-spun, which is the present practice with acrylic fibers. Most other major noncellulosic fibers, such as nylon, polyester, and olefin types, are melt-spun. If the new acrylic can be made melt-spinnable, it could then be introduced into many plants now using nylon, etc., particularly the smaller installations that buy resin to spin fiber. In addition, the new dimer is expected to improve acrylic's fiber properties such as "hand" and dyeability.

In thermoplastics, methylene glutaronitrile polymerizes to ABS-type products designated by USI as "A²BS". About 110 million lb of ABS resins were made in 1964, and forecasts of between 350–400 million lb have been made for 1970.

In nitrile rubbers with high oil resistance, present practice has been to hold the acrylonitrile content under 40%. Introduction of MGN increases the oil resistance and other desirable characteristics of the rubber without sacrificing flexibility.

Complete hydrogenation of MGN using nickel or cobalt catalysts yields 2-methyl-pentamethyl-enediamine. Although nylon-66 and nylon-6 (from caprolactam) have been the only products to reach high-volume markets via polyamides, it is believed that this new diamine will offer manufacturers an attractive substitute for the normally scarce hexamethylenediamine. In 1964, slightly over 800 million lb of nylon in all forms were produced.

The new diamine also has potential in the manufacture of isocyanates used in making poly-urethanes. Phosgene and the diamine combine to form an aliphatic diisocyanate which might fit into the polyurethane field. Nearly 300 million lb of isocyanates were made in 1964, of which about 90% were aromatic. The remainder of the market was largely aliphatic monoisocyanates such as methyl monoisocyanate. Thus, this new, inexpensive source of diamine is expected to spur interest in the use of aliphatic diisocyanates. 2-Methyl-pentamethylene diamine also is of interest for dimensional stabilization of wool by interfacial polymerization.

2-Methylglutaric acid, produced by hydrolysis of 2-methyl-glutaronitrile, is a branched dibasic acid that can be used in the synthesis of poly-amides, polyesters, and plasticizers.

Methylene glutaronitrile and its derivatives are expected to find outlets in other areas such as thermosetting resins for coatings, acidulants, extraction solvents, and pharmaceuticals, i.e., niacin via 3-pipecoline.

LOUIS F. MOORMEIER

METHYLSTYRENES

Following the wide acceptance of styrene monomer in the plastics industry, efforts have been made to alter certain of its properties by substitution of a methyl group either on the ring or side chain and thereby improve its suitability for specific uses. Two such monomers are presently in commercial production.

The first, α-methylstyrene, is a derivative of propylene and benzene and contains the methyl group attached to the α-carbon atom in the side chain.

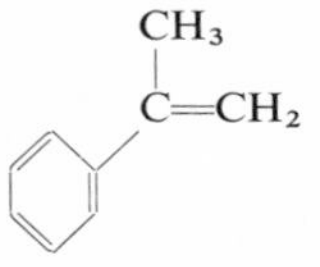

α-Methylstyrene

The second, vinyltoluene, is a derivative of ethylene and toluene with the methyl group attached to the *ortho*, *meta* or *para* position of the aromatic ring.

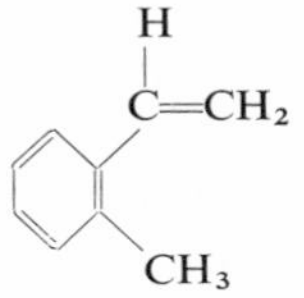

ortho-Vinyltoluene

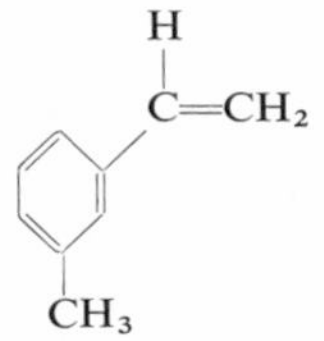

meta-Vinyltoluene

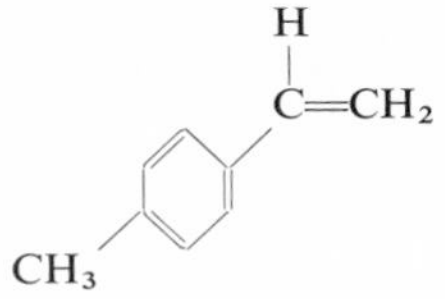

para-Vinyltoluene

Use of the name "vinyltoluene" for this monomer is a purely arbitrary commercial practice to reduce the possibility that it might be inadvertently substituted for α-methylstyrene in a polymerization reaction. Reaction rates for polymerization of the two monomers are quite different and a serious safety hazard could exist if such a substitution occurred.

Table 1 summarizes the typical physical properties of these monomers. These data were obtained on pure compounds prepared in the laboratory and may be somewhat different from commercial production lots of material. In addition, the isomers of vinyltoluene have slight differences in properties.

α-Methylstyrene

The basic raw materials, propylene and benzene, are reacted in the presence of a promoted

TABLE 1. PHYSICAL PROPERTIES OF METHYL STYRENES.

Property	Vinyltoluene[a]	α-Methylstyrene
Refractive Index,D line		
20°C	1.5422	1.5386
25	1.5395	1.5359
30	1.5342	1.5331
35	1.5346	1.5304
Viscosity, cps		
20°C	0.837	0.940
40	0.644	0.715
60	0.518	0.575
80	0.428	
100		0.395
Surface tension, dynes/cm		
20°C	31.66	32.40
40	29.52	30.11
100		23.31
Density, g/cc		
20°C	0.8973	0.9106
40	0.8805	0.8928
60	0.8639	0.8751
80	0.8469	0.8574
100		0.8396
Boiling point, °C at		
760 mm Hg abs.	172	165
Freezing point, °C	−77	−23.2
Flash point Cleveland		
Open Cup, °F	140	136
Fire point, Cleveland		
Open Cup, °F	155	136
Auto ignition temperature, °F	1067	
Explosive limits, % in air	1.9–6.1	0.7–3.4
Vapor pressure, mm Hg.		
20°C	1.15	1.90
40	4.40	6.28
60	13.2	18. 0
80	35.0	44.0
100	81.0	98.0
120	170.0	200.0
140	320.0	380.0
160	560.0	665.0
Critical pressure,atm.	41.5	43.2
Critical temp., °C	382	384
Critical volume, v_c, ml/g	3.33	3.26
Critical density, d_c, g/ml	0.30	0.29
Liquid specific heat,		
cal/g/°C 40°C		0.489
60		0.502
80		0.511
100		0.520
Vapor specific heat,		
cal/g°C 25°C	0.2936	0.2953
Latent heat of vaporization,		
cal/g 25°C	101.8	96.7
boiling point	83.47	78.0
Heat of polymerization,		
kcal/mole	16.0	9.5
Solubility in H_2O,		
% at 25°C	0.0089	0.056
Solubility of H_2O in monomer,		
% at 25°C	0.047	0.010

[a] Commercial *m,p*-vinyltoluene (65% *meta*, 35% *para*).

aluminum chloride complex to form cumene or isopropylbenzene.

Benzene   Propylene

Cumene
or
isopropylbenzene   α-Methylstyrene

The reaction is exothermic and is conducted at moderate temperatures and pressures in a continuous reaction, with an excess of benzene to minimize formation of di, tri and higher substituted compounds. An equilibrium mixture, containing about 40% cumene is purified by distillation, with unreacted benzene and poly substituted by-products being recycled to the reactor.

Cumene is then dehydrogenated by being vaporized, mixed with superheated steam and passed over a fixed bed of catalyst at a temperature in excess of 600°C. By-product, benzene, toluene, ethylbenzene and styrene, as well as unreacted cumene, are removed by distillation and α-methylstyrene monomer is recovered with purity in excess of 99.5%. Pressures below 50 mm Hg abs. and inhibitors are used in the fractionation columns to suppress polymeric residues and/ or oxidation. Ten to twenty ppm of p-tertiary butylcatechol is usually added to the pure monomer to protect it against polymerization and oxidation in storage and shipment. This inhibitor has the advantage of not imparting objectionable color to the monomer and normally does not need to be removed prior to use.

Substantial amounts of α-methylstyrene are available as a by-product from the cumene route to phenol. It may be purified by distillation for use as a monomer or hydrogenated to cumene for recycle to the oxidation step.

Uses of α-Methylstyrene

α-Methylstyrene does not polymerize by means of free-radical catalysis so familiar in styrene polymer technology, though it may copolymerize. In general, it slows the polymerization rate and forms lower molecular weight and more thermally-sensitive copolymers. The copolymerization reaction has been widely studied and methods established to estimate the copolymerization rates. Advantageously, it increases

the heat distortion temperature. Copolymers of styrene with 25% or less of α-methylstyrene have been commercially available for years which exhibit better heat and solvent resistance than polystyrene. Recent improvements in polystyrene have narrowed this gap. Relative newcomers are the copolymers of methyl methacrylate. These have been reported as having food approval, with heat distortions approaching 250°F. Substitution of α-methylstyrene for 25–35% of the styrene in styrene-modified drying oil formulations serves to moderate the reaction rate and improve product homogeneity. Recent trends, though, have been towards the use of solvent to accomplish this same result.

α-Methylstyrene is readily polymerized by ionic catalysts. Alkaline earth catalysts are used to make viscous liquid polymers with molecular weights in the range of 300–600. These materials are excellent plasticizers with a wide range of commercial applications, in paints and finishes, wax formulations, pressure-sensitive adhesives, molded and extruded plastics, and coatings. They have a wide range of solubility and compatibility, good electrical properties, low acid and unsaturation values, and are water white. Still another group of brittle resins find application in the floor tile industry. The unsaturated dimers are known and used   and are commercially available. Their preparation involves a highly exothermic and rapid reaction associated with the lower energy of activation characteristic of ionic polymerization. As a word of caution, this reaction can be violent and with some acid catalysts, especially HCl contaminated with a trace of iron, can become uncontrollable in larger reactors.

The Szwarc and Ziegler-Natta catalyzed type polymers are still of academic interest. Sodium has been used on a semi-commercial scale to make a polymer of α-methylstyrene with heat distortion in the range of 125–150°C. The polymer is harder, somewhat more brittle and more solvent resistant than polystyrene. It is more difficult to fabricate, molding temperatures being close to that of thermal decomposition.

Vinyltoluene

The chemistry of the present commercial process for the manufacture of vinyltoluene is very similar to that described for α-methylstyrene. Dry toluene and ethylene are continuously reacted in the presence of an aluminum chloride-hydrocarbon complex to form the three isomers of ethyltoluene.

An excess of toluene is used to suppress the formation of di- and tri-ethylated toluenes and other higher-boiling compounds. The product from the reactor contains approximately 50% toluene,

CH₃

$+ CH_2{=}CH_2 \xrightarrow{\text{AlCl}_3}$

Toluene   *Ethylene*

CH₂CH₃   CH₂CH₃   CH₂CH₃

CH₃

CH₃

CH₃

ortho-   *meta-*   *para-*
Ethyltoluenes   *Ethyltoluenes*   *Ethyltoluenes*

35% ethyltoluenes, and 15% of polyethyltoluenes and highers, with small amounts of benzene, ethylbenzene and xylenes as by-products. The monoethyltoluene portion of this mixture is normally about 60% meta, 30% para and 10% ortho.

In the dehydrogenation step, it was found that conditions which give satisfactory conversions and yields of *m*, *p*-vinyltoluene convert substantial amounts of *o*-ethyltoluene to indene and indane. This is a serious yield loss, a by-product disposal problem, and poses a rather formidable distillation problem in the final finishing steps for vinyltoluene. For these reasons the ortho isomer is removed for recycle to the alkylation reactor,

along with unreacted toluene and dealkylable polyethyltoluenes.

The dehydrogenation reaction is carried out over a fixed catalyst bed in the presence of steam. Operating temperatures fall in the range of 575–625°C. The reaction, represented as follows, is taken to about 40% conversion.

CH₂CH₃   CH=CH₂

$\xrightarrow{\text{Heat}}$ $+ H_2$

CH₃   CH₃

(*m*, *p-Ethyltoluene*)   (*m*, *p-Vinyltoluene*)

The product is condensed, decanted from water, and a series of exacting distillation steps removes the by-product benzene, toluene, ethylbenzene, styrene and xylenes, the *m*, *p*-ethyltoluene for recycle and tars and highers. This is a critical step in the process. Operating pressures on the columns range down to 20 mm Hg abs and a combination of inhibitors is used to suppress polymerization. To the final product is added 10–50 ppm of *p-tert-*butyl catechol to prevent oxidation and polymerization in storage.

An alternate route to vinyltoluene manufacture is the reaction of toluene with acetylene in the presence of mercuric sulfate and sulfuric acid to yield a mixture of asymmetrical di-toly-

FIG. 1. Vinyltoluene production facilities. (*Courtesy The Dow Chemical Co., Midland, Mich.*)

ethanes. These are cracked in the presence of steam to toluene and a 65% *para*, 33% *ortho* and 2% *meta* mixture of vinyltoluenes, with ethyltoluenes as by-products.

Uses of Vinyltoluene

Certain properties of vinyltoluene make it very useful as a specialty monomer for paints and varnishes in the coatings industry. Its higher boiling point compared to styrene permits faster reactions at reflux temperatures in closed kettle equipment. The methyl group attached to the aromatic ring offers two advantages, first in improvement of solubility in aliphatic solvents and second in activation of the vinyl group to faster polymerization rates. The higher flash point is a safety advantage.

Drying Oils and Alkyds. Vinyltoluene is used extensively as a modifier for drying oils and alkyd resins in paint vehicles because of the improved dry-time it contributes. Vinyltoluene has excellent compatibility with all of the commonly-used drying oils such as soybean, linseed, dehydrated castor and safflower. Because of the improved film toughness of the modified alkyds, vinyltoluene is used more widely as a modifier of alkyds than of drying oils. Monomer modified alkyds can be synthesized by a number of ways, however the preferred method is to prepare the alkyd first and then react it with the monomer. A typical procedure consists of reacting a polyhydric alcohol (glycerine) and drying oil (linseed) to form mono- and di-glycerides followed by esterification with a dibasic acid (phthalic anhydride), thinning with a suitable solvent (mineral spirits), and reacting at reflux temperature with a mixture of vinyltoluene and peroxide catalyst. From 30–50% vinyltoluene is generally required to give optimum properties. There is some disagreement concerning the manner in which the monomer combines chemically. What effect the conjugation of the oil has, and whether a true vinyltoluene-oil copolymer or a homopolymer is formed is not completely understood.

Substitution of vinyltoluene for styrene in these finishes thus yields a product with much better solubility in less costly solvents. Also, vinyltoluene has superior compatibility with drying oils, linseed oil for example, and yields clear films in formulations where styrene will not do so.

Polyesters for Reinforced Plastics. Another important use for vinyltoluene is in the formulation of polyester premix compound. A typical polyester cook starts with a condensation polymerization of a dibasic acid and a dihydric alcohol. Isophthalic acid, phthalic anhydride and maleic anhydride are commonly used acids; ethylene glycol, diethylene glycol and dipropylene glycol, typical dihydric alcohols. The product is blown dry with an inert gas and vinyltoluene which is inhibited with *p-tert*-butylcatechol is blended in to give about 30% monomer in the final mixture. Reinforcing agent and inert fillers, such as glass fibers, cloth, silicates and clays, are added to improve physical properties and reduce cost. The resulting product is an extremely versatile thermosetting resin which is widely used for molding of automobile, household appliance and electrical parts. Because of its higher boiling point, the use of vinyltoluene as the monomer in such premix compounds reduces odor problems during molding and allows high molding temperatures without porosity. Also, finished parts are more resistant to crazing and thereby may have better electrical properties.

Copolymers. As a homopolymer, there is no known commercial product per se. This is because of the unique contribution of each isomer. Table 2 serves to illustrate this in either the random or isotactic structure. Put two isomers together, which one of necessity gets from the aforementioned processes, and slower rates of polymerization or intermediate products result, thus *o,p*-polymer, did have higher distortions but the *m,p*-polymer offered nothing over polystyrene. One item of novelty is the ease of sulfonation of polyvinyltoluene or copolymers which are water soluble and useful as viscosity control agents and adhesives.

Several copolymers have reached the stage of product recognition, namely, with acrylonitrile, butadiene, and α-methylstyrene. Looking at each of these separately, the *o,p*-methylstyrenes with acrylonitrile did offer a thermoplastic with improved heat resistance as one might expect and its withdrawal might be presumed not due to property deficiencies. With butadiene, vinyltoluene produces a group of commercially important resins characterized by good solubility in aliphatic solvents and are used for traffic paint, adhesives, printing inks, abrasion resistant coatings, and multi-colored paints and lacquers. Likewise, commercially important copolymers with α-methylstyrene have water white color, hardness and good aliphatic solubility. They are used as paint modifiers and extenders for heat sealable hot melts, imparting improved hot tack. They are also of interest in the formulation of "re-stick" adhesives.

Hazards, Storage and Handling

Vinyltoluene and α-methylstyrene are not likely to cause a serious health hazard in most industrial operations. They are low in single dose oral toxicity. Their warning properties make the inhalation of toxic amounts unlikely. However, both may be toxic by inhalation if exposure occurs at high levels of contamination. While eye contact with these materials may result in

TABLE 2. HOMOPOLYMERS OF METHYLSTYRENE.

Isomer	T_G,°C	Copolymers Parameters		Isotactic		
		e	Q	Crystallization Rate	%	M.P., °C
Ortho	115–125	−0.78	0.90	high	65–75	360°
Meta	72–82	−0.72	0.91	low	35–40	215
Para	101	−0.88	1.10	—	None	—

irritation, there is little likelihood of serious eye injury occurring. Like many cyclic hydrocarbons, an occasional short skin contact with them showed no significant irritation. However, they may cause irritation, even blistering and a mild burn, if the exposures are frequent or if the materials are confined to the skin.

The normal precautions which are observed in handling flammable hydrocarbons apply to vinyltoluene. The vapor pressure (Table 1) is such that it will not form an explosive mixture with air at room temperature. However, space around processing equipment operating at elevated temperatures should be well-ventilated. Fires may be extinguished with foam, carbon dioxide or other techniques suitable for hydrocarbons lighter than water.

Vinyltoluene in drums should be stored out of the sun and away from heat sources at a temperature below 90°F. Best practice for bulk storage of vinyltoluene is an insulated, refrigerated tank maintained at less than 50°F. Recommended materials are aluminum or stainless steel; if carbon steel is used, it should be lined with a phenolic resin base paint suitably resistant to the monomer. A few ppm of O_2 dissolved in the monomer is necessary for p-$tert$-butylcatechol to function as an inhibitor. Therefore, bulk storage tanks should be vented to the atmosphere and not blanketed with an inert gas.

The foregoing comments also apply in general to the storage of α-methylstyrene except that nonrefrigerated mild steel tanks and lines are normally used.

LEE CRAMPTON
STEVENS S. DRAKE

MOLD RELEASE MATERIALS

Mold releases are necessary aids to help the plastic molder remove molded articles from the dies. When a molded piece sticks in the mold, valuable production time is lost when the press is shut down to remove the sticking piece. Expensive or irreparable damage may be inflicted on the die in an attempt to extract the recalcitrant piece. An efficient mold release is good insurance against these hazards. Further, it often enhances the molded article by improving the surface finish.

Early mold releases were usually proprietary mixtures developed by individual molding shops and applied by hand. A time honored compression molding release still in use today is carnauba wax. In practice, a piece of carnauba wax is wiped over the surface of the hot compression mold and the molten wax distributed with the aid of a compressed air hose.

Cellulose acetate was invented in 1927, and first injection molded in 1929. This was the beginning of shorter cycles for molded plastic parts.

A reliable mold release for plastic injection molding is zinc stearate. This is a white powder which in practice is dusted over the surface of the injection mold, and affords release for three or four cycles, depending upon the severity of the sticking.

When labor costs were lower and cycles longer, mold releases were applied by hand. In the succeeding years the state of the art has steadily improved and technology has led to increasingly shorter cycles, with a demand for more efficient mold releases and faster ways to apply them.

A release for polyester fiberglass or epoxy fiberglass systems consists of polyvinyl alcohol resin coated with a wax. The wood, plaster, or metal mold form is first coated with a layer of polyvinyl alcohol resin which has been dissolved in water. Alcohol may be added to this water solution to improve the drying rate.

After the PVA is dry, a layer of paste wax is applied and hand polished. The mold form is then ready for the glass-resin system. PVA wax is usually used on large molds such as boat hulls, automotive cabs, bodies and fenders.

Where one or both sides of the die surface are either plano or curved in one plane only, it is possible to use a slip sheet to release the plastic part. In the manufacture of melamine or phenolic counter top laminates, a sheet of cellophane functions as a releasing medium and remains attached to the molded part, thereby protecting the surface until installation. This technique also works well with fiberglass-resin panels. Slip sheets can be of other plastic films such as polyethylene and polypropylene, or a plastic coated or silicone treated kraft paper.

Goodhue and Sullivan, of the United States Department of Agriculture, during World War II, developed a high pressure aerosol insecticide utilizing low boiling propellants and diluents. The postwar development of low pressure mold release formulations, utilizing these inexpensive low pressure propellants and containers, initiated the beginning of the aerosol type agents. These mold release sprays do not mar the surfaces of the molds and are ideal for a rapid and efficient application of mold releases.

Silicone oils in the form of dimethyl fluids offer unique qualities as mold releases. When silicone-based mold releases were first introduced, the principal injection molding plastics were general purpose polystyrene and the cellulosics. As time went on, injection machines rapidly became larger, and the dies and the molded parts increased in size. The operating cost of injection molding machines increased rapidly to the point where it was more economical to quickly spray a mold release from an aerosol bomb than it was to interrupt the machine cycle and apply a mold release by hand. The saving in machine time paid for the extra cost of the aerosol mold release, as compared with the hand applied releases. Further, the new aerosol releases provided up to 75 releases per application, compared to 3 or 4 releases for a hand-applied release agent such as zinc stearate.

During the period of 1953–1960, aerosol mold releases formulated around dimethyl silicone oils increased in popularity until there were approximately 44 suppliers to the plastics industry. The popularity of these aerosol releases was due to easy, rapid application; improved surface finish of the molded piece; relatively little piece marking and a clean, dustless molding shop.

This basic type of silicone oil formulation was an efficient release for plastics in the 1950's, but the dimethyl silicone oils have disadvantages. They interfere with post molding decorating such as painting, hot stamping, and vacuum metalizing. They also interfere with gluing operations. Further, a number of new plastic materials have been developed which are degraded by silicone oils. The polyolefins such as polypropylene, linear polyethylene, and polyethylene, exhibit stress cracking when subjected to silicone oils. Polyvinyl chloride shrinks and hardens. Acetal resins stiffen and craze, and cellulose acetate butyrate stiffens when subjected to silicone oils.

These disadvantages have led to a search for improved mold releases which would be compatible with the newer plastics, and not interfere with post molding decorating or assembling operations.

Satisfactory mold releases for plastics should offer low release pressures, a large number of releases per application, be inert to the plastic material, not mark the surface of the molded piece, be rapidly applied, be nontoxic, noncorrosive to metal dies, and noncombustible.

In view of today's wide range of plastic materials, no one mold release satisfactorily fills all these requirements for all plastics. This has led to the development of individual mold releases tailored to the specific demands of each plastic molding material.

Today, specific mold releases are available for practically every type of plastic molding material. These specific releases supply the specific requirements necessary to obtain the lowest release pressures and a maximum number of releases with each type of plastic.

In addition, new developments in the aerosol mold release field offer directional spray control designed for continued industrial use, rather than intermittent household use, "spray-any-way" features which permit the aerosol container to be used in any position, and micro-fine atomization which minimizes piece marking. Mold releases seem definitely committed to aerosols for plastic molding.

ROBERT M. BARTH

MONOMERS, POLYFUNCTIONAL

The term "polyfunctional monomer" can be broadly construed as covering any monomer having more than one reactive site. This could include condensation reactants and a wide range of monomers having unsaturation and other functional groups such as acids, hydroxyls, amine, halogens, aldehydes, epoxies, sulfer compounds, lactones, nitro, organometallic, as well as many other functional groups.

For the purpose of this discussion polyfunctional monomers are defined as having more than one non-conjugated unsaturation. These are also often known as cross-linking monomers.

A vast number of polyallyl esters or ethers, polyacrylate or methacrylate esters, divinyl and other polyfunctional unsaturated compounds such as dicyclopentadiene or 1,6-hexadiene are known. Generally these monomers are capable of participating in several types of polymerization reactions:

(1) They may homopolymerize either to form a soluble product or an infusible cross-linked gel.

(2) They may copolymerize with resins having double bond functionality such as unsaturated polyesters.

(3) They may act as radical acceptors with polymers which are vulcanized by peroxides or radiation to increase cross-linking efficiencies where the polymers are active at other sites than unsaturation.

(4) They may copolymerize with difunctional monomers such as styrene, methyl acrylate, methyl methacrylate or vinyl acetate.

In general, the function of polyfunctional monomers is to produce a final product—a resin —which is insoluble and infusible as a three-dimensional network. Many reactions produce this infusible state in the initial reaction. However, many systems have been designed to produce a soluble "B Stage" polymer which can be poured or molded and then post cured or vulcanized to form an insoluble infusible product.

Polyfunctional monomers have been prepared and studied since the development of radical polymerized monomers. Standing has extensively studied divinyl benzene polymerizations with styrene and had been able to explain the insolubilizing functions of the divinyl benzene in terms of physical structure. Carlton Ellis, in 1937, suggested the use of allyl esters in insolubilizing unsaturated polyester resins. Dimethacrylates had also been prepared at about the same time for use as insolubilizing agents by Crawford.

Theory of Multifunctional Gelation

A number of studies of gelation of a combination of monofunctional units (A) and difunctional units (B–B) have been made. Many of these have been based on:

(1) Equal rate of reactivity of A and B.
(2) Equal reactivity of the two groups of B–B.
(3) No short chain or long chain rings in the polymerization chain.
(4) No entanglement gelation.
(5) Complete polymerization of both ends B–B.

In many polymerization systems the theoretical gelation points have been very close to those obtained. This gelation point is reached with a very low conversion at high percentage of the polyfunctional monomer, or at very low concentration of the polyfunctional monomer at high conversions. Thus these monomers can, in very low concentration, radically change those physical and chemical properties dependent on molecular weight, chain branching and cross-linking.

However, in most polymerizations involving polyfunctional monomers, wide diversification from this simple approach occurs. A study by Fox and Loshack indicated that the length of the glycol chain between dimethacrylate groups had an effect on the efficiency of polymerization of the second group after one end of the dimethacrylate had been incorporated into the polymer. The short chain glycol dimethacrylate apparently became unavailable or buried, particularly at high conversion.

An even more striking divergency from this simple theory occurs in producing a prepolymer of diallyl phthalate. This monomer has a very strong tendency to form a ring structure on polymerizing, so much so that very high conversions of the pure monomer can be formed without gelation so that a soluble polymer is formed which can be post cured, usually with additional catalyst and other monomers, or polymers to form an infusible insoluble polymer.

There are a large number of polymer systems containing polyfunctional monomers which have been found to diverge radically from this first approximation of gelation point. This generally involves leaving dangling end groups and cyclization. The polymers so formed do appear to have interesting properties.

The use of polyesters containing unsaturation, as well as diallyl prepolymers in reinforced plastic laminates in conjunction with polyfunctional monomers is a large industry and specializes in obtaining properties very difficult to obtain with other materials. These special properties include high temperature resistance, low mold shrinkage and good electrical properties. The high boiling point of the monomers allows high curing temperatures without vaporization to the formation of bubbles in the finished laminate.

The use of polyfunctional monomers as polymerizing coagents, with radical initiators such as peroxides or radiation, has developed considerable interest—particularly in the rubber industry as a vulcanizing system for ethylene-propylene rubber. However, the potential of a peroxide-polyfunctional coagent vulcanization is much broader than simply the ethylene-propylene rubber. The vulcanization which generally involves a hydrogen abstraction, can be used on many different rubbers and tends to produce a high modulus rubber with good aging characteristics. The monomers, such as ethylene dimethacrylate, act as radical acceptors and increase the efficiency of cross-linking. Although the peroxide cure systems have been known for fifty years, the development of high temperature peroxides has made it practical to use peroxide-polymerizable coagent.

The use of dimethacrylates is particularly indicated where good aging properties with light color is desired. Monofunctional monomers do not appear to be effective for this use. Polyfunctional monomers have also been utilized as polymerizable coagents in radiation cross-linking of plastic sheet such as polyethylene or polypropylene. There is evidence indicating that these monomers tend to prevent chain fracture or depolymerization and can actually enhance many fold the cross-linking efficiency of gamma or alpha radiation.

Copolymerization of polyfunctional monomers with difunctional monomers has been extensively utilized to produce cross-linked plastic compositions. Cast sheet has been produced which is cross-linked to resist crazing and to improve scratch resistance. The diethylene glycol bis (allyl carbonate) has been used, either as the major component or as a part of a casting composition to produce transparent optical components with high abrasion resistance and excellent solvent resistance. Similarly large sheets of cross-linked polymethyl methacrylate can be formed and post treated to give craze resistant clear formed sheets suitable for airplane windows and enclosures. Ethylene dimethacrylate has been used extensively as a cross-linking agent in the dental industry. Dentures are molded in individually constructed plaster (or stone) molds from a polymer powder-monomer slurry mixture. Without the cross-linking agent, the molded denture was sensitive to solvents such as alcohol, and could craze, thus producing premature breakage. Similarly, plastic teeth were found to be more resistant to aging when cross-linked. These cross-linked plastic teeth also showed improved wear resistance. Watch crystals and acrylic buttons were also improved by using cross-linking agents, which prevent the formation of crazing under moderate stress. Uncross-linked plastic watch crystals and acrylic buttons suffer from crazing. The use of dimethacrylates has alleviated this problem.

JOHN CORNELL

N

NONWOVEN MATERIALS

The use of nonwoven fabrics as reinforcement for structural plastics is steadily rising. Great advances have been made in developing new fibers and resins, in new chemical finishes given to the fibers, in methods of bonding the fiber to the resin, and in mechanical processing methods. Nonwoven fabrics are inherently better able to take advantage of the developments than are woven sheets.

The strength of commercial reinforced plastics is far below that calculated from theoretical values. Ordinary glass fibers are three times stronger and stiffer for their weight than steel. Nonwoven glass fiber laminates usually have strengths about 50% below that of woven fabric lay-ups. In special constructions properly treated fibers have produced laminates as strong as the woven product, better in some cases.

Reinforced plastics are usually applied as laminates of several layers. Many variables are important in determining the performance of the finished product. Some of these are:

(1) Orientation of plies of the laminate.
(2) Type of resin.
(3) Fiber-resin ratio.
(4) Type or types of fibers.
(5) Orientation of fibers.

Types of Nonwovens Used as Plastic Reinforcements

By definition, a nonwoven fabric is an engineered product consisting of a fibrous web structure where the fibers are mechanically or chemically locked together. The characteristics of the nonwoven fabric depend upon the basic fibers and resins used and the method of locking them together.

A number of bonding or stabilizing methods are used in nonwoven production. Binders may be added through saturation, spraying or pattern application (print bonding). Mechanical bonding is done by a needle loom. Some less common methods employ thermoplastic and thermosetting fibers and binders in the web itself, chemical bonding with a solvent or salt solution, heat shrinking or combinations of various other methods.

By combining mechanical bonding (needle punching) with other processes, many unusual fabrics have been developed, some of which are particularly suitable for plastic reinforcements.

Recently an asbestos-phenolic molding mat in felt form was announced by a large United States firm. This mat was specially developed to provide exceptionally light weight thermal shielding and high strength-to-weight ratio. The thermomat is composed of an unbonded felt containing 100% ASTM grade AAAA long, randomly dispersed chrysotile asbestos fibers and light weight fillers saturated with phenolic resins. Flexible before curing, the saturated felt conforms to the mold shapes and the random fiber dispersion provides uniform and maximum reinforcement to the cured mat. The unique characteristics of the felt allow easy working together of the joints and permit free flow of the fiber during processing. The versatility of the felt makes it adaptable to laying up, low pressure vacuum bag molding, pressure laminating and match die molding when properly "B" staged.

The same heat shielding effect is obtained with a thermomat having 1/3 the thickness and 1/9 the weight of standard asbestos-phenolic molded parts.

The French have developed a new fiber-reinforced plastic using low cost Kenaf fiber and powdered phenolic resins. A high strength fiber-reinforced plastic is produced that is fire and heat resistant, light weight, and low in cost. The product starts as a nonwoven needle felt Keraf, and is saturated with a powdered phenolic. The combination is subjected to the desired shape in a heavy press. Products may be made which range from thick discs for gears, to thin sheets for motor covers, chairs, trays and corrugated sheets.

Another range of glass fiber reinforcing mats has been developed by Fiberglas Industries known as "Format" and "Rovmat". The glass fiber-resin sheet is treated by heat and pressure for molding into permanently shaped glass fiber-reinforced plastic articles. Molding resin is applied in powder form to the glass mat prior to the needling operation to partially activate the resin and bond some of the glass fiber strands together.

Nonwovens versus Wovens in Reinforced Plastics

Nonwovens have a number of advantages as plastic reinforcements. Processing costs are usually lower than for woven fabrics. Maximum strength and other physical properties of the original fiber are retained in nonwovens because the fiber has not been subjected to twisting and looping. Certain fibers with a low shear value have, under special nonwoven techniques, been produced into reinforced plastics which are substantially stronger than if the same fiber had been used in a woven or knitted fabric. Nonwoven structures present a very high surface area which permits a maximum reinforcement per unit area to the resin. The uniformity of fiber-resin blend distributes the load more efficiently.

Nonwoven reinforcing sheets or mats are usually plied up into several layers to form a laminated structure. In order to achieve the maximum desired physical properties in the reinforced plastic several variables must be considered. These variables are type of fiber, denier, length, fiber finish, fiber orientation of the web on the ply, orientation of the ply in the laminate, fiber-resin ratio, type of resin and fiber surface bonding.

The conclusion that short staple fiber will not produce maximum physical properties is incorrect. Both experiment and theory have concluded that with proper adhesion between fibers and matrix maximum strength can be achieved by using relatively short staple fiber rather than continuous filament construction.

In the case of glass fiber constructions, high strength properties have been developed with fiber approximately 0.5 in. in length. The commercial glass mat using 0.5 in. fiber lengths will have strength approximately 50% below maximum properties obtainable in woven fabric lay-ups. However in special constructions, properly treated fibers form laminates equivalent to high strength woven laminates.

In general a maximum length of approximately 0.5 in. will result in maximum strength properties. Shorter fiber lengths are used to obtain maximum strength for certain fiber such as asbestos and whiskers of metal or ceramics. Whiskers are single crystal filaments possessing greater strength than the ordinary fiber, actually approaching the maximum theoretical strength of the material. Strength is inversely related to whisker diameter. The high strength is due principally to the absence of dislocation or imperfect shear planes. Fiber surface defects are practically nonexistent. Metal whiskers are usually of high purity and free of work hardness. Whiskers which show promise

in these areas are refractory oxides of aluminum (melting point 3722°F) and silica (melting point 2670°F), and metals such as iron (melting point 2920°F), and copper (melting point 2000°F).

Laminate Overlays

Glass fiber-reinforced laminates of epoxy and polyester resins have become important construction materials for hundreds of applications. These laminates offer many advantages over traditional design materials, but their usefulness and life can be considerably improved by the use of over-lay fabrics.

"Dynel" modacrylic fiber nonwoven laminate over-lays improve the laminate from several standpoints. When these over-lay fabrics are applied to one or both sides of the glass fiber-reinforced laminate, the fibers exposed at the load bearing surface are "Dynel," not glass. Since "Dynel" has high resistance to attack from chemicals, water, and abrasion, it actually improves the laminate by its use.

These over-lay fabrics are recommended for such applications as tanks, ducts, fume hoods, boats, industrial structural panels, and wherever the ordinary glass-reinforced resin laminate gives limited service because of weather damage, abrasion, salt water, chemicals or corrosive fumes.

FRANCIS M. BURESH

NYLON INTERMEDIATES

The term nylon refers to synthetic polyamide resins having film, fiber, or plastic-forming properties. The polymer chains are characterized by repeating hydrocarbon units linked by amide (—CO—NH—) groups. Accordingly, the preferred ingredients for this class of polyamides are dicarboxylic acids, diamines, amino acids, and lactams. These are known as nylon intermediates. Nylons are customarily named for the number of carbon atoms in the basic units of the polymer chains, with the diamine unit numbered first. Thus, the polymer of adipic acid and hexamethylene diamine is called nylon 66, sebacic acid and hexamethylene diamine give nylon 610 and caprolactam is nylon 6. By far the most common nylons are Types 6 and 66. Figure 1 shows schematically the variety of chemistry which has been applied to the manufacture of intermediates for these nylon types. Nylon fibers are widely used as textile and industrial yarns, staple fibers, and monofilaments. Nylon molding resins are used to make a variety of machine parts, electrical components, films, and other applications where toughness, inertness, and high tensile strength are required.

Dicarboxylic Acids

The most important class of dicarboxylic acids for nylons are the saturated aliphatic acids. The

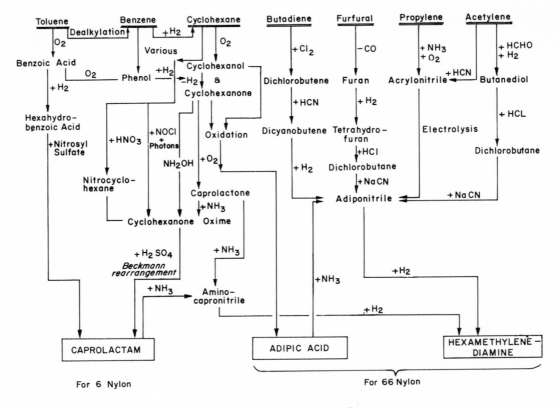

Fig. 1. Routes to nylon intermediates.

lower members of this series are listed in Table 1, together with a few of their physical properties. Some of these properties vary with the number of carbons in the molecule in a saw-tooth fashion. The acids having an even number of carbon atoms tend to have higher melting points, lower water solubility, and higher decomposition temperatures than their odd carbon neighbors. These property variations are utilized to separate pure acids from the crude acid mixtures often obtained in the oxidation reactions which characterize the synthesis of dibasic acids.

Dicarboxylic acids undergo all the normal organic acid reactions. In addition, their difunctional nature imparts special characteristics. The lower members of the series liberate carbon dioxide readily on heating. Thus, oxalic acid goes to formic acid and malonic acid to acetic acid. The next higher acids, succinic and glutaric, tend to form ring compounds with the elimination of water.

As a result of the tendency of the dicarboxylic acids of 5 carbons or less to decompose or ring close to monofunctional compounds at polymerization temperatures, the lower acids are not used to manufacture commercial homopolymers.

In addition, polyamides made from these acids are generally high melting and intractable. In the higher members of the dicarboxylic acid series, the distance between carboxyl groups is greater and less interaction results.

Only adipic acid and sebacic acid are commercially important dibasic acids for nylon homopolymers in this country.

Dibasic acids are produced by two general methods: (1) the oxidation of linear precursors such as natural oils, fatty acids, and other monocarboxylic acids, or (2) the oxidation of cyclic compounds with air, ozone, nitric acid, or other oxidizing agents. This latter route is more specific and of increasing utility as syntheses of cyclic hydrocarbons become more highly developed.

Adipic Acid

Adipic acid was first synthesized in 1902 from tetramethylene bromide. It occurs in nature as a natural constituent of sugar beet. Commercial production was initiated in 1939. United States annual production capacity in January, 1966, was estimated to be 845 million lb, and consumption is expected to increase at a rate of about 12% per year through 1970.

TABLE 1. DICARBOXYLIC ACIDS.

Name	Formula	Melting point,°C	Decarboxylation temperature, °C	Solubility in H$_2$O, g/100g at 20 °C
Oxalic	HOOC COOH	189	170	8
Malonic	HOOC (CH$_2$) COOH	135	150	73
Succinic	HOOC (CH$_2$)$_2$COOH	186	300	6
Glutaric	HOOC (CH$_2$)$_3$COOH	97.5	285	64
Adipic	HOOC (CH$_2$)$_4$COOH	153	310	2
Pimelic	HOOC (CH$_2$)$_5$COOH	103	—	5
Suberic	HOOC (CH$_2$)$_6$COOH	140	350	.16
Azelaic	HOOC (CH$_2$)$_7$COOH	106	330	.24
Sebacic	HOOC (CH$_2$)$_8$COOH	134.5	360	—
Undecanedioic	HOOC (CH$_2$)$_9$COOH	110	—	—
Dodecanedioic	HOOC (CH$_2$)$_{10}$COOH	131	—	—
Tridecanedioic	HOOC (CH$_2$)$_{11}$COOH	114	—	—

Adipic acid is a white crystalline odorless solid, whose properties are summarized below.

Properties of Adipic Acid

Molecular weight	146.14
Melting point	152.1°C (305.8°F)
Boiling point	at 760 mm Hg = 330.5°C with decomposition
	at 100 mm Hg = 265.1°C
	at 10 mm Hg = 205.5°C
Crystals	Monoclinic needles
Heat of combustion	668.6 kcal/g-mole
Heat of fusion	4.0 kcal/g-mole
Heat of vaporization	19.120 kcal/g-mole
Heat of solution	
at 10°–20°C	7.46 kcal/g-mole
at 90°–100°C	15.80 kcal/g-mole
Specific heat of solid	0.583 cal/g

Ionization constant

k_1 at 18°C	4.6×10^{-5}
at 25°C	3.6×10^{-5}
k_2 at 18°C	3.6×10^{-6}
at 25°C	2.9×10^{-6}

Market specifications:

Assay	99.6% min
Ash	20 ppm max
Iron	2.0 ppm max
Water	0.2% max
Color	25 APHA max
Volatile Acids	20 ppm as acetic max
Reducible nitrogen compounds	20 ppm as HNO$_3$ max

Adipic Acid Manufacture

Benzene is the basic raw material for most adipic acid. Generally, benzene is hydrogenated to cyclohexane which is air oxidized to a mixture of cyclohexanol-cyclohexanone, although at least one large manufacturer is believed to convert the benzene to phenol before hydrogenating to cyclohexanol. Some natural cyclohexane is recovered from petroleum fractions, but a complex refining operation is required to achieve the purity of over 98% cyclohexane which is desired for the manufacture of polymer grade adipic acid.

Cyclohexanol-cyclohexanone from Cyclohexane

Of the several commercial routes to adipic acid, the two-step oxidation process is of major importance. In the first step, cyclohexane is oxidized by air to a mixture of cyclohexanol and cyclohexanone.

In the original Loder process, cyclohexane was oxidized by air at a temperature of 140–180°C under sufficient pressure, 100–300 psig, to maintain a liquid hydrocarbon phase. This technology still forms the basis for today's air oxidation process. The oxidation may be carried out without a catalyst, but smoother reaction and better yields are achieved by the use of traces of metal salts.

In spite of much study, the mechanism of the oxidation is still not thoroughly understood. Cyclohexane hydroperoxide is the first compound formed. Peroxide decomposition and further oxidation leads to cyclohexanol, cyclohexanone, adipic acid, cyclohexanol esters, lower dibasic and monobasic acids, and higher boiling by-products. With a cobalt stearate catalyst, the oxidation passes through three stages, characterized by cobalt valence changes, during which cyclohexanol and cyclohexanone were formed in different ratios.

Oxidizer performance has been studied in both batch and continuous operation. A continuous stirred reactor gave average yields of cyclohexanol + cyclohexanone of about 79% and 67% at 5 and 10% conversion respectively. It was concluded that the optimum reactor system consisted of three stirred autoclaves in series. The hot hydrocarbon flows in series through three autoclaves with air entering the bottom of each autoclave.

The off-gas from the oxidizers, nitrogen containing cyclohexane, water, and traces of unreacted oxygen, passes through a condenser where water and cyclohexane are removed and discharged to a decanter. The cyclohexane is refluxed to the oxidizer and the water is discarded. The condenser off-gas is scrubbed with oil to recover the final traces of cyclohexane. The condenser on each autoclave provides a simple means for removing the heat of reaction via the vaporized cyclohexane.

The crude product from the last autoclave is stripped of unreacted cyclohexane and refined by distillation to separate the cyclohexanol and cyclohexanone from the tars and other high boiling by-products. Somewhat higher yields can be obtained by hydrolyzing the crude product to convert the by-product esters to alcohol before recovering the cyclohexanol.

Boric Acid Assisted Oxidation of Cyclohexane. It has long been recognized that improved yields of cyclohexanol could be achieved if the oxidation of cyclohexane could be arrested at the alcohol stage through the use of boric acid. The process involves carrying out the oxidation of cyclohexane in a slurry of metaboric acid or boric anhydride so that the alcohol is esterified by the boric acid as soon as it is formed. No cobalt or other catalyst is added. Depending on the ratio of boric acid present to alcohol formed, the following reactions may occur.

$$C_6H_{12} + \tfrac{1}{2}O_2 + HOBO \rightarrow (C_6H_{11}O)BO + H_2O$$

$$2C_6H_{12} + O_2 + HOBO \rightarrow (C_6H_{11}O)_2BOH + H_2O$$

$$3C_6H_{12} + O_2 + HOBO \rightarrow (C_6H_{11}O)_3B + 2H_2O$$

There is some evidence that the boric acid may react directly with the peroxide and thereby influence the decomposition products. In any case, the boric ester is quite resistant to further oxidation and effectively arrests the oxidation at this step. As a result, at a 10% conversion the yield of cyclohexanol + cyclohexanone is about 77% when using boric acid, compared with 67% without this additive when operating a single continuous stirred reactor. A batch reactor employing boric acid at this conversion gives a yield of about 88%. These higher yields also permit higher conversions to be employed, thereby reducing the size of the reactors and hydrocarbon recycle system. On the other hand, additional facilities are required for product work-up and boric acid recovery.

In the oxidation reaction, the use of low oxygen concentrations by the dilution of the inlet air with inert gas or recycled dry off-gas is recommended. The lower oxygen concentration is said to reduce the oxidation rate and give the alcohol more time to react with the boric acid. The increased volume of inert gas also assists in stripping the water of

reaction. This dehydrating action is important since a low water content in the oxidizer is required to avoid hydrolysis of the boric esters and serious loss of yield.

Work-up of the crude product involves contacting with hot water to hydrolyze the boric acid esters and regenerate cyclohexanol. The aqueous phase is decanted off and cooled to crystallize the boric acid which is recovered, dehydrated, and returned to the oxidizer system. The organic phase is stripped of cyclohexane and the alcohol passed on to the next oxidation step.

Several commercial plants employing boric acid assisted cyclohexane oxidation technology are reported to be in operation or under construction. This process, while more complex than the air oxidation process, offers a substantial yield improvement in cyclohexanol-cyclohexanone manufacture.

Cyclohexanol from Phenol. As indicated earlier, benzene may first be converted to phenol and then hydrogenated to cyclohexanol. This route to adipic acid, which is attractive if a large-scale phenol operation is available, is in commercial use today by at least one manufacturer. The hydrogenation of phenol proceeds with high yields over a nickel, copper, or chromium oxide catalyst. Cyclohexanol produced from phenol is of high purity and makes an excellent feed stock for further oxidation to adipic acid.

Nitric Acid Oxidation of Cyclohexanol-Cyclohexanone Mixtures. Early manufacture of adipic acid in Germany employed batch oxidation of pure cyclohexanol at 65°–70°C with make-up 54% nitric acid and recycled mother liquor. No catalyst was employed. The reaction mixture was cooled to precipitate the adipic acid, which was recovered by centrifugation, washed, and then recrystallized from water. The yield from alcohol was 81–85% at a nitric acid consumption of 1.5 lb/lb of adipic acid. Later operation, using 68% nitric acid, 40–45°C and manganese acetate catalyst, improved the yield to about 87.5%. The use of the vanadium catalyst system gives a yield of adipic from the alcohol of 86% at 60°C. But at 80°C the yield falls to 79%. Copper conversely shows improved yields as temperature is raised through this range. A combination of the two has a synergistic effect. The addition of .25% copper and .1% vanadium to a reaction mixture of 50% nitric acid gives a yield of 92–93% adipic acid at 65°C. Similar results are achieved with mixtures of ketone and alcohol. The weight ratio of nitric acid to organic feed can be varied widely. At the low ratio of 2.5 : 1 the temperature must be kept below 30° because of the highly exothermic nature of the reaction. With a ratio of 40 : 1 or higher, the reaction proceeds smoothly at 70–80°C and is 90% complete in five minutes. The mechanism of the nitric acid oxidation process is not easily established because of the complexity of the reaction mixture, the many reaction steps involved, and the rapidity of the reaction. It is suggested that the main reaction route may go through cyclohexyl nitrite to iso-nitroso-cyclohexanone to 2-nitro-2-nitroso-cyclohexane-1-one, which hydrolyzes with ring splitting to give adipic acid and liberates nitrous oxide in about the observed quantity. The lower dibasic acids are formed by the nitration of two different carbons in the cyclohexane ring. Glutaric, succinic, lower acids, carbon dioxide, and water are the main byproducts. The gases leaving the oxidizer include N_2, N_2O, NO, and NO_2. The nitrogen and nitrous oxide represent the products of nitric acid consumption since the nitric oxide and dioxide are scrubbed from the off-gas, reconverted to nitric acid, and returned to the oxidizer.

Two processes for the continuous nitric acid oxidation of cyclohexanol-cyclohexanone mixtures have been developed. In one process the organic mixture is fed continuously to a stirred autoclave from which the off-gas is vented through a scrubber. Nitric acid flows countercurrently down the scrubber into the autoclave. Reaction temperature is controlled by recirculating the reaction product through an external shell and tube cooler. Autoclave product flows to a bleacher where the dissolved nitrogen oxides are stripped from the liquid by air and passed to the scrubber.

Higher oxidation yields and through-puts are claimed by feeding the reactants through two shell and tube circulating reactors in series. The first operates at about 70°C and the second at about 100°C. Off-gas from each step is removed by separators in the circulating systems.

Adipic Acid Refining

One method for the recovery of adipic acid from the crude oxidation product is as follows: Before entering the crystallizer, the product is concentrated by vacuum stripping to remove excess water and monobasic acids; acetic, propionic, butyric, valeric, and caproic acids, which would otherwise contaminate the refined adipic. Recovery of adipic acid from the still tails is accomplished by crystallization at about 50°C. Crystals are separated by filtration or centrifugation. The mother liquor, consisting of adipic, succinic, and glutaric acids in about 50% nitric acid, is recycled to the oxidizer. To prevent buildup of by-product dibasic acids in the oxidation system, a portion of the mother liquor is purged continuously. The crude adipic acid cake is redissolved in water and crystallized in one or two stages to give refined cake which may then be dried by air in tray, rotary, or boiling bed dryers.

Other Oxidation Processes

The manufacture of adipic acid from cyclohexane by three consecutive oxidation steps is extensively described in the patent literature. The cyclohexanol-cyclohexanone mixture produced in the two-step process is separated and the cyclohexanol converted to cyclohexanone by catalytic dehydrogenation over a zinc-iron catalyst. The resulting ketone is combined with that produced in the first oxidation step and further air oxidized to adipic acid. In one reaction system the cyclohexanone is dissolved in acetic acid solvent and oxidized at about 80°C using a mixed catalyst of manganese and barium acetate.

A process for converting cyclohexane to adipic acid in one step has long been the objective of intensive research. Air oxidation of the hydrocarbon in a solvent such as acetic acid or acetone gives adipic acid, but the yields are too low to compete with the two- or three-step processes. One step nitric acid oxidation can give attractive yields when the by-product nitrocyclohexane is recycled. However, limited studies of this reaction system indicate that it may be uncontrollable and, hence, unsuitable for commercial operation.

Uses of Adipic Acid

The predominant use of adipic acid is in the manufacture of nylon 66. However, as a nontoxic, inexpensive, and high-purity acid, adipic has found a wide range of other uses. Mono- and polyesters of adipic acid are important adhesives and plasticizers. Adipate plasticizers impart outstanding low brittleness temperatures to polyvinyl chloride, and have been used with polystyrene, ethylcellulose, and nitrocellulose. Adipic acid is used in the manufacture of hydraulic fluids, for tanning of leather, in foods such as gelatin desserts, baking powders, canned vegetables, flavoring extracts, and beverages. It is used in the manufacture of detergents, and in the preparation of such drugs as antiseptics and effervescent powders. Adipate salts and resins are employed in various textile treating operations.

Sebacic Acid

This 10-carbon acid is produced commercially by the hydrolytic splitting of castor oil. Castor oil is reacted either with a suspension of solid caustic in mineral oil at 250-260°C or with aqueous caustic in a pressure autoclave. Hydrogen and 2-octanol are evolved as by-products. The sebacic acid is recovered as a fine white precipitate in 40-65% yield by acidification of the sodium sebacate.

$$CH_3(CH_2)_5CHOHCH_2CH{=}CH(CH_2)_7COOH \xrightarrow[-H_2]{NaOH}$$
Ricinoleic acid

$$CH_3(CH_2)_5CHOHCH_3 + NaOOC(CH_2)_8COONa$$
Capryl alcohol   *Sodium sebacate*

An alternate manufacturing method involves the oxidation of castor oil by a mixture of air and ozone. Sebacic acid may also be produced by the electrolysis of the methyl acid ester of adipic acid. The resulting dimethylsebacate is acidified to recover the acid.

Uses of Sebacic Acid

Sebacic acid is of importance as a nylon intermediate because its polyamide with hexamethylenediamine nylon 610 is less water sensitive than nylon 66. As a result, nylon 610 loses less of its stiffness when wet and hence makes a superior monofilament for brushes and applications where dimensional stability is required under varying humidity conditions. Sebacic acid is also used to produce plasticizers, alkyd resins, polyurethanes and urea resins. Sebacate esters are employed as aircraft lubricants, thinners, ingredients of metal soaps, and plasticizers for polyvinyl chloride and other film-forming polymers. Sebacic alkyds have stability and flexibility which make them useful as textile coatings and in paints and lacquer systems.

Diamines

Of the saturated aliphatic diamines, ethylenediamine and hexamethylenediamine are in large-scale commercial use. Only the latter is an important intermediate to nylon.

Hexamethylenediamine

Hexamethylenediamine is a water-white liquid which freezes at $40.87°C$ and boils at $196°C$. It is miscible with water and ethanol. While this diamine is a relatively stable compound, an aqueous solution gradually absorbs oxygen and liberates ammonia. Hot diamine tends to decompose to hexamethylenimine and polymers, particularly in the presence of iron, copper, or nickel. It is usually shipped as an $80-95\%$ aqueous solution to avoid freezing. Like other strong amines, contact of hexamethylenediamine with the skin or by breathing of the vapors should be carefully avoided.

Methods of Manufacturing Hexamethylenediamine

Of the many routes which have been commercialized, one is reported to start with cyclohexane oxidation products and proceed through 1,6-hexanediol to the diamine. All the other routes lead to the intermediate, adiponitrile, which is readily hydrogenated to hexamethylenediamine:

$$NC(CH_2)_4CN + 4H_2 \rightarrow NH_2(CH_2)_6NH_2$$

The latter reaction is carried out in the liquid phase over a cobalt or cobalt-copper catalyst feeding ammonia and adiponitrile in a 4/1 weight ratio together with a large excess of hydrogen. The ammonia reduces the formation of by-products. Reaction conditions are $100-135°C$ and a pressure of 600–650 atm. The reaction product, containing more than 90% hexamethylenediamine, is refined to high purity by distillation.

The adiponitrile for the above hydrogenation step may be made from adipic acid, furfural, acrylonitrile, butadiene, or acetylene, as follows:

Adiponitrile from Adipic Acid. Adiponitrile was first made on a large-scale by the vapor phase reaction of adipic acid with excess ammonia over a dehydration catalyst:

$$2NH_3 + HOOC(CH_2)_4\text{-}COOH \rightarrow NC(CH_2)_4CN + 4H_2O$$

The reaction involves a number of consecutive reactions and the product is a complex mixture which includes adiponitrile, cyanovaleric acid, adipamide, adipamic acid, and tars. The extensive patent art indicates the complexity of purifying this crude adiponitrile. Distillation coupled with chemical treatment with acids, bases, or oxidizing agents such as permanganates can be used.

Adiponitrile from Butadiene. The steps for the synthesis of adiponitrile from butadiene involve the following reactions:

$$CH_2{=}CH{-}CH{=}CH_2 + Cl_2 \rightarrow ClCH_2{-}CH{=}CH{-}CH_2Cl$$

$$2HCN + CH_2Cl{-}CH{=}CH{-}CH_2Cl \rightarrow NC{-}CH_2{-}CH{=}CH{-}CH_2{-}CN + 2HCl$$

$$NC{-}CH_2{-}CH{=}CH{-}CH_2{-}CN + H_2 \rightarrow NC{-}(CH_2)_4{-}CN$$

In the first reaction, chloride is mixed with an excess of butadiene vapor without a catalyst. A mixture of chlorinated products, predominately, 1,4-dichlorobutene-2 and 3,4-dichlorobutene-1 is formed. Control of the reactant ratio and reaction temperature is important to avoid substitution reactions forming HCl. The excess butadiene is recycled and the product refined by distillation.

The cyanation reaction is carried out in the liquid phase at a pH of 4–6 using HCN, a soluble copper catalyst and an acid acceptor, such as calcium carbonate, to neutralize the hydrochloric acid formed. The organic compounds in the reaction product are separated by extraction with a solvent such as chloroform, and dicyanobutene is recovered by distillation. Yields of $95-96\%$ for this step are reported.

The hydrogenation of dicyanobutene to adiponitrile is conducted over a fixed bed of palladium on charcoal catalyst. Pressure of 200–500 psig and temperature of $75-150°C$ are reported to be used. A yield to adiponitrile above 95% is achieved.

Adiponitrile from Furfural. Furfural, obtained from corncobs or bagasse, may be decomposed to furan, hydrogenated to tetrahydrofuran, hydrochlorinated to dichlorobutane, and reacted with cyanide to give adiponitrile.

In the first step furfural vapor and steam at 400°C are passed over a mixed catalyst of zinc chromite with iron or manganese chromite. The resulting furan is hydrogenated over a nickel catalyst in the second step to form tetrahydrofuran. Tetrahydrofuran and aqueous hydrogen chloride under 200–300 psig pressure are passed through a reactor at 180°C containing a dehydrating agent such as sulfuric acid. Achievement of high yields requires the recycling of reaction by-products. In the last step, sodium cyanide and 1,4-dichlorobutane are reacted in a solvent to give adiponitrile which is refined by distillation. The changing economics of furfural and petroleum products have made this route less attractive in recent years.

Adiponitrile from Acetylene and Formaldehyde. A process related to the furfural route which produces tetrahydrofuran or adiponitrile was commercialized in Germany during World War II. Two moles of formaldehyde react with one mole of acetylene to give 1,4-butyn-2-diol.

$$2HCHO + C_2H_2 \rightarrow HO-CH_2-C\equiv C-CH_2-OH$$

Close control of reaction conditions and the copper acetylide catalyst is required to safely operate this hazardous reaction. The diol is then hydrogenated to butanediol and dehydrated to tetrahydrofuran for further processing to adiponitrile as indicated above. Alternatively, the 1,4-butyn-2-diol may be hydrogenated to 1,4-butene-2-diol, hydrocyanated to 1,4-dicyanobutene, and finally further hydrogenated to adiponitrile and hexamethylenediamine.

Adiponitrile from Acrylonitrile. A recently commercialized process for the manufacture of adiponitrile is based on the electrolytic coupling of acrylonitrile. This process has attracted wide interest because of the rapidly declining cost of acrylonitrile as the result of the development of processes for the direct synthesis of acrylonitrile from propylene, ammonia, and air.

Acrylonitrile may be hydrodimerized to adiponitrile in over 60% yield through reduction by

contact with sodium amalgam or by electro-reduction. In one process the hydrodimerization is performed inside a series of cells constructed of polypropylene with neoprene gaskets, supported in a plate and frame filter press. Each cell consists of a lead cathode separated from a platinum-on-titanium anode by a cationic, selectively permeable membrane made from sulfonated polystyrene resin. A porous spacer about 6 mm thick is inserted in each compartment to separate the electrodes from the membrane and to induce turbulence in the anolyte and catholyte streams flowing through the cell compartments. The electrolytes flow through the cells in parallel with a potential of about 6 volts across each cell. The catholyte feed solution consists of about equal weight of acrylonitrile, water, and a quaternary ammonium sulfonate salt. The latter serves to increase the solubility of acrylonitrile in water and to improve the conductivity of the catholyte. The anolyte is a sulfuric acid solution. Oxygen is released at the anode. The hydrodimerization mechanism is not fully understood, but the reaction can be represented by:

$$2CH_2{=}CH-CN + 2H_2O + 2e \rightarrow$$
$$NC-(CH_2)_4-CN + 2OH^-$$

Precise control of catholyte composition and pH is required to minimize side reactions forming propionitrile, bis (2-cyanoethyl) ether, and acrylonitrile polymers. Yields of over 95% to adiponitrile are achieved.

The adiponitrile is separated from the catholyte solution leaving the cells by extraction with acrylonitrile and water to give an aqueous phase containing the quaternary salt and an organic phase of adiponitrile in acrylonitrile. The adiponitrile is recovered and refined by distillation. The acrylonitrile, after purging any by-products formed in the electrolysis, is returned to the cell along with the recycled quaternary salt.

Uses of Hexamethylenediamine

No large markets for this diamine, except as a polyamide intermediate, have been developed. Limited quantities have been used to synthesize pharmaceuticals and insecticides, as a rubber accelerator, and for corrosion inhibition.

Lactams

Lactams are anhydrides (inner amides) of amino carboxylic acids. They may be considered as lactones in which the heterocyclic oxygen is replaced by NH. This may be accomplished in some cases by heating lactones with ammonia under pressure. Of the many lactam candidates, only caprolactam is important as a nylon intermediate. Valerolactam is too stable to polymerize easily. Butyrolactam can be polymerized at low temperatures, but polymer stability is unsatisfactory.

Dodecalactam is polymerized commercially in Germany. Other lactams having greater than 7-membered rings can be expected to become of increasing industrial interest in the future.

Caprolactam is a white crystalline material having a molecular weight of 113.16, a melting point of 69.2°C, and boiling of 120°C at 6 mm Hg. Contact with the skin should be avoided as it may be an irritant. When heated to decomposition caprolactam may emit toxic fumes so that adequate ventilation should be provided.

Manufacture of Caprolactam

Four processes for the manufacture of caprolactam are of commercial interest. The earliest process, and still the most widely used, involves the reaction of cyclohexanone with a hydroxyl amine salt to give cyclohexanone oxime which is then treated with concentrated sulfuric acid to yield caprolactam via the Beckmann rearrangement. In one application of this process, cyclohexanone, made as described under adipic acid manufacture, is added to an agitated reactor together with an excess of hydroxyl amine salt solution.

$$\text{[cyclohexanone]} + NH_2OH \cdot 1/2H_2SO_4 \xrightarrow{+NH_3}$$

$$\text{[cyclohexanone oxime]} - NOH + 1/2(NH_4)_2SO_4 + H_2O$$

The mixture is cooled to hold the temperature below 50°C. Anhydrous ammonia is then added to the solution to form the oxime which precipitates as a crystalline solid. Cooling is required to remove the heat of reaction. The reaction product is then filtered to recover the wet oxime. The oxime is melted and pumped to an agitated and water-cooled autoclave where it mixes with concentrated sulfuric acid at a temperature of 115–140°C. The reaction is vigorous. Intimate mixing, good temperature control, and close ratioing of acid to oxime feed streams are required to carry out the reaction safely. The crude product is cooled to below 75°C.

$$\text{[cyclohexanone oxime]} - NOH + \xrightarrow[NH_3]{1/2H_2SO_4}$$

$$(CH_2)_5 \quad CO + 1/2(NH_4)_2SO_4$$
$$\quad\quad\quad NH$$

In the final step, the caprolactam-sulfuric acid solution is neutralized with ammonia while being cooled. The crude lactam solution is decanted and refined in a vacuum distillation train.

One disadvantage of this process is that the ammonium sulfate in the aqueous solution decanted from the crude lactam must be recovered for sale to make the process economically attractive. From 2.8–5 lb of ammonium sulfate per lb of caprolactam are produced, depending on what hydroxyl amine salt is employed.

In the second process, toluene is oxidized with air in the liquid phase using a bromine promoted manganese salt catalyst or ketone promoted cobalt catalyst to yield benzoic acid. The acid is readily hydrogenated over a precious metal catalyst to cyclohexane carboxylic acid. This acid is reacted with a slight molar excess of nitrosyl sulfuric acid at 55–65°C in oleum solution. Carbon dioxide is released and crude caprolactam is formed in about 61% conversion per pass and 90% yield.

$$\text{[toluene]} -CH_3 \xrightarrow{O_2} \text{[benzoic acid]} COOH \xrightarrow{H_2} \text{[cyclohexane carboxylic acid]} COOH$$

$$\xrightarrow[H_2SO_4 + NH_3]{NOHSO_4} (CH_2)_5 \begin{array}{c} C=O \\ \\ N-H \end{array} + CO_2 + (NH_4)_2SO_4$$

Another process for caprolactam manufacture involves the reaction of cyclohexane with nitrosyl chloride. In the first step, product gas from a standard ammonia oxidation converter is absorbed in concentrated sulphuric acid to produce a sulfuric acid solution of nitrosylsulfuric acid.

$$2H_2SO_4 + N_2O_3 \rightarrow 2HNOSO_4 + H_2O.$$

Preheated hydrogen chloride gas is reacted with the sulfuric solution to generate a gaseous mixture of nitrosyl chloride and hydrogen chloride. The remaining nitrosylsulfuric acid is recycled to the ammonia oxidizer gas absorber.

$$HNOSO_4 + HCl \rightarrow NOCl + H_2SO_4$$

The heart of the process involves the reaction of nitrosyl chloride and hydrogen chloride with liquid cyclohexane in the presence of visible light emitted from a battery of mercury lamps.

$$\text{[cyclohexane]} + NOCl + HCl \xrightarrow{h\nu} \text{[cyclohexanone oxime]} =NOH \cdot 2HCl$$

The resulting cyclohexanone oxime hydrochloride is very slightly soluble in cyclohexane and separates as a heavy oil at the bottom of the reactor. The oil is decanted and treated with oleum to effect the Beckmann rearrangement to caprolactam as described in the standard process. HCl gas is liberated during the rearrangement and recycled to the nitrosyl chloride generator. The newer photochemical reaction vessels contain 20 kw lamps. Power requirements are less than 2 kwh per lb of oxime.

A recently developed process involves the hydrogenation of nitrocyclohexane, made from cyclohexane and 35% nitric acid, to cyclohexanone oxime at 140°C and 500 psig over a catalyst of 10% PbO or Pd on activated carbon black. A yield of 75–79% is claimed. As an alternative, the nitrocyclohexane may be reacted with ethylene and a hydrogenation catalyst in a solvent to give the oxime in 70–80% yield. Ethylene oxide is a by-product of this BASF development.

The oxime is converted to caprolactam by the Beckmann reaction or by vapor phase rearrangement at 370°C over a borophosphoric acid catalyst. The yield is rather low in the latter case, but the formation of by-product ammonium sulfate is avoided.

Future Trends

Several significant trends are discernible in the future of the nylon intermediates field. The search for lower cost raw materials and processes for the manufacture of nylon intermediates will intensify as more producers enter the business and competition increases. Secondly, the variety of nylon intermediates can be expected to expand rapidly. To date, variations in properties of nylon fibers have largely been achieved by physical means: drawing, twisting, heat-treatment, fiber cross section variation, and surface treatment. The technology of tailor-making new nylon polymers and copolymers from more sophisticated diamines and acids to satisfy new end-use requirements is just beginning to develop.

J. V. E. HARDY

O

ODORS AND PERFUMES

Plastics that are suitable from the standpoint of physical and chemical properties for any given application are often rejected because of their inherent odor when they are considered for automobile upholstery, table covers, shower curtains, wearing apparel, etc. It is feasible and economical to incorporate odorants into such materials to cover a malodor or to employ perfumes to impart attractive and appealing fragrances to the finished product. In such applications, the use of odor modifiers or perfumes will nullify an objectionable odor that will otherwise preclude the intended use of the finished article.

It is also practical through the use of odor modifiers to obviate the accumulation of latent offensive odors which would deter the utilization of the finished plastic article. Such offensive odors as are encountered in plastics arise for a number of reasons, two of the most important being the plastic composition and the procedures involved in fabrication. Although malador may be characteristic of the basic plastic, it frequently arises from the plasticizers or materials added in the course of fabrication.

Some resins inherently possess objectionable odors. The phenolics and cellulose acetate butyrate fall into this category. Materials which are to be added, particularly stabilizers, present definite odor problems. Cadmium naphthanate and thio-organic compounds used as stabilizers, and some plasticizers such as dioctyl phthalate (DOP) and diisooctyl phthalate (DIOP) may be cited as examples. Furthermore, objectionable by-odors may arise at any stage in the processing, so that odors characteristic of the fillers, colorants, and hardeners, as well as of the stabilizers and plasticizers, will be encountered. All of these may exert chemical effects that are responsible for malodor in plastics.

Heat treatment at any stage in the processing of plastics can accelerate characteristic odors. Finally, objectionable odors may be imparted from materials that are extraneous to the plastic itself, such as an odoriferous lacquer or a surface treatment which is applied to the finished article.

The use of industrial odorants and perfumes in plastics involves their direct incorporation. More frequently the addition of odorants takes place before the plastic is set. When the odorant is applied, it can take the form of a concentrated oil, or it can be incorporated as a solution of odorant in a suitable solvent which might even be the plasticizer itself. In this procedure the mixing of the odorant with the base material is a simple process.

Inasmuch as many plastics undergo heat treatment, especially those that are to be extruded, good odor fixation is required in order to achieve maximum performance of the odor modifier or of the perfume, as well as to minimize the loss of odorant during the heating process. It is important that perfumes and odor modifiers be formulated to have a high heat resistance, especially when temperatures of the magnitude of 300°F or higher are employed in the plastic manufacture.

Experience has shown that perfumes are released slowly in the more porous plastics, whereas thermosetting materials require a surface dressing with the perfume, rather than direct incorporation, since the perfume when added is actually entrapped and cannot serve its function as odorant.

In the cases indicated, both perfumes and odor modifiers can be applied during some convenient stage of manufacture, or they can be used as a surface dressing. If utilized as a surface dressing the finished plastic item may be sprayed or dipped into a suitable solution of the odorant. For example, the perfume may be made into solubilized form by combining it with a suitable solubilizer which will render it dispersible in water. The plastic article can be dipped into this aqueous solution so that the odorant adheres to the surface. When properly formulated, solubilized odorants demonstrate good adherence to the plastic and corresponding odor modification or perfume effect, as the case may require.

If the surface of the plastic has a degree of porosity, this is helpful in fixing the odor. When the resins are extremely hard and do not possess this porosity, odorants can still be used in the form of a surface dressing, providing such dressings contain a carrier or coating into which the odorant can be incorporated.

While mention is made of a water solution of the solubilized odorant, in some cases a volatile solvent may be employed to dilute the concentrated odorant which will adhere to the plastic after this solvent has volatilized. It naturally follows that odorants and perfumes employed in this manner must be well fixed or stabilized in order to retain the desirable odor on the surface. Furthermore, if the perfume is to be employed in the form of a water bath, as in the aforesaid procedure, about 2% of the odorant is added to the water. When a volatile solvent is utilized as a carrier, a 0.5% solution of odorant will insure good results.

The selection of odor types will depend on the requirements of the finished article. Woody or cedar notes, camphoraceous or sassafras blends are generally employed. Table covers or shower curtains will require a light, pleasant fragrance. If the odorant is to be incorporated into such personal articles as toothbrushes, a food type odor is useful, among these being orange, lemon and mint blends. In fact there, are a multitude of fragrance types which are available, depending upon the odor effect desired. The selection of such odorants as noted will depend on the end use of the finished plastic article. To carry this example further, it can be readily seen that plastic belts, brief cases and luggage might require the customary leather odor. On the other hand, some manufacturers of pocketbooks made of plastics desire a floral perfume. Personal articles, such as mattress covers, can be best perfumed with a neutral, indefinable odor type. Very frequently, manufacturers of shower curtains think in terms of a fresh, clean odor. When the odor is to be incorporated directly into the plastic and the plastic is of such composition that the odor modifier or perfume can migrate freely, the perfume concentrate may be added directly at the rate of 0.5–1.0%.

In the aforesaid procedures for the use of either an odor modifier or of a perfume, it can be stated, experience has shown, that satisfactory results are usually attained when the compounder or fabricator of the plastic will work in close cooperation with the odor specialist. The practical knowledge of plastics and their formulations provided by the fabricator, conjoined with the experience of the odor specialist in handling aromatic materials, will achieve this cooperation because it will facilitate the manufacturer's obtaining a plastic that not only serves the intended use of the product, but is esthetically pleasing to the customer as well.

E. LAWSON

OLEFIN MONOMERS

Olefins are that class of aliphatic hydrocarbons each of which contains one carbon-carbon double bond. In this article particular attention will be paid to those olefins used in plastics, which can be referred to as olefin monomers. In this connection the members of the olefin family which find the greatest usage are ethylene, propylene, and certain of the C_4 olefins such as isobutylene and butene-1. Olefins in general are highly reactive, because of the above mentioned carbon-carbon double bond. Chemical configuration is not only the basis for reactivity of olefin monomers but thus the basis for their tremendous importance as raw materials for the plastics industry. Olefins are the most versatile of the basic petrochemical intermediates and are produced for petrochemical usage in the largest tonnage, with the exception of ammonia. For the convenience of the reader, physical properties of the important olefin monomers are shown by Table 1.

Ethylene finds its principal uses as an olefin monomer for plastics in the production of high and low density polyethylene, in the production of styrene for polystyrene, and in the production of ethylene dichloride for subsequent production of vinyl chloride and polyvinyl chloride. A discussion of the chemistry of the above mentioned processes and the many others which use ethylene is beyond the scope of this section, but it can be said that ethylene specifications are set by the requirements of commercial high and low density polyethylene processes. This is because virtually every large ethylene producing facility has a significant part of its production consumed by a related polyethylene facility, and it is in general economic to produce all the ethylene from a given plant to meet the stringent specifications set by polyethylene processes. Thus, almost all ethylene plants now being built, and which will be built in the future, will produce ethylene with a gross purity specification of about 99.9% ethylene, with ethane and methane, the next higher and lower boiling components, being principal contaminants. However, it is especially important that polymerization poisons be held to low parts per million in the ethylene monomer. Thus, acetylene, total sulfur, water, oxygen, carbon monoxide and carbon dioxide are variously specified at 5–15 ppm max, and each is usually held well below this range in normal operation. Purification of ethylene monomer usually is achieved by fractionation at low temperature. Sulfur and carbon dioxide are removed by amine and caustic wash, water by solid bed dehydration, and carbon monoxide and oxygen removed as a part of the low temperature separation between methane and ethylene.

Propylene is a highly versatile olefin which

TABLE 1. PHYSICAL PROPERTIES OF PRINCIPAL OLEFIN MONOMERS.

Compound	Formula	Molecular wt	Boiling point, °F, 14.696 psia	Freezing point, °F, 14.696 psia	Critical constants Pressure, psia	Temp., °F	Volume, ft³/lb	Liquid Sp. Gr. 60°F/60°F Saturation pressure (In vacuum)	Liquid density, lb/gal 60°F Saturation pressure, (In air)
Ethylene	C_2H_4	28.052	-154.68	-272.47^a	742.1	49.82	0.0706	—	—
Propylene	C_3H_6	42.078	-53.86	-301.45	667.	197.4	0.0689	0.5220^b	4.343^b
1-Butene	C_4H_8	56.104	$+20.73$	-301.63^a	583.	295.6	0.0689	0.6013^b	5.004^b
cis-2-Butene (high boiling)	C_4H_8	56.104	38.70	-218.04	600.	324.3	0.0503	0.6271^b	5.219^b
trans-2-Butene (low boiling)	C_4H_8	56.104	33.58	-157.99	600.	311.9	0.0503	0.6100^b	5.076^b
Isobutylene	C_4H_8	56.104	19.58	-220.63	579.8	292.51	0.0513	0.6004^b	4.996^b

Compound	Specific heat ratio Cp/Cv Btu/lb-°F, at 60°F, Ideal gas	Heat of vaporization, Btu/lb 14.696 psia Normal boiling point	Surface tension, dynes/cm Air saturated liquid 14.696 psia	Absolute viscosity, CP 32°F 14.696 psia Gas	Heat of formation, Btu/lb, mole of ideal gas at 0°R	Heat of combustion gross, Btu/ft³ of real gas at 60°F	Sp. Vol., ft³/lb of real gas at 60°F 14.696 psia
Ethylene	1.243	207.57	16.5^c	0.0093	26,139.6	1608.5	13.4524
Propylene	1.154	188.18	16.7^c	0.0078	15,242.4	2371.7	8.8736
1-Butene	1.112	167.94	13.12	0.00708	8928.0	3177.9	6.5571
cis-2-Butene (high boiling)	1.121	178.91	15.49	0.0069	6264.0	3168.	6.561
trans-2-Butene (low boiling)	1.107	174.39	14.19	—	4032.0	3163.	6.561
Isobutylene	1.106	169.48	12.84	0.0073	1764.0	3156.	6.561

[a] At saturation pressure (triple point).
[b] At saturation pressure.
[c] At boiling point.

Data Sources:
Miller, Clara E., and Rossini, F. D., "Physical Constants of Hydrocarbons, C_1 to C_{10}," American Petroleum Institute (July 1961).
American Petroleum Institute Research Project 44—"Surface Tension," Carnegie Institute of Technology (Oct. 31, 1960).
Brown, G. G., Katz, D. L., Oberfell, G. G., and Alden, R. C., "Viscosity," Natural Gasoline Association of America (1948).

finds use in a dozen or more major tonnage chemicals. The principal propylene-based plastic is polypropylene, although other propylene derivatives are plastics related. For example, cumene, or isopropyl benzene, is used for manufacture of phenol, which in turn goes into phenolic plastics; acetone is used in methacrylate production; and acrylonitrile in ABS plastic. In general, propylene is available as a by-product of thermal cracking operations to produce ethylene, or from refinery operations, as a concentrate varying from 60–93% propylene, with propane being the principal impurity. For chemical uses propylene is marketed in either a so-called chemical grade of 90 minimum % purity, and a polymerization grade of 99 minimum % purity. In each case propane is the principal contaminant, and small amounts of ethylene and ethane may be present

depending on the precision of the deethanization step during purification of the propylene. As regards propylene for use in polymerization, principal catalyst poisons are methyl acetylene, propadiene, sulfur, water, oxygen, carbon monoxide and certain other oxygenated compounds for which specifications are set generally from 10–50 ppm max each, depending on the needs of the specific polymerization process.

The members of the butylenes family are used for significant volumes of chemicals, principally butadiene, but only two are used directly to any extent in plastics. The first is butene-1 which is used as a comonomer in small percentages in polyolefins. The second is isobutylene which is used to produce a family of polyisobutylenes varying from viscous liquids to solid polymers, useful for blending with polyolefins to improve their properties. Butene-1 monomer is sold in purities no less than 95%, with a trend toward 98 and 99% specifications. Trace contaminants, or polymerization catalyst poisons, in butene-1 sold approximate the levels of those in propylene. Polymer grade isobutylene is usually 99 minimum % purity, again with very low level catalyst poisons.

Manufacturing techniques for olefin monomers vary in different locations in the world principally because of feedstock and by-products considerations. For example, in the United States there is a very large supply of olefins as a by-product of crude oil refining. United States refineries practice a large amount of catalytic cracking for motor fuel production, which also makes available ethylene, propylene and butylenes. On the other hand, in the other two large olefin monomer consuming areas of the world, Western Europe and Japan, refineries do not practice to any large extent catalytic cracking for motor fuel production. Olefins instead are produced in Europe and Japan almost entirely by thermal cracking of the light fraction of crude oil, commonly called light naphtha. To a lesser extent, olefins are also produced from refinery gases and other sources in these areas.

Figure 1 shows an estimated 1965 United States olefin material balance. This figure illustrates the part which refinery gases, principally from catalytic cracking operations, play in the availability of olefin monomers in the United States. It shows in fact that chemicals consume only a small fraction of the available propylene and butylenes from refineries, and that the bulk of these olefins go to motor fuel (via

alkylation or catalytic polymerization). Refinery gases also supply a significant portion of the ethylene (about 30%) which is produced for chemical usage in the United States. Ethylene recovery from refinery gases is regarded as a more expensive route to ethylene because of the dilute form of the ethylene and the treating operations usually required. The remaining 70% comes from thermal cracking of ethane, propane, and to a lesser extent heavier components, extracted from natural gas. From 1965 to 1970 it is expected the consumption of ethylene, propylene and butylenes respectively will grow at the rate of 6–7%, 7–8% and 4–5% per year in the United States. The pattern of olefin production as regards feedstock source will not change significantly in the United States in the foreseeable future, unless the policy of the government should change with respect to importation of light naphtha for use as a chemical feedstock.

A material balance on olefins for Europe or Japan, similar to Figure 1, is virtually impossible to prepare because of lack of complete published data. The following tabulation of ethylene and propylene production and growth rates summarizes Western Europe and Japan:

	1965 Estimated consumption, million lb	Estimated growth rate per year 1965–1970, %
Western Europe		
Ethylene	3960.	19 – 20
Propylene	2470.	8 – 9
Japan		
Ethylene	1440.	20 – 22
Propylene	880.	18 – 25

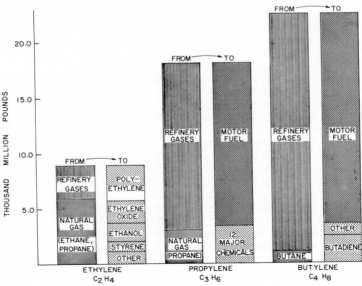

FIG. 1. Estimated 1965 U.S. olefin material balance.

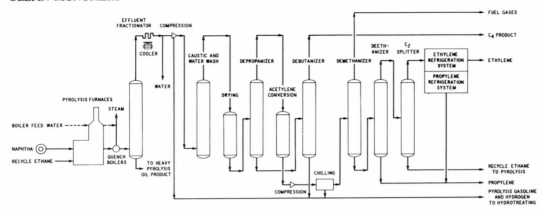

FIG. 2. Olefin monomer flow diagram. (*Courtesy M. W. Kellogg Co.*)

A butylene projection is not included since in the United States butylenes are closely related to the demand for butadiene and rubber in Europe and Japan. However, in these areas butadiene is mostly supplied as a by-product of naphtha cracking. Butylenes, which are largely excess, will probably continue to be so.

Consumption of all olefins in Europe and Japan seems destined to grow faster than in the United States for a number of years. Naphtha cracking to produce ethylene in Europe and Japan has thus far produced more than adequate propylenes and butylenes for chemical usage. However, alkylation of propylene and butylene for motor fuel production is not practiced to any significant extent as yet outside the United States, and part of the propylene and butylenes produced along with the ethylene are excess. For example, in Europe a large amount of the propylene produced goes to fuel gas. In Japan thus far the excess propylene which is produced as a part of ethylene operations is consumed in the rapidly growing LPG industry.

A typical flow scheme for a naphtha cracking plant to produce olefins is shown in Fig. 2. Plants which use ethane or propane are similar, except that an olefin plant is slightly less complex as the feedstock becomes lighter, because there are smaller volumes of by-products to recover and purify.

As can be seen, an olefin plant consists principally of thermal cracking furnaces, compressors and low temperature fractionation equipment. The by-product propylene may be concentrated to chemical or polymer grade propylene by hydrotreating to remove methyl acetylene and propadiene, and fractionation to remove propane. After by-product butadiene is extracted, polymer grade isobutylene may be produced by sulfuric acid extraction from the remaining C_4 mixture. Butene-1 is the only other C_4 olefin monomer

used directly in plastics. It is presently produced as a co-product of butadiene manufacture and linear olefin manufacture from ethylene.

Process trends of future importance are those which will permit the producer of olefins to tailor or adjust the olefin ratio, particularly of ethylene to propylene, and to a lesser extent of butylenes. For example, thermal cracking furnaces which can operate with more severe cracking conditions and thus maximize the yield of ethylene will be used increasingly. Likewise processes which can cheaply convert one olefin to another and thus enable operating flexibility will find application. One such process for converting propylene to ethylene and butylenes, called the "Triolefin" process, has been developed. Finally, competition is forcing higher purity olefin production with increasingly rigorous specifications, and the construction of larger plants in the range of 200,000 metric tons and up per year of ethylene.

J. W. DAVISON

ORGANIC COLORANTS, SOLUBLE DYES

Organic colorants are those colorants which are based on high molecular weight, complex organic compounds. When these colorants retain their particulate structure, they are classified as "pigments"; when these colorants are completely dispersed, they are classified as "dyes". Such complete dispersion occurs when an organic colorant is completely soluble in the polymer or when completely dispersed during the milling or extrusion of the polymer.

Organic colorants in their soluble or completely dispersed form have the following advantages: they yield brilliant colors, complete transparency, excellent tinting strength, and ease of incorporation into the polymer. Their disadvantages include their tendency to migrate

or bleed, their poor chemical stability, generally poorer light stability than pigments and their expense when purified to the degree required for plastic operations.

Methods of Using Dyes with Plastics

Dyes may be applied to the surface of plastics in the classic method of dyeing textiles (which are fibrous polymers). This procedure is known as "substantive dyeing", or the application of the colorant from a solution to the surface of an object. Adhesion of the dyestuff occurs through chemical combination with a reactive group or through the attraction of secondary valence (Van der Waal's) forces. This method is in regular use for small nylon, cellulose acetate, and urea-formaldehyde moldings. The materials and procedures used are the same as those used for nylon and cellulose acetate textiles. The techniques of substantitive dyeing are adequately explained in references on textile chemistry.

"Solution dyeing" or "mass coloration" are the terms used to describe the physical incorporation of the dye *into* the plastic. This refers to the complete dispersion (by solution or by melting) of the colorant within the body of the polymer and is similar to the procedure used with pigments.

Classification of Organic Colorants

Dyes are classified according to (1) their solubility when considered for use in plastic, or (2) for their method of application when used in textiles. There is little relationship or coordination between these two classification systems, and their chemical structure and care must be taken to specify end-use when discussing their characteristics.

Solubility Class Name	Textile Class Name	General Chemical Types in Class
(1) Oil soluble	(Old name for dyes now classed as hydrocarbon soluble)	
(2) Hydrocarbon soluble	Basic dyes	Triphenylmethane
(3) Alcohol or spirit spluble	Acid dyes	Miscellaneous
(4) Solvent soluble	Premetallized acid dyes	Azo dyes chelated with a metal atom such as Al or Cr

Oil Soluble Dyes. The term "oil soluble dyes" has been used to describe dyes that are soluble in hydrocarbons and vegetable oils. With the new development in dyes for plastics, this classification must be considered obsolete.

Hydrocarbon Soluble Dyes. These include most of the classic oil soluble dyes of commerce. They are soluble in aliphatic and aromatic hydrocarbons. Occasionally, they may also be soluble

in alcohols, ketones, or other oxygenated solvents. They have excellent tinting strength and yield brilliant colors. They are limited by their poor heat stability and light-fastness.

Spirit Soluble Dyes. This term is applied to a series of textile dyes that demonstrate a marked solubility and development of color strength in ethyl alcohol. They are insoluble in hydrocarbons. These dyes contain a water solubilizing group as part of the chromophore molecule. In addition, the standardizing agents (salts, dextrins, etc.) characteristic of the textile dyes of commerce are present.

Spirit soluble dyes are relatively inexpensive and yield brilliant colors. They are, however, highly reactive unless used in small amounts (up to 0.05% by weight of the polymer). The residual salts may result in haze in the plastic and in reduction of electrical properties.

Solvent Soluble Dyes. This newest class of dyes has been developed for use in polymers of the plastics and coatings industries. They have been purified to remove all of the inorganic salts and extraneous standardization materials. The metallic salts and other portions of the water solubilizing groups have been neutralized or removed. The dye (single chromophore or mixture of chromophores) is therefore water insoluble.

Solvent soluble dyes are soluble in alcohols, ketones, esters and in polymers or plasticizers containing these linkages. Many of the dyes in this class have melting points below 450°F and may be milled into polystyrene or the polyolefins.

Use of Dyes in Plastics

Dyes are of value in plastics because of their brilliance and transparency. Under normal circumstances a very small amount of dye will provide a satisfactory color with no effect on tensile strength, modulus, or other engineering properties of the plastics.

Their chief restrictions are their tendency to migrate and the possibility of their reactivity with stabilizers, accelerators, residual polymerization catalysts, etc.

Selected dyes have shown adequate stability as well as requisite color value in acrylics, cellulose acetate, and polystyrene plastics. They have not as yet shown a great deal of value in vinyls, ABS, polyolefins, or the thermosetting plastics.

MELVIN M. GERSON

Cross-reference: COLORATION OF PLASTICS.

ORGANIC PEROXIDES, GENERAL

The polymerization of terminally unsaturated compounds (monomers) is today generally initiated by a free radical produced from a peroxide. There are other physical methods however like heat alone, high energy radiation and use of ultraviolet light. There are other chemical methods like strongly basic anions (butyl lithium), strongly acidic cations (boron trifluoride) and azo compounds (azobisisobutyronitrile).

Organic peroxides under suitable reaction conditions produce free radicals and these acting on a monomer cause it to grow by addition to itself to produce a polymer or by addition to another monomer to yield a copolymer. Organic peroxides should not strictly be called catalysts as the peroxide fragments are built into the polymer and are not recoverable. True catalysts can be recovered unchanged. Hence organic peroxides used in polymerizations are frequently called initiators.

Free radical catalysts are preferred in most industrial applications because of the ease of usage and because they give suitably rapid rates of conversion at reasonable cost and predictable control.

Nomenclature

Organic peroxides contain the —O—O— group attached to at least one carbon atom. Thus, R—OO—R, where R is a methyl group, would give H_3C—O—O—CH_3, named methyl peroxide or dimethyl peroxide. If one R was methyl and the other benzoyl, we would have H_3C—OO—COC_6H_5, methyl benzoyl peroxide. Organic peroxides may be considered derivatives of hydrogen peroxide, H—OO—H, in which one or both hydrogens are replaced by an organic radical. Indeed most of the commercial organic peroxides are made from hydrogen or sodium peroxides by direct replacement of hydrogen or sodium by organic groups.

When only one hydrogen of H—OO—H is replaced by an organic group, like R—OO—H, the product is known as an alkyl hydroperoxide, but R—CO—OO—H is a peroxy acid or simply peracid, (R—CO—O—)₂ is a diacyl peroxide, and (R—O—CO—O—)₂ is a peroxycarbonate.

There are a number of so-called peroxides like urea peroxide and melamine peroxide which are not true organic peroxides but are in fact hydrogen peroxide addition products.

Production of Radicals

Organic peroxides contain a weak valency bond in the —O—O— group. These oxygens are precisely the reason why a molecule containing them dissociates to radicals at relatively low temperatures. It is often important to know the rate and temperature at which a given organic peroxide will decompose to form radicals. The rate determining step is the scission of the peroxy bond. Some peroxides can decompose by more than one mechanism. The rate of decomposition varies from one type of solvent to another and

frequently in a given solvent the velocity constant will show dependence on the concentration. If this occurs, induced decomposition has set in, so that radicals are attacking molecules of undissociated peroxide.

The primary dissociation of hydroperoxides, of which t-butyl hydroperoxide and cumene hydroperoxide are best known, show the formation of alkoxy radicals:

$$R\text{—}O\text{—}O\text{—}H \rightarrow R\text{—}O\cdot + \cdot OH$$

But hydroperoxides also show induced decomposition to give peroxy radicals:

$$R\text{—}O\cdot + R\text{—}O\text{—}O\text{—}H \rightarrow R\text{—}OH + R\text{—}O\text{—}O\cdot$$

and the whole process might not be even this simple as other evidence indicates interaction of peroxide with monomer.

The dialkyl peroxides such as di-t-butyl peroxide, are less susceptible to induced decomposition and transfer reactions and are thus more reliable than the alkyl hydroperoxides in expected action. They dissociate to alkoxy radicals:

$$R\text{—}O\text{—}O\text{—}R \rightarrow 2R\text{—}O\cdot$$

The diacyl peroxides, well known in benzoyl and lauroyl peroxides, dissociate primarily into aroyloxy radicals when reactive substances are present,

$$R\text{—}CO\text{—}O\text{—}O\text{—}CO\text{—}R \rightarrow 2R\text{—}CO\text{—}O\cdot$$

If the reactive substances are absent, as in the thermal decomposition of diacyl peroxide alone, then an almost quantitative yield of carbon dioxide is apparent:

$$R\text{—}CO\text{—}O\text{—}O\text{—}CO\text{—}R \rightarrow 2R\cdot + 2CO_2$$

The peroxyesters have intermediate rates of decomposition between those of the respective dialkyl and diacyl peroxides to which they are related. The peroxyesters are a source of alkoxy and acyloxy radicals:

$$R\text{—}CO\text{—}O\text{—}O\text{—}R' \rightarrow R'\text{—}O\cdot + R\text{—}CO\text{—}O\cdot$$

The dialkyl peroxydicarbonates dissociate at low temperatures and give alkyl carbonate radicals as expected:

$$R\text{—}O\text{—}CO\text{—}O\text{—}O\text{—}CO\text{—}O\text{—}R \rightarrow 2R\text{—}O\text{—}CO\text{—}O\cdot$$

Further decomposition yields alkoxy radicals and carbon dioxide,

$$R\text{—}O\text{—}CO\text{—}O\cdot \rightarrow R\text{—}O\cdot + CO_2$$

These free radicals react with monomer molecules in a polymerization and thus start the formation of each growing chain to polymer. The rate of polymerization is dependent upon the rate of decomposition of the peroxide. And this rate of decomposition is invariably controlled by close temperature domination with or without chemical additives known as accelerators. The rate of decomposition should not be so fast that the free radicals cannot be fully utilized and thus become wasted. In general, higher rates of polymerization can be obtained with increased amounts of peroxide because more polymer chains are started. Also, lesser amounts of peroxide mean fewer free radicals and polymer chain can grow to larger size yielding higher molecular weights. All of this can be worked out for practical application by selection of the proper organic peroxide, temperature control, chemical additives and proper medium in critical usages.

Classification

Organic peroxides have been arranged in various ways to put in order such a listing. Here is one system to include the commercially available materials.

Alkyl hydroperoxides	R—OO—H
Dialkyl peroxides	R—OO—R'
Acyl peroxyacids	RCO—OO—H
Diacyl peroxides	RCO—OO—COR'
Dibasic acid peroxides	[HOOC—(CH$_2$)$_x$—CO]$_2$O$_2$
Esters of acyl peroxyacids	R—CO—OO—R'
Aldehyde peroxides	[R—CH(OH)]$_2$O$_2$
Ketone peroxides	[RR'C(OOH)]$_2$O$_2$; [RR'C(OH)]$_2$O$_2$
Dialkyl peroxydicarbonates	R—OOC—OO—COO—R'
Esters of alkyl peroxy-carbonic acid	R—OOC—OO—R'

Commercial Peroxides

Alkyl Hydroperoxides. *t-Butyl Hydroperoxide.* *t*-Butyl hydroperoxide is a colorless liquid, $C_4H_{10}O_2$, molecular weight (M.W.) 90.12, active oxygen (A.O.) 17.75%, with d_4^{20} 0.8960, n_D^{20} 1.4010, boiling point (B.P.) of 35°C at 20 mm, and a melting point (M.P.) of 4°C. About 12% will dissolve in water. It readily forms a salt with sodium hydroxide.

t-Butyl hydroperoxide is prepared from *t*-butyl alcohol by reaction with hydrogen peroxide in strong sulfuric acid:

$$(CH_3)_3C—OH + H—OO—H \rightarrow (CH_3)_3C—OO—H + H_2O$$

When prepared by this method, it invariably contains substantial quantities of the related peroxide.

Commercial *t*-butyl hydroperoxide is available in 70, 80, and 90% concentrations. The 70–72% is most in demand and contains mainly *t*-butyl peroxide as associative material with much lesser amounts of *t*-butyl alcohol and water. The open cup flash point is about 38°C (100°F). It is shipped in polyethylene containers with 1, 7 and 35 lb net of the peroxide, under red label. The principal polymerization usage is for acrylics, polyesters and vinyl acetate. It is the raw material for peroxyester preparation.

2,5-Dimethylhexyl-2,5-dihydroperoxide. 2,5-Dimethylhexyl-2,5-dihydroperoxide is a colorless, crystalline solid, $C_8H_{18}O_4$, M.W. 178.22, A.O. 17.96%, with M.P. 104–105°C. It is soluble in alcohols and ketones, slightly soluble in water and esters, and nearly insoluble in hydrocarbons.

This hydroperoxide is prepared from dimethyl hexanediol by reaction with hydrogen peroxide in strong sulfuric acid:

$$(CH_3)_2C(OH)(CH_2)_2—C(OH)(CH_3)_2 + 2H—OO—H \rightarrow (CH_3)_2C(OOH)(CH_2)_2—C(OOH)—(CH_3)_2 + 2H_2O$$

The commercial product has about 90% peroxide content and a M.P. of 102–104°C. It is packed in individual single lb containers; 25 or 50 such units are shipped per outside case. It has found use as a catalyst for polyesters, polystyrene, and silicone cross-linking.

Cumene Hydroperoxide. Cumene hydroperoxide is manufactured from cumene and air under controlled conditions. The acidity of the reaction medium must not become too high as the hydroperoxide is sensitive to decomposition at low pH conditions:

$$C_6H_5CH(CH_3)_2 + O_2 \rightarrow C_6H_5C(OOH)(CH_3)_2$$

Cumene hydroperoxide is a colorless liquid, $C_9H_{12}P_2$, M.W. 152.19, A.O. 10.51%, with d_4^{20} 1.0619, n_D^{20} 1.5242, and a B.P. of 53°C at 0.1 mm.

The commercial product is 80–85% with an open cup flash point of 80°C (177°F), and a d_{25}^{25} of 1.0458. The impurities are cumene, alcohol and ketone derivatives of cumene. The material is shipped in drums and tank wagons. It has found use as a catalyst in synthetic rubber manufacture, polyester polymerizations, and the styrenation of alkyds. Its greatest captive use is for the preparation of phenol and acetone. These products result when the hydroperoxide is heated with dilute mineral acid.

Diisopropylbenzene and p-Menthane Hydroperoxides. Both these hydroperoxides are prepared from the air oxidation of the hydrocarbon much like cumene hydroperoxide. The end products are hydroperoxides of about 55% content, and both contain isomers. Diisopropylbenzene hydroperoxide is $C_{12}H_{18}O_2$, M.W. 194.26, and A.O. 8.24%. *p*-Menthane hydroperoxide is $C_{10}H_{20}O_2$, M.W. 172.26, and A.O. 9.29%.

Commmercial diisopropylbenzene hydroperoxide is a liquid with $d_{15.6}^{15.6}$ of 0.956, and an open cup flash point of 79°C (175°F).

Commercial *para*-menthane hydroperoxide is a liquid with $d_{15.6}^{15.6}$ of 0.932, and an open cup flash point of 71°C (160°F). Both products are soluble in most organic solvents, but insoluble in

309

water. They are catalysts for synthetic rubber manufacture, polyester polymerization, and have a moderate exotherm with bulk polyester polymerizations. Shipment is in drums as oxidizing agent and in tank wagons.

Dialkyl Peroxides. (1) *t-Butyl peroxide. t*-Butyl peroxide is a colorless liquid, $C_8H_{18}O_2$, M.W. 146.22, A.O. 10.94%, vapor density 5.03, and vapor pressure at 20°C is 19.5 mm. It has a B.P. of 111°C at 760 mm, and an open cup flash point of 18°C (65°F) with d_4^{20} 0.7940 and n_D^{20} 1.3890.

t-Butyl peroxide is prepared from *t*-butyl alcohol and hydrogen peroxide in the presence of sulfuric acid:

$$2(CH_3)_3C—OH + H—O—O—H \xrightarrow{H+}$$
$$(CH_3)_3C—O \cdot O—C(CH_3)_3 + 2H_2O$$

The peroxide is also prepared by direct oxidation, with oxygen of the branched hydrocarbon in the vapor phase catalyzed by hydrogen bromide.

The commercial product is of excellent purity and will assay 98–99%. It is shipped in 6 lb (1 gal) and 30 lb (5 gal) metal containers. *t*-Butyl peroxide is used to catalyze olefines, styrene and silicones, and is the preferred peroxide for styrenation of alkyds.

(2) *Cumyl Peroxide.* Cumyl peroxide is a colorless solid, $C_{18}H_{22}O_2$, M.W. 270.26, A.O. 5.91%, and melting point 39°C. The super-cooled liquid at 21°C has a refractive index of 1.536.

Cumyl peroxide is prepared from cumene hydroperoxide and cumyl alcohol by heat and a trace of acid:

$$C_6H_5C(CH_3)_2—OOH + C_6H_5C(CH_3)_2—OH \rightarrow$$
$$C_6H_5C(CH_3)_2—OO—(CH_3)_2CC_6H_5 + H_2O$$

Commercially, cumyl peroxide is available as a 40% active peroxide intimately mixed with calcium carbonate or with carbon black, These are free flowing powders with d_{25}^{25} of 1.53 and 1.33 respectively. A 90% active and 95% recrystallized product is also offered having d_{25}^{25} of 1.023 and 1.018.

Cumyl peroxide is used for rubber and silicone vulcanization in the supported forms and as a polymerization catalyst for vinyl monomers and polyester resins in the carbonate and purer materials.

Acyl Peroxyacids. (1) *Peroxyacetic acid.* Peroxyacetic acid is $C_2H_4O_3$, M.W. 76.05, A.O. 21.04,% and has a melting point of 0.1°C in pure form. It is prepared by the action of hydrogen peroxide on acetic anhydride in presence of 1% sulfuric acid:

$$CH_3CO—O—COCH_3 + H—O \cdot O—H \xrightarrow{H+}$$
$$CH_3CO—O—O—H + CH_3COOH$$

or by the vapor phase oxidation of acetaldehyde:

$$CH_3CHO + O_2 \rightarrow CH_3CO—O—O—H$$

Commercially, a 40% colorless solution in acetic acid is available, containing about 5% hydrogen peroxide, with 11.0% active oxygen of which 2.4% is due to the hydrogen peroxide present. It is miscible in all proportions in water, and has a solubility like acetic acid in other solvents. The pungent odor is characteristic, has specific gravity of 1.15 at 20°, and is not shock sensitive. The flash point is 40°C (105°F), and fires are easily extinguished with water.

Peroxyacetic acid is much used as a convenient epoxidation, hydroxylation, and oxidizing agent. It finds use in bleaching and sterilizing, but not much as a polymerization agent.

(2) *Peroxylauric acid.* Peroxylauric acid is $C_{12}H_{24}O_3$, M.W. 216.31, A.O. 7.40%, and melting point of 52°C. It can be prepared in excellent yield from lauric acid and hydrogen peroxide in cold concentrated sulfuric acid.

(3) *Peroxybenzoic acid.* Peroxybenzoic acid is $C_7H_6O_3$, M.W. 138.12, A.O. 11.58%, M.P. of 41°C and B.P. 110–112° at 15 mm. It sublimes readily and is volatile with steam. It can be prepared from benzoyl peroxide and sodium methoxide in cold chloroform solutions:

$$C_6H_5CO—O—O—COC_6H_5 + CH_3ONa \rightarrow$$
$$C_6H_5CO—O—O—Na + C_6H_5COOCH_3$$
(acidify to free acid, 85% yield)

The stability of peroxybenzoic acid is quite limited, and the solution must be kept cold (2°C) and used within 2 weeks. This material is often used in structural determination of organic compounds to ascertain the number of double bonds, and for epoxidations and hydroxylations.

(4) *Meta-Chloroperoxybenzoic acid.* m-Chloroperoxybenzoic acid is $C_7H_5O_3Cl$, M.W. 172.57, and A.O. 9.27%. The commercial product is available as an 85% material with about 15% of the related acid. It is a white, crystalline solid, slight pungent odor, 7.8% A.O., M.P. 92°C, and decomposing at 100–104°C. The best solvents are ethyl alcohol, ether and ethyl acetate. m-Chloroperoxybenzoic acid is said to be an effective epoxidizing agent for olefines.

Diacyl Peroxides. *Acetyl Peroxide.* Acetyl peroxide is $C_4H_6O_4$, M.W. 118.09, A.O. 13.55%, a colorless solid, highly explosive, M.P. at 30°C. It is prepared directly in a plasticizer by the reaction of acetic anhydride and hydrogen peroxide in basic solution:

$$2CH_3CO—O—COCH_3 + H—O—O—H \xrightarrow{NaOH}$$
$$CH_3CO—O—O—COCH_3 + 2CH_3COOH + 2H_2O$$

The commercial product is a 25% solution of the peroxide in dimethyl phthalate. This mixture melts at −8°C, has a flash point of about 79°C (175°F), A.O. of 3.4% and d_{25}^{25} 1.17. It is available in 1, 9 and 45 lb units.

Acetyl peroxide is useful for acrylic, olefin and polyester polymerization. It has also found application in organic synthesis.

Propionyl Peroxide. Propionyl peroxide is $C_6H_{10}O_4$, M.W. 146.14, A.O. 10.95%, a colorless, shock sensitive, and very flammable material. It is prepared directly in a solvent by the reaction between propionic anhydride and hydrogen peroxide in basic solution.

The commercial product is a 25% solution of the peroxide in heptane, with A.O. 2.74%. The material is catalyst for olefin polymerization, and can be used for acrylic and styrene conversions to polymer.

Octanoyl (Caprylyl) Peroxide. Octanoyl peroxide is $C_{16}H_{30}O_4$, M.W. 286.40, A.O. 5.59%, a colorless liquid, with M.P. 22°C. It is prepared by the action of caprylyl chloride on hydrogen peroxide in alkaline solution or on sodium peroxide in aqueous solution:

$$CH_3(CH_2)_6CO-Cl + Na-O-O-Na \rightarrow$$
$$[CH_3(CH_2)_6CO-]_2O_2 + 2NaCl$$

The commercial product is a 50% solution of the peroxide in mineral oil, A.O. 2.8%. It has poor stability at room temperatures and above, but when stored at 2°C, may be kept for prolonged times without substantial loss of activity. The material freezes at 16°C, and storage in the solid state is desirable. Product is useful in emulsion and vinyl type polymerizations.

Decanoyl Peroxide. Decanoyl peroxide is $C_{20}H_{38}O_4$, M.W. 342.50, A.O. 4.67%, a colorless solid, M.P. 41°C. It is prepared by the action of capric acid chloride on sodium peroxide in aqueous solution.

The commercial product is a high purity material of 97.0% assay and A.O. 4.53%, consisting of soft white granules. It melts at 41°C, has slight odor and good solubility in benzene, carbon tetrachloride, and monomers. Decanoyl peroxide has excellent stability when stored cold, and holds up well even when held at room temperature for 13–15 weeks. The material is preferred for olefin polymerization, when shorter time and shorter length free radical is desired in the reactor. The product is shipped in drums of 100 lb capacity in refrigerated trucks to insure good quality.

Lauroyl Peroxide. Lauroyl peroxide is $C_{24}H_{46}O_4$, M.W. 398.61, A.O. 4.01%, a colorless crystalline material, M.P. 55°C. It is prepared by the action of lauroyl chloride on sodium peroxide in water solution.

The commercial product is of high assay, in excess of 97%, A.O. 3.9% and granular form. It has good normal room temperature stability. Lauroyl peroxide is very safe to handle, and burns only slightly faster than the lauric acid from which it is produced. This product is shipped in 100 lb units. Large quantities are employed as catalyst in vinyl chloride and olefin polymerizations and for polyacrylates. Lauroyl peroxide imparts good color stability and makes possible non toxic, food grade polymer products.

Benzoyl Peroxide. Benzoyl peroxide is $C_{14}H_{10}O_4$, M.W. 242.24, A.O. 6.60%, a colorless, odorless, tasteless rhombic crystalline material. The d_{25}^{25} is 1.26 and n_D^{20} 1.545. It melts at 105–106°C with decomposition, and is easily soluble in acetone, benzene and chloroform, but insoluble in water. Benzoyl peroxide is prepared by the reaction between aqueous sodium peroxide or alkaline hydrogen peroxide and benzoyl chloride:

$$2C_6H_5CO-Cl + Na-O-O-Na \rightarrow$$
$$C_6H_5CO-O-O-COC_6H_5 + 2NaCl$$

The commercial product is a high purity (98%), crystalline, agglomerated, granular substance, with A.O. 6.5%. It has excellent stability at normal room temperatures, but is highly flammable and somewhat shock sensitive in this high purity form. Benzoyl peroxide is probably the peroxide produced in largest tonnage of all the organic peroxides; the United States Tariff Commission reports production for 1963 in excess of $4\frac{1}{5}$ million lb. All dry benzoyl peroxide must be packed in individual single pound units, and shipped in celled boxes not exceeding 50 lb net weight. The celled material must be flame proofed and cushion protecting. It is available in powdered form.

Producers offer the same benzoyl peroxide wet with 10, 20 to 25 and 30% water. This material is much safer to handle and use, and is highly recommended if the water can be tolerated. Shipment is allowed in drum units with inner plastic bags.

Other available mixtures include dry, finely divided powders with inorganic salts, pastes of 50–55% peroxide mixed with plasticizers and silicone fluids. All of these diluted products serve a useful purpose in various segments of industry, and are much safer than others when exposed to heat or flame. Shipment is again allowed in drums because of the improved safety of such products.

For certain applications, benzoyl peroxide can be accelerated with tertiary amines such as N,N-dimethylaniline, or N,N-dimethyl-*p*-toluidine, and thus room temperature polymerizations of methacrylates and polyesters occur.

Benzoyl peroxide can be used in nearly any polymerization reaction; it is used with allyls, acrylics, vinyl chloride and acetate, polyesters, styrene and silicones for vulcanization. Its great versatility and relatively inexpensive cost makes benzoyl peroxide quite attractive.

Aside from polymerization uses, benzoyl peroxide is used for bleaching of oils, fats, waxes, milk products and flour, for organic synthesis, and certain skin creams of limited use.

p-Chlorobenzoyl Peroxide. p-Chlorobenzoyl peroxide is $C_{14}H_8O_4Cl_2$, M.W. 311.13, A.O. 5.14%, with M.P. 140°. It is a colorless, crystalline solid, soluble in acetone, benzene and chloroform, but insoluble in water. The peroxide is prepared from p-chlorobenzoyl chloride and alkaline inorganic peroxides.

The commercial product is a granular or powdered material of 96% assay and A.O. 4.94%. It has a faint odor and off white color, with melting point 133–136°C. It can be promoted with tertiary amines useful in certain applications. This peroxide is used in instances where benzoyl peroxide might be employed in certain operations it is a little faster acting than the unsubstituted peroxide, but is more costly. It is shipped in individual single pound units in celled boxes. As with other peroxides, the wet-with-water material is much safer to handle than the dry.

2,4-Dichlorobenzoyl Peroxide. 2,4-Dichlorobenzoyl peroxide is $C_{14}H_6O_4Cl_4$, M.W. 380.01, A.O. 4.21%, with M.P. 103°C. It is a colorless, odorless, crystalline solid, soluble in acetone, benzene and chloroform, but insoluble in water. The peroxide is prepared from 2,4-dichlorobenzoyl chloride and alkaline inorganic peroxides.

The commercial product is *always* sold in dilute form, since it is too flammable to be an article of commerce in its pure form. It is therefore available as a 35% dry powder with calcium phosphate, as a 50% paste with dibutyl phthalate, and 50% paste with silicone fluid. The pastes are available in 50 lb net drums.

This peroxide is very reactive and is an excellent low temperature catalyst. It has a relatively low peak exotherm, and is suitable for large castings where considerable heat buildup can result. Silicone vulcanization with this peroxide uses hot air processing.

Dibasic Acid Peroxides. *Succinic Acid Peroxide.* Succinic acid peroxide is the only commercial representative of this class of peroxides. It is a colorless crystalline material, $C_8H_{10}O_8$, M.W. 234.08, A.O. 6.84%. The peroxide must be stored below room temperature to prevent loss of active oxygen. It is prepared from succinic anhydride and hydrogen peroxides.

$$2OC—(CH_2)_2—CO + H—OO—H \rightarrow$$
$$[HOOC—(CH_2)_2—CO]_2O_2$$

The commercial product, also known as "Alphozone," has 90% assay, A.O. 6.1%, and M.P. 125°C. It is a white powder, somewhat soluble in water and oxygenated organics. It has germicidal and antiseptic properties, and has been used for vinyl fluorocarbon polymerization. It is also available in individual single pound containers.

Peroxyesters—*Tertiary Butyl Peroxyacetate, Benzoate, Isobutyrate, Pivalate and Phthalate.* *t-Butyl peroxyacetate* is a colorless liquid, $C_6H_{12}O_3$, M.W. 132.16, A.O. 12.11%, d_4^{22} 0.883, n_D^{25} 1.40. It is somewhat volatile, and is sold as a 75% solution in benzene with A.O. 9.0%, d_{25}^{25} 0.923, and n_D^{25} 1.421. It is used for olefin and styrene conversion to polymers. Preparation is from t-butyl hydroperoxide and acetyl chloride or anhydride in alkaline medium.

t-Butyl peroxybenzoate is a colorless liquid, $C_{11}H_{14}O_3$, M.W. 194.22, A.O. 8.24%, d_4^{22} 1.043, n_D^{22} 1.5007, and B.P. 76°C at 2 mm. It is sold as a 95% liquid having M.P. 8°C and flash point about 82°C in 8 and 40 lb containers. This peroxide can be used in the polymerization of acrylics, polyesters, olefins, styrene, vinyl acetate and vulcanization of silicone rubbers. Preparation is from t-butyl hydroperoxide and benzoyl chloride in alkaline solution.

t-Butyl peroxyisobutyrate is $C_8H_{16}O_3$, M.W. 160.21, and A.O. 9.99%. It is sold commercially as a 75% solution in benzene, under refrigeration in 45 lb carboys. Primary use is for the preparation of polyolefins. Preparation is from t-butyl hydroperoxide and isobutyryl chloride in alkaline solution.

t-Butyl peroxypivalate is $C_9H_{18}O_3$, M.W. 174.23, A.O. 9.18%. It is commercially sold as a 75% solution in mineral spirits, and transported in refrigerated truck. Use is for preparation of polyvinyl chloride, polyolefins and polystyrene. The peroxide is made from t-butyl hydroperoxide and pivaloyl (trimethylacetyl chloride in alkaline solution.

Di-t-Butyl diperoxyphthalate is $C_{16}H_{22}O_6$, M.W. 310.34, A.O. 10.31%, a colorless crystalline solid, with M.P. 57°C. The commercial product is a 50% solution in dibutyl phthalate, with d_{25}^{25} 1.056 and n_D^{25} 1.489. The flash point is above 65°C, and it too is shipped in 8 and 50 lb containers. This product has limited use for the curing of polyesters. The peroxide is prepared from t-butyl hydroperoxide, and o-phthalyl chloride in alkaline solution.

2,5-Dimethylhexyl-2,5-diperoxy benzoate is $C_{22}H_{26}O_6$, M.W. 386.2, A.O. 8.28%, and is a colorless, crystalline solid. The commercial product has M.P. 113–116°, is 91% pure with 7.5% A.O., and is fairly soluble in acetone. It is packaged in individual single pound containers, with as many as 50 units to a shipping case. This peroxide is often preferred in polyester premix compounds because of good shelf life for the premix, and smooth-surfaced parts which result from its uses. The material is prepared from the dihydroperoxide, with 2 moles of benzoyl chloride in basic solution.

Aldehyde Peroxides. There are few aldehyde peroxides on the market. One of them is hydroxyheptyl peroxide, a colorless, needle-structured material, possessing faint odor, M.W. 262.4, A.O. 6.10%, and M.P. 73°C. The product keeps well stored below room temperature, but above it, gradually loses activity beyond a month's storage. This peroxide is prepared by reacting heptaldehyde with hydrogen peroxide in dilute acid medium:

$$2CH_3(CH_2)_5CO{-}H + H{-}O{-}O{-}H \rightarrow$$
$$[\,CH_3(CH_2)_5CH(OH)]_2O_2$$

The technical peroxide is a granular to powdered product with a characteristic odor, soluble in many organics, but insoluble in water. It is 95% pure, A.O. 5.8%, and has infrequent use with polyester polymerization. The product is packaged in individual single pound units, as many as 50 of which can be shipped in an outside case.

Ketone Peroxides. *Methyl Ethyl Ketone Peroxides.* When methyl ethyl ketone is peroxidized with $1\frac{1}{4}$ moles hydrogen peroxide in strong acid media, several peroxides results, chiefly (about 50%):

$$2CH_3COC_2H_5 + 3H{-}O{-}O{-}H \xrightarrow{H+}$$

$$
\begin{array}{ccc}
& C_2H_5 & C_2H_5 \\
& | & | \\
CH_3{-}C{-}O{-}O{-}C{-}CH_3 & + & 2H_2O \\
& | & | \\
& OOH & OOH
\end{array}
$$

The next predominant entity is the trimeric peroxide in about 25%. This mixture is very shock sensitive and extremely flammable. The dihydroperoxide, of the equation above, is a colorless solid, M.W. 210.22, A.O. 22.83%, M.P. 42°. When the mixture of peroxides is made into a solution of 60% peroxides in dimethyl phthalate, the commercial product results, and is safe to handle. The products of different manufacturers show variations, as changes in ratio of ketone: hydrogen peroxide: acid, temperature, pH, water, etc., yield a multiple number of materials. These ketone peroxides can be promoted with cobalt salts, and have found great favor with polyester fabricators because no external heat is necessary to start them off. The U.S. Tariff Commission for 1963 reports production of over 1.1 million lb of 2-butanone peroxide. The mixture is shipped in 8 and 40 lb polyethylene containers with vented caps for pressure release.

Methyl Amyl Ketone Peroxide. MAK Peroxide is the peroxidized product resulting from $1\frac{1}{2}$ moles hydrogen peroxide on methyl amyl ketone in strong acid media. The predominant peroxide,

a liquid, is presumably $C_5H_{11}(CH_3)C(OOH)-OO-C(OOH)C(CH_3)C_5H_{11}$, M.W. 294.38, A.O. 16.31%.

The technical product has 15.5% A.O., and about 95% peroxide content. It is a colorless, oily, viscous liquid with $d_{25}{}^{25}$ 1.002, $n_D{}^{25}$ 1.443, flash point about 50°C. It serves as a polyester polymerization catalyst, but its high cost has made it unpopular.

Cyclohexanone Peroxides. Cyclohexanone reacted with hydrogen peroxide in strong acid media yields a number of peroxides, but the main one is 1-hydroxy-1'-hydroperoxydicyclohexyl peroxide, a white crystalline solid, $C_{12}H_{22}O_5$, M.W. 246.30, A.O. 12.99%, M.P. 78°C.

$$2C_6H_{10}O + 2H{-}O{-}O{-}H \xrightarrow{H+}$$
$$C_6H_{10}{-}(OH){-}O{-}O{-}(OH){-}C_6H_{10} + H_2O$$

The commercial product is diluted with dibutyl phthalate in its preparation so as to give an 85% peroxide product, 11.0% A.O., M.P. 70°C, flash point 106°C. This is a safer product to handle, and is a convenient granular solid. Also commercially available is a 50% paste product containing additional dibutyl phthalate. Both products are extensively used as catalysts for polyesters, and are favored over other peroxides for low color and low temperature action. The peroxide can be promoted with cobalt for room temperature applications.

Bis(hydroxycyclohexyl) Peroxide. Cyclohexanone reacted with hydrogen peroxide in trace acid media yields a single peroxide, a white fluffy powder, $C_{12}H_{22}O_4$, M.W. 230.30, A.O. 6.95%, M.P. 71°C.

$$2C_6H_{10}O + H{-}O{-}O{-}H \rightarrow$$
$$C_6H_{10}{-}(OH){-}O{-}O{-}(OH){-}C_6H_{10}$$

The commercial product is a bulky, readily soluble product with 90% assay, 6.25% A.O. and M.P. 67°C. A 50% paste in plasticizer is offered to reduce bulk and improve safety and solubility. The material can be promoted with cobalt for fast room temperature gelation of polyester.

Other Peroxides

2,5-Dimethyl-2,5-di(t-butyl peroxy)hexane. This peroxide is a colorless liquid, $C_{16}H_{34}O_4$, M.W. 290.43, A.O. 11.02%, B.P. 51°C at 0.1 mm, $d_4{}^{25}$ 0.873, $n_D{}^{25}$ 1.4184. It is prepared by reacting t-butyl alcohol with 70% sulfuric acid and the dimethylhexane dihydroperoxide.

The commerical product is 90% assay, 9.9% A.O. flash point 84°C, and is soluble in common organic solvents. It may be used for polymerization of polyesters, olefins, styrene, and for crosslinking operations when absorbed on a filler.

2,5-Dimethyl-2,5-di(t-butyl peroxy)hexane-3. This is a colorless liquid peroxide, $C_{14}H_{30}O_4$,

M.W. 262.38, A.O. 12.20%, B.P. 66°C at 2 mm, d_4^{25} 0.881, n_D^{25} 1.4219. It is prepared by reacting t-butyl alcohol with 70% sulfuric acid, and the dimethyl hexyne dihydroperoxide.

A commercial product is 90% assay, 11.0% A.O., but the product containing 45% peroxide absorbed on enert filler is more common, and is presently used for cross-linking of polyethylene.

Diisopropyl Peroxycarbonate. This material is a liquid at room temperature but has M.P. 9°C. It must be kept frozen at all times, and therefore stored below the M.P. It is $C_8H_{14}O_6$, M.W. 206.19, A.O. 7.76%, with d_4^{15} 1.08 and n_D^{20} 1.4034. The material is prepared by reaction of isopropyl chloroformate with alkaline hydrogen peroxide or sodium peroxide:

$$2(CH_3)_2\text{—}CH\text{—}O\text{—}COCl + Na\text{—}O\text{—}O\text{—}Na \rightarrow$$
$$[(CH_3)_2CH\text{—}O\text{—}CO]_2O_2 + 2NaCl$$

The commercial product is of high purity and must be shipped and stored under refrigeration. It has been used for polymerization of ethylene, styrene, vinyl chloride, acrylates, and mixtures of monomers. It is sold in 1 and 9 lb trays.

t-Butyl Peroxyisopropyl Carbonate. This peroxide is a liquid ester, $C_8H_{16}O_4$, M.W. 176.21, A.O. 9.08%, produced from t-butyl hydroperoxide and isopropyl chloroformate in alkaline solution. It is used for conversion of ethylene to polymer, and available in 8 and 40 lb containers. This technical grade contains about 6–10% of t-butyl peroxide.

Selection of a Peroxide

The selected peroxide is frequently the one with the lowest price. Conditions are made to fit the activity of four or five of the lowest priced catalysts. Because of the large number of peroxides available an attempt is presently being made to fit the needs of the process. One criterion for selection is based on half-life decomposition in benzene; Tables 1 and 2 evaluate such. A catalyst should be chosen with a half-life between 10 and $\frac{1}{2}$ hr, and then applied to the system for final decision.

Methods of Analysis

The best methods for determining purity have been iodometric. The oxidizing power of the various classes of organic peroxides show wide variation, and therefore a specific method has been devised for certain classes. Potassium iodide, sodium iodide, and hydriodic acid are invariably the inorganic source of iodide. Many solvents, acetone, glacial acetic acid, isopropyl alcohol, acetic anhydride, and mixtures have been used with some success. Esters respond nicely to catalytic amounts of iron for complete liberation of iodine. Some solvents require an inert atmosphere of CO_2 or N_2 to obtain low blanks and heat is often required for quantitative results.

Health and Safety

Most of the peroxides have not undergone extensive health investigations. Prolonged inhalation of vapors of most organic peroxides, and most volatile chemicals for that matter, will cause headache and throat irritation. When constantly used, they should be employed in well ventilated rooms to protect the daily worker. After use, washing of the skin with soap and water will reduce the chance of irritation.

The greatest hazard of all organic peroxides is their flammability and sensitivity to shock and friction. The commercial products are largely free of shock, but some show increased sensitivity with rise in temperature —all peroxides are flammable in varying degrees. When involved in a fire or

TABLE 1. HALF LIFE OF ORGANIC PEROXIDES (IN HOURS).

Peroxide	Temperature, °C											
	30	40	50	60	70	80	90	100	110	120	130	140
Diisopropylperoxycarbonate	19	6.2	2.2	0.84	0.33	0.14						
2,4-Dichlorobenzoyl peroxide		18		4.6	1.4	0.40	0.14					
t-Butyl peroxypivalate		20		5.1	1.5	0.47	0.16					
Lauroyl peroxide				13	3.4	0.93	0.30	0.09				
Decanoyl peroxide				13	3.4	0.93	0.29	0.09				
Octanoyl peroxide				13	3.4	0.95	0.28	0.09				
Propionyl peroxide				17	4.5	1.2	0.36	0.10				
Acetyl peroxide				32	8.0	2.1	0.57	0.16	0.05			
Benzoyl peroxide				45	13	3.8	1.2	0.40	0.14	0.05		
p-Chlorobenzoyl peroxide				73	19	5.4	1.6	0.50	0.16	0.06		
t-Butyl peroxyisobutyrate					29	7.2	1.9	0.55	0.15	0.05		
Hydroxyheptyl peroxide					29	14	6.8	3.4	1.8	1.0	0.56	0.33
Cyclohexanone peroxides							11	3.8	1.3	0.52	0.20	0.08
t-Butyl peroxyisopropyl carbonate							28	8.3	2.8	1.0	0.36	0.14

TABLE 2. HALF LIFE OF ORGANIC PEROXIDES (IN HOURS).

Peroxide	100	110	120	130	140	150	160	170	180	190	200	210	220	230
2,5-Dimethyl-2,5-di-(peroxybenzoate)	10	2.8	0.85	0.27	0.09									
t-Butyl peroxyacetate	12	3.4	1.1	0.34	0.12	0.04								
Methyl ethyl ketone peroxides	15	6.1	2.7	1.2	0.56	0.28								
t-Butyl peroxybenzoate	18	5.4	1.7	0.55	0.19	0.07								
di-t-Butyl peroxyphthalate	18	4.8	1.4	0.40	0.13	0.04								
Cumyl peroxide		25	6.5	1.8	0.50	0.16	0.05							
2,5-Dimethyl-2,5-di-(t-butylperoxy) hexane		35	9.4	2.6	0.71	0.23	0.07							
t-Butyl hydroperoxide, 70%			11	3.2	1.0	0.33	0.11	0.04						
t-Butyl peroxide			21	6.4	2.2	0.85	0.32	0.13	0.06					
2,5-Dimethyl-2,5-di-(t-butylperoxy) hexyne-3			28	8.2	2.5	0.90	0.31	0.12	0.05					
p-Menthane hydroperoxide, 55%				13	5.0	2.2	0.93	0.41	0.20	0.09				
Pinane hydroperoxide, 75%					11	4.7	2.1	0.95	0.47	0.22	0.11			
2,5-Dimethylhexyl-2,5-dihydroperoxide						13	6.1	2.9	1.5	0.73	0.39	0.20	0.11	
Cumene hydroperoxide, 85%						18	7.8	3.5	1.7	0.77	0.39	0.19	0.10	
t-Butyl hydroperoxide, 90%								12	5.2	2.2	1.0	0.49	0.23	0.11

otherwise exposed to sudden high heat shock, they often explode violently. Care must then be exercised in the storage and handling of peroxides at all times. A separate reasonably cool building for exclusive storage of stocks is highly recommended.

ALLAN A. WAHL

ORGANIC PEROXIDES FOR POLYESTER RESINS

The availability of numerous peroxide catalysts for polyester resins makes possible a greater degree of control, not only in terms of cure times, gel times and initiation temperatures but also in the appearance and performance of the end product. However, such a variety of peroxide catalysts presents problems as well as advantages: namely the selection of the very best curing agent for the polyester system involved.

In general, the organic peroxide groups for use in polyester reinforced plastic systems fall into three categories: the ketone peroxides for room temperature polyester curing; medium temperature range peroxides, including both aromatic and aliphatic diacyl peroxides, and a third group of high temperature polymerization initiators, including alkyl peroxides and hydroperoxides, peroxyesters and diperoxyesters.

Only the commercially available peroxide chemicals will be mentioned here. Others have been for the most part omitted unless they have a unique or specific characteristic which is not attainable with standard materials.

Ketone Peroxides

For initiation of polyester polymerization or cross-linking at room temperature, ketone peroxides are most widely used. This group of peroxides includes methyl ethyl ketone peroxide (MEKP), cyclohexanone peroxide and bis(1-hydroxycyclohexyl) peroxide. Spray-up and hand lay-up techniques are usually used with these groups.

MEK peroxides in a 60% solution of dimethyl phthalate with three levels of reactivity or speed are most generally used for hand lay-up and rudimentary methods of fabrication. MEK peroxides are available in standard, fast (10-30% faster than standard) and extra fast (10-30% faster than fast) grades. Pot life, gel time, exotherm peak temperature, degree of cure, hardness and cure time desired dictate which of the three speeds a fabricator should choose in addition to atmospheric conditions of temperature and humidity.

For spray-up systems, special MEKP formulations are available. One example is diallyl phthalate (DAP) extended formulations of MEKP The DAP cross-links with the polyester resin, providing, in most cases, better physical properties in the finished product than solvent-extended MEKP. An extended MEK peroxide is safer in that it not only has a significantly higher flash point (DAP flash point 330°F) but also does not form potentially hazardous by-products as in a solvent-extended system. Since the DAP cross-links with the polyester, pinholing and blistering as a result of solvent boil-off is eliminated.

If a solvent is used with MEKP in a spray system, ethyl acetate or isobutyl acetate are recommended. Since acetone has a tendency to form acetone peroxides (which are extremely hazardous, shock-sensitive materials) its use should be avoided.

All of the above MEKP formulations are available with color tints. Use of blue, green or red tinted MEKP in spray systems is helpful as a visual means of assuring catalyst flow and continuity.

Another commercially available ketone peroxide is cyclohexanone. It is available in either a nonseparating homogeneous paste in a 50% concentration with dibutyl phthalate diluent or in powder form consisting of 85% cyclohexanone peroxide and 15% dibutyl phthalate. The latter, with a low plasticizer content, is usually used in applications where plasticizer content must be minimized.

Another commonly used organic peroxide catalyst is bis(1-hydroxycyclohexyl) peroxide. A single isomer of cyclohexanone peroxide, bis(1-hydroxycyclohexyl), is a 90% pure ketone peroxide which provides extremely fast gelation and low discoloration in polyester curing.

The ketone peroxides are sometimes used for moderate temperature cross-linking. For instance, MEK peroxide can be successfully used as the initiator in the application of polyester resin films to wood. The wood is first heated, then a coating of MEK peroxide is rolled on. The wood is then sent through a curtain flow of noncatalyzed polyester resin and finally baked for 15–30 min in an ascending temperature oven. The heat actually promotes decomposition of the peroxide, thus initiating the cure.

Another major area for room temperature curing of polyester based resins is in the auto body putty field. Both MEKP and benzoyl peroxide pastes are employed as catalysts in properly promoted auto body putty formulations. The paste catalyst, which is now available in a variety of colors, has been gaining wide popularity in this application. The color pigment in the paste catalyst is used to assure the body repair man a thorough catalyst mix and dispersion in the putty.

The choice of proper promoter for the ketone peroxides and, as a matter of fact, for any room temperature curing system is an important consideration affecting not only color but also pot life, speed of cure, finished properties, etc. Cobalt naphthenate and cobalt octoate, both metallic soaps, are most commonly used as promoters for ketone peroxides. A 12% concen-

tration of cobalt octoate is actually less expensive than a 6% concentration of cobalt naphthenate and provides less discoloration and is more efficient.

Where discoloration is not a prime consideration, faster gel and cure can be accomplished through a doubly promoted system using cobalt octoate and a tertiary amine, such as dimethyl aniline or diethyl aniline. However, in addition to causing a yellowish or brownish discoloration, the presence of the amine promoter tends to result in poor polyester resin stability. One important feature of doubly promoted systems is that they permit the use of high temperature peroxides, such as benzoyl peroxide, for room temperature cures as illustrated by the use of benzoyl peroxide paste in auto body putties.

For clear polyester cures, it may be necessary to design specific catalyst promoter systems. For instance, cobalt naphthenate causes a yellow-pink cast when used with MEK peroxide. This can be virtually eliminated by using less cobalt naphthenate and adding a small amount of lauryl mercaptan. Substitution of cyclohexanone or bis-(1-hydroxycyclohexyl) peroxide for MEKP may further eliminate the discoloration problem.

Aromatic and Aliphatic Diacyl Peroxides

For polyester resin cures between 120–200°F, the aromatic and aliphatic diacyl peroxides are generally used. The aromatics include benzoyl peroxide, 2,4-dichlorobenzoyl peroxide and para-chlorobenzoyl peroxide. Less important for polyester systems are the aliphatics such as myristoyl, lauroyl and decanoyl peroxides.

Benzoyl peroxide, both in high purity and formulated forms, is probably the most widely used peroxygen chemical for polyester reinforced plastics application. It is inexpensive and provides dependable and rapid curing especially in matched metal die molding, transfer molding, bag molding, rubber plug molding and many other medium and high temperature techniques. Benzoyl peroxide exhibits long pot life in unpromoted polyester resin and in granular form is fairly soluble in styrene, the diluent usually used to disperse it prior to its addition in the resin. Benzoyl peroxide paste does not require predissolution in styrene as it is soluble directly in the polyester.

While benzoyl peroxide is generally used in a temperature range of 180–220°F, the temperature required may vary with the specific resin to be cured. A number of factors must be considered in determining the optimum temperature, particularly glass-to-resin ratio, cross-sectional thickness of the laminate, ultimate rigidity or flexibility of the polyester and speed of cure required. While benzoyl peroxide is a versatile catalyst, it has one significant drawback when used in granular form, and that is hazard. The granular product is shock sensitive and extremely flammable and it is always mandatory that precautionary measures are taken, not only when the granular benzoyl peroxide is shipped, but in its storage and handling. It is important that all instructions on the shipping label and in the technical literature are explicitly followed.

There are several formulations of benzoyl peroxide which have proven highly successful in all but the most exacting circumstances and are considered completely safe. These range from a free flowing granular material which contains 70% benzoyl peroxide and 30% moisture, all the way down to a 10% peroxide content with a nonflammable inert filler as diluent. The wetted form has been successful in most applications; however, instances of blistering have occurred in extremely hot, matched metal die molding operations.

Benzoyl peroxide formulations are also available in paste form. For safety, ease of handling and consumer acceptance, this form has proven most popular. There are two basic formulations: one using tricresyl phosphate (TCP) as a diluent and the other using butyl benzyl phthalate. The availability of non-separating paste formulations of benzoyl peroxide has been the most important reason this formulation has gained such wide preference.

Benzoyl peroxide in a 50% paste of tricresyl phosphate is particularly suitable for applications which call for superior electrical properties, or ones which will be molded at higher temperatures. One drawback of TCP is that it tends to discolor upon aging. This characteristic, however, does not destroy its effectiveness as a polymerization initiator. There are three formulations using butyl benzyl phthalate as a diluent containing respectively 45, 50 and 55% benzoyl peroxide. These formulations do not discolor upon aging and are significantly less toxic.

A 10–20% benzoyl peroxide in a thixotropic liquid formulation has also been developed recently. This liquid formulation, although experimental, has proven successful where a double dip tank is employed in a filament winding process. The liquid catalyst eliminates problems of pot life and, with tertiary-amine promotion, provides fast cures at room temperature which can later be post-cured in an oven.

For exceptionally fast cures, 2,4-dichlorobenzoyl peroxide in a 50% formulation with dibutyl phthalate diluent can be used. It is also available in 50% formulation in a silicone oil diluent for vulcanization of silicone resins. In polyester systems this chlorinated aromatic diacyl peroxide operates at a temperature range of 120-140°F. It has a tendency to discolor.

Another organic peroxide available in dibutyl phthalate or silicone oil diluent is p-chlorobenzoyl peroxide. However, it is a fairly weak catalyst in terms of conversion rates and degree of cure and is used only in specialized applications.

The aliphatic diacyl peroxides are primarily used to produce low density polyethylene and polyvinyl chloride resins. However, in some polyester systems a fatty acid peroxide such as lauroyl peroxide may be used as a replacement for benzoyl peroxide when a high degree of color integrity is required.

In a promoted system lauroyl peroxide will initiate a cure anywhere from room temperature to 110–125°F. In an unpromoted system, it will operate at 140–160°F. Lower exotherm temperatures can be expected when lauroyl peroxide is used as a replacement for benzoyl peroxide.

Myristoyl peroxide contains less active oxygen than lauroyl peroxide and, although it has a similar half-life, is a less potent catalyst.

Decanoyl peroxide, on the other hand, contains more active oxygen than lauroyl peroxide and this, combined with far greater solubility in a polyester resin, makes it somewhat advantageous to use. The major drawback to use of decanoyl peroxide is the fact that its melting point is 104–107°F.

Both aromatic and aliphatic diacyl peroxides can be doubly promoted with cobalt and tertiary-amines to produce room temperature cures. Doubly promoted systems are widely used for spray-up applications, auto-body putties and patching compounds requiring low or room temperature cures.

To increase cure speed without increasing mold or oven temperature, aromatic and aliphatic peroxides are often singly promoted with tertiary-amines. For example, benzoyl peroxide promoted with tertiary-amine will cure at temperatures as low as 120–125°F. Unpromoted benzoyl peroxide will cure in the same resin in the same amount of time at approximately 180°F.

Promoters, of course, will decrease the pot life of a resin and this must be considered if a promoter is to be used.

High Temperature Curing Agents

Organic peroxides for use as initiators in high temperature polymerization fall into these general groups:

(1) Aryl peroxides, such as di-tert-butyl peroxide.

(2) Alkyl hydroperoxides, such as tert-butyl hydroperoxide.

(3) Peroxyesters, such as tert-butyl perbenzoate.

(4) Diperoxyesters, such as 2,5-dimethylhexane-2,5-diperbenzoate.

(5) Dihydroperoxides, such as 2,5-dimethylhexane-2,5-dihydroperoxide.

Because of its extreme stability and uniform decomposition rate, di-tert-butyl peroxide is by far the most commonly used high temperature initiator. Due to its thermostability it may be used with certain prepolymers that are in a solid state and have a melting temperature below 190°F. With a material of this type the DTBP may be mixed into the molten prepolymer and frozen with no decomposition of the TBP, thus preserving its activity for later molding operations. However, for molding compounds or premix, DTBP which has a high volatility and vapor pressure, is not particularly suitable.

For polyester clear casting for decorative or biological purposes, *tert*-butyl hydroperoxide will provide clear water-white cures in high quality casting resins. In general, hydroperoxides are sensitive to surrounding media and therefore are less predictable initiators in rate of decomposition and side chain effects. As might be expected, dihydroperoxides are also unpredictable with regard to their activity. None the less, 2,5-dimethylhexane-2,5-dihydroperoxide has recently been successfully used in high electrical specification molding work which had heretofore been almost impossible to fabricate with polyesters.

tert-Butyl perbenzoate, a peroxyester, is most commonly used where long shelf-life is required, as in premix, prepreg and some molding operations. A relatively new group of compounds, the diperoxyesters, has recently become commercially available and offers significant advantages over many of the monoperoxyesters. For instance, 2,5-dimethylhexane-2,5-diperbenzoate provides cures in the same temperature range as tertiary-butyl perbenzoate but exhibits greater catalyzed shelf-life in a given molding or premix than the monoperbenzoate. Faster gel times and cure times, better flow characteristics, greater economy longer shelf-life, lower volatility and better surface finish are possible with the diperbenzoate.

For example, a 0.2% concentration of the diperbenzoate provides the same flexural strength values as 1.0% of *tert*-butyl perbenzoate in a molded premix part. Initiation temperature of the diperbenzoate can be reduced as low as 130-140°F using cobalt naphthenate as a promoter.

For molding temperatures of the order of 300-335°F, 2,5-dimethyl-2,5-di-*tert*-butyl peroxyhexane is useful. This product can also be promoted and is best suited for polyester premix and diallyl phthalate moldings where long shelf-life is employed and high molding temperatures are required. A liquid organic peroxide, 2,5-dimethyl-2,5-di-*tert*-butyl peroxyhexane lends itself to applications calling for lower volatility.

As pointed out, di-*tert*-butyl peroxide is extremely stable and relatively unaffected by promoters. However, dimethyl aniline, N,N-dimethyl-*p*-toluidine and diethylaniline will cause slight promotion whereas the cobalt promoters have an inhibiting effect on DTBP.

The diperoxyester 2,5-dimethylhexane-2,5-diperbenzoate can be promoted with cobalt to reduce curing temperatures to as low as 130°F.

tert-Butyl hydroperoxide reacts to promotion in much the same manner as di-*tert*-butyl peroxide; however, cobalt naphthenate in this case does have a promoting rather than inhibiting effect. In addition, TBHP is more sensitive to lauroyl mercaptan promotion than is TBP.

The dihydroperoxide, 2,5-dimethylhexane-2,5-dihydroperoxide is unpredictable with any given resin; therefore, effective promoters cannot be suggested with any degree of accuracy. It is known, however, that dimethyl aniline and cobalt naphthenate both have some effect on reducing the initiation point of this material.

MARTIN E. MARKS

P

PAINT MATERIALS

Plastics are painted for either decorative or functional purposes, or both. While some designs can be made in plastics during the molding process, it is not possible to add color coordination or multicolor images. Most painted plastics have a flat, uninteresting appearance; it is painting that adds "life" to a molded piece of plastic. Decorative finishes can impart the appearance of a metallic gleam or add a color tint, make an item easy to identify, or provide a uniform color for parts not color-matched as basic raw materials.

A functional finish adds a utilitarian quality to a plastic which is not basic to the plastic itself. A coating can make a part a conductor of electricity, or give a finished product greater resistance to chemicals, solvents, or water. The possibilities of applying paint to plastics are endless, but it is difficult to determine the proper coatings that combine with the right plastics to achieve the desired results.

The fact that the plastic part is to be painted must be kept in mind throughout all the steps of product design, mold design, and the molding operation itself. Thoughtful planning and careful workmanship throughout these stages can mean the difference between the success and failure of the painting operation. For example, if a part is to be silk screened, the area must be flat or smoothly curved, or if the part is to be hot stamped, the design must allow for this operation. Parts designed for spray painting should have a minimum number of narrow grooves or small holes. Parts should be molded as strain-free as possible, because in some cases painting can add to strain and cause crazing and cracking. It may be necessary to anneal parts before they are painted to eliminate strain, and it is sometimes essential to clean the parts or dip them in an antistatic solution to reduce the attraction of dust.

The different types of plastics vary in their physical and chemical properties. These differences are an important factor in the composition of paint appropriate for each type. For example, resins used in paint for thermosetting plastics may be unsuitable for a thermoplastic which would warp or melt at the curing temperatures required by the resins. Again, thermoplastics vary greatly in their resistance to solvents, and this limits the choice of resins to those soluble in the prescribed solvents.

Paints used on plastics are divided into two classes: lacquers and enamels. Lacquer films harden by solvent evaporation; when dry, the thermoplastic film has exactly the same properties as the resins used in making the lacquer. The film hardens quickly and completely without baking. When enamel is applied to a surface, the solvent evaporates, leaving a soft, tacky film which hardens or "cures" by oxidation, polymerization, or other chemical reactions. This film is totally different from those of the resins used to make the enamel. Baking is usually required to induce the polymerization which produces top quality enamel film.

Paint is a dispersion of pigment in a liquid, compounded to form a solid adherent film when applied to a surface. The basic components are resins, solvents, and pigments. Pigments are insoluble materials which "hide" the surface, color the coating and may also serve other functions. The liquid portion of the paint formula, called the "vehicle," acts as a mixing medium for the pigment.

The solvent system compounded for any paint depends on the type of plastic to be painted, the resin system selected, and the method of application. The solvent system must definitely not etch the plastic severely enough to give a rough or frost surface. Even slight etch disturbs the surface of most thermoplastics and results in a poor paint film, particularly on the second (the back) surface of the part. This is most important in vehicles for metallics and pigmented metallics; etch can cause irregular leafing of the powder and color change in the painted surface. It is equally important that the solvents do not craze or crack the plastic.

Solvents are classified as high, intermediate, and low boiling. High boiling solvents are slow-drying; low boiling evaporate quickly. To assure a continuous, smooth film, the high boiling solvent must hold the resin in solution until the film is completely dry. In spray coating it is common practice to use a mixture of high, intermediate, and low boiling solvents, balanced to give high viscosity when the paint reaches the plastic surface. The low boiling portion evaporates or is "blown away" during the spray operation, increasing the solids content and the viscosity of the wet paint film. The percentage of high boiling solvent used in a paint must be adjusted carefully because it controls the degree of flow or leveling of the wet film laid on the surface.

While pigments serve many functions in paint they are used mainly to "hide" the substrate and add color to the surface. When a paint film is exposed to outdoor light for an extended period of time, there may be some change in the color. Only light-stable pigments and vehicles should be employed to prevent these color changes. It is of utmost importance that the paint formulator know about these exposure conditions or any other unusual requirement before he makes up the paint. Specifications for the sign field and the automotive industry often call for light-stable colors.

Although few organic pigments have good light stability in tint tones, this property can be found in some of the phthalocyanine and indanthrene colors. Non-chalking rutile titanium dioxide white, carbon black, and some iron oxides make pigments with good light stability. Hansa yellow and toluidine red have outdoor light stability in mass tone, but tend to fade out when mixed with titanium dioxide in tint tones. Light stability may be reduced when these pigments are blended in color matches.

Often a color submitted for matching calls for organic pigments, yet light stability is required. It becomes a choice between sacrificing an exact color match to obtain this durability, or accepting the higher cost of light stable pigments. This choice can be avoided if the original designer will use light-stable colors in creating his design. Color matches can then be made later on with the same pigments the designer's paint was made from.

The properties required of a paint depend upon the end use of the product. A toy manufacturer needs good adhesion, nontoxicity, and high gloss for his paint; an appliance manufacturer demands adhesion, plus resistance to stains, soaps and detergents, temperature changes, as well as other properties.

Proper adhesion is an essential requirement for any kind of paint. All other properties compounded into the paint are worthless if the paint will not adhere to the surface. The adhesion of paints for plastics is governed by complicated physical and chemical considerations. Paint adheres to plastic through intermolecular attraction, solvent etching, or a combination of both.

Properly formulated paints rely more on chemical attraction than on solvent attack. Intermolecular attraction is based on polarity. Polar groups of molecules provide "magnetic" forces which assist in adhesion.

For practical purposes, hardness and abrasion resistance often go hand-in-hand—both are frequently required. Besides consideration of the paint itself, the hardness of the substrate and the effect of pigmentation must be taken into account. A paint applied to acrylic may be exceptionally hard, but may appear to have lost hardness when applied to a soft-flow butyrate. It must be remembered that thin paint films are not self-supporting and must have firm backing to display their true characteristics. Usually, high gloss colors have more mar or abrasion resistance than semi-gloss or flat colors.

Quality paints are seldom pigmented with dyes; almost always durable "indoor" pigments are used. For outdoor applications, such as signs or window displays, special fade-resistant pigments are used. The paint formulator must be told if the part will be subjected to direct sunlight.

Quality spray coatings can be expected to withstand 1,000 hrs in a humidity cabinet at 110°F, and 100% relative humidity with no softening, blistering, or loss of adhesion. Normal pigmented coatings are not affected by salt spray, except those made with bronze powders. Plastics are not affected by salt; tests for salt spray resistance are little more than humidity tests. They have some pertinence in testing paints for vacuum metallized plastics.

Color is an essential factor in decorating plastics, and the maintenance of color uniformity is of prime importance to the entire plastic finishing industry. Everything possible is done to minimize color variation, even though many things that affect color are not under the control of the company producing the paint. For example, manufacturers of automobiles, appliances, and many other finished products may purchase the same plastic part from several suppliers, demanding that parts be identical in all respects, of course including color. The manufacturers may order a large number of different plastic parts from several suppliers; these parts are later assembled into units, and colors must match.

Color control begins with the acceptance of standard, consistent procedures, so that both the paint formulator and the finisher use the same methods for measuring and matching colors. Many companies prefer to use north daylight to match colors because it is uniform and available to everybody. Standard artificial light is available from a number of sources. Production colors are usually checked under the fluorescent light used in the plant. Two colors made with different pigments may look exactly alike under natural light, and still may appear dissimilar under artificial light. Production standards should be prepared with the same type of paint used in forming the finished piece so that both panels will look the same under any light. When there is a question of color variation during production, the standard panel can be compared with the painted part, using the same light source.

The industry uses two terms, "first surface" and "second surface," to designate the area on which the finish is applied. The first surface is the front of molded or sheet plastic; the finish is seen from the same side on which it is applied. A second surface (the back of a transparent molding or sheet) finish is seen through the plastic, though it may also be decorative, viewed directly as a first surface finish. In most cases, first and second surface applications require different finishes, and some allowances must be made in the paint formulation. For example, plastics considered colorless and transparent often do have some slight tinge of color. On second surface painting, this color may visually alter the apparent color of the paint.

It is not always possible to match colors with only opaque pigments; sometimes transparent or translucent pigments must be used. As a result, many paint films allow the color of the plastic to show through slightly and affect the tone or color of the paint film. If the paint is used over similar type material of a harmonious color and the film thickness is constant, the film color will be uniform. But if any one of these factors is changed, the apparent color of the paint film will also change. These paints certainly can be satisfactory in every respect, but it is important when matching colors to examine the plastic to be covered in order to obtain as much information as possible about the specific application. It may be necessary to spray the part with an opaque coat and then follow up with the desired top coat if engineering or production cannot use a standard color base stock for the product.

Variation in color can also result from thin or irregular film thickness allowing the substratum to show through in patches. This is often caused by incorrect thinning or improper adjustment of application equipment.

The decision on what method of paint application to use is governed by factors such as the size and shape of the plastic item, the quantity to be decorated, the variations in color required, the equipment available, and the working area. The most widely used methods of decorating plastics are spray, spray-and-wipe, screen process printing, dip coating, roller coating, hot stamping, vacuum metallizing, and gravure printing.

For spray work, paint must be thinned to a viscosity suitable for the particular job. It must spray evenly and still be viscous enough to hang on corners and edges while the film dries. Parts are spray painted in more than one color by using metal masks to shield certain areas while others are painted.

Depressed letters, figures, and designs are easily and rapidly painted by the spray-and-wipe method. Depressions must be deep and narrow enough to avoid removal of the paint during the wiping or buffing operations. An entire area is spray painted and then the areas around the depressions are wiped or buffed clean.

Screen process printing is used primarily for painting flat surfaces, although the process can also be adapted to certain cylindrical surfaces. A silk screen (now usually made of nylon) is held in a wooden frame and covered by a design cut into a stencil. A squeegee moves paint across the entire screen; the paint can go through the screen only where the design in the stencil leaves open spaces. Multicolor decorating is done by using different screens in succession. For painting elaborate designs, silk screen is more economical than spraying.

Dip coating is a method widely used to decorate novelties, toys, and other objects that require only one color, and can be designed so that the paint can drain off freely. The solvent system of dip finishing paint must allow good flow-out, and must drain without sagging. The gel time and film thickness may be controlled to some extent by using the proper combination of high, medium, and low boiling solvents. Paint in dip tanks may lose solvent and become too viscous. This is corrected by adding the proper thinner.

Small raised areas like letters, figures, and designs may be decorated by roller coating. On some parts this works better than spray coating because simple, loose-fitting block masks may be used, or the part can even be rolled without a mask. The paint must have good adhesion, since raised areas are often subjected to hard wear. The solvent system must be balanced to allow flow-out, but the film must gel or become immobile to prevent it from running off the raised area.

Hot stamping is used to decorate plastics when numerals or raised letters cannot be spray painted or roller coated, where indentations are too shallow for spray-and-wipe operations, or where no provision is made for lettering in the design of the part. A foil tape of gold, silver, or any other color is placed over the part, and a heated metal die having the desired pattern pressed the foil against the surface of the part.

Modern wood graining is the application of photography, photo engraving, and printing to reproduce the natural beauty and warmth of authentic wood grains. The process can also reproduce marble, fieldstone, brick, textured cloth, leather, and many other manufactured or artist-created designs. The complete wood graining system consists of three coatings: ground (base) coat, graining ink, and top coat. Many different types of each coat are available, each formulated to work on one of a group of substrates, each designed to be compatible with the other components in the system. The ground coat is a pigmented coating used as a background for the grain pattern. The graining ink is used to reproduce the pattern on the photo engraved plate. The top coat is determined by the type of substrate used and the end use of the grained product. Materials come in a broad selection of surface glosses and degrees of texture, hardness, toughness, and abrasion resistance. Many of these meet the specifications of the automotive industry.

Color control is extremely important in *all* wood graining. Sometimes it is desired to vary or adjust the intensity of the graining ink. Although over-thinning will reduce the color strength, this procedure may adversely affect viscosity and give a blurred print. The correct way to lower color strength is to add clear ink without pigmentation. Strengthening is done by adding ink without thinner.

If it is necessary to change the color of the ground coat or graining ink, one should use only the tinting colors recommended by the supplier. Almost always these will be pigmented materials of the same type used in the original color, and therefore compatible with the original. Color matching is an art, acquired through experience. It is far from an exact science, and visual color matches are not easily obtained without experienced personnel, even under controlled laboratory conditions.

Problems in color variation can occur during production from color bleeding, solvent etching, powder settling, leafing, and flooding. The paint manufacturer usually is able to furnish paints made from non-bleeding materials. Solvent-soluble dyes are bad bleeders, and must be used with caution. Color variation due to etching can be reduced or eliminated by using less active thinners but they must be added with care to avoid precipitating resins out of solution.

When a gradual change of color is noted during spray painting, the cause is most often pigment settling. The problem can be acute when metallics or pigmented metallics are used. While most spray-room personnel know that materials must be thoroughly mixed before they are used, they are not always aware of how far color can be thrown off by the gradual settling of metallic powders if agitation is not continued during use. Color change due to poor application usually involves flooding, the separation of pigments in wet paint film. In lacquers and enamels containing only milled pigments, this can often be controlled by proper solvent adjustment. Metallics and pigmented metallics often require mechanical adjustments in the spraying operation to provide the answer to flooding problems.

There are certain problems especially important in the field of plastics, although they also occur in other kinds of industrial and commercial decoration. Loss of paint adhesion is a common problem. Even with paint that has been designed for proper adhesion to a particular substrate, the condition can be caused by excessive mold lubricant, oil or water in the air lines, oil from an outside source, or humidity blush.

Humidity blush results when water condenses into the paint from the air during application and drying. Coatings vary greatly in their resistance to blushing, but the condition can usually be corrected by using thinners recommended for high humidity surroundings. Loss of gloss in a normally glossy coating is most frequently due to humidity blush. The flattening effect caused by the water condensation may not necessarily be accompanied by lack of adhesion, but the correct use of proper thinners can correct both problems.

Orange peel and cratering are defects in paint film which mar the beauty of the decorated parts. Orange peel resembles the surface of an orange. It results from poor leveling of the paint film; the viscosity of the paint may have been too high when it hit the plastic surface. The answer to the problem may be either adjusting the gun to spray wetter, or using a paint with more high boiler thinner. Plastic parts which contain excessive lubricant or other types of contamination tend to develop craters when painted. This results when the paint runs out to a very thin film which ruptures and leaves pinholes. The solution is to spray clean parts and use a little less thinner. Some spray paints string when not adequately thinned. This makes a cobweb between the nozzle and the surface. The answer to cobwebbing is the use of additional thinner.

The vacuum metallizing process deposits a thin, continuous layer of metal film onto a prepared surface by vaporizing the metal and condensing it on the surface under high vacuum. The result is a reflective, chrome plated, mirror-like surface. The formulation of these coatings is far more critical than that of conventional coatings and must be designed as an integral component.

The base coat serves a multiple purpose and is the most critical part of the system. It levels the surface, providing markedly improved brilliance to the plating. It also forms the adhesion link between the substrate and the metallic film, and can be used to color the part when applied on the second surface of clear plastics. The top coat applied over the first surface metallizing primarily protects the aluminum film from wear. The back up coat, usually opaque, protects the metallic film on second surface metallizing.

The back up coating can also be designed to be decorative viewed from the first surface.

The vacuum metallizing process can be performed on plastics, metals, glass, paper, textiles, and other materials. It is often combined with painting to achieve highly decorative effects. Unlike electroplating, the process does not require an electrically conductive surface. Direct electrolytic deposition of metal on plastic is precluded by their nonconductivity.

Metallizing produces a thin, highly opaque coating. A vacuum-deposited aluminum film less than 0.0005 mil in. thick completely conceals the color of a plated object. Scrap plastic which would be rejected for ordinary molding because of its appearance can be used for metallized products.

All major plastic materials—acrylics, ABS plastics, acetals, cellulose acetate butyrate, nylons, polycarbonate, polyolefins, polystyrene, and phenolics—can be metallized to make appliance trims; automotive horn buttons, instrument panels, arm rests, tail light rings and other auto components; bottle closures; costume jewelry; displays; escutcheons and nameplates; plaques; radio and television parts; and an endless variety of toys and novelty items.

Victor H. Rampelberg

Cross-reference: COLORING OF PLASTICS.

PAPERS USED IN PLASTICS

Papers have been used as resin carriers, decorative elements, and reinforcements since the beginning of the plastics laminating industry. The end products made with these laminating papers and the resins with which they are combined include flat and tubular precision machined parts having outstanding mechanical and electrical properties, and decorative laminates and moldings, famous for their beauty and utility. Because of the many special processing and end-use properties which must be built into industrial and decorative laminates, there are many kinds of papers used, employing a wide range of fibers, basis weights and thicknesses.

To be properly prepared for the laminating operation, the laminating papers are impregnated with resins usually in liquid form, and usually with fairly standard equipment. In practice, the paper in roll form is led into a resin saturating tank, and the excess resin removed by carefully adjusted squeeze (metering) rolls or wiping bars to a controlled resin content. The impregnated paper is then passed through a curing oven, either horizontal or vertical, where the volatile matter is evacuated and the resin advanced to the desired degree of polymerization. The combination of impregnating and curing equipment is called a "treater". To obtain consistently good results in the finished laminate, it is necessary, during the treating operation (impregnation and drying), to control the resin content, volatile content and "flow" of the treated paper to within fairly narrow limits. After passing through the treating operation, the paper is wound into rolls for later cutting into sheets, or is cut into sheets as it comes out of the oven. To preserve their proper volatile and flow values, the treated papers are generally stored in air-conditioned bays until needed. The above treating process applies generally to decorative, industrial, and electrical grades. In some cases where special electrical properties are needed in the final laminate, more than one pass through the treater is required.

Because of processing requirements and precise end-use properties to be met in the finished laminate, the laminating papers themselves have usually been designed to rather rigid specifications, including basis weight, thickness, fiber furnish, filler type and content, color and surface smoothness. Uniformity of properties is most important.

Industrial Laminating Papers

Industrial laminating papers such as are used in flat or tube stock, from which parts are to be machined or shaped by punching, are generally made from cotton fibers, purified wood fibers, or kraft fibers. Where special mechanical properties such as cold punchability, machineability, or impact strength are required in conjunction with good electrical properties, cotton fibers generally have been used. Papers made from purified wood fiber especially find usage where the mechanical and electrical requirements of the finished laminates are less critical. Where mechanical properties in the laminate are more important than the ultimate in electrical properties, papers made from unbleached kraft would probably be used. Glass fibers combined with cellulose and/or other fibers (synthetic and natural) have been made into papers for electrical grade laminates having superior strength properties. It is technically possible to make industrial laminating papers from almost any fibrous material extant. Hence, where the need might arise, laminating papers can be made from metal fibers, asbestos fibers, nylon, glass fibers, ceramic fibers, other synthetic or natural fibers, or combinations thereof. Resin impregnated papers have been used as macerating stock to produce molding compounds having unusually uniform resin-to-fiber distribution. Papers made by compounding special fibers plus fillers have found use as aerospace molding materials, where light weight combined with reliability of extreme heat resistance and strength at elevated temperatures are required. Naturally, the influence of the resin system to be employed in any application is of prime importance, but papers to be used with those particular resin systems can be designed to cover an enormous range of processing and end-use properties, and because of the uniformity inherent in properly constructed papers, their use often may make possible a better finished product at lower cost, compared to other web materials such as fabrics.

Decorative Laminating Papers

In the manufacture of decorative laminates for table tops, counter-tops, furniture, panelling, etc., three types of papers have commonly been used; they are core stock papers, decor (print base and solid colors) papers, and transparent overlay papers.

There are mainly two types of core stock papers which have been used in decorative laminates. The most commonly used type is a well formed unbleached kraft paper having a basis weight of approximately 97 lb per 3000 ft², and a thickness of approximately 11 mils. These core stock papers are carefully engineered for uniformity of formation, basis weight, thickness, and phenolic resin receptivity. It is very important in modern high-speed impregnating equipment that these properties be precisely controlled—otherwise, excessive waste, lower production rates, and poor quality of the finished laminate will result.

The other main type of core stock paper commonly used in decorative laminates is essentially an unbleached kraft grade which has been crêped in two opposing directions. Use of this crêped core stock permits the finished laminate to be postformed readily, without the usual danger of cracking in the laminate. There have been developed core stocks which are fire retardant; although use of these papers has been somewhat restricted due to cost considerations, there may be more need for such materials as building codes become tighter.

In the manufacture of decorative laminates, "decor" papers designed to provide a decorative surface to hide the dark brown color of the laminate core are used. Such decor papers are made from so-called "alpha" (highly purified bleached wood) fibers or from bleached kraft fibers, and usually contain an opacifier such as titanium dioxide plus colored pigments where color is required. The decor papers are commonly made in a range of weights extending from 65 lb/3000 ft²–125 lb/3000 ft². Although the custom has been to use papers as close as possible to the 95–105 lb weight range, there is currently a strong trend toward the lower weight ranges down to 65 lb/3000 ft². The advantages of using these lighter weight papers are lower cost per square foot of paper, lower resin costs, higher treating speeds, and better postformability in the finished laminate. Prior to melamine resin impregnation, the decor papers are usually printed by rotogravure process, with patterns such as wood grains, fabrics, or abstract designs. However, a significant quantity is not printed, but used as "solid color"; these solid color papers are obtainable in a wide range of colors covering the normal spectrum. Within recent years, impregnated decorative laminating papers have been increasingly used in the plywood, particle board, and hardboard industries to provide pre-finished, decorative panels for a variety of markets. In such cases, the usual 65 lb weight decor paper, after resin impregnation, is laminated directly over the smooth particle board or hardboard substrate at pressures ranging from about 175 psi and upward. The finished panel so produced outperforms natural wood in scratch and mar resistance, resistance to color change, stain resistance, heat resistance, ease of maintainance and in many other ways.

Transparent overlay papers are incorporated in decorative laminates to provide high surface abrasion resistance. They perform two basic functions, namely:

(1) They are *resin carriers* for depositing the relatively thick layer of resin necessary over the decor sheet to give the desired abrasion resistance.

(2) They are *reinforcements* within the thick resin layer, and provide craze resistance thereto.

Without transparent overlays, present day decorative laminates in horizontal applications such as table and countertops, would soon become unsightly due to the normal abrasion encountered in everyday use. The weight and thickness of such papers are carefully controlled to assure uniformity of processing and end-use characteristics. The range of weights currently used in flat decorative laminates is 15 lb–29 lb per 3000 ft². Thickness generally falls within the 3.0–6.5 mils range. In order to insure maximum transparency, these papers are manufactured from rayon fibers, purified cotton fibers and/or highly purified wood fibers. The overlay papers are available in uncolored or colored form, the latter type being used with wood grain patterns to give an illusion of depth.

Film Reinforcements

In other plastics fields, papers are used mainly as reinforcements for films in packaging applications. Here, in combination with otherwise dimensionally unstable resin films such as polyethylene, etc., paper provides the advantages of added strength under mechanical stress, resistance to heat distortion, and workability in processing. In the case of packaging films, etc., the resin and paper can be combined by impregnation or coating in a variety of ways.

L. L. R. PHILLIPS

Cross-reference: PREPREGS.

PARTICLE SIZE FOR PLASTICS INGREDIENTS

The sizes of several types of particles constituting basic materials for plastics have marked effects on the finished products, on the choice of manufacturing process, or both. For convenience, the particles can be classified into four types. One type consists of the macromolecules themselves. A second consists of the droplets of monomer making up the discontinuous phase employed in emulsion and suspension polymerization. A third is the particles or granules of the bulk plastic used for manufacturing various objects, and the fourth includes the particles of plasticizers, pigments, fillers, and other additives.

Particle Statistics

In any discussion of particle size effects, it is important to specify what is meant by the terms particle and particle size and to include considerations of the effects of variations in size distribution. In a granular bulk polymer the particles of interest may be the macromolecules or the individual granules. However, the distinction is not always so obvious. For instance, the particles of significance in a pigment may be firmly bound agglomerates rather than the "ultimate" particles.

Particle size is usually defined either as a statistical property based on the measurement of each of a large number of particles in a powder or suspension, or in terms of some property of the powder which is related to particle size. Measurements involving optical or electron microscopy, and sieving, are based on definitions of the first type, while measurements of settling rate and permeability are based on the second type of definition.

When large numbers of particles are measured, some method of averaging is generally employed. Perhaps the most common is the number mean diameter, which is defined as $(1/n)\Sigma d$, while other common averages are the mean surface diameter:

$$\sqrt{\frac{1}{n}\Sigma d^2}$$

and the mean volume (or weight) diameter:

$$\sqrt[3]{\frac{1}{n}\Sigma d^3}$$

where n is the number of particles measured and d is the diameter of each particle.

The distribution of sizes is often represented graphically, for example, by plotting the percentage of total number, surface, or volume of particles greater than a given size against size. The distribution can often be represented conveniently by one of a number of mathematical expressions termed distribution functions. Examples are the normal distribution, the log-normal distribution, and the Rosin-Rammler function.

Sizes of Macromolecules

The process of polymerization produces very large molecules (macromolecules), the size and size distribution of which markedly affect many properties of the finished product. The size of a macromolecule is usually indicated by its molecular weight, although chain length and degree of cross-linking are also indications of particle size as well as shape. In general, tensile strength, impact strength, and melt viscosity increase with increasing molecular weight. Usually a minimum molecular weight must be achieved before measurable strength is attained, appreciable tensile strength being the first to appear. On the other hand, the melting points of crystalline polymers are rather insensitive to molecular weight.

The distribution of molecular sizes and shapes is also very important. For example, although strength depends largely on the average molecular weight, flexibility and workability vary with the molecular weight distribution.

Numerous methods are available for determining average molecular weights of polymers. Those which involve analyzing end groups or measuring colligative properties such as osmotic pressure yield number average molecular weights ($M_n = \Sigma M/n$). Methods based on measuring turbidity or the rate of sedimentation yield a weight average molecular weight ($M_w = \Sigma M^2/\Sigma M$). The ratios M_w/M_n can be used as a measure of the range of distribution of the molecular weights. The assumption is often made that the distribution is log normal. Then the geometric standard deviation (s_g) is given by the expression:

$$M_w/M_n = \exp[\tfrac{1}{2}(\ln s_g)^2]$$

Furthermore, if this assumption is made, the determination of any two averages establishes the distribution function for the molecular weights.

The standard deviation of the number distribution (s_n) can be calculated from M_w and M_n without making assumptions concerning the distribution function:

$$s_n = (M_w M_n - M_n^2)^{\tfrac{1}{2}}$$

Numerous techniques in addition to the one mentioned above are available for calculating molecular weight distribution functions from averages weighted in different ways. Some, but not all, make an assumption concerning the form of the distribution function.

Emulsion and Suspension Polymerization

Emulsion polymerization is conducted in a dispersion of a hydrophobic monomer in an aqueous solution containing a catalyst and an emulsifying agent. The catalyst is a water-soluble free-radical initiator and the emulsifying agent aids in producing and maintaining the dispersion. Polymerization is rapid and the heat of reaction is carried off by the continuous (aqueous) phase. The droplets have diameters of about $0.01-2\mu$, sufficiently small that suspensions of spheres of polymer (the latex) can be used in a latex paint.

The particles can be collected by "breaking" the emulsion through heating, freezing, or adding appropriate electrolytes. Unfortunately the separated polymer is contaminated with the solids dissolved in the aqueous phase, and emulsion polymerization is used largely for producing latex paint and synthetic rubber.

The polymer particles in a given batch may all be nearly the same size. Samples from such a batch have been used extensively for fine particle research, for example, for comparing light-scattering theory with experimental results.

Suspension polymerization is similar to emulsion polymerization in that small monomer droplets are dispersed in another liquid which is usually water. However, the monomer contains the catalyst which must be insoluble in the continuous phase. Various stabilizing agents are added to the latter. As in emulsion polymerization, the heat of polymerization is rapidly removed by the continuous phase.

Both liquids and gases can be polymerized in this manner, by means of the "high-pressure free-radical" process or the "low-pressure ionic catalyst" process.

The monomer and polymer particles are hundreds or thousands of microns in diameter. As a result, maintaining them in suspension must be accomplished by stirring. The resulting beads of polymer are removed and washed in a centrifuge, dried, and classified by sieving according to size.

A closely related process is precipitation polymerization. The reaction starts in a homogeneous solution of the monomer, but the polymer, being relatively insoluble in the solvent for the monomer, precipitates. Very fine powders can be produced in this manner, the particle size depending largely on the rate of nucleation.

Bulk Plastic Materials

Granules and powders of polymeric materials are converted into finished products in a number of ways. A very important method is injection molding of thermoplastic polymers. The plastic is fed into a chamber in which it is heated and softened. It is forced out of the chamber through a nozzle into a mold to produce the finished product.

The granular material used should flow freely and not trap large amounts of air. The variation in particle size is wide, depending to a large extent on the method of polymerization. It is important to maintain a constant granule size during volumetric feeding since a variation in size (or size distribution) will result in a variation in the weight of material fed to the chamber per unit time and this must be carefully controlled.

Extrusion is similar to injection molding in that granular plastics plus other ingredients are fed from a hopper into a machine, the plastic is softened by heat, and the resulting material is forced out the other end. However, the softened material is extruded through a die to form a continuous form. Extrusion is accomplished by means of a screw which is not only a conveyer but also compresses and mixes the ingredients. The design of the screw depends in part on the bulk density of the granular material to be handled, and this is related to the particle size distributions of the various ingredients in the mixture fed from the hopper. In general, the greatest bulk density is achieved by having sufficient fine material present to fill the spaces between larger particles. Bulk density is also affected by the particle shape. For example, in principle, cubes can be fitted together to obtain a bulk density essentially the same as that of the product.

Although most thermoplastic material is processed by injection molding or extrusion, numerous other methods are used for particular purposes. An example is compression molding. The powdered plastic may be very fine, such as that produced by suspension polymerization, and when the molds are intricate such a powder is desirable. However, for many purposes the loose powder is first compressed into tablets of various shapes called preforms. The compaction is a cold, high-pressure process.

Powders used for preforming should have a size distibution such that the pores between large particles are filled by finer ones. A very large percentage of very fine material should be avoided, since this may cause bridging and entrapment of air.

Foamable powders which contain a blowing agent in addition to the polymer are used for many purposes. Rotational and stationary molding in 1963 used about 8 million lb of polyethylene powder. Powder coating of automobile carpeting, metals, and other surfaces is used extensively. Powder coating of sheeting is also employed to some extent. Polyethylene and polyvinyls are used extensively for all of these purposes and are commercially available in a wide range of sizes but mainly in the range 0.1–1 mm diameter. The best size for a particular application is usually determined empirically but cost must be considered, the finer powders generally being more expensive.

Non-polymeric Materials

Various fillers, plasticizers and pigments are mixed with many plastics. The main powders are fillers, which can be classified into "reinforcing fillers" and "inert fillers," the former being those that improve mechanical properties. Reinforcing fillers are generally fibrous, and include asbestos, glass fibers, and various organic substances. Their presence improves the impact strength, but usually not the tensile strength. Inert fillers cheapen and harden the product and may aid in heat dispersion during thermosetting. In general, fillers should have very small diameters but the particle size distribution of the entire granular mix must be considered, as discussed above.

Pigments are usually organic. The particle size of insoluble pigments can greatly affect their covering power, tinting strength and tone. Pigments consisting of particles about 0.2μ in diameter are about optimum for covering power (opacity) and tinting strength. Carbon particles are in an entirely different size range than the particles of most other pigments. Apparently the "blackness" increases with decreasing diameter, but the tinting strength decreases.

RICHARD D. CADLE

PETROLEUM PRODUCTS

White mineral oils, petrolatums, light hydrocarbon distillates, high viscosity compressor lubricants, and waxes are the most significant of the specially refined petroleum products used today by the plastics industry.

These products have met many needs in the continual search for improved plasticizers, lubricants (both internal and external), mold-release agents, and other processing aids for the industry. Confirmation of F.D.A. clearances covering the use of these petroleum products for food grade applications has enhanced their position in this field.

The basic properties of each of these petroleum based materials that make them particularly useful in plastics applications are as follows:

White Mineral Oils

White oils are fully refined saturated paraffinic and naphthenic hydrocarbons which will not enter into the polymerization reaction. They can be safely used with the knowledge that they will in no way affect the chemical structure of the polymer.

White oils are highly resistant to coking at normal polymerization temperatures. Less coking occurs when higher viscosity white mineral oils are used such as those having a 185/500 Saybolt viscosity at 100°F.

White oils are free from unsaturated aromatic and polynuclear hydrocarbons, this characteristic makes them suitable for use in plastics coming in contact with food.

White oils conform with F.D.A. specifications as covered under CFR 121.1146.

Petrolatum

USP and NF petrolatums are purified mixtures of semi solid hydrocarbons obtained from petroleum. They are nonreactive and as such do not affect the chemical structure of the polymer.

USP and NF petrolatums are of "food grade" quality, and can thus be used in plastics which will come in contact with food. They conform with F.D.A. regulation CFR 121.1166.

Light Hydrocarbon Distillates

Light hydrocarbon distillates are fully acid-treated to an iodine number of zero. Acid treatment removes aromatic, unsaturated and polynuclear hydrocarbons. These distillates are of "food grade" quality and conform with F.D.A. regulation CFR 121.1182, which enables them to be used in those plastics which may come in contact with food. At the same time these distillates are nonreactive, thus minimizing the possibility of their affecting polymer structures.

High Viscosity Compressor Lubricants

These lubricants have been developed to withstand the high pressures at which polyolefins are polymerized. They may migrate into plastic and in accordance with F.D.A. regulations such lubricants must be of "food grade" quality. Compressor lubricants can meet F.D.A. specifications, and range in Saybolt viscosities at 100°F from 600–1700—higher viscosities can be made available.

Waxes

Two types of waxes are found in crude oil. One of them is paraffin wax. This is found in low boiling fractions, and consists of straight chain hydrocarbons having average molecular weights of 360–420, and melting points from 120–above 150°F. The second type is microcrystalline wax. This is found in high boiling fractions that are primarily alkylated naphthenes and isoparaffins having average molecular weights of 580–700, and melting points of 147–196°F.

Both paraffin and microcrystalline waxes can be classified as food grade, providing they conform with F.D.A. specifications as covered under CFR 121.1156.

These petroleum products are generally used

in one or more of the following plastics processing operations:

Extrusion. White oils or petrolatums are used for lubricating the orfice of extrusion equipment. These lubricants are equally effective on either screw-driven, ram-driven or simple drawing equipment.

Injection Molding. Addition of white oils to the molten resin will adjust its consistency to optimum levels so as to increase the rate at which the resin is forced through the orifice. As a secondary benefit, the oil serves as a lubricant for the resin as it passes through the orifice.

Vacuum and Pressure Forming. White oils serve as an excellent mold release agent, replacing the more expensive materials such as silicone oils.

The use of these products in specific resin systems is described in further detail below. The resin applications are listed in alphabetical order.

Acetal copolymers. A 70 Saybolt viscosity white oil is used as an annealing agent in molding acetal copolymer resins that may come in contact with food. The oil is heated to 305°F ± 5°F, and the molding is then immersed for a predetermined time. Annealing improves the dimensional stability of the moldings, especially if they require precise control of dimensions in long term exposure at temperatures exceeding 180°F.

Thin wall sections generally derive greater benefit from an annealing application than do moldings with thick wall sections. Oil is preferred for this application because its use makes temperature uniformity easier to maintain.

Coumarone indene. In producing coumarone indene polymerized from coal tar derivatives, white oil is added to function as a plasticizer and internal lubricant. A 350 or 500 Saybolt viscosity white oil is used in quantities of from 5–10% by weight of resin, depending on individual conditions.

Ethylcellulose. White oil is added to ethylcellulose resin to act as a plasticizer and internal lubricant. Quantities of white oil used for this purpose range from between 20–25% by weight of resin.

In applications for ethylcellulose, such as plastic skin and strippable coatings, white oil is used in amounts of from 65–70% of the total resin mix. The white oil acts both as a secondary plasticizer and as vehicle for the ethylcellulose.

In both of these applications, white oil of from 100–325 viscosity is used depending on the particular application for which a formulation is designed.

Polyamide (nylon). Wide application has been found for a 350 Saybolt viscosity white mineral oil as an annealing agent for molded and extruded parts and shapes. After rough machining, bar or rod stock is annealed to obtain maximum toughness and good dimensional stability as well as to

reduce stresses. As soon as annealing is accomplished, the white mineral oil must be removed by immersion of the part or shape in a light hydrocarbon distillate.

Polyethylene. U.S.P. white mineral oils of approximately 325–500 Saybolt viscosity at 100°F are used as a catalyst carrier in both high pressure and low pressure systems. The metal catalyst is dispersed in the oil in quantities of about 0.8% based on the total polyethylene produced.

White mineral oil is also used as a compressor lubricant in some low pressure systems. Since the polyethylene producer is unable to tell whether or not the plastic will be used for food applications, the compressor lubricant must be F.D.A. approved. These F.D.A. approved compressor lubricants have Saybolt viscosities at 100°F from 350–1700. They are also used in some high pressure systems.

Polypropylene. A light hydrocarbon fraction, highly refined, is used as a diluent in the polymerization of a polyolefin.

A U.S.P. white mineral oil having a Saybolt viscosity at 100°F of 325–500 is used as a compressor lubricant because of the compressor's low (600 psi) operating pressure.

Polystyrene. To increase the ease, uniformity and rate of flow during molding without appreciably affecting other properties such as heat distortion temperature, tensile strength and impact strength, from 1–4% of white mineral oil of 70–350 Saybolt viscosity, and sometimes 500 viscosity is added to the resin mix. This serves as a colorless internal lubricant.

Another advantage is that white mineral oil acts as a mold release agent and, being colorless in itself, the molded or extruded articles are clear.*

Polysulfone. When polysulfone parts are thermoformed, post annealing of the formed parts in a 350 viscosity white mineral oil at 330–340°F improves creep resistance and solvent crazing properties. Best annealing results are obtained by immersion for a few minutes.

Polytetrafluoroethylene (PTFE and TFE). After polymerization, the PTFE or TFE resin is in the form of round and oblong particles. It is mixed with a fully acid-treated light hydrocarbon distillate in 1 part to 4–5 parts PTFE or TFE ratio by weight of resin. The light hydrocarbon distillate is mixed at a temperature of 60–66°F and is added to enable the particles to elongate when extruded through a tapered die at 70–80°F. The PTFE or TFE is then heated to 620–725°F at which time it becomes an amorphous mass and ready for production extrusion. It is important

*The use of white mineral oils having a Saybolt viscosity range of 59–324 is covered by U.S. Patent No. 2, 619, 478 (Nov. 24, 1952), assigned to Dow Chemical Co., Midland, Michigan.

that a fully acid-treated and F.D.A. approved hydrocarbon solvent is used, as it will prevent possible contamination of the resin, especially when used in applications where the PTFE and TFE will come in contact with food.

Polyurethane. There are two types of foamed urethane plastics. One type has the unique ability to foam in place (at actual utilization site) using the heat of reaction and CO_2 gas generated by the reaction to foam the plastic. The other type requires inert gases under pressure as the blowing agent, and obviously cannot be foamed in place, but must instead be foamed at the point of manufacture.

Despite the convenience of the former procedure, the more prevalent plastic is the one which requires the external gas as the blowing agent. This is due to the fact that since these gases are added under controlled conditions, the plastic will usually be of more uniform cell size and density. It is this latter procedure which is used almost exclusively in making cushions for furniture or padding in automobiles, etc. The foamed-in-place plastic has found application in areas where the structure of the foam is not of critical importance, e.g., in the insulation of refrigerators and buildings.

Both of the above described procedures have one thing in common—both require high pressure in one phase or another of the foaming process. In the foamed-in-place procedure, the polyurethane constituents are contained in separate vessels and forced by pressure through a mixing head and into the area that must be filled. It is of great importance that no contaminant be allowed to enter the reaction field since it is extremely likely that such contaminants could alter the character of the foamed plastic.

In the procedure which uses inert gases as the blowing agent, high pressure must be used to force the inert gases through the resin to produce the uniform foam. Again, it is important to avoid contaminating the reaction field.

The high pressure required in both of the above applications can be gained only through the use of the compressors. It is in these compressors that white oils find application. Since white oils are fully acid-treated and thus non reactive, they do not in any way interfere with the urethane reaction should they somehow find their way into the reaction field. 350 U.S.P. viscosity white oil has been approved by a number of basic suppliers of the constituents of urethane foams as the lubricant for compressors.

Polyvinyl Chloride. The advantages of using white mineral oil of an 85 or 350 Saybolt viscosity that is added in quantities of from $\frac{1}{4}\%$–$2\frac{3}{4}\%$ (by weight of resin) in blow molding, injection molding and extrusion are that they give a better surface gloss, eliminate the need of a secondary buffing operation, offer excellent lubrication and act as a primary release agent.

Polyvinylidene Chloride. White oil, 1–2% by weight of resin of a 70–100 Saybolt viscosity, serves as an aid in extrusion, and in addition, helps reduce formation of static electricity.

Pigmenting Thermoplastics

Both white mineral oil and petrolatum are used in pigmenting plastic materials.

White mineral oil of a 350 viscosity is used as the vehicle to hold oil-insoluble powdered colorants in suspension after stirring. This will then be milled on either a three-roll mill or a ball mill. The resulting product is a paste color concentrate, which in turn can either be milled into the plastic or added in a blending operation by using a ribbon blendor until the color is uniformly distributed.

Petrolatums, white for pastel shades, yellow for darker shades, are heated to a clear liquid at which time the powdered pigment is added and thoroughly dispersed by stirring. The mixture is then milled with the plastic (pellets, beads or powder) until the color is uniform.

Wax Applications

The addition of varying percentages from 10%–40% (generally 20-25%) of certain polymers such as ethylene vinyl acetate (EVA), polyethylene, polypropylene and styrene copolymers to high melting point paraffin and microcrystalline waxes enhances the properties of both the waxes and the polymers.

The properties that are gained are as follows: A high gloss and excellent scuff resistance, excellent flexibility at low temperatures, improved moisture vapor transmission rate (MVTR), i.e., moisture barrier, excellent heat sealability, and improved grease resistance.

The above properties are important when the waxes are used for the following applications.

(1) *High Gloss Coatings.* They can be applied by either a hot melt or solvent system. Average formulations consist of a wax with a melting point above 150°F, high molecular weight copolymers, and sometimes terpene-based resins.

(2) *Laminations.* These are divised into two groups. Wax laminations, with melting points above 150°F, are used to join two sheets of cellophane, glassine, foil or polyethylene. Wax polymer laminations utilize copolymer wax blends that can be applied to both sides of glassine paper. Preprinted polymer coated cellophane is added and laminated. The other wax coating allows a face-to-back seal.

(3) *High Heat Sealable coatings.* These are modified wax coatings which contain up to 15% by weight of the modifier and range in temperature from 150–375°F.

Other Uses of Waxes. These include lubricants, extenders, and mold release agents. A $\frac{1}{2}\%/2\%$ high melting point paraffin of approximately 165°F is used, for example, in place of stearates as a lubricant in the polyvinyl chloride (PVC) extrusion of rigid compounds.

D. C. SCHRECK

PHENOL

Phenol is the common name for monohydroxy benzene, (C_6H_5OH.) but is sometimes used to designate substituted hydroxy benzenes.

Phenol is a white crystalline substance, melting at about 41°C. It is partly soluble in cold, completely soluble in hot water. It has a characteristic odor and is poisonous to the human body. Externally applied it corrodes the skin and is absorbed through it. Internally it acts as a nerve poison.

Originally phenol was used as a disinfectant, but later found considerable use as a raw material for dyes and medicinals, particularly salicylic acid, and the explosive picric acid. When Baekeland discovered the reaction between phenol and formaldehyde, the use of phenol as source material of phenolic resins began to develop. This use has been growing ever since and constitutes now about one half of the total phenol consumption. Another 30% goes into other, more recently developed plastics, so that use as raw material in plastics account for about 80% of the total production.

Phenol finds its outlet in the plastics and related industries mainly through five channels:

(1) Phenolic resins and molding compounds.
(2) Polyamide intermediates.
(3) Epoxy resins, including phenoxy resins.
(4) Polycarbonate resins.
(5) Polyphenylene oxide resins.

Phenolic Resins. The two ortho and the para hydrogen of phenol are reactive with formaldehyde, some other aldehydes, and certain derivatives of aldehydes. In principle each –COH group of the aldehyde connects two phenolic nuclei by means of a methylene linkage, resulting finally in a cross linked, three dimensional, insoluble and infusable plastic symbolically represented by Eq. (1).

$$2n\,C_6H_5OH + 3n\,CH_2O \rightarrow$$

$$(1)$$

Cured phenolic plastic

This end stage is reached through several more or less soluble and fusible stages. A typical procedure is, for example, the formation of a novolak by reacting a molecule of phenol with less than one molecule of formaldehyde under the influence of acidic catalysts, according to the schematic Eq. (2).

$$(n+1)\underset{n\sim1-6}{C_6H_5OH} + n\,CH_2O \rightarrow$$

Novolak

mixing the novolak with fillers and hexamethylenetetramine, a derivative of formaldehyde and ammonia, which under the influence of heat and pressure completes the reaction to the molded product (two-step or two-stage process).

In another typical procedure a one-step, or single stage, resin is formed by reacting phenol with an excess of formaldehyde in the presence of an alkaline catalyst under conditions carefully supervised to form a resin chain linked by methylene groups and containing enough methylol ($-CH_2OH$) groups to be curable.

There are innumerable modifications and variations in these procedures, involving incorporation of numerous organic or inorganic additives, fillers, promoters, etc., into the phenolic resins.

Polyamide Intermediates. Phenol has served for many years and is still serving as the raw material for cyclohexanol $C_6H_{11}OH$, formed by hydrogenation of phenol in the presence of nickel catalysts. Cyclohexanol can be oxidized further to cyclohexanone, leading, through cyclohexanone oxime, to caprolactam and its plastics derivatives, or to adipic acid, one of the constituents of nylon-66, and in some cases to other constituents of polyamide plastics.

Epoxy Resins. Epoxy resins use the properties of the epoxy group for building the plastic

chain. Phenol is used as raw material in epoxy resins mainly in two forms, as novolak (see above) and as bisphenol A.

Bisphenol A is produced by condensation of 2 moles of phenol with 1 mole of acetone under the influence of acidic catalysts according to Eq. (3).

$$2C_6H_5OH + O{=}C(CH_3)_2 \rightarrow$$

$$(3)$$

Formation of the epoxy resin chain is effected by reaction of the phenolic hydroxyl with epichlorohydrin, as represented by Eq. (4) for bisphenol A.

$$n \; HO\!\!\langle\rangle\!\!C(CH_3)_2\!\!\langle\rangle\!\!OH \; +$$

$$(n+1) \; ClH_2C\!-\!\overset{O}{\overset{\triangle}{CH}}\!-\!CH_2 \rightarrow$$

$$H_2\overset{O}{\overset{\triangle}{C}}\!-\!C\!-\!CH_2\!\!\left[O\!\!\langle\rangle\!\!C(CH_3)_2\!\!\langle\rangle\!\!O\!-\!CH_2\!-\right.$$

$$\left.-\!H(OH)\!-\!CH_2\right]_{n-1}\!O\!\!\langle\rangle\!\!C(CH_3)_2\!\!\langle\rangle\!\!O\!-\!CH_2\!-$$

$$-\!\overset{O}{\overset{\triangle}{CH}}\!-\!CH_2 \tag{4}$$

The analogous reaction forms the epoxy resin on novolak basis, the characteristic group of which is shown in Eq. (5).

$$\left[\overset{O-CH_2-\overset{O}{\overset{\triangle}{CH}}-CH_2}{\underset{CH_2-}{\langle\rangle}}\right] \tag{5}$$

The curing of the epoxy chain to an insoluble and infusible state is effected by reaction of the epoxy groups with either diamines, diacid anhydrides, or similar difunctional compounds reactive with the epoxy group.

The phenoxy resins are in their general structure similar to the epoxies on bisphenol A basis. Main differences are, that they do not contain unreacted epoxy groups and therefore remain thermoplastic, and that they have a much greater chain length.

Polycarbonates. In the thermoplastic polycarbonate resins, the hydroxyls of bisphenol A are linked together by reaction with phosgene forming a chain according to Eq. (6).

$$\left[\!O\!\!\langle\rangle\!\!C(CH_3)_2\!\!\langle\rangle\!\!O\!-\!\overset{}{\underset{O}{C}}\!\right]_n \tag{6}$$

Polycarbonate resins

One of the prime requirements of bisphenol A used in this reaction is its purity, particularly absence of chain breaking or cross-linking substances, and of substances causing discoloration.

This can be achieved by distillation, followed by an extractive pressure crystallization.

Polyphenylene Oxide Resins. This is the youngest member of the class of phenol-based plastics, having been introduced in 1964. In this class molecular chains are formed by oxidizing the hydroxy hydrogen from one and the *para* hydrogen from another molecular, leading to the formation of a phenyl ether chain, according to Eq. (7).

$$HO\!\!\underset{CH_3}{\overset{CH_3}{\langle\rangle}}\!\!-\!\!\left[-O\!-\!\underset{CH_3}{\overset{CH_3}{\langle\rangle}}\!-\right]_n\!\!O\!-\!\underset{CH_3}{\overset{CH_3}{\langle\rangle}} \tag{7}$$

Structure (7)

The preferred raw material in this reaction is 2,6-xylenol. It occurs in coal tar, but with increasing consumption in polyphenylene oxides the necessity of synthesizing it by methylation of phenol (or *o*-cresol) can be anticipated.

Table 1 gives an estimated use pattern of the phenol consumed in 1964.

TABLE 1. USE PATTERN ESTIMATED FOR 1964.

Phenolics	50%
Epoxies	6%
Polycarbonates	1%
Polyamides	23%
Alkyl-phenols	6%
Salicylic acid	4%
Exports	3%
Miscellaneous	7%
Total	100%

Extrapolating the present trends into the future, it may be expected that the percentage of phenol going into polyamides will decline, because it will gradually be replaced by cyclohexane as a raw material, its percentage as raw material for phenolics will remain more or less stationary, while its uses in epoxies, polycarbonates, and polyphenylene oxides will grow.

Another outlet for phenol in the future may be its use as raw material in the production of *para*-hydroxybenzoic acid, as starting material for polyester fibers.

Phenol Synthesis

There are few organic bulk chemicals for which as many sources and processes are available as for phenol.

Natural Phenol. This is extracted from coal tar and petroleum. The crude tar or oil is distilled, the fractions boiling between about 160 and 250°C are treated chemically or physically to extract the phenolic compounds which are then purified by distillation. The typical chemical extracting agent is dilute sodium hydroxide. The

PHENOL

hydroxyl hydrogen of phenol and its lower homologs is of a sufficiently acidic character to form salts (phenolates or phenates) with sodium hydroxide which are soluble in water.

Phenol, however, is a very weak acid and even carbon dioxide replaces it in its salts. A typical procedure therefore is to pass the phenol containing distillate counter current to a 10% sodium hydroxide solution through an extractor, which yields on one side phenol-free hydrocarbons and on the other side a dilute solution of sodium phenate, cresylate, etc.

This solution is passed down a column in counter-current to a gas containing carbon dioxide, which "springs" (liberates) the phenol by converting the caustic to sodium carbonate. The oily layer of tar acids is separated by distillation into phenol, *ortho*-cresol, *meta-para* cresol, etc., while the solution of sodium carbonate can be regenerated, for instance by "causticizing" with lime, for further extractions.

Sulfonation Process. Benzene is converted by treatment with sulfuric acid or oleum to benzene monosulfonic acid, which is then neutralized and subjected to a fusion with caustic soda. The reaction yields sodium phenate with sodium sulfite as the by-product. The phenate is neutralized, and the resulting phenol purified by distillation. Numerous modifications of this process have evolved over the years. In the earlier versions, the water formed in the sulfonation reaction was permitted to dilute the sulfuric acid to the point where it lost its ability to sulfonate. In more modern versions the water is removed from the equilibrium mixture, for instance by benzene vapors, leading to a better utilization of the sulfuric acid. In earlier versions neutralization of the sulfonation mixture was effected by sodium carbonate, sodium hydroxide, etc., while in the modern versions the sodium sulfite formed in the fusion reaction is used for that purpose, thereby lowering the formation of by-products sodium sulfite, sulfate, etc. Similarly the technique of fusion has undergone considerable changes. The most modern sulfonation process could probably be represented, for example, by the following equations, although it appears doubtful that any actual operation follows all these equations in detail.

$$C_6H_6 + H_2SO_4 \rightarrow C_6H_5SO_3H + H_2O$$
$$C_6H_5SO_3H + 1/2Na_2SO_3 \rightarrow C_6H_5SO_3Na + 1/2SO_2 + 1/2H_2O$$
$$C_6H_5SO_3Na + 2NaOH \rightarrow C_6H_5ONa + Na_2SO_3 + H_2O$$
$$C_6H_5ONa + 1/2SO_2 + 1/2H_2O \rightarrow C_6H_5OH + 1/2Na_2SO_3$$
$$\overline{C_6H_6 + H_2SO_4 + 2NaOH \rightarrow C_6H_5OH + Na_2SO_3 + 2H_2O}$$

The economy of this process depends essentially on the utilization of the by-product sodium sulfite.

Chlorobenzene Process. This process was developed by Dow Chemical Company Midland, Michigan. It may be represented by the equations:

$$C_6H_6 + Cl_2 \rightarrow C_6H_5Cl + HCl$$
$$C_6H_5Cl + 2NaOH \rightarrow C_6H_5ONa + NaCl$$
$$C_6H_5ONa + HCl \rightarrow C_6H_5OH + NaCl$$
$$\overline{C_6H_6 + Cl_2 + 2NaOH \rightarrow C_6H_5OH + 2NaCl + H_2O}$$

Benzene is chlorinated to monochlorobenzene. A mixture of monochlorobenzene and dilute caustic is then passed at a high temperature under pressure through a tubular autoclave, where the hydrolysis to sodium phenate and sodium chloride takes place. The phenate is neutralized by the hydrochloric acid produced in the first stage and the phenol is then purified by distillation. Sodium carbonate can be substituted in place of the caustic soda, yielding phenol directly from the hydrolysis reaction, thus avoiding the neutralization step.

One of the initial difficulties of the process was the formation of phenyl ether instead of phenol, according to the equation:

$$C_6H_5Cl + NaOC_6H_5 \rightarrow C_6H_5OC_6H_5 + NaCl$$

The discovery that formation of phenyl ether could be suppressed by recycling of phenyl ether made this process commercially highly successful. Its main drawback is that it consumes chlorine and caustic in quantities proportional to the phenol produced, converting them to a practically valueless solution of sodium chloride.

Raschig Process. The phenol processes discussed so far, requiring proportional quantities of caustic, sulphuric acid or chlorine, were designed to fit into the complex of a general chemical production. The first process designed to convert benzene into phenol without the use of auxiliary chemicals and without forming proportional quantities of by-products was developed by the Dr. F. Raschig G.m.b.H., Ludwigshafen am Rhein, Germany, in the early thirties. This "Raschig" or "Regenerative" process is typically represented by the equations:

$$C_6H_6 + HCl + 1/2O_2 \rightarrow C_6H_5Cl + H_2O$$
$$C_6H_5Cl + H_2O \rightarrow C_6H_5OH + HCl$$
$$\overline{C_6H_6 + 1/2O_2 \rightarrow C_6H_5OH}$$

The original process did not fully reach the goal of no auxiliary chemicals and no by-products Dichlorobenzenes were formed as a by-product to the extent of about 10% of the phenol produced, and the corresponding quantity of hydrogen chloride was consumed. In a modification of the Raschig process, by the Hooker Chemical Company, the formation of dichlorobenzenes

332

was avoided and the goal of very little or no by-products and a minimum consumption of auxiliary chemicals except for incidental and mechanical losses, was achieved.

In this process benzene, hydrogen chloride, water, and air are passed over a catalyst, where the oxychlorination of benzene takes place to form monochlorobenzene with some dichlorobenzene. The chlorinated benzenes are separated from the reaction products and passed in vapor form together with water over a catalyst where the monochlorobenzene is converted to phenol, which is then purified by distillation.

Cumene Process. During World War II, Hercules in America and I.C.I. in England independently developed the cumene phenol process, which may be represented by the equations:

$$C_6H_6 + H_2C = CH—CH_3 \rightarrow C_6H_5CH(CH_3)_2$$
$$C_6H_5CH(CH_3)_2 + O_2 \rightarrow C_6H_5COOH(CH_3)_2$$
$$\underline{C_6H_5CO_2H(CH_3)_2 \rightarrow C_6H_5OH + CH_3COCH_3}$$
$$C_6H_6 + C_3H_6 + O_2 \rightarrow C_6H_5OH + CH_3COCH_3$$

Propylene is reacted with benzene to form cumene (isopropyl benzene). Oxidation with air, usually carried out in an emulsion of cumene in water, converts the cumene to cumene hydroperoxide, which when treated with acids, is hydrolyzed to phenol and acetone, which are recovered by distillation. Approximately 60 parts by weight of acetone are formed for each 100 parts by weight of phenol. The economy of the process depends largely on the selling price of the acetone. The process represents the simultaneous conversion of benzene into phenol and of propylene into acetone, and where the economics of both processes are favorable, the cumene process represents one of the most economical methods of producing phenol.

Benzoic Acid Process. The Dow Company has the distinction of being the only company to develop two phenol processes. The new Dow phenol process starts with toluene, rather than benzene, as the source material. The toluene is oxidized to benzoic acid, which is then further converted to phenol in a reaction which can be visualized as an oxidation of the benzoic acid to salicylic acid, followed by splitting off the carboxyl group. It seems that this process depends economically on a rather large price difference between toluene and benzene in order to make it competitive with the processes starting from benzene.

Cyclohexanol Process. Although considerable quantities of cyclohexanol are being made from phenol for conversion to nylon intermediates, a process developed fairly recently by Scientific Design reverses this reaction. This process starts with cyclohexane, oxidizes it to cyclohexanol and then dehydrogenates the cyclohexanol to phenol, according to the equations:

$$C_6H_{12} + 1/2O_2 \rightarrow C_6H_{11}—OH$$
$$C_6H_{11}OH \rightarrow C_6H_5OH + 3H_2$$

As far as is known, this process has not reached plant scale yet in the United States.

An estimate of the share of the different phenol processes in the 1964 production is given in Table 2.

TABLE 2. 1964 PRODUCTION OF PHENOL IN THE UNITED STATES BY THE DIFFERENT PROCESSES.

Process	%
Cumene	29
Chlorobenzene	20
Dow II	3
Natural[a]	4
Raschig	23
Sulfonation	21
	100

[a] The share of natural phenol from petroleum has risen from less than 10% in 1955 to over 25% in 1964, with the difference coming from coal tar.

Physical and Chemical Properties of Phenol

Chemical formula	C_6H_5OH
Molecular weight	94.11
Freezing point	40.93°C
Boiling point	181.75°C
Density 41°	1.0576
Vapor pressure	$\log p_i = 7.84376 — 2043/(T+230.1)$ mm
Heat of fusion	25.37 cal/mole
Heat of combustion	732 cal/mole
Heat of vaporization	11.42 cal/mole (atm pressure)

PHENOLIC RESINS, INGREDIENTS

The basic raw materials for phenolic resins can be conveniently divided into five categories:

(A) The phenolic constituent.
(B) The aldehydic constituent.
(C) The catalyst.
(D) The modifier or modifiers (if required).
(E) The other ingredients used in molding compounds.

The Phenolic Constituent

Types of Phenolic Constituents. (1) *Phenol.* Phenol (hydroxybenzene) is by far the most frequently used constituent in the manufacture of phenolic resins. It is a solid at room temperature, having a melting point of 40.9°C. In the pure state, phenol is best handled as a liquid at a temperature 10–20°C above its melting point.

The addition of relatively small amounts of water greatly depresses the melting point, and, if water is not objectionable, phenol can be handled more conveniently when mixed with from 5–18% of water.

(2) *Ortho- and Meta-substituted Phenols.* In this tar acid category, the most important members are the *ortho-* and *meta*-cresols (2-methyl- and 3-methylphenol), and the xylenols, one example of which is 3,5-dimethylphenol. They are most often used as blends of cresols, xylenols and higher boiling homologues. The term "cresol" is used in the industry to describe a tar acid blend in which at least 50% of the constituents boil under 204°C. When more than 50% of the constituents boil over 204°C, the raw material is described as a "cresylic acid." As will be evident later, such blends inevitably contain some para-substituted constituents.

The proportion of cresols, xylenols and higher boiling fractions in a tar-acid blend determine the reactivity of the blend with the aldehydic component and can thus be used to control the properties of the resin. Also, cresols and xylenols, having less affinity for water than phenol, are recommended for products, such as electrical-grade laminates, where minimum water absorption is required.

(3) *Para-substituted Phenols.* Homologues of phenol in which the substituent is in the *para* position with respect to the hydroxyl group, are an important class of raw materials. A resin prepared from a *para*-substituted phenol cannot be cross-linked to give the normal three dimensional network, and thus cannot be cured to a hard, infusible, insoluble product. Phenols in which the *para* position is blocked by a long side chain are particularly useful in the manufacture of oil-modified coatings, the side chain providing compatibility with the oil.

Dihydric Phenols. Resorcinol is the only one of the three dihydroxy benzenes used in the manufacture of resins. Because of the *meta* position of the two hydroxy groups, its use results in resins which are extremely fast-curing. The only other commercially important member of this class is bisphenol A which, chemically, is 2,2′-bis-(hydroxyphenol)propane.

Manufacture of Phenolic Constituents

Phenolic constituents used in the preparation of phenolic resins are either manufactured synthetically, or are derived from natural sources.

Phenolic Constituents Manufactured Synthetically. (1) *Phenol.* Phenol is made by a number of commercial processes. The main chemical reactions utilized in these processes may be summarized as follows.

(a) Sulfonation Process. Benzene is reacted with sulfuric acid to benzenesulfonic acid, which is then neutralized with sodium sulfite to form the sodium salt, sulfur dioxide being a by-product. The sodium salt is fused with sodium hydroxide to yield sodium phenate and sodium sulfite. The sodium phenate is subsequently acidified with sulfur dioxide to give phenol.

(b) Chlorination Process. Benzene and chlorine are reacted in the presence of a catalyst (ferric chloride has been commonly used) to produce monochlorobenzene, with hydrochloric acid as by-product. The chlorobenzene is then hydrolyzed with aqueous sodium hydroxide to give sodium phenate, from which phenol is obtained by acidification with the hydrochloric acid produced in the first step.

(c) Raschig Process. This is also a chlorination-hydrolysis process. However, a mixture of air and hydrogen chloride is used to chlorinate the benzene. The resulting chlorobenzene is hydrolyzed by steam in the presence of a catalyst at high temperatures.

(d) Cumene Process. Cumene is air-oxidized to cumene hydroperoxide in the presence of a catalyst. The cumene hydroperoxide is then decomposed with sulfuric acid to produce phenol and acetone along with small amounts of acetophenone and alpha-methylstyrene. The phenol, acetone and other by-products are separated by a combination of washing and fractional distillation.

(e) Oxidation Process. Although the direct oxidation of benzene has been carried out in the laboratory, no commercial process has been based on this route. Recently, however, two new processes are understood to involve an oxidation step. In one of these, benzene is hydrogenated to cyclohexane which is then oxidized to cyclohexanol. This, in turn, is dehydrogenated to phenol. In the other process, toluene is oxidized to benzoic acid, which is hydrolyzed to salicylic acid. The salicylic acid is decarboxylated to phenol.

(2) *Ortho- and meta*-substituted phenols. *Ortho-* and *meta*-cresol, as well as 2,6-xylenol are produced by synthetic methods, but there has been no great use of these products in the resin-producing industry. They are still relatively high in cost, and inexpensive broad-cut mixtures (see phenol from natural sources) satisfy industry requirements.

(3) *Para-substituted Phenols.* Three *para*-substituted phenols prepared synthetically have assumed importance in the commercial manufacture of phenolic resins.

(a) *p-tert*-Butylphenol. Isobutylene or *tert*-butyl chloride react with phenol in the presence of a catalyst to give the *ortho-* and *para*-isomers. By heating, most of the *ortho-* is converted to the *para*-compound: the remaining *ortho*-isomer is separated by distillation.

(b) *p-tert*-Amylphenol. The process for the manufacture of *p-tert*-amylphenol is similar to that for *p-tert*-butylphenol, except for the use of amylene or *tert*-amyl chloride.

(c) *p*-Phenylphenol. This raw material is a by-product of the Raschig process for the manufacture of synthetic phenol. The process conditions can be modified to increase the yield of *p*-phenylphenol at the expense of phenol, from which it is separated by distillation.

(3) *Dihydric Phenols*. In the industrial method for the manufacture of resorcinol, benzene is sulfonated under carefully controlled conditions to give *m*-benzenedisulfonic acid. The crude sodium salt of this acid is fused with sodium hydroxide. The melt is dissolved in water, acidified with hydrochloric acid, filtered, and the resorcinol extracted with solvent. It can be purified by vacuum distillation, sublimation or crystallization.

Bisphenol A is made by the reaction of phenol and acetone in the presence of a catalyst.

Phenolic Constituents Obtained from Natural Sources. (1) *Monohydric Phenols*. Most of the naturally occurring monohydric phenols are obtained as a by-product from the coking of coal, or from cracked petroleum residues.

Coal tar is a black, viscous liquid which is produced during the destructive distillation of coal to make coke. When this tar is fractionally distilled, the portion distilling below approximately 235°C, commonly referred to as carbolic oil, contains, among other chemicals, most of the phenolic constituents present in the original tar. Washing of the carbolic oil with dilute sodium hydroxide removes these tar acids which can subsequently be sprung by acidification. The crude tar acids are distilled to give fractions containing various proportions of phenol, the three isomeric cresols, and the six xylenols. These fractions can be blended to give "tar acid blends" meeting many different specifications. The respective quantities of the various monohydric phenols obtained from this source are governed by a large number of factors, such as, the type of coal, the type of coke oven, the temperature of coking and the type of fractionation equipment.

The process for recovering monohydric phenols from cracked petroleum distillates is very similar to that described for coal tar distillates. One difficulty encountered with petroleum oils is the presence of sulfur compounds, which must be removed to give a satisfactory product. It is, therefore, necessary to include an additional step, e.g., the oxidation of the mercaptans present to disulfides. These are removed by decantation or solvent extraction prior to liberation of the phenols with acid.

(2) *Dihydric Phenols*. Dihydric phenols from naturally occurring sources find use mostly as extenders (q.v.).

The Aldehydic Constituent

Of the aldehydic constituents which might possibly be used for phenolic resins, only two are of commercial importance—formaldehyde and furfural.

Formaldehyde. Pure formaldehyde is a gas at ordinary temperatures. In this form, it cannot be readily handled in a manufacturing process. Therefore, in the preparation of phenolic resins, three types of formaldehyde are employed:

(1) Water solution.
(2) Paraformaldehyde.
(3) Hexamethylenetetramine.

(1) *Water Solution*. Most processes for the manufacture of formaldehyde involve passing a mixture of methanol vapor and air over a catalyst and absorbing the product in water. All three major raw materials, methanol, air, and water, are carefully purified to remove trace chemicals which might poison the catalyst. Since certain proportions of methanol and air form explosive mixtures, the feed mix must be carefully controlled.

Two types of process are in commercial use. When a methanol-free product is required, a mixture low in methanol content is employed with an iron/molybdenum oxide catalyst. On the other hand, a mixture with a low proportion of air with a silver or copper catalyst yields a product containing unreacted methanol. Product vapor is passed to a series of scrubbers where it is cooled and dissolved in water. The methanol and formaldehyde contents are then adjusted to meet specifications.

In aqueous solution, formaldehyde is present as an equilibrium mixture of the monohydrate, methylene glycol, $CH_2(OH)_2$ and a number of low molecular weight polymeric hydrates having the general formula $HO(CH_2O)_n H$. When n is greater than 3, the polymers are only partially soluble in water, and this accounts for the instability of formaldehyde solutions, from which these polymers will precipitate on standing. Low concentrations of formaldehyde favor the formation of the monohydrate and this accounts for the popularity of the 37% formaldehyde grade. High temperatures also favor the monohydrate, and water solutions as high as 55% are successfully handled commercially, especially in bulk quantities, since they can readily be transported and stored at temperatures around 65°C. Use of high concentrations of formaldehyde results in greater yields of resin per batch. Water solutions having improved stability can also be prepared by "inhibition" with methanol, the quantity of the latter varying from 2–15%. Such solutions, of course, react more slowly with the phenolic constituent, resulting in longer batch times. Small though increasing quantities of formaldehyde are manufactured by the oxidation of hydrocarbon gases.

(2) *Paraformaldehyde.* Paraformaldehyde is a mixture of polymeric hydrates containing 91–99% formaldehyde. It is a white solid which depolymerizes on heating to give a mixture of formaldehyde and water vapor. It also depolymerizes when dissolved in polar solvents to give solutions of formaldehyde. Thus it reacts as formaldehyde at a rate which depends on the rate of depolymerization. This rate increases with temperature and decreases as the molecular weight of the paraformaldehyde increases. The pH of the solvent system is also very important. The chief advantage of paraformaldehyde is the large yield of resin which can be obtained from a batch and the saving in cycle time due to the small amount of water to be removed from the reaction kettle. It is extensively used in the production of solid resins.

(3) *Hexamethylenetetramine* (*Hexa*). Hexa is a special source of formaldehyde which finds wide use in the manufacture of resins and molding powders. It is made by reacting ammonia with aqueous formaldehyde:

$$6CH_2O + 4NH_3 \rightarrow C_6H_{12}N_4 + 6H_2O$$

It is a colorless solid which has no odor and is thus more readily handled than other forms of formaldehyde. Its chief use is to supply the additional formaldehyde needed to effect the cross-linking of novolaks. Since it contains no oxygen, it produces no water during cure, so "bubble-free" products are obtained. Since it decomposes to formaldehyde only under the influence of heat or in the presence of catalysts, its reactions are more easily controlled.

Furfural. Furfural is the only other aldehyde which finds some application in the manufacture of phenolic resins. Even so, the extent of its use is slight compared to formaldehyde. It is made from agricultural waste products, especially corn cobs, and when used in molding compounds, it gives materials that have a long flow and are slow curing, but are very dark in color.

The Catalyst

There are four types of catalyst system which are common in the manufacture of phenolic resins. By varying the molar ratio of formaldehyde to phenol and by using one or more of these catalysts, resins having a wide variety of properties can be obtained.

(1) Acids (strong or weak).
(2) Strong bases.
(3) Weak bases.
(4) Salts and oxides.

(1) *Acids.* Acid catalysts are used with reaction mixtures in which the molar ratio of formaldehyde to phenol is less than 1, to produce novolaks. Since novolaks contain predominantly compounds of the dihydroxydiphenylmethane type having no reactive methylol groups, they do not condense further on heating. When mixed and heated with formaldehyde donors such as hexa, they become cross-linked and harden to insoluble, infusible resins.

Sulfuric acid is probably the most popular acid catalyst because of its low corrosive action on metals. Oxalic acid is used where light colored products are desired, since it can be decomposed after reaction has taken place. Toluenesulfonic acid finds use because of its complete solubility not only in the resin but also in modifying oils.

(2) *Strong Bases.* When a strong base is used as a catalyst with a formaldehyde to phenol ratio in excess of 1, phenol alcohols are preferentially formed. Since these contain reactive methylol groups, they polymerize readily under the influence of heat.

Sodium hydroxide is probably the most popular basic catalyst. It produces resins having good water dilutability. It may be neutralized after reaction to give a relatively stable resin, or this step may be omitted to produce a fast-curing resin, although at the expense of stability. When sodium hydroxide is used as a catalyst for mixtures having a formaldehyde to phenol ratio of less than 1, and this reaction is followed by neutralization with sulfuric acid and removal of the sodium sulfate by washing with water, products are obtained which are used for cross-linking rubber.

The hydroxides of lithium, potassium and calcium are all used to obtain special effects as is sodium carbonate. Barium hydroxide is used to obtain ash-free resin. On neutralization with sulfuric acid, barium sulfate is formed which can be removed by filtration.

(3) *Weak Bases.* The most frequently used weak base is ammonium hydroxide. It is employed with molar ratios of formaldehyde to phenol of around 1 to give heat-hardenable products. Resins catalysed with ammonia have low water tolerance and are usually dissolved in organic solvents, especially denatured alcohol, to yield "varnishes". The use of ammonia results in the presence of nitrogen in the resin molecule.

(4) *Salts and Oxides.* The oxides of zinc and magnesium, as well as the acetates of these metals are used as catalysts to produce novolaks having special properties.

The Modifier

It would be impossible to treat comprehensively the many modifiers which are used with phenolic resins. This short discussion covers the most important ones, and the properties which they confer on the resins. Although there is considerable overlapping, modifiers may be classified very generally into three types:

(1) Internal modifiers.
(2) External modifiers.
(3) Extenders.

(1) *Internal modifiers.* An internal modifier is one which is added at some stage during the manufacture of the resin. The most common modifier is probably rosin, a solid resinous material obtained from the stump wood of pine trees. The principal reactive components of rosin are conjugated acids of the abietic type. Reacting phenolic resins with rosin during the final stages of preparation renders them oil-soluble. A number of drying oils find wide use as modifiers for phenolic resins. For best results, drying oils should have some conjugated unsaturation, e.g., tung oil or linseed oil. Oils can be incorporated into resins by partial ester interchange, by chroman-ring type condensation, etc., to obtain materials useful in brake-linings, grinding wheels and molding materials. Phenolic resins modified with aniline have particularly good electrical properties.

(2) *External Modifiers.* External modifiers can be defined as products which are added to or reacted with phenolic resins prior to their use. As an example of the overlapping of these categories, it may be mentioned that both rosin and drying oils are used as external modifiers. Rosin is often added to varnishes to provide additional plasticization in an attempt to overcome the inherent brittleness of unmodified phenolics. Drying oils are reacted with novolaks prepared from *para*-substituted phenols and the products are used in the coating industry. Dibutyl phthalate is used as plasticizer in the manufacture of industrial laminates. A great many different polymers are used with phenolic resins to give a co-polymer or a polymer blend having some special property, but this modification is beyond the scope of this article. The addition of phosphate esters results in resins which confer flame retardant properties on the end-product.

(3) *Extenders.* There is a third class of materials, most of them derived from natural sources, which are not true modifiers, but are better described as extenders. This is due to the fact that they are employed commercially as inexpensive partial replacements for phenol rather than for any specific property which they confer on the products. Of these, the most important are the phenolic bodies which are obtained as by-products of the wood-pulping industry. Considerable attention has been given to the possible use of lignin or modifications thereof as phenolic resin extenders. In the wood structure, lignin serves largely as a cementing material which holds the cellulose fibers together. When wood chips are subjected to the action of pulping liquor, lignin is dissolved setting free the fibers. When the liquor used is one of the alkaline pulping liquors, the recovered lignin is known as alkali lignin. When acid is used, the lignin is obtained as lignosulfonates. The structure of lignin is complex, but it has been established that certain units are related to catechol and would be expected to undergo phenolic type condensation. Both alkali lignin and lignosulfonates are employed in the production of resins. Another common extender for resins is a dark colored high-melting, thermoplastic resin derived from southern pinewood. There are a number of natural tannin materials which contain phenolic bodies, and certain resins are in use which contain extracts from quebracho. Bagasse, the residue from the cane sugar extraction process, has also found application as a phenolic resin raw material.

Molding Compounds

A large and important use for phenolic resins is in compounds employed in the manufacture of molded articles. Besides the phenolic resin, these molding powders usually contain:

(1) A reinforcement.
(2) A filler.
(3) A lubricant.
(4) A colorant.

(1) *Reinforcement.* Cotton fabric or cotton flock are the most widely used reinforcing materials. They impart good finish and low water absorption properties to the molded part. Relatively good impact strength can be obtained by increasing the resin content. Glass fiber, although expensive, is used as reinforcement where exceptional strength is necessary. Molding materials containing glass fiber require careful processing due to the possibility of fiber degradation when excessive stresses are applied to this reinforcement. Sisal fibers are used to impart good impact strength. However, this material has a high affinity for water, and molded parts from sisal-filled compounds have a characteristic orange-peel effect which prevents its use in many applications. Partial use of asbestos results in compounds having good heat resistance, while mica gives excellent electrical properties.

(2) *Filler.* Wood flour is the most widely used filler for phenolic molding compounds. It is low in specific gravity, and although inexpensive, it gives molded articles with good strength. Bark derivatives are available which contain natural resins. When these are used in molding compounds, the phenolic resin content can be reduced, which decreases the cost of the compound. They also contain natural acids which must be neutralized since their presence will decrease the cure rate of the compound. Limestone is often used as a filler. Because of its white color, the resulting

articles have good surface appearance. It also offers a background for colored compounds.

(3) *Lubricants.* Lubricants, such as metallic stearates and low molecular weight polyethylene, are used in molding powders to aid in processing and in removal of the part from the mold. Being largely incompatible with the other components, these materials migrate to the surface where they form a thin film between the molding compound and the mold.

(4) *Colorants.* Phenolic resins are not color stable, gradually turning from yellow to reddish-brown. Light colored articles are, therefore, not manufactured from phenolic resins. Various dyes or pigments can be added to molding materials to give black, brown, dark green or dark red colors.

A. DAVIES

Cross-reference: PHENOL.

PHENYLETHYL ALCOHOL

One of the simplest of the aromatic alcohols, phenylethyl alcohol [(2-phenylethanol), $C_6H_5CH_2$—CH_2OH], is a colorless liquid of faint rose odor and has the reaction characteristics of a primary alcohol, forming esters, halides, ethers, etc. Although primarily used in the manufacture of perfumes, phenylethyl alcohol, because of its antifungal or fungicidal properties, is used in the manufacture of plastics where the end product is likely to be subject to high humidity, heat, and other conditions conducive to fungal attack, particularly in tropical countries. It also finds uses in the dye industry and in chemical engineering generally as a surfactant or surface-active agent.

Phenylethyl alcohol occurs in either free or ester form, in various essential oils such as attar of rose, oils of neroli (orange blossoms), carnation geranium, and pine needles. It has even been isolated from orange juice, Japanese tobacco-leaf oil, beer, and cigarette smoke. Large-scale commercial manufacture is by the Friedel-Crafts reaction, in which a short carbon chain is attached to a benzene ring by the use of heat and aluminum chloride. Phenylethyl alcohol is extremely difficult to crystallize, as it tends to supercool to a glassy state. Its solubility is 1 part in 50 parts of water, 1 part in 11 parts of 30% ethyl alcohol, 1 part in 1.5 parts of 50% ethyl alcohol; viscosity, 0.0758 P at 25°C, 0.0319 P at 50°C. The alcohol combines with anhydrous calcium chloride to give a solid "addition compound," and it forms acetals with many aldehydes. With nitric oxide the major product of oxidation is phenylacetic acid, with similar amounts of phenylacetaldehyde.

WILLIAM F. RINGK

PHOSPHONITRILIC CHLORIDE

Phosphonitrilic chloride has only recently become available in pilot plant quantities. Phosphonitrilic chloride is actually a family of cyclic and end-stopped linear polymers, however, our interest here will focus on the cyclic members, especially the trimer and tetramer (see below) because of their commercial availability and the high-heat stable properties of various resinous products in which they are incorporated:

Trimer   *Tetramer*

Syntheses

Recent methods are improvements on the Schenk and Römer synthesis which involves the partial ammonolysis and cyclization of pentavalent phosphorus chloride in an inert solvent. Ammonium hexachlorophosphate which is first formed is unstable. From this is formed two different series of cyclic and linear compounds, roughly separable on the basis of solubility in nonpolar solvents, e.g., hexane, in which the cyclics are soluble and the linears insoluble. Further separations of individual members can be accomplished by other physical methods such as fractional distillation, solvent extraction, chromatography or fractional crystallization.

Recent studies include Bilger's synthesis, employing the use of an inexpensive solvent, chlorobenzene, and the preparation of PN derivatives by further reaction with ammonia in methanol solution. Catalysts, e.g., Co(II), Al, Mn(II), Cu(II), Sn(IV), are advantageous in shortening the reaction time from ten hours to about 2.5 hr. Also quinoline is recommended as the catalyst in preparation of PNC by reaction of PCl_5 and NH_4Cl in chlorobenzene.

The process by Hooker Chemical Company is reported to yield a higher proportion of cyclic trimer. Chlorine is passed into a mixture of phosphorus trichloride, finely divided ammonium chloride, and *sym*-tetrachloroethane at refluxing temperature. The mixture is refluxed until hydrogen chloride evolution ceases. After cooling, the excess ammonium chloride is filtered off and the solvent removed from the filtrate by distillation. The product contains:

	%
Linear polymer	17
Trimer	59
Tetramer	10
Higher cyclics	14

A recent Japanese process may be summarized as follows: To dried, finely divided, ammonium chloride suspended in tetrachloroethane, phosphorus trichloride is added slowly with stirring at 110–115°C while chlorine is introduced. When the evolution of hydrogen chloride gas stops, the reaction is finished and the suspended unreacted ammonium chloride is filtered. To the filtrate is added sulfur dioxide to decompose the phosphorus pentachloride, and the solution is evaporated *in vacuo* to remove $POCl_3$, $SOCl_2$, and $C_2H_4Cl_4$ and the residue vacuum distilled to give the cyclic trimer in 40% yield.

A process for converting the cyclic trimer in 74% yield to the (oily pet-ether-insoluble) linear polymer consists of heating it with phosphorus pentachloride in an autoclave at 350°C for 2.5 hr. The linear polymer is more reactive (chloride atoms easily hydrolyzed) and less volatile than the cyclic trimer.

Resin-Forming Reactions

PNC may be condensed in inert solvents with various (mono-functional) amines, alcohols and mercaptans to produce derivatives which on high-heating yielded "pale yellow, hard, glassy solids, stable to heat, insoluble in water and organic solvents, and acid and alkali resistant." The reaction of PNC with polyhydroxyaromatics, preferably hydroquinone, yields dark rubbery resins which on heating with typical formaldehyde-type curing agents yielded hard polymers said to be useful for moldings, laminates, coatings adhesives, fire-proofing agents, etc. The nature and appearance of this type of resin may be improved by the use of acid acceptors such as pyridine which lead to soluble white resins of low chlorine content and good hydrolytic stability, capable of being cured to hard tenacious films or laminates able to withstand extreme environmental stresses.

Currently a resin of similar type and improved quality (PH 990) is being made available commercially. This resin, which also contains hydroxyphenyl end groups, can be cured with conventional phenolic curing agents, e.g., hexamethylenetetramine and magnesium oxide. The cured resin does not burn, resists heat continuously in air at 500°F, intermittently at up to 1000°F (losing only 2% after 6 hr at 700°F) and is relatively resistant to hard radiation. The uncured resin is soluble in most polar solvents and compatible with polar resins and elastomers. This polymer is considered to be in competition with aromatic and heteroaromatic polymers being developed for high temperature uses—e.g., the polyimides and polybenzimidazoles, which it surpasses in flame retardency and high temperature oxidation resistance. Some rather unique undisclosed aerospace applications utilizing PN-resins of this general type are in current development. In the non-military markets commercial development is progressing in the areas of diamond abrasive wheel fabrication and high-temperature electrical insulations.

While reaction of trimer with hydroquinone or resorcinol leads to coupling of adjacent PN rings with resultant resin formation, the use of pyrocatechol (*o*-dihydroxybenzene) yields principally the high melting (244°) non-resin cyclic condensate, tris(*o*-phenylenedioxy)phosphonitrile trimer.

One technical obstacle to the wider use of the cyclic trimer as a resin-making chemical is the presence of six reactive chlorine atoms which causes it to behave as a hexafunctional monomer. This can be a serious drawback since polymers derived from it tend to become inflexible and intractable due to crosslinking at relatively low degrees of polymerization. The resins described above have shown this defect in varying degrees, a fact which has eliminated their consideration from some applications.

Flame-resistant, thermoplastic resins, useful as adhesives or coatings are formed from the reaction of PNC with an aliphatic diamine in polar solvents (dioxane, diethyl ether, tetrahydrofuran) at room temperatures. These high-heat stable resins may be used to coat aluminum, titanium and stainless steel.

Earlier resin developments in phosphonitrile technology have been directed toward their use in high-temperature gaskets, brake linings, abrasives and insulators, glass and asbestos fiber coatings (to form electrical insulators with improved heat, flame and moisture resistance). Phenolic resins with improved thermal stability are formed from mixtures of phosphonitrilic chlorides, polyhydric phenols, and inorganic chlorides such as boron trichloride or phosphorus oxychloride. Resins useful as rubber additives have been made by reaction with butyl amine or urea.

One of the more unusual recent developments is a copolymer of PNC and acrylonitrile (heated to 75°C in presence of benzoyl peroxide) to form a white resin powder. Film obtained on evaporation of a DMF solution of this resin has the properties of a semi-conductor (resistivity, 10^3–40×10^3 ohms sq cm/cm. A flame-proof elastic polyurethane foam may be obtained by reacting the cyclic phosphonitrile amidate (trimer-condensed with sodium phenate and ammonia) with tolylene diisocyanate using dibutyl tin as the catalyst, then with a polypropylene glycol (M.W. ~ 3000) and finally with water. Laminates, moldings, coatings and bonding agents based on this cured resin proved temperature resistant to 600°C.

Toxicity

The physical irritation and discomfort that phosphonitrile chlorides can cause to eyes, lungs and mucous membranes differs from the typical results of overexposure to a volatile acid chloride. The fumes can irritate the lungs and produce a mild conjunctivitis of the eyes, beyond what might be expected from the amount of hydrogen chloride that could be evolved. The susceptibility varies with the individual, and severe eye pain has been reported. The effects are similar to acid burns, but fortunately recovery appears to be complete. No dermatitis has been reported, but in view of the potential biological activity of many phosphorus compounds, appropriate protective measures are indicated for the present.

T. F. BANIGAN

PHOSPHORUS ESTERS

Although many phosphorus esters have been known for over 100 years, compounds of this type did not gain commercial importance until about 1920 when tertiary phosphates were first introduced as improved replacements for camphor in the plasticization of cellulose nitrate. Since then they have gained acceptance in many plasticizer applications, especially in polyvinyl chloride, polyvinyl acetate, polyvinylidene chloride, and cellulosics.

Types and Properties

Phosphates, $(RO)_3P{=}O$, in which R is alkyl, haloalkyl, alkoxyalkyl or aryl group or mixed alkyl and aryl, are the most useful type of phosphorus esters for plasticizer applications. Other types of less commercial importance are trialkyl phosphorothioates, $(RO)_3P{=}S$, dialkyl alkylphosphonates, $(RO)_2P(O)R$, and trialkyl and triaryl phosphites, $(RO)_3P$. Phosphites are used primarily in stabilizer compositions.

A compilation of phosphorus esters used as plasticizers is found in Table 1. All are liquids at room temperature except triphenyl phosphate, tris(p-tert-butylphenyl) phosphate, and tris(p-tert-amylphenyl) phosphate. In most cases they are either odorless or else possess a mild pleasant odor. Only triethyl phosphate and diethyl ethylphosphonate have appreciable water solubility. Most of the esters are soluble or miscible with common industrial solvents such as alcohols, esters, and ketones. While a few of the esters of Table 1 have flash points of less than 150°C, the

more important commercial ones have values of 190°C or greater.

Production volumes for 1964 of phosphate esters for plasticizer usage taken from U.S. Tariff Commission Publication 167 are as follows:

Cresyl diphenyl phosphate	16,061,000 lb
Tricresyl phosphate	32,419,000 lb
Triphenyl phosphate	8,982,000 lb
Acyclic phosphates	11,731,000 lb

The listing is incomplete because data on certain items were accepted in confidence and cannot be published. The quantities given for cresyl diphenyl phosphate and tricresyl phosphate also include material produced for use as motor fuel additives.

Manufacture

The trialkyl phosphates, including the alkoxyalkyl analogs, are usually manufactured by reaction of an excess of the appropriate alcohol with phosphorus oxychloride. Titanium, aluminum, and zinc chlorides have been reported to catalyze the reaction. Rapid removal of byproduct hydrogen chloride, to avoid ester cleavage with the formation of alkyl chlorides, is essential for high yields. An alternate route is the condensation of ethers with phosphorus pentoxide under pressure; this is the preferred method for triethyl phosphate. Tris(2-chloroethyl) phosphate is manufactured by the reaction of ethylene oxide with phosphorus oxychloride in the presence of catalytic compounds containing vanadium, titanium, and aluminum; alternatively, the corresponding phosphite is oxidized to phosphate.

Triaryl phosphates are usually manufactured by the reaction at elevated temperatures of the appropriate phenol with phosphorus oxychloride in the presence of catalysts such as aluminum and zinc chlorides until hydrogen chloride evolution is complete. The purification techniques employed vary. They are reported to include either preliminary or final distillation as well as dilute caustic and water washes to remove unreacted phenols and partial esters. Activated carbon and permanganate treatments have also been suggested to improve color and oxidation stability.

Two routes are available for the manufacture of alkyl diaryl phosphates. In the first method, phosphorus oxychloride is reacted with the appropriate alcohol to give an alkyl phosphorodichloridate which is then treated with a sodium phenate using the Schotten-Baumann technique. Alternately, a diaryl phosphorochloridate which is prepared from phenol and phosphorus oxychloride is reacted with the alcohol. Work-up of the product is similar to that for triaryl phosphates.

O,O,O-Trialkyl phosphorothioates are prepared by the reaction of thiophosphoryl chloride with either a sodium alkylate or an alcohol in the

TABLE 1. PHOSPHORUS ESTERS.

Name	Structural formula	Specific gravity	Boiling point, °C/mm	Flash point, °C (Cleveland open cup)
Triethyl phosphate	$(C_2H_5O)_3PO$	1.064 at 25°/4°C	75/5	116
Tributyl phosphate	$(C_4H_9)_3PO$	0.973 at 25°/4°C	177–8/27	146
Tris(2-ethylhexyl) phosphate	$[C_4H_9CH(C_2H_5)CH_2O]_3PO$	0.926 at 20°/20°C	220/5	207
Tris(2-chloroethyl) phosphate	$(ClC_2H_4O)_3PO$	1.428 at 15°/20°C	210–220/20	216
Tris(2-butoxyethyl) phosphate	$(C_4H_9OC_2H_4O)_3PO$	1.020 at 20°/20°C	223–230/15	224
2-Ethylhexyl diphenyl phosphate	$[C_4H_9CH(C_2H_5)CH_2O]$ $[C_6H_5O]_2PO$	1.088–1.093 at 25°/25°C	230/5	224
Triphenyl phosphate	$(C_6H_5O)_3PO$	1.268 at 60°/20°C	245/11 (mp 49–50°C)	220
Cresyl diphenyl phosphate[a]	$(CH_3C_6H_4O)\,(C_6H_5O)_2PO$	1.203–1.213 at 15°/25°C	258/10	232
Tricresyl phosphate[a]	$(CH_3C_6H_4O)_3PO$	1.157–1.173 at 25°/25°C	240–265/4	243
Trixylyl phosphate[a]	$[(CH_3)_2C_6H_3O]_3PO$	1.145 at 25°C	225–295/10	233
2-Biphenylyl diphenyl phosphate	$(2\text{-}C_6H_5C_6H_4O)\,(C_6H_5O)_2PO$	1.20 at 60°/4°C	250–285/5	225
Bis(2-biphenylyl) phenyl phosphate	$(2\text{-}C_6H_5C_6H_4O)_2(C_6H_5O)PO$	1.20 at 60°/4°C	285–330/5	250
Tris(p-tert-butyl phenyl)phosphate	$[p\text{-}(CH_3)_3CC_6H_4O]_3PO$	—	300–320/5 (mp 95–100°C)	275
Bis(p-tert-butylphenyl)phosphate	$[p\text{-}(CH_3)_3CC_6H_4O]_2[C_6H_5O]PO$	1.08 at 60°/4°C	260–275/5	250
Tris(p-tert-amylphenyl) phosphate	$(p\text{-}C_5H_{11}C_6H_4O)_3PO$	—	305–345/5 (mp 62–3°C)	—
Diethyl ethylphosphonate	$C_2H_5P(O)\,(OC_2H_5)_2$	1.026 at 20°/4°C	82–83/11	105
Dibutyl butylphosphonate	$C_4H_9P(O)\,(OC_4H_9)_2$	0.946 at 25°/4°C	127–128/2.5	155
Bis(2-ethyl-hexyl) 2-ethylhexyl-phosphonate	$C_4H_9CH(C_2H_5)CH_2P(O)$ $[OCH_2CH(C_2H_5)C_4H_9]_2$	0.908 at 20°/4°C	160–161/0.25	215
O, O, O—Triethyl phosphorothioate	$(C_2H_5O)_3PS$	1.074 at 20°/4°C	93.5–94/10	107
O, O, O—Tributyl phosphorothioate	$(C_4H_9O)_3PS$	0.987 at 20°/4°C	142–145/4.5	146
O, O, O—Triisooctyl phosphorothioate	$(C_8H_{17}O)_3PS$	0.933 at 20°/4°C	160–170/0.2	210
Tris(2-chloroethyl) phosphite	$(ClCH_2CH_2O)_3P$	1.353 at 20°/4°C	119/0.15	191
Triphenyl phosphite	$(C_6H_5O)_3P$	1.191 at 25°/25°C	220/11	154

[a] Mixture of isomers.

presence of a hydrogen chloride acceptor. An alternate route is the addition of sulfur to the corresponding phosphite.

The preferred route for most trialkyl phosphites is the reaction of an alcohol with phosphorus trichloride in the presence of a hydrogen chloride acceptor. Tris(2-chloroethyl) phosphite is best obtained by reaction of ethylene oxide and phosphorus trichloride. Triaryl phosphites are prepared directly from a phenol and phosphorus trichloride.

Dialkyl alkylphosphonates are produced by the Michaelis-Arbuzov rearrangement of the corresponding trialkyl phosphate with a trace of alkyl halide as catalyst.

Chemical Properties

Tertiary phosphates in general are very stable compounds especially to oxidation. Triaryl phosphates are quite stable thermally while the alkyl esters are somewhat less stable and will undergo decomposition at elevated temperatures. Acids catalyze this decomposition in which clevage of an unsaturated aliphatic hydrocarbon occurs.

Hydrolysis is both acid and base catalyzed. In basic media the reaction stops at the secondary ester stage while with acid hydrolysis the end-product is phosphoric acid. The reaction in aqueous basic solutions is first order in both hydroxide ion and ester.

The alkyl phosphates will undergo alcoholysis or ester interchange in the presence of small quantities of basic catalysts to give mixed esters. The aliphatic esters also react with amines, phenates, thiourea, and mercaptide ions to form alkylated products of these reactants. Treatment with phosphorus oxychloride replaces the alkoxy groups with chlorine. Dry hydrogen chloride cleaves the alkyl phosphates, forming alkyl chlorides.

Applications of Phosphates

Phosphates have wide utility as plasticizers for many commercial plastics due to their outstanding compatibility. Table 2 lists important areas for phosphate use. Compatibility is defined as the ability of a plasticizer to form a homogeneous product with the resin without exudation or crystallization.

Normally, plasticizers are used for two purposes: to lower the working temperature during fabrication and to impart desirable properties such as flexibility, gloss or flame retardance to the finished article. Phosphates are generally excellent plasticizers and excel in adding flame resistance to many resin systems.

Polyvinyl Chloride (PVC) and Copolymers. Outstanding properties provided by phosphate plasticizers in flexible PVC are flame resistance, excellent processing, and permanence. Selected members, however, can also add outdoor durability, low-temperature flexibility, nontoxicity, good flow characteristics, oil resistance, and fungal resistance.

Tricresyl phosphate (TCP) has been the standard among phosphates because of its good permanence, low volatility, and flame resistance in spite of its poor T_f – the temperature at which

TABLE 2. RESINS NORMALLY PLASTICIZED WITH PHOSPHATES.

Resin	Triethyl phosphate	Tributyl phosphate	Tris (2-butoxy-ethyl) phosphate	Tris (2-ethyl-hexyl) phosphate	2-Ethyl-hexyl diphenyl phosphate	Cresyl diphenyl phosphate	Tricresyl phosphate	Trixylyl phosphate	Triphenyl phosphate
PVC	—	C	—	C	C	C	C	C	—
PVC copolymers	—	C	—	C	C	C	C	C	—
PV butyral	—	C	C	C	C	C	C	C	C
PV acetate	—	C	C	—	C	C	C	—	C
Polvinylidene chloride	—	—	—	—	C	—	—	—	—
Cellulose nitrate	C	C	C	C	C	C	C	C	C
Cellulose acetate	C	—	—	—	—	—	—	—	C
Cellulose acetate-butyrate	C	C	C	C	C	C	C	C	C
Ethylcellulose	C	C	C	C	C	C	C	C	C
Acrylic	C	C	C	—	—	C	C	C	—
Polystyrene	C	—	C	—	C	—	C	C	—
Chlorinated rubber	C	C	C	—	C	C	C	C	—
GR-S rubber	C	—	—	C	C	C	C	C	—

TABLE 3. PROPERTIES OF PLASTICIZED PVC.
(40% Plasticizer in Polyvinyl Chloride plus 1/2 PHR Dibasic Lead Stearate)

Plasticizer	T_f, °C	Shore A Hardness	Volatility, % Plasticizer Loss 87°C	Kerosene Extraction, % Plasticizer Loss, 24 hr	Water Sensitivity, % Absorption 24 hr, 50°C	% Weight Loss
ASTM Designation:	D–1043	D–676	D–1203	D–1239	D–1239	D–1239
Tricresyl phosphate	−10	78	1.0	2.4	0.26	0.03
Trixylyl phosphate	−8	79	1.1	2.2	0.30	0.02
Cresyl diphenyl phosphate	−15	76	3.6	2.1	0.30	0.04
2-Ethylhexyl diphenyl phosphate	−39	65	7.4	7.3	0.36	0.06
Tris(2-ethylhexyl) phosphate	−68	72	7.0	78.0	1.70	0.06
Di(2-ethylhexyl) phthalate	−38	67	4.5	33.0	0.26	0.04

plasticized PVC attains a definite stiffness modulus. A serious toxicity hazard exists with TCP if care is not exercised to use "ortho-free" cresylic acid. Cresyl diphenyl phosphate (CDPP) is also noted primarily for low volatility and permanence to oil extraction. 2-Ethylhexyl diphenyl phosphate (2EHDPP) offers improved T_f with slight sacrifice in volatility and oil resistance. Tris(2-ethylhexyl) phosphate (TEHP) has excellent T_f but suffers from poor oil resistance and high water sensitivity. Several other phosphates, such as tris(2-chloroethyl) and tris(2-butoxyethyl), are not considered primary plasticizers for PVC since they are only compatible while hot.

The results of screening evaluations for compatible phosphates compared with the industry standard di(2-ethylhexyl) phthalate (DOP) are given in Table 3. The alcohol portion of the ester has a profound influence on the properties imparted to plasticized PVC. As the molecule is changed to aliphatic character an improvement in T_f and softening efficiency is noted. At the same time volatility and kerosene extraction resistance become poorer while in some cases water sensitivity is increased.

Fusion. Plasticizers influence the formation of a homogeneous product from PVC resin. Normally in flexible PVC, fusion is accomplished by heat with or without external mixing. Laboratory tests attempt to measure fusion as a function of temperature or time. In actual practice rapid fusion could be related to either faster processing or equivalent processing at lower temperatures. In either case the net result is lower production costs.

PVC fusion will be considered in two cases: hot processing and plastisol techniques. Measurement of fusion characteristics for hot processing requires dynamic mixing and heating as in a Banbury, calender or extruder. Plastisol technology contrasts with hot processing in that mixing is done at normal (room) temperature while physical properties are developed later with heat. Thus, fusion is related to the rate of development of physical properties (film integrity as

evidenced by tensile strength and elongation). Laboratory studies by both techniques show excellent fusion characteristics of phosphates compared to DOP. An exception is TEHP which by some tests has poorer fusion than DOP.

Flame Resistance. All compatible phosphates produce self-extinguishing PVC films and have slow burning rates. More important is their effect in plasticizer mixtures. Aryl phosphates produce self-extinguishing blends with DOP when the phosphate is present as 20% of the plasticizer. Those phosphates containing alkyl moieties are less effective in mixtures and require more than 20% to improve flame resistance.

The phosphates have an advantage of producing clear flame resistant film while antimony oxide as a flame retardant yields an opaque film.

Outdoor Durability. As sole plasticizers in PVC phosphates suffer from poor weatherability. Early yellowing and tackiness are problems.

One member of the phosphate family does offer a tremendous advantage in outdoor application. 2EHDPP as a 10% replacement in combination with phthalate plasticizers in thin, clear film offers outdoor exposure life vastly superior to phthalates alone and slightly superior to phthalates containing expensive ultraviolet light (UV) screeners. Addition of UV screeners to the 2EHDPP/phthalate system further improves weatherability. This effect of 2EHDPP is even more pronounced in opaque systems where its value is not restricted to thin films. Interestingly, UV screeners are not particularly effective in thin, opaque systems. These results are shown in Figure 1.

Heat Stability. Phosphate-plasticized PVC is generally more difficult to stabilize against long-term heat degradation than phthalate-plasticized PVC. Present stabilization technology to improve heat stability suggests an increase in both epoxide and organic inhibitor over the amounts recommended for phthalates.

Viscosity and Viscosity-Stability. Initial viscosity and viscosity-stability are of prime concern in plastisol technology. These applications range

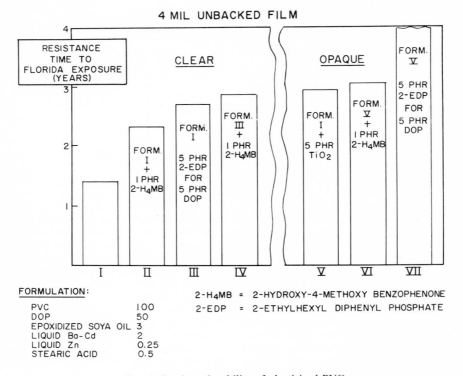

FORMULATION:

PVC	100
DOP	50
EPOXIDIZED SOYA OIL	3
LIQUID Ba-Cd	2
LIQUID Zn	0.25
STEARIC ACID	0.5

2-H₄MB = 2-HYDROXY-4-METHOXY BENZOPHENONE
2-EDP = 2-ETHYLHEXYL DIPHENYL PHOSPHATE

FIG. 1. Outdoor durability of plasticized PVC.

from high shear techniques for roll or knife coating to low shear for dip coating or slush molding. Ideally, plasticizers would have no effect upon resins at low temperatures. Seldom is this the case. A plasticizer giving rapid fusion does exert solvating action at storage temperatures resulting in increased viscosity.

2EHDPP gives DOP-like initial viscosity but with rapid viscosity buildup on storage. 2EHDPP because of its shear thinning characteristics under conditions of high shear has good utility in roll or knife coating applications. TEHP produces low initial viscosity and is relatively stable on storage. In contrast the initial viscosity of TCP is quite high with little increase on storage.

The phosphates offer a wide range of properties in plastisols. Fusion and viscosity data show the advantage of 2EHDPP for rapid fusion. For low viscosity applications TEHP is suggested.

Nontoxic Applications. The U.S. Food and Drug Administration has declared 2EHDPP acceptable for food packaging applications. Regulations have been published for resinous and polymeric coatings, adhesives, resinous and polymeric coatings for paper and paperboard, and polyolefin films. In addition 2EHDPP has been approved by the Bureau of Animal Industry.

The other phosphates have not received approval and cannot now be used in food-contact applications.

Fungal Resistance. Fungi are not able to utilize phosphates as carbon sources. Thus, by proper choice of plasticizer and stabilizers, fungal resistance can be built into PVC formulations.

Electricals. Phosphates have a position in electrical insulation applications based on their flame resistant characteristics. Electrical properties poorer than phthalates are entirely adequate for a number of applications. Flame resistant insulation increases safety, especially in multiwire installations, by preventing complete destruction in the event of fire caused by either a short circuit or an external source.

Polyvinyl Chloride Solutions. Coatings prepared by solution techniques can be given the desirable properties of permanence, flame resistance, fungal resistance or nontoxicity by using phosphates as plasticizers. Phosphates will incorporate easily in these systems. Vinyl maintenance paints based on phosphates have outstanding chemical resistance for metal, concrete, and other substrates. Of particular importance is the alkali resistance afforded by TCP-based swimming pool paint.

Polyvinylidene Chloride. Polyvinylidene chloride films for packaging applications can be prepared by melt extrusion, solvent casting or latex coating. Phosphates add desired flexibility, good fusion, and heat sealing characteristics. 2EHDPP is the only phosphate which has been approved for food packaging.

Polyvinyl Acetate. Polyvinyl acetate offers excellent adhesion in adhesives and good resistance to oily extractants in coatings. Phosphate plasticizers can improve performance by adding flexibility and water resistance and by lowering heat-sealing temperature. TCP, 2EHDPP and TEHP are used in these applications.

Cellulosics. Phosphates are useful as plasticizers in cellulose esters and ethers where their flame retardant qualities help overcome the inherent flammability of cellulosic derivatives. Additionally, the excellent solvent power of phosphates is important. In the end-use application, phosphates also improve flexibility and low temperature properties. Care must be exercised since compositions containing phosphates may be less heat stable than unmodified resins.

Cellulosic compositions are used in lacquers of all types and as adhesives, hot melts, and strippable coatings. Table 2 reviews compatibility with the more important resins of this class. Triethyl phosphate and triphenyl phosphate are industry standards for cellulose acetate, while TCP holds the same position for cellulose nitrate. Triphenyl phosphate, a solid plasticizer, is extremely useful in hot melts to yield final products with high modulus.

Self-Polishing Floor Waxes. Tris(2-butoxyethyl) phosphate (TBEP) is one of the principal plasticizers used in both polystyrene and acrylic self-polishing floor waxes. It has utility in both alkali- and acid-sensitive resin systems. The excellent compatibility of phosphates to bind together the synthetic resin and wax components is evident in this application. TBEP in floor polishes adds to gloss development, depth perception, and leveling of the coating. All these properties are critical in final performance of the polish. TBEP can be used as the sole plasticizer or in combination with either dibutyl phthalate or butyl benzyl phthalate. Typical formulations for these applications are given in the trade literature.

Application of Phosphites

The phosphites hold a unique place as stabilizers for plastics. They function as noncoloring antioxidants to prevent color buildup or degradation during manufacture or processing. They have been recommended in polyvinyl chloride, natural and synthetic rubber, cellulosics, polyolefins, polyurethanes, polyesters, phenol-formaldehyde resins, and alkyd resins.

In flexible PVC, triphenyl phosphite in combination with metallic soaps found early use as a chelator to form complexes and to prevent clouding resulting from metallic halide precipitation. Currently a number of proprietary compounds called either chelators or organic inhibitors containing triphenyl or other phosphites are available from stabilizer manufacturers to improve both heat and light stability.

Toxicity

Published reports indicate that the phosphorus esters utilized as plasticizers are generally of low to moderate mammalian toxicity in animal tests. They have been used safely in plasticizer applications since 1920. Tricresyl and cresyl diphenyl phosphates are primarily mixtures of *para* and *meta* isomers. The *ortho* isomers are considered to be too toxic and are unsafe for plasticizer usage. 2-Ethylhezyl diphenyl phosphate is essentially nontoxic and is the only phosphorus ester approved for use in plastics and films which come in contact with foods.

JOSEPH W. BAKER
NORMAN W. TOUCHETTE

PHOTOTROPIC ADDITIVES

Color matchers in the dye industry have found while testing their dyes for light fastness that some fabrics change their shade markedly in sunlight, but return to their original shade after storage in the dark. This property of certain dyes and chemicals to undergo a reversible change in the colors they absorb when exposed to different wavelengths of light is known as phototropism or photochromism.

Phototropism involves a temporary change in color due to a change in visual light intensity. This means in most cases a temporary change in the distribution of electrons in the molecule. However, a rule of thumb is generally applied to predict photochemical activity. The next few years will undoubtedly see much activity in the determination of the physical properties and chemical reactivity of phototropics in their various states.

A number of phototropic products are presently available on a commercial basis.

The preparation of most phototropic additives for molding and extruding with plastics is a simple and inexpensive procedure. The phototropic additive powders are supplied in a consistently fine particle size. The additives should be incorporated with the plastic pellets at the loading specified. If drying of the plastic is required, it is preferable to do this before dry-blending the additives with the plastic. Dry-blending can be accomplished by using a tumbler, ribbon or cone blender, or by any other suitable method. To compound these additives with plastic pellets, the following steps should be followed:

(1) Charge a weighed amount of resin pellets into a clean tumbling drum. The resin charge should be 50–60% of the drum capacity.

(2) Add the specified amount of powder. An accurate balance or scale should be used to assure reproducibility of results.

(3) Tumble the resin-powder mixture for one hour at 30–40 rpm. End over end tumbling is preferred.

(4) If necessary, plastics drying can be done at this point in the procedure. Drying should be controlled to the temperature and time period specified by the plastics manufacturer. Drying temperatures of above 200°F, however, should be avoided. Drying at 160°F for 2–3 hr is adequate for most plastics.

(5) The tumbled resin is now ready for molding or extrusion. Transfer the resin to the processing equipment carefully, to minimize pigment separation.

(6) Most phototropic additives can withstand processing temperatures of up to 400°F for long periods without decomposition or loss in activity.

Accurate records should be kept of the resin type, the additive type, the additive-to-plastic weight ratio, drum size, charge size, tumbling speed and time, and processing cycle. This will assure the ability to duplicate results, since color control, as is the case with ordinary dye-stuffs, requires the batches to be processed in the identical manner.

Some additives are available mixed with plastic powder or flake, ready for processing. As such, processing can be accomplished by the method normally used to obtain mixing and intimate dispersion of plastics ingredients such as stabilizers and plasticizers.

Phototropic additives have been used with a wide variety of plastics. Included are polymethyl methacrylate and other acrylate derivatives, polystyrene, polyethylene, polypropylene, polyvinyl chloride, acetate and butyral, cellulose acetate, propionate and butyrate, polyesters, and mixtures and copolymers of these.

By now considerable experience and data have been collected on the effects of many variables on the performance of phototropic plastics. Some of these include light level, temperature and humidity, plastic type, plasticizer type and concentration, and the use of selected chemical additives.

Highly plasticized cellulose acetate additive formulation, will darken to about only 80% of normal value but it will recover about 25% faster at 50°F above room temperature. On the other hand, at 50°F below room temperature, the plastic will become about 25% darker than normal and the recovery rate will be slowed by more than 25%. The temperature effect can be reduced by lowering the plasticizer concentration and by the use of certain selected plasticizers. Also, the temperature dependence varies from plastic to plastic.

Phototropic materials have applications whenever a light induced dynamic change in transmittance of color is desired. These applications may be functional or decorative. Let us for a moment consider a transparent panel of phototropic plastic.

On exposure to bright light, a phototropic plastic acts as a "valve" which automatically adjusts itself to the light level. The depth of color varies with the intensity of the light received. This principle could be applied to sunglasses, sun shields, and windows for automobiles, airplanes, spacecrafts, homes and office buildings. These plastics might also be used for the construction of variable transmitance or translucent windows, skylights, or wall paneling to moderate the sunlight entering buildings on particularly bright days.

In a typical eyewear application, phototropic sunglasses darken within a few seconds in the presence of sunlight (or any bright light) to a level corresponding to the light intensity. When the light intensity is reduced to normal, the lenses automatically change back to their original transmitting state. Thus, the light reaching the eyes is automatically adjusted to a safe and comfortable level.

Sunglasses now available commercially provide a normal transmittance of about 65% under low level brightness conditions (below 1000 ft-candles) and adjust to a transmittance of about 20% under bright sunlight conditions (10,000–12,000 ft-candles). The time for reaction to its equilibrium transmitting condition in bright sunlight is about 15–30 sec. The recovery time to its normal transmitting state is about 2–3 min; but more than 50% recovery is obtained in under 1 min. Phototropic sunglasses in the near future will feature substantially increased recovery rate characteristics and it is anticipated that recovery times will be less than 30 sec.

In experimental work for the Ford Motor Company on a 1966 Mercury automobile, the glass in the upper windshield area and in the rear window was treated with the phototropic material. Although the treated glass in this case consisted of a resin coating on its surface, phototropic windshields in the future will be constructed with the additives incorporated into the laminate polyvinyl butyral film.

PAUL M. STEGINSKY

Cross-reference: ADDITIVES.

PHTHALIC ACIDS AND ANHYDRIDE

There are three isomeric phthalic acids, *ortho*, *meta* and *para*, as shown in the following structural formulas:

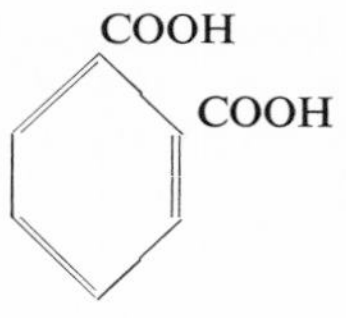

(*ortho*)
Phthalic Acid

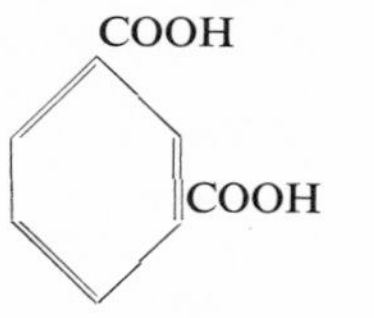

(*meta*)
Isophthalic Acid

(*para*)
Terephthalic Acid

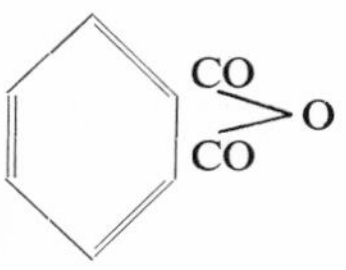

Phthalic Anhydride

The *ortho* acid is the more important commercially and is manufactured almost exclusively in the form of the anhydride. It is the only one of the acids, capable of forming the anhydride because its carboxyl groups are adjacent to each other for interaction. All three acids and the anhydride are white crystalline solids, and show properties characteristic of dicarboxylic acids, forming simple esters, mixed esters, polyesters, acid chlorides, acid amides and other carboxyl derivatives. In addition, substituted phthalic acids may be prepared by replacing the hydrogens of the benzene nucleus with chloro-, nitro-, sulfo-, amino- and other similar groups.

Until fairly recently only the ortho acid in the form of phthalic anhydride was produced commercially. With the advent of low cost, high purity xylene isomers from petroleum, it has been possible to produce the *meta* or isophthalic acid and the *para* or terephthalic acid from the corresponding *meta* and *para* xylenes by oxidation.

I. Phthalic Anhydride

The adjacent carboxyl groups of the *ortho* acid permit ready dehydration to the anhydride. Because of the relatively low melting point of the

water per molecule of anhydride in ester formation and similar reactions. It reacts almost instantaneously at moderate temperatures with most alcohols and glycols to form the corresponding mono- and di-esters of phthalic acid.

The physical properties of phthalic anhydride are shown in Table 1 below:

TABLE 1. PHYSICAL PROPERTIES OF PHTHALIC ANHYDRIDE.

M. Pt. °C	130.8°
B. Pt. °C	284.5
Density 4°C (solid)	1.527
Density 150°C (liquid)	1.197
Sp. heat 30°C	0.2627 cal/g /°C
Ht. fusion	5.48 kg-cal/mole
Ht. vaporization	12.91 kg-cal/mole

The chemical properties of phthalic anhydride are characteristic of the carboxyl groups, in forming acid derivatives and substituting the hydrogens of the benzene nucleus to form substituted phthalic anhydrides. Some of the typical derivatives of phthalic anhydride are discussed below:

Esters. Half esters, simple ester, mixed esters and polyesters may be formed in the reaction of phthalic anhydride with monohydric and polyhydric alcohols.

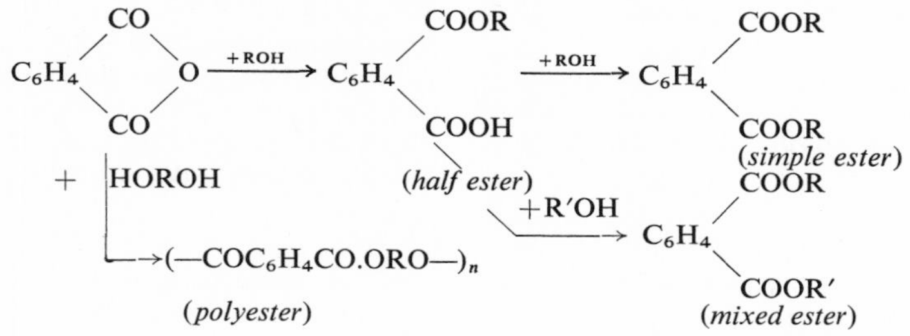

anhydride (131°C) it is often stored and shipped in the molten liquid form in tank cars and drums equipped with steam coils. It finds large uses in the manufacture of ester plasticizers, alkyd resins, pharmaceuticals, dyes and benzoic acid. Being an anhydride, it evolves only one molecule of

Acid Chloride is phthaloyl chloride C_6H_4<COCl COCl

which is formed by heating phthalic anhydride with phosphorous trichloride, pentachloride or other similar chlorinating agents.

Amides. The reaction of phthalic anhydride with ammonia gives rise to several types of amino acid products, depending on the mole ratio of ammonia to phthalic and the temperatures employed. The schematic diagram below, indicates the various amide products which may be formed:

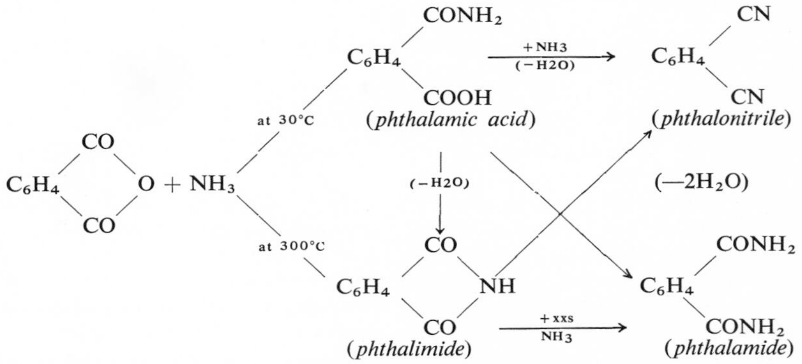

reaction of the phthalic anhydride with chlorine. At moderate temperatures using the molten anhydride and ferric chloride as the catalyst, dichorlorophthalic anhydride is obtained. At much higher temperature in the vapor phare, using antimony trichloride as the catalyst, the tetrachlorophthalic anhydride is the chief product.

Benzoic Acid is formed by the decarboxylation of the ortho acid, in the reaction of the anhydride with steam at elevated temperature, in the presence of a decarboxylating catalyst.

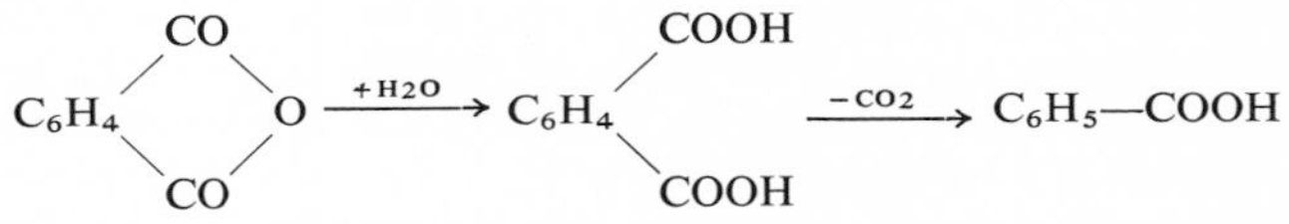

Phenolphthalein is the condensation product from the reaction of phthalic anhydride with two moles of phenol.

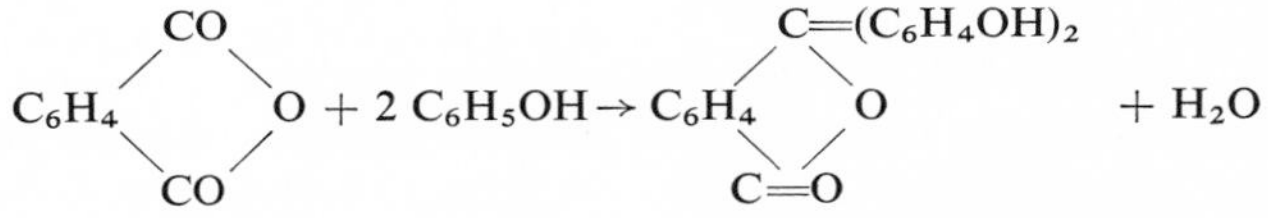

Similar reactions with other phenols yield phthaleins of a great variety. For example, thymol gives thymolphthalein and resorcinol gives fluorescein.

Anthraquinone is obtained from the intermediate product, *o*-benzoyl benzoic acid which is formed in the reaction of phthalic anhydride with benzene.

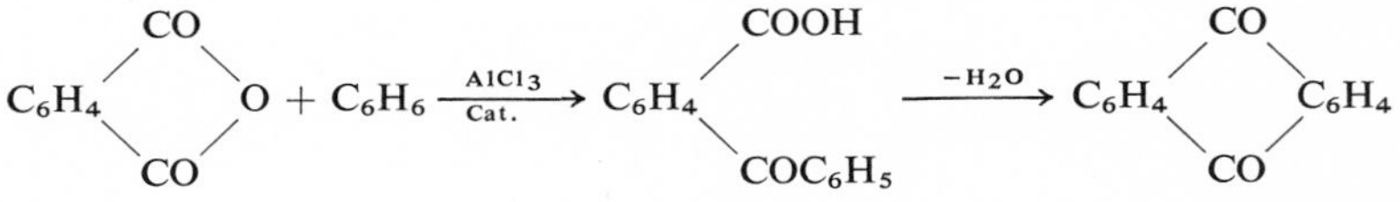

Likewise substituted anthraquimone derivatives may be formed using a substituted benzene such as chlorobenzene.

Chlorophthalic Anhydrides are formed in the

Manufacture of Phthalic Anhydride

Until 1950, most of the phthalic anhydride was produced by the catalytic air oxidation of pro-phthalene in vapor phase at 500°C over a vanadium pentoxide catalyst. More recently with an abundance of low cost high purity orthoxylene available from petroleum feed stocks, a considerable amount of the phthalic anhydride has also been obtained in a similar catalytic air oxidation process from sylene.

Naphthalene is first melted and then pumped to a vaporizer where it is volatilized with a current of preheated primary air and the resultant mixture diluted with secondary air in a mixing section to adjust the air-naphthalene ratio to 25 : 1 by weight. After preheating to 300°C it is passed over vanadium pentoxide catalyst coated on silica pellets and packed in a multi-tubular type

$$\text{(naphthalene)} \xrightarrow[\text{(V$_2$O$_5$ cat)}]{+4\frac{1}{2}O_2 \ \text{(air)}} C_6H_4 \begin{matrix} CO \\ \\ CO \end{matrix} O + C_6H_5COOH$$

(naphthalene)   (phthalic anhyd)   (benzoic acid)

$$\text{or} \quad \text{(orthoxylene)} \xrightarrow{+3 \ O_2} + \begin{matrix} CHCO \\ \\ CHCO \end{matrix} O + CO + CO_2 + H_2O$$

(orthoxylene)   (maleic anhyd.)

reactor. Although the heat of formation of the phthalic anhydride is only 1500 cal/lb of naphthalene, the actual heat of reaction is over 3000 cal/lb due to a considerable amount (20%) of complete combustion of the naphthalene. This excess heat must be removed in order to maintain control of the reaction temperatures by use of a suitable fluid heat-transfer medium at 500°C. Both mercury and molten salts (nitrate-nitrite) have been used in the shell of the reactor for this purpose.

From the converter the hot reaction gases are passed into a vapor cooler where the temperature is reduced to below the dew point (125–130°C) by the use of water, for the condensation of the crude phthalic anhydride product as a liquid melt. Exit gases from the vapor cooler are passed first to a naphtha scrubber for the removal of the maleic anhydride by-product and finally to a water scrubber to remove traces of acid gases and naphtha, before venting to the air.

The crude phthalic anhydride from the vapor cooler is purified by continuous fractionation in packed distillation columns under diminished pressure, giving a water white molten product of high purity of the following specifications:

Color of melt, A.P.H.A. Hazen Scale	50 max.
Solidification point	130.7°C min.
Total acid as phthalic	99.7% min.
Oxidizable material as maleic	0.15% max.
Ash	0.03 max.
Benzene turbidity in a 5% Solution	nil

An innovation in the naphthalene oxidation process in recent years has been the use of a fluidized catalyst bed. Air from the preheaters is passed into the bottom of the reactor containing the powdered catalyst consisting of vanadium oxide coated onto silica spheres. Melted naphthalene is sprayed directly into the bottom of the reactor where it vaporizes and mixes with the air. Consequently some of the fine powdered catalyst is carried out the reactor continuously in the overhead product stream and is recovered for recycling back to the reactor in cyclones and filters. Advantages to be claimed are 1) lower air ratios, 2) less explosion hazard, 3) lower and more uniform operating temperatures, 4) less labor and 5) higher purity of product.

The first of the production of phthalic anhydride from ortho-xylene occurred as early as 1946 but the final commercialization of the process for any appreciable production from this raw material did not take place until nearly ten years later. This came about with the discovery that other aromatic and paraffin hydrocarbon impurities in the ortho-xylene feed stock were completely oxidized to carbon dioxide and water. Thus a less pure more economical grade of ortho-xylene could be used. The main advantages of using ortho-xylene as the starting material are the lower air requirements and resulting lower heat generation, and the ease of vaporization, as compared with naphthalene, with no melting equipment required. Otherwise, much the same type of process equipment could be used and this has resulted in a change over of the naphthalene convertor units with only minor modifications for the use of ortho-xylene as the starting material.

Uses of Phthalic Anhydride

The remarkable growth in phthalic anhydride production during the past forty years or more has been due to the versatility in the use of this basic material for a great variety of products. First there was the dye stuff intermediates, which were developed during the nineteen twenties. These were followed by the dibutyl phthalate plasticizer era of the thirties and War II and the accompanying development of the phthalate alkyds during this same period. Although the latter has predominated for much of the phthalic utilization in recent years, the post War II era saw the development of the phthalate polyesters used for reinforced plastics applications. Also the newer phthalate plasticizer ester, dioctyl phthalate, which is used almost exclusively in the plasticizing of polyvinylchloride resins has been one of the big uses for phthalic anhydride in recent years. It is anticipated that both the use of phthalic anhydride in alkyd resins and polyvinyl resin plasticizers will continue to grow at even a greater rate and thus maintaining the ever increasing expansions in plant capacity for a greater production of this important chemical product.

The largest single use for phthalic anhydride is in the production of alkyd and polyester resins of a great variety. Combinations with glycols, glycerol, pentaerythritol and other polyhydric alcohols, with and without added drying or non-drying fatty acid glycerides has enhanced the use of phthalic anhydride in alkyd resin production.

A second large use for phthalic anhydride is the production of a large number of phthalate esters, by the reaction with monohydric alcohols, which find wide-spread application as plasticizers for various types of snythetic resins and plastics. The dioctyl phthalate [di(2-ethylhexyl) phthalate] known as D.O.P. in the plastics industry, is perhaps the biggest item among phthalate plasticizers. The dimethyl phthalate D.M.P. finds uses not only in plasticizer combinations with the cellulose ester plastics, but is also an effective insect repellent and is widely used in insect and fly sprays for this purpose. Diallyl phthalate is useful as a plasticizer and also as a crosslinking agent, since the allyl groups of this monomer can be used to couple with unsaturated linkages in other resin monomers or polymers. It can be polymerized by itself and forms one of the strongest of the crossed linked polyester resins, known in the trade as "DAPON."

Other uses for phthalic anhydride are in the production of dyes and dyestuff intermediates of various types. The most important of these is anthraquinone and anthraquinone dyes, from the intermediate o-benzoylbenzoic acid and derivatives, made from phthalic anhydride and benzene or substituted benzenes. The xanthene dyes and the phthalocynanine dyes are other examples of dyestuffs also derived from phthalic anhydride intermediates.

Another outlet for phthalic anhydride has been its use for the production of benzoic acid by the decarboxylation of the ortho acid. Until recent date, most of the benzoic acid was produced commercially from phthalic, but lately the development of the liquid phase oxidation of toluene has offered competition to phthalic for benzoic acid manufacture. Some small quantities of phthalic anhydride are used in pharmaceutical products such as phenolphthalein and sulfathalidine. Other minor uses include a variety of phthalate salts such as the copper lead, or cobalt salts of the half esters of phthalic, which are used as driers in paint and plastic compositions employing synthetic resins. Among the derivatives of phthalic anhydride are the chlorinated compounds such as the tetrachlorophthalic anhydride, whose esters find limited uses as plasticizers in plastic products, where flame retardancy is of major interest.

JAMES M. CHURCH

II. Isophthalic Acid

Isophthalic acid may be described as an aromatic dibasic acid. It is the 1, 3- or meta-phthalic acid isomer.

Isophthalic's largest outlets are alkyd resins for coatings, unsaturated polyesters for reinforced plastics, and high polymers for fibers and film.

The commercial significance of isophthalic (IP) can best be appreciated by comparing it to the other phthalic isomers, ortho-phthalic anhydride (PA) and terephthalic acid (TPA), in properties and uses.

PA has been available commercially for many years. TPA was second to be offered, and the third, IP, was introduced commercially in 1956. Isophthalic is priced intermediate between PA (lowest) and TPA.

Properties

Isophthalic is a high melting, low solubility, white crystalline powder. Some of its physical properties in comparison to those of phthalic anhydride (PA) and terephthalic acid (TPA) as shown in Table 1.

Linear PA polyesters would be more "kinked" than corresponding polymers of TPA or IP because of the position of its carbozylic acid groups. Evidence also indicates that PA forms a certain amount of cyclic intra-esters with glycols and polyols and cyclic imides with primary amines. For these reasons, it is not well suited for the preparation of high polymer esters or amides.

Cyclic intra-ester formation also results in a reduced effective functionality for PA in polyfunctional systems, such as coating alkyds.

By contrast, terephthalic acid is very high melting and relatively insoluble and is, therefore,

TABLE 1.

	Isophthalic acid	Phthalic anhydride	Terephthalic acid
Molecular weight	166.1	148.1	166.1
Equivalent weight	83	74	83
Commercial form	White, granular crystals	White flake or molten liquid	White, granular crystals
Melting point, °C	348	131	436
Acid number (theor.)	675	757	675
Hygroscopicity	No	Yes	No
Solubility (g/100 g)			
Water at 25°C	0.01	0.6	Very slightly soluble
at 200°C	25	Soluble	1
Xylene at 25°C	0.07	Soluble	0.04
at 130°C	0.1	Soluble	0.07

difficult to esterify by normal moderate techniques. Isophthalic is intermediate in these respects and, in fact, forms high quality unsaturated polyesters and alkyds. Neither IP nor TPA can form monomeric anhydrides. They are both capable of forming high molecular weight, linear polyesters —although TPA (including DMT) is the one used in greatest volume in these high polymers.

Chemistry

Isophthalic undergoes most reactions characteristic of organic carboxylic acids, such as esterification, amidation, acid chloride formation. In addition, it undergoes certain reactions of substitution or addition directly to the aromatic benzene nucleus.

Ester Formation

Isophthalic can be esterified using conventional techniques. With monofunctional alcohols, monomeric diesters are formed (Eq. 1). With diols (glycols), polyesters are produced (Eq. 2); high polymers result if suitable techniques are used. With polyols, such as glycerin or pentaerythritol, such as in formulating alkyds for coatings, branched chains are formed.

Esterification is by far the most widely used reaction of isophthalic in its major commercial applications—alkyds, unsaturated polyesters, polyester high polymers, and monomeric diesters.

Amide Formation

Isophthalic forms salts with ammonia and amines. The ammonia salt dehydrates to the amide and then to the nitrile which can be hydrogenated to the diamine, m-xylylenediamine (MXDA). The diamine can be further converted with phosgene to the diisocyanate. The isophthalic salts of diamines can be converted to the polyamides (Eq. 3).

$$+ 2R\text{—OH} \rightleftarrows \quad\quad + 2H_2O \quad\quad (\text{Eq. 1})$$

$$x \cdot IP + x \cdot HO\text{—R—OH} \rightleftarrows \quad\quad + (2x - 1)H_2O \quad (\text{Eq. 2})$$

$$x \cdot IP + x \cdot H_2N\text{—R—NH}_2 \rightleftarrows \quad\quad + (2x - 1)H_2O \quad (\text{Eq. 3})$$

Formation of Anhydride

Because of the spatial configuration of the two carboxylic acid groups in isophthalic acid, it is impossible for the intramolecular anhydride to form as it does with *ortho*-phthalic acid. However, with acetic anhydride, a linear intermolecular anhydride forms.

Formation of Acid Halides

Isophthalyl halides are prepared by reaction with acetyl halide, phosphorous oxyhalide or pentahalides. Thionyl chloride produces isophthalyl dichloride.

Formation of Hydrogenation Products

Reduction of isophthalic by electrolysis produces *m*-xylyleneglycol and a hydrogenated acid. Sodium amalgam reduction gives the tetrahydro acid.

Formation of Substitution Products

Halogenation of isophthalic in fuming sulfuric acid gives the tetrahalogen derivatives.

5-Nitroisophthalic acid is formed by nitration with fuming nitric acid.

Sulfonation with SO_3 in fuming sulfuric acid gives isophthalic-5-sulfonic acid.

Supply and Demand

The Oronite Chemical Company introduced isophthalic commercially in 1956. Amoco Chemicals entered the picture about three years later.

An acute shortage of phthalic anhydride in 1959–60 accelerated the commercialization of many alkyd and polyester products based on isophthalic.

Present plant capacity for the manufacture of isophthalic is difficult to assign because there is considerable capacity that can be used to produce either IP or TPA, as required. However, a rough estimate of isophthalic capacity (Chevron and Amoco) in 1965 might be 75–100 million lb per year. Usage in 1965 is estimated to have been in the neighborhood of 50–60 million lb.

Rapid growth is projected for isophthalic in high polymers. Continued growth is also expected in unsaturated polyesters and specialty alkyds.

Manufacture

Isophthalic acid is prepared by oxidation of *meta*-xylene:

meta-Xylene is derived from petroleum. Oxidation processes based on different oxidants, promoters, media and operating conditions have been disclosed in the patent and trade literature.

Applications

Alkyds. The largest early growth of isophthalic was in oil-modified alkyds for coatings. Alkyds are used widely in a full range of coatings—exterior house and trim paints, interior gloss and flat paints, maintenance and equipment primers and enamels, automotive and appliance finishes, and many other varied paints and varnishes. Most alkyds are combinations of a natural vegetable oil (either drying or non drying; examples are linseed, soyabean, and coconut oils), a polyol such as glycerin or pentaerythritol, and a dibasic acid such as PA or IP.

Other modifiers—such as a glycol, a monobasic acid, or rosin—are often used.

Direct comparison between IP and PA in alkyds is difficult because these two acids cannot be directly interchanged without altering the over-all formulation. For example, if equal moles of IP were substituted for the PA in a phthalic alkyd, the product would "gel" (cross-link to a non-useful state) in the reaction kettle before reaching an acceptably low acid number. Because of this higher "effective" functionality of isophthalic, its alkyds must be formulated at a higher mole ratio polyol/IP (generally in range 1.12 ± 0.05) than the corresponding PA formulation (about 1.0, sometimes less).

The "iso-alkyd" counterpart is generally 5–10% longer in oil length. (Alkyd formulating principles and preparative techniques are beyond the scope of this article.)

"Iso-alkyds" often possess a better combination of air-drying rate and hardness, along with flexibility, impact resistance, and abrasion resistance. In certain formulations, they exhibit better exterior durability as denoted by gloss and color retention. They often also possess better resistance to water and other corrosives.

Isophthalic is used in alkyds covering the entire range of oil length and type—alkyd oils (very long), long oil alkyds, medium oil alkyds, and short oil alkyds. One formulation example for each class is given in Table 2. In the medium and short oil ranges, isophthalic is particularly effective in providing an excellent combination of fast dry, hardness, impact resistance, and gloss.

Isophthalic is better suited than PA for making the very long oil "alkyd oils" which find use in house paints and printing inks. This preference is due to the greater effective functionality and greater stability of IP at the very high oil-bodying temperatures required to achieve the desired viscosity. In exterior house paints these "Iso-oils" are more resistant and durable than conventional

TABLE 2. TYPICAL ISO-ALKYD FORMULATIONS.

Oil length: type enamel:	Short appliance (baked)	Medium 4-hr mach. and maint.	Long general-purpose ext. wood and metal	Iso-oil ext. wood house
Coconut oil, refined	330			
Soyabean oil, nonbreak			700	
Safflower oil, nonbreak		550		
Tall oil fatty acids (<2% rosin)				803
Glycerin, 100%		165		
Trimethylolethane	316			
Pentaerythritol, tech.			120	156
Litharge	0.5	0.2	0.5	
Isophthalic	450	364	230	116
Total	1096	1079	1050	1075
Theor. water	96	79	50	75
Theor. yield	1000	1000	1000	1000
Solvent	Xylene	Min. spts.	Min. spts.	—
Viscosity	Z_2–Z_4	Z–Z_2	Z_2	Z_2–Z_4
% Solids	50	50	70	100
Acid No. (solids)	10–15	7–13	5–8	4–7

linseed oil house paints, yet they are flexible enough not to fail by embrittlement with cracking and peeling.

Polyesters. Unsaturated polyesters are widely used in fiberglass-reinforced plastics (FRP or "fiberglass" products). Among these are sports car bodies, boats, translucent building panels, corrosion-resistant equipment, seating, trays, skis, etc. In non-reinforced applications, polyesters are used in making imitation pearl buttons, synthetic marble, tile-like finishes, repair putties, and as casting resins by both the electrical and hobby industries.

Polyesters are prepared by esterification of a combination of unsaturated dibasic acids (such as maleic anhydride or fumaric acid) and saturated acid (PA, IP, and/or adipic) with a dialcohol (glycol or "diol") to form a linear resinous polyester. This material is then diluted in a vinyl monomer (such as styrene). Upon later initiation of "cure" by organic peroxides, the monomer copolymerizes with the maleic unsaturation in the polyester chain to convert the viscous liquid to a hard, thermoset material. (A detailed description of polyester formulations, mechanisms, and methods of manufacture is beyond the scope of this article.)

In unsaturated polyesters, isophthalic gives a higher molecular weight product which exhibits greater impact resistance or toughness, greater chemical resistance, and greater heat resistance than phthalic anhydride. With IP, a product with a higher "balance of properties" is obtained. IP finds large use in polyesters for fiberglass auto bodies, chemical-resistant products and linings, gel coats, body putties, and patching compounds.

Examples of formulations representing rigid, high-impact, and semi-flexible "isopolyesters" are given in Table 3.

High Polymers

The best known example of a linear polyester high polymer is poly(ethylene terephthalate), the polycondensation product of ethylene glycol and either dimethyl terephthalate or terephthalic acid. Its uses in the forms of textile fibers ("Dacron," "Fortrel") and film ("Mylar") are well known. Isophthalic can be incorporated in similar polyesters to beneficially modify properties desired for certain applications.

Isophthalic can also be used alone or in combination with other dibasic acids to make high molecular weight polyamides (i.e., nylons). For example, such polyamide copolymers based on hexamethylenediamine have softening points, toughness and impact strength in the range required for industrial molding resins.

Metaxylylenediamine (MXDA) can be made from isophthalic by the classical route: organic acid → ammonium salt → amide → nitrile → amine. The polyamide from MXDA and adipic acid exhibits fiber properties of considerable interest.

Reaction of MXDA with phosgene gives metaxylylene diisocyanate (MXDI), which can be used to form urethane polymers.

High molecular weight ethylene glycol polyesters of mixtures of isophthalic and aliphatic dibasic acids, such as adipic or azelaic acid, are tough and rubbery and can be used to form urethane elastomers by further reaction with diisocyanates.

TABLE 3. TYPICAL ISOPOLYESTER FORMULATIONS.

	Rigid		High impact		Semi-flexible	
	Mole ratios	lb per 1000 lb theor. yield	Mole ratios	lb per 1000 lb theor. yield	Mole ratios	lb per 1000 lb theor. yield
Isophthalic	1.0	454	3.0	355	1.0	260
Maleic anhydride	1.0	268				
Fumaric acid			4.0	331	1.0	181
Adipic acid					1.0	228
Propylene glycol	2.05	426				
Diethylene glycol			5.6	424	3.015	500
Ethylene glycol			1.58	70		
Total		1146		1180		1169
Theor. water		146		180		169
Theor. yield		1000		1000		1000
Hydroquinone (inhibitor)		0.2		0.2		0.2
Styrene		667		425		425
Acid No. (solids)		15–20		15–20		15–20
Viscosity (Gardner-Holdt)		X–Y		Z–Z$_1$		Y–Z
% styrene		40		30		30

Tough, moldable polycarbonates can be made from isophthalic and bisphenol A. Isophthalic can also be used to modify the more conventional polycarbonates based on phosgene and bisphenol A.

High temperature polybenzimidazoles are made from diphenylisophthalate (derived from IP) and tetraaminobiphenyl.

The over-all field of high polymers is considered to be one of the greatest growth areas for isophthalic in coming years.

Other Uses

Plasticizers. Di-2-ethylhexyl isophthalate, commonly called dioctyl isophthalate or DOIP, is a plasticizer for polyvinyl chloride (PVC) resins. DOIP has lower volatility and exhibits greater resistance to lacquer marring than the more widely used dioctyl phthalate, DOP.

Allyl Ester Monomers and Polymers. Diallyl isophthalate (DAIP) is used as a low volatility monomer for unsaturated polyesters where high heat resistance is desired. Polymers of DAIP are operable at higher temperatures than the corresponding polymers of diallyl phthalate, DAP.

Isophthalic is also used in alkyds, polyesters, and urethanes designed specifically for wire enamels, varnishes, and adhesives for the electrical industry.

DONALD G. HUGGINS

III. Terephthalic Acid.
See Dimethyl Terephthalate and Terephthalic Acid.

PIGMENTS, EXTENDER

The major function of extender pigments (or more accurately, bulk fillers) is to extend the polymer—to lower compound costs by adding a relatively inexpensive filler to an expensive resin.

The term "pigment" is often somewhat erroneously applied to such filler and extender materials as mineral powders, fibers, and the variety of ground natural organic materials used chiefly in thermosets.

Although the emphasis is on the cost factor in some instances an extender makes a substantial contribution to improved processing or physical properties of the plastic compound. Calcined clay in PVC, for example, enhances electrical resistivity; epoxy resin adhesives require precipitated calcium silicate to attain suitable application viscosity; fine particle silica reduces blocking of polyethylene film. Other contributions of extender pigments in plastics include opacifying, weather resistance (titanium dioxide and carbon black), flame-proofing (antimony oxide), heat resistance, and improved processing properties for calendering, extrusion, and molding.

However, in only a few cases do extender pigments reinforce plastics in terms of large increases in tear, abrasion, and tensile strengths. It is because of this that extender pigments for plastics include materials such as precipitated silica and calcium silicate which in the field of rubber technology would be considered quite separately from relatively inert fillers.

In the absence of any major improvement in a plastic's physical properties, a suitable extender pigment must be evluated by negative criteria. In other words, a material is desired which will reduce costs without detracting from the plastic's desirable basic properties. This condition has proved to be a severe limitation so that in commercial practice there are only two polymer types—vinyls and polyesters—in which substantial amounts of extender pigments can be used. In other cases, particularly polyolefins and polystyrenes, the loss of physical properties (such as flexibility or impact strength) due to the presence of extenders cannot be tolerated.

A typical situation, for polystyrene, is illustrated in Table 1. Here only ground whiting did

TABLE 1. EXTENDER PIGMENTS IN POLYSTYRENE.

Extender, 20 phr loading	Notched impact strength, ft lb/in.	Tensile strength, psi
None	0.8	12,300
Ground whiting	0.8	12,100
Precipitated calcium silicate	0.3	8,300
Precipitated silica	0.3	7,700

not degrade physical properties. The precipitated pigments reduced tensile and impact strengths by over 50%.

Types of Extender Pigments

The major extenders are clay and calcium carbonate and each appears in a wide variety of types. Other extenders include aluminum hydrate, barium sulfate (barytes), calcium silicate (natural and precipitated), calcium sulfate (gypsum), diatomaceous earth, lithopone, magnesium silicate (asbestine and talc), mica, silica (ground and precipitated), slate flour, and zinc oxide.

Calcium Carbonate

It is seen that the two principal forms of calcium carbonate, ground or precipitated, differ mainly in particle size, surface area, and price. Dry ground calcium carbonate is probably the cheapest extender available for plastics or rubbers. It is made by grinding soft limestone and is frequently a by-product of the building stone and agricultural industries. Water ground whiting is made with more uniformity, less foreign matter, whiter color and smaller particle size because of the water floating and classification involved in its manufacture.

Although the term "whiting" is now used somewhat indiscriminately to describe any ground calcium carbonate, it originally applied only to ground chalk. This material is easier to grind than limestone and often provides smaller particle sizes. The oyster shell calcium carbonate (aragonite) has particles with platy rather than spherical shape, which in some cases leads to improved extrusion properties.

The precipitated calcium carbonates are all made by reacting a milk of lime suspension with carbon dioxide, soda ash, or ammonium chloride and soda ash. Reaction variations in temperature, time, and concentration allow the production of a range of particle sizes and surface areas. Coatings of tall oil, coconut oil, and fatty acids are frequently used to provide improved ease of mixing and processing.

Kaolin Clay. This offers an equally wide range of extender pigments for plastics compounding. Chemically all kaolins are hydrated aluminum silicate produced in nature by the weathering of feldspar and mica; variations in particle size or or purification provide the differentiation found in the following types:

	$\% < 2\mu$	$\% > 5\mu$
Hard clay	87–92	3–5
Soft clay	50–55	25–30
Calcined clay	—	—

The designations "hard" and "soft" relate to rubber properties; a hard clay provides more reinforcement and stiffening in elastomers than does a soft clay. Calcined clays have been processed at high temperatures to remove water of hydration and volatile salts which restrict regular

TABLE 2. TYPES OF CALCIUM CARBONATE.

Form	Sp. gr.	Particle size, μ	Surface area, M^2/g	Price, ¢/lb
I. Natural				
(A) Limestone whiting				
(1) Dry ground	2.71	5–30	1–5	1/2
(2) Wet ground	2.71	0.5–10	2–10	1 1/2
(B) Chalk whiting	2.70	0.2–10		
(C) Oyster shells	2.70	1.5		
II. Precipitated				
(A) Untreated	2.65	0.1	20–26	3–6
(B) Coated		0.04–0.1		4–8
(C) Ultra-fine particle size	2.55	0.04	30–35	6–8

types from electrical insulation uses. Ultimate particles are plate-like and hexagonal in shape.

Silicas and Calcium Silicate. Both are used as extenders in two markedly distinct forms:

	Particle size, μ	BET Surface area, M²/g
(1) Fine particle silicas		
Precipitated (Hi-Sil);	.022	140–160
Fumed (Cab-O-Sil)	.015	190
(2) Ground silicas	5–20	1–5

Properties in Relation to Compounding

Particle size and its corollary, surface area, are the most significant properties of extenders in respect to their use in plastics compounding. The preferred range for particle diameters appears to be between 0.1 and 5μ. Materials smaller than 0.1μ tend towards difficult dispersion; fine particle calcium carbonates, in particular, are prone to aglomeration and caking during mixing. Coating the pigment with 2 or 3% fatty acid, tall oil or metallic soap helps to remedy these processing deficiencies. Above a particle diameter of 5μ the decline in physical properties such as abrasion or scratch resistance is prohibitive.

Surface area (measured by BET nitrogen absorption or oil absorption) is inversely proportional to particle size for nonporous pigments. It is a property of prime importance in liquid systems such as polyesters, DAP, epoxies, or plastisols and in plasticized compounds.

In liquid systems surface absorption controls viscosity; wherever plasticizers are present, surface absorption reduces flexibility. Coated pigments show lower absorption effects for equal particle size. These factors are discussed further in the following sections on PVC and polyester compounding.

Specific gravity in its relation to cost reduction is an important consideration in the use of extenders. In any situation where raw materials are purchased on a weight basis and the product sold on a volume or number basis, specific gravity is a major economic factor. Obviously, higher gravity compounds provide fewer finished molded items or feet of extrusions. Since the gravities of extender pigments are all two to three times those of resins, the use of any extender at all must result in a higher compound gravity. Thus, cost advantages gained by the use of extenders are frequently lower than a simple price-per-weight calculation would indicate. A comparison of extenders on a cost basis ought only to be made by multiplying pound price times specific gravity.

TABLE 3. EXTENDER PIGMENTS IN PLASTICIZED PVC.

Base Formula

PVC Resin	100
Dioctyl Phthalate	50
Stabilizer	2
Extender	10–20–40

Type of extender and particle size	PHR	Tensile, psi	Elongation, %	100% Modulus, psi	Hardness, shore A	Tear, lb/in.
None		2880	330	1500	85	500
Fine particle precipitated silica (.022μ)						
	10	2760	260	1780	90	540
	20	3010	220	2270	93	560
	40	3210	120	3050	96	610
Precipitated calcium carbonate (.100μ)						
	10	2970	300	1580	87	510
	20	2820	300	1530	87	490
	40	2650	260	1800	90	530
Water ground whiting (3μ)						
	10	2990	340	1500	89	520
	20	3010	310	1630	90	550
	40	2980	220	2280	95	600
Medium particle precipitated silica (.080μ)						
	10	2920	310	1700	90	550
	20	2920	270	2050	93	610
	40	2480	240	2130	93	600
Ground calcium silicate (Wollastonite) (10μ)						
	10	2710	300	1520	89	500
	20	2730	310	1530	88	500
	40	2300	300	1230	85	420

The importance of chemical composition of extender pigments resides in the nature of the impurities rather than in the pigment itself. Soluble salts, for example, are detrimental to electrical properties. Thus only clays which have been purified by thorough washing or calcining are suitable for use in PVC insulations. An equally important consideration regarding impurities is their effect on catalyst reactivity and stability. For example, in polyester premix compositions it is often necessary, in comparing various extenders, to adjust the type and amount of catalyst to maintain the desired storage life. This assumes that impurities are a constant and integral part of the extender. Thus, uniformity in terms of both minor and major constituents is a basic requirement for acceptable extender pigments.

PVC Compounding with Extenders

The performance of extender pigments in vinyl chloride polymers and copolymers follows the general behavior previously described. Table 3 summarizes the results of a loading study of several calcium carbonates and precipitated silicas in plasticized PVC. The lack of any significant reinforcement (in tensile or tear) regardless of particle size is apparent. The small increases which have occurred are generally accompanied by increased hardness and stiffness. This indicates reduction in plasticizing efficiency rather than reinforcement, and reflects the absorption of plasticizer by filler.

Plasticizer absorption must be countered—to maintain flexibility—by the addition of more plasticizer, and the resulting cost increase mitigates the original cost advantage provided by an extender. For this reason, low absorption is a prime requirement for extenders. Table 4 illustrates the variation among extenders in their plasticizer requirements. This same phenomenon

TABLE 4. PLASTICIZER ABSORPTION BY FILLERS.

Filler type, 100 phr	Plasticizer to give equal hardness, phr
Precipitated calcium carbonate	25
Ground whiting	20
China clay	35
Calcium silicate	45
Carbon black	65

in relation to plastisol compounding is discussed below.

In terms of *processing*, that is, calendering, extrusion and molding operations, a number of valuable contributions are provided by extenders in PVC. For example,

(1) Extrusion rates of garden hose and similar products are increased by 10–20 phr of precipitated, coated calcium carbonate (0.1μ particle size range).

(2) Plate-out (pigment film on mill and calender rolls) can be reduced by aluminum oxide.

(3) Blocking (self-adhesion) of PVC film and sheeting at the calender is avoided by 3–10 phr of fine particle silica.

(4) Trimming and cutting of translucent vinyl compounds are achieved at higher production rates and with improved appearance by 10–20 phr of precipitated fine particle silica.

Film and Sheeting. Both employ either low amounts of extenders, or none at all. The extender function here is essentially one of quality rather than cost reduction. For example, automotive upholstery requires a uniform non-gloss (matte) surface finish. This is obtained from small amounts (3–8 phr) of fine particle calcium silicate or silica.

Vinyl Tile. This furnishes a special case of a very highly extended plastic compound. In this product the stiffening and hardening effects of extender addition are of real benefit to perfor-

TABLE 5. EXTENDER PIGMENTS IN PVC COMPOUNDS.

Typical Formulations*

	VA tile	Homogeneous tile	Hose and gasket	Calendered sheeting	Upholstery, unsupported	Wire insulation
PVC polymer or copolymer	100	100	100	100	100	100
Plasticizers	35	40	90	44	46	55
Water ground whiting	125	75	50	35	10	—
Precipitated calcium carbonate	—	—	25	—	—	15
Calcined clay	—	—	—	—	—	15
Hard clay	—	75	—	—	—	—
Soft clay	100	—	—	—	—	—
Asbestos 7 R	100	—	—	—	—	—

* Excluding stabilizers, lubricants, colors, etc.

mance as they provide indentation resistance, hardness, and dimensional stability. Adequate abrasion or scuff resistance requires that extender particle size be less than 5μ. Typical formulas for tile and other compounds which contain extenders are listed in Table 5.

PVC Plastisols

Although extender pigments are used in plastisols to provide cost reductions, they have an additional and important function in controlling the viscosity of the liquid phase, chiefly through plasticizer absorption. Particle size and surface area are critical pigment properties here. Oil absorption tests are frequently used to evaluate the ability of extenders to effect viscosity changes. High oil absorption extenders provide high thixotropy.

The most effective viscosity increasing extenders are the fine particle silicas and precipitated calcium silicate (Silene EF). Table 6 compares several

TABLE 6. EXTENDERS FOR PVC PLASTISOLS.

Pigment	Oil absorption, g/100 g oil
Ground calcium carbonates	20–40
Precipitated calcium carbonates	40–60
Calcined clays	50–70
Precipitated calcium silicate	80–120
Fine particle silicas	120–160

extenders for plastisols listed in order of increased effect on viscosity.

Polyester Compounding with Extenders

The extender pigment contribution to cost reduction in polyesters is almost matched by numerous benefits obtained in the processing properties of the pre-mix and prepreg phases. The liquid phase operations of mixing, curing, and molding depend heavily on extenders for improvements which include:

(1) Viscosity control to insure proper mold flow and pressure.

(2) Reduce exothermic heat during cure.

(3) Reduce porosity and internal stress.

(4) Reduce shrinkage and crazing.

(5) Improve surface smoothness and gloss.

The effects of fillers on physical properties are much the same as those described for PVC and other plastics. Tensile is lowered, compressive strength rises slightly, flexural strength and modulus remain relatively constant.

Major extenders types are clays and calcium carbonates. A wide variety of other useful materials include silicas, slate flour, talc, alumina, mica,

pumice, gypsum, barytes, vermiculite and diatomaceous earth.

Thermal properties, particularly low expansion coefficients, are improved by all extenders and the improvement is proportional to the amount used. Certain materials are preferred to obtain specific properties:

Electrical insulation	Mica
	Ground silica
	Calcined clay
High temperature resistance	Clay
	Ground silica
	Talc
Moisture resistance	Ground silica
	Clay

Extender requirements center around the necessity of adding large amounts of filler—loadings of 60% are not uncommon—without undue increases in viscosity. As was previously discussed for plasticized PVC and plastisols, this absorption behavior is directly related to particle size and surface area. The lower limit of particle size which avoids excessive viscosity increase is near 0.1μ; above an upper limit of 5μ physical and processing properties deteriorate. Fine particle silicas (precipitated and fumed) and precipitated calcium silicate with particle sizes in the 0.015–0.030μ range are used only in small amounts for thixotropic effects alone.

Other plastics

Compounding epoxies with extenders follows much the same lines described for polyesters. Ground silica is the preferred general purpose filler since high loadings do not raise viscosity excessively. Calcium carbonate and talc are restricted to lower loadings but provide improved machinability.

Although phenolics employ more organic than mineral loading, clay and mica provide heat and chemical resistance and mica improves electrical properties.

Polyethylene makes little or no use of extenders but approximately 1% of fine particle precipitated silica is used to reduce blocking in extruded film. Cross-linked polyethylene sometimes contains 60–100 phr of medium thermal (MT) carbon black.

N. L. HEWITT

PIGMENTS, WHITE

White hiding pigments are finely divided solids, insoluble in the medium in which they are used, which nonselectively reflect and diffuse visible light. These pigments have substantial opacity and whitening value when thoroughly dispersed.

The ideal white pigment must reflect and diffuse equally well all the wavelengths of visible light. It should retain this property under all normal conditions for an indefinite period of time. It should also be economical to use—that is, it should have good covering power, which means both high opacity and high tinting strength. In addition, it should be of a fine particle size and not protrude above the binder film and thus impair the gloss.

The substance should be chemically inert, free from soluble salts, insoluble in all media used, and unaffected by normal temperatures. It should be easily dispersed, nontoxic, and with low oil-absorption characteristics. As outlined below, titanium dioxide pigments fulfill all these requirements best of all of the known white hiding pigments.

Titanium Dioxide Pigments

Titanium dioxide pigments are the most important prime white pigments in use today. They are manufactured in two crystalline forms—rutile, with a refractive index of 2.71, and anatase, with a refractive index of 2.55. The difference is manifested in a much closer packing of the atoms in the rutile crystal as compared with the anatase. This close packing of atoms is part of the basis for its higher refractive index. Rutile has 20–30% more hiding power than anatase. Because of their inertness, brightness, high hiding power, fineness, ease of dispersion, etc., titanium dioxide pigments are used in many industries and end products, including paint, paper, floor coverings, printing inks, plastics, rubber, roofing granules, textile fibers, cement, ceramics, cosmetics, shoe polish, welding rods, cutting oils, sunburn and flash-burn creams, and metal and glass polish.

Besides the rutile and anatase forms, there are the "extended" titanium dioxide pigments composed of rutile titanium dioxide and 70 or 50% anhydrous calcium sulfate (anhydrite). The primary advantage of the extended titanium pigments is their low cost combined with high quality, although the nonflexibility of composition is often considered a disadvantage. With every 70 or 50 lb of calcium sulfate, one must purchase and use 30 or 50 lb of rutile titanium dioxide. As extender manufacturers further improve the quality of their products, the specific advantages of titanium calcium pigments diminish. Further, calcium sulfate is slightly soluble and may cause stability and crystallization difficulties if used in water-thinned paints. At present there are about 30 anatase and 60 rutile grades manufactured by the seven American producers. Many grades have been developed for specific uses so that it is necessary to use the correct grade instead of seeking an all-purpose type.

Lead Pigments (White)

Basic Carbonate White Lead. Basic carbonate white lead is the oldest white pigment in current use. It was known at least as early as 400 B.C. Its composition is usually given as $2PbCO_3 \cdot Pb(OH)_2$. Actual composition is much more complex, being a mixture of basic carbonates and normal lead carbonate. Manufacturing techniques have been developed so that composition and particle size can be controlled to produce tailor-made grades.

With the development first of lithopone and second of titanium dioxide the use of basic carbonate white lead as a prime hiding pigment in paints has declined. Today there is only a small amount of lead pigments used in oil pastes and paints. Relatively small amounts are used in combination with other pigments in the manufacture of house paints.

Basic Sulfate White Lead. Basic sulfate white lead was developed in the mid-nineteenth century. It is represented approximately by the chemical formula $2PbSO_4 \cdot PbO$. It resembles basic lead carbonate in many of its properties. Since it was easier to manufacture it was often substituted for the basic carbonate. Practically all present production is used either in house paints or as the basic lead sulfate portion of blended zinc oxides.

Basic Silicate White Lead. The newest of the basic lead pigments is basic silicate of white lead. It is intended for use in multiple-pigment exterior paints in combination with other pigments. It may be substituted for basic carbonate white lead, basic sulfate white lead, and the basic sulfate portion of leaded zinc oxide. Commercial grades of basic silicate of white lead contain either 48% of 84% PbO. Basic silicate white lead is being recommended for use in exterior latex paints. The unique chemical and physical properties of basic silicate white lead provide a means of controlling staining by tannins and other water-soluble materials present in wood. About $1\frac{1}{2}$ lb of basic silicate white lead are used in the formulation of latex primers and top coats, especially the primer, where cedar or redwood staining is the problem.

Zinc Pigments (White)

Zinc Oxide Pigments. Zinc oxide pigments are produced lead-free or leaded—that is, blended or co-fumed with basic lead sulfate. Zinc oxide has complete opacity to ultraviolet rays with wavelengths of less than 3600 Å. It protects a paint film by converting the short waves to heat, which tends to minimize film deterioration. Zinc oxide neutralizes the vehicle decomposition acids. This buffering action may be helpful in prolonging the life of exposed films. It is also used in oil-type house paint to control mold.

Leaded Zinc Oxides. Leaded zinc oxides, first introduced to the paint industry about 1896, are available in at least five different types—50%,

35%, 20%, 18%, and 12%, the figure referring to the amount of basic lead sulfate combined with the zinc oxide in the pigment. The paint industry consumes practically all of the production of leaded zinc oxide.

Lithopone. Lithopone was a very important white pigment in the early 1900's, but in the United States it has been largely replaced by titanium dioxide. Lithopone is a mixture of approximately 29% zinc sulfide and 71% barium sulfate made by the double decomposition of zinc sulfate and barium sulfide. The pigment derives its hiding power from the zinc sulfide, as the $BaSO_4$ is essentially without hiding power. Lithopone has decreased in importance because of its unfavorable cost/hiding-power ratio.

Antimony Oxide Pigment. Before the development of chalk-resistant rutile titanium dioxide pigments, a considerable amount of antimony oxide pigment was used in automotive enamels to retard the chalking of anatase. Today it is used in many of the fire-retardant paint formulations to increase flame retardancy. Antimony oxide is also used in the plastics industry, in porcelain enamel frits, and in glass as a decolorizer.

WILLARD H. MADSON

PLASTICIZERS

The first use of a plasticizer was in the 1860's when Parks and Hyatt used camphor to plasticize cellulose nitrate. Later, cellulose nitrate was plasticized to make motion picture film in 1882. The commercial use of the vinyl resins was delayed until tricresyl phosphate was used to plasticize polyvinyl chloride in 1930. Today, over 1 billion pounds of organic plasticizers are produced annually. About 70% of the total production is used for the plasticization of polyvinyl resins alone.

As shown in the accompanying figures, cross-linked or thermosetting plastics are rigid because the polymer chains are bonded together. Some thermoplastic polymers such as polyethylene are flexible because of the ability of the polymer chains to slide by each other. In contrast, thermoplastic polymers with strong polar groups, like polyvinyl chloride, lack flexibility because of the presence of strong attractive forces which prevent the chains from moving independently from each other. These secondary valences, or Van der Waals' forces, are unaffected by temperature. When the temperature is raised, the kinetic energy is increased and this aids in overcoming the attractive forces. However, some decomposition occurs when the temperature of polyvinyl chloride is increased sufficiently to provide flexibility and processibility.

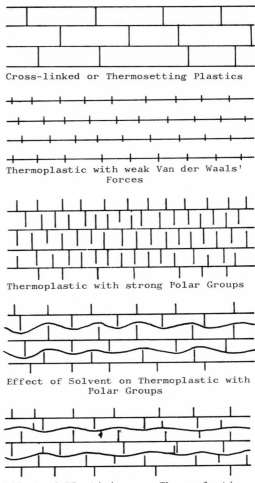

Cross-linked or Thermosetting Plastics

Thermoplastic with weak Van der Waals' Forces

Thermoplastic with strong Polar Groups

Effect of Solvent on Thermoplastic with Polar Groups

Effect of Plasticizer on Thermoplastic with Polar Groups

FIG. 1.

As shown by the bottom figure, the addition of appropriate plasticizers reduces the Van der Waals' forces so that the product may be readily processed below its decomposition temperature. Dioctyl phthalate, one of the most versatile compounds of this type, accounts for almost 25% of the total plasticizer production. In the past, isooctyl alcohol was used for the production of this ester for economical reasons. However, straight chained alcohols are now produced economically from the oxo process. Esters from these alcohols yield plasticized products with superior low temperature properties.

Esters of phosphoric acid such as tricresyl phosphate make up about 10% of the plasticizer production. Esters of adipic acid are the principal aliphatic plasticizers, but they contribute only about 7% to the plasticizer market. The total production of aliphatic plasticizers is less than 30% of the entire plasticizer production.

The effectiveness of a plasticizer is dependent on the relative polarity of the polymer and the plasticizer. Plasticizer efficiency may be determined from solubility parameters as measured by the temperature at which the resin-plasticizer mixture develops suitable strength characteristics. Other tests are based on the time required for the resin-plasticizer mixture to develop torque in a mechanical mixer.

Plasticizer efficiency is defined as the amount of plasticizer required to provide a desired degree of flexibility. Plasticizers must be compatible with the resin and the acquired properties must be retained during the life of the plastic product. The long time acceptance of plasticized polyvinyl butyral in shatterproof glass and the desirable properties of quality vinyl upholstery, tile and film serve to demonstrate the optimum properties that are obtainable in plasticized products.

A typical plasticized vinyl plastic will consist of about 35% weight of plasticizer. Several different plasticizers may be used in order to obtain the optimum properties desired in the end product.

Chlorinated biphenyl and tricresyl phosphate provide flame resistant properties. Esters of adipic and sebacic acids yield plasticized products which retain flexibility at lower temperatures. Resins plasticized with alkyl diphenyl phosphates or epoxidized oils have superior resistance to outdoor exposure.

Linear polyesters produced from ethylene glycol and dibasic acids are polymeric plasticizers, and are not readily extracted by soap and detergents. These products are available in various molecular weight ranges.

Properties of Typical Plasticizers

Plasticizers	D_{25}	N_{25}	B.P.,°C atm.
Di-*n*-octyl phthalate	0.978	1.482	225–250 (5 mm)
Tricresyl phosphate	1.136	1.554	265
Di(2-ethylhexyl) adipate	0.927	1.446	214
Epoxidized soybean oil	0.966	1.472	150+

Classification of Plasticizers

Compound

Abietates
Methyl abietate
Hydrogenated methyl abietate

Adipates
di-(*n*-hexyl)adipate
dicapryl adipate
diisooctyl adipate
dinonyl adipate
di-(butoxyethyl) adipate
dicyclohexyl adipate

Azelates
di(2-ethylhexyl) 4-thioazelate
diisobutyl azelate

Citrates
tributyl citrate

Glycol and polyol esters
diethylene glycol dibenzoate
dipropylene glycol dibenzoate
glycerol triacetate
glycerol tripropionate
triethylene glycol diacetate
triethylene glycol dipropionate
triethylene glycol di-2-ethylbutyrate
triethylene glycol di-2-ethylhexoate
polyethylene glycol di-2-ethylhexoate

Glycolates
methyl phthalyl ethyl glycolate
ethyl phthalyl ethyl glycolate
butyl phthalyl butyl glycolate

Phosphates
triethyl phosphate
tributyl phosphate
tri-(butoxyethyl)phosphate
triphenyl phosphate
tricresyl phosphate
monophenyl di-xenyl phosphate
diphenyl mono-xenyl phosphate
di-(*t*-butylphenyl) mono-(*t*-butylcresyl) phosphate

Phthalates
dimethyl phthalate
diethyl phthalate
dibutyl phthalate
diamyl phthalate
dihexyl phthalate
di-(methylisobutylcarbinyl) phthalate
butyl octyl phthalate
butyl isohexyl phthalate
di-(*n*-octyl)phthalate
diisooctyl phthalate
di-(2-ethylhexyl)phthalate
n-octyl-*n*-decyl phthalate
dicyclohexyl phthalate
butyl cyclohexyl phthalate
di-(methoxyethyl)phthalate
di-(ethoxyethyl) phthalate
di-(butoxyethyl) phthalate
methylcyclohexyl isobutyl phthalate
dibenzyl phthalate
diphenyl phthalate
butyl benzyl phthalate
2-ethylhexyl benzyl phthalate
hexamethylene bis(2-ethylhexyl phthalate)
diisodecyl-4,5-epoxytetrahydrophthalate

Sebacates
dimethyl sebacate
dibutyl sebacate
dioctyl sebacate
diisooctyl sebacate
di(2-ethylhexyl) isosebacate
dibutyl isosebacate
butyl benzyl sebacate
dibenzyl sebacate

Classification of Plasticizers (continued)

Sulfonates and Sulfonamides
    ethyl *p*-toluenesulfonate
    o-cresyl *p*-toluenesulfonate
    p-toluene sulfonamide
    cyclohexyl *p*-toluenesulfonamide

Miscellaneous
    tetrahydrofurfuryl oleate
    chlorinated paraffin
    benzyl benzoate
    ethylacetanilide
    triphenylguanidine
    diphenyl ether
    methyl pentachlorostearate
    camphor
    dibutyl tartrate

RAYMOND B. SEYMOUR

POLYETHERS FOR URETHANE FOAM

The predominant class of hydroxyl compounds used today in making urethane foams are the polyethers. Structurally they are usually propylene oxide adducts of diols and polyols, but ethylene oxide-capped propylene oxide adducts are gaining favor. The polyethers of low functionality and relatively high molecular weight (2000–3000) are generally used to make flexible urethane foam; those of higher functionality and lower molecular weight (350–700) produce a rigid foam. Blends are useful for semi-rigid (or semi-flexible) foam.

Hydroxyl-terminated polyesters were used to make the early urethane foams, but except for the chlorendic acid derivatives in fire retardent rigid foams, and specialty molding applications of flexible foam, the lower cost polyethers have replaced polyesters almost completely.

The first commercial polyether flexible foams were based on poly(1,4-oxytetramethylene) glycol (DuPont trademark, "Teracol 30"); the first rigid foams were made using polyoxypropylene sorbitol (Atlas Chemical G-2410).

Preparation

Polyethers for urethane foam are made by the addition of propylene oxide to an initiator having active hydrogens.

TABLE 1. INITIATORS.

Diols	Triols
Propylene glycol	Glycerine
Dipropylene glycol	Trimethylolpropane
	1, 2, 6-Hexanetriol
	1, 1, 3-Tris (4-hydroxyphenyl) propane

Tetrols	Hexol
alpha-Methyl glucoside	Sorbitol
Pentaerythritol	

Octol	Amines
Sucrose	Ethylenediamine
	Diethylenetriamine
	Aniline formaldehyde dimers and trimers

Most of the polyethers now under development are designed for rigids and appear to be based on aromatic initiators such as aryl formaldehyde condensates and aromatic polyamines. Degraded starch and cellulose products are also under study as possible initiators.

The addition reaction is usually carried out under pressure at elevated temperature. Catalysts may be either acids or bases, but an inorganic base is generally used and produces mainly secondary hydroxyl groups. With acid catalysis the reaction yields primary and secondary hydroxyl groups in equal amounts. A product high in primary hydroxyls can be made by capping the polyoxypropylene derivative with ethylene oxide.

Initiators of high functionality containing small amounts of water are used to prepare most

TABLE 2. SPECIFICATIONS, TYPICAL POLYETHERS FOR FLEXIBLE FOAMS.

	Diol[a]	Triol[b]	Triol[c]
Molecular weight	2000	3000	3000
Acid number, mg KOH/g	0.20	0.20	0.20
Hydroxyl number, mg KOH/g	56	56	50
% Water (max)	0.10	0.10	0.10
pH	6.5	6.5	6.5
Viscosity, cps at 25°C	270	458	458
Specific gravity, 25°C	1.002	1.018	1.018
Flash point, °F	445	435	445
Refractive index, 25°C	1.450	1.452	1.452

    [a] poly(oxypropylene)glycol.
    [b] poly(oxypropylene)glycerine.
    [c] poly(oxypropylene)poly(oxyethylene)glycerine.

TABLE 3. SPECIFICATIONS, TYPICAL POLYETHERS FOR RIGID FOAMS.

	Tetrol[a]	Hexol[b]	Octol[c]
Acid number, mg KOH/g	0.05	0.50	Not given
Hydroxyl number, mg KOH/g	560	490	465
pH	7.0	6.0	Not given
Viscosity, cps at 25°C	2800	9000	26,000
Specific gravity	Not given	1.09	Not given
% Water (max)	0.10	0.10	0.10
Ash, ppm	Not given	10	Not given
Sodium and potassium, ppm	100	—	Not given

[a] poly(oxypropylene) pentaerythritol.
[b] poly(oxypropylene) sorbitol.
[c] poly(oxypropylene) poly(oxyethylene) sucrose.

polyethers for rigids. In some cases the lower molecular weight glycols formed by reaction of propylene oxide and water are removed by vacuum distillation; in others, the glycols are retained to produce a low-viscosity polyether.

Inorganic cations that may be troublesome in some polyether applications can be removed by ion exchange.

Reactions

The polyethers undergo reactions typical of hydroxyl compounds. The reaction of alcohols with isocyanates is fundamental to urethane chemistry, and many categories of compounds with active hydrogen react with isocyanates in a similar manner.

The classes of active hydrogen compounds of most interest in urethane foam technology, in order of descending reactivity with isocyanates, are as follows:
primary amines > primary alcohols > water > secondary and tertiary alcohols > urethanes and ureas > carboxylic acids.

Properties

Physical and chemical properties must be held within narrow limits for a polyether to be classified as a urethane-grade product.

The urethane-grade polyethers are nonvolatile liquids of low to very high viscosity. They range in color from water-white to dark brown.

Most polyethers are soluble in the common organic solvents. The lower molecular weight polyethers are generally water soluble, the solubility decreasing as the molecular weight increases. Ethylene oxide capping increases water solubility.

Chemical specifications of most significance are hydroxyl number, acidity, and water and ash content.

Because water reacts with the isocyanate component to form carbon dioxide which contributes to "blowing" the foam, water content must be low. Metallic ash, usually of potassium or sodium, must also be low; alkali metals influence catalysis and may cause prepolymers to gel. (Prepolymers are formed by reaction of an isocyanate with a portion of the polyether required for complete conversion.)

Improved production methods have reduced unsaturation and carbonyl content to very low levels.

Toxicity

The urethane polyethers as a group are very low in oral toxicity and are not considered to be skin irritants. They should not cause problems in normal use.

Applications

All polyethers used for general purpose flexible urethane foam (mattresses, furniture cushions, etc.) are low viscosity diols or triols, or their blends. The choice of polyether for a particular application is based on the processing variables of the foaming equipment as well as the specifications for the final foam product. The polyether most commonly used for flexible foam is the propylene oxide adduct of glycerine with an average hydroxyl number of 56 and molecular weight of 3000.

Ethylene oxide-capped diols and triols have made the process of molding flexible foam more reliable. They yield improved flexible foams and, because primary hydroxyls require less catalyst, foam production costs are lower than with equivalent polyethers containing only secondary hydroxyl groups.

Semi-flexibles (sometimes referred to as semi-rigids) are generally made from prepolymer formulations using high molecular weight triols (M.W. 2000–3000) blended with minor quantities of a polyether of higher functionality. Molded semi-flexible foams are used extensively by the automotive industry for arm cushions and dashboard padding.

Most non fire-retardant rigid urethane foams are made using sorbitol or sucrose based polyethers with hydroxyl numbers in the 450–500

TABLE 4. COMMERCIAL POLYETHERS FOR URETHANE FOAM.

Chemical designation	Polyol types	Avg. mol. wt. Range
Poly(oxypropylene) glycols	Diols	150–4000
Poly(oxypropylene) poly(oxyethylene) glycols (block copolymers)	Diols	1000–3700
Poly(oxypropylene) adducts of glycerine	Triols	400–5000
Poly(oxypropylene) adducts of trimethylolpropane	Triols	300–4000
Poly(oxypropylene) poly(oxyethylene) adduct of trimethylolpropane	Triols	4500
Poly(oxypropylene) adducts of pentaerythritol	Tetrols	400–600
Poly(oxypropylene) adducts of ethylene-diamine	Tetrols	320–470
Poly(oxypropylene) poly(oxyethylene) adducts of ethylenediamine (block copolymers)	Tetrols	1000–5000
Poly(oxypropylene) adducts of alpha-methyl glucoside	Tetrols	477–615
Poly(oxypropylene) adducts of ethylenediamine		450
Poly(oxypropylene) adducts of diethylene-triamine	Pentols	400–600
Poly(oxypropylene) adducts of sorbitol	Hexols	518–687
Poly(oxypropylene) poly(oxyethylene) adducts of sucrose	Octols	975
Poly(oxypropylene) adducts of sucrose	Octols	850–1280

range. The two polyethers used most widely are poly(oxypropylene)sorbitol—hydroxyl number 490—and poly(oxypropylene) poly(oxyethylene) sucrose—hydroxyl number 460. The higher molecular weight polyethers are used most often for higher density foams (4.0 lb/cu ft and up), whereas the lower molecular weight polyethers provide lower density foams of greater strength. The aliphatic amine-based polyethers are generally blended, in quantities up to 20%, with more conventional polyethers. They contribute to catalysis and improve processing.

The aromatic polyethers are more expensive than sucrose and sorbitol analogs and are specified in general only where fire retardance is required.

ROBERT H. VARLAND

POLYISOBUTYLENES

Polyisobutylenes of a wide range of molecular weights are supplied by Badische Anilin- & Soda-Fabrik AG., under the registered trademark "Oppanol" B.

The history of polyisobutylene goes back to 1931, when a patent (DRP 641 284) was awarded to Otto and Müller-Cunradi. This described the polymerization of isobutylene at temperatures below –10°C, with the aid of volatile inorganic halides, particularly BF_3. At first the polymers were obtained in the form of low-molecular, viscous oils. At a later date, monomers of greater purity allowed high-molecular polyisobutylenes to be produced at the boiling point of liquid ethylene, which was used as a cooling agent and solvent.

Properties

The "Oppanol" B range embraces all polyisobutylenes, ranging from oligomers to high-molecular products with molecular weights as high as 5×10^6 (see Table 1).

The figure is the Staudinger molecular weight divided by 1000. Measurements by Flory and others have revealed that the viscosity average molecular weight of polyisobutylene is more than ten times greater than the Staudinger molecular weight, which is also based on viscosity measurements.

The number average molecular weight of the low-molecular "Oppanol" B types is easier to determine than the viscosity average.

Physical Properties. At room temperature polyisobutylene is a liquid. Its viscosity depends on its average molecular weight, and decreases with rise in temperature. The glass temperature is of the order of –50°C. Polyisobutylenes, in which the molecular chain consists only of about 6 monomeric units, clearly display the characteristics of a liquid whose viscosity is comparable to that of a mineral oil. At an average chain length of about 15 monomeric units, the polymers have a syrupy consistency. The limiting viscosity which can be measured by conventional methods is 10^6 poise, and this value is attained at room temperature by polyisobutylene with an average degree of polymerization of about 150. The highest molecular weight polyisobutylenes that can be manufactured in practise have an average of 10,000 monomeric units in the molecular chain.

High-molecular polyisobutylenes display the property, common to all high polymer melts, of being visco-elastic. At a first glance they appear to be elastic solids. Their property of remaining in the liquid form in the whole temperature range within which they are employed clearly distinguishes them from thermoplastic polyolefins, to which group they belong chemically. Its rigidity, expressed as the shear modulus, hardly decreases with rise in temperature in the range in which it is usually employed. As opposed to this, the shear modulus of thermoplastic polyolefins, which is higher in the temperature range of application, drops within the softening range to the very much lower level typical of the melt. Melts of thermoplastic polyolefins have lower shear moduli than "Oppanol" B 200 at the same temperature, because commercial thermoplastics have very much smaller molecular weights.

Mixtures of polyolefins with high-molecular "Oppanol" B exhibit obliteration of the discontinuity occurring in the melting range of polyolefines in the shear modulus-temperature curve. In the temperature ranges normally encountered, the blends are softer than the pure thermoplastic, but their melts are more viscous and rigid.

In respect of mechanical properties, high-molecular "Oppanol" B is much more closely related to cross-linked natural rubber than to the thermoplastic polyolefins. The curves of torsion modulus plotted against temperature are very much the same for cross-linked natural rubber as for high-molecular "Oppanol" B 200, The characteristic difference in mechanical behavior between cross-linked natural rubber and high molecular "Oppanol" B is apparent from the change in slope of the shear modulus-temperature curves in the temperature ranges normally encountered. The values for damping in the torsional vibration test for high-molecular "Oppanol" B are about ten times higher than those for cross-linked natural rubber in the temperatures normally occurring in practice. In other words, vibrational energy is much more rapidly expended by the internal friction of the flow mechanisms in "Oppanol" B. The flexibility of the high molecular "Oppanol" B between −40 and +150°C is an enthropy elasticity, just as in the case of rubber. Although the long chain molecules may be orientated by tensile or shear forces, the extremely high viscosity opposes flow. Thus when short-term deformation stresses are relaxed, the material resumes its original form. The molecular network in cross-linked rubber takes the form of chain entanglements in high molecular "Oppanol" B. Thus if the deformation stresses are sustained, high molecular "Oppanol" B also exhibits its properties as a liquid. This is referred to as "cold flow."

Electrical Properties. "Oppanol" B displays the dielectric properties typical of polyolefins. In other words, it is an outstanding insulating material. The dielectric properties hardly depend on the molecular weight. The only case in which a slight decrease in insulation properties can be noted is with the low-molecular types.

Chemical Properties. From the point of view of chemical properties as well, "Oppanol" B behaves similarly to polyolefins. At room temperature it is resistant to inorganic and organic acids and bases. It is not attacked by oxidizing acids such as nitric acid and chromic acid. It is charred by concentrated sulfuric acid at 80°C.

Polyisobutylene is degraded by radiation or by peroxides at high temperatures. Special conditions are required for cross-linking polyisobutylene. It can be cross-linked by heating it with

TABLE 1.

Grade of "Oppanol"	Intrinsic, viscosity dl/g	Molecular weight, viscosity average	Molecular weight, number average	Viscosity poise, 20°C	100°C
B 1	—	—	300	30.1×10^{-2}	2.6×10^{-3}
B 3	—	—	820	249	2.03
B 10	0.33	50,000	8,000	5×10^5	2.2×10^3
B 15	0.50	95,000	13,000	5×10^6	3.0×10^4
B 50	1.3	380,000	—	1.1×10^6	5×10^6
B 100	2.7	1,300,000	—	3.6×10^6	6.7×10^8
B 150	4.5	2,700,000	—	—	—
B 200	6.3	4,700,000	—	1.5×10^{12}	1.0×10^{10}

di- *tert*- butyl peroxide and sulfur. In addition polyisobutylene swollen with 15% if allyl acrylate, can be cross-linked by $Co^{(60)}$ radiation.

Solubility. At room temperature, "Oppanol" B is just soluble in solvents in which crystalline polyolefins are soluble at temperatures above their melting points. "Oppanol" B is soluble at room temperature in a number of faintly polar or nonpolar organic solvents, such as aliphatic and aromatic hydrocarbons, petroleum fractions, carbon tetrachloride and carbondisulfide. Strongly polar solvents, such as alcohols, ethers, and esters, do not dissolve polyisobutylene, but some of them can swell it. Polyisobutylene is completely inaffected by water, even at the boiling point.

Application and Processing. The main fields of application for the various grades of "Oppanol" B are discussed below. Medium and high viscosity "Oppanol" B types are hardly ever used by themselves but usually in blends.

Plastics Film for the Building Trade. The bulk of high-molecular "Oppanol" B is processed to extended films. By virtue of its good compatibility with fillers, films with an extender content of 50–60% by volume may be prepared. Suitable fillers are carbon black, chalk, ground slate, ground quartz, etc. The addition of small amounts of thermoplastic polyolefins facilitates homogenizing of the blend. It also reduces the sheer forces occurring during mixing, and thus hinders degradation of the "Oppanol" B. The high resistance to chemicals in the temperature range −50 to +100°C is exploited in cladding of vessels. In the building trade the flexibility of the film and the good resistance to aging are of great value. A recent innovation is laminated film manufactured from low density polyethylene and extended "Oppanol" B. This pairs the good chemical resistance of polyethylene, particularly towards solvents, with the good adhesion of "Oppanol" B. These laminated films are used for special cladding applications. The good compatibility of high molecular "Oppanol" B with fillers is exploited in the manufacture of magnetic sections for refrigerator door seals and for doors on other types of furniture.

Blends with Thermoplastic Polyolefins. Below the melting point of the polyolefines concerned, blends of "Oppanol" B with polyolefins are softer than the polyolefin's themselves. The tendency to environmental stress cracking of low density polyethylenes is considerably reduced by blending with "Oppanol" B. Blends with polypropylene become brittle at lower temperatures than polypropylene itself.

Blends with Paraffin and Other Waxes. Blends of "Oppanol" B with paraffin and other waxes are used for impregnating, coating, and laminating paper, metals, or plastics. They have a higher melt viscosty and a lower permeability to water vapor than the waxes themselves. The coatings are much more supple, and their adhesion and heat sealing properties are improved.

Adhesives. All types of "Oppanol" B are used in adhesives. The formulations include resins and fillers. The mechanical strength of the adhesive film is increased by the high molecular grades, and the tack by the low molecular grades of "Oppanol" B. Consequently, adhesives for any given purpose can be designed by varying the ratio of low-molecular to high-molecular grades.

Sealing Compounds. Sealing compounds of high flexibility retention can be prepared from any type of "Oppanol" B. The ratio of the ingredients can be adjusted to suit the requirements imposed on the suppleness and adhesion of the compound.

ERNST KÖHNLEIN

POLYMERIC PLASTICIZERS

In general terms, a polymeric plasticizer is any polymer which is used to plasticize another polymer. Many different materials have been used or suggested for this purpose. By far the most important in commercial usage are the linear saturated polyesters. Liquid and solid addition polymers of several different chemical types constitute the only other important class. However, they are of very limited commercial interest.

The history of polymeric plasticizers began with the introduction in 1929 of a liquid sebacic acid based alkyd resin for use in nitrocellulose lacquers. This plasticizer and several related products were later used to plasticize polyvinyl butyral. In 1943 the first polymeric plasticizer designed for use in polyvinyl chloride (PVC) was introduced. This high molecular weight linear sebacic acid polyester made possible the production of highly migration resistant vinyl jacketing for coaxial cables during World War II. From these early beginnings, a sizeable industry making a diversity of products has developed. Total United States production of polyester plasticizers in 1964 was estimated at over 56 million lb with a market value of approximately 23 million dollars.

From the beginning the primary advantage sought and gained in the use of polymeric plasticizers was permanence. Simple esters with molecular weights in the range of 200–600 have been, and are widely used as plasticizers. However, for many applications they are lost from the plastic composition too readily by volatilization, migration or extraction. The use of properly chosen polymeric plasticizers can minimize or eliminate such loss problems. As a result, they have found widespread use in PVC applications such as high temperature wire insulation, refrigerator gaskets, pressure sensitive tape, shoe liners, and high quality upholstery sheeting.

Chemistry

Almost all commercial polymeric plasticizers are linear saturated polyesters. The dibasic acids which are available and are used in commercial products are adipic, azelaic and sebacic. Similar acids such as glutaric are also suitable. Ring structure acids such as the three isomers of phthalic acid are sometimes used in mixture with the linear acids, primarily to reduce cost. The dibasic acids are reacted with a variety of diols such as propanediol-1,2, butanediol-1,3, and 2,2-dimethyl-1,3-propanediol. Some of the very high molecular weight polyesters are hydroxyl terminated. However, most polyester plasticizers are terminated with long chain monobasic acids or monohydric alcohols. A typical commercial product might be an *n*-12 polyester made from propylene glycol (propanediol-1,2) and adipic acid, with lauric acid as the terminator. The *n* number refers to the number of repearing units, in this case mono-esters of propylene glycol and adipic acid in the polyester molecule. In commercial practice, average molecular weights of polyesters for use as plasticizers range from 700 to over 10,000.

The literature contains many references, frequently in the form of patents, to possible structures for polyester plasticizers. However, the composition of commercial products of this type is very rarely revealed by the manufacturer.

There are two types of addition polymers offered commercially as plasticizers. These are low molecular weight polymers of α-methyl-styrene and liquid butadiene-acrylonitrile polymers. Neither enjoys very wide usage. In addition, the solid butadiene-acrylonitrile rubbers have been studied intensively as plasticizers for vinyl chloride polymers. These rubbers have found some use in food wrapping films and in electrical insulation applications.

Interesting plasticizers made by copolymerizing ethylene with ethyl acrylate or vinyl acetate have been described. These are liquid polymers with molecular weights in the vicinity of 1000. Unfortunately, these materials have not been made available for commercial use.

Uses

Polymeric plasticizers are used to advantage in a variety of polymers for applications in plastics, coatings and elastomers. Their primary utility is in homopolymers and copolymers based on vinyl chloride. However, their unique properties are also used to advantage in coatings based on other polymers such as nitrocellulose, polyvinyl acetate, cellulose acetate and polymethyl methacrylate . A review of the use of polyester plasticizers in vinyl coatings has been published.

Many important applications of plasticized vinyl chloride (PVC) resins have been made possible by the use of polymeric plasticizers. Some examples are:

(1) Electrical insulation for use at high temperatures (e.g., 105°C).
(2) Gasketing for the doors of refrigerators and freezers.
(3) High quality upholstery for furniture and automobiles.
(4) Pressure sensitive tapes for medical and electrical uses.
(5) Non-migratory jacketing for high frequency electrical cables.
(6) Dry-cleanable garments and draperies.

To meet the requirements of these and many other demanding applications, a large number of different polyester plasticizers have been developed. These products cover a wide range of physical properties, and of performance properties in PVC. Some properties of a selected group from the products of a major manufacturer are shown below to illustrate this diversity.

TABLE 1.

Polyester	Molecular weight	Viscosity 25°C (cps)	Specific gravity 25°C
A	1000	290	1.02
B	2000	5500	1.115
C	2000	2300	1.08
D	3500	5000	1.08
E	8000	220,000	1.06
F	>10,000	40,000,000*	1.13

*Soft gum

Note that in general, viscosity is dependent on molecular weight. The one exception, Polyester B, is quite high in viscosity because of a structural variation.

As would be expected, the performance properties of these plasticizers in PVC cover a wide range. The most important performance properties in the characterization of polymeric plasticizers are those having to do with the permanence of plasticization in the composition. These may be divided into three categories: loss of plasticizer by volatilization, loss by extraction into various liquid media, and loss by migration into adjacent solids. Some examples of liquids which may extract plasticizer are soap and detergent solutions, oils, and organic solvents such as gasoline or dry-cleaning fluids. Some solids into which plasticizer may migrate are organic coatings, other plastics, fabrics, foam rubber and dry powders.

Another important aspect of performance is the physical properties of the plasticized vinyl composition. The first of these to be considered is the softness or flexibility imparted by the plasticizer. A plasticizer which produces a softer composition at a given concentration is said to be more efficient. This characteristic is assessed by measuring tensile modulus, indentation hardness, or flexural modulus. Another very pertinent physical characteristic is performance at low temperatures. This is assessed by determining the temperature at which embrittlement or marked stiffening occurs.

Many other performance properties are useful is the study of plasticized PVC compositions. However, those noted above are of greatest use in characterizing the performance of polymeric plasticizers.

To illustrate the range of performance found among commercial products, the plasticizers of Table 1 were tested and compared with a popular simple ester plasticizer, DOP [di(2-ethylhexyl) phthalate]. The vinyl formulation used was as follows:

All of the extraction and migration tests were run on 10 mil thick sheeting made on a two-roll laboratory mill at a roll temperature of 163°C. The Shore A hardness measurements were made on molded slabs stacked to a thickness of $\frac{1}{4}$ in. *Tf,* the low temperature performance measurement, is the temperature at an elastic modulus of 135,000 psi (ASTM D-1043-61T). The results of these tests are shown in Table 2.

It is apparent that all of the polyester plasticizers are somewhat less effective than the simple ester, DOP, at room temperature and at lower temperatures. On the other hand, they are without exception much more resistant to loss from the vinyl composition, by volatilization, by extraction or by migration.

Among the six polyesters, a relation between increasing viscosity and decreasing extractability is apparent. However, it must be noted that this relationship is at best a semi-quantitive one. Prediction of the specific utility of a given polyester plasticizer from simple properties such as viscosity is not practical. Only actual performance data such as that shown in Table 2 can be used for this purpose.

Manufacture

The synthesis of polyesters for use as plasticizers has been the subject of considerable study. In addition to the extensive patent literature, several investigations have reported on the effects of structural variables in the synthesis and performance of polyester plasticizer.

Polyesters for use as plasticizers are of two general types, products with terminal hydroxyl groups, and products terminated with monofunctional acids or alcohols. Hydroxyl termination is normally confined to plasticizers of high molecular weight. The structure may be represented as follows, where A is a dibasic acid and G a diol.

$$[G\text{—}A]_n\text{—}G$$

Similarly, a polyester terminated with a monobasic acid (L) may be represented as:

$$L\text{—}[G\text{—}A]_n\text{—}G\text{—}L$$

and one terminated with a monohydric alcohol (H) as:

$$H\text{—}A\text{—}[G\text{—}A]_n\text{—}H$$

In making a terminated polyester, the dibasic acid and terminator are charged to a reactor in amounts calculated to yield a product having the desired value of *n* and calculated from the relationship:

$$n = \frac{2(A)}{L}$$

where the letters A and L are moles of dibasic and monobasic acid respectively, as noted above. The amount of glycol charged is from 5–25% in excess of the stoichiometric requirement. A catalyst (e.g., zinc chloride) is normally used to increase the rate of reaction.

The reaction proceeds in two stages. The first stage consists of the formation of adducts of one mole of dibasic acid with two moles of glycol,

TABLE 2. PERFORMANCE OF POLYESTER PLASTICIZERS IN PVC.

	A	B	C	Polyester D	E	F	DOP
Shore A hardness (ASTM D–1706–61)	73	81	75	75	79	88	68
Tf, °C (ASTM D–1043–61T)	—23	—1	—14	—13	—10	+3	—35
Volatile loss, % 24 hr/90°C (ASTM D–1203–61T, Method A)	1.1	0.8	1.1	0.5	0.3	0.1	7.1
Hexane extraction, % 2 hr/25°C	13.6	1.5	2.4	1.9	0.6	0.1	31.5
Perchloroethylene extraction, % 2½ hr at 25°C with agitation	29.0	21.8	—	19.9	14.2	1.3	32.1
Extraction by 1% Ivory Soap solution, 24 hr/90°C, %	3.0	2.5	8.3	3.2	0.2	0.2	8.5
Migration into latex foam Rubber, % loss 168 hr/60°C and 0.25 psi	7.1	3.0	1.4	1.1	+0.2	+0.3	14.5

low molecular weight hydroxyl terminated polymers, and adducts of glycol and monobasic acid. During this stage, the water formed is removed and the vaporized glycol is returned to the batch by reflux. The progress of this stage is followed by determination of free acid (as acid number). When the acid number reaches a satisfactorily low value (i.e., 10 or lower), the second stage is begun. In this stage, the largely hydroxyl terminated products of the first stage are linked together by transesterification into a polymer of the desired molecular weight. The excess glycol is freed during the transesterification and is removed by distillation. The progress of the process is followed by determination of product viscosity. When the viscosity reaches a reasonably constant value, the process is completed. Since the entire process is carried out at high temperatures, in the region of 200–220°C, it is important that it be conducted under a blanket of inert gas.

The product of this polyesterification process is a polymer ranging somewhat in molecular weight above and below that corresponding to the desired n value. Such products have made possible the use of vinyl compositions in many difficult and demanding applications. They are a vital adjunct in the continuing rapid growth of this important polymer.

WARREN J. FRISSELL

Cross-reference: PLASTICIZERS.

POLYPROPYLENE ADDITIVES

Modifying polypropylene through the use of additives requires skills in chemical effects, polymer mixing, resin fabrication and applications development. Much of the research on polypropylene modification has been carried out by the resin supplier or the additive supplier; therefore, finished, modified compounds are prepared by the resin supplier and supplied to the market as finished compounds. Nearly all the polypropylene fabricated contains at least one additive (a stabilizer), and significant quantities containing a variety of additives are processed into film, fiber, sheet, monofilaments and molded articles. Some of the additives used in polypropylene are also used in other plastics.

The additives for polypropylene can be listed according to their function as in Table 1, and related to the fabrication process where these additives find primary use.

Impact Strength Improvers

Polyisobutylene and other elastomers are added to polypropylene in quantities dependent on the end use of the compound. As much as 25% polyisobutylene, with a Staudinger viscosity average molecular wt of 100,000, is added to produce a high impact grade. Low impact grades contain about 10 wt %. Grades containing elastomers can vary in molecular weight so that the finished compounds can be used for molding, extrusion, and other applications. Newer elastomers, such as ethylene-propylene copolymer, or ethylene-propylene terpolymer, are now also being used with success. The ethylene-propylene rubber modified polypropylenes seem to have some advantage in extrusion quality over the polyisobutylene modified materials, probably due to the character of the rubber.

Low pressure polyethylene has been added to polypropylene on occasions to increase the low temperature impact strength. The selection of polyethylene depends mostly on its compatibility with the base polypropylene. Because of the difference in crystalline melting points (260°F vs. 335°F), and the difference in the effect of temperature on melt viscosity, a low pressure polyethylene having about the same high shear viscosity at the planned mixing temperature as the

TABLE 1. CLASSIFICATION OF INGREDIENTS.

	Injection molding	Blow molding	Fiber spinning	Extruded shapes	Mono-filaments	Film	Rot. casting
Impact strength improvers	X	X	–	X	–	X	X
Reinforcing agents	X	X	–	X	–	–	–
Pigments and opacifiers	X	X	X	X	X	X	X
Processing aids	X	–	–	–	–	X	–
Dye acceptors	–	–	X	–	–	–	–
Stabilizers	X	X	X	X	X	X	X
Crystal nucleators	X	X	X	X	X	X	–
Optical brighteners	X	X	X	X	–	–	–
Antistatic agents	X	X	X	X	X	X	X
Antiblock and slip additives	–	–	–	–	–	X	–
Perfumes	X	–	–	X	–	–	–
Flame retardants	X	–	–	X	–	–	–

base polypropylene is chosen. For example, a 0.2 melt index (190°C) Phillips process polyethylene, and a 5.0 melt flow (230°C) polypropylene can be mixed at a temperature of around 380°F.

Several other materials are used to increase the low temperature impact strength in special applications. For example, the plasticizers normally associated with vinyls have been used experimentally in film grades of polypropylene. These are dioctyl adipate (DOA) and dioctyl phthalate (DOP). The mechanism for improving the low temperature impact strength of polypropylene that is normally associated with all the impact strength modifiers is a reduction in glass transition temperature. Actually, tests show that blends do not exhibit a change in the normal glass transition temperature, but instead show a shift of the brittle-ductile transition to a lower temperature.

Figure 1 illustrates the effect of the addition of polyisobutylene on the impact strength of polypropylene when measured by the ASTM-D-256 (Izod) Test. High speed impact tests, carried out in equipment where a ball is shot through the sample at speeds up to 50 m per sec show a more rapid transition from brittle to ductile type failure. Energy to break is affected accordingly.

Because of the difference in viscosity and elasticity of polypropylene and most impact strength modifiers, intensive mixing of the two materials is necessary. Generally, the additive is masterbatched in high shear mixing equipment and then extended with the base polypropylene by extrusion.

Reinforcing Agents

The objective of adding any filler to polypropylene is a functional one, done to enhance the physical properties, not to lower the cost by extending the compound. Additive cost plus compounding cost, coupled with the need to assure the consumer of the quality of the blend, eliminates any possibility for reducing the cost of the compound.

The modulus of polypropylene can be increased several fold by the addition of mineral fillers. Along with the increase in modulus, other properties are also affected. Generally, with non-fibrous materials, the increased rigidity is attained at the sacrifice in impact strength. Fibrous materials do not generally result in a decrease in impact strength, and on some occasions, an increase in impact strength as well as modulus is obtained with fibrous fillers, as long as the fibrous nature of the additive is preserved. Preservation of the fibrous nature of the additive is important. High shear mixing of asbestos or glass fiber causes complete break-up of the fiber. However, extruder blending (with a deep channel, low compression screw) of the glass fiber and polypropylene will produce a satisfactory blend.

Asbestos, talc, wood flour, cellulose, and all the common fillers found in other plastics have been evaluated in polypropylene, the main emphasis being on asbestos and talc. Five types of asbestos (chrysotile, amosite, anthophylite, crocidolite, and tremolite) exist, but anthophylite $[(MgFe)_7Si_8O_{22}(OH)_2]$ is the one most often used in polypropylene. Asbestos concentration can range up to 50% in commercial applications, depending on end use requirements.

Talc-filled polypropylene performs similar to asbestos filled polypropylene (Table 2.).

TABLE 2. PROPERTIES OF FILLED POLYPROPYLENES.

	40% Asbestos	40% Talc	Unmodified polypropylene
Flexural modulus, psi			
0.2 in./min, secant, 0.1 in.	360,000	340,000	170,000
Izod impact strength,			
ft-lb/in. notched, 72°F	0.5	0.5	0.9
Deflection temperature °F			
66 psi	275	275	220
264 psi	190	170	140

Both talc and asbestos for use in polypropylene have to be carefully selected to obtain the maximum performance of the blend and to minimize any chemical effects of the filler on the heat stability of the base polymer. Oven life of polypropylene can be reduced by as much as 75% by the addition of 40% asbestos, and 60% by the addition of 40% of talc if appropriate stabilizers are not used to compensate for this effect.

Fillers such as barium ferrite, calcium carbonate, zinc oxide, wood flour, cotton flock, alpha cellulose, and the many other materials used in filling thermosets do not find significant use in polypropylene.

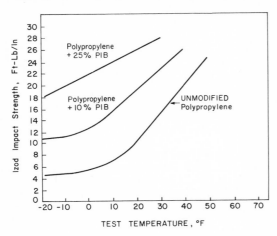

FIG. 1. Effect of polyisobutylene

Glass-fiber reinforcement promises to become of commercial significance. Reinforcement with glass fiber, if the fiber integrity is maintained into the molded part, will increase the modulus of the compound as well as the impact strength. The property improvement is shown in Table 3.

TABLE 3. PHYSICAL PROPERTIES OF FIBROUS GLASS-REINFORCED POLYPROPYLENE.

	30 w% Glass fiber	Poly-propylene
Flexural modulus, psi 0.2 in./min, secant, 0.1 in.	600,000	170,000
Izod impact strength ft-lb/in. notched, 72°F	3.0	0.9
Deflection temperature, °F 264 psi	250	140
Molding shrinkage, in./in. ⅛ in. specimen, MD	0.004	.017
Oven life, days, 320°F	17	17

Mixing technique is especially important with fibrous additives for reinforcement. Excessive shear destroys the fibrous nature of the additive. Special patented techniques are now used which assure a uniform blend yet do not cause severe breakdown of the fibrous additive.

Pigments and Opacifiers

Polypropylene is colored with pigments that are used for nearly all plastics. Translucent colors can be obtained with some pigments which can be dispersed well enough to avoid agglomeration. Opacity in pigmented articles is generally obtained by the addition of metal oxides (titanium or zinc oxide) for light colors, and by the addition of carbon black if consistent with the color formulation. Dispersion of the pigment significantly affects the development of color. For this reason pigments are usually masterbatched with high shear mixing equipment. The masterbatch is then extended to the final color by extrusion.

The effect of pigmentation on the properties of polypropylene can be significant. Some pigments affect the heat resistance of the compound, probably due to the presence of traces of copper. Pigments can also reduce the stability of the molecular weight during processing. Still other pigments are known to act as crystallization nucleation sites and thereby change the spherulitic structure of the base resin. This nucleation effect generally causes increase in stiffness and impact strength.

Processing Aids

Processing aids are not used often in the fabrication of polypropylene. Occasionally, calcium or zinc stearates are added during ram injection molding to reduce pellet to pellet friction in the rear zone of the cylinder. These are generally referred to as external lubricants. In contrast, internal lubricants are generally those materials which lower the melt viscosity, such as paraffin waxes or other low molecular weight polymers.

Dye Acceptors

Polypropylene is a nonpolar material, i.e., it contains no chemically functional groups. Since chemical functionality is necessary for dyeability, chemical compounds are added for this reason. These compounds are usually additives rather than comonomers because of the difficulty in copolymerizing polar monomers with propylene with polyolefin catalysts. Process know-how and economics will be the basis for decisions between the additives and polymerization approaches to gaining dye sites.

The additives that are used either metallic or polymeric. Metallic compounds reported to perform satisfactorily are: (a) inorganic metallic compounds, (b) carboxylic acid salts, and (c) organometallics such as alkoxides or nickel-containing compounds. The alkoxides decompose to metal oxides at fiber spinning temperatures.

Polymeric additives can be either natural or synthetic polymers such as cellulose or polystyrene. The synthetic polymers are more often those containing nitrogen, such as polyamines or polyvinylpyridines. The nitrogen-containing polymers have been selected because of the wide range of anionic dyes available for use with polypropylene containing these additives.

Stabilizers

Stabilizers for polypropylene retard the effects of heat, oxygen and light on the reduction in molecular weight. Generally, a stabilizer "package" (one or more stabilizers) is specified for a given end use requirement.

Phenols and bisphenols are most effective as processing stabilizers. The use of these materials in concentrations as high as 0.2 wt % is adequate to stabilize the molecular weight during injection molding or other fabrication processes. Because these phenols are volatile at processing temperatures, some stabilizer is lost during processing, requiring restabilization if excessive regrind is used. The dramatic effect of a process stabilizer such as 2,6-di-t-butyl-4-methylphenol is shown in Table 4.

The use of a co-stabilizer, i.e., dilauryl thiodipropionate with a phenol, improves the oven life of the fabricated part. The use of the thio ester with a phenol is effective because of a regenerative effect of the combination. Other additives are sometimes used along with the phenol and the thio ester, but their compositions are generally not disclosed.

POLYPROPYLENE ADDITIVES

TABLE 4. EFFECT OF INJECTION MOLDING ON
MOLECULAR WEIGHT.

| Sample treatment | Viscosity average molecular weight | |
	Stabilized[a]	Unstabilized
None	273,000	273,000
After "normal" injection molding[b]	252,000	165,000
After "severe" injection molding[c]	221,000	112,000

[a] With 0.2 wt % 2, 6-di-*t*-butyl-4-methylphenol.
[b] 500°F cylinder temperature, 30 min cylinder residence.
[c] 550°F cylinder temperature, 45 min cylinder residence.

The mechanism of molecular weight reduction in the presence of ultraviolet light is considered by some to be the same as that resulting from exposure to heat, but with the ultraviolet light acting as a catalyst. With this catalytic effect, molecular weight reduction can occur at much lower temperatures. Because of this mechanism, it is necessary to use heat stabilizers along with the light stabilizers for an effective system. Thus, the heat stabilizer action is chemical, while the purpose of an ultraviolet light stabilizer is to screen or shield the polymer from the uv light. This can be accomplished by either organic compounds or specific inorganic compounds. The inorganic compounds are largely represented by carbon black, whereas the organic compounds are more numerous. Typical organic compounds are the substituted benzophenones, nickel phenol chelates and alkyllauryl salicylates.

Both carbon black and the organic compounds can be used in concentrations up to 2 wt %. However, because of the cost, the organic compounds are usually used at the 0.5–1.0% level. The additives can be added to the polymer during the normal stabilizer addition step by either direct addition or masterbatching followed by extrusion. Compounds containing a uv stabilizer and molded into $\frac{1}{8}$ in. specimens which were exposed to the sun in the South retained 90% of their physical strength for up to 3 years. Superior compounds, utilizing improved heat stabilizers, are projected to demonstrate as much as 5 years' life under such conditions.

Nucleation Promoters

The crystallization nucleation rate and crystal growth rate of polypropylene can be increased substantially by the addition of nucleating agents. Inert, finely divided solids are one class of materials which will nucleate polypropylene. This includes some pigments as well as catalyst residues, silica, high melting polymers and even dust. Other materials which effectively nucleate

are metal salts of organic acids and mono- or dicarboxylic acids. These additives are compounded into the polypropylene by any one of the melt mixing techniques.

There are clear, well established improvements to be gained by the addition of nucleating agents. Impact strength, stiffness, molded part dimensional stability, and clarity are generally improved. Molding shrinkage, although generally more uniform, is slightly greater for nucleated polymers than for polymers with low nucleation rates. Of most importance to processors is that polymers containing nucleating agents generally develop stiffness upon crystallization more rapidly, thus resulting in improved molding production rates.

Two major problems still exist with the use of polymers containing certain nucleating agents. Of most concern is the problem of mold "plate-out," where the nucleating agent volatizes and deposits at the mold vents and because of the acidity of some of these compounds, corrosion of the mold is possible. The other problem is that of filling thin sections in injection molds. Polypropylene with a high rate of nucleation will be difficult to mold in thin sections due to "freeze-off" in the cavity prior to completion of filling of the mold.

Optical Brighteners

Several additives are available for improving the appearance of unpigmented polypropylene articles. These additives absorb light in the 250–400 mμ range, and emit light in the 400–550 mμ range. Derivatives of substituted disulfonic acid, azoles and coumarin are compounds used for improving optical brightness. The ultraviolet light stability of polypropylene containing optical brighteners is generally decreased by a small but measurable amount.

Antistatic Agents

Polyolefins can develop a surface electrical charge which dissipates slowly. Both the buildup and discharge rate is affected by the surface conductivity of the plastic. This electrical charge is responsible for undesirable effects in the handleability of film and the pickup of dust on fabricated articles. These effects can be minimized by the addition of antistatic agents directly to the base resin in a compounding step or by the application of materials to the surface of molded parts. Since the additive technique works by a process of additive exudation, it produces a longer lasting effect than the technique of surface application.

Compounds which have been used as additives for reducing the static electricity effect on polypropylene are fatty acid esters and fatty acid amides. These compounds may be used in concentrations ranging from 0.5–1.0 wt. %.

372

Antiblock and Slip Additives

Antiblock and slip additives, although they perform different functions, are discussed together because both are usually added to polypropylene film grades.

Blocking of film, not unique to polypropylene, is the condition of apparent fusing of layers of film. Finely divided silica, referred to as an antiblock additive, is added to alter the surface characteristic of the film to minimize blocking. Slip additives also alter the surface character of the polymer. Slip additives, usually fatty acid amides, are compounded into the polymer. These compounds then exude, forming a layer of low coefficient of friction. The exudation occurs over a period of time due to crystallization of the polymer and is partially diffusion controlled. It is in this manner that the coefficient of friction of the film is reduced and thereby improving the film handleability.

Perfumes

Compounds having odors similar to leather, vanillan, etc., are sometimes added to the polymer prior to fabrication to achieve special effects. Generally, these materials are not capable of effectively masking the odor of reprocessed or off-grade polymers.

Flame Retardants

Polymers containing halogens (PVC, PTFE) are self-extinguishing after exposure to flame while, in contrast, polyolefins are classed as slow burning. For many electronic, electrical and construction applications, polypropylene must be self extinguishing. Self-extinguishing (or even non-burning) polypropylene is manufactured by adding antimony trioxide, borates, phosphates and chlorinated hydrocarbons. In the presence of flame, the chlorinated hydrocarbon decomposes, liberating chlorine. The chlorine may react with antimony oxide, possibly forming antimony trichloride. The dense, white decomposition (and subsequent reaction) products exclude oxygen from the flame front.

The additive "package" in a flame-retardant grade can run as high as 50% by weight. Because of this high loading of additives, the moldability and physical properties of a flame-retardant grade are different from the base polymer.

Most significantly changed properties are hardness, density and processability. Hardness is increased from 70 Rockwell R to 80 Rockwell R and density from 0.90 to 1.19 g/cc.

Care must be taken to avoid fabricating flame retardant grades above their recommended processing temperature. Some systems begin decomposing at 400°F, whereas others can withstand molding temperatures as high as 500°F.

Some flame-retardant polypropylenes do not oven age as well as the material without the additive. This poor performance is due primarily to the slow decomposition of the chlorinated hydrocarbon. Certain chlorinated hydrocarbons have now been developed which, when added to polypropylene and oven aged at 250°F, retain their fire-retarding quality for periods as long as 200 days. The use of these newly developed chlorinated hydrocarbons has resulted in flame-retardant polypropylene which can be used for high heat resistance.

R. L. TUSCH

POLYPROPYLENE MONOMERS

Polypropylene, one of the five most commonly used thermoplastics today, is produced with the aid of stereoselective catalysts which have the effect of "ordering" or giving uniformity to the structure of the polymer chains as they build up during the polymerizing process. Polypropylene's "ordered" structure in turn produces molecules that crystallize into homogeneous bundles, so that the resulting resin has high strength, hardness, and good heat resistance, combined with high rigidity and high dielectric strength. There are two types of polymer chain involved in the development of polypropylene—"atactic" and "isotactic," the latter describing the structure in which all side-chain methyl groups appear on alternate carbons of the polymer chain on the same side of the backbone, which presumably accounts for its better molecular symmetry and crystallinity as compared with "atactic," which has a random distribution of side chains.

Every process for producing isotactic polypropylene involves three key steps—polymerization, purification, and finishing. During polymerization, a solution of the monomer propylene in an inert hydrocarbon diluent is converted to a slurry containing insoluble, crystalline polymer of high molecular weight. Any noncrystalline or amorphous polypropylene formed in the process is removed from the crystalline product during the purification step. The dried powder is then suitably compounded by the addition of various materials necessary for specific end uses, pelletized, and packaged for shipment.

Monomer

The monomer or unpolymerized form of the product must be essentially free of all nonhyrocarbon impurities which may react with and deactivate the catalyst. Water, carbon monoxide, carbon dioxide, acetylenes, oxygen, and non-hydrocarbons containing oxygen, nitrogen, and sulfur are some of the most common contaminants found in propylene. These contaminants poison the catalyst to different degrees, reducing its efficiency and causing a falling of quality in the end product. As little as 5–10 ppm of some of these poisons will drastically reduce polymerization rate. High-quality, polymerization-grade monomer (i.e., propylene), has a typical analysis as follows:

Propylene	99.7%
Propane	0.3%
Ethane	50 ppm
Water	10 ppm
Other hydrocarbons (ethylene, acetylenes, diolefins)	Nil
Sulfur, total	2 ppm
Carbon monoxide	Nil
Carbon dioxide	1 ppm
Oxygen	4 ppm
Carbonyl sulfide	1 ppm

High purity can be achieved by precise fractionation in combination with treatment by caustic soda, ethanolamine, solid adsorbents, and the like.

Propylene recovered from normal cracking operations in petroleum refining is generally low in acetylenes. When high-temperature cracking of naphtha is used specifically to make propylene (and ethylene), acetylenes tend to be high (up to 100 ppm). Because acetylenes can also be polymerized to give unsaturated homopolymers or copolymers which affect polypropylene properties adversely, it is sometimes necessary to remove acetylenes by adsorbents or selective hyrodgenation.

During polymerization, certain impurities tend to accumulate and must be removed. Propane tends to build up gradually and should be distilled out. Hydrocarbon diluent, often carried with the propylene, may or may not have to be removed, depending on the process. Allowance must also be made for the removal of impurities brought in with the various raw materials, required for polymerization and polymer purification; decomposition products of the catalysts themselves represent a type of impurity which may be undesirable in recycle diluent or corrosive to equipment, and should be removed by distillation and/or suitable scrubbers or absorbers. Propylene monomer may be transferred to the polymerization site by pipeline or by high-pressure or refrigerated tank cars, or by 6500 gal tractor trailers. Normal temperatures of from 75–90°F have corresponding pressures of from 150–210 psi. In storage, care should be taken to prevent contamination and thus eliminate the need for additional purification.

THOMAS J. KELLY

Cross-reference: PROPYLENE.

POLYURETHANE ELASTOMER MATERIALS

Urethane elastomers are condensation polymers made by the reaction of aromatic diisocyanates with polyols which have an average molecular weight greater than about 750. The end products are obtained by several different routes through intermediates which require different processing techniques and have different degrees of stability. Metering and mixing machines have been developed to handle the liquid systems. The use of machine processing greatly improves the control and the economics of urethane casting systems. The recent concept wherein a complete system including the chemical intermediates and a machine tailored to a specific application are available from a single source systems supplier has greatly advanced the processing technology of liquid systems. The solid urethane elastomers are processed using either conventional rubber machinery or thermoplastic processing machinery depending upon the types of urethanes involved and the application.

In addition to the several types available based on the processing requirements, two chemical types are available in one or more of these classifications. The chemical types are polyether urethanes and polyester urethanes. The aromatic isocyanates used in the elastomers are tolylene diisocyanate (TDI) and diphenylmethane diisocyanate (MDI).

The physical properties of the different types available decrease in the following order in a general way: polyester MDI, polyester/TDI, polyether/TDI.

The polyester types are more stable to the effects of oxidative environments, especially in the presence of uv light, than the polyether types. The latter are more stable to hydrolytic influences than conventional polyester types. However, lactone-derived polyester types are reported to be as good in hydrolysis aging as polyether types. Polyester types are improved in hydrolysis aging by additives, and polyether types are improved in oxidative and ultraviolet light aging by additives. Such additives are commercially available.

The types available based on processing characteristics are as follows:

(1) One shot.
(2) Prepolymer.
(3) Thermoplastics.
(4) Millable gums.

One-shot Systems

The term "one shot" refers to systems in which the elastomers are produced by direct machine mixing of the diisocyanate and polyol together with a catalyst. Casting is done directly from the machine into the mold, and gel times are fast. No prepolymer intermediate is involved.

The use of the one-shot technique is generally influenced by the economics of the situation. Such a technique is more difficult to control to get the high quality characteristic of prepolymer elastomers. However, it is used in certain high volume operations where the competitive climate is intense and the property variances are not critical. The large volume application of these systems is in polyether-TDI elastomeric sealants.

Prepolymer Systems

Urethane prepolymers are available as liquids or low melting solids. Both the polyether and polyester types are on the commercial market. Systems are available to produce elastomers in the hardness range of about Shore A 20–Shore D 75.

The aromatic isocyanates used to make the prepolymers are tolylene diisocyanate (TDI) and diphenylmethane diisocyanate (MDI). Prepolymers made from he latter are generally less stable, and the elastomer systems are less reproducible than the TDI systems when all factors are considered. The MDI systems are faster in general than TDI systems and have a shorter working life. Many TDI systems are available which can be used for hand casting because the working life is relatively long.

The prepolymer systems are used by mixing the prepolymer with a curing agent which, chemically speaking, is a chain extender or crosslinker. This is usually done at temperatures up to about 110°C, but some systems can be mixed at room temperature. The materials are degassed by vacuum either prior to mixing, in the case of machine operation, or after mixing in the case of hand mixing. Then the liquid mixture is cast into molds and cured according to a schedule recommended by the supplier. This may be at room temperature in some cases. In most instances the cure is at 70–120°C for periods up to about 24 hr. After the elastomer is cured by the recommended procedure the ultimate properties are obtained in most cases after standing about four to seven days at ambient conditions.

The properties of several typical systems are given in Table 1.

Thermoplastic Systems

Two types of thermoplastic urethane elastomers are in commercial use. These materials are supplied as a ground or pelletized stock suitable for thermoplastic processing in operations such as injection, compression and transfer molding.

The first type are isocyanate-terminated polymers which have been reacted to a degree which permits further thermoplastic processing to a limited extent. All the elements are present for a complete cure by heat so that only limited reprocessing is possible with retention of the best properties. The free isocyanate groups make the materials relatively unstable in storage and readily susceptible to moisture from the atmosphere. Materials of the polyester/MDI types are available to make elastomers of this class in the Shore A 80–95 or Shore D 35–55 range.

The second type are high molecular weight hydroxyl-terminated urethane elastomers which receive no additional cure upon processing by thermoplastic techniques. These materials are stable in storage and do not tend to cure by moisture from the air. A wide range of products are available to cover the hardness range from about Shore A 50 to Shore D 70. These materials

TABLE 1.

	Polyester[a]/ MDI[b]	Polyester[a]/ MDI[b]	Polyester[c]/ TDI[d]	Polyester[c]/ TDI[d]	Polyether/ TDI[d]
NCO content, %	6.5	6.5	4.2	4.2	4.1
Mixing ratio Prepol/curing agent	100/12.5	100/14	100/27	100/4.8	100/4.1
Casting temp., °C	110	110	100	100	100
Work life, min	2	3	10	20	30
Shore hardness	52D	90A	85A	55A	55A
Tensile, psi	5500	4500	5600	3000	1500
Modules 100°, psi	2350	1500	700	300	250
200%, psi	2800	1900	900	400	375
300%, psi	3600	2500	1250	550	500
Tear, pli	650	350	210	195	150
Elongation, %	430	550	500	460	650
Elongation set, %	—	45	nil	nil	—

[a] Conventional polyester.
[b] MDI = diphenylmethane diisocyanate.
[c] Coprolactone—derived polyester.
[d] TDI = tolylene diisocyanate.

have good abrasion resistance, high tear and tensile, but the solvent resistance is poorer than the heat cured type mentioned above. A number of these polymers are recommended for solution coatings. The high molecular weight of the elastomers produces films of excellent strength without additional cure.

Millable Gum Systems

The materials referred to in this class are polyester urethane elastomers which are hydroxyl-terminated and not crosslinked. These materials are stable in storage and do not tend to cure by moisture from the air as do the thermoplastic isocyanate-terminated type described in the foregoing section.

These gums are processed on conventional rubber machinery. They are cured by milling with a crosslinking agent such as a peroxide or a polyisocyanate, and, after forming by conventional techniques, by heating as recommended by the supplier.

W. R. McElroy

POLYURETHANES, INGREDIENTS

Polyurethanes are generally classified as the reaction products of diisocyanates with compounds containing active hydrogens. In commercial practice, many polyhydroxy compounds may be reacted with various diisocyanates to form many types of useful polyurethane polymeric products. Many of these polyurethane products include polyurethane foams, both flexible and rigid, also semi-rigid, coatings, adhesives, and many types of elastomeric materials, including fibers.

The basic raw materials that are generally used in the manufacture of polyurethanes may be listed as follows:

(1) Organic Diisocyanates

$(O=C=N-R-N=C=O)$

The organic diisocyanates are generally produced by the reaction of an organic diamine compound with phosgene to yield the corresponding diisocyanate. The most commercially used diisocyanate in present day urethane technology is tolsene diisocyanate, 80% and 20% mixture of the 2.4 and 2.6 isomers.

There are also many other types of diisocyanates of the aromatic and aliphatic types, which are being utilized in elastomers, coatings, and fibers. When these various diisocyanates are reacted with various polyhydroxy compounds, they produce products with a wide range of physical properties. There are also available types of polymeric diisocyanates which are presently being utilized in the production of rigid polyurethane foam.

(2) Polyhydroxy Intermediates

The general types of polyhydroxy intermediates utilized in the preparation of polyurethanes may be classified as follows:

Polyester Resins. For polyurethane foams, many millions of pounds of polyester resins are used in the manufacture of foam for laminates, coatings, fibers, and elastomers. These are polyesters of the saturated type which may vary in molecular weight and the degree of crosslinking and hydroxyl functionality. They are generally the reaction products of glycols such as diethylene glycol and organic acids such as adipic acid and may be cross-linked with such materials as trimethylol propane. The polyesters may vary in viscosity, molecular weight, and reactive functionality. When these polyesters are reacted with the various available diisocyanates, they give resultant polymers with varying physical properties. The resulting polymer may be very rigid or extremely flexible.

Polyethers. The second type of polyhydroxy intermediate is classified as *polyethers*. The polyethers are by far the largest group of hydroxyl terminated foam intermediates that are presently utilized in the urethane industry. There are numerous types of polyethers which are commercially available—however, the bulk of the polyethers consists mainly of adducts of propylene oxide diols and triols, or higher functional alcohols. Many of these triols are adducts of glycerol and propylene oxide. As with the previously discussed polyesters, the polyethers, when reactivated with various isocyanates, produce polymers which may vary from very soft and flexible to very hard and stiff polymers. In general, the bulk of the polyethers are utilized in the furniture cushioning and seating foams because of their superior comforting and cushioning qualities. The resulting foam products are generally more resilient and have better hydrolysis resistance than polyesters. The polyester based urethanes, however, do have greater tensile and elongation properties and better resistance to oils, solvents, and oxidation.

Amine Compounds. A third type of active hydrogen intermediate the various diamines or amine compounds. These materials may vary in molecular weight and functionality and, in most cases, are extremely fast reacting with the isocyanates. Some of the higher molecular weight polymeric amines are useful in the manufacture of various elastomers and coatings and fibers.

Other minor raw materials utilized in the manufacture of Polyurethane resins may be listed as follows:

Blowing Agents—Primary and Auxiliary. Commercial flexible urethane foams utilize, as the self-generated blowing agents, carbon dioxide. This is generated when the reaction of an isocyanate takes place with water. The amount of water incorporated into a foam formulation will determine the density and, to a certain degree, the firmness of the foam. In addition to the self-manufactured blowing agent, auxiliary blowing agents may be incorporated in the foam formulations to further reduce the density and also soften the foam. Fluorocarbons, such as trichloromonofluromethane and methylene chloride, have been successfully employed as auxiliary blowing agents in polyurethanes.

Catalysts. There are many types of catalysts with various degrees of activity which are utilized in the production of polyurethanes. The type and amount of catalyst, the degree of polymerization, and the strength of the resulting polymer or foam can be greatly affected by the type of catalyst used. The broad general classes of catalysts that are utilized are the tertiary amines and the organometallic compounds. In the case of the amines, the most widely used are N-ethylmorpholine and triethylene diamine. In the case of the organometallic compounds, the most widely used catalyst is dibutyltin dilaurate. The amines are generally used to catalyze the reaction between the water and the isocyanates where the organometallics generally catalyze the reaction between the polyhydroxy intermediate and the diisocyanate.

Surfactants. The role of surfactants in a foam formulation is to give stability to the foaming system and to aid in regulation of the cell size. Many different classes of surfactants have been used and include the nonionic and anionic organic surfactants, also the use of various types of silicones. The type of surfactant utilized depends on the method of foam preparation and the type of foam prepared.

Miscellaneous Additives. Many other additives may be incorporated in polyurethane polymers and products, and in foaming systems. The additives may include flame retardants, plasticizers, inert fillers, pigments, antioxidants, dyes, crosslinking agents. In general, these are added for some specific, desired, additional physical property and in specialty applications.

MICHAEL A. RICCIARDI
MARK E. FRENCH

POLYVINYL ALCOHOL

Polyvinyl alcohol is obtained when polyvinyl acetate is hydrolyzed using either basic or acidic catalysts:

$$(-CH_2-CH-)_n \xrightarrow[\text{or base}]{\substack{+H_2O \\ \text{Acid}}} -[CH_2-CH]_n + CH_3 COOH$$
$$\quad | \qquad\qquad\qquad\qquad | $$
$$\quad C=O \qquad\qquad\qquad OH$$
$$\quad | $$
$$\quad CH_3$$

The monomeric vinyl alcohol does not exist because only its ketoform, acetaldehyde, is stable.

A wide variety of polyvinyl alcohols can be obtained by varying the molecular weight of the parent polyvinyl acetate, and by controlling the degree of hydrolysis. Fully hydrolyzed polyvinyl alcohols have less than 2 mole% residual acetate groups whereas partially hydrolyzed polyvinyl alcohols are manufactured having from 2–20 mole% residual acetate group.

Polyvinyl alcohols are white to yellow powders which are soluble in water; the fully hydrolyzed grades only in hot water; the partially hydrolyzed also in cold water. With increasing amounts of residual acetate groups, their aqueous solutions exhibit "cloud points" on heating. Polyvinyl alcohols are insoluble in organic solvents, but the resistance to swelling by such solvents decreases with increasing acetate group content.

The molecular weight of a particular polyvinyl alcohol is generally expressed by its 4% solution viscosity. There are at the present three main molecular weight grades on the market having 4% solution viscosities of approximately 60 cps, 25 cps, and 5 cps, which corresponds roughly to a molecular weight of 100,000, 70,000 and 16,000, respectively.

Polyvinyl alcohols are sold under the trade marks of "Vinol" (Airco Chemical Co.), "Lemol" (Borden Chemical Co.), "Elvanol" (DuPont Co.), "Moviol" (Farbwerke Hoechst), "Poval" (Kurashiki Rayon Co.), "Gelvatol" (Shawinigan), and "Polyviol" (Wacher-Chemie).

The applications for polyvinyl alcohols are varied. They include uses as protective colloids in polyvinyl acetate emulsion manufacture, in paper and wood adhesive formulations, as pigment binders and sizing agents in the paper industry, as warp sizing agents for cotton and synthetic fibers, and, finally as the raw material for synthetic fiber and film manufacture. There are many more specialized uses.

In the adhesives industry, polyvinyl alcohols are added to polyvinyl acetate emulsions to allow the preparation of lower solids adhesives having the desired properties of quick tack, high viscosity, water sensitivity or insolubility as desired, and having generally the known advantages of all water-based systems. At the same time the excellent film forming characteristics allow for fast drying. The resulting adhesive films have a high cohesive and adhesive strength. Polyvinyl alcohol is often plasticized with glycerol, glycols or ethoxylated butyl phosphates. The adhesives made using polyvinyl alcohol are mainly used as wood glues and packaging adhesives for high speed packaging machines.

Large quantities of polyvinyl alcohol are used as an adhesive to produce a laminated fiber board. The polyvinyl alcohol can be borated for this use and compounded into adhesives of high wet tack. A typical formulation is as follows:

	Parts
Polyvinyl alcohol (Vinol 125)	88
Boric acid	9
Concentrated HCl	1/2
ASP-400 clay	60
Dowicide B	1
Water	842

In the paper industry fully hydrolyzed polyvinyl alcohols are used as pigment binders alone or in combination with a latex to produce paper and paper board with excellent printing qualities, brightness and opacity. A typical coating formulation consists of 100 parts coating clay, 6 parts polyvinyl alcohol, and 10 parts latex solids and water to give 60% solids. Unpigmented or very lightly pigmented polyvinyl alcohol solutions are used as size press coatings and board sizes to improve oil and grease resistance.

In the textile industry, polyvinyl alcohol is being used as a warp size agent for cotton and synthetic fibers. It can be used alone or in combination with starches. A typical warp size formulation is as follows:

	Parts
Polyvinyl alcohol (Vinol 165)	16
Hydroxyethylated starch (Penford Gum 280)	60
Wax (Texsize W-20)	12
Water to make 40 gal. of solution	

Yarns sized with polyvinyl alcohol show very little shedding during the weaving operation. The removal of the size after weaving can be accomplished simply with hot water. Polyvinyl alcohol is also dissolved as an ingredient in wash-wear formulations. A typical formulation for cotton is as follows:

	Parts
Thermosetting resin (melamine-formaldehyde)	50
Polyvinyl alcohol (Vinol 165)	9
Softener (CA-100)	12
Catalyst (Mg Cl$_2$)	6
Penetrant	1/4
Optical bleach	1/4
Water	340

Partially hydrolyzed polyvinyl alcohols are used as protective colloids and emulsifying agents in the vinyl acetate emulsion polymerization process. Normally, 3–6 parts on the weight of the vinyl acetate are employed.

Polyvinyl alcohol film is used for some specific applications such as polyester bag molding. Cold water soluble polyvinyl alcohol film is used to package detergents, bleaches, pesticides and other chemicals to allow for easy handling.

In Japan a large synthetic fiber industry is based on polyvinyl alcohol. Fibers are spun from aqueous solutions into salt solutions and subsequently they are treated with formaldehyde for insolubilization. Polyvinyl alcohol fiber is the only synthetic fiber with hydrophilic properties like cotton, but having much higher strength.

There is a multitude of other smaller uses for polyvinyl alcohol. For example, polyvinyl alcohol increases the green strength of ceramics; it can be used as a temporary protective coating, as a release agent, as a solid erosion preventive, and as a plastic for fuel line tubing.

Martin K. Lindemann

POTTING AND ENCAPSULATING MATERIALS

Definition

Potting, encapsulation, and embedding of electronic components and assemblies comprise the creation of a protective covering over the component or assembly to assure that there will be no operating failure, electrical or mechanical, due to environmental effects.

In potting, the component to be protected is placed in a container, the protective material in liquid state is poured into the container, and cured or otherwise hardened to a solid state. The container or "pot" becomes an integral part of the finished assembly. Embedding involves a similar process, except the container serves only as a mold for casting the protective material around the component. Encapsulation usually refers to the use of a coating which conforms to the contours of the protected components. Encapsulation is usually accomplished by dipping the component or by spraying the protective coating on the component.

The enviromental hazards that bring about the need for potting, encapsulation or embedding may include low and high temperature conditions, moisture, oils, abrasive dusts, chemicals, vibration, mechanical shock, and other challenges to satisfactory performance. The selection of the protective material calls for consideration of the environmental hazards, consideration of the processing and handling requirements of the materials, and consideration of the overall economics of using one protective material in preference to another to meet the required conditions.

Potting and encapsulation are terms most often associated with the electronics industry, although the protective coating concept is far from new, and is in fact about as old as the electrical industry. Asphalts, tars, waxes, and phenolics have been in use as potting and embedding compounds for years, and these materials continue to offer a low cost protection in electrical industry applications where the temperature range of operation, and the electrical requirements are not demanding.

In the electronics industry, the epoxies are

FIG. 1. Encapsulation—Object is encapsulated by dipping, painting or spraying process. Above, a transformer is encapsulated by dipping method in liquid silicone rubber. (*Courtesy General Electric Co.*)

widely used potting and encapsulating materials. Silicones were developed during and after World War II, and found considerable use in aerospace electronics. In recent years they have been widely used in non-military electronics as well. The combined sale of silicones for both military and non-military applications places them in second position for electronic potting and encapsulating use. Other materials that are used include urethanes, polyesters, vinyls and polysulfides.

Epoxies

The popularity of the epoxies for electronic potting and encapsulation is related to both properties and versatility. Available in a wide range of viscosities, the epoxies through choice of curing agent may be cured at either room temperature or elevated temperature. The cured resin may be hard and rigid, or, through the use of modifiers, can be altered to provide a soft, flexible material. Shrinkage is relatively low

for a thermosetting resin, about 2% as compared to 8–10% for polyesters. Polymerization is by addition reaction and the ether linkages, protected esters and carbon nitrogen bonds are quite stable. Epoxies have excellent chemical resistance, outstanding adhesion to most materials, and good electrical properties. They provide a tough hard coating of considerable rigidity and strength, and are particularly well suited for making electronic assemblies resistant to vibration and mechanical damage.

Using the same basic epoxy resin it is possible to obtain many different properties through the choice of curing agent, the use of flexibilizers, and the use of fillers. Typically tertiary amine curing agents are used for room temperature cure. Aliphatic primary amines will cure at room temperature or slightly elevated temperature. Cure is very rapid with considerable exotherm, and pot life is short. Acid anhydrides are used for elevated temperature cure. With this type curing agent, "one-part" systems with a long useful pot life are achieved. Typical epoxy flexibilizers are polysulfides, polyamides, and polyamines. Fillers are used in epoxies to reduce curing exotherm and shrinkage, to reduce cost, to increase thermal conductivity, and to improve thermal stability. Silica fillers, mica, glass, and aluminum oxide are among the typical materials used.

FIG. 2. Potting—Potting method involves placing the object to be protected into a case and pouring a protective compound around it. (*Courtesy General Electric Co.*)

Some of the general purpose epoxy resins sell for under $1.00 lb, with a typical price of perhaps 70¢ lb. There are many manufacturers and formulators of epoxy resins readily found in material supplier catalogues. A wide range of formulations are available off-the-shelf, and custom formulations can be provided to meet unusual potting and encapsulation needs.

Perhaps the biggest disadvantage to the use of epoxy resins is related to handling properties. Some of the curing agents used do pose toxicity problems, particularly in relation to skin irritation, and precautions are necessary in handling these materials. The exothermic cure of some epoxies and resultant shrinkage can set up stresses on delicate electronic components resulting in damage to parts, particularly when the assembly is subjected to thermal cycling in use. In some instances the use of elastomeric encapsulants, such as RTV silicone rubber, around the components prior to potting serves to cushion the component against epoxy potting stresses. Fillers are also often used in the epoxy to reduce the shrinkage.

The epoxies, together with the silicones, are the most widely used electronic potting and encapsulating materials.

Silicones

The earliest uses of silicones as potting, encapsulating, and embedding materials was primarily related to their utility over an extremely wide temperature range, from temperatures as low as $-150°F$, to as high as $600°F$. This continues to be an important reason for their use, but an equally important consideration in their selection is the ease of use of these materials. Silicones are generally nontoxic, odorless, and easy to handle, both on small scale and production line applications.

Silicones have excellent electrical properties that are maintained over the wide temperature range. They have very low moisture absorption characteristics, and will maintain good electrical properties, even immersed in water.

The most popular silicones for potting and encapsulation are the RTV (room temperature vulcanizing) silicone rubber compounds. These are available in a range of consistencies, from easy pouring liquids to spreadable pastes. With the addition of a curing agent, typically dibutyl tin dilaurate or tin octoate, the RTV's cure to a solid elastomer ranging in hardness from about 15–60 Shore A durometer. Most of the silicones cure by condensation reaction. There is no exotherm on curing, and shrinkage is vitually nil. The cure rate may be adjusted by the type and amount of curing agent, and cure may be accelerated with elevated temperature.

Until recently, RTV's unlike epoxies, did not adhere to a variety of materials. Improved adhesion can be achieved with a paintable silicone resin-containing material. In addition, silicones are repairable. The cured material may be cut with a knife, a faulty electronic component removed and replaced, and the assembly resealed by pouring more catalyzed RTV in to fill the cutaway portion. There are, in fact, clear transparent grades of room temperature curing silicones designed to facilitate potted component identification and repair.

Recently introduced silicone products for electronic applications include the ready-to-use silicone adhesive sealants. These materials require no seperate curing agent. The moisture from the air catalyzes the condensation reaction and causes cure to take place at room temperature. These products, supplied in sealed containers such as collapsible tubes and plastic caulking cartridges, will bond to most materials without the need for primer. They find use as adhesives as well as elastomeric encapsulants. Because moisture from the air is required for cure, these materials are generally used in thicknesses of $\frac{1}{8}$in. or less.

Another recent development in silicone potting materials are room temperature curing compounds which cure by a vinyl addition reaction rather than a condensation reaction. These materials yield no by-products during cure, nor require any air for cure to take place, and will cure in sections of unlimited depth or in completely sealed assemblies. A primer is sometimes used to improve adhesion.

The biggest disadvantages to silicone potting materials is their relatively high cost, typically about $4.00 per lb. In spite of this, their excellent properties and ease of handling make them often the best choice and many times the lowest overall cost way of meeting the application requirements.

Polyurethanes

Rigid polyurethane foams are used extensively in potting low power, high frequency electronic assemblies. The low dielectric constant, dissipation factor, and light weight make them particularly useful for high frequency aerospace applications. The ability of the foams to absorb mechanical shock is also a plus for assemblies that must be potted to withstand high impact and mechanical shock. They have good thermal shock resistance, and a low coefficient of thermal expansion.

The disadvantages of the polyurethane foams are poor thermal conductivity, low dielectric strength, and poor handling properties from the standpoint of short pot life and toxicity problems that must be factored into their use.

Solid polyurethane materials have found limited use in electronic applications. Their

ELECTRONIC PACKAGING MATERIALS—TYPICAL PROPERTIES.

	Unfilled Epoxy	Polysulfide	RTV Silicone	Polyurethane Foam	Polyvinyl Chloride	Unfilled Polyester
Specific gravity	1.0 − 1.2	1.3	1.0 − 1.5	0.16	1.3	1.1
Cured hardness	>80 Shore D	40 Shore A	15–65 Shore A	—	80 Shore D	>80 Shore D
Tensile strength, psi	10,000	300	350–800	250–400	3000	8000
Elongation, %	1–5	400	100–200	—	100	<5
Linear expansion, in./in. °F	4×10^{-5}	10×10^{-5}	12×10^{-5}	2×10^{-5}	3×10^{-5}	6×10^{-5}
Heat resistance	up to 400°F	up to 250°F	up to 600°F	up to 300°F	up to 225°F	up to 300°F
Volume resistivity, ohm-cm	10^{14}	10^9–10^{11}	10^{14}	$10^{11} - 10^{13}$	$10^{12} - 10^{14}$	10^{13}
Dielectric strength, volts/mil	450	150	550	250	400	350
Dielectric constant	2.8–3.5	7–14	3–4	1.2–1.3	3.5	3.5
Dissipation factor	0.01–0.02	0.1	0.02	0.003	0.05	0.05
Approx. cost per lb	$0.70	$1.00	4.00	$2.00	$0.25	$0.40
Advantages	Excellent chemical resistance. Excellent adhesion. Good electrical properties. Hard and tough.	Solvent and oil resistance. Resistance to weathering.	Outstanding thermal stability. Nontoxic, easy to use. Excellent electrical properties.	Light weight low electrical loss at high frequency. Low thermal expansion.	Low cost. Tough for use as conformal coating, as plastisol or organosol.	Low Cost Low viscosity. Ease of use.
Disadvantages	Toxicity problems in handling. Exothermic cure with resultant shrinkage.	Relatively poor electricals. Limited thermal stability.	Relatively high cost. Most grades require primer for adhesion.	Poor thermal conductivity. Short pot life. Toxicity problems in handling.	Limited temperature stability. Relatively high moisture absorption.	High shrinkage. Relatively high moisture absorption.

electrical properties are not good at elevated temperature, and handling properties are difficult.

Vinyls

Polyvinyl chloride in the form of plastisols or organosols is sometimes used as a conformal encapsulant. The component is dipped into a suspension of polyvinyl chloride particles in plasticizer and the adhering particles baked to fuse to continous coating. A polyvinyl organosol, which is a solution of polyvinyl chloride in solvent, may be applied by brushing, dipping, or spraying. Baking is also used to form the continuous coat.

These coatings are limited in use temperature to about 100°C, have relatively high moisture absorption characteristics, and relatively poor electrical properties at high frequencies.

Polyesters

Once used widely in electronic work, the polyesters have given way, for the most part, to epoxies. Supplied as liquids, the polyesters cure using a peroxide catalyst and heat. The reaction is an addition reaction but shrinkage is high, in the order of 6–8%. The high shrinkage and resultant problems with cracking or component damage, high moisture absorption, and a maximum use temperature of about 125°–150°C, have

resulted in a decline in the use of polyesters in favor of other materials.

Polysulfide Rubber

Polysulfide rubbers are available as liquids for use in electronic applications. The cured rubber compound has good resistance to solvents, oxidation, and weathering. Electrical properties are poor compared to silicone elastomers, and their use is limited to applications where low volume resistivity and a high dielectric constant can be tolerated. Their good oil and solvent resistance make them useful in electronic packaging applications where exposure to oils and fuels is a problem.

JAMES W. HAWKINS

POWDERED METALS

Metallic fillers lend many useful qualities to plastics materials, depending on their size, shape, concentration and surface chemistry. Some metallic fillers are highly decorative, while others are chosen for their functional attributes. Although manufacturers of powdered metals are concerned primarily with applications to the field of powder metallurgy, the growing volume and useful combinations with plastics are encouraging more interest on their part.

The incorporation of metallic powders into plastics depends upon the form of the plastic at the time of blending and the processing aids available. Liquid plastics permit the easiest addition—a stir in proposition with adequate shear action and formulating techniques to maintain reasonable suspension of the metallic fillers. Solutions of plastics which are low in viscosity will permit copious additions of metallic fillers, but because they are solutions, volatiles must be removed and the end product is usually in film form after solvents are evaporated. Solid thermoplastics or Stage B solid thermosetting plastics may be fluxed on a mill and while semi-fluid, be blended with finely divided metallic fillers. This operation may also be accompanied by further attrition grinding operations to attain a fine mesh size and further filler distribution. Another alternative method of blending solid resin particles and metallic powders is by ball or pebble milling. In all instances, care must be exercised to prevent the hazards of explosive dusts and the pyrophoric qualities of some of the metallic fillers. Health and safety measures must be rigorously observed.

In the following paper an analysis will be made of the functional requirements of plastics filled with powdered metals. There are many reasons why plastics and powdered metals are brought into combination. The background leading to unique combinations will be reviewed and appropriate examples cited of blends of plastics and metals.

Among the functional classifications of powdered metals and plastics are the following groups.

Electrical. The electrical conductivity of metal filled plastics depends upon the identity of the metallic filler and its concentration in the plastics matrix. Minor additions of copper, aluminum or silver powder to a plastics material does not necessarily produce marked improvements in the electrical conductivity. In general, the metallic particles surrounded by non-conductive plastic, offer negligible contribution to electrical or thermal conductivity. Only when the metallic particle concentration is sufficiently high so as to entail frequent, though random physical contacts of the metal particles with one another at their interfaces, does the electrical resistivity markedly drop in value. When one reaches that desirable concentration, viscosity of the system of resin plus metallic filler is inordinately high and the pouring of a liquid system or flow of a thermoplastic system are sluggish. Resistivity of the

Fig. 1. Steel-filled epoxy-tooling resins used as back ups for explosive forming die. (*Courtesy Furane and North American Aviation.*)

order of .05 ohm-cm may be attained. The actual value may vary within a given mass due to gravitational separation of the conductive filler and its resin binder.

Cure shrinkage of a thermosetting resin matrix or thermal shrinkage of a resin binder, suggest that a processing of resin and metallic filler, if concluded with a volume reduction of the resin, will bring the metallic particles into closer and tighter contact with one another, and hence better electrical conductivity.

In practice, the development of conductive resin adhesives has resorted primarily to finely divided powder dispersed 80% to 85% on a weight basis. Price savings may be effected with silver coated copper flakes, which are available at much lower cost than the pure silver. Conductive adhesives are a typical application of silver filled plastics, running into many hundreds of pounds per year for the electronic industries. They are used on some semiconductor circuits where the heat of welding or brazing is detrimental to the components.

For semiconductive plastic formulations, to bleed off static charges or to reduce sparking hazards, as on hospital floors, lesser amounts of copper or silver may be used in plastic coatings and maintained in suspension by thixotropic agents which may well be acetylene black. The latter is useful in its own right as a semiconductive type of filler. The resistivities for antistatic coatings are usually at or under 10^6 ohm-cm.

Thermal. The principles of close, intimate contact of metal particles, as noted above for electrically conductive systems, are likewise true of metallic fillers selected for their thermal conductivity. Greater heat stability is not contributed by the metallic filler (though some of the oxides such as arsenic trioxide will help), but better thermal conductivity, among the major requirements for improved thermal conductivity in plastics formulations. Applications to high temperature, nonmetallic tooling and heat sinks for dissipating heat arising in electrical systems are major uses for improved thermally conductive systems. The more massive requirements preclude the use of silver and copper, and aluminum fillers are preferred. Due to the macroscopic nature of the requirements, physical limitations on particle sizes are no longer deterrent. In the accompanying photograph of a high temperature (300° to 400°F) service in nonmetallic tooling, there is a liberal use made of acicular grades of aluminum. Typical needles averaging $\frac{1}{4}$ inch in length and fine pellets of aluminum are also used. In practice, one will find a combination of finely divided powders and granules densely packed to achieve a maximum volume percentage of metallic fillers and hence a maximum thermal conductivity.

One system, extensively used for the manufacture of good thermal conductivity systems is described as the Veritool process (developed by Boeing Airplane Company). Comprised of high temperature epoxy resins and curing agents, the

FIG. 2. EPOCAST 8230–1 Veritool material used to make high heat transfer molds. Smooth gel coated surface fashioned from EPOCAST 8251 (Verigel).

aluminum filled mixtures are cured at elevated temperatures to provide back-up for nonmetallic tooling. Typical properties include:

Density	100 to 110 lb/cu ft
Heat distortion temperature	475°F
Coefficient of Thermal expansion	$29. \times 10^{-6}$ in./in./°C
Thermal conductivity	2.34×10^{-2} gm cal/ cm/cm²/sec/°C
Compressive strength at 70°F	4,900 psi
at 450°F	3,000 psi

Metallic fillers may also take on another guise to enhance thermal conductivity—that of fine fibers. Some equipment has been designed to spray metallic fibers, in conjunction with metallic (aluminum) powdered filled resins to achieve good thermal conductivity. Many hundreds of aluminum powder and needle filled epoxy castings have been used as nonmetallic tooling for the preparation of reinforced plastics, under heat and pressure, as bonding fixtures for metal assemblies, and as vacuum forming tools for heated thermoplastics.

Strength. Metallic powders do not contribute much to the strength of plastic matrices. However, if the reinforcements are in the form of fibers or woven wire lamina, the strength imparted may be substantial. Boron fibers are a noteworthy example of a semi-metal showing promise of contributing substantially to the strength of a plastics system. However, one must not overlook the considerable improvement vouchsafed through glass fibers at a reasonable cost. In principle, fine metallic whiskers have innate strength factors which may be considered should they become commercially available at moderate cost. The strength of fine iron whiskers is very high and properly distributed in an appropriate matrix, the fine whiskers will contribute to the strength of the composite structure.

Density. The concept of variable density in a machine element has practical significance. High density and maximum strength at regions of high probable stress concentration are good design precepts. Metallic powder filled materials introduced in the required concentrations and over a planned program may achieve a planned density distribution. In casting a liquid system, the more dense metal particles settle downward due to gravity or outward due to centrifugal force— either means a convenient process for effecting a density distribution.

Radiation. The shielding of gamma radiation is most practically accomplished through the inclusion of high density lead fillers. The shielding against thermal neutrons is best achieved through boron fillers (as B_4C). Effective radiation shields against a broad spectrum of radiation may be prepared from combinations of finely divided metallic elements dispersed in plastics matrices. Efficient radiation shields are obtained from specific metallic elements which in combination with plastic binders achieve results which are impractical in metallurgy processes. The preparation of conformable coatings as radiation resistant shields and the design of radiation shields for personnel protection, in nuclear power plants, require the design and selection of specific metallic-filled plastics.

One other illustration entails the use of flexible aprons of lead filled, rubber-like compounds of value to X-ray laboratories and operating technicians. Highly resilient, lead filled, cast polyurethanes would represent another radiation shield.

Prevention of Marine Growths. Copper and copper oxides dispersed in coatings formulations are marked deterrents to barnacles and other marine growths. The bottom coating developed for marine service is formulated so that there is a slow erosion over a period of years, slowly exposing fresh copper and copper oxide. Other organic deterrents may be used, but historically, powdered copper occupies a favored position on military specifications. Many thousands of gallons of copper filled bottom paints are specified and used by marine establishments each year.

Decorative. Perhaps the most widely used reason for the inclusion of metallic fillers in plastics is for their decorative appeal. Appearances as a silvery article or as a bronzed article offer sales advantages in numerous circumstances. Special leafing grades of aluminum, copper, or brass are introduced into all manners of plastics formulations with pleasing results. Thermoplastic sheets of the cellulosics and vinyls feature specular grades of metallic particles which lend much sales appeal. The distribution and selection of decorative uses of metallic fillers are limited only by the imagination of the designer or the fabricator of these sheet stocks

Corrosion Control. The sacrificial qualities of zinc have been used to advantage in the manufacture of zinc-rich coatings for application as primers to steel surfaces. The quantities of zinc are large in these formulations, usually in the neighborhood of 90% by weight. However, functioning as a primer coating, the presence of zinc as a sacrificial element will protect the steel structure. The safest practice for the inclusion of zinc dust is to add the material as a dry powder to a liquid resin blend. If premixed and added to closed containers there is always the probability of the zinc reacting with traces of water to liberate hydrogen and build up a pressure within the container. Hence dry, powdered zinc is added to the resin mixture just prior to its application as a coating.

Summary of Metallic Fillers and Important Applications to Plastics

	Property emphasized	Used in
Powdered iron	Machineability and reduced shrinkage	Nonmetallic tooling
Iron whiskers	High strength	Experimental structures
Powdered aluminum	Machineability and thermal conductivity	Nonmetallic tooling and heat sink
Aluminum needles	Improved thermal conductivity	Nonmetallic tooling
Powdered zinc	Corrosion protection	Sacrificial element in coatings
Powdered stainless steel	Machineability and reduced shrinkage	Repair compounds with optimum chemical resistance
Powdered lead	High density and shielding from radiation and sound dampening	Shielding compounds and ballast noise control in machinery
Powdered bronzes and brasses	Decorative	Many decorative coatings and sheets
Aluminum leafing grades	Decorative	Many decorative coatings and sheets
Boron fibers	High strength	Experimental structures. Radiation shields.
Powdered nickel and cobalt	Semiconductive properties	Limited
Powdered magnesium	Pyrophoric qualities	Fireworks and flares
Powdered silver	Electrical conductivity	Conductive adhesives
Powdered copper	Electrical conductivity and thermal transfer	As heat sink and some uses in nonmetallic tooling

JOHN DELMONTE

"PREPREGS"—PREIMPREGNATED LAMINATE MATERIALS

Reinforced plastics refer to the class of composite materials consisting of a cured resin and a structural reinforcement, combined to yield unique properties. The raw materials are available in two basic forms:

(A) Liquid resin, filler, and reinforcement, combined just prior to cure (wet layup).

(B) Prepreg, wherein the reinforcement is preimpregnated with liquid resin, and partially cured to a relatively non-liquid state.

The relative advantages and disadvantages of wet layup vs. preimpregnated materials are shown in Table 1. Experience has indicated that consistency of strength properties is slightly better when "B" staged materials are used, and that strengths are generally higher.

Hidden advantages of preimpregnated fabrics (especially for smaller molders without laboratory facilities) are:

(1) Knowledge of resin chemistry and resin handling need be minimum.

(2) Research facilities of impregnators are available.

(3) Custom designed materials are available.

(4) Initial investment in equipment is low.

Impregnation Process

The impregnating of the carriers or reinforcements is basically accomplished by application of the resin from a solvent solution or a hot melt. This usually is followed with the application of heat and advancing the cure of the resinous material to a partially cured state.

Very little information on the impregnation cycle appears in the literature. Impregnators have had to develop their own techniques and specially modified equipment to perform the job required by industry. Both horizontal and vertical towers, with accurate temperature control in heating zones, have been used successfully.

The addition of a synthetic resin in a solvent solution ("A" stage) to a woven fabric or mat from a dip pan necessitates precise control of web tension, resin viscosity, resin solids, speed and temperature. Other factors come into play, but these are the most important.

The degree of "B" stage (partial advancement of the resin on the cloth to give desired drape, flow, tack, etc.) is a function of temperature, speed (or time at a given temperature), resin content, and resin type. It is the unique balancing of these factors that determines the quality of a particular piece of impregnated goods.

TABLE 1. COMPARISON OF WET LAYUP AND PREIMPREGNATED MOLDING SYSTEMS.

Resin types	Wet layup Polyester; epoxy	Preimpregnated Polyester: phenolic silicone, epoxy
Resin/glass control	Poor	Good
General strength properties	Fair–good	Good–excellent
Reproducibility	Fair–good	Excellent
Direct labor costs (molding)	High	Low
Material costs	Low	High
Items inventoried (number)	3–6	1
Cost of impregnating equipment	Low–medium	High
Dermatitis problems	High	Low

385

During the curing process, resins pass through three stages, designated "A," "B," and "C". Initially in the "A" stage, the resin is soluble and fusible. Upon application of heat (e.g. during impregnation) the resin advances to the "B" stage, where it becomes a fusible solid with limited solubility. Further heat (e.g. during final cure) advances the resin into the fully cured "C" stage, where it is hard, infusible and insoluble. An example of this process is outlined in Figure 1, Schematic Diagram of Impregnating Process.

A further example of the flexibility of the process can be illustrated. Phenolic resins may be impregnated and transformed to the "B" stage when exposed to temperatures of about 300°F, for a period of about 4 min, when the desired resin and volatile contents are 32% and 5% respectively.

Upon temperature increase, perhaps to 350°F, and reduction of the time of exposure so that an end product of the same resin and volatile content is attained, on the surface it would appear that we have an identical product, and have produced it at higher speeds. Actually, the product is more advanced (to a further "B" stage). This is evidenced by a sharply reduced percentage flow during laminating. This phenomenon is due to the effect of temperature on the rate of polymerization of phenolic resins. It is an exponential function, while time at a given temperature more closely approximates a straight line relationship. The above facts must be taken into consideration by impregnators for each of the resin systems used.

Resin Systems

The resin binds together and stabilizes the reinforcements into a solid, cured, composite material, usually exhibiting anisotropic properties.

The resin must perform this function by acting like a controlled flow casting, during both the impregnation and the final curing. It must thoroughly "wet" the reinforcement and fill its interstices. This process is aided by application of positive pressure, vacuum, or both during cure. These resins are usually thermosetting in nature, but some thermoplastic resins also are used for impregnating.

The thermosetting resin is one which cures into a relatively hard infusible state. The cure is normally induced by external or internal (chemical) heating. When cured, the thermoset will not soften, even though the temperature is raised substantially above the curing temperatures.

Thermoplastic resins will soften at a given temperature and harden on cooling below this temperature. They will continue to function almost indefinitely in this manner each time they are heated to this temperature and cooled.

Resins of thermoset thermoplastic mixtures will exhibit some or both of its constituent resin characteristics. The resulting material may or may not be superior to either of its counterparts, depending on formulation and use.

The introduction of reinforced thermoplastics is fairly recent. The initial use was in areas where end users found the unreinforced thermoplastic resins to be marginal or failing. Since then, these compounds have come into their own as engineering materials, and fit the performance gap between metals and base resins. Many injection molders find them superior in processing, thanks to shorter cycles and ease of flow. As with thermosets, the chief reinforcing material used with thermoplastics is fibrous glass, with limited work done with asbestos, fluorocarbon, and other fibers. Typical resins used are "Nylon," acrylonitrile-butadiene-styrene (ABS) family, acetals,

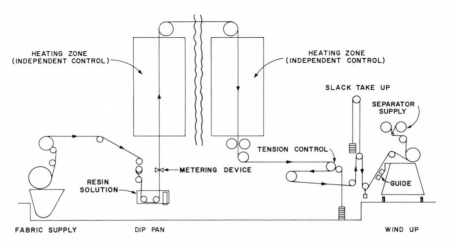

FIG. 1. Schematic diagram of impregnating process.

polycarbonates, styrenes, and styrene-acrylonitriles, and polypropylene.

Unlike reinforced thermosets, the reinforced thermoplastics are almost entirely processed by injection molding. Hence, the reinforcing material is in the form of chopped fibers, the molding compounds are in pellets, and the length of the reinforcing fibers is an important factor.

Applications range from automobile crash pads to clothes hangers, precision molded machine parts, bearings, gears, coil forms, blower wheels, appliances, power tools, and electronic equipment. They are often used as direct replacements for die cast or stamped metals, or for applications where unreinforced plastics do not have adequate physical properties or good working characteristics.

Thermosetting resins are most popular because they provide rigidity, dimensional stability, and good bond strength under a wide range of operating conditions. While there are a large number of resins that can be employed, the five groups most extensively used today are as follows:

(The balance of this article will deal with the thermoset prepreg materials.)

Phenolics. These are the most common of the resins. The total production of phenolic resins for all uses in the United States is many hundreds of millions of pounds per year. Only a very small portion of this is used for preimpregnated materials. The largest consumption in this area is impregnation of paper and canvas for electrical and industrial uses. A relatively small, but extremely important application is the impregnation of glass, asbestos, graphite, carbon, and silica woven fabrics for high temperature structural and ablative applications in the aerospace and aircraft industry.

Phenolic resins cure to a straw yellow or a dark brown color, and have good electrical properties, high mechanical strength, and excellent chemical resistance. Their resistance to high temperatures (500°F and higher) is good.

Low pressure or high pressure techniques can be used with these materials and this, in combination with their low cost, makes them a desirable material.

The major limitations of "B" stages phenolic prepregs are color, color control, and by-products of the condensation reaction. The resin, in the liquid form ("A" stage), contains about 10%–15% water. During advancement to the "B" stage, more water is produced and driven off, along with solvent, leaving from 2.0%–5.0% volatiles (largely water) in the impregnated web. (This is the volatile content.)

During cure some volatile matter remains trapped in the laminate. As a result, it is difficult to produce translucent, void-free laminates. Some work has indicated that the presence of these gas pores in the laminate is of definite aid in attaining high temperature strengths. Differences in the rate of expansion of the resin and glass under high temperature exposure produce stresses and strains that, if not relieved by the presence of minute gas pockets, would materially reduce strength.

One of the major advantages of the phenolic-impregnated glass cloth is the variety of properties that can be controlled for the user. Variations in flow, drape, resin content, tack and other properties can be built into the material during the "B" stage process. Thus, material can be designed for specific applications, with equipment and production problems in mind.

Because phenolic resins are supplied in solvent solutions, pre-loading the reinforcement is necessary to remove solvents during advancement to the "B" stage.

For specially high temperature applications, phenyl-silanes are used in prepreg form. Their handling properties are similar to the phenolics, but more critical in nature.

Epoxy Resins. The major use of impregnated epoxy resins is for printed circuits. Other uses are tooling (which consumes the major portion of liquid epoxy resins, using wet layup methods), aircraft parts, ducts, and tubular sections. Many experimental materials are under investigation, and over the past few years there has been a resurgence of interest in the epoxy impregnated materials for structural aircraft applications.

The epoxy resins are characterized by low shrinkage during polymerization (2% or less compared to 4%–8% for polyesters), excellent mechanical, electrical and chemical resistance properties, very low water absorption, and excellent dimensional stability. While the base resins are higher in cost than phenolics or polyesters, in impregnated form the price differentials are not as great.

In "B" stage impregnated form, the catalyzed epoxies can be tailored to give high or low flow, drape, tack, and other handling properties that are desirable for specific applications. Other characteristics of the preimpregnated materials are the generally excellent storage life of the cloth, the production of almost colorless, translucent, high density laminates; and suitability for both high and low pressure molding. A major advantage of the epoxy system is the low volatile content and the absence of volatile by-products during cure.

Some of the disadvantages of the epoxy resins, in general, are extreme adhesion to mold surfaces, generally poor high temperature resistance (although this is being improved), slightly longer cure cycles, and generally higher cure temperatures than required for polyesters.

Silicone Resins. The silicones have gained in

popularity where good high temperature properties and unusual electrical properties are required. Based on organo-silicon compounds, they are the most heat stable materials, presently in production, for fiberglass-reinforced plastics. Since they are available as solvent solutions only, they must be supplied in a "B" stage preimpregnated web. Here again, as in the case of the phenolics, volatile by-products are given off.

While the initial strengths of silicone resin laminates are low, strengths are retained over long periods of exposure to high temperatures (500°F or higher). Molding and curing cycles are critical and long. These materials are also suitable for high and low pressure molding, but require extensive postcuring to attain ultimate strength.

F–12 glass is generally recommended for silicone resins, but recent work has indicated that superior strengths can be attained with specially designed pre-finishes. Actual increases recorded have been as high as 25% initial strength. The use of "Volan" pre-finished cloth is definitely not recommended.

The "B" staging of silicone resins is a critical operation. The amount of "B" staging, or advancement, has a definite effect on strength. This is not generally so with other resin systems. It appears that a minimum exposure to certain temperatures is required if high ultimate strengths are desired. This generally means that the silicone-preimpregnated fabrics, whether designed for high or low pressure applications, will appear dry and stiff to the touch. This is accentuated by the rapid loss of solvent (toluene) when exposed to room conditions.

The major disadvantages of silicone resin-preimpregnated glass cloth are high cost, low initial mechanical strengths, difficulty in handling, extensive postcuring, high curing temperatures and critical curing conditions.

The advantages of the silicone-preimpregnated glass cloth are good mechanical strength of laminates for long-time exposure to high temperatures and good electrical properties.

Silicone resins are not designed to be competitive with other organic resins which function satisfactorily under prevailing conditions, but rather to *supplement* these resins in more severe applications, and to span the gap between organic resins and ceramics or metals. As a result, expected usage will be small, but growth should be steady.

Polyester Resins. The volume of preimpregnated polyester-fiberglass is fairly small; the great majority of reinforced fiberglass parts are produced using wet layup and spray-up techniques.

Included in the preimpregnated polyesters are the crystalline types (hot melt or solvent dip application), of which some new ones are appearing for evaluation; diallyl phthalate (DAP)

catalyzed with tert-butyl perbenzoate (impregnated from a solvent solution); and DAP-modified polyesters. These materials, with the possible exception of DAP, are not truly "B" staged. Passage through the heating zones merely removes solvent, since catalyzed polyesters will generally continue to react once polymerization begins.

The disadvantages of polyester-fiberglass are high shrinkage during cure, resulting in poor surfaces and poor water resistance (offset somewhat by use of fillers); flammability; temperature limitations (generally not used above surface temperatures of 250°F, except TAC modified types); and cost compared to wet layup.

The advantages of preimpregnated polyesters are ease of handling by the molder; colorless, sometimes translucent, high density laminates; short cure times at relatively low temperatures (220°–275°F); and generally adequate mechanical, electrical and chemical properties for most applications.

Melamine Resins. The consumption of melamine preimpreganted materials is directed mainly towards the electrical and housewares trade. Melamine is a high cost resin whose laminate strength is high. High pressure is generally required for adequate molding, and resultant laminates are somewhat brittle. New grades have been developed for low pressure applications. Melamine face sheet materials (paper) are generally used for table top and wall covering applications because of the toughness of the resin and resistance to abrasion. They are particularly noted for resistance to arcing and tracking, and are used extensively for electrical applications.

Other Resins. Industry is in need of high performance laminating resins and adhesives for structural radomes, wing tips and fairings on future supersonic transports and bombers (SST). These materials must have better high temperature strength and oxidation resistance than the phenolics, phenyl-silane, and silicone resins which are the current standards for high temperature applications. Significantly higher thermal and oxidative stability is obtainable from polymeric systems comprised of heterocyclic recurring units. Two polyaromatic resin systems, polybenzimidazole and polyimide, are now commercially available as glass fabric prepregs. Test data are shown in Table 6.

Reinforcements. Reinforcements usually take the form of organic, inorganic, or metallic fibers. They may be used individually as filaments, or grouped as roving, in random orientation and direction as a mat, or in woven fabrics. The contribution of the reinforcement is to provide most of the strength and stiffness of the cured prepreg composite.

Prepregs are available with various finishes on

the reinforcement. A finish, when applied to the reinforcement prior to impregnating with resin, affects the handling characteristics, moisture absorption, fatigue, creep, and static strength of the cured prepreg composite. The finish or sizing of the fiber must be compatible with the resin system used, as well as provide good adhesive strength to the reinforcement. This is particualrly true for glass fiber reinforcements.

The type of reinforcement also affects the handling characteristics of the prepreg to a great degree. Thickness, strength, and stiffness affect its drape characteristics. Table 2 shows specific reinforcement material types most commonly used.

TABLE 2. SPECIFIC REINFORCEMENT MATERIAL—TYPES MOST COMMONLY USED.

Inorganic	Metallic	Organic	Composite
E-Glass	Steel	Nylon	Boron-Tungsten
S-Glass	Aluminum	Polypropylene	Metal coated-inorganic
Carbon	Beryllium	Acrylic	Metal coated-organic
Graphite	Tungsten	Cotton	
Quartz	Copper	"Dacron"	
Silica			
Asbestos		"Rayon"	
		"Paper"	

The engineer must choose his material for strength, stiffness, environmental resistance, and thickness per ply for end-product application. The thorough knowledge of the reinforcing materials in their various forms is necessary for the proper selection of reinforcements for efficient, producible, and economical structural designs.

Fillers

While the primary reinforcements in preimpregnated materials are in fibrous form, fillers are often used for specific reinforcement properties. The presence of fillers in the resin tends to reduce crazing, shrinkage, coefficient of expansion, and porosity, and can improve moldability. In the finished cured products, surface appearance, dimensional stability, wearability, strength, and resistance to temperature, moisture, flame, and cold flow can be improved by the selection of appropriate resin fillers. Filler materials range from wood flour to cotton flock, alpha cellulose, silica, lignin, glass flake and beads, microballoons, mica, clay, talc, alumina, and powdered metals. The specific filler chosen for a resin/reinforcement combination is a highly engineered choice based on the chemistry of the resin and end use application.

Properties

Mechanical and physical properties taken from randomly selected manufacturer's woven prepregs are shown in Table 3. These properties were attained using standard test methods for woven glass cloth reinforcements. The preparation of the test laminates was usually done within ASTM or government specifications and usually with the manufacturer's recommended modifications.

In Table 4, the mechanical, physical and electrical properties are shown for a typical non-woven glass reinforcement prepreg. In this case the material is 3M Company, "Scotch Ply" 1002, which is an E-glass reinforced epoxy composite. Although these materials exhibit superior properties to the woven materials in specific orientations, they are harder to handle during layup and more expensive. However, where specific strengths are required in highly oriented structures, these disadvantages are more than offset by the excellent properties of the material. Table 4 does show the effect of orientation which is critical with woven materials and must be taken into consideration in the design of structures containing woven or orientated materials. Table 5 shows some mechanical properties of filament winding materials comparing both wet layup and prepreg. It can be seen that these NOL ring test data are about the same for prepregs or wet layup. In general, prepreg filament winding materials are more expensive but have the major advantage of close control and testing prior to application.

Table 6 shows the ultimate strength of the heat resistant resin systems, PBI and polyimide, compared to the phenolics.

Molding Processes

There are basically many methods for molding preimpregnated materials. Some of these are shown in Figs 2, 3, 4, and 5. These are vacuum bag, shrink tape wrap, pressure bag, and matched die molding. Typical curing cycles for these various systems are outlined in Table 7.

Vacuum Bag Molding. Layers of impregnated material are placed by hand against the mold surface (which has been coated with release agents), usually using heat guns and/or hot irons. When the desired number of plies have been mounted, a layer of perforated cellophane

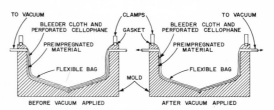

FIG. 2. Vacuum bag molding.

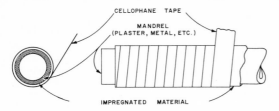

FIG. 3. Shrink tape molding.

(necessary with phenolics and silicones to assist in removing volatile by-products), followed by a layer of heavy glass fabric (bleeder cloth), and possibly some hair felt, are generally added. (Epoxy systems do not require bleeder materials.) These absorptive layers will tend to equalize pressure and facilitate removal of the volatile constituents. A pressure membrane such as polyvinyl alcohol (PVA) or synthetic rubber is then used to completely encase the layup, with provision for a vacuum outlet. Obviously the maximum pressure developed will be 14.7 psi, which is sufficient for most preimpregnated fabrics.

Vacuum bag molding is generally recommended where the number of parts to be produced

cannot justify the construction of expensive tooling, and the ultimate in properties is not required.

Shrink Tape molding. For specialized applications (such as ducts, fishing rods and general tubular shapes), shrink tape wrapping has been very successful. Here the mold or mandrel is wrapped with the preimpregnated material and then spirally wound with cellophane tape ("Vinylite" or PVA tape can also be used), overlapping somewhat on each revolution. This assembly is then placed in an oven and heated to

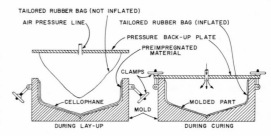

FIG. 4. Pressure bag molding.

TABLE 3. TYPICAL GLASS CLOTH LAMINATE PROPERTIES[ab]

Prepreg material (Woven glass cloth)	Mechanical						
	Tensile F_{TU} ksi	Compressive F_{CU} ksi	Bending F_{BU} ksi	Johnson shear F_{SU} ksi	Flexural E kksi	Rigidity G kksi	Poisson's u ratio
Phenolic (181 Volan A)	60.0	48.0	74.0	16.0[i]	3.8		
Polyester Supplier #1 (181 Volan A)	57.0	36.0	70.0	22.7	2.85		
Supplier #2 (181 Volan A)	58.1	47.9	70.0	24.6	3.30		
Cordopreg UVFR (181 MPC-1[c])	50.0	53.2	87.3		3.09		
Epoxy (181 Volan A)	57.0	52.0	88.0		3.70		
(181, I–550[e])	51.8	57.5	78.9		3.30	0.95[h]	0.16[g]
Silicone (181 Cloth)	30.0	25.3	37.0		2.90		
Polybenzimidazole (PBI) Imidite 1850 (1581)	90.0	68.0	115.0		5.60		

[a] All properties obtained on press cured (30 psi) at mfg's recommended temp. on ⅛ in. thick parallel laminates (except as noted) parallel with the warp (0° orientation) (see mfg's data sheets for other orientations).
[b] Wet properties may or may not be less than these.
[c] Proprietary glass cloth finish, Cordo Division Ferro Corp. (ultraviolet cure).
[d] Based on 0.027 in. thick laminate.
[e] Proprietary glass cloth finish, J. P. Stevens Co.
[f] Tested at 8500–10,000 mc.

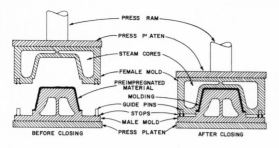

FIG. 5. Matched die molding.

curing conditions. The heat will cause the cellophane (or other wrapping) to shrink about 5%. This shrinkage provides the pressure required for adequate flow of resin. Quite often, when complex ducts are made, a combination of shrink tape wrap and vacuum bag molding is used. This insures adequate pressures at critical areas, such as sharp bends in ducting. Here, the vacuum bag generally encases the spirally-wound part. No bleeder cloth is required. Tension wrap molding is an inexpensive method for molding tubular shapes.

A modification of this process is the high-tension wrap process "SAMSON WRAP" (TM).* Tubular and conical shapes are manufactured by first tape wrapping the prepreg material onto a steel mandrel (cylinder or cone), and then over-wrapping the prepreg with a high strength woven tape, applied under very high tension. The proper application of the over-wrap is critical, especially for large structures and where high pressures are required. The over-wrapped assembly is then cured in an oven. High pressures are generated with this process. resulting in high density structures, without the need for expensive pressure cure vessels.

Pressure Bag Molding. Here the layup is identical to that used in the vacuum bag process, except that a solid sheet (not perforated) of cellophane is used, and no bleeder cloth is necessary. A tailored bag is placed against the cellophane— when this is inflated, pressures of 100 psi or more are applied against the preimpregnated material. This system is used where pressures higher than those developed with the vacuum bag are desired, but equipment costs must be low. The limitation

*Harvey Industries, Inc.

(Randomly Selected Manufacturers' Published Information on Woven Glass Cloth Prepregs).

	Physical				Electrical		
Fatigue[j] limit F_N, ksi	Barcol hardness	Resin content, % by wt (Cured lam.)	S.G.	Thermal coefficient of expansion, in./in./°F $\times 10^{-6}$	Thermal conductivity, $\dfrac{\text{Btu-in.}}{\text{hr-ft}^2\text{-}°F}$	Diel.[f] const.	Loss[f] tang.
12.0		35		5.0	0.80	4.89	0.0510
	67	42		8.5	0.95	4.13	0.0106
	73	35	2.00			3.23	
	70	40	1.86			3.73[d]	0.0200[d] (Max.)
		42				4.6	0.0200
	82	33	1.80			4.27	0.0181
	73		1.93	5.0	0.70	3.98	0.0012
		17				4.70	0.0065

[g] 7581 reinforcement autoclave cured at 50 psi.
[h] Volan A finish, autoclave cured at 50 psi.
[i] In-plane panel shear.
[j] Endurance limit stress at 10 million cycles.

TABLE 4. TYPICAL NONWOVEN GLASS FIBER LAMINATE PROPERTIES—DRY—AT R.T. MECHANICAL, PHYSICAL, AND ELECTRICAL. (3M Co. Scotchply 1002; E-Glass Epoxy)

| Type material | Orientation of reinforcement relative to load | Mechanical | | | | | | | | Physical |
		Ten. F_{TU}, ksi	Comp. F_{CU}, ksi	Bend. F_{BU}, ksi	Stiff. E, ksi	Creep limit F_{CC}, ksi/100 hr	Stress rupture limit F_{SR}, ksi/100 hr	Flexural fatigue F_N, ksi endurance limit*	IZOD impact (edgewise), ft–lb / in. notch	Thermal coefficient of expansion, in./in./°F $\times 10^{-6}$
Unidirectional	0°	160	90	165	5.3		125	38	60.8	4.8
	45°	3.6	25	20	2.0				6.8	
	90°	2.9	20	10	1.6				0.9	12.3
Crossplied	0°	75	75	120	3.5	43	49.5	26.5	35.2	7.1
	45°	22	23	50	2.0				59.2	
	90°	75	75	120	3.5	43	49.5	26.5	35.2	7.1
Isotropic	0°	57	60	80	3.0	37	40	19	40.8	8.4
	45°	43	51	73	2.8	37	40	19	42.3	
	90°	43	51	79	2.7	37	40	19	38.6	

*10⁷ cycles.
Notes: 1. Resin content—36% by weight.
2. Barcol hardness—70.
3. Specific gravity—1.8.
4. Thermal conductivity—2.35 Btu/°F-ft²-hr for 1-inch thick laminate.
5. Dielectric constant at 30 mc—4.4.
6. Dissipation factor—0.023.

TABLE 5. SUMMARY OF ROUND-ROBIN TEST DATA[a].
(Task Group A, Section H, Subcommittee XVIII of ASTM Committee D-20 on Plastics; Average of all Laboratories)

Method	3M S–P 1002 Prepreg	OCF 20E–801 Epoxy[b]	3M S–P 1009 Prepreg	OCF 20E–HTS Epoxy[b]	1/0–890 Epoxy	3M XP–230 X–994(S–901) Prepreg
Split disk method: NOL-Ring						
Tensile strength, psi	147,800	154,100	166,500	210,100	212,400	270,600
Hydraulic method: NOL-Ring						
Tensile strength, psi	143,200	161,800	161,100	219,200	196,500	256,000
Modulus of elasticity, psi $\times 10^6$	6.33	8.25	7.16	8.14	7.73	9.06
Horizontal shear method: Bending						
Shear strength, psi	8515	6069	9022	8945	7736	9351
Ash content, %	72.8	84.8	79.5	85.3	83.6	83.7

[a] ASTM Task Group Report, p. 247.
[b] Wet layup.

TABLE 6. ULTIMATE STRENGTH OF HEAT-RESISTANT LAMINATES.[a]

	Polybenzimidazole[b] S-Glass (psi $\times 10^3$)	Polyimide[c] E-Glass (psi $\times 10^3$)	Phenolic[d] S-Glass (psi $\times 10^3$)	Phenolic[d] E-Glass (psi $\times 10^3$)
0° Tension				
Room temp.	103	54	84	60
Elev temp. $\frac{1}{2}$-hr exp	55	40	66	45
Elev temp. 200-hr exp	20	22	69	—
45° Tension				
Room temp.	26	19	38	—
Elev temp. $\frac{1}{2}$-hr exp	12	2.4	20	—
Elev temp. 200-hr exp	2	5.6	23	—
Stress concentration				
Room temp.	61	31	60	40
Elev temp. $\frac{1}{2}$-hr exp	41	25	46	32
Elev temp. 200-hr exp	15	17	44	—
Bearing				
Room temp.	62	37	54	62
Elev temp. $\frac{1}{2}$-hr exp	37	14	44	32
Elev temp. 200-hr exp	16	16	32	—
Shear tear-out				
Room temp.	17	10	18	16
Elev temp. $\frac{1}{2}$-hr exp	11	6	10	10
Elev temp. 200-hr exp	4	4	12	—
Interlaminar shear				
Room temp.	2.1	1.3	1.2	—
Elev temp. $\frac{1}{2}$-hr exp	1.2	0.37	0.96	—
Elev temp. 200-hr exp	0.16	0.38	0.96	—

[a] E. L. Strauss, SPE Journal, Sept. '66.
[b] Polybenzimidazole test temperature: $\frac{1}{2}$-hr exposure—700°F; 200-hr exposure—600°F.
[c] Polyimide test temperature: $\frac{1}{2}$-hr exposure and 200-hr exposure—600°F.
[d] Phenolic test temperature: $\frac{1}{2}$-hr exposure—500°F; 200-hr exposure—400°F

TABLE 7. TYPICAL CURING PROCEDURES.
(for $\frac{1}{8}$ in. laminates)

	Vacuum bag (oven cure)		Matched die molding		
	Cure	Postcure	Precure	Cure	Postcure
(DAP, polyester)	15 min @ 150°F 30 min @ 310°F	None	None	10–30 min @ 310°F	None
(Phenolic)	½ hr @ 250°F	½–1 hr @ 300–350°F	0–2 min @ 325°F Contact pressure	(a) 30 min @ 325°F or (b) 45 min @ 300°F or (c) 1½ hr @ 275°F	½–1 hr @ 300–350°F
(Silicone)	10 min @ 250°F 2 hr @ 350°F	16 hr @ 200°F 2 hr @ 250°F 2 hr @ 300°F 2 hr @ 350°F 2 hr @ 400°F 2 hr @ 440°F 12–48 hr @ 480°F	2–3 min @ 350°F Contact pressure	30 min @ 350°F @ 30–200 psi	16 hr @ 200°F 2 hr @ 250°F 2 hr @ 300°F 2 hr @ 350°F 2 hr @ 400°F 2 hr @ 440°F 12–48 hr @ 480°F
(Epoxy)	1 hr @ 275°F 1 hr @ 310°F	None	2–4 min @ cure temperature Contact pressure	30 min @ 275–310°F @ 30–500 psi	None

of this system is that the mold must be a female, or cavity type.

Another technique of pressure bag molding is the flexible plunger molding method. Here the layup is identical with that used in the pressure bag method, only instead of a tailored rubber bag, a medium hard rubber plug shaped like the part is used to provide pressure against the preimpregnated cloth. This is similar to matched metal die systems, except that the male die is flexible. Obviously, this system may be used only for applications where simple shapes and a cavity type are called for.

Autoclave Molding. Still another modification is the vacuum bag/autoclave method. Here the vacuum bag layup is placed in the autoclave (gas-pressure vessel), so that higher pressures (25–200 psi) can be attained, while volatile by-products can be removed by the vacuum pump. Wherever autoclaves or vacuum bags are used, the membrane must be completely sealed. Various sealing compounds are used, such as a PVA solution in water, or zinc chromatic ribbon.

Hydroclave Molding. This is identical to the autoclave method, except that the pressure medium is water or oil, and pressures of 500–1500 psi are attained. The bag material must be synthetic rubber of special design to resist the cure temperature and pressure, and is generally cured into the shape of the desired part.

Matched Die Molding. This system is used for high production runs and for parts generally small in area (say up to 60 sq ft), since die costs are high, and large heavy duty presses are expensive. The method uses two heated metal molds with a telescoping area which seals in the resin and trims the fiberglass or molding material. Pressure ranges are limited only by size of equipment, and may go as high as 10,000 psi. On long runs, matched die molding gives the lowest cost and highest production rates.

General Considerations

To make thick laminates ($\frac{1}{4}$ in.–2 in.), the above systems can be used if care is taken to control high exotherms by careful control of temperature. "Bumping," which is the alternate application and release of pressure, may also be required to facilitate removal of trapped gases. Another method involves partial curing of thinner laminates in stages, and superimposing one on the other, with prepreg or adhesive systems interspersed.

Various other combinations of the above molding processes can be used to give the desired end effect. In each of the above systems, however, care must be exercized to choose the correct preimpregnated material within the desired resin system.

Effect of Resin Content

Experience has shown that with most resin systems with glass fiber reinforcement, resin content of the cured laminate is probably from 28–32%. In this range, maximum physical properties are realized. Below 28% there is insufficient resin to bond the layers, while above 32% the excess resin effectively reduces the allowable stress (since the strength of cured resin is less than the strength of the reinforcement).

In vacuum bag molding, the excess resin is absorbed by the bleeder cloth, so that a resin content of preimpregnated cloth as high as 40% will still produce a laminate in the correct range. This is wasteful, and the excess resin may actually cut off the vacuum from the part. As a result, resin contents of about 35% are generally recommended (based on 181 glass cloth).

In positive pressure applications (pressure bag, autoclave, matched die and shrink tape molding), there is less opportunity for the resin to escape. As a result, a resin content of about 32% will produce the desired laminates. Thin fabrics and mat materials will generally require higher resin contents. Filament winding materials will range from 18–22% resin solids for most applications.

Effect of Resin Flow

The control flow of the resin under curing conditions is important if high quality parts are to be produced. The flow of a resin is controlled by the degree of "B" staging (advancement), volatile and resin content of the preimpregnated web, gel time of the resin system, and temperature and pressure at which it is measured. For vacuum bag molding, high flows are required. In higher pressure molding, lower flows are needed. The volatile content is of little value by itself. It sometimes indicates the flow level and is mainly used by the impregnator as a control measure. As pointed out above, the flow can be radically altered by variation of temperatures and speeds during the impregnation process.

DAP and silicone impregnated materials have flows lower than those of the phenolics, in general. The epoxy impregnated materials, however, generally have higher flows. Here, the resin system stays very liquid for a longer period under curing conditions.

Fabricators can control the flow during molding by any of three basic methods. The first is temperature and pressure control. By starting at lower mold or oven temperatures and/or lower pressures, flow can be retarded or advanced. With vacuum bag layups, the use of lower entering temperatures increases the period of high flow and allows better release of volatiles.

A second method is precuring or staging. Here the layup is subjected to medium temperatures (150–200°F) for a short period of time prior to application of final pressure and cure temperature. The flow is retarded and sufficient pressure is applied prior to gelation of the resin.

A third method is enveloping the layup in sheeting, such as cellophane. This essentially prevents the resin from flowing from the laminate during the cure.

It should be noted that adequate flow is necessary if high-strength, well-bonded laminates are desired. Quite often, the flow of resin is the mechanical means of removing excess volatile matter. Since nonporous laminates are generally associated with high strength, the removal of these volatiles is critical. As a result, the percentage of flow is one of the most important properties to molders of preimpregnated materials.

Effect of Postcure

As indicated in Table 7 postcuring of phenolics and silicones is recommended. For DAP, polyesters and epoxies, no postcure is necessary. For silicones, the postcuring cycle is very critical, and full strengths are not realized if deviations are made from the correct schedule. It was found that after 2–3 min exposure to 500°F, the strength of the phenolics decreased by about 30% and then recovered within a short period. Thus, a short postcure is recommended to eliminate any possible failure in application. In general, a short postcuring cycle for phenolics is recommended in order to relieve stresses set up during the cure and to remove excess volatiles within laminate (residual volatiles).

Tooling For Prepreg Parts

Good tooling is an absolute necessity for making satisfactory parts from prepreg materials. Tooling materials can be reinforced plastic, metal, ceramic, plaster, or a combination of these.

Although numerous types of plastics have been used successfully for tooling, the most satisfactory ones are epoxy, resin castings and laminates. Epoxy resin plastics tooling, especially the reinforced and/or laminated variety, provide low cost, durable, easy to manufacture contoured tools with good heat up rates if properly designed. They also have compatible thermal coefficient of expansion characteristics with that of the prepreg materials. Tooling laminates are usually of the wet layup type, but some prepregs are used in the manufacture of molds.

Aluminum is a popular tooling material. The prepreg materials, however, under fluid pressure during cure, will expand or grow with the aluminum tool during heat up and cure hard at cure temperatures. On cooling, the aluminum will shrink considerably more than the cured part. This can be a serious problem if not properly anticipated in the tooling design. This problem is multiplied considerably as the parts become larger and/or the contours become more pronounced.

For filament wound parts, the condition

becomes worse. The aluminum mandrel expands more than the glass fibers, and additional pre-stress is applied and bonded into the structure during cure. Mandrel materials with thermal co-efficients of expansion more compatible with those of the prepreg should be used.

Steel is an excellent tooling material for pre-pregs but is very expensive. It has excellent durability. The thermal coefficient of expansion is compatible with most prepreg materials. It is an excellent material for filament winding and tape winding mandrels. However, its weight is usually excessive, and the labor cost involved in forming or machining accurate contours is very high when compared to other types of tooling. Press molding generally requires steel tooling for large production runs. Only large quantity production would justify the cost of steel tooling for compound contoured parts.

Kirksite has also been used successfully and exhibits many desirable characteristics, but is usually more expensive than plastics tooling. These alloys make good molds for short to medium runs, but for longer service a fine grain cast iron such as "Meehanite" is more satisfactory.

Molds made of plaster or gypsum are satisfactory for a short run where low pressure and heat are used. Surfaces are porous and should be sealed. More durable plaster molds can be made by impregnating the materials with a liquid resin, such as "Furane". Plaster is often used for single-use molds to produce parts with expensive undercuts or complex configurations. After cure, the mold is simply broken apart and removed in pieces.

Regardless of the material selected, the tool must present molding surfaces that are as smooth as the surfaces desired on the molded reinforced plastics pieces.

Pattern Cutting

Because prepregs are relatively stable and may have protective backing on one or both sides, they are especially suitable to precutting with a template. This results in smoother production flow of parts. The parts can be laid up with more accurate fiber orientation, and the correct number of plies. Precounting of the precut plies and proper storage in kits assures a high degree of reliability and efficiency, and makes the prepreg material more adaptable to automated mass-production techniques.

Release Agents

These materials take the form of waxes, silicones, fluorocarbons, and sprayable thermoplastic films which are strippable or water soluble. Not all of these types are usable with all types of prepregs. Selecting the proper parting agent for

resin system, mold type, and end product use is important.

For instance, silicones exhibit some of the best and worst characteristics of parting agents. Some types provide an easy method of parting for certain types of epoxy resins that are otherwise very difficult to part clean from the tool. Other types of silicones will not stop the bonding of certain epoxy base materials to the tool. In addition, the silicones are almost impossible to completely remove from the part short of ply peeling, sandblasting, or heavy sanding. A silicone coated surface may be desirable if the mold finish is the final part finish, but it provides an impossible situation whenever painting or secondary bonding is to be performed on the part. Also, the silicone materials are very difficult to remove from tooling, hand tools, and one's hands in one washing. This then becomes a serious problem because contamination of the prepreg surface during layup can cause delaminations or weakened interlaminar properties on the finished part. For these reasons, the silicone base parting agents must be selected carefully and then checked out prior to production.

Some of the paraffin, carnauba, and dammar base waxes work very well but require considerable labor to apply properly. These may require three coats with each coat followed by buffing and polishing.

The water soluble polyvinyl-alcohol liquid release material works very well for the low temperature curing polyesters prepregs (curing temperature below 200°F). The material is low cost and washes off easily with water.

Cellophane plastic film has been used successfully as a parting film on polyesters, phenolics, and silicones. It usually strips off with a minimum of scraping and is inexpensive.

The fluorocarbon films like TFE and FEP "Telflon" make excellent parting films but usually have to be made with glass fabric reinforcement to be reusable. The cost of one time usage would be prohibitive, but the long life of the reinforced variety makes them a possible candidate. These materials can also be coated onto the tools for permanent parting, as with the fluorocarbon coated cookware. Fluorocarbon coated papers for one time use are also excellent but too expensive for some operations. High temperature resistant contact adhesive backed fluorocarbon tape is available and can be used for lining tools which have flat or mildly contoured surfaces. An ideal application is press-platens. This approach is also expensive except for quantity production. Fluorocarbon liquid spray parting agent is available in pressurized spray cans. Although these sprays work well in some cases, a trial run should be made before utilization on an important and expensive part. The fluorocarbon films are generally superior to the spray materials.

The material and surface condition of the tool to be covered with parting agent is extremely important for proper release.

Layup Techniques

This is a basic part of the manufacturing process and it is here prepreg materials exhibit significant advantages over wet layup techniques. The prepreg materials can be programmed for layup by precutting to size the required number of piles for each part and programming the application of each ply. The actual layup characteristics can be measured and controlled to a high degree by proper designation of certain properties of the prepreg such as drape, tack, and resin content. These properties are interrelated to some degree, but can be controlled to give a wide variation of handling characteristics.

In building honeycomb structures the tack characteristics of the prepreg are quite important. The honeycomb must be located and fixed in position and held there for the application of subsequent piles of material. If the prepreg exhibits the correct tack characteristics this process becomes quite straightforward.

The winding process for prepreg filament winding is quite different. Important winding process characteristics are speed and angle of winding, fiber tension, temperature of the mandrel, and method of cure. The material variables which affect the winding process can be readily controlled by the prepreg supplier. This provides simplicity of manufacture not available for wet process filament winding.

Tape winding of cylindrical or conical shapes is readily accomplished with prepreg materials using sufficient heat and pressure during tape application to insure adequate tack. The tape winding process, used extensively in the aerospace industry for high temperature ablative structures such as exit cones, nose cones, and blast tubes, is dependent on the material characteristics to a high degree. The preimpregnated tape must have a high degree of hot tack so that the wrap, when applied to the mandrel with heat, will maintain its integrity. Extremely high density tape wrapping is possible when the prepreg materials are carefully controlled.

Bagging Materials

For vacuum bag, autoclave, and hydroclave molding, the prepreg layup must be sealed in a leakproof bag. Knowledge of bag materials and their characteristics is very important. These materials can be divided into two categories: (1) throw away bags, (2) permanent bags.

Expendable bag materials are the most widely used and, except for long production runs, are usually less expensive. Permanent bag materials are usually made of silicone rubber, or rubber materials modified for high temperature application, which are formed to the shape of the part.

Sufficient bag material must be allowed at contour changes to prevent "bridging". "Bridging" of the bag will encourage collapse of honeycomb core in a sandwich construction and prevent application of full pressure, resulting in delaminations or resin rich areas.

After bagging is complete, the bag must be checked for leaks and if necessary, resealed. The bagging process is critical, for a leak during the cure cycle will result in a rejected part. Care and study of the bagging techniques used can result in significant economics.

Material Selection, Structural Design and Analysis

These three functions are grouped together because of the importance of integrating them for efficient design. Traditionally, the designer creates the component design within the dimensional, load, and environmental requirements set forth. Prepreg composite materials are neither homogenous nor isotropic, so the structural analyst has a serious and difficult problem. The approach and method used for a solution must be different from that of metallic structures.

Seldom is a material substitute design efficient, although it may be adequate and useful in some circumstances. The strict use of standard "strength of materials" formulas will be inadequate except for secondary and non-structural parts and even here may provide inefficient structures.

Another problem is that the materials lack complete characterization. The material properties presented in Tables 3, 4 and 5 do not completely characterize those composite materials. For instance, the properties listed are somewhat time-dependent (viscoelastic), and on the bias (45° to the reinforcement direction, except for isotropic layups), the static properties are highly viscoelastic and approximate 50–60% of the longitudinal properties for strength and 70–80% for stiffness. It is doubtful that the question of how to completely characterize a composite material which exhibits elasticity, viscoelasticity, and elastoplasticity during various types of loading has been completely answered.

The most practical approach is to utilize the best isotropic and/or anisotropic formulas currently available and verify all conditions by experimental testing. The benefits to be gained from such prepreg composite structures, however, usually outweigh their added design cost.

Honeycomb sandwich construction is one of the favorite structural configurations used with prepreg reinforced plastics. For cloth laminate faces, sufficiently accurate formulas are available. Although similar to metal-faced sandwich, both the theoretical and fabrication aspects are somewhat complicated by the use of anisotropic faces. However, the knowledge of metal-faced sandwich construction and test methods will provide a good foundation from which to design with reinforced plastics.

One of the major advantages of prepreg reinforced plastics design is that large components can be made in one piece, eliminating many joints and detail parts. There is, however, a limit to the size of tooling which can be made, so the problem of joints is still a consideration.

The designer must have material test data to characterize the material, configuration development information for efficient application, and then design the component and material simultaneously for the most optimum application. The interrelated factors which must be considered for composite structures design are:

(1) Dimensional requirements.
(2) Load-environmental-electrical requirements.
(3) Material selection.
(4) Processing-quality control-producibility requirements.
(5) Reliability and cost requirements.

Typical applications

In spite of some of the design difficulties outlined above, many fine examples of successful, efficient, and competitively economical prepreg composite components are in use today.

With the exception of the rotor, the helicopter is a prime example of a lightly loaded structure, with extremely tough requirements for fatigue and external damage resistance. The helicopter fuselage is an outstanding application of prepreg glass cloth laminates. These materials have excellent fatigue resistance, damping characteristics, damage resistance, and repairability—and it is highly competitive with metal on a fabricated cost basis. Boeing-Vertol, Bell Helicopter and Sikorsky Aircraft all have flying examples of prepreg applications to helicopter fuselages.

The rotor blade of a helicopter is an area where the loads are high, the stiffness critical, and the vibration resistance and damping extremely important. Much development work has been done on fibrous composite rotor blades, but to date only one company, Vertol, has a production vehicle flying with a major portion of the blade made of fibrous composite materials.

Almost every military and commercial aircraft flying has at least one radome made of fibrous reinforced composite materials. In addition, many of the commercial and private aircraft have wings and empennage tips, tip tanks, engine cowls, prop spinners, wheel fairings, main gasoline tanks, and cockpit coverframes made from composite materials. Examples of these are the Piper Aircraft Company, Cherokee Line, and the Boeing

727 and 737 airliner (control surfaces and exterior structural members for improved strength, and reduced weight). For military aircraft, the General Dynamics B-58 Hustler supersonic bomber is a perfect example of the extensive use of not only reinforced plastics, but adhesive bonding, brazing and sandwich construction. The major portion of the primary structure and external surface of the aircraft is adhesive bonded metal and glass phenolic honeycomb sandwich, utilizing both fiberglass phenolic and aluminum foil honeycomb. This aircraft is one of the best examples of the tremendous advances made in the state-of-the-art of materials and processes, design, fabrication, and quality control of aircraft structures during the decade from 1950–1960. Grumman Aircraft, in the primary structures (empennage and rotodome) of its E 2A Aircraft, utilized prepreg composites with fiberglassplastic honeycomb.

In the missile field, General Dynamics provides another excellent example of the use of prepreg phenolics on the Atlas D and later models. These included complete construction of the aft skirt, bulkheads, and fairings with honeycomb sandwich. Another noteworthy example is the filament wound rocket motor case of the Lockheed Polaris missile. The extensive application of prepreg composites to the area of high heat ablators are numerous. The reentry nose cones of many missle payloads, the heat shields of the manned spacecraft, and the rocket engine nozzles of most millile propulsion systems utilize prepreg materials, generally based on "exotic" reinforcements.

In the electronics and ground support equipment fields, use of prepreg composite materials is extensive. Examples are electronic circuit boards, housings, racks, truck bodies and frames, gasoline tanks, equipment housings, etc., have found many applications for prepreg materials.

Preimpregnated laminating stock is highly engineered raw materials designed for technically oriented production processes and end use applications, and, as such, should find increasing use, both in aircraft and commercial applications.

S. G. SALZINGER
GLENN C. GRIMES

PRINTING INKS, FOR FILMS

A recent compilation of commonly used packaging films lists some 50 different trademarks of more than 20 different types of plastic films, not counting the various grades of cellophane. The list is steadily growing. Most of these plastic films used in the packaging industry are printed by either the flexographic or gravure printing process. Both of these processes utilize inks which dry rapidly by evaporation, and thus permit continuous web printing of these films at speeds up to 1000 ft/min. The printed ink films are dry and tack-free at the rewind end of the press, at these speeds, so that the printed film may be rewound into rolls or fed directly into other converting operations at the end of the printing and drying operation.

The number of different types of plastic packaging films available and the almost unlimited variety of end-use and product requirements make it impossible to do more than generalize within the scope of this article. The dynamic, fast moving nature of the plastic film industry and of the printing ink formulation technology combine to further compound the problem. Therefore here we will attempt to discuss only the subject of flexographic and gravure inks for plastic packaging films.

Flexographic Inks

Flexographic inks for printing various plastic packaging films comprise an almost infinite variety, but we will attempt to bring some degree of order out of this chaos by dividing them into three general and very broad categories which may overlap on occasion. Our broad classifications will first be polyamide resin based flexo inks, sometimes referred to as "co-solvent" inks. Our second classification will be flexographic inks containing significant portions of nitrocellulose as a major constituent of the formula, while our third classification will cover that group of flexographic ink formulations based on such miscellaneous resin binders as acrylics.

The most widely used family of flexographic printing inks, with respect to the printing of plastic packaging films, as this is written, are those inks formulated essentially from the various polyamide type resins. The original polyamide resins available were most soluble in a mixture of alcohol and naphtha-type solvents. The inks were formulated with such solvent mixtures and the recommended solvent mixtures for press side use were blends of about equal parts of isopropyl or normal propyl alcohol and a narrow-cut, essentially odor-free aliphatic hydrocarbon solvent, preferably with a drying rate similar to that of the alcohol used with it. Such a mixture helped to maintain an acceptable solvent balance in the ink throughout the press run, and explains the "co-solvent" designation frequently applied to this broad family of polyamide type flexo inks.

These polyamide or "co-solvent" flexo inks generally have excellent adhesion to a wide variety of plastic films, notably polyolefins. Generally speaking they have excellent gloss, excellent resistance to water and wet pack applications, excellent block resistance, and excellent printing and handling characteristics. These

Polyamide based ink films, however, have relatively low heat resistance and they tend to be somewhat soft, therefore having limited abrasion resistance.

Where heat resistance and abrasion resistance are not primary considerations, the polyamide based inks are almost universally used for printing treated polyethylene and treated polypropylene films, polyvinylidene chloride coated films of all sorts, including polyesters, uncoated polyester films, cellulose acetate films, and oriented and expanded polystyrene films and Polyamide films.

Nitrocellulose-based Inks

Nitrocellulose-based flexo ink formulations include a very broad family of flexo inks, because nitrocellulose is frequently combined with and modified with an extremely wide variety of resins, modifiers, etc. All of the nitrocellulose-based inks are reducible in varying degrees, with anhydrous proprietary ethyl alcohol as the primary solvent. Better solubility results from a mixture of this sort of alcohol, plus from 10–20% of an ester solvent such as isopropyl acetate or normal propyl acetate. For this reason, it has become almost a universal practice to use such a solvent blend for most inks in this category.

Generally speaking, nitrocellulose-based flexo inks have a little less gloss than the best grades of polyamide-type flexo inks. Most nitrocellulose-based inks have fair to good heat resistance, generally ranging from 250°F to as high 350°F, and sometimes in excess of this where heat resistance is a primary requirement. Nitrocellulose-based flexo inks generally have better abrasion resistance than polyamide inks, with a harder and "slicker" surface. These inks are frequently used on plain cellophanes, cellulose acetate films, on ethyl cellulose film, on some grades of polystyrene and in the case of nitrocellulose-polyamide modifications, on various polyolefin films, especially where more heat resistance is necessary than the polyamides alone will provide.

Acrylic and Miscellaneous "Special" Flexo Ink Formulations

This family of flexo ink formulations is in a sense a sort of "catch-all." Obviously, it may include virtually all flexo ink formulations not covered by the Polyamide or nitrocellulose categories. In an effort to avoid overgeneralization to the point of meaninglessness, we will refer in this category primarily to those flexo ink formulations which utilize some acrylic type resin in their formulation. Generally speaking, this family of inks has about the same order of gloss as the nitrocellulose-based inks. Their heat resistance usually ranges from about 300°–400°F. Dried ink films based on acrylic resins are usually very hard and tough, with excellent abrasion resistance. Most of the flexo inks in this category require a mixture of a minimum of 20% ester solvent with anhydrous proprietary ethyl alcohol. In some cases higher percentages of ester solvent are recommended, and because of this either natural rubber printing plates and rollers or butyl rubber printing plates and rollers are often recommended. In addition to excellent adhesion characteristics on many "difficult" plastic film surfaces, acrylic-type flexo inks are distinguished for good block resistance, excellent resistance to grease and many other difficult product requirements, excellent water resistance, and, when suitably formulated, these qualities are frequently combined with good heat-sealing characteristics.

Acrylic-type flexo inks are most widely used where substantial heat resistance together with their other unique properties are required for printing a wide range of polyvinyl chloride and polyvinylidene chloride films and coatings, oriented polystyrene, rubber hydrochloride, some grades of polyester films, some grades of cellulose acetate films, Polyamide films and some oriented polypropylene films.

Rotogravure Inks for Plastic Films

The above discussion on flexographic inks for plastic films is substantially also true for rotogravure inks, but there are some exceptions.

One important difference between gravure and flexo inks for plastic films is in the field of polyamide inks. While polyamide based inks are frequently used in printing some plastic films, notably polyethylene, by the rotogravure process, their use is not nearly as universal in connection with rotogravure printing. For one thing, polyamide type inks do not "wipe" very well, for another thing polyamide ink films do not dry hard enough between colors to work well at high press speeds in the rotogravure process, and perhaps even more to the point is the fact that a relatively small volume of polyethylene film is printed by the rotogravure process, because the stretchable nature of polyethylene film, particularly in low gauges, results in difficult register problems on most rotogravure presses. Where polyamide inks are used in the rotogravure process, all or part of the naphtha content is frequently replaced with an aromatic hydrocarbon solvent such as toluol, for better solubility. This is possible in connection with rotogravure printing since the solvent does not come in direct contact with any rubber compound as is the case in flexographic printing.

Nitrocellulose based inks are widely used for rotogravure printing of the same variety of plastic films mentioned in the section on flexographic inks. The main difference here is that the rotogravure process does not involve any solvent restrictions such as apply in the case of flexographic printing so that the common solvent mixtures for nitrocellulose based inks used in rotogravure printing are such mixtures as isopropyl acetate, toluol, etc. Alcohol is frequently used as a part of the blend but in rotogravure printing it is more likely to represent a minor portion of the solvent blend.

Acrylic-type rotogravure inks are quite widely used for the same combination of properties, product resistance and end-use requirements as those listed in this category of flexographic inks. Here again, however, the solvent or thinner mixture for the acrylic inks in rotogravure printing normally consists primarily of ester solvents such as isopropyl acetate. Little or no alcohol may be present in rotogravure ink versions of the acrylic-type formulations.

Because the rotogravure process does not involve any solvent restrictions, certain materials can be used in ink formulations which are unique to the rotogravure process and not permissible in the case of flexographic inks. Perhaps the most important type of rotogravure ink in this category is the family of "rubber based" gravure inks. These are usually formulated with vehicles comprised essentially of chlorinated rubber compounds. They are essentially soluble in aromatic hydrocarbon solvents such as toluol, and are commonly used for printing a variety of plastic films such as rubber hydrochlorides, various grades of cellophane, and most vinyl films.

From the foregoing, it should be obvious that the choice of the proper ink to use in printing any given plastic film for a particular end-use may be a very difficult problem. This is due to the endless combinations of possible requirements, and this fact emphasizes the importance of cooperating closely with a reputable and experienced source of printing inks to assure success in any important plastic film printing project.

Douglas E. Tuttle

PROPYLENE OXIDE

Propylene oxide is an extremely reactive compound which reacts readily with water, alcohols or amines. It is consequently used chiefly as the intermediate for the production of propylene glycol, polypropyleneglycols, propylene glycol ethers and esters, and propanolamines. Likewise, polymeric materials with active hydrogen atoms such as starch or cellulose, and will also react with propylene oxide. Propylene oxide may be grafted on other polymers, thus yielding new polymers with interesting properties. The principal product is a polypropylene oxide elastomer.

Propylene oxide may be prepared by liquid phase chlorohydrination of propylene at 90–100°C at atmospheric pressure. The feed stock with a low chlorine to propylene ratio is mixed with a slight excess of lime to maintain a pH of 8–9. The effluent gas passes through a condenser and the unconverted chlorohydrin is recycled. The overall yield based on propylene is 80%. Propylene dichloride and chloroisopropyl ether are obtained as byproducts.

The principal reactions in the chlorohydrination process are as follows:

$$CH_3—CH{=}CH_2 + H_2O + Cl_2 \rightarrow$$
$$CH_3CH(OH)CH_2Cl$$

$$CH_3CH(OH)CH_2Cl + Ca(OH)_2 \rightarrow$$

CH₃—CH—CH₂ + CaCl₂ (with epoxide O ring)

In an alternative process, propylene is oxidized by air in the vapor phase. Silver is often employed as the catalyst. The oxidation product is neutralized by sodium bicarbonate and a pH of 6.4 ± 0.1 is maintained. Over 94% yields of product are obtained when the mixture is extracted with water at 10°C. Propylene glycol is obtained as a by-product.

Propylene oxide is a colorless liquid, boiling at 33.9°C. Its specific gravity at 28°C is 0.8304. The flash point for propylene oxide is −35°C. Propylene oxide is soluble in both water and ethanol. In addition to being a monomer for rubbery polymers, propylene oxide is used as a low boiling solvent for cellulose nitrate and other coating compositions.

RAYMOND B. SEYMOUR

PYROMELLITIC DIANHYDRIDE

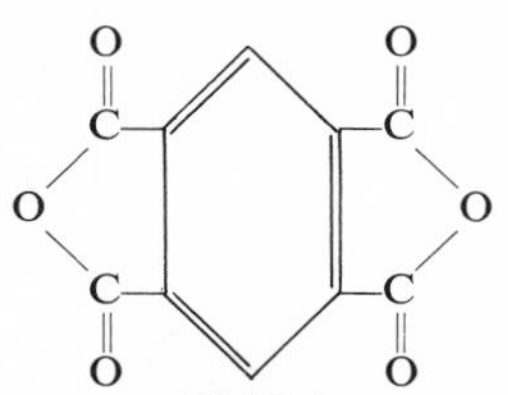

PMDA

Pyromellitic Dianhydride (1, 2, 4, 5-benzene-tetracarboxylic dianhydride), most commonly referred to as PMDA, has been known for many years, but only within the last decade has this chemical become commercially important as an intermediate for the manufacture of resins and plastic materials.

PMDA was first reported by Erdman in 1851, derived from the dry distillation of mellitic acid obtained from the honey-colored mineral $Al_2O_3 \cdot C_{12}O_9 \cdot 18H_2O$. This mineral is found in brown coal and was originally called "Honigstein." Translated to New Latin (mell for honey), it is now known as "Mellite." Despite this early beginning, PMDA remained very much a laboratory curiosity until it was offered in development quantities in the early 1950's.

The first commercial interests in PMDA were in curing or hardening of epoxy resins. Many applications have been investigated, such as esters for plasticizers, additives for lubricating oils, dyestuffs, polyester resins and others, many of which are still in an active development stage. In nearly all applications, the ability of PMDA to impart heat resistance to the end product is the key to its success.

One of the most significant new developments is the class of polyimide polymers made from PMDA and aromatic diamines. These materials have softening points over 700°C. Films, coatings and molded plastics made from these polyimides offer new engineering materials with properties previously unavailable.

Physical Properties

A listing of the known physical properties of PMDA is given in Table 1, and solubilities in Table 2. Since most commercial products have been supplied with a minimum assay of 98% PMDA, their typical properties are very close to those in the tables below.

TABLE 1. PHYSICAL PROPERTIES OF PMDA.

Appearance	White powder
Formula	$C_{10}H_2O_6$
Molecular weight	218.12
Melting point	287°C
Boiling point	397–400°C at 760 mm Hg
	305–310°C at 30 mm Hg
Specific gravity	1.68
Heat of combustion, kcal$_{15}$/mole	776
Neutralization equivalent	54.53
Anhydride equivalent	109.06
Dissociation constants (of the acid) at 0.03 ionic strength	$pKa_1 - 1.92$
	$pKa_2 - 2.89$
	$pKa_3 - 4.49$
	$pKa_4 - 5.64$
Equivalent electrical conductivity, ohm^{-1}, aqueous solution at 25°C 0.014 milli-equivalents/liter	260

TABLE 2. SOLUBILITY OF PMDA.

Solvent	% PMDA in saturated solution	
	Room temp.	Reflux temp.
Acetonitrile	7	16
Acetone	7	9
Benzonitrile	<1	>92
Cellosolve acetate	1	>13
Diacetone alcohol	<1	24
Diethylene glycol dimethyl ether	4–5	29
Dioxane	1	5–6
Ethylene glycol dimethyl ether	5–6	18
Methyl ethyl ketone	4	7
Methyl isobutyl ketone	1	6
N-Ethyl-2-pyrrolidone	6	>16
Tetraethylene glycol dimethyl ether	4	>22
Tetrahydrofuran	11	12
Triethylene glycol dimethyl ether	3–4	156

	Gms. PMDA/100 ml solvent	
	25°C	Reflux temp.
γ-Butyrolactone	15	80
Dimethyl formamide	15	110
Dimethyl sulfoxide	15	95
Water (forms acid)	2	42

Preparation

There have been reported in the literature many different methods for the synthesis of PMDA. Nearly all of these involve first the preparation of pyromellitic acid, PMA, followed by a dehydration step to the anhydride, usually by heating at elevated temperatures. PMA may also be converted to PMDA with acetic anhydride.

PMDA was first made by Erdman by heating mellitic acid (benzene hexacarboxylic acid), either alone or with sulfuric acid. Benzene pentacarboxylic acid, heated at 270–300°C, also gives PMDA.

Pyromellitic acid may be obtained in low yield by the oxidation of wood charcoal in the presence of sulfuric acid. This was a convenient way to prepare PMDA in small laboratory runs before its commercial introduction. Oxidation of coal with sulfuric acid, oxygen or nitric acid produces PMA, as does the electrolytic oxidation of graphite in an alkaline medium or the oxidation of lignin in aqueous systems.

Most of the recent work has centered about the oxidation of 1, 2, 4, 5-tetra-substituted benzenes. Durene, isopropyl pseudo cumene, octahydroanthracene, 2, 4, 5-trimethyl benzyl acetate, diisopropyl xylenes, 2, 4-dimethyl-α-α'-di-chloro-m-xylene and others can be oxidized to PMA by such agents as nitric acid, chromic acid, $KMnO_4$ and NaOBr.

Considerable research has been done on the vapor phase oxidation of durene over catalysts such as V_2O_5, or modifications of V_2O_5 at temperatures around 500°C. It is particularly of interest because this type of continuous process now used for phthalic and maleic anhydrides is capable of producing PMDA of very high purity in large volumes at relatively low costs.

Manufacture

Two processes are currently used to manufacture the major portion of PMDA for industrial consumption. One reportedly utilizes the nitric acid oxidation of durene and the second uses a vapor phase catalytic air oxidation of durene at elevated temperatures.

While durene is the preferred feedstock at the moment, other materials can be used. In the future, detailed economic studies of yields, materials cost and availability and product quality will be necessary to determine the best starting material.

Sales specifications for commercial PMDA are 98% minimum assay. This quality is generally satisfactory for chemical reactions and for curing epoxy resins. However, for polymer formation a higher assay may be needed to obtain high molecular weight polymers, particularly for polyimide resins.

The identity of the 1–2% of impurities is also important. These can be entirely the acid from hydrolyzed PMDA or contain incompletely oxidized materials, residual solvents and other impurities introduced by the oxidizing agent. Their nature and proportion will depend upon the process and method of purification.

Chemical Reactions of PMDA

PMDA readily undergoes the typical reactions of organic anhydrides. It will also undergo reactions of the benzene ring and form complexes with other aromatic compounds. The following examples show the large number of derivatives that can be made from PMDA. In the equations, no attempt has been made to show the two position isomers possible when PMDA reacts with an alcohol or amine.

Esterification. PMDA reacts readily with alcohols to form di- and tetra-esters.

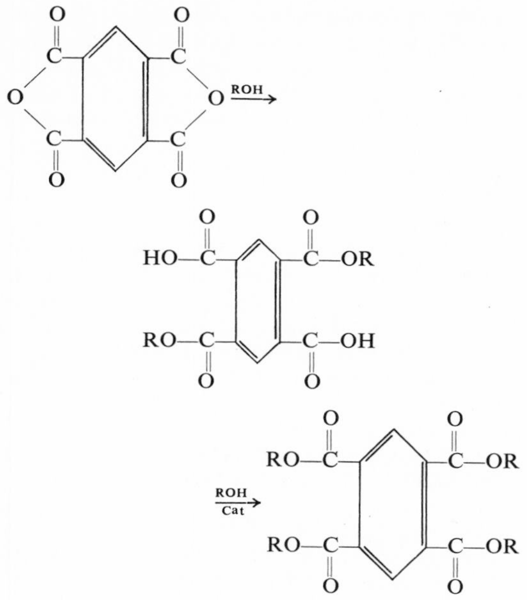

200°C. Treatment of the imide with ammonia gives pyromellitamide:

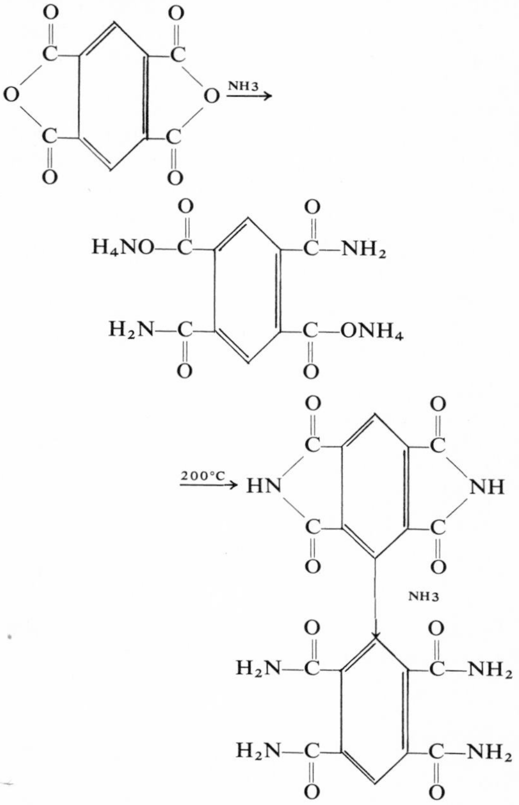

Although diesters are easily formed without catalysts by heating PMDA with an alcohol for a short period, azeotropic and catalytic techniques are necessary to form the tetra-esters. Tetra-allyl pyromellitate is best prepared, however, by the reaction of allyl alcohol and pyromellityl chloride.

Another technique is the preparation of esters by transesterification; vinyl acetate and PMA give the tetra-vinyl ester. Salts of PMA reacted with certain alkyl halides also give tetra-esters.

Acid Chloride Formation. Pyromellityl chloride may be made by reacting PMDA with PCl_5 or $SOCl_2$:

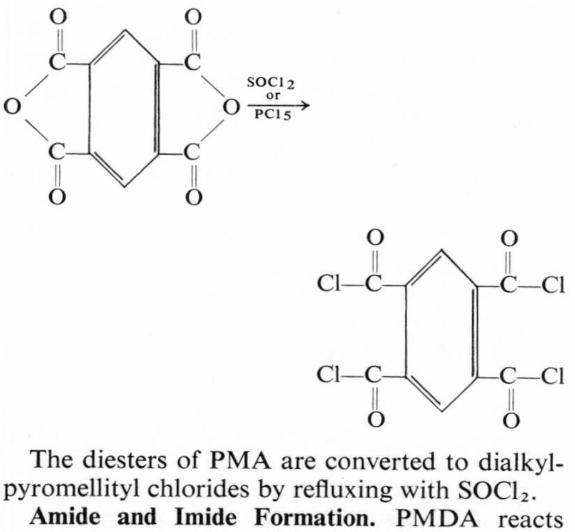

The diesters of PMA are converted to dialkyl-pyromellityl chlorides by refluxing with $SOCl_2$.

Amide and Imide Formation. PMDA reacts with ammonia at a low temperature to give the ammonium salt of pyromellitamic acid. This salt is converted to pyromellitimide by heating at

N-substituted pyromellitimides are prepared by the reaction of PMDA with primary amines to form the pyromellitamic acid, which is converted to the N-substituted imide by heating at about 350°C:

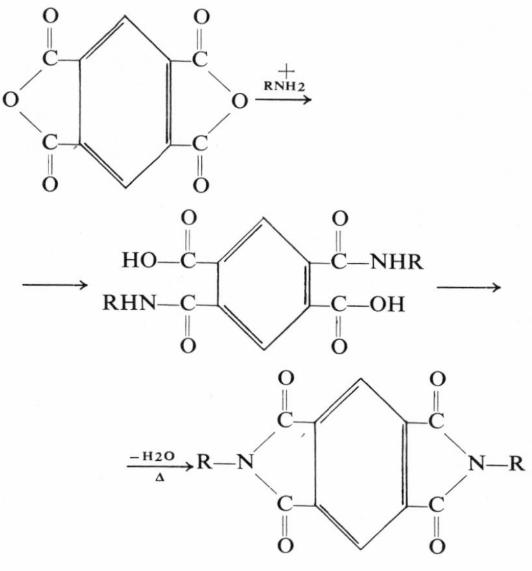

Hydrazine and PMDA similarly react to form the dihydrazide. Secondary amines react with PMDA to give the corresponding pyromellitamic acid, which, however, cannot be converted to the imide. Tertiary amines form only the amine salts of PMA.

Hydrogenation. The benzene ring in PMA may be reduced by catalytic hydrogenation of PMA at 250°C and 250 atm pressure in aqueous Na_2CO_3 to give cyclohexane tetracarboxylic acid. Reduction with sodium amalgam gives a

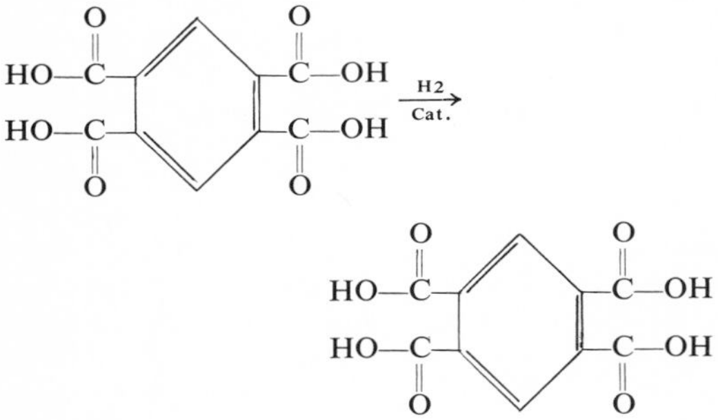

mixture of hydro- and isohydro-pyromellitic acids.

Reduction of tetramethyl pyromellitate with $LiAlH_4$ produces the tetraol in 90% yield:

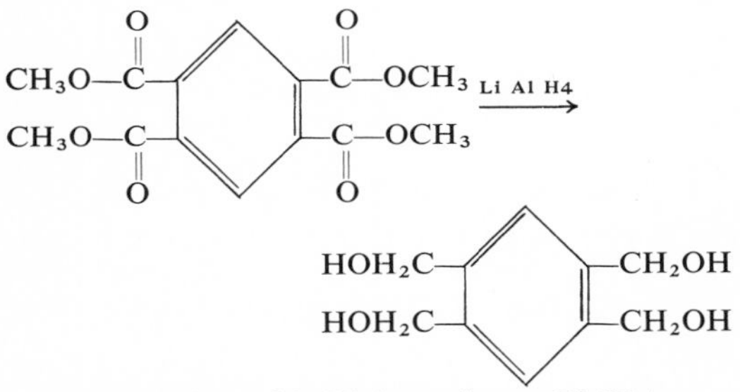

Condensation with Hydrocarbons. PMDA undergoes a Friedel-Craft Type reaction with aromatic hydrocarbons such as benzene, toluene, bromobenzene, xylenes and naphthalene to give mixtures of the corresponding iso- and terephthalic acids.

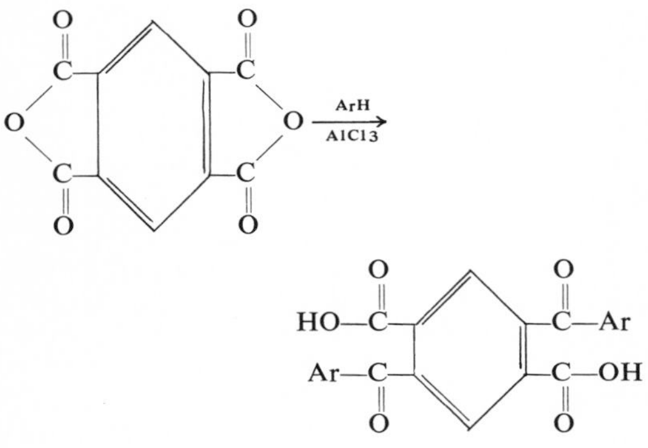

Miscellaneous Reactions. Metallic salts may be prepared by adding PMDA to an aqueous suspension of the metallic carbonate or by addition of an aqueous solution or suspension of a metallic acetate, chloride, nitrate or sulfate to an aqueous solution of sodium pyromellitate. The sodium salt, prepared from sodium hydroxide and PMA, is soluble in water, but other metallic salts are insoluble.

PMDA forms complexes with many aromatic compounds such as benzene, xylenes, tetralin, anisole and veratrol. PMDA can be regenerated from these complexes.

Pyromellitonitrile is prepared by the reaction of pyromellitamide with $SOCl_2$. This material may be converted into polymeric phthalocyanine pigments and polymers.

The thioanhydride of PMDA may be prepared from sodium sulfide and PMDA. Chlorination of the thioanhydride is an excellent way to prepare pyromellityl chloride.

Pyrolysis of PMDA under basic conditions at 425°C yields terephthalic acid.

Applications for PMDA

The ability of PMDA to react with alcohols and amines has led to extensive use in curing or hardening of epoxy resins and in preparation of the new polyimide class of heat resistant polymers. Non-polymeric derivatives such as esters of PMDA have been useful as vinyl plasticizers and lubricant additives. Details of these applications are presented below.

Curing Epoxy Resins. The reaction of PMDA with an hydroxyl group to form an acid-ester followed by reaction of the acid with epoxide groups is the basis by which PMDA cures epoxy resins. PMDA has four reactive points for crosslinking which result in very high heat distortion points and faster cure rates than monoanhydrides.

One anhydride group is theoretically needed to cross-link one epoxide group. However, in practice, the ratio of anhydride to epoxide is usually somewhat less than 1 : 1 unless an amine catalyst is used. A heat cure is normally required.

Casting, Potting and Encapsulation. Liquid epoxy resins and PMDA form uniform dispersions which dissolve on heating to yield clear castings. Mixtures of PMDA with other anhydrides like phthalic may be used to speed the solution and reduce the activity of PMDA but with some loss of heat resistance. More rapid cures are achieved by adding tetrahydrofurfuryl alcohol containing dicyandiamide and impact resistance is improved by adding glycols.

These resins are characterized by heat distortion points as high as 550°F. Weight loss on heat aging is low and electrical properties and chemical resistance are excellent.

Laminates. Laminates that have outstanding mechanical properties at 500°F may be obtained by either a "wet layup" system or the "prepreg" method.

Dispersions of PMDA and liquid resins may be used with glass fabric in a heated press. A press cure at 250–350°F is usually followed by a postcure in an oven at over 400°F to develop maximum heat resistance.

The prepreg method is more versatile, since use of a solution of the resin formulation in methyl ethyl ketone allows more freedom in choice of liquid or solid resins and various modifiers. Prepregs prepared from these varnishes may be stored for limited periods before pressing into a laminate.

Molding Powders. PMDA is especially useful here because it is a highly reactive dianhydride as well as a free flowing powder. Formulations are prepared by mixing PMDA with a solid epoxy resin to which solid catalysts may be added. Solid prepolymers of liquid epoxy resins and PMDA or solid adducts of glycols and PMDA may also be used.

These powders are useful in fluidized-bed coatings, compression moldings, and transfer moldings. Coatings and molded items with exceptional heat resistance and good electrical properties are obtained.

Coatings. PMDA is best adapted to epoxy resin coatings by first reacting two moles of PMDA with 1 mole of a glycol in a solvent like methyl ethyl ketone. These adducts are much more soluble than PMDA and can be used to formulate a number of different coatings. A wide variety of properties can be achieved such as excellent chemical resistance, extreme hardness, good abrasion resistance, good flexibility, high heat resistance, impact resistance and excellent adhesion.

A very reactive adduct made from PMDA and the propylene oxide reaction product of bisphenol A will cure epoxy resins at room temperature. Other glycol adducts can be used for baked coatings. The reactivity of the epoxy resin will determine the extent of baking required. Air dried coatings are obtained with reactive adducts and epoxidized novolac resins.

Polyimide Resins. The reaction of PMDA with equal molar amounts of primary diamines gives a polymeric amide-acid which is converted to a polyimide by heating at high temperatures. Polyimides so derived from aromatic diamines like *meta*-phenylene diamine or oxydianiline can withstand temperatures up to 500°C for short periods, and retain good physical and electrical properties for service at 200–300°C. Their resistance to X-ray and gamma radiation is outstanding. These new products offer entirely new engineering materials with properties previously unknown. Conversion of the polymer to useful end products is difficult and costly by present techniques.

Several polyimide products are in use commercially. A varnish is available for coating copper magnet wire. A transparent film is made in thicknesses as low as 1 mil. Diamond cutting wheels with polyimide binders are available as are molded plastic items.

A recent new development is the preparation of "ladder"-type polymers by reacting PMDA with aromatic tetra-amines like 3,3′-diaminobenzidine, to form polyimidazopyrrolones, referred to as "Pyrrones." These also have extremely high heat resistant properties and radiation resistance.

Esters as Plasticizers. Tetra-esters of PMDA are effective primary plasticizers for polyvinyl chloride resins. Tetrabutyl pyromellitate and tetra-2-ethylhexyl pyromellitate are two examples.

The low volatility of these esters approaches that of the polymeric plasticizers. The heat resistance and oxidative stability are greater than the corresponding trimellitate and phthalate esters.

This combination of properties gives them superior performance in heat resistant wire coatings, in non-fogging plasticizers for vinyls in automobiles, and in vinyls exposed to water or heat.

Health and Safety Precautions

PMDA has been handled in many industrial plants without serious problems. However, proper safety precautions must be observed at all times.

Persons who handle PMDA should avoid contact of the material with the skin, eyes, nose, or throat, and should not inhale its dust. Ventilation should be provided to remove dust from the working area. Protection is provided through the use of proper face masks and rubber gloves. Exposed areas should be washed with soap and water where possible, or flushed thoroughly with water. As happens with many anhydrides, some individuals are quite sensitive to PMDA, while others will have no irritation.

Storage Stability

PMDA will hydrolyze slowly to PMA when exposed to moist air. For this reason, all containers must be tightly sealed when not in use.

PMDA is supplied in polyethylene bags placed in fiber drums having a built-in vapor barrier. PMDA can be stored for long periods of time in this manner, provided the bags are tied and the drums properly sealed.

FRANK W. LONG

R

RADIATION OF PLASTICS

Among the wide variety of applications in which radiation is being used in the plastics industry today are the cross-linking of polyethylene film to induce plastic memory for use in shrink packaging, cross-linking of wire insulation for increased heat resistance, and the cross-linking of polyvinyl chloride and polyethylene tubing to make shrinkable fitting for cable and electrical connectors. In addition there are a number of other applications which promise to become commercial in the near future—radiation vulcanization of rubber, radiation curing of factory-applied coatings and finishes, graft copolymerization of vinyl monomers to natural and synthetic polymers, controlled depolymerization of cellulose for viscose rayon production, and solid-state and emulsion polymerization of monomers to produce specialty polymers which are difficult or impossible to prepare by other means.

Methods for producing plastic foams have been proposed in which the blowing agent is decomposed under the action of radiation, thus foaming and at the same time inducing cross-linking in the polymer. Radiation has also been suggested to reduce the permeability of polyethylene to various gases through cross-linking, grafting, or polymerizing a coating *in situ* with radiation. Additional benefits from radiation are: improvements in sealability, shrink memory, stress crack and fire resistance, and improved clarity.

General Effects

All polymers which are exposed to radiation fall into two groups—those that undergo cross-linking reactions, and those that exhibit degradation or chain scissions. Generally, both occur to a limited extent at the same time in any polymer, but the net effect depends on which outweighs the other. For vinyl polymers it has been found that if each carbon atom of the main chain has at least one hydrogen atom, the polymer predominantly exhibits cross-linking. If the monomer unit, on the other hand, has a tetrasubstituted carbon atom present, then degradation generally outweighs cross-linking. It should be emphasized, however, that through the use of correct irradiation conditions and/or incorporation of chemical cross-linking promoters, many polymers that normally degrade under radiation can be made to cross-link. For example, the rate and degree of cross-linking can be affected by the presence of oxygen; polyethylene in oxygen requires a higher dose of radiation to achieve the same degree of cross-linking than if irradiated in the absence of oxygen. Polypropylene, which cross-links in the absence of air, is degraded in its presence. The form of the polymer and the dose rate both affect the irradiation in the presence of oxygen. Thin films often cross-link less efficiently, especially at low dose rates.

Most linear polymers exhibit enhanced cross-linking when irradiated at temperatures above their melt temperature. It may be desirable, therefore, to carry out irradiation at elevated temperatures—or, alternatively, a postirradiation annealing treatment can be used. This enables the free radicals trapped in the crystalline areas of the polymer to cross-link with adjacent chains instead of causing chain scissions as oxygen diffuses into the materials and reacts with the radicals.

Cross-linking additives found to be effective include allyl acrylate, allyl methacrylate, ethylene glycol diacrylate, ethylene glycol dimethacrylate, (2), n-phenylmaleimide, m-phenylene dimaleimide (3), and many others. Use of these monomers in concentrations of about 5% by weight in the polymer has been found to increase cross-linking efficiency by up to a factor of 5 or more. The presence of phenyl groups or other resonant structures in the polymer structure tends to increase the overall radiation resistance of the polymer.

Cross-linking Techniques

The enhancement of the properties of polyethylene by economically low radiation has resulted in a great emphasis on the study and manufacture of irradiated products made from this resin. Irradiation also greatly increases stress-cracking resistance, and tensile and impact strength, and decreases ultimate elongation while affecting electrical characteristics only very slightly. Irradiated polyethylene sheet with thin copper sheet laminated on both sides is being used for microwave stripline and associated components used in phased-array antenna systems. At the extremely high frequencies used in microwave systems, dimensional stability at elevated temperatures is of critical importance, slight changes of dimensions in waveguide components leading to distortion and noise. Irradiated polyethylene finds an ideal application in this use.

The largest volume of irradiated polyethylene film used today is in shrinkable film applications for food and other types of packaging. The electron irradiation is employed to impart cross-linking and increased elastic memory to the film. In this process the extruded tubular film is irradiated, expanded, or stretched by an air bubble type of mandrel, then cooled while still expanded. When packaging an object, sufficient heat is applied to raise the film above its unirradiated melting point, whereupon, because of the cross-linking imparted by the irradiation step, the material "remembers" its unstretched dimensions and reverts to them, forming a tightly fitting, attractive package.

Graft Polymerization

A most promising application of radiation in the near future appears to be that of radiation grafting. The preparation of radiation graft copolymers is often simpler than that using conventional chemical methods. Because the absorption of radiation by monomers and polymers is nonselective, radiation grafting is widely applicable to practically any of the various types of polymeric systems currently known. Three methods are in general use—(1) the mutual technique, in which the polymer is exposed while immersed in the monomer to be grafted, (2) the peroxidation by preirradiation of the polymer and (3) the preirradiation technique which utilizes the trapped free radicals produced by the irradiation of the polymer to react with the monomer when the former is subsequently exposed to it. Irradiation has been used to prepare grafts of chloromethyl-styrene to polypropylene to make the polymer dyeable. Various vinyl monomers have been grafted to wood to stabilize the material against dimensional change on exposure to moisture. Radiation has also been used to prepare graft copolymers of vinyl polymers in which the object is in general to increase solvent and heat resistance.

Polymerization by means of radiation has the advantage that no chemical catalyst is needed, the initiation rate does not depend on temperature, and many polymers unobtainable by other means can be prepared.

Costs

The cost of irradiation is directly related to the dose or amount of radiation required and to the power output of the accelerator. The cost is also naturally influenced by the total capital cost including accelerator, auxiliary and process equipment, installation cost and shielding, and operating cost consisting of both direct and indirect labor, maintenance, and plant overhead. For example, the capital investment involved in a line utilizing a typical 500-kV, 10-kW single 48-in. accelerator will amount to about $135,000, of which $88,000 is for accelerator system, $20,000 for shielding and installation, $7000 for auxiliary equipment and spares, and $20,000 for process equipment. Total operating costs are estimated to be about $85,000 based on a three-shift operation.

DONALD E. SMITH

REINFORCEMENTS

The physical limitations of many plastics have been overcome by judicious selection of a reinforcement. Vinyl asbestos flooring is a prime example of a highly filled, very weak composition, made durable by the use of asbestos reinforcement. Another example is woven nylon mesh tubing in clear vinyl garden hose for rigidity and resistance to crimping. Many other applications serve purposes which correlate with strength improvement. Certain properties, such as electrical, relate to composition of the reinforcement.

Forms and Properties of Reinforcements

The properties imparted to various plastics (see Table 1) can be stated only in a very general way. The form of the reinforcement determines the properties imparted and its applications. Much ingenuity has been applied to the development of particular forms of reinforcement to suit fabrication technique, part size and shape, cost, polymer to be reinforced, combination with other reinforcements, strength requirements, decorative properties, etc.

Fiberglass is frequently combined with the reinforcements listed in the table to take advantage of its many forms and generally superior properties. Almost each type of reinforcement listed is available in several compositional varieties as well as the forms listed. Asbestos, for example, is available in several fiber lengths, upon which its form as a fiber, mat, fabric or felt depends. Long fibers are woven after being fabricated into yarn. Shorter fibers may be used as is or formed into mats or felted.

Metallic reinforcements are the most varied. Rods, such as used in concrete, have considerably lower tensile strengths than very fine wire. The particular metal also determines the degree of

TABLE 1. REINFORCEMENTS FOR THERMOSETTING AND THERMOPLASTIC POLYMERS.

Type of Reinforcement	Fiber	Filament	Mat	Fabric	Felt	Mesh	Whisker	Flakes	Flexural strength	Tensile strength	Stiffness	Dimensional stability	Thermal resistance	Electrical insulation	Lubricity	Impact resistance	Chemical resistance	Water resistance	Weather resistance	Thermoplastics	Thermosets
Inorganic																					
Asbestos	X		X	X	X	X			M	M	M	H	VH	M	L	MH	H	MH	M	X	X
Metal	X	X		X	X	X		X	H	H	H	H	VH	VL	L	VH	L	VH		X	X
Single crystals		X					X		VH	VH	VH	VH	H								X
Carbon	X	X		X	X				L	L	H	M	H	L	L		VH	VH			X
Graphite	X	X		X	X				VH	H	VH	VH	VH	L	VH		VH	VH			X
Glass		X	X					X	H	M	H	H	H	H	L	M	M	H	H		X
Organic																					
Synthetic	X	X	X	X		X			L	L	L	L	L	M	M	VH	M	M	VH	X	X
Wood flour	X								L	L	M	M	L	L	L	M	L	L	L		X
Jute	X	X		X					L	L	L	L	L	L	L	M	L	L	L		X
Sisal	X		X						L	L	M	M	L	L	M	M	M	L	L		X
Paper		X			X				H	M	H	M	M	M		M	L	L	L	X	X
Cotton	X			X	X				L	M	L	M	M	H	L	M	L	L	L		X
Alpha-cellulose	X								L	L	M	L	L	H	L	L	L	L	L		X
Lignocellulose	X								L	L	L	M	M	L	M	M	VL	VL	VL		X
Keratin	X								L	L	L			L	M	L	VL	VL	VL		X

VH = Very high   MH = Medium high   H = High   M = Medium   L = Low   VL = Very low electrical and thermal conductivity, thermal resistance, dimensional stability, and other properties.

Single crystal whiskers have attracted much attention due to their extremely high strengths and moduli. Their use in plastics is limited by their costs of $25 to several thousand dollars per lb. As producing methods are refined and costs decline, such products will doubtlessly become important factors in plastics composites.

Rapid changes are occurring in the production of superior carbon and graphite fibers to keep pace with whiskers. Theoretical strength for graphite is among the highest and tensiles of 3×10^6 psi have been obtained experimentally.

Glass flake provides the particular property of high flexural strength and stiffness in two planes, and is amenable to orientation.

Fabrication

Reinforcements have been adapted to almost every plastics fabrication technique, and several have been developed to accommodate a particular type or form. Compounds which are mixtures of powdered resins and fiber may be injection or compression molded or extruded. Dough-like compounds (premix) also employ fibers in a more easily handled and measured form, using the same techniques but usually employing liquid thermosetting polymers or solutions of these in monomers (styrene-polyester solutions).

Liquid thermosetting resin mixtures may also be spread upon a mat, felt or preformed reinforcement, and then compression molded.

Filament winding often employs wire for special purposes in conjunction with fiberglass.

Thermoplastics sheets are also heated and compression molded with fabric, mat and felt (paper) reinforcements. Crêpe paper is printed for decoration and is easily conformable to contours.

Spray-up methods are used with fibers or filaments blown onto a form with the liquid thermosetting resin serving to bond the structure.

Continuous dipping of mat fabric or felt and curing or subsequently combining with other materials is employed in heat curing laminating processes.

The more rigid reinforcements are also placed in molds and room temperature castings resins, and mixtures poured to encase them.

Applications

So varied are the applications for these agents that only a few can be mentioned. Wherever improvement in the properties listed are required, there is certain to be a reinforcement to serve the purpose. Lightweight tools for metal forming or compression molding have been made possible by castings and hand lay-up methods. Resistance wire embedments act as reinforcements as well as

heating elements and wire mesh and expanded metal provide exceptional impact strength and rigidity, as well as conductivity. Low-cost casting molds may be made by the same method.

Thermoplastics have benefited considerably by the use of nylon and wire mesh to improve impact resistance. Electrical insulators with adequate compressive strength and heat distortion properties are made possible by the inclusion of asbestos. Wire rims in polyethylene buckets have extended their sizes and usefulness.

Previously it was believed that reinforcements were more compatible with the more rigid thermosets, but recent research directed toward thermoplastics indicates that fiber reinforcement often enables these polymers to replace metals in gears and other moving parts. Direct molding of the part also eliminates machining. Although carbon and graphite reinforcements and whiskers were developed for rocket nozzle and nose cone applications, they undoubtedly will become more extensively used in plastics for super-duty requirements at low manufacturing costs, weight, conductivity, maintenance and other properties resulting from the complementary nature of plastics and reinforcement.

THOMAS H. FERRIGNO

REINFORCEMENTS: CERAMIC WHISKERS

True whiskers are tiny, single-crystal fibers having a highly perfect crystalline structure. When compared with bulk (large) crystals, whiskers contain far fewer flaws (dislocations), impurities, voids, point defects and have a high degree of surface perfection. As a consequence, whiskers have exhibited phenomenal strengths approaching the cohesive bond strength between adjacent atoms, which is estimated (based on theoretical considerations) to be about 10% of the elastic modulus.

Whiskers usually grow along a prominent crystallographic direction and display polyhedral (not circular) cross sections. They are generally quite small in length, which may average between 1/16 to 1 in.; a few exceptional whiskers have been as long as 6 in.

Over 30 elements and 50 compounds, including organic, ceramic and metallic compositions, have been grown in whisker form. However, for reinforcing purposes, the ceramic whiskers probably will be used the most widely because of a combination of desirable properties, which include: low density, high hardness, high elastic modulus, and chemical inertness (low reactivity).

A typical photomicrograph of aluminum oxide whiskers is shown in Fig. 1. These whiskers are about 1×10^{-4} in. in diameter, and have lengths

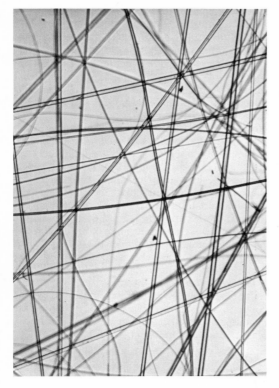

FIG. 1. Photomicrograph of Al_2O_3 whiskers having diameters falling between 1×10^{-5} to 1×10^{-3} inches, and having length-to-diameter ratios of 1,000 to 50,000 (Transmitted light, Mag. 400X).

averaging from $\frac{1}{2}$–1 in. long (not shown here). However, an important fact is that they have high length-to-diameter ratios (1000-50,000) which should be sufficient for reinforcing plastic materials.

Although high tensile strengths of the order of a few million pounds per square inch were predicted early in the 1920's, thirty years elapsed before materials (whiskers) were discovered which had these phenomenally high strengths. Since that time, considerable interest has been generated in these materials, but primarily to learn more about their properties, how they are grown, and why they are so strong. They have been an excellent media in which to observe solid-state phenomena in near-perfect materials. However, it was not until 1960 that studies were undertaken to see whether the high strength of the whiskers could be utilized by incorporating them into various materials as reinforcements. Most of the efforts were concerned with the reinforcement of metals, although recently, increasing attention is being directed towards the use of polymeric materials as the matrix or binder. At present, there is little data available on whisker-reinforced plastics, so that this discussion will be concerned more with their future potential.

Properties

The rapidly increasing interest in whiskers today has resulted chiefly from their ultra-high strengths and their potential as plastics reinforcing agents. The observed maximum tensile strengths of various materials are compared in Fig. 2, which clearly indicates the superior reinforcing potential of the whiskers. The strength values of the whiskers represent the maximum values tested to date, and do not necessarily mean that the (highest) theoretical strengths have been yet achieved. For example, graphite whiskers should theoretically be stronger than aluminum oxide whiskers, although the limited number of tests have not been sufficient to confirm this. In general, the strength of whiskers increases with decreasing size, so that the smallest whiskers tend to be the strongest. This fact can be used to separate high strength whiskers from their large, weaker counterparts for reinforcement applications.

In Table 1, some mechanical properties of various whiskers are compared with those of continuous filaments of glasses and metals. Although the glass and metal fibers have high strengths, the whisker materials are considerably stronger and exhibit specific strengths which may be as much as 10 times greater. In addition, the whisker materials have very high elastic moduli and very high specific moduli. The highest specific modulus for glass filaments is about 150 million in., whereas ceramic whiskers have specific moduli ranging from 500-2400 million in. Thus, the usefulness of whisker materials will depend on how effectively they can be incorporated into a suitable matrix, and how efficiently the matrix is able to transfer the stresses to the whiskers. This means that new processing techniques will be necessary for separating the whiskers according to their strengths, for handling and orienting the whiskers, and for developing a design and fabrication technology to produce composites having the desired tailor-made properties.

Applications

It appears that the greatest potential gains in using whisker reinforcement will be in both the strengthening and in the stiffening of the plastic materials. The whiskers, because they are short, can be combined in a variety of ways with the plastics —e.g., impregnated yarns, papers, tapes, threads, sheets and pre-pregs. Thus, it will be possible to build up a wide variety of structures which will not depend solely on filament winding techniques. Complex body shapes, even without centers of revolution, are able to be formed. The

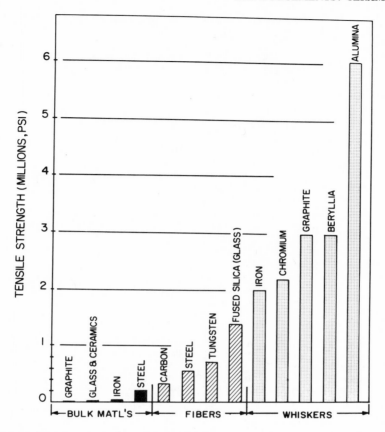

FIG. 2. Measured maximum tensile strengths of various materials in bulk, fiber, and whisker form.

fact that many plastics will wet and bond directly to whiskers is encouraging, and should help to simplify the fabrication process.

In order to achieve the full potential advantages of whiskers, they should be oriented in a direction parallel to the applied stress (or stresses). This can be accomplished by selecting a suitable compositional and geometric combination of whiskers and matrix. However, other applications are becoming evident. It has been reported for example, that by adding as little as 1% whiskers, along with continuous glass filaments during a filament winding process, the interlaminar shear strength of the reinforced material was increased by as much as 20%. This indicates that whiskers can be incorporated advantageously along with other fibers, tapes, and yarns used in filament winding processes. In the case of glass filaments, the high modulus of the whiskers could be used to increase the stiffness of the overall composite. Other properties of the plastics, such as abrasion resistance (hardness), optical effects (luster, opacity), thermal expansion, and electrical and thermal conductivity can be greatly modified as desired, depending on the type, packing density,

and orientation of the whiskers used.

It should be emphasized that whiskers and whisker-reinforced plastics are still in the early exploratory stages of development, and that the whiskers produced today exhibit a wide scatter in strength. This means that there is much to be done in improving the yield of the high-strength varieties, and new techniques will have to be developed for orienting and incorporating these whiskers into the plastics. Nevertheless, it appears that whisker reinforced materials will lead to a new class of materials which have far superior properties over those being made and used today. About two years ago, whiskers were available in only small (gram quantity) amounts. However, recently it has been announced that some whiskers, such as SiC, are available in tonnage quantities at costs as low as $200/lb. It has been predicted that in a few years whisker prices will approach $100/lb.

Thus the use of whiskers opens up a new approach to the development of reinforced plastics having unique and superior properties. The chief gains in the whisker-reinforced plastics will be (1) high tensile, and high specific strengths

TABLE 1. PROPERTIES OF REINFORCING FILAMENTS.

Filament Reinforcement	Melting or Softening Pt. (°C)	Density (D, lb/in^3)	Tensile Strength ($S_f \times 10^{-3}$ psi)	Young's Modulus ($E \times 10^{-6}$ psi)	Specific Strength ($S_f/D \times 10^{-6}$ in.)	S_f/E Ratio	Specific Modulus ($E/D \times 10^{-6}$ in.)
I. *Continuous*							
A. Glass							
E-glass	840	0.092	250	10.5	2.72	1/42	114
E/HTS	840	0.092	500	10.5	5.43	1/21	114
YM 31A	840	0.103	500	16.0	4.85	1/32	155
S–994	840	0.090	650	12.6	7.22	1/19	136
29–A	900	0.096	800	14.5	8.33	1/18	151
SiO$_2$	1660	0.079	850	10.5	10.75	1/12	133
B. Metal							
B	2100	0.09	300–500	55–60	4.44	1/144	639
W	3400	0.697	580	59	0.83	1/102	85
Mo	2622	0.369	320	52	0.87	1/163	141
Rene 41	1300	0.298	290	24.2	0.97	1/83	81
Steel	1400$^+$	0.280	600	29.0	2.14	1/48	104
Be	1284	0.066	185	35	2.80	1/189	530
II. *Discontinuous* (whiskers)							
A. Ceramic							
Al$_2$O$_3$	2040	0.143	6200	62–67	43.4	1/11	524
BeO	2570	0.103	2800**	58–60	27.1	1/21	971
B$_4$C	2490^d	0.091	934	70	10.3	1/81	835
SiC	2690^d	0.115	1650	70$^+$	14.3	1/75	1078
Graphite	3650$^{[s]}$	0.060	2845	142	47.4	1/50	2367
B. Metal							
Cu	1083	0.322	427	18	1.33	1/42	56
Ni	1455	0.324	560	31	1.73	1/55	96
Fe	1540	0.283	1900	29	6.71	1/15	102
Cr	1890	0.260	1290	35	4.96	1/27	135

**Flexure Test
d = decomposes
s = sublimes

(2) high stiffness, (3) improved shear strength, and (4) improved compressive strength. Also great improvement in abrasion resistance, in hardness, and in a wide variety of electrical, magnetic, and optical properties will be possible through the choice of the metallic and ceramic whisker materials, which will be available in the near future.

WILLARD H. SUTTON

Cross-reference: BORON FIBERS.

ROLL LEAF

Roll leaf for marking and decorating plastics is widely used by plastics finishers. Obtaining the proper formulation of roll leaf is of utmost importance. Roll leaf consists of a thin carrier strip of acetate, cellophane, or "Mylar" polyester film coated on one side. There is a wide variety of coating formulations that are designed to give

maximum adhesion with the various materials. Naturally, if the formulation is not compatible with the particular plastic being marked, the coating will not release properly from the carrier strip.

In general, there are three different types of pigment foils and three types of metallics. Pigments are available that will stamp with a matté (non-glossy) finish, gloss finish, and transparent colors. Gloss colors are the most popular because of appearance and excellent abrasion resistance. Transparent foils are actually dye coatings rather than pigment colors. These foils are used for decorating automotive deck medallions, horn buttons, etc. The part is usually hot stamped from the back (second surface), and then vacuum metallized for an interesting metallic effect. Transparent foils are also used on household appliance dials and escutcheons that are to be back lighted. Special "masking" colors, simulated wood grained foils, and "day glow" colors are also available.

Metallic foils are coated with suspensions of bronze or aluminum powder, with vacuum-plated aluminum, and with pure gold. Within the past few years, the vacuum metallizing process has been adapted to roll leaf manufacturing. The use of roll leaf stamping as a method of decorating molded plastic items has increased tremendously with this development. The finisher can now "selectively metallize" well-defined areas of a part in a simple stamping operation.

The manufacture of metallized imitation gold, silver and colors is a complex operation requiring several steps. When making a metallized foil, "Mylar" polyester film must be used as the carrier. Acetate and cellophane will give off gas and become brittle during the metallizing process. The "Mylar" is first coated with a release agent which releases the coating off the carrier strip and on to the plastic during the stamping operation. If the foil is to be chrome finished, the release coating is clear. If the finish is to be gold colored, the release coating is dyed to the desired shade of yellow. Naturally, other color metallics can be made, using the appropriate dye. It is important that the dyes used are as colorfast as possible to prevent fading. The carrier strip is then vacuum metallized in a chamber. A final sizing coat is applied to facilitate adhesion to the plastic.

One of the big advantages of roll leaf stamping as a method of marking and decorating is that "difficult-to-mark" materials such as polyethylene, polypropylene, etc., can be marked without any surface treatment.

Roll leaf normally is supplied in 200 ft lengths wound on a 1-in. diameter core. It can also be purchased in rolls up to 1000 ft for high speed applications. Roll leaf is usually manufactured in 24-in. widths. The leaf supplier cuts it to whatever width the job calls for.

When ordering roll leaf it is important to specify the plastic being marked, whether a metal or silicone rubber die will be used, and whether the part will be painted or vacuum metallized either before or after the stamping operation.

FRANK J. OLSEN

Cross-reference: DECORATIVE.

ROSIN ESTERS

Rosin is a thermoplastic, resinous solid obtained from the cells of living pine trees or extracts of aged pine stump wood. It occurs in such sources in widely distributed warm temperate areas of the world. In the United States, it is produced chiefly in the southeastern section of the country, from two species of tree, the longleaf pine (*Pinus palustris*) and the slash pine (*Pinus caribaea*). Rosin consists largely of resin acids, as well as smaller amounts of neutral compounds. It varies in color from pale yellow to dark red, depending on the source and method of collecting and processing.

There are three major methods of obtaining rosin commercially: solvent extraction of aged pine stump wood (wood rosin), collection of the oleoresin or gum from the living tree (gum rosin), and separation from tall oil, a by-product from the manufacture of paper from wood pulp (tall oil rosin). In the gum rosin process, the flow of oleoresin is induced by cutting V-shaped incisions in the bark. The collected oleoresin is separated by a simple distillation process into its components, rosin and turpentine. Wood rosin is obtained by solvent extraction of shredded pine stump wood. The crude extract is separated into liquid terpenes and a dark resinous fraction. Refining the dark resin to remove colored components yields a range of color grades of pale, refined rosin. Tall oil contains approximately 90% of acidic material which is composed of essentially equal parts of fatty and resin acids. The most effective commercial means of separating the rosin and fatty acid components is by fractional distillation at reduced pressure. Although each fraction remains contaminated with small percentages of the other, a commercially available grade of tall oil rosin is obtained by this method.

Pine stump extraction yields a nonresinous fraction composed mainly of: (1) terpene hydrocarbons: monocyclic (dipentene, terpinene, terpinolene, p-menthane and p-cymene) and bicyclic (alpha-pinene, the chief constituent of turpentine) and (2) oxygenated terpenes, the pine oils, which are mixtures of terpineols, terpins, borneol and fenchyl alcohols. The rosins derived from the oleoresin of living trees and from the extraction of aged stump wood are composed of approximately 90% resin acids and 10% nonacidic material.

Resin acids are monocarboxylic acids of alkylated hydrophenanthrene nuclei. Those acids with two double bonds have the empirical formula $C_{19}H_{29}COOH$. Rosin consists of a very complex mixture of these resin acids, as well as certain dihydro, tetrahydro and dehydro variations of them. Abietic acid may be considered as representative of those resin acids which comprise a major proportion of rosin constituent acids:

The resin acid molecule possesses two chemically reactive centers, the double bonds and the carboxyl group. Oxidation is one of the more troublesome, and therefore important, reactions of resin acids at the double bonds. The abietic-type acids with conjugated unsaturation readily take up oxygen to produce darker colored, less soluble products. Since oxidation of rosin depends on the conjugated system of double bonds, altering these double bonds is necessary in order to minimize oxidative action. Such reactions as hydrogenation, disproportionation and polymerization are employed commercially to produce more stable types of rosin.

Hydrogenation is one of the most satisfactory methods for decreasing the susceptibility of rosin to oxidation. Molecular hydrogen in the presence of catalysts such as palladium, platinum or Raney nickel will effectively eliminate the conjugated double bonds and produce the desired stability by conversion to the dihydro derivatives.

Disproportionation is another means of modifying rosin to improve its resistance to oxidation. In effect, the reaction creates a third double bond by removing two atoms of hydrogen from the abietic-type acids. These double bonds then rearrange to form an aromatic nucleus (dehydroabietic acid). Concurrently, the hydrogens removed add to other resin acids to produce the more stable dihydro and tetrahydro resin acids.

The conjugated double bond types of resin acids in rosin that are susceptible to oxidation can also be stabilized under conditions which produce polymerization. The effect of this reaction is to polymerize the abietic-type acids to dimeric resin acids. Compared to the starting rosin, the resulting product exhibits a lower acid number, higher softening point, higher solution viscosity and greater degree of oxidation resistance.

Certain of the resin acids, notably levopimaric acid, having the conjugated double bonds within one ring, react readily with maleic anhydride by a Diels-Alder mechanism to form an adduct. The reaction is carried out commercially to produce modified rosins that are composed of over 50% adduct. Such adducts, containing a significant proportion of tribasic acid, exhibit higher softening points and greater acidity than the starting rosin. As a result of their higher degree of functionality, these polybasic acids find great utility in the production of hard resins and as size additives in the paper industry.

Modified, oil-soluble, phenolic derivatives may be prepared by condensing rosin, phenol and formaldehyde. It is generally accepted that this condensation consists of an addition reaction between the methylolphenol and the resin acids. The condensation products are usually further modified by esterification with polyols to yield hard, high-melting synthetic resins which find utility in coatings, inks and other related applications.

The second important reactive center of resin acids is their carboxyl group. Salts and esters of rosin and of modified rosins are produced commercially in large volumes for use in a variety of industrial applications. Other reactions involve reduction of the carboxyl to a primary alcohol and conversion to a nitrile group which can be reduced to a primary amine.

Alkali metal salts of rosin are readily formed and find wide commercial applications. The sodium salt or soap of rosin is used widely in soaps, paper sizes and emulsions. In the sizing of paper, the sodium resinate is added to the pulp suspension and precipitated in the form of a complex aluminum salt by the addition of alum.

The esterification of rosin and modified rosins with monohydric and polyhydric alcohols yields a vast family of synthetic resins which offer a wide range of physical properties. The structurally hindered nature of the resin acid carboxyl group makes it necessary to use higher reaction temperatures to effect esterification. Temperatures of 250°C or higher are normally required to achieve a commercially practical rate of esterification.

The rosin esters of short-chain, monohydric alcohols are usually viscous liquids or soft, balsamic solids. The most important commercial product in this group is the methyl ester which is produced in a continuous esterification process under conditions of elevated temperature and pressure. This ester is converted to a more stable derivative by catalytic hydrogenation. The hydrogenated methyl ester of rosin finds application in a variety of applications including nitrocellulose lacquers for wood and metal, adhesives, printing inks, chewing gum and many other related industrial end uses.

The polyhydric alcohols, glycerine and pentaerythritol, offer great utility in the conversion of rosin and modified rosins to essentially neutral, high-melting synthetic esters. Esterification of rosin with glycerine yields ester gum, which offers decided advantages over ordinary rosin or rosin salts with regard to durability, solubility, moisture resistance and inertness to certain basic pigments in coatings. Ester gum is compatible with many elastomers and plastic materials including nitrocellulose, ethyl cellulose, natural and synthetic rubbers, waxes, vinyl resins, chlorinated rubber, casein, zein and many natural and synthetic resins.

The use of pentaerythritol as the esterifying alcohol enables the production of rosin esters having higher softening points and greater resistance to the effects of heat, oxidation, water and chemical saponification than the corresponding glycerine esters. The pentaerythritol counterparts are compatible with essentially the same group of elastomers or film-formers as those of the glycerine esters, with the exception of the cellulosic derivatives.

In addition to the glycerine and pentaerythritol esters of rosin, the corresponding esters of many modified rosin types are produced commercially. Thus, the counterpart products made from hydrogenated rosin, polymerized rosin and disproportionated rosin serve useful functions in applications requiring a higher degree of oxidation resistance than can be attained in esters from ordinary rosin. These more stable resins, therefore, find utility in a variety of solvent and emulsion adhesives, pressure-sensitive adhesive compositions, coatings, printing inks and hot melt, heat-sealable, barrier coatings for paper, metallic foils and plastic films.

All of the ester-type resins mentioned in the preceding text result only from the simple combination of a resin acid with an alcohol or polyol. Additional resins can be produced by the introduction of a third or fourth modifying reactant. The commonest of these modifiers include maleic anhydride, fumaric acid, phthalic anhydride and a group of phenol-formaldehyde condensates. A vast multitude of synthetic resins is thus possible by the appropriate choice of the kind and amount of modifiers used, as well as by the polyol chosen.

Maleic anhydride modification of rosin, followed by esterification of the adduct with glycerine or pentaerthritol, yields a group of hard, brittle, polyester-type resins commonly known as maleates or modified maleics. The high degree of cross-linking in these resins contributes a lower level of solubility, high softening points and high solution viscosities. These properties alone suggest the use of the maleic resins in nitrocellulose wood lacquers, oleoresinous varnishes, gravure printing inks and similar applications in which such properties are a prerequisite to good performance.

Phthalic anhydride and fumaric acid modified rosin esters are usually considered in a specialty class and find application in certain end uses where their unique properties are beneficial to the performance of the final product. These include moisture-set inks, nitrocellulose wood lacquers, self-polishing emulsion floor waxes and processing aids for vinyl floor tiles. In some cases, the fumaric-modified types are rather similar in properties and performance characteristics to the maleics. In others, however, the fumaric acid is the key to the unique properties and performance of this group of resins.

Although the dibasic acid-modified rosin esters comprise a rather extensive list of products, the combinations available through phenolic modification would appear to be endless. Wide variations in physical properties and performance characteristics can be achieved through such variables as the choice of substituted phenol type,

the molar ratio of phenol to formaldehyde, the amount of phenolic modification of the rosin ester, type of rosin, type of polyol and even the use of additional modifiers such as dibasic acids. These rosin ester resins are generally described as "modified phenolics" in contrast to the "pure phenolics," which contain no rosin or rosin ester modification.

The phenolic-modified rosin esters are generally oil-soluble, hard resins having relatively high softening points and high viscosities when dissolved in drying oils or organic solvents. They find the greatest utility in coatings applications, such as varnishes and enamels, as well as in printing inks, particularly oil-based gloss inks for the lithographic and offset printing trade. In these end uses, the modified phenolic resins exhibit good hardness, rapid solvent release and drying characteristics, excellent gloss and other desirable properties resulting from their chemical nature. Certain of these modified phenolics also find application in specialty solvent-based adhesives in which natural or synthetic rubbers are used as the elastomers. High tensile strength characteristics and good adhesion are contributed to solvent adhesives by the inclusion of resins of this type.

Certain rosin ester resins are specially formulated to be soluble in aqueous ammonia or in alcohol. These are designed very carefully so that a high degree of cross-linking occurs before the esterification reaction has been carried to completion. The resulting products, therefore, are relatively high in softening point even though the acid number remains as high as 150-200. The high acid number is the key to solubility in both aqueous ammonia and alcohol.

Ammonia solutions of such resins find wide application in the modern, synthetic polymer-based emulsion floor polishes of the self-polishing type, where they function as excellent leveling agents and gloss promotors. Other notable performance features imparted by these alkali-soluble resins to floor polishes are good water resistance, removability and recoatability. The same resins are generally completely soluble in ethyl alcohol or in the many proprietary alcohol blends available commercially. This property makes them useful also in flexographic printing inks, which are chiefly alcohol-based, for printing on paper, metal foils or films of polystyrene, cellophane, polyethylene, polypropylene, poly (vinylidene chloride) or similar plastic materials. Flexographic inks based on alcohol-soluble, modified rosin esters exhibit the desirable properties of low odor, high gloss, heat-smear resistance and good adhesion which are so necessary to modern packaging methods, particularly where food products are involved.

Rosin and its ester derivatives constitute a valuable and diversified group of resinous products which find utility in a wide variety of to-day's commercial applications. Through the proper choice of resin acid type as the starting material and the selection of appropriate polyols and modifying agents, a host of resins can be produced having a wide range of properties. Compatibility with various film-formers, dispersibility in vegetable oils, solubility in aliphatic and aromatic hydrocarbons, as well as alcohol and aqueous alkali, are all characteristics which can be acquired by the proper modification of rosin ester resins. The particular properties of these products have led to commercial acceptance in the fields of varnishes, lacquers, printing inks, vinyl floor tiles, adhesives, chewing gum, plastics, emulsion-type floor polishes, and hot melt, barrier coatings, among other widely differing industrial applications.

J. S. AUTENRIETH

S

SILICA FIBERS

High silica fibers and textiles have been used in the plastics industry only during the last ten years in any significant quantity. Prior to approximately 1955 high silica fibrous materials were used only as thermal insulation in such applications as jet engine tail cones and aircraft hot air ducts where existing insulation materials such as fiber glass were unable to withstand the service temperatures of 1000–1800°F. However, in the latter half of the fifties when solid propellant rockets and ballistic reentry vehicles necessitated thermal protection materials to operate in 3000°F to above 10,000°F environments, high silica fibrous materials came into prominence. This new application was as an integral part of ablative plastics where the silica fibers provided reinforcement for the resin—hence reinforced plastics. This application was somewhat unique however, in that the reinforcement provided more than just a strengthening function since the high melting "point" and very high melt viscosity of silica was utilized.

In an ablative plastic where silica is used as reinforcement the fibers will melt and diffuse through the porous char layer and form a tenacious liquid film over the ablating surface. The film then holds the pyrolyzing resin in the ablation layer until the polymer degrades into elemental gases rather than being swept away as large polymer fragments. The polymer retention and attendant degradation increases the energy absorption severalfold in the silica reinforced plastics. In addition the silica melt stays on the surface long enough for some vaporization to occur rather than just being swept away in the molten form.

The ablative plastics usage for silca materials which for several years has exceeded 1 million lb per year has dwarfed any other silica reinforced plastics application. This application has been almost totally restricted to fabric and chopped fiber forms with emphasis in properties being placed upon resin compatibility, silica content, and laminate mechanical properties.Some limited usage has existed for silica materials in radomes or electrical applications where the low dielectric constant and loss tangent of fused silica has been required.

In most ablative components the principal purpose is thermal protection and the secondary purpose is structural integrity, with cost a still important consideration. Consequently, silica fibers in use today are limited to two types, as defined by manufacturing processes and origin. The two general types are fused silica and leached glass fibers.

Fused silica fibers which are also referred to as quartz are produced by a direct melt process. These products are marketed primarily by the General Electric Company, and by J. P. Stevens & Company.

The leached glass products are also commonly called high silica, and are produced by a precursor conversion process. They are marketed by Haveg Industries Inc., J. P. Stevens & Company, and by H. I. Thompson Fiber Glass Company (HITCO) under the trademarks "Siltemp," "Astrosil," and "Refrasil," respectively.

In the precursor conversion process normal borosilicate glass fibers, E-glass, in any one of several forms, are leached in acids. The principal acid is hydrochloric, but other acids, excluding phosphoric and hydrofluoric, can be used with some success. The leaching is performed under closely controlled conditions of time, temperature and concentration. The glass which originally consists of twelve or more metal oxides is "purified" during leaching, and the silica content increases from an original level of less than 60–99% or greater. After leaching, the fibers are water washed to remove all traces of soluble salts and residual acid. The removal of these contaminants must be thorough or the subsequent heat treating operation and final properties can be drastically affected. The material is then heat treated to temperatures between 1500°F and 2200°F to consolidate the pore structure, dehydrate the silica and increase the mechanical strength. As would be expected, the silica content can be increased by extending or accelerating the leaching cycle through higher acid concentrations, higher temperatures or variations in the leaching solution. However, the leaching procedure is relatively complex because of the differing solubilities and reaction rates of each cation, the reactivity of silica and the high surface area of the fibers.

It is of significance to note that the precursor conversion process is based upon prior formation of fibers in whatever form the end application requires. For example, if silica fabric of a certain weave construction and count is required E-glass fabric in the same form (plus a shrinkage allowance) is the starting material. Similarly, if random fiber is required the producer uses chopped E-glass yarn or strand as a starting material.

This characteristic is in contrast to fused silica fibers where the fused silica fiber is formed in the final intended composition and then progresses through the normal plying, twisting, weaving etc. operations used to process glass fiber into the finished form. Figure 1 shows several of the forms in which "Refrasil" products are available.

In the silica fiber heat treating procedure, the consolidation process reduces the surface area from the 400–500 sq/m/g level to something less than 100 sq/m/g. This heat treating procedure is performed in gas or electric fired furnaces on a batch or continuous basis depending largely upon the fiber form being processed. The type of heat source and atmosphere during heat treating have some effect upon subsequent properties

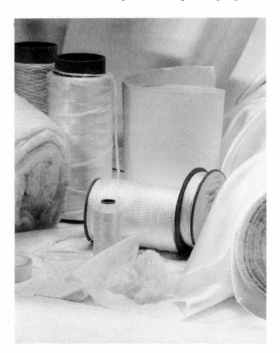

FIG. 1. Common forms of leached glass silica fibers (Refrasil).

of the fibers but end use requirements are not sufficiently defined to show preference in exact processing conditions.

High silica fibers are also made via the leaching-heat treating method using a different starting material. In this method a high silica content sodium silicate glass is blown into staple fibers of a fine diameter (1μ or less). These fibers are converted to silica fibers by the leaching-heat treating technique.

Because these fibers are staple and non-oriented, they have been used little in the plastics industry and used almost exclusively in fibrous thermal insulation systems. This type does offer some potential for reinforced plastics because of an extremely high purity and potentially higher strength than other leached products.

Several methods have been reported for producing fused silica filaments and these revolve around either fusing quartz rods and drawing/blowing filaments from the molten tip or else flowing molten silica through orifices and drawing filaments from the globule on the end of the orifice tip in the same manner continuous glass filaments are formed.

Recently, fused silica has been marketed in fabric or non-woven forms for use in ablative plastics so that it is now available in forms comparable to the high silica types. However, the price is five to six times that of a comparable leached glass product. For this reason fused silica fibers are used in reinforced plastics only where high purity or high strength requirements offset the cost difference.

In the use of silica reinforced plastics as mentioned previously purity and melt viscosity are of preliminary importance. Laminate strength is of next importance. Figure 2 shows the viscosity relationship between silica fibers with silica contents of 99.97, 99.1, and 98.7%. It is apparent that as purity increases viscosity increases manyfold for any particular temperature above 1700°C.

Also, as these ablative components are used extensively in reentry vehicles purity with the absence of alkali or alkali earth elements has become significant. These elements affect detectability during reentry and hinder communication. Consequently, the absence of these elements is an added requirement over silica content. In this characteristic, the fused silica products are superior to leached glass products because in the former the raw materials are devoid of these contaminants as opposed to the leached glass raw material that has appreciable quantitites which can never be completely removed.

It has been estimated that approximately 95% of all silica reinforced plastics use phenolic resins which are encompassed by the specification MIL-R-9299 high temperature phenolic specification. Several manufacturers are producing

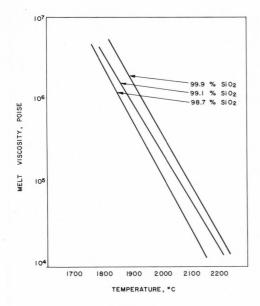

FIG. 2. Silica fiber melt viscosity.

resins meeting this callout. The general types are phenolformaldehydes, phenyl-silanes (silicone modified) and novalacs (nylon modified). The latter types were developed primarily for greater high temperature stability and higher mechanical strength respectively. Several other modifications have been developed to accelerate cure, reduce cure shrinkage to minimize the distribution of polymer chain lengths in the uncured resin prior to impregnation and to generally facilitate fabrication.

Table 1 shows some of the relative properties of fused silica and leached glass products in the virgin and composite states.

It must be remembered that when mechanical properties are cited for silica reinforced ablative plastics the values are meaningless unless the following as an absolute minimum are identified:

(a) Reinforcement and resin specific identification.
(b) Reinforcement orientation.
(c) Reinforcement and resin content.
(d) Curing time, temperature and pressure.
(e) Molding method.
(f) Composite density.

Fabrication methods of silica reinforced plastics are highly controlled by configuration of finished product especially since phenolics are the principle resin system and most components are cylindrical or conical. These methods can be classified either by reinforcement orientation or molding pressure. According to orientation, the methods are flat layup, tape winding (parallel to centerline or shingle angle), rosette layup, and matched tool molding. For flat layups, plies

of the impregnated reinforcement are precut and stacked in a tool or on a backing plate and the part is then ready for debulking or curing.

In tape winding, continuous impregnated tape is applied to a rotating mandrel at some angle between parallel-to-center line and perpendicular. A rosette layup is one in which precut plies are placed in a female tool with edges of the plies extending from inside to outside surface and from both ends of the component. The ply orientation can also be defined as one in which the surface of the individual layers are radial and tangential to the inner and outer surfaces of the component.

With the above methods, the part (and mandrel) is then encapsulated in a protective film which may be PVA or a rubber "bag," and fitted with bleeder lines and thermocouples. The part is then cured in ovens, presses autoclaves or hydroclaves.

During cure, special precautions must be taken to allow for release of evolved volatiles. The volatiles originate from solvents used in impregnation and from condensation products released during resin polymerization.

Curing temperatures are varied between 175°F and 400°F, and pressures between 15 psi and 2000 psi—in some rare cases, 5000 psi. Retention times are a function of part geometry and mass, but may vary from 3–4 hr, to 20–30 hr.

Part densities can be varied between 20 and 115 lb/cu ft, and sizes range from fractions of a pound to several thousand pounds.

TABLE 1. COMPARATIVE PROPERTIES OF SILICA FIBERS[a].

Property	Type		
	Fused silica	Leached glass	Regular glass
Silica content, %	99.9	99.0+	
Fiber diameter, in.[b]	.0004	.0004	
Fiber strength, psi	300,000	<100,000	
Fabric breaking strength lb/in. (184 cloth equivalent)	100++	70	
Softening point, °F	3,100	3000+	
Specific gravity	2.2	2.13	
Laminate properties[c] flexural strength, ksi	40–45	30–35	9–10[d]
tensile strength, ksi	26–30	18–24	5–7
tensile modulus, X10⁶ psi	—	2.5	—
flexural modulus, X10⁶ psi	3.4	2.75	2.2

[a] These values are typical averages only.
[b] Several diameters available for both types.
[c] In MIL-R-9299 phenolics without fillers.
[d] Random fiber molding compound.

J. PAT STERRY

SILICON CARBIDE WHISKERS

Reinforcement of plastics is achieved by the incorporation of high strength and high modulus particles whose geometry is such that they can best carry the load transmitted by the deformed low modulux matrix. The higher the modulus of the reinforcing phase the lower will be the total deformation produced by a particular stress. High strength of the reinforcing phase per se is not sufficient if the elastic modulus is sufficiently low that large strains are required to produce the desired load carrying stress. In a large proportion of engineering applications large strains cannot be tolerated.

For other applications where weight is a major factor, the density of the reinforcement must be minimized, or better the strength to weight ratio must be maximized. As before, if total strain must be kept small the specific modulus, the modulus to density ratio, must be maximized.

The three most important properties of a structural reinforcing material then are high elastic modulus, high ultimate strength, and low specific gravity.

The class of reinforcing materials on which many place their hope for the future of reinforced composites are the microcrystalline fibers of refractory materials, the "whiskers", for the following reasons. The moduli are extremely high, the ultimate strengths are orders of magnitude greater than those of massive materials and since they are typical inorganic compounds their specific gravities are low. Other properties, not normally considered, favor "whiskers," namely their refractoriness, and chemical inertness.

Rather than present another comparison of the properties of various whiskers and fibrous materials, the properties of SiC whiskers alone are tabulated below. Not only do silicon carbide whiskers have the necessary high modulus, high strength and low density properties; they offer a unique combination of secondary properties which are unmatched by any other reinforcement. They have high thermal and electrical conductivity, comparable to metals, refractoriness and creep resistance, chemical inertness and oxidation resistance. Lastly they do not melt, but on exposure to temperature extremes, decompose to yet another refractory material, graphite, without the presence of a liquid phase. The hardness and abrasion resistance of silicon carbide are well known and need no further description.

Reinforcement of epoxy and phenolic matrices with silicon carbide whiskers has been demonstrated. With volume fractions of 20% whiskers, composites having over 35,000 psi tensile strength have been produced.

Epoxy resin composites, containing silicon carbide whiskers in a thin layer on the tensile side have shown remarkable, and as yet unexplained flexural properties. In flexure, the unreinforced bar fractured at low stress (approximately 5000 psi) and low strain. The second, containing a layer of silicon carbide whiskers 0.050 in. thick, oriented as a paper, yielded at over twice the load (approximately ~ 12,000 psi) and deformed severely without fracture. This test has been repeated a number of times with identical results.

An application in which silicon carbide whiskers may prove to be exceptional is in reinforced ablating structures. The absence of a liquid phase, and the formation of residual graphite fibers in the char layer produce a composite which resists high heat fluxes.

The subject of this discussion might better have been amended to include other microcrystalline forms of silicon carbide. Though very different in appearance, the various microcrystalline forms of silicon carbide are closely related structurally Figure 1 shows typical silicon carbide whiskers. Each reinforcement type is characterized by at least one dimension in the micron range. Powders, of course, have micron dimensions in all directions, whiskers in two directions and ribbons and flakes in one direction.

Randomly oriented, each form will provide stiffening and reinforcement in all directions. For specific stress applications, the different geometries can be applied, at least in theory, to provide more nearly optimum performance. For example, in a unidirectional tensile stress application, the obvious choice would be whiskers arranged parallel to the direction of the applied stress. For compression and shear stresses, the flake form, oriented with the flakes normal to the applied

FIG. 1.Silicon carbide whiskers—Crude single crystal silicon carbide fibers magnified forty times.

compressive stress or parallel to the shear stress would be ideal. Epoxy resins reinforced with SiC flakes have been prepared having elastic moduli up to 20 million psi.

The whisker and submicron powder forms of silicon carbide are the only ones which have been produced in commercial quantities. The others, the ribbon and flake are as yet available only in research quantities.

As opposed to certain other whiskers such as sapphire and beryllium oxide which have highly perfect, smooth, regular crystal facets, silicon carbide whiskers, particularly in the small diameters($<10\mu$), show no facets but instead grow in a "bamboo" type of structure. It is not known just what causes this structure, however, it may be due to the fact that SiC crystals rarely form true prism facets. This "bamboo" structure might well lead to an improved bonding between whiskers and the matrix. It should be stressed that these irregular shaped whiskers do not represent a low strength fraction but are the typical high-strength whiskers. Nearly all silicon carbide whiskers show this structure to some degree.

Structurally silicon carbide is at the same time both simple and complex. Both atoms are tetrahedrally bonded to four of the other atoms in what might be called a "diamond-like" structure providing a simple short-range structure. Successive layers of tetrahedra can be arranged either with the atoms of the upper tetrahedron directly above those of the lower (parallel), or rotated to be directly opposite (antiparallel). Over extended distances the various stacking sequences lead to a number of different crystal structures (polytypes), falling into three crystallographic types. These show cubic, hexagonal and rhombohedral symmetry. The various polytypes, of which over 100 have been identified, frequently occur as successive layers in crystals. This intergrowth of polytypes might also be an explanation for the "bamboo" structure of silicon carbide whiskers. Strength measurements on SiC whiskers representing several of the more common polytypes have shown no significant differences among them.

In summary, SiC whiskers (and other micro-crystalline forms) possess the physical properties required for reinforcement, namely high modulus, high ultimate strength, low density and refractoriness. Other secondary properties such as high thermal conductivity and hardness may in certain applications be used advantageously.

Structural composites utilizing the extreme properties of microscopic whiskers represent an entirely new generation of materials, and present a new system of engineering problems. Though far from optimum, composites with SiC whiskers have demonstrated the practicality of reinforcement of plastics with whiskers. It remains now for engineers to learn to improve composites and utilize the full potential of whiskers.

TABLE 1. PROPERTIES OF SiC WHISKERS.

Elastic modulus	100×10^6 psi	
Ultimate strength	$>3 \times 10^6$ psi	
Density	3.21 g/cc	
Specific modulus	8.6×10^8 in.	Modulus-density ratio
Specific strength	$>2.6 \times 10^7$ in.	Strength-density ratio
Thermal conductivity	1.17 cal/cm-sec-°C	Measured on macroscopic crystal
Electrical resistivity	0.03–0.3 ohm/cm	
Melting temp.	>2200°C	Sublimes
Creep resistance	>1750°C	No creep detected in macroscopic crystal
Oxidation resistance	>1500°C	No severe degradation in air or O_2 at 1500°C

PETER T. B. SHAFFER

Cross-reference: REINFORCEMENTS.

SILICONE INTERMEDIATES

Silicones are polymers having a backbone structure containing alternating silicon and oxygen atoms, with significant proportions of organic material attached to the silicon atoms by silicon-carbon linkages. Examples are compounds of the type shown in Fig. 1.

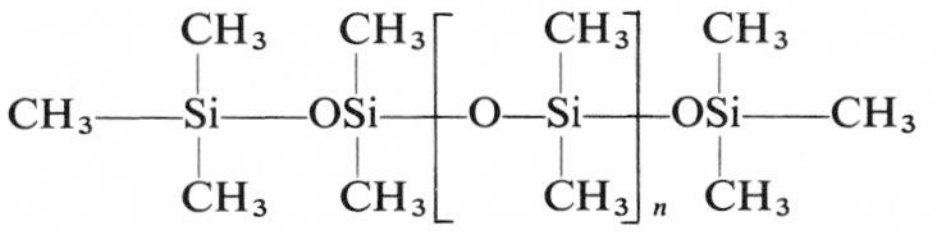

$$CH_3-\underset{\underset{CH_3}{|}}{\overset{\overset{CH_3}{|}}{Si}}-O\underset{\underset{CH_3}{|}}{\overset{\overset{CH_3}{|}}{Si}}\left[-O-\underset{\underset{CH_3}{|}}{\overset{\overset{CH_3}{|}}{Si}}\right]_n-O\underset{\underset{CH_3}{|}}{\overset{\overset{CH_3}{|}}{Si}}-CH_3$$

FIG. 1. A silicone molecule.

Compounds with the —SiOSi-group are called *siloxanes*, and silicones are *polysiloxanes*. By substituting some or all of the methyl groups with other organic groups such as phenyl or vinyl, by varying the ratio of oxygen to silicon, and by changing the size and shape of the polysiloxane skeleton of the molecules, an enormous variety of fluids, elastomers, and resins can be made. Originally developed to provide insulating materials stable at temperatures up to 250°C, silicones proved to be broadly useful because of their stability, their flexibility at low temperatures, and their surface properties. They are now of worldwide technical importance, with an annual world production of the order of 20 or 30 thousand tons (1965).

The monomers on which these polymers are based are called silanes. The simplest member of the group is silane itself, SiH_4. When the substituents attached to silicon are chlorine, methoxy, or methyl instead of hydrogen, the monomers are chlorosilanes, methoxysilanes, or methylsilanes. Some of the properties of technically important chlorosilanes are shown in Table 1.

Chlorosilanes are the usual starting materials for the preparation of other useful silanes and of oligomeric siloxanes. The properties of some of these are shown in Table 2.

Generally speaking, silicon-carbon bonds are strong, and such groups as Si—CH_3 or Si—C_6H_5 are stable to heat and to hydrolysis, oxidation and other chemical attack. On the other hand groups such as Si—Cl, Si—OCH_3, Si—$N(CH_3)_2$ and Si—$OCOCH_3$ are easily hydrolyzed. Reaction with water proceeds in two stages, the second resulting in the formation of siloxanes, as can be seen in Fig. 2.

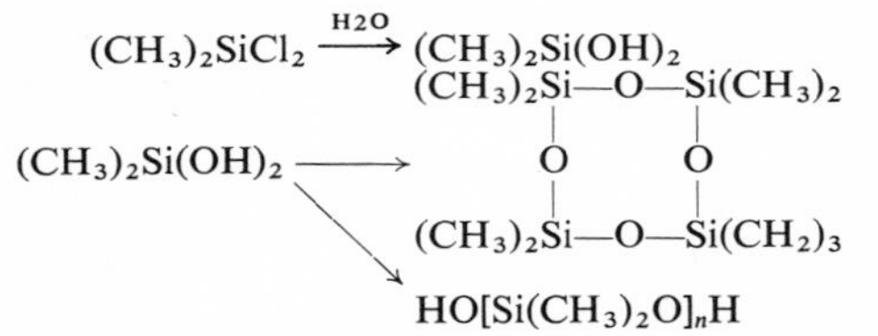

Fig. 2. Hydrolysis and condensation.

The linear polysiloxane produced in Fig. 2 resembles that shown in Fig. 1, except that in the first the chain-terminating groups are trimethylsiloxy $(CH_3)_3SiO$- instead of hydroxyl. These are derived from trimethylchlorosilane. If, on the

TABLE 1. PROPERTIES OF CHLOROSILANES.

Compound	Boiling point °C	Melting point, °C	d_4^{20}
CH_3SiCl_3	66.4	−77.8	1.275
$(CH_3)_2SiCl_2$	70	−76.1	1.069
$(CH_3)_3SiCl$	57.9	−57.7	0.858
CH_3SiHCl_2	41	−90.6	1.105
$(CH_3)_2SiHCl$	35.5	−103	0.854
$C_2H_5SiCl_3$	98	−105.6	1.237
$(C_2H_5)_2SiCl_2$	130.4	−96.5	1.050
$C_2H_5SiHCl_2$	75.4	−107	1.093
$C_3H_7SiCl_3$	124		1.185
$C_4H_9SiCl_3$	149		1.161
$C_5H_{11}SiCl_3$	169		1.133
$CH_2:CHSiCl_3$	92	−95	1.243
$(CH_3)(CH_2:CH)SiCl_2$	93		1.087
$(CH_3)_2(CH_2:CH)SiCl$	83		0.88
$C_6H_5SiCl_3$	201.5	−39.8	1.324
$(C_6H_5)_2SiCl_2$	305	−22	1.222
$(C_6H_5)(CH_3)SiCl_2$	205		1.187
$HSiCl_3$	31.9	−126.6	1.342
$SiCl_4$	57.6	−68.8	1.481

TABLE 2. PROPERTIES OF DERIVATIVES OF CHLOROSILANES.

Compound	Boiling point, °C	Melting point, °C	d_4^{20}
$[(CH_3)_2SiO]_3$	134	64.5	
$[(CH_3)_2SiO]_4$	175.8	17.6	0.956
$[(CH_3)_3Si]_2O$	100	−66	0.759
$CH_3Si(OCH_3)_3$	103		0.955
$CH_3Si(OC_2H_5)_3$	143		0.895
$(CH_3)_2Si(OC_2H_5)_2$	113	−87	0.840
$(CH_3)_3SiOC_2H_5$	75.7		0.757
$CH_2CHSi(OC_2H_5)_3$	160.5		0.903
$C_6H_5Si(OC_2H_5)_3$	236		0.996
$[(C_6H_5)_2SiO]_4$	335/1 mm	201	
$(C_6H_5)_2Si(OH)_2$		168	
$[(C_6H_5)(CH_3)SiO]_4$	237/1.5 mm	99	1.18
$CH_3Si(OCOCH_3)_3$	200	41.4	1.175

other hand, methyltrichlorosilane or silicon tetrachloride are components of the system, centers with three or four oxygen atoms attached to silicon result on hydrolysis, and branched chain or cross-linked siloxane polymers result.

Organosilicon Monomers

Several processes are used for manufacturing organosilicon monomers. The direct process involves the reaction of an organic halide with silicon in the presence of a catalyst. For example, methyl chloride reacts with powdered silicon and copper at about 250–350°C to give mixtures of methylchlorosilanes (see list, Table 1) and other compounds. The process can be controlled to give dimethyldichlorosilane as the major product:

$$2CH_3Cl + Si \xrightarrow{Cu} (CH_3)_2SiCl_2$$

The chlorosilane mixtures are separated by distillation to give the pure compounds, which are then processed to make silicones.

The direct process is also useful for making trichlorosilane from hydrogen chloride and silicon, and for making phenylchlorosilanes from chlorobenzene and silicon. The latter reaction proceeds at about 500–600°C, and produces mixtures containing diphenyldichlorosilane and phenyltrichlorosilane, which are separated by distillation.

The practical usefulness of the direct process declines rapidly as the organic portion of the halide becomes larger. Ethylchlorosilanes can be made readily, but propyl and larger give increasing difficulty. Vinyl and allyl chlorosilanes can be made by the direct process.

Phenylchlorosilanes can also be manufactured by other processes. In one of these benzene reacts with trichlorosilane to give phenyltrichlorosilane:

$$HSiCl_3 + C_6H_6 \xrightarrow[\substack{1000 \text{ psi} \\ BCl_3}]{300°} C_6H_5SiCl_3 + H_2$$

In another, chlorobenzene and trichlorosilane also give phenyltrichlorosilane, with hydrogen chloride byproduct. Still another uses benzene, silicone tetrachloride and silicon to give phenyltrichlorosilane.

Trichlorosilane reacts with olefinic hydrocarbons such as ethylene, propylene, or hexene to give ethyl-, propyl-, or hexyltrichlorosilane. Reactions of this type may be induced by heat (200–300°C), or may be catalyzed by (1) free radical initiators such as benzoyl peroxide, (2) metals such as platinum, (3) metal compounds such as chloroplatinic acid, or (4) Lewis acids or bases, such as BCl_3 or tertiary amines.

Acetylene and trichlorosilane yield vinyltrichlorosilane, similarly:

$$C_2H_2 + HSiCl_3 \xrightarrow{\text{Pt}} CH_2{=}CHSiCl_3$$

Acrylonitrile gives cyanoethyltrichlorosilane:

$$CH_2{=}CHCN + HSiCl_3 \xrightarrow{\text{Et3N}} Cl_3SiCH_2CH_2CN$$

Reaction of this product with ethyl alcohol gives cyanoethyltriethoxysilane, which can be hydrogenated to give aminopropyltriethoxysilane:

$$(C_2H_5O)_3SiCH_2CH_2CN \xrightarrow{\text{H2}}$$
$$(C_2H_5O)_3SiCH_2CH_2CH_2NH_2$$

Many so-called *carbonfunctional* silanes have been made available by such procedures. The properties of some of these silanes are shown in Table 3.

Organosilicon compounds can also be made from chloro- or alkoxysilanes by reaction with organomagnesium, organosodium, or organoaluminum compounds; for example:

$$SiCl_4 + 3C_6H_5MgCl \rightarrow (C_6H_5)_3SiCl + 3MgCl_2$$

Because of the large amount of solvent required and byproduct metal salts produced, Grignard processes are of limited interest in the manufacture of silanes.

Chemical Properties

Some of the chemical reactions and characteristics of silanes, chlorosilanes, silanols, and siloxanes have been mentioned above. For this brief account it seems best to point out some of the ways in which silicon compounds differ from those of carbon. These differences are largely due to the lower electronegativity of silicon and to the ability of silicon to use its 3d-orbitals for bond formation.

SiH. The hydrogen in SiH tends to react as a hydride ion. The SiH bond is rather easy to hydrolyze, especially in the presence of bases or catalysts such as platinum. SiH compounds are reducing agents. They add across olefinic double bonds to form alkylsilanes.

SiCl. The SiCl bond is easily hydrolyzed, resembling COCl rather than CCl. It reacts not only with water but with other protonic materials such as alcohols, primary and secondary amines, and phenols. It also reacts more readily with organometallic compounds such as Grignard reagents than CCl does.

SiOC, COC, and SiOSi. Whereas either (COC) and siloxane (SiOSi) bonds are hydrolytically stable, SiOC is not. This is true of alkoxysilanes and of acyloxysilanes, which are much more susceptible to hydrolysis than organic esters or anhydrides are. The SiOSi bond is 50% ionic and is attacked by alkalies and strong acids.

Si—C, C—C, and Si—Si. Both of the former are stable, although electronegative substituents on the carbon of $\equiv$SiC (as for example in $\equiv$SiCCl$_3$) can make the SiC bond unstable. The SiSi bond, however, is moderately reactive to water, acids, or bases.

Si—N. Silazanes or silylamines are easily hydrolyzed to form silanols and amines.

Redistribution and Scrambling Reactions. The groups and atoms on silanes and siloxanes can be

TABLE 3. CARBONFUNCTIONAL SILANES.

	Boiling point, mm Hg.	d_4^{20}
$NH_2CH_2CH_2CH_2Si(OC_2H_5)_3$	221/760	0.951
$CH_2{=}CHSi(OCH_2CH_2OCH_3)_3$	285	1.035
$CNCH_2CH_2Si(OC_2H_5)_3$	160/70	0.979

$CH_2{=}C{-}COOCH_2CH_2CH_2Si(OCH_3)_3$
     |
     CH_3
	147/30	1.045

$CH_2{-}CH{-}CH_2OCH_2CH_2CH_2Si(OCH_3)_3$ (epoxide O bridge)	120/2	1.070
$CH_3CH_2OCCH_2CH_2Si(OC_2H_5)_3$ (C=O)	246	0.986
$NH_2CH_2CH_2NHCH_2CH_2CH_2Si(OCH_3)_3$	146/15	1.01

made to move from one silicon atom to another, thus:

$$CH_3SiCl_3 + (CH_3)_3SiCl \xrightarrow[\text{heat}]{\text{AlCl}_3} 2(CH_3)_2SiCl_2$$

In the absence of catalyst, the Si—C bonds are not involved but other groups move about:

$$(CH_3)_2SiCl_2 + (CH_3)_2Si(OC_2H_5)_2 \xrightleftharpoons{\text{heat}}$$
$$2(CH_3)_2SiCl(OC_2H_5)$$

Both of these are, as indicated, equilibrium processes.

The equilibration of siloxanes is related to the latter (scrambling) reaction. A simplified example of this complex reaction is:

$$(CH_3)_3SiOSi(CH_3)_3 + [(CH_3)_2SiO]_4 \xrightleftharpoons[\text{catalyst}]{\text{heat}}$$
$$(CH_3)_3SiO[Si(CH_3)_2O]_4Si(CH_3)_3$$

Actually a complex ring-chain equilibrium reaction occurs here.

Polymerization to form elastomers is a special case of this, in which the concentrations of chain-stoppers, such as $(CH_3)_3SiO$, and of catalyst (such as KOH) are very small.

Silanol condensation (Figure 2) occurs readily with methylsilanols. It is an equilibrium reaction in which formation of siloxane is favored:

$$2(CH_3)_3SiOH \xrightleftharpoons{\text{catalyst}} (CH_3)_3SiOSi(CH_3)_3 + H_2O$$

Reaction rates and equilibria are strongly influenced by the substituents on silicon. Thus dimethylsilanediol condenses so readily it is difficult to prepare and store, diphenylsilanediol is stable under ordinary conditions, and di-*tert*-butylsilanediol cannot be condensed even under drastic conditions.

Reactions of the organic portions of silicones are in general those to be expected from ordinary organic chemistry. Of special interest to users of silicones are those involved in vulcanization of silicone rubber. Free radical initiators such as benzoyl peroxide cause two types of cross-linking to occur:

$$C_6H_5\overset{\overset{O}{\|}}{C}OO\overset{\overset{O}{\|}}{C}C_6H_5 \rightarrow 2C_6H_5COO\cdot$$

$$C_6H_5COO\cdot + HCH_2Si\equiv \rightarrow$$
$$C_6H_5COOH + \cdot CH_2Si\equiv \quad (1)$$

$$2\cdot CH_2Si\equiv \rightarrow \equiv SiCH_2CH_2Si\equiv$$

$$C_6H_5COO\cdot + H_2C\!=\!CHSi\equiv \rightarrow \quad (2)$$
$$C_6H_5COOCH_2\dot{C}HSi\equiv$$

The latter then causes vinyl polymerization via chain reactions.

The special chemistry of organosilicon compounds is well described in several texts, i.e., Eaborn's "Organosilicon Compounds" (Butterworth's, London 1960), and Bazant, Chvalovsky, and Rathousky "Organosilicon Compounds" (Academic Press, 1965).

Applications

There are hundreds of silicone products and many times that number of applications. These are found in many industries, in medicine and surgery, and in the home. Only those pertaining to the manufacture and fabrication of plastics will be considered here.

Silicone Fluids: These are manufactured by hydrolysis of chlorosilanes, and equilibration of the resulting siloxanes. Figure 2 shows that linear and cyclic siloxanes are formed by hydrolysis of dimethyldichlorosilane. The resulting liquid mixture separates into silicone and hydrochloric acid layers on standing. The silicone is separated, washed, and neutralized. A similar operation carried out with trimethylchlorosilane gives hexamethyldisiloxane:

$$2(CH_3)_3SiCl + H_2O \rightarrow (CH_3)_3SiOSi(CH_3)_3 + 2HCl$$

When mixtures of hexamethyldisiloxane and the siloxane fluid prepared from dimethyldichlorosilane are heated in the presence of strong acidic or basic catalysts, the siloxane bonds rearrange and chain-stopped fluids (Figure 1) are produced. This process is called equilibration because it tends toward formation of an equilibrium mixture of cyclic and long- and short-chained linear siloxanes. After removal of the catalyst the products are heated *in vacuo* to remove volatile components. The viscosity of the product is a function of the relative proportion of hexamethyldisiloxane in the raw materials used.

Silicone fluids are low or medium molecular weight polysiloxanes. The ordinary fluids of commerce are poly(dimethylsiloxanes) with trimethylsiloxy end grounds, as in Fig. 1. Fluids in which some of the methyl groups are replaced by phenyl are also available. Properties of representatives of these two classes are shown in Table 4.

These fluids, especially the first class, show unusually small changes of viscosity with temperature, over a wide temperature range. They have excellent stability to heat and oxidation, are chemically inert, have low surface tension (16–24 dynes per cm at 77°F), high compressibility, excellent shear stability, and good dielectric properties. The dimethyl silicones are not compatible with most organic systems.

The fluids and their emulsions in water are useful as mold release agents in fabricating metal, rubber and plastic parts. Their efficiency seems to be due to their stability and to their incompatibility, which allows them to remain as an insoluble, nonadherent film at the surface of the mold. They are also used as lubricants for rubber and plastic parts, as antiblocking agents for rubber and plastic sheets, and as extrusion aids.

TABLE 4. PROPERTIES OF SILICONE FLUIDS.

Viscosity, 25°C	Viscosity-temperature coefficient[a]	Sp. Gr., 25/25°C	Refractive index, 25°C	Pour point °F	Flash point °F	Dielectric constant
Dimethyl Fluids:						
0.65	0.33	0.759	1.375	−90	30	2.20
5	0.53	0.916	1.397	−120	275	2.60
10	0.56	0.940	1.399	−100	410	2.60
20	0.58	0.953	1.401	−85	>450	2.68
50	0.59	0.963	1.402	−67	>535	2.72
100	0.59	0.968	1.403	−67	>575	2.75
500	0.60	0.973	1.403	−58	>600	2.75
1000	0.60	0.974	1.4035	−58	>600	2.75
5000	0.60	0.975	1.4035	−56	>600	2.75
10000	0.60	0.975	1.4035	−53	>600	2.75
100000	0.60	0.978	1.4035	−40	>600	2.75
Methyl Phenyl Fluids:						
125	0.76	1.07	1.495	−50	575	2.88
50	0.62	0.99	1.425	−100	540	2.79
100	0.62	0.99	1.425	−100	560	2.80
500	0.65	0.99	1.425	−100	580	2.80

$$^{a} \; 1 - \frac{\text{Viscosity at } 210°F}{\text{Viscosity at } 100°F}$$

They are useful as antifoaming agents in the manufacture of latex and paint. Foam control increases kettle capacity and decreases processing time. The fluids are also useful as additives to paint, to improve pigment dispersion and to defoam varnishes.

Silicone Elastomers. These are based on fluids of very high molecular weight (500,000). These may have vinyl groups replacing a fraction of a percent of the methyl groups, to facilitate cure. Phenyl or ethyl groups may be introduced to give flexibility at lower temperatures (−130°F). Polar groups such as trifluoropropyl or cyanoethyl improve resistance to certain solvents and fuels.

These viscous fluid siloxanes are mechanically mixed with fillers such as silica aerogels, carbon black, titanium dioxide, or calcium carbonate, and with catalysts such as benzoyl peroxide, ditertiarybutyl peroxide, or *tert*-butylperbenzoate. The mixtures (called "compounds" in industry) are fabricated by freshening, molding and heating. Typical cure conditions are 225–350°F for 5–20 min at 800–1500 psi. Volatile components present after cure may be removed by an oven post bake if desired.

Alternatively the polymer-filler mixture can be dispersed in a solvent such as toluene and applied as a paste to glass cloth or other fabrics.

Room temperature vulcanizing silicones are made by mixing fluids of the type shown in Fig. 2 with cross-linking agents such as ethyl silicate, and catalysts such as tin (or organotin) salts. Vulcanization is greatly accelerated by these catalysts, which are therefore added only shortly before the mixture is to be used. This method necessitates a two-package system. By proper choice of cross-linking agent one-package systems containing all three components can be made. These depend on hydrolysis by moisture in the environment for their cure.

Silicone elastomers are not plastics, but they compete with plastics (including silicones) for applications such as electrical insulation, and as caulking and sealing material in construction and industry. RTV silicone rubber is used as a mold material.

The ranges of properties of heat-cured and room-temperature-cured silicone elastomers are given in Tables 5 and 6.

Their outstanding characteristics are their resistance to high temperature (450°F and up), their flexibility at low temperature, their electrical properties, and their resistance to ozone and corona. They offer an unusual combination of thermal, oxidation, and radiation resistance.

Heat-curing silicone rubber may be molded by compression, transfer, or injection, and can be extruded, calendered, knife or dip-coated, and bonded. It is used in making o-rings, gaskets, hot air ducts, tapes, tubing, sponge, and insulation for wire and cable.

RTV silicone rubber is available in liquid or paste form. The two-package types cure at room temperature to a tack-free condition in 1–16 hr, and are firm in 8–48 hr. The one-package types are tack-free in 15–30 min, and cure through in about a day. The RTV silicones are used for adhesives, sealants, and caulking materials, for

TABLE 5. RANGE OF PROPERTIES OF HEAT-CURED SILICONE ELASTOMERS.

Type	Durometer shore A	Tensile psi	Elongation, %	Compression set, 22 hr/300°F	Useful range of temp., °F Min.	Max.
General purpose	40–80	700–1000	100–400	15–50	−75	500
Low compression set	50–80	700–1000	80–400	10–15	−75	500
Extreme low temperature	25–80	800–1500	150–600	20–50	−150	500
Extreme high temperature	40–80	700–1100	200–500	10–40	−75	600
Wire and cable	50–80	600–1500	100–500	20–50	−75/−150	500

example in potting electrical terminal connections, in sealing and encapsulating electronic equipment, as sealants for aircraft and missiles, as bonding agents, for caulking joints in buildings, as roof and traffic coatings, and as flexible mold materials.

Silicone Resins. The resins are made by cohydrolysis of mixtures of mono-, di-, and tri-, methylchlorosilanes or mono-, di- and tri-, phenylchlorosilanes (or alkoxysilanes) in solvents. After hydrolysis the aqueous layer is separated, and the organic layer is neutralized. The resin solution is then concentrated and heated until the proper degree of polymerization has been reached. Catalysts such as zinc octoate are used to accelerate this process and to aid in curing the resin during fabrication.

Such resins have varying concentrations of silanol, $\equiv$SiOH, remaining in the polymer structure. Cure is achieved in fabricating the resin, after removal of the solvent, by heating until further condensation of these silanols to siloxanes has caused the polymer to reach the proper state of polymerization.

These silanols can also be used to effect copolymerization with hydroxyl-containing organic resins such as epoxies, polyesters, and alkyds. In such cases higher concentrations of silanol are left in the silicone resin, to provide more points for reaction with the organic resin. Copolymerization is accomplished by mixing and heating. The silicones used for such purposes are designed to be compatible with the organic resin; this in general means a higher content of phenyl and higher alkyl siloxanes, and relatively little methylsiloxane.

Copolymerization can also be accomplished through "carbonfunctional" groups on the siloxane (Table 8), using conventional organic reactions such as transesterifications, vinyl polymerizations, amide formation, and reaction with epoxides.

Silicone resins are based on highly branched and crosslinked siloxane polymers. They are usually supplied as solutions in organic solvents, but dry powder resins are available.

Silicone resins are useful in electrical insulating systems designed to tolerate hot-spot temperatures of 180°C. They have good electrical properties and generally adequate mechanical strength, and they retain their properties on prolonged exposure to high temperature. Some properties of a silicone impregnating resin are shown in Table 7.

Silicone molding and laminating resins are used to bond fibrous or particulate fillers, or glass cloth, to make rigid shapes for mechanical or electrical applications. Typical properties of silicone-glass cloth laminates are shown in Table 8. The glass used was type 112 fabric.

Silicone resins are used as impregnating varnishes for electrical coils, as mica bonding resins, as resins for coating glass cloth to produce flexible insulating tapes, as laminating material for electrical and mechanical applications, and as adhesives, paints, release agents, and water repellents. They are especially useful where long-term exposure to high temperature and high humidity are involved. Silicone-insulated motors are capable of giving long service in steel mills, rubber factories, and so on. Glass-silicone laminates are used for terminal boards, slot wedges for motors, switch gear and transformer tubes, and for aircraft firewalls and ducts.

Silicone paints are used for mufflers, exhaust stacks, space heaters, and chemical plant equipment. Silicone-aluminum paints give protection up to 1000°F. Silicone and silicone-alkyd paints

TABLE 6. RANGE OF PROPERTIES OF CURED RTV SILICONE.

Type	Durometer shore A	Tensile, psi	Elongation %	Tear strength	Electric strength, V/M
Two part	45–65	350–850	110–220	15–75	575–650
One part	30–40	300–350	400–500	40–45	550

TABLE 7. PROPERTIES OF A SILICONE IMPREGNATING RESIN.

Heat endurance at 250°C		
Flex life	250 hr	
Craze life	750 hr	
Electric strength (2-in. electrodes)		
	Dry	Wet
Volts per mil	1500	1000
Power factor at 25°C		
100 cycles	0.0084	0.0085
10^6 cycles	0.0043	0.0047
Dielectric constant at 25°C		
100 cycles	3.0	3.0
10^6 cycles	2.9	2.9

TABLE 8. PROPERTIES OF SILICONE-GLASS LAMINATES.

Flexural strength, psi	
25°C	25 — 45,000
250°C	4 — 14,000
Tensile, psi, 25°C	20 — 40,000
Arc resistance, sec	200 — 240
Dielectric constant, 1 mc	3.8 — 4.2
Electric strength, VPM	200 — 400
Dissipation factor	
Dry	0.001 — 0.002
Wet	0.004 — 0.05

Silicone Coupling Agents

Resin System	Vinyl $Si(OCH_2CH_2OCH_2)_3$	$NH_2CH_2CH_2CH_2Si(OEt)_3$	$CH_2{=}C{-}COOCH_2CH_2CH_2Si(OMe)_3$ (CH_3)	$CH_2CH{-}CH_2O{-}CH_2CH_2CH_2Si(OMe)_3$ (epoxide)
Polyesters	*		*	
Melamine		*		*
Phenolics		*		
Epoxy				*

Certain reactive silanes such as $(CH_3SiHO)_n$ and $(C_6H_5)_2SiH_2$ have been found useful as components of Ziegler-type catalysts for polymerizing ethylene and propylene. These probably act to help control molecular weight by adding to terminal double bonds. Thus they provide means of controlling melt viscosity and increasing melt index.

ROBERT N. MEALS

SILICONE MOLD RELEASE AGENTS

The purpose of a release agent in the molding industry is to aid in easy removal of a molded part from its mold. In addition, release agents may be used on conveyors, spray booths, processing machinery and other equipment that becomes contaminated with spilled materials, to facilitate easy removal of the spillage. Papers can be impregnated or coated with a fluid silicone release agent for many industrial applications, but usually a silicone resin is used which can be polymerized into three-dimensional crosslinked polysiloxanes to achieve a final "touch-dry" paper.

The plastics and rubber industries depend heavily upon silicone release agents, and almost every type of plastic or rubber can be successfully released from its mold with the proper silicone release. The choice, however, sometimes must be arrived at by simple trial and error. But considerable time can be saved by following a few simple principles in choosing a mold release. In brief, the principles are: The release agent must be highly incompatible with the material being released, it must be heat stable (if heat curing is involved), it must be of low surface tension to thoroughly wet and coat all surfaces with the smallest possible film thickness and it should be easy to apply.

have excellent heat-resistant and weatherability characteristics, and gloss retention.

Copolymers of silicones and polyoxyalkylenes (ethylene or propylene oxide polymers and copolymers) are used to control foaming in the production of one-shot polyurethane foams. Without silicone, these foams tend to be uneven in texture, with large and small holes, rather like a sponge. With a silicone copolymer foam control agent, an even-textured foam with uniform pore size is obtained. For prepolymer-type polyurethane foams, silicone fluids alone are used for cell size control.

Treatment of glass cloth or fiber with reactive organosilicon compounds brings about improved adhesion of the glass to organic resins. The principal benefit from this treatment is greatly improved retention of tensile and flexural strength of the glass-resin composite under humid conditions. The silanes used are of the R'Si(OR)₃ type and are believed to act by hydrolysis of the alkoxysilane bonds and condensation of the resulting silanols with the silanols always present on a glass surface. The R' group is chosen to be reactive with the resin. Some useful resin-silane combinations are:

Silicone releases are one of the few materials that satisfy these four principles exceptionally well.

In the past, some problems have been encountered with silicone releases when the molded part is subsequently painted. Residual silicone left on the molded part will prevent the paint from covering in a uniform film thickness due to the incompatibility between silicone and the coating formulation. This problem has been largely solved now through the creation of "paintable" silicone releases which will give good release of the molded part but which are compatible with a particular type of coating. A compatible release will not "repel" the coating film.

Silicone Fluids

The great majority of commercially available silicone fluids are dimethyl siloxanes with the following structure:

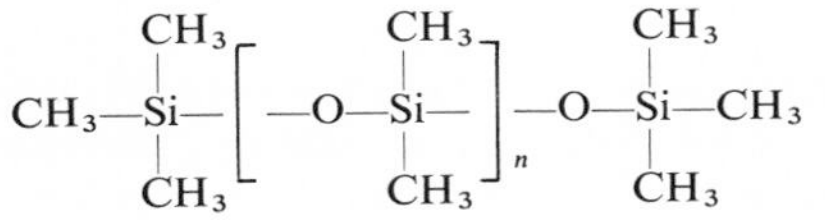

$$CH_3-\underset{\underset{CH_3}{|}}{\overset{\overset{CH_3}{|}}{Si}}-\left[-O-\underset{\underset{CH_3}{|}}{\overset{\overset{CH_3}{|}}{Si}}-\right]_n-O-\underset{\underset{CH_3}{|}}{\overset{\overset{CH_3}{|}}{Si}}-CH_3$$

As the valve of n increases, so does the viscosity. Some of the other silicone fluids may contain phenyl (C_6H_5), or other organic groups in place of methyl (CH_3) groups to achieve a particular desirable end product. Although the structure shown above is of a straight linear chain, in practice some of the dimethyl siloxanes contain branch chains such as:

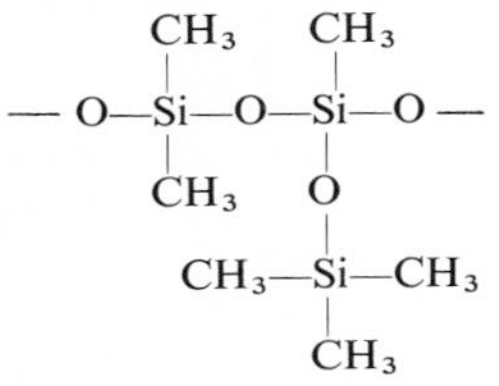

$$-O-\underset{\underset{CH_3}{|}}{\overset{\overset{CH_3}{|}}{Si}}-O-\underset{\underset{\underset{\underset{\underset{CH_3}{|}}{Si}-CH_3}{|}}{\overset{\overset{CH_3}{|}}{\underset{O}{|}}}}{Si}-O-$$

However, the most common silicone fluids are essentially straight chain dimethyl polysiloxanes with a maximum of 5–10% branching.

Silicone fluids, as a class, are characterized by low surface tension, extreme stability over a wide range of temperatures, low viscosity with changes in temperature, excellent foam controlling ability, good releasing properties, high electrical resistance and water repellency.

Because of the unusually low surface tension in silicone fluids, only a very small amount added into many liquid compounds will radically alter the surface characteristic of the entire compound. Under appropriate conditions silicone fluids can also function as defoamers, foam stabilizers, wetting agents, water repellents, leveling agents and anti-leveling agents, depending upon the type of silicone fluid, the concentration used and the nature of the other compound with which it is being mixed.

By adding as little as 1 part per million of a silicone fluid to many liquid materials, the tendency of that material to foam is virtually eliminated. In industry, undesirable foaming occurs while mixing or moving liquid materials, caused by entrainment of air. If the surface tension of the liquid is high, the bubbles do not break after rising to the surface causing many processing difficulties. It is believed that silicone's effectiveness as a defoamer is derived from both its low surface tension and its incompatibility with the remainder of the liquid formulation. The property of incompatibility in defoaming is an important one because it allows the silicone to be entrapped into the bubble structure as a concentrated area of low surface tension and thus destroy the bubble somewhat like a pin prick in a balloon. If the silicone were compatible with the liquid it would merely lower the bubble's surface tension to an average level depending upon the concentration used.

Compatible silicone fluids however do play an effective role in controlling and stabilizing foam rather than destroying it. Polyurethane foam depends greatly upon using the proper silicones to aid in producing a final product with a uniform cell structure. Many of the aerosol foam formulations contain silicones as foam stabilizers.

One interesting new development in the plastics and foundry industries is to incorporate certain silicone releasing agents into the molding material itself, which is inherently much cheaper than recoating each mold every cycle. The internally mixed silicone seems to "seek" the surface of the mold and achieve, in many cases, releasing characteristics as successful as the more time consuming method.

Although most of the usage in the electrical-electronic industries is for the silicone resins or rubbers, certain silicone fluids have found a place in applications requiring a liquid dielectric that possesses superior resistance to oxidation and high temperature degradation, while giving good low temperature fluidity and relatively constant dielectric properties over the entire range of operating conditions.

Silicone fluids are also used as hydraulic fluids, where their inertness, constant viscosity and overall resistance to degradation gives them an advantage over conventional organic fluids, where conditions require these properties. Fluid damping devices are making use of silicone's constant viscosity and resistance to breakdown under shear. Fluid drives, liquid "springs," heat transfer mediums and diffusion pump fluids are some of the other applications for silicone fluids.

CHARLES E. CHASTAIN

SILICONES, INGREDIENTS OF

The usual starting material for the manufacture of silicones is high grade quartzite rock, which is almost pure silica (SiO_2). Although silica is already composed of silicon and oxygen, both of which are necessary for silicone, their molecular arrangement is much too stable for polymerization. Thus it is necessary to tear down this arrangement and begin over again in order to achieve a new molecular arrangement more to our desires. The disassociation of silicon and oxygen is accomplished by heating silica white hot in the presence of charcoal, at which time oxygen will split off from silicon, combine with the carbon in the charcoal, forming CO_2 and leaving essentially pure silicon (Si) metal in its molten state. The pure silicon is then drawn off, cooled and ground into fine powder for processing.

For many practical reasons it is next necessary to form intermediate chlorosilanes before proceeding to reintroduce oxygen into combination with silicon again. Only in this manner can many hundreds of different organic groups be easily attached to the silicone, giving an extremely large number of possible new compounds.

Three different methods have been used for producing chlorosilanes: the Direct method, the Grignard method, and the olefin addition method.

Direct Method. In a simplified equation, the Direct method can be illustrated as follows:

$$2CH_3Cl + Si \xrightarrow{Cu} (CH_3)_2SiCl_2$$

The Direct method was discovered by Dr. E. G. Rochow of General Electric, and was patented by that company. Essentially, it involves reacting various organic halides (methyl chloride is shown) in the presence of a copper catalyst. The catalyst is sometimes a copper salt or silver, but the reaction will take place even without a catalyst at much higher temperatures, although with some accompanying degradation of the reaction products.

Grignard Method. The Grignard method was the first industrial method for the large scale manufacture of organosilicon compounds (by Dow Corning Corporation) and was based upon the "coupling" reaction between silicon tetrachloride and organic magnesium chloride, which can be represented as follows:

$$CH_3MgCl + SiCl_4 \rightarrow CH_3SiCl_3 + MgCl_2$$

or:

$$CH_3MgCl + CH_3SiCl_3 \rightarrow (CH_3)_2SiCl_2 + MgCl_2$$

There is however a tendency in the Grignard method to form also several other products which subsequently require costly separation procedures. Other disadvantages of the method include the generation of a considerable amount of heat, with explosive dangers and also, only organic radicals that are compatible with organometallic compounds may be used. Nevertheless, the Grignard method has considerable versatility and is the only method which can be presently used to manufacture certain types of chlorosilanes.

Olefin Addition Method. Starting with simple compounds containing the SiH linkage, such as $SiHCl_3$ or others of the simple chlorosilanes, olefin addition builds them into more complex chlorosilanes which can then be used for the manufacture of silicones. The Olefin addition method can be illustrated by this reaction:

$$HSiCl_3 + CH_2{=}CH_2 \rightarrow CH_3CH_2SiCl_3$$

Usually catalysts such as organic peroxides, platinum, organic bases or ultraviolet light are used, but the addition will take place at higher temperatures without a catalyst.

Reintroduction of oxygen into combination with silicon can be done easily now, chiefly because of the reactivity of the chlorine on the end of each chlorosilane. Reacting a chlorosilane with water may form many different compounds, depending upon the conditions involved. One such reaction involves a monochlorosilane and water, yielding a monosilanol,

$$CH_3{-}\underset{\underset{\textstyle CH_3}{|}}{\overset{\overset{\textstyle CH_3}{|}}{Si}}{-}Cl + H_2O \rightarrow CH_3{-}\underset{\underset{\textstyle CH_3}{|}}{\overset{\overset{\textstyle CH_3}{|}}{Si}}{-}OH + HCl$$

which can subsequently condense by the elimination of one molecule of water yielding a siloxane:

$$2(CH_3)_3SiOH \rightarrow CH_3{-}\underset{\underset{\textstyle CH_3}{|}}{\overset{\overset{\textstyle CH_3}{|}}{Si}}{-}O{-}\underset{\underset{\textstyle CH_3}{|}}{\overset{\overset{\textstyle CH_3}{|}}{Si}}{-}CH_3 + H_2O$$

More important than the monosilanols are the disilanols formed from dichlorosilanes under controlled conditions, for these are used to manufacture the linear polymeric chains broadly termed silicones. The following simplified equation illustrates one such condensation reaction of a disilanol into a siloxane.

$$2HO{-}\underset{\underset{\textstyle CH_3}{|}}{\overset{\overset{\textstyle CH_3}{|}}{Si}}{-}OH \rightarrow HO{-}\underset{\underset{\textstyle CH_3}{|}}{\overset{\overset{\textstyle CH_3}{|}}{Si}}{-}O{-}\underset{\underset{\textstyle CH_3}{|}}{\overset{\overset{\textstyle CH_3}{|}}{Si}}{-}OH$$

Under controlled conditions, further condensation results in the formation of linear polymers of the type:

$$HO{-}\underset{\underset{\textstyle CH_3}{|}}{\overset{\overset{\textstyle CH_3}{|}}{Si}}{-}\left[O{-}\underset{\underset{\textstyle CH_3}{|}}{\overset{\overset{\textstyle CH_3}{|}}{Si}}{-}\right]_n{-}O{-}\underset{\underset{\textstyle CH_3}{|}}{\overset{\overset{\textstyle CH_3}{|}}{Si}}{-}OH$$

or under other conditions and with certain mixtures of various chlorosilanes, a siloxane linear polymer is formed with essentially nonreactive methyl terminal groups. One typical linear compound is:

$$CH_3-\underset{\underset{CH_3}{|}}{\overset{\overset{CH_3}{|}}{Si}}-\left[O-\underset{\underset{CH_3}{|}}{\overset{\overset{CH_3}{|}}{Si}}-\right]_n-O-\underset{\underset{CH_3}{|}}{\overset{\overset{CH_3}{|}}{Si}}-CH_3$$

This particular compound is a methylpolysiloxane and is the basis for many of the familiar silicone fluids, lubricants, antifoams and gums.

Starting however with an aryl or alkyl trichlorosilane we will obtain resinous polymers which are normally quite brittle and hard. But by proper copolymerizing with other chlorosilanes they can be made more flexible and become extremely useful products. One such silanol resin is:

$$HO-\underset{\underset{OH}{|}}{\overset{\overset{CH_3}{|}}{Si}}-O-\underset{\underset{OH}{|}}{\overset{\overset{CH_3}{|}}{Si}}-O-\underset{\underset{OH}{|}}{\overset{\overset{CH_3}{|}}{Si}}-O-\underset{\underset{OH}{|}}{\overset{\overset{CH_3}{|}}{Si}}-OH$$

The reactive OH groups make it relatively easy to attach other linear silicone polymer chains to the molecule as well as permitting easy attachment of a multitude of other organic resins. A strong, tough three-dimensional network is thus easily achieved through condensation with other polymers. Silicone resins are used extensively as protective coatings for specialized applications such as those requiring high temperature resistance and water repellency.

Other organic atoms or groups which are commonly attached to the siloxane linkage are hydrogen (H), oxygen (O), phenyl (C_6H_5), vinyl (C_2H_3) and amino (NH_2). Each of these can serve as a useful reactive site when manufacturing a particular type of silicone compound.

CHARLES E. CHASTAIN

SODIUM CHLORIDE AND SALT CHEMICALS

Salt has a variety of functions in the plastics field. In addition, as a source for sodium or chlorine-containing compounds, it is involved in practically the whole spectrum of plastics. The applications of sodium chloride and the following salt-derived chemicals in plastics preparation and processing will be elaborated in this discussion: calcium chloride, chlorine, hydrogen chloride or hydrochloric acid, sodium bisulfate, sodium carbonate, sodium chlorate, sodium cyanide, sodium hydroxide, sodium nitrate and sodium sulfate.

Table 1 summarizes the production methods of these chemicals.

Uses of Sodium Chloride

Salt is employed primarily as a polymerization catalyst and as a latex coagulent. As a catalyst

sodium chloride initiates polymerization through the surface electronic defects, "F"-center, "U"-center, etc.

Butadiene, styrene and isoprene can be polymerized with Alfin catalysts (allyl sodium, sodium isopropoxide and sodium chloride) or other organosodium compounds and salt. The olefins, ethylene, propylene and butene, have been polymerized with a catalyst consisting of an aluminum alkyl, titanium halide and sodium chloride. The salt increases the yield, reaction rates and amorphous fraction and decreases wax formation. Sodium chloride, alone or in combination with a variety of other compounds, has been a polymerization catalyst for acrylics, styrene, formaldehyde, acetylene, ethylene oxide, and for the preparation of polycarbonates. Sodium chloride may also be used simply as an additive in the polymerization system.

Salt is widely used to coagulate latexes of butadienestyrene rubber, polystyrene, polyacrylate and polyvinyl alcohol. Polymers isolated from latexes coagulated with sodium chloride have better physiomechanical characteristics; however, they exhibit less heat stability.

Miscellaneous applications occur in synthetic fiber processes, in forming pores in polyvinyl chloride, in compounding synthetic rubbers and in antistatic coatings for plastics.

Uses of Salt-derived Chemicals

The two major chemicals, chlorine and caustic, are the backbone for a vast majority of plastic materials. The role played by them, along with the other chemicals are illustrated in the following plastic resins.

Acetals. Polyoxymethylenes can be formed by reaction of formaldehyde with a sodium or sodium hydroxide catalyst although the common commercial catalysts for the polymerization of formaldehyde are anionic catalysts which include cyclic nitrogen compounds, arsines, and phosphines. Chlorine has been shown to polymerize trioxane to polyoxymethylene. Trioxane is usually polymerized with Lewis acid catalysts to afford high molecular weight polyoxymethylene.

Acrylics. The acrylic and methacrylic esters as well as acrylonitrile utilize several salt chemicals. Ethylene oxide and hydrogen cyanide, or ethylene chlorohydrin and sodium cyanide, react to form ethylene cyanohydrin which produces acrylonitrile on heating with sodium bisulfate. Also acetylene and hydrogen cyanide form the acrylonitrile with a sodium cyanide catalyst. Acrylonitrile can be polymerized with sodium nitrate, sodium chlorate-sodium sulfite, or with sodium or other free radical catalysts. Frequently a zinc chloride-calcium chloride solution is the medium for polymerization, and calcium chloride can be used in the spinning bath for polyacrylonitrile

TABLE 1. SALT-DERIVED CHEMICALS AND THEIR PRODUCTION METHODS.

Calcium chloride ($CaCl_2$)	Ammonia-soda process (Solvay)
	$2NaCl + CaCO_3 \rightarrow Na_2CO_3 + CaCl_2$
	Cyanamide electric furnace
	$2NaCl + CaCN_2 + C \rightarrow CaCl_2 + 2NaCN$
Chlorine (Cl_2)	Chlorine-caustic electrolytic cell
	$2NaCl + 2H_2O \rightarrow 2NaOH + H_2 + Cl_2$
	Downs sodium electrolytic cell.
	$2NaCl \rightarrow 2Na + Cl_2$
Hydrogen chloride (HCl)	Mannheim furnace
	$2NaCl + H_2SO_4 \rightarrow Na_2SO_4 + 2HCl$
	Hargreaves process
	$4NaCl + 2SO_2 + O_2 + 2H_2O \rightarrow 2Na_2SO_4 + 4HCl$
	Nitre cake retort
	$NaCl + H_2SO_4 \rightarrow NaHSO_4 + HCl$
Sodium (Na)	Downs sodium electrolytic cell
	$2NaCl \rightarrow 2Na + Cl_2$
Sodium bisulfate ($NaHSO_4$)	Nitre cake retort
	$NaCl + H_2SO_4 \rightarrow NaHSO_4 + HCl$
Sodium carbonate (Na_2CO_3)	Ammonia-soda process (Solvay)
	$2NaCl + CaCO_3 \rightarrow Na_2CO_3 + CaCl_2$
	Hargreaves-Bird electrolytic cell
	$2NaCl + CO_2 + H_2O \rightarrow Na_2CO_3 + Cl_2 + H_2$
Sodium chlorate ($NaClO_3$)	Chlorate electrolytic cell
	$NaCl + 3H_2O \rightarrow NaClO_3 + 3H_2$
Sodium cyanide (NaCN)	Cyanamide electric furnace
	$2NaCl + CaCN_2 + C \rightarrow CaCl_2 + 2NaCN$
Sodium hydroxide (NaOH)	Chlorine-caustic electrolytic cell
	$2NaCl + 2H_2O \rightarrow 2NaOH + H_2 + Cl_2$
Sodium nitrate ($NaNO_3$)	Nitrosyl chloride process
	$3NaCl + 4HNO_3 \rightarrow Cl_2 + 3NaNO_3 + NOCl + 2H_2O$
Sodium sulfate (Na_2SO_4)	Mannheim furnace
	$2NaCl + H_2SO_4 \rightarrow Na_2SO_4 + 2HCl$
	Hargreaves process
	$4NaCl + 2SO_2 + O_2 + 2H_2O \rightarrow 2Na_2SO_4 + 4HCl$

fibers. Polyacrylonitrile fibers are commonly prepared commercially by a dry spinning process. A hydrogen chloride treatment of polyacrylonitrile prevents discoloration of the polymer.

Methyl acrylate also is manufactured via ethylene cyanohydrin. Methyl methacrylate is produced from acetone cyanohydrin and is polymerized with hydrogen chloride, or with sodium or other free radical catalysts. This polymer is frequently chlorinated.

Cellulosics. The cellulose synthetic fiber, rayon, and the film, cellophane, utilize sodium hydroxide in their manufacture. In the viscose process pulp is soaked in sodium hydroxide and treated with carbon disulfide to form the xanthate. The soluble cellulose xanthate is extruded into an acid regeneration bath, which may contain sodium sulfate, to form rayon or cellophane. In the cuprammonium process sodium bisulfate can be used to coagulate the fibers. Rayon treated with caustic has improved dyeability. A formaldehyde-hydrochloric acid treatment of rayon fabric increases the fabric's weight, crease resistance and tensile strength; it also smooths and softens the fabric.

The acetylation of viscose with acetic anhydride vapor to form acetate rayon makes use of a hydrogen chloride catalyst, after pretreatment with sodium hydroxide. Ethyl cellulose is prepared by soaking alpha-cellulose in caustic, followed by treatment with ethyl chloride. Ethyl chloride is manufactured from ethanol and hydrochloric acid, or from ethylene and chlorine or hydrochloric acid.

Epoxies. The condensation product of epichlorohydrin with bisphenol A in the presence of a base, sodium hydroxide, gives an epoxy resin. Epicholorohydrin is made from glycerol and hydrochloric acid, or allyl chloride and oxygen, while bisphenol A is the reaction product of acetone and phenol.

Fluorocarbons. Tetrafluoroethylene and chlorotrifluoroethylene are produced from chloroform and acetylene, respectively. Many steps are involved in preparation of fluorocarbons; chlorine, caustic and hydrochloric acid are required in the various steps of the synthesis. Sodium nitrate can be used to promote their polymerization. Treating such polymers with sodium in liquid ammonia improves their adhesion properties.

Phenolics and Urea-Formaldehyde Resins. One method of phenol production consists of sulfonating benzene, neutralizing with sodium sulfite and running the solution into fused sodium hydroxide. The melt is treated with water and carbon dioxide to liberate the phenol. A second process (Dow) runs accordingly:

$$C_6H_6 + Cl_2 \xrightarrow{FeCl3} C_6H_5Cl \xrightarrow{NaOH} C_6H_5ONa \xrightarrow{HCl} C_6H_5OH$$

The third process (Raschig) takes place as follows:

$$C_6H_6 + HCl + 1/2O_2 \xrightarrow[Cu-Fe\ cat.]{heat} C_6H_5Cl \xrightarrow[heat\ cat.]{H2O} C_6H_5OH$$

Resorcinol is synthesized from sodium m-benzene disulfonate and caustic soda.

To produce cast phenolics, phenol and formaldehyde are heated with sodium hydroxide or sodium carbonate, as basic catalysts. In compression molding, phenol and formaldehyde may be heated with a hydrochloric acid catalyst. Likewise phenol and furfural can be condensed with sodium hydroxide or hydrochloric acid catalysts to afford thermosetting resins. Urea and formaldehyde are condensed with sodium carbonate or sodium hydroxide catalysts to form a cross-linked polymer.

Polyamides. One of the raw materials for the production of nylon 66 is hexamethylenediamine. Salt chemicals are involved in the preparation of adiponitrile which is hydrogenated to hexamethylenediamine. Hydrocholoric acid and sodium cyanide are reactants when tetrahydrofuran is the starting material, and chlorine and sodium cyanide are used if butadiene is the starting point.

Another polyamide, nylon 6, is formed by the polymerization of caprolactam with sodium hydroxide, sodium carbonate, sodium or hydrochloric acid acting as the catalyst.

Polycarbonates. Both sodium hydroxide and sodium promote the bisphenol A-phosgene reaction to form polyacrylcarbonates. Phosgene is produced catalytically from chlorine and carbon monoxide, and bisphenol A from phenol and acetone.

Polyesters. The glyptal alkyd resins, i.e., reaction products of phthalic anhydride and glycerol, require salt-derived chemicals for their preparation: chlorine, sodium hydroxide and sodium carbonate. Glycerol can be obtained by the saponification of fats with caustic, or by alkaline hydrolysis (caustic and sodium carbonate) of glycerol alpha-chlorohydrin. Chlorine, water and allyl alcohol react to form the latter.

Linear polyesters formed from diols and diacids which contain unsaturation can be cross-linked by graft copolymerization with vinyl monomers. Such a cross-linked polyester can be prepared by reacting unsaturated polyesters, prepared from maleic anhydride and ethylene or propylene glycol with styrene, using a free radical catalyst.

Ethylene and propylene glycol can be manufactured by the addition of water and chlorine to the olefins, treatment with base to form the alkylene oxides, and subsequent hydrolysis by the addition of water.

Polyethylene terephthalate can be produced from methyl terephthalate and ethylene glycol with a sodium hydroxide promoter. A chlorine treatment improves this polymer's heat sealability.

Polyethers and Polyethylene Oxide. Sodium hydroxide catalyzes polyether formation from alkylene oxides and glycerol, alkylene oxides and phenols, and epichlorohydrin and polyphenols. The production of polyethylene oxide monomer was mentioned under *Polyesters*.

Polyolefins. The polymerization of ethylene or propylene can be catalyzed by calcium chloride or hydrochloric acid with various aluminum and titanium compounds, by sodium alone or in combination with aluminum and titanium compounds, or by sodium hydroxide. Olefins are also polymerized with alfin and sodium naphthalene catalysts. Treatment of the polyolefins with hydrochloric acid removes metallic catalyst impurities, and surface chlorine treatment improves their adhesion properties and dyeability. These polyolefins are often chlorinated.

Polystyrene. Styrene and alpha-methylstyrene can be polymerized with sodium catalysts. Sodium sulfate promotes the emulsion polymerization of styrene, and hydrochloric acid accelerates the polymerization when a stannic chloride catalyst is used. Chlorinated polystyrene foams containing copper antimony salts are flame-retardant.

Polyurethanes. The polyurethanes are synthesized by the reaction of diisocyanates and diols or diacids with sodium carbonate or sodium hydroxide catalysts. Isocyanates can be formed from alkyl sulfates, alkali metal cyanates and sodium carbonate, or from sodium amide, sodium nitrate and acyl chlorides although they are usually prepared commercially from diamines and phosgene. The addition of ethylene oxide to ethylene glycol yields polyethylene glycol. Sodium carbonate can be used as a foaming agent for these plastics.

Polyvinyl Plastics. Vinyl acetate is synthesized from ethylene and chlorine with calcium chloride and copper or iron, and subsequent addition of sodium acetate. A common commercial route to vinyl acetate involves acetylene and acetic acid. Saponification of polyvinyl acetate with a catalyst such as sodium hydroxide, sodium carbonate or hydrochloric acid produces polyvinyl alcohol. Polyvinyl alcohol and acetaldehyde react in dilute hydrochloric acid to form polyvinyl acetal. Likewise polyvinyl butyral is made by substituting butyraldehyde for acetaldehyde. Sodium sulfate is used in the spinning solution for polyvinyl alcohol fibers.

Vinylidene chloride is produced from the reaction of chlorine with vinyl chloride, ethylene, or acetylene. Heat and ethylene chloride, or chlorine and ethylene, or hydrogen chloride and acetylene produce vinyl chloride. Sodium carbonate and calcium chloride can catalyze the polymerization of vinyl chloride although it is usually polymerized with free radical initiators. A chlorination reaction is frequently carried out on polyvinyl chloride. Chlorine treatment improves its heat and light stability and solvent resistance; hydrogen chloride treatment also improves heat stability. The addition of chlorinated polyethylene to polyvinyl chloride produces an impact-resistant material.

Silicones. Hydrolysis of dialkyldichlorosilanes with sodium hydroxide yields diols which lose water and condense in the presence of a hydrochloric acid catalyst to give silicone plastics. The dialkyldichlorosilanes can be prepared either by combination of silicon and methyl chloride or by reaction of silicon tetrachloride with a Grignard reagent:

$$CH_3OH + HCl \longrightarrow CH_3Cl \xrightarrow{Si(Cu)}$$
$$CH_4 + Cl_2 \longrightarrow \quad \nearrow \quad (CH_3)_2SiCl_2$$
$$CH_3Cl + Mg \longrightarrow CH_3MgCl \xrightarrow{SiCl_4} \nearrow$$

SHARAN STELLRECHT

SORBITOL

Sorbitol, one of the higher polyhydric alcohols ("sugar alcohols"), contains six alcohol groups, as shown in the following structural formula:

$$HOCH_2 \underset{\underset{H}{|}}{\overset{\overset{OH}{|}}{C}} \underset{\underset{OH}{|}}{\overset{\overset{H}{|}}{C}} \underset{\underset{H}{|}}{\overset{\overset{OH}{|}}{C}} \underset{\underset{H}{|}}{\overset{\overset{OH}{|}}{C}} CH_2OH$$

Sorbitol is a hygroscopic white crystalline substance with a pleasant, sweet taste. It is available in powder or granular form. The compound has a stable form melting at about 96°C and a metastable form melting at about 93°C.

Sorbitol is soluble in water, glycerol or propylene glycol; slightly soluble in methanol, ethanol, acetic acid and phenol. It is practically insoluble in other common organic solvents. The commercial product contains under 1% of sugars.

Polyethers based on sorbitol have definite advantages when used in the production of urethanes. Since there are six hydroxyl groups in sorbitol, ethers having a wide range of hydroxyl numbers can be produced when sorbitol is condensed with a compound such as propylene oxide. Higher hydroxyl number polyethers provide more rigid foams, higher heat distortion temperatures and higher cross-linking densities. Rigid urethane foams produced from a sorbitol-based polyether can be poured in place, molded or sprayed. Depending on the density of the foam, compressive strengths ranging from 20–1300 psi can be attained. Sorbitol polyethers also can be used to make resilient urethane foams and urethane coatings.

Other uses of sorbitol in plastics manufacture are reported in various patents. A mixture of glycerol and sorbitol can be used as a plasticizer in the production of a strong, tack-free water-soluble film from a salt of carboxymethylcellulose. Sorbitol can be used as a plasticizer in the manufacture of a flame-retardant coating composition based upon polyphosphorylamide and an aldehyde amine resin. The addition of sorbitol is said to aid in stabilizing chloride-containing vinyl resins against discoloration and degradation by heat and light.

Varnishes based on sorbitol resins have high adhesion, flexibility and durability. Lacquers similarly based have excellent rubbing characteristics and cold check resistance. Used together in varying proportions, resin esters of sorbitol and pentaerythrytol or glycerol yield varnishes and lacquers with a wide range in hardness, viscosity and melting point. Coatings based on sorbitol esters of tall oils offer advantages with respect to drying rates, adhesion and weathering qualities. Alkyds prepared with sorbitol provide coatings with high gloss and durability, as well as excellent drying and adhesive characteristics. In most cases, sorbitol esters should be used in conjunction with esters of other polyols.

D. F. CHICHESTER

STABILIZERS, ELECTRICAL

General Considerations

Polyvinylchloride resins have excellent electrical properties when manufactured by processes which result in low levels of residual ionic impurities. In formulating electrical insulation compounds, it is necessary to select judiciously the other components as well as the resin to maintain the ionic content at a minimum. This applies not only to the original plasticizers, fillers, pigments and stabilizers, but also to the reaction products formed during the processing and service life of the electrical insulation compound. Choice of stabilizer is particularly critical with reference to the reaction products formed.

Heat degradation induced during processing, usually extrusion, and in actual service, occurs principally by a dehydrochlorination mechanism. One of the primary functions of a stabilizer is to neutralize and inactivate the resulting hydrogen chloride. In electrical compounds it is essential that the reaction products of the hydrogen chloride and the stabilizer result in insoluble and non-ionizable end products. Of all the metals known, only silver, mercurous mercury, and lead form insoluble chlorides. As a result, some form of reactive lead compound is the most suitable practical source of "hydrogen chloride acceptor" for electrical insulation. The anion portion of the lead salt can exert an influence on electrical properties since the resultant acid formed can vary in its ionic character. Basic lead salts provide a highly reactive coordinated PbO over and above the normal lead salt; thus they postpone and minimize the formation of anion derived acid in accepting the hydrogen chloride.

Based upon the considerations noted above, it is readily apparent why lead compounds, and more particularly basic lead compounds, have been preeminent as stabilizers for electrical insulation. Their relatively low cost and very good stabilizer holding power have contributed to their wide acceptance. Their opacity and tendency to stain in the presence of hydrogen sulfide are not the handicaps they might be in film and sheeting applications. Much more important are unexcelled electrical properties and long term stabilizing power without abrupt failure.

Stabilization against heat degradation extends past processing. Higher than ambient temperatures generated by the local environment and current within the wire in home and building use, instrument cabinets, radio and applicance wire, necessitate long holding power to meet the required extended safe and useful service life.

Lead Compounds

Litharge, PbO, free of ionic impurities was used in the early electrical insulation compounds. It is highly reactive and its yellowish-buff color is difficult to mask. Further, its color changes under heat and light presents additional problems. Its high degree of reactivity frequently leads to major interactions with plasticizers and other components.

Basic lead carbonate, $2PbCO_3 \cdot Pb(OH)_2$, commonly known as white lead, was initially widely used due to its color and high percentage of lead, 85% PbO. However, of this, only 31% is available before CO_2 is formed, producing blisters or "gassing", with a resultant porosity in the finished product. If relatively high levels of stabilizer are employed, it may be used in building ($60°C$ T and TW), and lower classes of wires. Lead carbonate is still fairly widely used in Europe because of its low cost, but usage has greatly diminished in the United States since it does not meet industry's demands for higher extrusion rates, higher temperature classes of wire ($80–105°C$), and thinner wall insulation.

Basic lead silicate, $3PbO \cdot 2SiO_2 \cdot 2H_2O$, was first used commercially in 1946. It provides reasonably good heat stability and electrical properties; the low order of reactivity makes it compatible with most plasticizers which are sensitive to more highly basic lead compounds— however, it is generally inferior in holding power. Lead silicate is a calcined product varying in moisture content. It has marginal dispersion characteristics, and this may present problems with modern processing of dry blends.

Tribasic lead sulfate, $3PbO \cdot PbSO_4 \cdot H_2O$, provides good heat stability and electrical properties without any danger of gassing. It is widely used in Europe in building ($60°C$) wire compounds, but in the United States it has been replaced with the more economical basic lead silicate sulfate. Tribasic lead sulfate is, however, too reactive for use with polyester plasticizers to meet the aging requirements of high temperature ($90–105°C$) insulation.

Tetrabasic lead sulfate, $4PbO \cdot PbSO_4 \cdot H_2O$, provides performance closely approaching tribasic lead sulfate—however, it has the disadvantage of being photosensitive, but not to the severe degree characteristic of litharge. It finds only limited use in electrical insulation, principally in Germany.

Basic lead silicate sulfate, an undisclosed complex, contains about 24% SiO_2 and 6% SO_3. This complex is widely employed in the United States for building wire and lower classes. It is an economical stabilizer having lower basicity and a lower specific gravity than tribasic lead sulfate. It retains its very good electrical properties during the prolonged $50°C$ water immersion aging required by Underwriters' Laboratories for the TW ($60°$) class of wire, and is compatible with most of the lower cost extender plasticizers used in this very competitive class of wire.

Basic lead chlorosilicate, a complex containing about 47% SiO_2 and 3% Cl, is an economical stabilizer with a low specific gravity. It is less basic than basic lead silicate sulfate, and thus is less reactive with sensitive plasticizers, but its heat stability holding power is somewhat inferior. It is used to advantage alone in $60°$ compounds, and in combination with more basic lead compounds in higher classes of wire.

Dibasic lead phthalate, $2PbO \cdot Pb(OOC)_2C_6H_4 \cdot \frac{1}{2}H_2O$, unlike the inorganic basic lead salts discussed above, is derived from an aromatic organic acid. It is much less reactive with plasticizers than its high PbO content (80%) would indicate. It is very widely used in high temperature electrical insulation due to its low reactivity with plasticizers, particularly the polyester type. It currently stands alone as the only significant volume stabilizer in use for the long term stability and retention of elongation required in 90 and $105°C$ Underwriters' Laboratories classes of wire.

Tetrabasic lead fumarate, $4PbO \cdot Pb(OOC)_2 C_2H_2 \cdot 2H_2O$, an aliphatic organic acid derived basic lead salt, provides unusually good heat stability and electrical properties. As with dibasic lead phthalate, it is much less reactive with plasticizers than its high PbO (90%) would indicate. It is slightly less reactive than dibasic lead phthalate. Although generally providing greater reserve heat stability than dibasic lead phthalate, it is relatively more expensive and therefore not as widely used. Usage is indicated with the most sensitive plasticizers, e.g., in flame-proof compositions based upon tricresyl phosphate plasticizer. It is also useful in semi-rigid electrical insulation where stabilizer demands are higher.

Tribasic lead maleate, $3PbO \cdot Pb(OOC)_2C_2H_2 \cdot \frac{1}{2}H_2O$, is closely related chemically and in PbO content (89%) to tetrabasic lead fumarate. However, its characteristic yellow color, significantly greater plasticizer reactivity, and its moderate photosensitivity restrict its use in electrical insulation. At least equivalent heat and electrical properties may be achieved with dibasic lead phthalate or tetrabasic lead fumarate without the color or photosensitivity problems.

Dibasic lead phosphite, $2PbO \cdot PbHPO_3 \cdot \frac{1}{2}H_2O$ provides a unique balance of properties. Although derived from an inorganic acid and having a high PbO (91%) content, its plasticizer reactivity is in the same range as dibasic lead phthalate. Its heat stability performance with polyester plasticizers in high temperature insulation is at least equivalent to dibasic lead phthalate. Electrical properties are superior. Dibasic lead phosphite would find much greater use in electrical insulation if it were not somewhat more costly than other good basic lead stabilizers. One unique property, its weathering resistance, explains worldwide usage in electrical compounds subject to outdoor exposure. It is the only stabilizer known which will provide the required electrical properties and weathering resistance in the absence of carbon black pigmentation. A properly formulated electrical insulation compound containing dibasic lead phosphite in combination with rutile type titanium dioxide will remain in serviceable condition for 15–20 years. Its outstanding weathering resistance is attributed to very high absorption in the ultraviolet region and to the antioxidant activity of the phosphite anion.

Normal lead orthosilicate, marketed as a coprecipitate with excess silica gel (total SiO_2 35–45%), has varying electrical properties depending upon the extent of removal of residual sodium ions from the sodium silicate reactant. Being a normal salt, it is essentially nonreactive with sensitive plasticizers, provides translucent stocks, and the excess silica gel minimizes spew and plating problems by absorbing incompatible components in the compound. It does not provide the reserve heat stability of the basic lead compounds. It is not widely used in primary insulation, but is employed in some less demanding electrical applications, particularly where translucent jacketing is desired.

Normal lead stearate, $Pb(C_{17}H_{35}COO)_2$, cannot be used as a primary stabilizer due to its lubricating qualities and because of compatibility considerations. It is used as a lubricant-stabilizer at 0.1 phr to 1 phr level in combination with basic lead stabilizers. Melting point is approximately 110°C. It generally lowers electrical properties, although this is dependent upon the electrical level of the primary stabilizer and the test temperature at which the measurements are made. In acting as a hydrogen chloride acceptor, normal lead stearate liberates stearic acid which has limited compatibility, and will spew or exude. Thus lead stearate is usually employed at relatively low levels.

Lead 2-ethylhexoate, $Pb(C_7H_{15}COO)_2$, is a normal lead salt which is a viscous liquid at room temperature. It is not used in primary insulation, but has found very limited use in translucent jacketing compounds having low electrical requirements. It has low lubricating qualities and thus may be used at higher levels than lead stearate—however, its poor compatibility and tendency to bloom sharply restrict its industrial use in electrical applications.

Dibasic lead stearate, $2PbO \cdot Pb(C_{17}H_{35}COO)_2$, is a basic lead salt analog of lead stearate, used as a supplementary lubricant-stabilizer. As anticipated from its composition, it offers significantly better heat stability. Electrical properties are generally equivalent, while it is less lubricating than normal lead stearate. The latter is attributed to the lower organic content, and due to the fact that it has a melting point above 250°C, thus remaining a solid during processing. Its lower lubricity and better compatibility permit the use of higher levels than lead stearate without presenting spew problems. It has wide application as a strong supplementary stabilizer with low basicity primary lead stabilizers.

Modification of Lead Compounds

The normal and basic lead salts listed above have been classified as to the chemical composition of the major component. Commercial products will vary somewhat in coatings and additives present, as well as freedom from ionic impurities. Thus heat stability and electrical performance will vary between suppliers and between grades from the same supplier. As a case in point, one might consider tribasic lead sulfate. It was originally produced, and still is to some extent, as an uncoated product. As manufactured, it has good electrical properties and reasonably good dispersion characteristics—however, there is an adverse effect upon ease of dispersion after a relatively short period of bag storage. This dispersion problem can be corrected by applying a stearate coating during its manufacture. The stearate coating provides slightly improved heat stability at a slight sacrifice in electrical properties at elevated temperatures.

The next improvement consisted of replacing the stearate coating with a paraffin coating. This provided the same improvement in dispersion, intermediate heat stability, without the sacrifice in electrical properties. Table 1 illustrates the effect of coatings upon volume resistivity at various test temperatures in a tribasic lead sulfate stabilized composition.

TABLE 1.

Formulation:

Electrical grade resin	100
Di-2-ethylhexyl phthalate	25
Diisodecyl phthalate	25
Electrical grade clay	10
Tribasic lead sulfate	5

Test temperature, °C	Relative volume resistivity, %		
	Uncoated	Stearated	Paraffin coated
30	100	125	105
50	100	110	100
70	100	70	100
90	100	60	100
100	100	50	100

Some stabilizers, such as dibasic lead phthalate, process very well, are highly resistant to moisture, and are unaffected by adverse conditions of storage. Special coatings can, however, still provide improved performance in these products. The most recent advance in coatings has been the "XL" grade stabilizers developed by National Lead Company. This coating, of undisclosed composition, upgrades the heat stability and

electrical properties. The "XL" modified products meet industry's demands for increased production rates, higher processing temperatures, better initial color and color stability, and improved retention of physical properties on aging. Laboratory test data given in Table 2 demonstrate the improved electrical performance. Volume resistivity was measured on test slabs at 20°C and 60% RH after 24 hr water immersion on a compound consisting of PVC 100, DOP 50, stabilizer 5.

TABLE 2.

Stabilizer	Volume resistivity, 10^{12} ohm-cm
Tribasic lead sulfate-stearated	45
Tribasic lead sulfate-"XL"	88
Basic lead silicate sulfate-stearated	30
Basic lead silcate sulfate-"XL"	137
Dibasic lead phosphite-uncoated	17
Dibasic lead phosphite-"XL"	139

Advantages of the coating modified products are often more effectively demonstrated in the actual plant extrusion of wire. They provide extended trouble-free plant operation combined with a better quality insulation. Table 3 is an example of comparative tests run on production cables by one manufacturer.

The above data show that varying degrees of efficiency can be expected from commercial stabilizers of generally similar composition, but modified by coating or additive to achieve special performance. It suggests that caution must be exercised in generalizing as to performance based upon the disclosed chemical composition of the product. Coatings and/or modifiers, although present in relatively low concentrations, can markedly influence heat stability and electrical performance.

Non-lead Stabilizers

Barium-Cadmium. The general heat stability performance of barium-cadmium stabilizer systems at relatively low levels (1.5–3 phr) and at

TABLE 3.

Stabilizer	Insulation resistance 24 hr immersion	Original properties		% Retention after aging 7 days at 121°C	
		Tensile strength, psi	Elongation, %	Tensile	Elongation
Basic lead silicate sulfate, stearated	1800	2290	267	108	81
Basic lead silicate sulfate, "XL"	3700	2040	225	115	92
Basic lead chlorosilicate, stearated	1000	2360	242	117	59
Basic lead chlorosilicate, "XL"	1600	2410	250	113	70
Dibasic lead phthalate, uncoated	170	2720	250	111	90
Dibasic lead phthalate, "XL"	181	2700	250	112	100

high processing temperatures experienced in calendering operations, naturally created interest as to their possible use in electrical insulation. Their lack of reactivity with various plasticizer types provided added incentive for testing their utility. Initial investigations showed that the standard film and sheeting grades of barium-cadmium stabilizers were ineffective electrically. Extensive development studies resulted in products which laboratory test data indicated would provide improved electrical performance. Results obtained from the actual wire extrusion trials were discouraging however. Electrical properties, particularly electrical properties during water immersion, were poor. The high shear and heat history during the extrusion process undoubtedly magnified the electrical deficiencies. This is presumably due to the greater stability demands than those experienced in standard laboratory tests, and the resulting higher levels of barium and cadmium chlorides formed in the process. These chlorides, unlike the un-ionizable lead chloride, markedly reduced the electrical properties. To date there are no commercial barium-cadmium systems which provide the necessary electrical performance for primary insulation. Further, cost considerations necessitate that the barium-cadmium stabilizers be employed at lower levels than the more economical lead stabilizers. At these levels their reserve stability and holding power during the actual service life of the electrical insulation must be established.

In Europe selected barium-cadmium stabilizers have been used as lubricants in combination with basic lead salts. Generally, superior properties can be achieved at a lower cost by the judicious choice of the basic lead stabilizer type combined with a more conventional electrical grade lubricant.

There is some limited use of barium-cadmium systems in electrical compounds where water immersion resistance and/or high level electrical properties are not required. These include clear and brightly colored jacketing stocks for instrument wires, novelty Christmas tree wire, and other low requirement wire coatings.

Epoxy Compounds. Use of epoxy plasticizers, such as epoxidized soybean oil, as a portion of the plasticizer system of electrical insulation compounds has been fairly widespread. The ability of the epoxy group or oxirane ring to act as an HCl acceptor is well known. While these materials are ineffective stabilizers when used alone, they provide synergistic activity with other stabilizers, particularly barium-cadmiums—however, their synergism with basic lead compounds is much less than with the barium-cadmiums. Their use in electrical insulation has declined steadily because expected values in retention of properties on aging have not yet been realized. Epoxy

compounds have a mild adverse effect upon electrical properties, and demonstrate a tendency to spew unless used at relatively low levels.

Antioxidants. Polyvinylchloride resins are known to degrade by an oxidative mechanism as well as by dehydrochlorination. Oxidative effects are more evident during mill and calender processing than they are in the extrusion operations used to coat wire. During extrusion the compound is subjected to high temperature and shear, essentially in the absence of air. During aging however, in both the Underwriters' Laboratories accelerated aging test and natural aging in service, the surface of the electrical insulation is subject to oxidative attack. In di-2-ethylhexyl phthalate plasticized compounds, the effect is not of major significance. With plasticizers based upon "Oxo process" derived alcohols such as diisooctyl phthalate (DIOP), diisodecyl phthalate (DDP), and ditridecyl phthalate (DTDP), it is necessary to add 0.1–0.5% based upon the plasticizer, of a hindered phenol antioxidant such as bisphenol A. The antioxidant is added to protect the plasticizer. It is necessary to meet U.L. retention of elongation requirements. In the United States it is common practice for the plasticizer manufacturer to add the bisphenol A, frequently designating the plasticizer containing this additive as "electrical grade." In Europe this practice is less widespread, and the compounder must add it when required.

Lubricants. Lead stearate and dibasic lead stearate have been previously mentioned as supplementary lubricant-stabilizers. Calcium stearate is employed to some extent, principally in Europe, in combination with basic lead stabilizers. Its heat stability is generally equivalent to lead stearate—however, electrical properties are inferior. It has a slightly higher melting point and somewhat better compatibility.

Stearic acid is also used as a lubricant. It does not contribute to heat stability; in fact, there are some data that indicate it is detrimental to long term stability. With some basic lead it is beneficial to original plastic color. Its effect upon electrical properties will vary with the formulation of the compound and test temperature. For example, it is sometimes helpful in compounds having only fair electrical properties, and then only when resistivity is measured at 25–50°C. In most cases, however, stearic acid lowers volume resistivity. The occasional exceptions that are found suggest caution in extrapolating specific results to other base compounds and test temperatures.

Microcrystalline hydrocarbon waxes, with melting points in the range of 165°F, and low molecular weight polyethylenes, enjoy fairly extensive use as lubricants for electrical insulation compounds. They are innocuous with reference to heat stability and, being nonionic in character, have good electrical properties. They are safe under high humidity conditions and generally do not show the marked variation in electrical properties with test temperatures noted for some of the other lubricants. Although they provide no supplementary heat stability, their use is increasing, particularly when combined with the newer stabilizer modifications which provide optimum heat stability and electrical properties.

Evaluation of Electrical Compounds

From the discussion above it is obvious that there is no universal stabilizer for vinyl electrical insulation. The different basic lead stabilizers offer particular advantages with specific plasticizers and to meet specific aging requirements. Stabilizer-plasticizer interaction due to the reactivity of these components, together with varying temperatures, contribute toward making the evaluation of an electrical compound a difficult task. In practice, decisions must be made on a relatively small amount of laboratory test data. This must be followed by the actual extrusion coating of the wire and performance tests on the finished wire. Underwriters' Laboratories, Canadian Standards and British Standards, and other groups responsible for maintaining the quality of electrical insulation, are only interested in the finished wire. They approve total insulation compounds rather than the components.

It is beyond the scope of the present discussion to consider all of the physical, thermal and electrical properties examined in the various classes of electrical insulation. Evaluation of heat stability, aging, and electrical characteristics will be considered in some detail. These are the primary properties examined initially.

Heat Stability. Underwriters' Laboratories imposes no requirements as to heat stability with reference to discoloration of the electrical compound. Discoloration is, however, usually indicative of compound degradation and loss in physical and electrical properties; thus it must be considered. Further, the electrical manufacturer does have color stability requirements per se, since he must provide electrical compounds with consistent colors. He is concerned also as to whether an experimental compound will have sufficient stability to get through the extrusion process and maintain its physical properties during the UL required aging test.

Laboratory heat stability comparisons are normally made by mill mixing the compound and then exposing samples in an oven at selected temperatures for varying periods. Comparison of the extent of discoloration usually indicates relative heat stability. These tests may be supplemented with closed mold heat stability tests where the compositions are held at elevated temperatures, under pressure, in the absence of

air. This test frequently produces colors more closely approximating colors developed during the extrusion process. A third method, which is receiving increasing attention, is to subject the electrical compound to conditions of high temperature and shear using a torque-rheometer such as the "Brabender Plasti-Corder". Data from these tests show improved correlation with extrusion experience. Processing as well as heat stability data are obtained. The time-torque curve indicates the lubricating characteristics at the beginning of the cycle, power requirements after fluxing, and time to decomposition. Useful color stability data may be obtained by the periodic withdrawal of small samples of the plastic melt during the course of the test.

Retention of Physical Properties. One of the more difficult UL requirements is the retention of elongation after aging at elevated temperatures. The accelerated test period is normally 7 days in a forced draft oven, with temperature varying with wire class. Retention of elongation is highly dependent upon the volatility and aging characteristics of the plasticizer, efficiency of the stabilizer and stabilizer-plasticizer interaction. Test data obtained on laboratory test slabs correlate well with data obtained on insulated wire, provided certain precautions are followed. The heat history imposed on the molded test slab should approximate that experienced by the wire insulation. Secondly, the thickness of the test slab should be in the same range as the wall thickness of the insulation. In examining compounds containing different types and levels of volatile constituents it is necessary to avoid a cross-contamination within the test oven. The new "tubular ovens," which provide individual tubes with carefully controlled air velocities, are useful in improving precision and reproducibility in stress-strain aging studies.

Electrical Properties. Insulation resistance is the most common measure of the electrical characteristics of vinyl insulation. Measurements are made on coils of the original wire under various temperature conditions and after varying periods of water immersion and/or oven exposure, dependent upon wire class. In the laboratory, volume resistivity measurements are made on milled or molded sheets. The most troublesome variation between laboratories is the particular temperatures used in making the measurement. The more widely accepted test temperatures are 25°C, 50°C, 70°C and 95°C. Test data presented in Table 4 show the effect of test temperature upon volume resistivity with a series of stabilizers. The base compound consisted of PVC 100, DOP 50, electrical grade clay 10, and stabilizer 5, except in the case of the electrical grade barium-cadmium-organic system where 3 parts were employed.

TABLE 4.

Stabilizer	Volume resistivity, 10^{12} ohm-cm							
	30°C	40°C	50°C	60°C	70°C	80°C	90°C	100°C
Tribasic lead sulfate, stearated	200	110	55	30	15	8	5	1.2
Tribasic lead sulfate, paraffin coated	195	110	55	30	20	15	10	3.2
Basic lead sulfate silicate, stearated	245	140	65	45	20	15	6	1.8
Basic lead sulfate silicate, paraffin coated	200	105	60	40	20	15	10	2.9
Basic lead chlorosilicate, stearated	115	40	20	7	4.1	2.8	2.2	1.0
Dibasic lead phthalate	205	110	65	35	20	10	6	1.6
Dibasic lead phosphite	290	180	125	60	30	20	11	2.0
Tetrabasic lead fumarate	405	205	120	70	30	20	12	2.7
Barium-cadmium, organic	160	85	20	8	2.5	1.1	0.50	0.15

Volume resistivity data of the type shown in Table 4 from slab specimens can be made to correlate fairly well with actual wire data if certain factors are considered. It is necessary to provide a heat history on the test specimens equivalent to that imposed on the insulation, and secondly, volume resistivity measurements should be made at the same temperature as the class of wire under investigation.

Practical Selection of Stabilizer

A detailed discussion of the factors to be considered in formulating an electrical insulation compound will not be attempted here. Since stabilizer and plasticizer selections are governed by the performance required, and there is an interaction between these components, some general remarks on several UL classes of wire might be helpful.

60°C Type T and TW wire. This is the high volume building wire where low costs are necessary to be competitive. These compounds generally contain relatively high levels of electrical grade clay and whiting fillers, and significant quantities of hydrocarbon and/or chlorinated paraffin extender plasticizers. Primary plasticizers such as DOP or DOP/DDP blends generally meet the 7 days at 100°C aging requirement. Since cost is of prime concern, basic lead silicate sulfate, basic lead chlorosilicate, basic lead carbonate or less frequently, tribasic lead sulfate or basic lead silicate are employed as primary stabilizers.

80°C Wire. Higher performance is required in this wire than in the T or TW wire. Lower levels of filler (30 parts), little, if any extender plasticizer, and higher ratios of DDP plasticizer are used to meet the 7 days at 113°C aging requirement. The same general stabilizers as noted for T and TW may be used, but some become marginal unless they contain additives or modified coatings.

90°C Wire. Requirements are still higher in this class of wire and a primary plasticizer such as ditridecyl phthalate alone or in combination with a polyester plasticizer is needed to meet the 7-day aging at 121°C. Stabilizer demands also increase, and dibasic lead phthalate alone, or combined with basic lead chlorosilicate to reduce cost, are usually employed.

105°C Wire. This is currently the highest class of PVC thermoplastic wire approved by U.L. Polyester or pentaerythritol esters, combinations of the two, and, more recently with some trioctyl trimellitate, are the plasticizers used to withstand 7 days at 136°C. Fillers are kept at a low level. Dibasic lead phthalate is used almost exclusively in this type of compound. Tetrabasic lead fumarate or dibasic lead phosphite should be equally suitable, but more expensive. The use of dibasic lead phosphite is restricted to, and required in, primary insulation or jacketing stocks subjected to extended outdoor exposure.

E. L. WHITE

STABILIZERS, HEAT

While polyvinyl chloride and its copolymers constitute one of the major categories used in the production of thermoplastic products, many processing problems had to be overcome before PVC could attain majority status. The major inherent deficiency in polyvinyl chlorides and its copolymers is a natural instability toward heat, with the accompanying liberation of irritating and corrosive HCl fumes. With the advent of suitable heat stabilizers, the processing of PVC forged rapidly forward.

With the exception of air-dry coatings, all PVC products are processed either by heat alone or by the combination of heat and mechanical work. The heat converts the raw chemical composition into a plastic and formable mass permitting the processor to shape it at will. For example, the end products may be in the form of garden hose, packaging film, pipe, phonograph records or floor covering, and in making each of these many different shapes, heat is employed to process the raw material into its finished shape ready for sale. In some applications, there are additional fabricating steps in the manufacture of a vinyl article which also employ heat. Such products must not only be able to withstand the effects of heat processing but also the secondary operations of heat conversion. These operations include sealing and, even more strenuously, the operation of laminating where sheets are built into blocks or are applied by means of heat to some additional surface. While not primarily a function of heat stability, many vinyl products are used outdoors where sun exposure can also have a harmful effect. In these cases, the processor looks toward a heat stabilizer which will also function to withstand the degradation accompanying this exposure. In general, then, the vinyl heat stabilizers must provide the processor with sufficient stability toward decomposition so that the normal heat processing operations can be carried out to make the finished merchandise with complete and economic operational safety.

The temperatures at which a heat stabilizer must function can vary from low temperatures slightly under 300°F, to as high as 450°F, encountered in selected processing methods. The application of heat may be for a relatively short period of time as in the calendering operation. On the other hand, the heat history of a compound used in extrusion and particularly in the extrusion of film or pipe from pellets, may be long and involved. The extrusion of PVC film has been handicapped by the rather complicated die design necessary to obtain good flow and consequently the extensive plumbing involved often leaves areas where perfect flow is not obtained. This results in dead pockets of material which are constantly exposed to high temperatures, and thus there exists an opportunity for lengthy exposure to relatively high temperatures. Once decomposition has started in these dead spots, it tends to spread to the rest of the stock with the result that discoloration and eventually decomposition shows up in the finished product. In the extrusion of film from pellets, the PVC composition must go through two heat cycles: a heat processing cycle to prepare the pellets and then through a second heat processing cycle for conversion to film. Additionally, the compound must be stable enough to permit the re-use of scrap produced in the fabricating operation. Generally, the heat stability of a vinyl compound should be sufficient to permit the reprocessing of scrap, as a small percentage of scrap is produced in all operations.

A brief examination of the extremes of temperature and processing conditions reveals only a bit of the complicated nature of selecting stabilizers for the commercial production of PVC products.

This brief summary will not attempt an historical review of the development of PVC heat stabilization; however, a brief review of some of the major stabilizer types will be covered. The literature, and particularly the patent art, indicates the progress made and the directions taken over the past 30 years evolving into the present day PVC stabilizers.

The evolution of PVC stabilizers has extended from early use of alkaline earth stearates, lead compounds, and tetravalent tin compounds to the more complex barium-cadmium types which currently dominate the industry. The use of lead compounds is still extensive and particularly prevalent in heavy-duty, opaque and nondecorative applications. The tin compounds are particularly of interest in the stabilization of rigid PVC compounds and constitute practically the sole stabilizer type used in the production of PVC pipe. The barium-cadmium type compounds constitute the general purpose stabilizers currently in broad commercial use and are formulated to produce either extremely transparent clears or brilliant highly stable colored compositions. By carefully controlling the auxiliary parts of the barium-cadmium systems, a great many useful properties may be brought into stabilizer compositions. A brief discussion of the effects of the various stabilizer ingredients may be helpful in a review of the functions of heat stabilizers.

Alkaline Earth Metals

Barium and calcium are the principal alkaline earth metals used in the manufacture of compounds for inclusion in PVC stabilizers, although there is some usage of magnesium and strontium. In general, these metal compounds aid in developing long-term heat stabilization by delaying decomposition due to liberation of HCl. Heat stabilization based solely on alkaline earth metals tends to produce sticks which rapidly become yellow, then orange, then brown.* Barium compounds may be considered the heavy duty portion of heat stabilization systems in which they occur and, in general, the other alkaline earth metals may be rated in effectiveness loosely in proportion to their atomic weight. The calcium and magnesium compounds are particularly useful in the compounding of stabilizers for vinyl products which are to be utilized in contact with food or medicinal products. For example, magnesium and calcium stearates have long been known as "safe" products in contact with food. Consequently, the magnesium and calcium stearates together with a number of other approved compounds are used in preparing the so-called "FDA approved" stabilizers for PVC food-packaging operations.

The barium compounds are utilized in the so-called "general purpose" stabilizers and are considered "toxic," as contrasted to the "nontoxic"

---

*To "enrich" the stabilizer systems of today, many auxiliary ingredients are added with these alkali earth metals which in turn slow down this visible color change.

calcium and zinc compounds. This use of the word "toxic" should not be construed as implying that the barium stabilizer compounds are necessarily very toxic or hazardous in handling; it simply means that such compounds are unsuitable for use in formulating PVC compositions for nontoxic applications.

Cadmium and Zinc

In the preparation of heat stabilizers for PVC, cadmium and zinc compounds are used to promote early water-white color and transparency. The use of these metals tends to accelerate the black decomposition so commonly observed in PVC degradation. Thus when the cadmium or zinc compounds are used by themselves, the PVC compound is characterized initially by brilliant water whiteness which may suddenly revert on prolonged exposure to heat to a black mass. This is often accompanied by a violent liberation of HCl. Furthermore, all commercial PVC resins show a variable tendency to respond to the presence of cadmium or zinc compounds, and consequently in many cases when the resin source is changed, a change in stabilizers must also be made. It can be noted here that many stabilizer manufacturers have characterized commercial resins with regard to "zinc" sensitivity.

Tin Compounds (*See* Stabilizer, Tin Compounds)

The majority of the effective tin compounds are based on tetravalent organotin compounds, and often contain sulfur in addition to tin. The sulfur may be present as the mercaptide, in which case the stabilizer tends to have a pronounced odor. This odor has been the cause of numerous personnel problems in processing plants, and because of such, consumers have been known to register complaints aimed at the finished product. The more recent developments in tin stabilizer compositions have been aimed at reducing this odor. The tin stabilizer does not contribute any appreciable value when the finished product is exposed to sunlight and consequently, the barium-cadmium compounds have been preferred in the preparation of PVC products for outdoor use. The more recent efforts in the development of tin stabilizers have included improved outdoor weathering properties. One outstanding feature in connection with many tin stabilizers is that they do provide crystal clarity and good heat stability. Generally, however, the cost of stabilizer per pound of resin is somewhat higher than equivalent stabilization with the barium-cadmium systems.

Bivalent tin compounds such as tin stearate have found limited utility in the formulation of nontoxic stabilizer compositions.

Lead Compounds (*See* Stabilizers, Lead Compounds)

Because of the high atomic weight of lead, the customary dosage with lead stabilizers is heavier than with other types of stabilization. This heavy dosage is usually offset due to the relatively low price of the lead compounds and consequently, massive dosage of lead stabilizers may be used with reasonable economics. Lead is still a preferable stabilizer in electrical PVC compounds where the inherent opacity is not a drawback. Lead compounds are also characterized by their tendency to sulfur stain and consequently, find limited use in decorative consumer products.

Nonmetal Additives

As the development of PVC stabilizers progressed, more sophisticated formulators added organic compounds either to enhance the extent of heat stabilization or to improve other properties such as transparency, freedom from haze, freedom from "bloom", etc. The patent literature discloses a broad range of compounds used in conjunction with metal stabilizer components, and it is presumed that many proprietary formulations contain one or more of these various additives. The most commonly used additive is one of the organic phosphites, often called "chelators" by those in the stabilizer field. The inclusion of the phosphites has demonstrated improved clarity and to some extent extended the time before the inception of a yellow color. The phosphites also provide a good solubilizer for many of the metal components. While not strictly a part of the normal stabilizer system, the use of epoxy compounds such as epoxidized oils and glycidyl ethers has been shown to have merit.

Other Variables

The variations possible in the formulation of stabilizers may briefly be summarized to include metals selected from magnesium, calcium, barium, zinc, cadmium, tin and lead, plus organic compositions including phosphites, oxirane-containing materials and numerous other proprietary compounds. Thus the number of possible stabilizer combinations is almost without limit. However, the stabilizer problems from a processor's standpoint are considerably more multitudinousness, inasmuch as simple changes in sources of PVC resin will make subtle differences in stabilizer performance. There is not as great a difference in stabilizer response in using various molecular weight resins from a single supplier as there is in shifting resins of equivalent molecular weight from one supplier to another.

Perhaps even more important than the resin source as a formulation problem is the choice of plasticizer blend which is utilized in getting and retaining the desired properties in the compounds. For example, were a processor to change from a standard phthalate type plasticizer system to one which incorporated in addition a portion of either a phosphate or an adipate plasticizer, it would be almost imperative to reevaluate the adequacy of the stabilizer system.

Furthermore, the use of various types of fillers, pigments, and extenders may all have a marked effect on the response of the composition to a previously established stabilizer system. Even the lubricant selected as a processing aid may affect the performance of a heretofore perfectly acceptable stabilizer system. Thus, no one stabilizer system or type of stabilizer system can be considered to be "all-purpose" with regard to the solution of production problems of the various processors. This in turn necessitates that processors handling large production output, in a diversified line of PVC products, must of necessity maintain a development lab for the purpose of selecting stabilizer systems for each production item. Such a development lab requires compounding skill combined with the processor's experience, plus a ready supply of recommended stabilizer systems from the many stabilizer manufacturers.

C. E. KLEIMAN and P. H. RHODES

Cross-reference: STABILIZERS, LIGHT.

STABILIZERS, LEAD

Inorganic lead compounds, namely litharge (PbO) and basic white lead carbonate ($2PbCO_3 \cdot Pb(OH)_2$), were among the first to be considered as stabilizers for polyvinylchloride polymers and copolymers. Both lead compounds were successful and well known in electrical insulation and surface coatings, many years prior to the advent of large-scale vinyl production. Since vinyl resins entered these fields in earliest applications, these lead compounds were logical choices. They functioned as hydrogen chloride acceptors, without being basic to the extent of promoting hydrogen chloride removal and polymer degradation. While many theories have been advanced to explain the mechanism of degradation and stabilization of PVC, stabilization remains essentially an empirical art. Hydrogen chloride acceptance is only one functional requirement of the stabilizer, so it is not unexpected that a variety of lead compounds have been developed for use as vinyl stabilizers. These include normal and basic salts of both inorganic and organic acids. They overcome the color (yellow) and reactivity deficiencies of litharge, the gassing problems with white lead (liberation of CO_2), and provide improved heat and light stability in a variety of plastic applications. Their utility is attested to by their high volume usage in PVC, although there is some question as to whether the lead compounds or the barium-cadmium mixtures are "most popular." In Europe the lead compounds are the most widely used stabilizers. In the United States one source noted that "the leads and barium-cadmium dominate—although which is the front runner will depend upon whether you consider pounds or dollars." Lead stabilizers are priced from 20 to 55¢ per lb and are used at 5 to 8 pph of resin, while barium-cadmiums sell for 55¢ to $1.00 per lb and are used at the 2 to $2\frac{1}{2}$ phr level. Actually, each type dominates certain specific applications, and shares others, while neither is widely used in still other areas. Lead stabilizers are used mostly in extrusions, rigids and electrical insulation; their opacity and sulfide staining restrict their use in film and sheeting, which is dominated by barium-cadmium, with and without zinc; while nontoxic applications generally require organo-tins or calcium-zinc stabilizers.

Lead Stabilizer Types

Commercial lead stabilizers are derived from both inorganic and organic acids. They include both normal lead salts and basic lead compounds, with the latter predominating. The basic lead compounds contain reactive coordinated PbO over and above the normal lead content, and thus provide greater available stabilizing power. The current commercial products may be classified as follows:

Normal Lead Salts

Inorganic Acids:
   Lead orthosilicate, marketed as a coprecipate with excess silica gel (SiO_2 35–45%)
Organic Acids:
   Lead 2-ethylhexoate, $Pb(C_7H_{15}COO)_2$
   Lead stearate, $Pb(C_{17}H_{35}COO)_2$
   Lead salicylate, $Pb(HOC_6H_4COO)_2$

Basic Lead Salts

Inorganic Acids:
   Basic lead carbonate (white lead),
      $2PbCO_3 \cdot Pb(OH)_2$
   Basic lead silicate, $3PbO \cdot 2SiO_2 \cdot 2H_2O$
   Basic lead silicate-sulfate, complex containing 24% SiO_2, 6% SO_3
   Basic lead chlorosilicate, complex containing 47% SiO_2, 3% Cl
   Tribasic lead sulfate, $3PbO \cdot PbSO_4 \cdot H_2O$
   Tetrabasic lead sulfate, $4PbO \cdot PbSO_4 \cdot H_2O$
   Dibasic lead phosphite, $2PbO \cdot PbHPO_3 \cdot \frac{1}{2}H_2O$
Organic Acids:
   Dibasic lead stearate, $2PbO \cdot Pb(C_{17}H_{35}COO)_2$
   Dibasic lead phthalate, $2PbO \cdot Pb(OCO)_2C_6H_4 \cdot \frac{1}{2}H_2O$
   Tribasic lead maleate $3PbO \cdot Pb(OCO)_2C_2H_2 \cdot \frac{1}{2}H_2O$
   Tetrabasic lead fumarate $4PbO \cdot Pb(OCO)_2C_2H_2 \cdot 2H_2O$

Reactivity

The lead stabilizers listed above have each been found to have specific chemical and physical properties that make them useful, either alone or in combination, for one or more of the varied plastic applications. Since all are lead salts they meet the requirement of being an "acid acceptor" and therefore contribute to the ultimate heat and light stability in vinyl compounds. Actually, litharge (PbO) would be the most efficient form of using lead as an "acid acceptor," but the requirements of vinyl stabilization go beyond mere acid acceptance, and various other chemical and physical properties must be incorporated into a desirable stabilizer compound or combination. It must be noted that litharge is not light and color stable and may be used only in certain black pigmented compounds.

A stabilizer may very satisfactorily impart good heat and light resistivity to the polymer, but in so doing, may react with the plasticizer and give rise to loss of plasticity or severe color formation or both. At the temperatures of processing used for the average vinyl application, plasticizer-stabilizer interaction is almost inevitable. Basic lead compounds do however vary in reactivity, and plasticizers vary in sensitivity. Thus in designing a compound for a given application, stabilizer-plasticizer interaction must be considered. The plasticizers present will influence performance of the stabilizer.

There are a great number of plasticizers, both primary and secondary, available to the vinyl compounder. Most of the plasticizers are esters, with those used in high volumes based upon dibasic acids. The primary plasticizers include both aromatic (phthalate, trimellitate) and aliphatic (adipate, azelate, sebacate) esters derived from alcohols of varying carbon chain lengths. This class of plasticizers is characterized by its low order of reactivity with stabilizers. Optimum stability is usually provided by the more highly basic lead stabilizers such as tribasic lead sulfate, dibasic lead phthalate, dibasic lead phosphite, tetrabasic lead fumarate or the somewhat less effective, but more economical, basic lead silicate-sulfate. Tetrabasic lead sulfate and tribasic lead maleate may be used but they are photosensitive and the latter is yellow in color. Basic lead carbonate provides good heat stability however, high levels are employed to minimize, but not always completely overcome, porosity problems due to the liberation of carbon dioxide.

Polyesters are closely related to the preceding class of plasticizers. They are reaction products of dibasic acids and glycols. The secondary functional groups, if present, in the glycol govern the reactivity of the polyester with basic lead compounds. Those containing simple glycols such as ethylene or propylene glycol are essentially nonreactive. Those based upon diethylene glycol, dipropylene glycol or triethylene glycol, all of which are ether-linked glycols, are susceptible to interaction. Tribasic and tetrabasic lead sulfates, the more reactive basic lead compounds, should be avoided since they react with ether groups. Dibasic lead phthalate and phosphite, and tetrabasic lead fumarate are preferred. The latter may be somewhat surprising, but in spite of its high PbO content it has low reactivity with susceptible organic functional groups.

For convenience, we may group in one plasticizer class ether-esters such as triethylene glycol dicaprylate, aliphatic unsaturated esters such as butyl acetyl ricinoleate, and ester epoxides such as octyl epoxy stearate. These materials contain aliphatic unsaturation or ether or epoxy groups all of which are reactive with the more basic lead compounds. The less reactive basic lead silicate, or chlorosilicates or normal lead orthosilicate stabilizers are generally preferred when these plasticizers are employed as a major component of the plasticizer system. In practice however, the limited compatibility of these plasticizers restricts the levels that may be employed, and when they are combined with the more common primary plasticizers, basic lead stabilizers such as dibasic lead phthalate, or basic lead carbonate or silicate-sulfate will provide good stability.

Phosphate esters represent another class of plasticizers which exhibit varying reactivities. Triaryl phosphates such as tricresyl phosphate, which are of prime interest where outstanding flame resistance is required, are quite reactive and present particular stabilization problems with the various types of commercial stabilizers. Highly reactive materials such as tribasic lead sulfate should be avoided. A normal lead salt such as lead orthosilicate would be an obvious choice due to its low reactivity; however, it generally does not provide adequate long term stability. This can be corrected by the co-use of basic lead silicate or chlorosilicate. A better choice however is tetrabasic lead fumarate. In spite of its high PbO content, it is relatively nonreactive and provides good heat stability.

Mixed alkyl-aryl phosphate plasticizers, such as the widely used octyl diphenyl phosphate, are much less reactive and, with the exception of the basic lead sulfates, most of the basic lead stabilizers may be employed. On the other hand, trialkyl phosphates, such as trioctyl phosphate, are reactive and stabilizer requirements are generally similar to the triaryl phosphates.

Miscellaneous other plasticizers include the pentaerythritol esters, hydrocarbons and chlorinated hydrocarbons. The pentaerythritol esters have low volatility and good heat stability, and thus are used in applications involving exposure

443

to relatively high temperatures for extended periods. The moderately reactive basic lead compounds such as dibasic lead phthalate or phosphite are most suitable. The hydrocarbons and chlorinated hydrocarbons are secondary plasticizers of limited compatibility. The hydrocarbon extender plasticizers usually contain aliphatic unsaturation and are susceptible to reactivity with the more basic lead compounds leading to color formation; however, these plasticizers are frequently of poor color themselves and not used where plastic color is of prime importance. On the other hand, the chlorinated hydrocarbons are nonreactive, have good color and can provide good stability. Highly efficient stabilizers such as dibasic lead phosphite are necessary however. Like PVC resin they are subject to thermal degradation and the resultant release of hydrogen chloride, so that an optimum stabilizer system is required.

In discussing stabilizer reactivity and plasticizer-stabilizer interaction, no reference has been made to lead salicylate, lead 2-ethyl-hexoate and the normal and dibasic lead stearates. All are used for special purposes. With the exception of dibasic lead stearate these materials have low reactivity. Lead salicylate was the first stabilizer available which eliminated the specific color stability problem in vinyl floor tile compositions containing asbestos filler. It has gradually been replaced by polyol and nitrogen containing chelating agents which also complex the impurities present in the asbestos. Lead 2-ethylhexoate, a viscous liquid, is used where a liquid lead stabilizer is desired. It has limited compatibility however, and must be used at relatively low levels.

Normal and dibasic lead stearates are widely used in conjunction (0.5–1.5 phr) with the other lead stabilizers to provide lubrication and supplementary heat stability. The normal salt is the more efficient lubricant while the dibasic salt provides much greater stability. The reactivity of dibasic lead stearate is in the range of tribasic lead sulfate; however, since it is used at much lower concentrations, it may be used with most plasticizer systems to provide strong supplementary|stabilization.

Applications

Lead stabilizers are used in a variety of products formed from flexible and rigid PVC. Lead stabilized flexible extrusion compounds include garden hose, belting, spline, gasketing and electrical insulation. Stabilization of electrical insulation, which is almost completely dominated by basic lead compounds, is quite complex in that in addition to the necessary heat stability, electrical and mechanical performance requirements are specified by regulatory groups such as Under-

writers' Laboratories and Canadian and British Standards. Criteria used in selection of stabilizers for electrical insulation are discussed in another section (see "Stabilizers, Electrical.)

The normal and basic lead compounds are also used in calendered film and sheeting and in plastisols and organosols. The only primary restriction on their use is that they are not suitable in applications where sulfide stain resistance or good clarity are necessary. The basic lead compounds, being pigments, opacify the plastic composition. Frequently this is advantageous in that it reduces the quantity of supplementary opacifying agent needed. Translucent film and sheeting may be obtained with the normal lead salts.

The selection of a stabilizer for a given flexible plastic application will be governed|by the properties and heat stability level required during processing and service life of the product and by the plasticizer present in the composition. With reference to the latter, the principles discussed above will serve as a primary guide. With plasticizers of low reactivity the more basic compounds such as tribasic lead sulfate and tetrabasic lead fumarate will provide the best heat stability. With mildly reactive plasticizer systems, dibasic lead phthalate and phosphite or the lower cost basic lead silicate-sulfate will be preferred, while the more reactive systems will require the less basic or normal lead compounds.

In applications where light stability must be considered, the different lead compounds will provide varying degrees of protection. Most of the normal and basic lead compounds will provide only moderate light stability and weathering resistance without help from a supplementary light stabilizer. Dibasic lead phthalate will however provide good light stability and dibasic lead phosphite outstanding light stability and weathering resistance. Dibasic lead phosphite is unique in its outdoor performance, although under some accelerated light stability test conditions it will appear to be quite ineffective. With a good weathering plasticizer such as dioctyl phthalate, 5–10 phr of rutile type titanium dioxide and 5–10 phr of dibasic lead phosphite, 10–20 mil sheets have remained flexible after over 12 years of outdoor exposure in the New York area. The outstanding weathering resistance imparted by dibasic lead phosphite is attributed to its antioxidant properties and to its high ultraviolet absorption of the wave lengths that are detrimental to PVC.

Lead stabilizers also find wide use in extruded and injection and compression molded rigid PVC compositions. An example of the latter is the use of normal and dibasic lead stearates, or preferably a combination of both (total 1.5 phr) in phonograph records. Tribasic lead sulfate is widely used in Europe in extruded pipe, including potable water pipes in Holland and Germany. In the United States, however, lead compounds have not received N.S.F. or F.D.A. approval so that they are restricted to pipe for chemical, irrigation, drain, waste and vent use. In these and other building products, the more basic lead compounds such as tribasic lead sulfate, tetrabasic lead fumarate and dibasic lead phosphite provide excellent heat stability under the rigorous high temperature and shear conditions encountered in the processing of rigid PVC. As with flexible plastic, where good weathering resistance is desired, dibasic lead phosphite most frequently in combination with tribasic lead sulfate, is required.

Commercial Products

In discussing the various lead compounds, they have been identified by their chemical composition. Most suppliers of lead stabilizers provide compositional data as to the primary component. This facilitates stabilizer selection better than the practices with most other types of proprietary stabilizers where only metal types are specified. It should be noted however that commercial lead stabilizers of the same base composition will vary in performance depending upon method of manufacture, degree of purity, additives present and coatings on the pigment particles. Coatings can have significant effects on performance. Some patented coatings impart not only improved wetting and dispersion, but also buffer the reactivity of the basic lead pigment and provide improved stability. The lead stabilizers are also marketed with low levels of mineral oil or plasticizer to minimize dusting, and also as dispersions at higher levels in plasticizer for direct use in plastisols and other applications.

It should be noted also that different lead stabilizer types are frequently used in combination to achieve special properties. Occasionally, lead stabilizers are combined with nonlead stabilizers. Lead orthosilicate, for example, is combined with tin or barium-cadmium stabilizers in film and sheeting to improve the long term stability, cost and to reduce spew and plate-out. Some combined lead types and lead-nonlead types are marketed as single-package products in Europe; however, this practice has not been adopted in the United States, where the combining of different stabilizers is left to the individual compounder.

E. L. WHITE

STABILIZERS, LIGHT

Light stabilizers protect polymeric substrates from photochemical degradation. Their purpose is to extend the useful life (color and/or physical properties) of plastic materials exposed to terrestrial sunlight, fluorescent lights, etc. Extraterrestrial environment demands UV absorbers with special properties. The solar energy spectrum above the earth's atmosphere consists of electromagnetic radiation with wavelengths of less than 100 nm.* Although the earth's atmosphere absorbs all the wavelengths below 280 nm and over 50% of the ultraviolet between 280 and 380 nm, materials such as plastics, rubbers, coatings, and colorants are photochemically degraded when exposed to solar radiation at the earth's surface.

Types of Light Stabilizers

UV-Absorbing. The major types of UV absorbing light stabilizers are the 2-(2′-hydroxyphenyl)-benzotriazoles (I), the o-hydroxybenzophenones (II), the substituted acrylonitriles (III), and the salicylates (IV). Figure 1 illustrates the relative absorbance for the major types of UV-absorbing light stabilizers.

Non- or Weakly Absorbing. The nonabsorbing light stabilizers consist mainly of metal chelates or complexes (V), nonabsorbing esters (VI) which rearrange photochemically to UV-absorbing

* Nanometer (nm) has replaced millimicron (mμ).

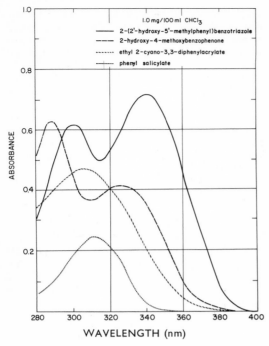

FIG. 1. UV—absorbing light stabilizers.

o-hydroxybenzophenones (VII), and hexamethyl-phosphoric triamide [(CH$_3$)$_2$N]$_3$PO.

(V)

(VI)   (VII)

Figure 2 compares the absorbance of "non-absorbing" light stabilizers with a typical absorbing light stabilizer, 2-(2′-hydroxy-5′-methyl-phenyl) benzotriazole.

Carbon Black. One of the oldest methods for stabilizing plastic materials against UV degradation is the use of carbon black. This approach has obvious color limitations. Besides improving the weathering properties of plastics, carbon black also serves as a filler and colorant; it not only functions as an ultraviolet light absorber, but is also believed to protect the substrate in a manner similar to antioxidants. Carbon black contains

stable free radicals which can function as chain stoppers, terminating the oxidative chain reaction and the photochemical-induced free radicals. It is used principally in polyethylene, phenolics, and poly(vinyl chloride) in applications such as wire and cable coatings, pipe, phonograph records, and film for mulches and tarpaulins.

Extraterrestrial UV Absorbers. In addition to the shorter and more destructive wavelengths of ultraviolet radiation above the earth's surface, extremely low pressures are encountered. In this environment, light stabilizers must be stable to, and be able to absorb, the shorter ultraviolet radiation; they must also have extremely low vapor pressures. The metal-cyclopentadienyl derivatives (VIII) have proved to be useful materials under these extreme conditions.

(VIII)

However, the addition of trifluoromethyl groups to the commonly used UV absorbers appreciably

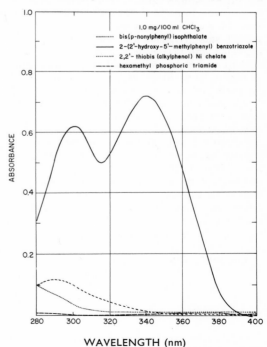

FIG. 2. Absorbing *vs.* non-absorbing light stabilizers.

lowers their vapor pressures and provides effective extraterrestrial UV absorbers.

Mechanism

Structural Requirements. A photochemically stable UV absorber is thought to function by preferentially absorbing ultraviolet radiation and dissipating the energy, either by transferring it to its surroundings or by reemitting it at longer wavelengths through phosphorescence, fluorescence, and heat. A characteristic of the two most commonly used plastics UV absorbers, the 2-(2′-hydroxyphenyl)benzotriazoles and the *o*-hydroxybenzophenones, is a molecular structure in which there exists an intramolecular conjugated chelated system involving a phenolic hydroxyl group (see I and II).

If the hydroxyl hydrogen is replaced by an alkyl or acyl group, no hydrogen bonding can exist and the materials can no longer function as effective UV absorbers. This essential feature is also illustrated by *p*-hydroxybenzophenone, which is characterized by the absence of intramolecular bonding and the presence of only intermolecular hydrogen bonding; *p*-hydroxybenzophenone does not therefore serve as a light stabilizer.

When an insulating group such as a methylene is inserted between the carbonyl and the phenolic moiety, or between the phenolic hydroxyl group and the aromatic ring, preventing conjugated hydrogen bonding, the resultant materials are ineffective light stabilizers. The importance of conjugated chelation is further illustrated by the following example: 2, 2′-dihydroxybenzophenone is a yellow, strongly UV-absorbing material, while the saturated compound bis(2-hydroxycyclohexyl) ketone is a colorless, weakly absorbing, inefficient light stabilizer.

Another desirable molecular feature of an effective, strongly absorbing UV absorber is the presence of an aromatic moiety conjugated with the triazole or carbonyl. For example, the acetophenones are less strongly absorbing and less effective as light stabilizers than the benzophenones. This is exemplified in Fig. 3 which compares the absorbance of equimolar concentrations of 2, 4-dihydroxybenzophenone (IX) with 2, 4-dihydroxyacetophenone (X).

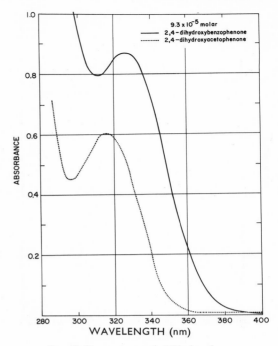

Fig. 3. Strong *vs*. weak UV absorbers.

The salicylates (IV) have an insulating oxygen separating the *o*-salicyloyl moiety from the aryl moiety. The salicylates are generally less effective light stabilizers than the 2-(2′-hydroxyphenyl)-benzotriazoles (I) or *o*-hydroxybenzophenones (II). This is so, in part, because the salicylates absorb more weakly in the UV region (see Fig. 1) and are less chemically stable materials when exposed to UV light. The alkyl salicylates are generally less effective than the aryl salicylates. This has been ascribed to the less absorbing characteristics of the alkyl salicylates, Fig. 4, and to a photochemical rearrangement of the colorless aryl salicylates to the yellow, more strongly absorbing hydroxybenzophenones. This may account for the initial yellowing upon light exposures of some plastics stabilized with salicylates.

It was shown above that nonabsorbing esters can also photochemically rearrange (VI→VII) to UV-absorbing materials. To illustrate, Fig. 5 shows the shift of the absorbance maxima to a longer wavelength and the increase in absorbance as a result of exposing a solution of bis(*p*-nonylphenyl) isophthalate (XI) to ultraviolet light

Not only is the acetophenone less strongly absorbing, but its maxima has been shifted to a lower wavelength compared with the benzophenone.

447

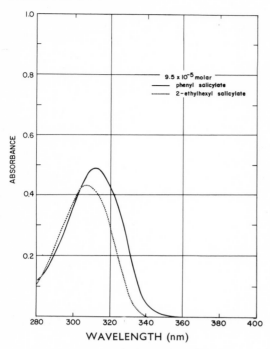

FIG. 4. Aryl *vs.* Alkyl salicylate absorbers.

substrate. As the rearrangement proceeds to the hydroxybenzophenone, the plastic increases in yellowness.

Another structural requirement is that the two aromatic rings be planar. When the available hydrogens ortho to the carbonyl are replaced with bulky groups, the two benzene rings are sterically prevented from lying in the same plane, and a less effective light stabilizer results.

The nickel chelate light stabilizers (V) are intended to function as antioxidants and free-radical chain terminators rather than as UV absorbers. An obvious disadvantage of the nickel chelates is their intensely green color. Less obvious is their heat sensitivity. They have a tendency to discolor (turn black) if fabrication temperatures are not carefully controlled. Their effectiveness as light stabilizers is enhanced when used in combination with a strongly absorbing stabilizer such as the 2-(2'-hydroxyphenyl)benzotriazoles.

Desirable Properties or Features

Factors to be considered in selecting light stabilizers are: substrate, method and conditions of fabrication, size and shape of the finished product, end-use, and environment during end-use.

The UV absorber should act as a "scavenger" and preferentially absorb the pertinent ultraviolet components of sunlight and/or fluorescent lights. Ideally, the UV absorber should strongly absorb

(combination of fluorescent sunlamps and black lights). This approach is not a satisfactory solution

for obtaining good light stability. Initially, the non-absorbing ester affords little or no protection to the polymeric substrate from UV radiation. The plastic may severely deteriorate before sufficient ester rearranges to an absorbing, protective stabilizer. Protecting the polymer at as early a stage as possible is extremely important; the more a polymeric substrate has been degraded, the more difficult it is subsequently to stabilize it. Another disadvantage: the rearranged absorber (XII) is yellow, and the color is imparted to the polymeric

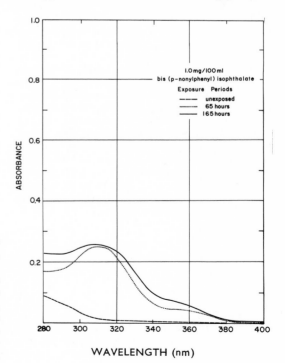

FIG. 5. Ester absorbers.

the wavelengths to which the polymer is photosensitive. In practice this is not readily accomplished because plastic materials are not pure compounds. Impurities, catalyst residues, functional end-groups, additives (pigments, antioxidants, plasticizers, thermal stabilizers, antistatic agents, hydrogen chloride scavengers, etc.), and oxidation products from polymer degradation all influence the absorption characteristics of the finished plastic material.

The UV absorber should be relatively stable to the electro-magnetic radiation. It should absorb ultraviolet light without itself undergoing any change in structure that would render it ineffective as a light stabilizer.

The UV absorber should be compatible with the material in which it is to be used. An effective UV absorber in one substrate may be much less effective in another. This, in part, can be attributed to compatibility. For example, 2-(2-hydroxy-5'-methylphenyl) benzotriazole is an excellent light stabilizer for relatively polar substrates such as poly(vinyl chloride), styrene polymers, and polyesters, but is less effective in nonpolar materials such as polyethylene and polypropylene. When longer alkyl groups are substituted on the 2-(2'-hydroxylphenyl)benzotriazole structure, a very effective polyolefin light stabilizer is obtained. This is also true in the case of o-hydroxybenzophenones. If the alkoxy substituent of 2-hydroxy-4-methoxybenzophenone is replaced with a longer-chained alkoxy group, a more

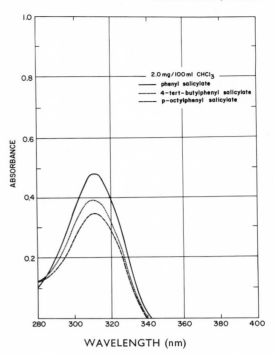

FIG. 7. Salicylate absorbers.

effective polyolefin stabilizer results. That this is not due to a difference in absorption characteristics is shown in Fig. 6 for the benzophenones, and in Fig. 7 for the salicylates. Carboxyl and hydroxyl groups are desirable to achieve compatibility with the polar substrates.

A UV absorber should be relatively nonvolatile and have a slow diffusion and evaporation rate. Permanence depends on the vapor pressure of the UV absorber itself and its solubility (compatibility) in the substrate. Volatility from a substrate, however, cannot always be predicted by the UV absorber's vapor pressure alone; in fact, the rate of loss of a UV absorber may vary widely from substrate to substrate.

The stabilizer should be thermally stable and should not decompose under the conditions imposed by processing. A UV absorber may be perfectly satisfactory for a given polymer but may fail completely in the same or a similar polymer processed at higher temperatures and pressures or subjected to the same conditions for a longer period. This can be an important factor when a considerable portion of the polymer is reprocessed. The nickel chelates (V), for example, are relatively thermally sensitive and have a tendency to discolor when overheated; careful control of processing conditions is therefore required.

The light stabilizer should be chemically inert during fabrication and subsequent use (weathering). It should be unreactive with other additives

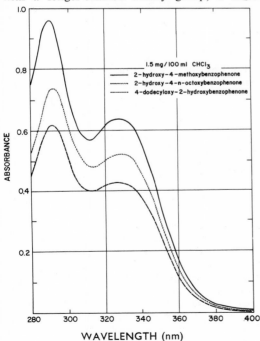

FIG. 6. Benzophenone absorbers.

present, with the polymeric substrate, or with the catalysts and curing agents used. In alkaline poly(vinyl chloride) stabilizer systems, the phenolic hydroxyl group of the UV absorber may form highly colored phenolates, resulting in an ineffective stabilizer. This effect can generally be alleviated by addition of a fatty acid, or avoided by modifying the structure of the UV absorber. The phenolic-hydroxyl can be sterically hindered and made less acidic by adding a large, bulky group ortho to the phenolic —OH. Some UV absorbers complex with metal-ion catalyzed or cured polymer systems, an effect that not only leads to a discolored product but may also inhibit the cure. This too can be eliminated by utilizing sterically hindered, less acidic UV absorbers.

In choosing a light stabilizer, both the chemical and the physical conditions to which the polymeric material will be exposed must be considered. Some applications demand stabilizers that are chemically inert and not readily extracted (washed out). Textile fibers, for example, are not only subjected to repeated washings and dryings in home and commercial laundries, but they are often exposed to rigorous scouring and dye baths. Significant improvements in wash resistance have been achieved by modifying substituent groups without materially affecting the UV-absorbing characteristics of the stabilizer. The benzotriazoles and the nonabsorbing nickel chelate stabilizers are considered to have good washfastness properties. Another way to obtain wash-resistance is by using either a polymeric light stabilizer or one that has a functional group capable of copolymerizing with the polymeric substrate. Molded materials which are exposed to continuous or intermittent washings (such as beverage cases, stadium seats and marine articles) may also require wash-resistant stabilizers.

Resistance to gas fading (discoloration attributed to reactions with nitrogen oxides) is an important consideration in the textile industry. The 2-(2′-hydroxyphenyl)benzotriazoles have proved to be relatively resistant to gas fading and are often used in synthetic fibers.

Polymers such as crystal polystyrene and acrylics demand efficient light stabilizers that impart little or no color (yellowness). Though the salicylates and the acrylonitriles add no color to these substrates initially, their light stabilizing properties are relatively quite poor. Ideally, an efficient, non-yellowing light stabilizer should absorb as much of the UV region up to 400 nm as possible but have a high transmittance in the visible region. For example, Fig. 1 shows that 2-(2′-hydroxy-5′-methylphenyl)benzotriazole has a much greater absorptivity between 300 and 400 nm than 2-hydroxy-4-methoxybenzophenone. Figure 8 compares the transmittance of the two UV absorbers in the visible region and illustrates

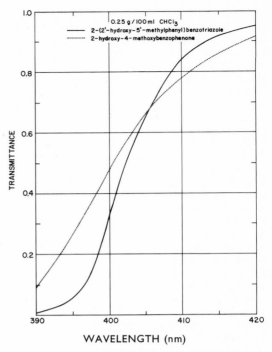

FIG. 8. UV absorbers in visible range.

that although the benzotriazole absorbs more of the UV region, it has a higher transmittance value in the visible range and is therefore less yellow. In other words, the benzotriazole provides better protection (absorbance) and discolors the substrate less.

Applications

UV absorbers may be applied in bulk (in the mass of the polymer), padded on, coated from solutions, or absorbed from baths. The ability of a given light stabilizer to absorb light and inhibit the photodegradation of a given polymer depends on the thickness of the polymer and the concentration (Beer's Law) of the light stabilizer. In very thick and/or opaque specimens, it may be desirable (if mechanically and economically feasible) to concentrate the UV absorber near the surface. This can be accomplished by applying a coating, laminate, or film which contains a relatively high concentration of UV absorber. The greater the surface area of the plastic product, the more critical are the volatility and compatibility properties of the stabilizer. Fibers, films, and coatings not only require high concentrations of UV absorbers to stabilize them effectively, but the volatility and compatibility of the light stabilizer are more critical than in thick sections.

The choice of a UV absorber is determined by both the degree and the type of protection desired. One application may require retention of physical properties only, while another may demand this in addition to good initial color and color retention after exposure. It should be emphasized that UV absorbers are not substitutes for the additives normally used to stabilize polymers. For example, UV stabilized poly(vinyl chloride) still requires HCl acceptors, and UV stabilized polyolefins still require antioxidants.

DAVID A. GORDON

Cross-reference: STABILIZERS, PVC; STABILIZERS, ULTRA-VIOLET; ULTRAVIOLET ABSORBERS.

STABILIZERS, ORGANOTIN

Polyvinyl chloride is subject to deterioration under the influence of heat or light. This deterioration becomes noticeable as a more or less pronounced formation of color, ranging from light yellow through orange and red to deep red, brown and even black, and under extreme conditions also in evolution of hydrogen chloride gas and charring. The deterioration is accelerated by the presence of oxygen and by soluble compounds of transition metals, particularly iron and copper.

The principle of minimizing at least the gross decomposition of polyvinyl chloride by the use of additives in modest concentration was discovered quite early in the commercial history of PVC. Patents for stabilizing PVC with sodium carbonate, basic lead salts, heavy metal soaps, 1,2-epoxides, and substituted phenols were all applied for before 1936. With any of these additives, the processor was able to work the polymer in many ways still used today without evolution of hydrogen chloride, damage to the equipment, or loss of the good mechanical properties of the polymer. However, these additives did little or nothing to prevent *discoloration*; some even accentuated it. Thus, PVC developed as a utilitarian industrial material, especially in Europe during World War II, with appearance considered secondary.

Production of esthetically attractive consumer goods made of PVC became possible with the discovery of the stabilizing properties of organotin compounds, i.e., compounds characterized by the presence of tin-carbon bonding, by Yngve, Quattlebaum, and their colleagues in the Union Carbide laboratories in the late 1930's.

Organotin PVC Stabilizers

Dibutyltin dilaurate (DBTDL) and Dibutyltin maleate (DBTM). These were the first organotin stabilizers to be used commercially and they are still used to some extent.

DBTDL is a liquid soluble in plasticizers and PVC solvents and compatible with the polymer itself. It provides both plasticized and unplasticized PVC materials with excellent clarity and also good light stability (i.e., resistance to discoloration on exposure to sunlight). As a heat stabilizer it is quite effective in minimizing discoloration as long as the plastic is worked at temperatures not much above 300°F (approximately 150°C); this is adequate for plasticized stocks and the "internally plasticized" vinyl chloride-vinyl acetate copolymers processed at relatively slow speeds, but quite insufficient for high-speed calendering and extrusion operations, or for working with unplasticized homopolymers of vinyl chloride. Thus, DBTDL must be considered obsolete. In the majority of articles made of plasticized PVC where clarity is important, DBTDL has been displaced by stabilizer solutions containing barium and cadmium organic salts and organic phosphites; these can be closely adapted by the supplier to the requirements of each application at substantial savings over the costly organotin materials.

In a number of uses where the special effectiveness of the organotin stabilizer is essential, DBTDL is gradually being replaced by the more effective organotin mercaptides and modified maleates.

Dibutyltin maleate is a much more effective heat stabilizer than DBTDL, and also provides excellent light stability and clarity. It is a solid, insoluble in plasticizers, but with proper care can be compounded directly with the polymer.

Clear and very pale sheets of unplasticized PVC can be prepared with this stabilizer, at least in the laboratory. However, several characteristics of DBTM are unfavorable for industrial practice. The stabilizer by itself has a tendency to stick to metal surfaces and, therefore, will give difficulties in calendering operations. Further, if used in a proportion of more than 1%, it will exude and produce a frosting effect.

Organotin Mercaptides. The outstanding effectiveness of this class of organotin stabilizers in PVC was discovered about 1950. These materials are compounds of the general formula $R_nSn(SR')_{4-n}$ where R is an organic group linked to tin through carbon (usually butyl) and n is the number of such groups, and R' is the organic moiety of the mercaptan R'SH used in preparing the stabilizer. Very many individual stabilizers of this class have been investigated and industrial practice has retained primarily the dialkyltin bis-alkyl mercaptides, e.g., dibutyltin bis-*n*-dodecyl-mercaptide, and the dialkyltin derivatives of mercaptocarboxylic esters, e.g., dibutyltin bis-isooctyl thioglycolate and di-*n*-octyltin bis-isooctyl thioglycolate.

These organotin mercaptides include the most powerful stabilizers known for crystal-clear PVC. They match and even surpass the performance of dibutyltin maleate, and are easier to handle and blend, whether dissolved in plasticizer or simply masterbatched with powdered polymer.

Another valuable property of the organotin mercaptide stabilizer is their hydrophobic nature. This means that they are unlikely to be extracted from the plastic by aqueous materials, and also that water will have no tendency to penetrate the plastic and produce cloudiness or "blushing".

Problems encountered with the organo tin mercaptides are relatively modest light stability and the characteristic odor.

Modified Organotin Maleates. Attempts to overcome the difficulties associated with DBTM have led to a series of products based on modification with either an aliphatic alcohol or an aliphatic monocarboxylic acid. These materials are usually liquids that combine the excellent heat and light stabilization of DBTM, the favorable handling and compatibility of the other liquid organotins, and avoid the odor associated with the mercaptides.

The modified maleates, alone or especially when formulated in synergistic combinations (see below) are economical and highly efficient stabilizers for crystal clear rigid PVC, vinyl latices, and terpolymer solutions for metal coating.

Synergistic Combinations Including Organotin Stabilizers. The principle of synergism (i.e., beneficial interaction) between several carefully selected PVC stabilizers has been well established for combinations of heavy metal organic salts (e.g., barium and cadmium, barium and zinc) or combinations of metal soaps with organic auxiliary stabilizers such as phosphites, epoxides, or both together. In the organotin stabilizer field, synergistic combinations are much more recent developments. The following proprietary materials have reached a certain prominence:

(1) Modified maleates with organic additives. These liquids offer excellent heat and light stability in rigid PVC and may be able to replace the mercaptides in a number of applications.

(2) Selected organotin mercaptides with organic additives for very much improved light stability along with the outstanding heat stability characteristic of PVC stabilized with the mercaptides. This development makes possible the utilization of the favorable properties of organotin mercaptides in PVC products for outdoor use.

Solid Organotin Stabilizers. Much of the early development of PVC stabilizers favored liquid materials for ease of incorporation with the polymer and maximum clarity of the final product. More recently, it has been noticed that even small additions of an organic liquid to unmodified PVC have an adverse effect on mechanical properties of the finished product, particularly the impact strength and heat distortion temperature. The resulting search for materials that avoid these drawbacks has yielded some stabilizers of industrial interest:

(1) Dialkyltin salts of mercapto-carboxylic acids, represented by the formula:

$$R_2Sn \begin{cases} S-R' \\ O-CO \end{cases}$$

where R is the organic group linked directly to tin (usually butyl or n-octyl), and R' is the nucleus of the mercapto acid.

This type of stabilizer provides heat stability equaling the best of the liquid organotin mercaptides, and avoids the adverse influence on heat distortion temperature. It is also stated that light stability of PVC with this stabilizer is better than with the liquid mercaptides.

(2) Polymeric butyl thiostannoic acid

$$[(C_4H_9Sn)_2S_3]_n$$

where n is the degree of polymerization, and can range from 1 to about 50.

The primary interest in this stabilizer is the very low degree of toxicity reported for it. The stabilizer has been approved for use in food packaging plastic in several European countries, although not yet in the United States. It is quite a good PVC stabilizer among those already approved for food-packaging use, although not as good as the mercaptide and modified maleate stabilizers in non-food uses.

(3) Stabilizers that show promise in the laboratory but have arrived too recently to judge their acceptance by industry include a solid stabilizer based on the modified maleate structure and a virtually odor-free solid stabilizer based on synergistic mixtures containing mercapto compounds. These stabilizers are recommended for extruded and blow molded articles made of rigid PVC.

Factors Affecting the Selection of a Stabilizer

Processing. It is usually desired that the operation of equipment in which plastic is heated and shaped continue for very long periods without interruption. This sounds like an impossibly severe stability requirement (i.e., days or weeks at processing temperature) until one stops to realize that *a given quantity of polymer* is exposed to processing temperatures for only the short time that it takes to pass through the equipment.

On the other hand, this points up the importance of insuring that no polymer entering the machine is by-passed or trapped within for any appreciable time. This, in turn, is accomplished by careful attention to the rate at which the polymer becomes softened or semi-fluid (i.e., truly plastic) in the equipment. It should be kept in mind that much less work is done by the machinery in moving a quantity of powder or pellets than in moving the same quantity of polymer as a viscous quasi-melt. Ideally, the transition from powder or pellets to polymer melt should occur as gradually and slowly as possible consistent with desired production rates. If fusion occurs too rapidly, the melt will be highly viscous, necessitating high power input to the extruder or other equipment, and the polymer will have a greater tendency to "hang up" in the extruder, and therefore require a greater degree of heat stability than a slower fusing material.

Polymer systems having a wide range of fusion rates can be successfully processed, as long as the type of equipment, nature of the polymer, and the additives used are properly balanced. Thus, rapid fusion may be desirable in an extruder with a short barrel. Slower fusion in a long extruder may be accomplished by adjusting the temperature profile, (i.e., cool through most of the barrel, maximum heat at the die), and the use of polymer with low surface area per unit weight and a stabilizer-lubricant combination that tends to retard fusion.

Available PVC resins vary substantially in their particle surface area, and this information is not always available from the suppliers. Fusion rate and peak viscosity of polymer-stabilizer-lubricant blends can be determined in the laboratory with a sigma-blade mixer in which the torque exerted by the blades is continuously measured and recorded, e.g., the Brabender Plastograph.

The organotin stabilizers vary in their effect on fusion rate of a particular resin and also in the degree to which the fusion rate is modified by lubricants. The following table lists the materials discussed earlier in decreasing order of fusion rate of a given resin:

Stabilizer type	Effect of lubricant
(a) Dibutyltin maleate	Very difficult to lubricate
(b) Butyltin modified maleates	Moderate
(c) Butyltin mercaptocarboxylic salts	Appreciable
(d) Butylthiostannoic acid	Appreciable
(e) Octyltin modified maleates	Appreciable
(f) Octyltin mercaptocarboxylic salts	Appreciable
(g) Synergistic mercapto-type mixture	Appreciable
(h) Dialkyltin alkyl thioglycolates	High
(i) Dialkyltin alkyl mercaptides	Not needed
(j) Dibutyltin dilaurate	Not needed

Synthetic waxes are excellent lubricants with stabilizers (b) through (h). Stearic acid is useful with types (c), (f), (g). Calcium stearate is a good alternate for types (b), (d), (e) and (h).

Mechanical Properties of the Finished Product. Liquid additives in rigid PVC must be used with caution and in minimal amounts because of their depressing effect on heat distortion temperature and impact strength. Where these properties are important and blending polymers which improve impact strength cannot be used, a solid stabilizer type should be selected.

Where impact modifiers (chlorinated polyethylene, ABS polymers) can be used, liquid stabilizers are most economical in terms of the quantity of tin needed. Both thioglycolate and modified maleate types are applicable. For high heat distortion, polyvinylidene chloride is used instead of conventional PVC. This rather recently introduced resin can be stabilized fairly well with dialkyltin alkyl thioglycolates.

Appearance of the Finished Product. Fine clarity and very pale color are qualities of PVC products that can be achieved in working with most of the organotin stabilizers, as well as with barium-cadmium systems. The special value of organotin compounds becomes apparent when these quantities are achieved together with other aspects that are also of great importance, i.e., the preservation of the fine appearance of an article as made for long periods of service life outdoors or in an unusually warm indoor environment. The synergistic combinations based on organotin modified maleates are outstanding for absence of discoloration on outdoor exposure and for minimal color change during long exposure at moderately warm temperature (about 180°F) in the absence of strong light.

Physiological Properties of the Finished Product. The choice of stabilizer may influence odor, taste, and toxicological acceptability of a plastic article. In this area it is dangerous to generalize; stabilizer suppliers should be consulted for recommendation of a stabilizer most suited to each individual plastic article and the way it is to be used. With the wealth of materials now available, stabilizers can be "tailored" to the end use as long as the problems are fully defined.

Some Examples of Products Made with Organotin Stabilizers

Potable Water Pipe	A	B
Resin (homopolymer)	100	85
ABS terpolymer	0	15
Dibutyltin alkylthioglycolate	2–3	1–2
Dibutyltin alkylmercaptide	0	0.75–1.5
Lubricant	0.5–2	0.5–2
Pigment	As required	As required

Clear Rigid Sheets	
Resin (low to medium molecular weight)	100
Dibutyltin modified maleate	2–3
Calcium stearate	0.5–1

High Impact Opaque Sheet	
Resin	85
ABS terpolymer	15
Dibutyltin alkylthioglycolate	2–3
Lubricant	0.5–2
Pigment	As required

Rigid Sheets for Outdoor Use	
Resin (homopolymer)	85–90
Chlorinated polyethylene	15–10
Special organotin mercaptide	3
Special uv absorber	0.5
Lubricant	0.5–1

Top Clarity Plasticized Stock

Resin	100
Plasticizer	15–70
Dibutyltin alkylthioglycolate	0.5–2
Stearic acid	0.25–0.5

Solution for Metal Coating

Vinyl chloride—vinyl acetate copolymer	80
Vinyl chloride-vinyl acetate-maleic acid terpolymer	20
Dibutyltin modified maleate	1–1.5
Aromatic solvent	150
Ketone solvent	250

(All quantities are parts by weight)

OTTO S. KAUDER

STABILIZERS, ULTRAVIOLET

Almost all of the well known plastics are synthetic organic polymers and undergo some degradation upon exposure to sunlight. This degradation is generally caused by the high energy solar radiation occurring in the ultraviolet region of the solar spectrum. The degradative action is largely nullified when a UV inhibitor such as 4-dodecyloxy-2-hydroxybenzophenone is incorporated into the plastic. Note that 4-methoxy-2-hydroxybenzophenone is not too effective in low-density polyethylene although it is suitable for other polymers. Thus it is necessary to correctly match the ultraviolet light inhibitor with the polymer system in order to obtain maximum protection.

A brief review of solar radiation in terms of the relationship between energy and wavelength will allow a better understanding of photochemically induced polymer degradation.

Solar electromagnetic radiation ranges from the extremely destructive gamma rays, which may be only 1.1 billionths of a centimeter long, to the very weak radio waves which may be miles in length. The portion of the spectrum that is visible to man is mainly contained between the wave lengths 380 and 760mμ. The UV range is generally considered to cover from 300–400mμ. The enormously powerful cosmic and gamma rays are screened by the ozone layer which exists as a band 13–15 miles high in the atmosphere. Although the uv radiation from the sun ranges down to 280mμ under ideal conditions, from a practical standpoint it may be considered to be from 300–400mμ. The energy in this region comprises about 5% of the total radiation incident on earth. Local atmospheric conditions such as haze or cloud cover often will reduce the effective radiation in this region to 1% or less.

The usual unit of measurement of exposure is the Langley which is defined as a gram calorie per square centimeter. This unit is a measure of total incident solar radiation and is not indicative of radiation from any portion of the spectrum. This total energy concept is of importance in solar heating and heat-energy considerations but is not fully significant in terms of polymer degradation. For example, polyethylene exposed in Arizona in 1960 showed seven times as much degradation in July as was observed in December, although the total exposure in terms of Langleys was equivalent.

In a photochemical degradation, the energy of activation is supplied by sunlight. Most ordinary chemical reactions involve energies of activation between 15 and 65 kcal per mole. This is equivalent energetically to solar radiation of wave lengths between 1900 and 440mμ. The energies required to break single covalent bonds usually range from 40–90 kcal per mole, which corresponds to solar radiation of wave lengths 710–320mμ.

Thus, it can be seen that the radiation at 300mμ with a relative energy of 95 kcal per mole of quanta, up to the radiation at 400mμ with a relative energy content of 71.5 kcal per mole of quanta, is the solar radiation usually involved in polymer degradation. It is not sufficient to measure total solar radiation as an indication of potential polymer degradation; the type must also be designated.

Other chemical phenomena can be caused by radiation outside the ultraviolet region. For example, in a recent article, it was noted that the fading of dyes could be caused by both radiation in the ultraviolet region and in the visible region (380–760mμ).

Let us now turn to the effect of the solar radiation, particularly the high-energy level radiation observed in the ultraviolet region of the spectrum, upon plastics. The term plastics as used here can be considered to include organic polymers, rubbers, and fibers. The most common effect of the absorption of solar radiation is the conversion of the radiant energy into thermal energy; the object gets warm or hot.

The energy of a quantum of solar radiation may be transformed in several different ways summarized as follows:

(1) *Heat*. The temperature of the absorbing system is raised.

(2) *Dissociation*. The molecule undergoes a chemical breakdown into smaller parts.

(3) *Excited molecule*. The molecule retains the absorbed energy until it can be used chemically by combination with some other molecule, or by transferring its energy to another molecule which, in turn, utilizes the energy to produce chemical change or to increase the translational energy of still other molecules.

(4) *Dissociation and excitation*. One of the excited fragments is produced in a photo dissociation.

(5) *Ionization*. An electron is driven out of the molecule leaving a positive-charged ion.

(6) *Fluorescence*. The excited molecule re-radiates part of the energy at a different wave length as the electron returns to a lower energy level. If there is a time lag in this reradiation, the phenomenum is known as phosphorescence.

(7) *Physical interaction*. The quantum of radiation is not absorbed and readmitted, but, rather, it imparts some of its energy to an electron or to atomic or molecular vibrations or rotations as observed in the Raman effect.

Degradation of plastics is initiated primarily through dissociation of the polymer molecule under the impact of the high-energy solar radiation. For example, with polyolefins this dissociation, through the cleavage a carbon-carbon or a carbon-hydrogen single bond, results in the formation of alkyl radicals, hydrogen atoms, and biradicals. Subsequent reaction of the cleavage particles which exhibit a high order of reactivity leads to the formation of hydrogen gas, olefins, radical recombination, and cross-linking. The alkyl radicals initiated by the solar radiation in the presence of oxygen are propagated through the formation of a peroxy radical with the subsequent formation of a hydroperoxide particle.

The decomposition of the hydroperoxide is a complex process and a wide variety of products has been observed. The primary mode of decomposition is probably the rupture of the oxygen-oxygen bond. The oxy radical is more liable to undergo scission reactions than the parent radical with resultant degradation of the polymer.

Thus, initially the solar radiation causes radical formation and embrittlement due to cross-linking, but subsequent reactions cause degradation of the polymer or plastic. Physical properties such as tensile strength, percent elongation and impact strength are drastically reduced. Colored degradation products are often developed. Surface crazing is also an indication that uv-induced degradation is occurring.

We have seen that the high-energy solar radiation when absorbed by polymers initiates the necessary photochemical reactions to cause breakdown of the polymer through two methods: (1) High-energy-induced dissociation, and (2) photocatalyzed-oxidative degradation. The role of the ultraviolet light inhibitor is to absorb the high-energy solar radiation and dissipate it harmlessly in such a manner that neither of these degradative phenomena occur.

The basic requirements of a good UV inhibitor are as follows:

(1) It must absorb strongly in the 300–370mμ range; some which absorb at or near 400mμ are good inhibitors but impart a yellow color to the plastic.

(2) The absorber itself must exhibit long-term stability toward ultra-violet light.

(3) The absorber must dissipate the solar energy in such a manner as to cause no degradation or color development in the plastic.

(4) It must be compatible with the plastic to be stabilized during processing and upon exposure.

(5) It must be relatively nontoxic.

(6) It must impart little or no color to the plastic material at the normal-use level.

The majority of the commercially-available ultraviolet light inhibitors are listed below. Most are derivatives of 2-hydroxybenzophenones or compounds such as benzoates and salicylates which can rearrange to form 2-hydroxybenzophenone derivatives. In addition to the 2-hydroxybenzophenones, the substituted (2'-hydroxyalkylphenyl) benzotriazoles and the substituted acrylonitriles are also important. Metal chelate complexes have also been developed for use in polypropylene as combination uv inhibitors and as sites for the retention of dyes.

The ultraviolet light inhibitors are used in plastics at the 0.25%–2.0% level. In coatings where very thin films (1–2 mils) of plastic are often encountered, the UV inhibitor level may be as high as 2–10%.

TABLE 1. COMMERCIALLY AVAILABLE ULTRAVIOLET LIGHT INHIBITORS.

Benzophenones:
4-Methoxy-2-hydroxybenzophenone
4-Octyloxy-2-hydroxybenzophenone
4-Dodecyloxy-2-hydroxybenzophenone
2,4-Dihydroxybenzophenone
4-Methoxy-2,2'-dihydroxybenzophenone
4-Octyloxy-2,2'-dihydroxybenzophenone
4-Methoxy-2-hydroxy-5-carboxybenzophenone
4-Methoxy-2-hydroxy-5-sulfobenzophenone trihydrate
2,4-Dibenzoylresorcinol
5-Chloro-2-hydroxybenzophenone
4,4'-Dimethoxy-2,2'-dihydroxybenzophenone
2,2',4,4'-Tetrahydroxybenzophenone
4-Methoxy-2-hydroxybenzophenone-5-sulfonic acid
Sodium-4,4'-dimethoxy-2,2'-dimethoxy-5-sulfobenzophenone
Benzotriazoles:
2(2'-Hydroxy-5'-methylphenyl)benzotriazole
Alkylated (2'-hydroxy-5'-phenyl)benzotriazoles
Salicylates:
Phenyl salicylate
4-*t*-Butylphenyl salicylate
p-Octylphenyl salicylate
Others:
Resorcinol monobenzoate
Substituted acrylonitriles
Metal organic complexes

The key to the effectiveness of the 2-hydroxy-benzophenones is apparently associated with the strong hydrogen bonding in the chelate structure which is formed. One way in which the solar-radiation energy may be dissipated is as follows:

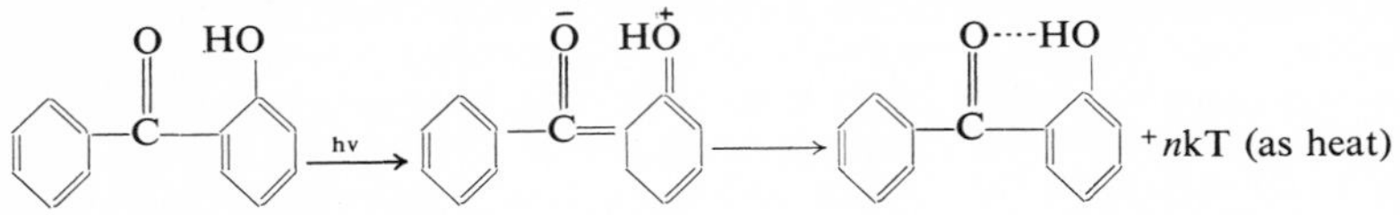

An internal ionic resonance structure resulting from photochemical excitation may be formed with the absorption of a quantum (hv) of solar radiation. In this structure the hydrogen atom would be expected to be shared more equally between the two oxygen atoms. The resonance energy of this system could feasibly be redistributed among the various vibrational modes in the molecule in returning to the nonionic stage and eventually be transferred harmlessly to the polymer as heat. After the energy transfer, the benzophenone would return to the original chelate structure and thus be receptive to the absorption of further quanta of solar radiation.

Because the energy from solar radiation is ultimately converted to heat and because photochemical catalyzed oxidative degradation is a factor in the stability of plastics, it can readily be seen that the use of an antioxidant in conjunction with the ultraviolet light inhibitor is generally indicated. Some compounds; such as organic phosphites, epoxy plasticizers, and organotin compounds; enhance the weathering characteristics of certain polymers without absorbing uv light and thus might be termed secondary absorbers.

Plastics properly formulated with carbon black exhibit the maximum resistance to solar degradation. Other pigments require specific evaluations. In many cases it is desirable to include a uv stabilizer and an antioxidant in the pigmented system. The resistance of plastic materials to solar radiation is most accurately determined by exterior exposure testing. Both surface appearance and physical properties of the plastic such as elongation, strength, and impact resistance are affected by weathering. Generally, weathering is a complex process involving the high energy effect of sunlight, of oxidation, and of the accumulative effect of humidity, wind and rain. Outdoor testing generally is carried out at a location which combines extreme weather conditions with a high level of solar radiation. In the United States, exposures in Florida, which involve high humidity, and exposures in Arizona, with its low humidity, are ofted used. In addition, it is usually desirable to expose in industrial environments.

Accelerated weathering test equipment is designed to accelerate the rate of aging. It attempts to produce the same physical effects as normal outdoor exposure but in considerably less time. Two widely-used devices are the "Fade-Ometer" and "Weather-Ometer" (products of Atlas Electric Devices Company). The "Weather-Ometer" uses a carbon arc with intermittent water spray; the "Fade-Ometer," an arc only. Accelerated aging is often valuable for initial screening and usually a correlation of results between outdoor and indoor testing can be established. An S-1 sunlamp is also valuable for conducting accelerated-aging tests.

Most plastics have good aging characteristics for indoor use. Neither incandescent nor fluorescent lighting degrades polymers appreciably under ordinary conditions. However, glass-filtered sunlight contains some damaging UV radiation, depending upon the severity of the climate. Germicidal UV lamps commonly used in appliances can be harmful to component plastic parts; the radiation is relatively intense and the extent of damage encountered will depend on type, size, and location of the bulb and also the type of plastic chosen.

Skin sunscreens differ from ultraviolet light stabilizers in their absorption characteristics. The erythemal radiation causing sunburning of the skin occurs between 290 and 320mμ; the radiation beyond 320mμ promotes tanning. Consequently, sunscreeners generally absorb below 330mμ and transmit beyond that point. The families of compounds most commonly used as sunscreening agents are paraaminobenzoates, anthranilates, salicylates, cinnamates, pyrrones, benzimidazoles, carbazoles, naphtholsulfonates, and quinine disulfate. Ordinary plate glass screens about 50% of the solar ultraviolet radiation and screens enough of the erythemal radiation to prevent sunburning.

In the plastics industry uv inhibitors are used to prepare formulations specifically designed for use in outdoor exposures. Physically the inhibitor is added by:

(1) Extrusion compounding.

(2) Mixing on a two- or three-roll mill.

(3) Banbury mixing.

(4) Forming a solution in a component of the system such as a plasticizer.

(5) Dry blending.

Weather-resistant formulas are offered by manufacturers, processors, and formulators. The concentrations used vary from 0.1–4% with the 0.5 to 1.0% range being the most common. With prices for the uv inhibitors ranging from less than $1 per lb to as much as $10 per lb, it is difficult to make a general statement concerning cost. Usually the cost of the uv inhibitor will be from one cent to six cents per pound of polymer. In any event the additional cost is more than justified since the ultimate consumer will receive a quality product with improved properties and an increased outdoor service life.

Cross-reference: STABILIZERS, LIGHT; ULTRAVIOLET ABSORBERS.

STABILIZERS, VINYL

The thermoplastic polymers and copolymers of polyvinyl chloride are unstable in the presence of heat, light and oxygen. They, therefore, require stabilizers in order to withstand the elevated temperatures of processing and the deleterious effects of weathering. The degradation of these polymers and copolymers, when unstabliized, is readily evident by the evolution of hydrogen chloride and by the formation of color bodies at elevated temperatures. The incorporation of stabilizers into polyvinyl chloride (PVC) results in the immediate, striking retardation of such decomposition.

Theory of Polyvinyl Chloride Degradation

There are numerous theories as to why PVC degrades. Basically, the reason lies within the polyvinyl chloride structure itself, and involves initiation, propagation and termination phases:

$$—CHCl—CH_2—CHCl—CH_2—CHCl—CH_2—$$

or,

$$–CH_2—CHCl—CHCl—CH_2—CH_2—CHCl—CHCl–$$

The liberation of hydrogen chloride (dehydrochlorination) will result in the formation of double bonds (unsaturation) which, through allyl activation of adjacent chlorines, will result, possibly through a "zipper-like" mechanism, in a polyene structure. The degradation products have structures analogous to those of the carotenoids, the familiar vegetable pigmentation, and possibly to those of diphenyl polyenes. These products produce the typical yellow, orange and red discoloration of degraded polyvinyl chloride, and offer a relatively simple means of determining the extent of PVC degradation at high temperatures (e.g., 300–400°F). These polyene structures also may result in cross-linking, chain scission, and carbonyl group formation, causing severe changes in the physical properties.

The decomposition of PVC may be considered a chain reaction, initiated, at specific points in the molecule, by heat, giving small amounts of hydrogen chloride which, in the opinion of some researchers, in turn catalyzes further degradation. The mechanism of PVC degradation is further complexed by the formation of free radicals, epoxides, and hydroperoxides, among others.

The photodegradation of polyvinyl chloride has been the subject of much study of quantum theory, photochemical effects, and energy absorption. While thermal stabilizers for PVC may also serve as light stabilizers, it is usually necessary to use ultraviolet light screening agents, in combination with the thermal stabilizers, where outdoor exposure is involved in the use of the finished product.

Function of Stabilizers

There is general agreement that good stabilizer systems must have an acid acceptor component which will form insoluble or slightly soluble chlorides with the hydrogen chloride at the point of elimination, thus reducing the catalytic action of the hydrogen chloride.

Other stabilizer components such as UV absorbers, antioxidants, and dienes are used to control the effects of ultraviolet light, oxidation, chain scission, etc.

Free radical initiators, or dienophiles, by virtue of addition to double bonds, inhibit the degradation effects of unsaturation within the PVC structure. The action of oxygen on PVC may be controlled by anti-oxidants, such as hindered phenolics. Anti-oxidants retard oxygen from reacting with the PVC molecule, or form stable complex bodies (deactivating inhibitors).

Although the emphasis in PVC stabilization is placed upon the metallic cation as an acid acceptor and, at times, as oxidation catalysts to destroy chromophoric groups, there is evidence that the anion constituent of the metallic compound also has an important function in PVC stabilization. The anion may, through an esterifying displacement of chlorine atoms in the PVC, form a more stable structure which, by virtue of carboxylate groups along the PVC chain, may block the "zipper-like" hydrogen chloride elimination.

Evaluation of Stabilizers

While a study of PVC degradation and the action of stabilizers on a research or academic level may involve hydrogen chloride liberation, molecular structure changes, infra-red and ultra-violet absorption spectra, and radio-active isotopes, the plant or technical development man is mainly concerned with the prevention of PVC discoloration and the retention of mechanical properties.

However, even before a detailed review of stabilizer activity is carried out, the following questions should be answered:

(1) Is the stabilizer or its decomposition

products compatible with the PVC system to be stabilized so that there will be no exudation or decrease in PVC stabilizing activity?

(2) Will the stabilizer, or decomposition products thereof, produce color bodies in PVC?

(3) Will the stabilizer volatilize at processing temperatures or produce objectionable odors?

(4) Is it economical?

(5) Are toxicity, water absorption, electrical properties, and sulfide staining of significant importance?

The stabilizer should be evaluated in the specific PVC system in which it would be utilized, including plasticizers, lubricants, fillers, epoxies, dyes, fungicides, bacteriastats, etc. Additives may inter-react with each other and/or with the PVC and affect the stabilizing activity of the stabilizer, thus making it necessary to evaluate stabilizer activity in the specific PVC system because of variations in the stability of different PVC resins (e.g., because of retained catalysts and compounds used during their preparation), plasticizers, etc.

A relatively simple method for the evaluation of stabilizers is to mill from 1–5% stabilizer into the PVC resin system, and then subject test pieces of the milled sheets to oven temperatures of 325–400°F (again duplicating as closely as possible PVC processing temperatures), for a period of 2 hours or more, removing test samples every 15 min (or 5 min for zinc system stabilizers). Discoloration (yellow, orange, red, black) will be an indication of degradation. More extensive studies could involve mechanical property measurements, embrittlement, clarity, etc.

In some instances, PVC stabilizer activity will change with age. It is advisable to make shelf-life studies, alone and combined with specific PVC resin systems.

Heat Stabilizers

Inorganic. Inorganic compounds such as litharge and basic lead carbonates were once extensively used for stabilizing PVC. Even today, for the stabilization of PVC electrical insulation and floor coverings, inorganic compounds such as tribasic lead sulphate monohydrate, basic lead silicates, and basic lead silicate sulphate are of commercial importance. Dibasic lead phosphite is of value for stabilizing PVC which will be subjected to the effects of weathering.

Among this class of stabilizers, lead orthosilicate is of value when transparent PVC films are desired. Transparency is obtained by the use of silica gel (of value also because of its absorption of fatty acid produced in the PVC system) to adjust the index of refraction.

The use of various alkali phosphates in the processing of PVC emulsion polymers also has an effect on stabilization.

Organic Compounds. Some organic compounds such as lead and cadmium soaps and organotins may be used by themselves as stabilizers. However, the synergistic value of multiple metal components favors the use of mixed metal compound systems, especially in the case of barium, zinc, and calcium.

Barium-Cadmium. Barium substituted phenolics, octoates, stearates, laurates, ricinoleates, etc., in combination with cadmium octoates, stearates, laurates, ricinoleates, etc., are economical, efficient stabilizers for PVC. A wide range of stabilizing activity is obtainable by varying the ratio of barium to cadmium in the stabilizer system. Normally, the barium content, on a per cent weight basis, is at a higher level than the cadmium content.

The powdered barium and cadmium soaps, especially in combination with polyols such as pentaerythritol, alpha methyl glucoside or anhydroenneaheptitol, are of value for the stabilization of rigid and flexible PVC. Organic phosphites, especially the solid ester or polymeric types, enhance the stabilizing activity.

Should there be a plating problem with Ba-Cd powdered systems, this may be remedied by increasing the cadmium soap content, by using less polar metallic soaps such as zinc soaps, or by substituting a metallic octoate for the stearate or laurate. Normally, the highly electropositive barium produces the most difficulty with plating. This is to be expected because plating is a phenomenon whereby rolls become coated with stabilizer components which have an affinity for metal.

Lubricating problems may arise with powdered barium and cadmium systems. Over-lubrication may result in surface defects and blisters in the processed PVC, while under-lubrication may result in PVC adhesion to the metal rolls. Since long-chain fatty anions have high lubricating value whereas short-chain, branched-chain, and aromatic anions have lower lubricating value, the proper lubricating balance may be obtained by varying the acidic constituents of the metallic compound.

Commercially, both powdered and liquid barium-cadmium systems are used, with liquid systems being the more versatile. A variety of acidic constituents may be employed to prepare the metallic satls: 2-ethyl hexoic acid, the newer neo-acids, substituted phenolics, cyclic acids, aromatic acids. Barium lends itself well to the formation of highly basic, solvent soluble complexes.

In addition, the PVC stabilizing activity of the liquid barium-cadmium systems may be enhanced by a variety of synergistic additives—organic phosphites (chelating agents) such as triisooctyl phosphite and diphenyldecyl phosphite; epoxy derivatives such as epoxidized soyabean oil; anti-oxidants such as butylated hydroxy toluene, bisphenol A, and other hindered phenolics alone or in combination with compounds such as dialkylthiodipropionates; esters such as organic borates, silicates, and titanates; anhydrides such as chlorendic anhydride and "nadic methyl anhydride."

Organic phosphites may have antioxidant activity. They also retard the deleterious action of bariumi and cadmium chlorides on PVC. Organic phosphotes may, in some instances, improve the clarity of PVC films.

Epoxy derivatives are effective thermal and light stabilizers, especially in combination with barium-cadmium systems. Epoxides are capable of reacting with hydrogen chloride. However, since there are possibilities of interreactions among epoxide and stabilizer and PVC components, the stabilizing activity of, for example, epoxidized soyabean oil and alkyl epoxystearates, is probably much more complex than simple HCl addition.

Zinc. Zinc soaps and organic salts degrade PVC and are not used alone. However, they are often used in combination with barium salts and barium-cadmium salts to synergistically improve PVC stabilizing activity; and in the latter system, to increase sulfide stain resistance. The percentage of zinc in PVC stabilizer systems must be closely controlled, otherwise severe degradation of PVC may result under prolonged processing at elevated temperatures.

Just as with barium-cadmium systems, a diversity of additives may be employed to increase the PVC stabilizing activity of the zinc systems. With the zinc systems, the results are rarely as vivid as those obtained with barium-cadmium systems.

Calcium. Calcium stearate and other calcium salts are not extensively used for PVC stabilization. They are often combined with zinc soaps to obtain F.D.A. approved nontoxic stabilizers. They have good lubricating properties and are of value in rigid PVC.

Lead. The lead compound stabilizers are very useful for electrical insulation. Dibasic lead stearate is preferred to the neutral stearate because of its high reactive lead availability and low stearic acid liberation in PVC. Lead compounds are synergistic in PVC stabilizing activity with zinc, cadmium, and tin compounds. (*See* Stabilizers: Lead, page 442.)

Tin. Tin salts, such as the stearate, are little used for PVC stabilization. The true organotin compounds are much preferred.

The organotin compounds, in general, produce stabilized PVC with excellent clarity, good heat resistance, and fair light resistance. They are among the most expensive stabilizers on a cost per pound basis, although this is somewhat compensated for by using lower amounts per weight PVC.

There are a variety of organotin stabilizers available. The more common commercial products are dibutyltin-R_1 types such as dibutyl tin dilaurate, dibutyltin maleate, and bibutyltin diacetate. The octyltin compounds, because of lower toxicity than the butyltin types, have been considered for food packaging.

Several organotin mercaptides, mercaptoamides, mercaptobenzothiazols, xanthates, sulphonamides, alcoholates, and dithiocarbamates have PVC stabilizing activity.

Synergistic combinations of organotin compounds with lead compounds and cadmium compounds are used commercially.

Light Stabilizers

While heat stabilizers based on barium-cadmium and zinc compounds offer good light stabilization, it is necessary in some cases to include light stabilizers in combination with the heat stabilizers, where severe exposure may be involved in the end use.

Phenyl salicylate was one of the first UV absorbers employed. However, its high volatility limited its use. Magnesium, lead calcium strontium, and tin salicylates are used.

The benzophenones are effective light stabilizers, as are also umbelliferones, hydroquinones, triazoles, and stilbenes.

Opacifying agents hinder the passage of light rays and are, therefore, of value—carbon black, titanium dioxide, clays, carbonates, silicas.

Colorless, transparent ultraviolet screening agents are commercially available.

The use of light stabilizers will become increasingly important as the large potential market for rigid vinyl in the construction industry develops.

Special Stabilizer Problems

Plastisol and Organosol Stabilization. The stabilization of plastisols (colloidal dispersions of PVC in plasticizer and organic solvent) is somewhat more complex than that of rigid or flexible PVC because factors such as air release and rheological properties must be considered. Because of the myriad of plastisol and organosol formulations used commercially, it is necessary that stabilizers be evaluated in the specific formulations.

In general, the types of stabilizer systems previously discussed are effective in plastisol and organosol systems. However, now the effect of the stabilizer on viscosity and air release must be considered. The stabilizer should not cause a marked increase in the viscosity of the plastisol or organosol.

The speed of deaeration may be altered by the stabilizer. Surface active agents are of value to coalesce small bubbles into large ones, and thereby instigate a rise to the surface of entrapped air.

Foamed Vinyl. The stabilization of PVC foam produced mechanically by means of an inert gas may be carried out with the typical stabilizers previously discussed. However, the influence of the stabilizer on cell structure and gas retention must be taken into consideration. Standard stabilizers may be modified to obtain a surfactant effect.

Problems unique to the stabilization of foamed PVC are encountered when chemical blowing agents (e.g., azobisformamide) are employed. The stabilizers may accelerate or retard the decomposition of the blowing agent, or they may have no effect at all. The stabilizers may produce closed cell or open cell structures. In view of these facts, it is a practical necessity to evaluate stabilizers in the precise PVC formulation being expanded.

Vinyl-Asbestos. When considering the use of asbestos in vinyl-asbestos formulations, it must be realized that these hydrated magnesium silicates may contain appreciable amounts of iron oxides. The simple magnesium silicate, chrysotile, may contain from 0.0–11.0% iron oxides. The complex magnesium iron silicate, anthophyllite, may have iron oxide contents of 3–12%. The familiar blue asbestos, sodium iron silicate, known as crocidolite, may have iron oxides contents as high as 40%.

Chrysotile is the most widely used asbestos. Amosite, crocidolite, and tremolite are less extensively used in plastics.

In the past, lead salicylate was used extensively for the stabilization of vinyl-asbestos. However, in order to obtain increased sulfide stain resistance and improved heat stability, barium-zinc compounds were employed. Later developments favored the use of polyols in vinyl-asbestos stabilizers. Although polyols did improve the heat resistance of vinyl-asbestos, they had a serious handicap because of low water resistance, even when used with barium, magnesium, and zinc salts.

In addition to high water resistance, the main problem with vinyl-asbestos stabilization is to inactivate the iron oxides in the asbestos, taking also into consideration that vinyl-asbestos may contain a high percentage of other materials such as calcium carbonate, clays, and silicas.

Among the latest developments in the stabilization of vinyl-asbestos has been the use of organic nitrogen compounds such as dicyandiamide and melamine. With these stabilizers, improved heat stability and water resistance have been obtained. However, the heat stability and water resistance properties of these organic nitrogen compounds will vary in different vinyl-asbestos formulations. Stabilizers for vinyl-asbestos should be studied in the actual vinylasbestos formulation being considered for an end use.

ROBERT E. LALLY
FREDERICK J. IHDE, JR.

STRIPPING AGENTS

It is sometimes desirable to remove a plastic coating or embedding compound in order to recover the component to which the plastic was applied. In other cases, it is desirable to employ a plastic film or coating as a temporary barrier capable of easy subsequent removal. In still other cases, it is desirable to soften the plastic so that it may be welded to itself. In order to determine which of the available practical methods is most suitable, it is first necessary to determine the type of plastic involved.

However, in view of the variety of plastic products on the market, it is not generally possible, without extensive testing, to make this determination on an unlabeled plastic. If the brand name is known, it is best to consult the manufacturer or distributor for recommendations. In the absence of identification, the most likely method for removing the plastic is with one of the proprietary strippers which are available through consumer and industrial outlets. Should this method fail, or be unsuited, mechanical abrasion or heat may be employed.

Generally speaking, paints and varnishes may be removed more or less easily with the proprietary chemical strippers. Films may be softened to the point where they may be rinsed or scraped off within a very few minutes. When larger sections of plastic are involved, as for example when stripping a plastic embedment, the difficulties are compounded. Long soak times may be required, and it may be necessary to employ heat to assist the chemical action.

To some degree, the problems involved may be considered to fall into three broad classes: those encountered with thermoplastic compounds, those encountered with thermosetting compounds, and those encountered with various films.

Thermoplastic Compounds

Some thermoplastic resins will melt substantially below their decomposition temperature. Most widely known and used of this type are polyethylene and polypropylene, both of which are quite resistant to chemical attack. These thermoplastics may be removed by exposure to a temperature above their melting points, usually in the range of 200–250°F. The plastic will then be soft enough to permit scraping or cutting away. By applying the elevated temperature to a limited area, sufficient flow may be obtained to permit spot-welding. The plastic is heated to its softening point and simultaneously joined under pressure. This heat sealing operation is quite commonly used on polyethylene films, and the resultant plastic weld is equal in strength to the remainder of the plastic.

Many thermoplastic compounds, while capable of some flow under heat and pressure, cannot be melted to even moderate viscosities. In this class, "Teflon" and "Kel-F" in particular are extremely resistant to the action of chemical strippers and other means must be used for their removal.

Most of the other, less inert thermoplastics which cannot be melted respond well to attack by oxygen-containing solvents, such as cyclohexanone or ketones. Chlorinated solvents, such as methylene chloride and trichloroethylene, are usually even more effective and do not provide the flammability hazards associated with the other species. Solutions of acetic acid, or acetic acid in combination with solvents are also often used.

Some of the thermoplastics respond specifically to one solvent and not to a closely related one. Polystyrene, for example, is readily attacked by toluene but is rather resistant to attack by xylene. Many of the thermoplastics may be dissolved in their monomers. Thus, either solvents or, preferably where applicable, the parent monomers may be used to cold weld the plastics as well as to strip them. Cold welding is accomplished by spotting the plastic with the liquid monomer or solvent and then joining the surfaces under pressure. Pressure is retained, usually for overnight, and the new joint, properly made, should be as strong as the parent plastic.

Thermosetting Compounds

Once having attained the thermoset state, the thermosetting plastics will not remelt nor permanently flow under heat and pressure. They cannot, therefore, be hot- or cold-welded as can some of the thermoplastics and must be adhesively joined.

The common classes of thermosetting compounds are the silicones, polyesters, phenolics, polyurethanes, and epoxies. As a general rule, the higher the heat resistance of the specific system and the more rigid it is, the more resistant it will be to attack by chemical strippers. For example, silicone, while providing exceptional thermal stability, is actually a synthetic rubber and thus is readily attacked by aromatic and chlorinated solvents which cause excessive swelling and facilitate mechanical removal. On the other hand, a room-temperature-curing polyester, suited to service at temperatures no higher than 250°F, is comparatively rigid, and overall, within its temperature range, will provide

greater resistance than the silicone to the action of strippers. From this it follows that the thermosetting plastic will be much more readily attacked by strippers at and above the temperature at which it becomes somewhat flexible or semi-rigid and correspondingly, below those temperatures it will be much more resistant to the action of chemical strippers.

The polyesters, phenolics, and epoxies are quite difficult to strip by chemical means, the difficulty bearing a direct relationship to the specific formulation. The polyesters and phenolics are perhaps somewhat more sensitive to bases and less sensitive to acids than the epoxies. However, in view of the number of commercial formulations involved, and the differences between them, such generalizations are hazardous at best.

The best of the strippers for the thermosetting compounds are based on chlorinated solvents, usually methylene dichloride in combination with a small amount of an acid or a base and perhaps in blend with other solvents such as chlorobenzene. Generally, to strip a molded phenolic component, for example, requires a soak of 16 hr or more at room temperature, depending on the thickness of plastic involved and the specific formulation and fillers used. Many formulations, of course, are virtually inert to the action of strippers.

In cases where chemical strippers are unsatisfactory, it is possible to remove the plastic through the application of a direct flame or of high heat. The thermosetting plastics will char and carbonize at temperatures in the 800–1000°F range and after relatively brief exposures to these temperatures may be manually removed rather easily. Epoxy-encapsulated motors are stripped for rewind by the burn-out technique. In this case, the amount of plastic involved may be as much as 20 lb or more and adequate ventilation should be provided through suitable exhausts, since the fumes are acrid and irritating.

Removal of Films

Films requiring removal may be of the permanent or temporary type.

Temporary Films. Generally temporary films are selected with a view to their easy removability. They are most frequently used as release agents for cast, laminated, or molded plastics. A release film of poly (vinyl alcohol), when practical to the application, is virtually ideal, since it may be removed with water and detergent and brushing. The most intractable of the temporary films are those based on silicone oils and greases. These will, whereas for example sintered "Teflon" films will not, transfer to the part being produced from the coated master. Should subsequent removal be required in order to facilitate bonding to the finished article, the only really satisfactory method is mechanical abrasion.

Permanent Films. Permanent films of paints, varnishes or lacquers may be removed by a variety of chemical strippers depending on whether the films are thermoplastic or thermosetting, and within each class, depending on its specific type and formulation. Among the more resistant of the organic films are those based on the thermosetting epoxy resins and suitable strippers are available for their removal: formulation of both liquid (immersion type) and paste (brush-on type) strippers are described in US Patent 3,138,556 (1964). The strippers described are based on methylene chloride and hypophosphorous acid. A specific paint remover formulation, suitable for use on epoxy and alkyd coatings, consists of the following, parts by weight:

Methylene dichloride	67.85
m-Cresol	12.0
90% formic acid	8
Dodecylbenzenesulfonic acid	6.5
Water	5
Dibutyl thiourea	0.65

The stripper is described in US Department Commerce OTS publication AD 602 923N.

Although chemical strippers are useful, particularly on items of wooden furniture, they are inherently somewhat messy, time consuming, and expensive. It is often more convenient and economical to remove paint films by sandblasting, sanding, or wire brushing. Removal in this fashion is especially well suited to metal structures, since the sanding operation automatically prepares the surface to accept a recoat. Sanding is also especially suited to stucco, concrete, and cement surfaces.

Alternatively, the paint may be burned off with a blow torch. The burn-and-scrape technique is not normally too satisfactory for metals, since carbonaceous deposits may remain to interfere with adhesion. The technique, however, if carefully done, is quite useful for removing old paint from frame residential buildings.

HENRY LEE
KRIS NEVILLE

STYRENE

Styrene is the monomer used in the manufacture of polystyrene plastics, as well as GRS synthetic rubber. Well over three billion pounds of styrene are being produced each year, with a good share of it going into polystyrenes of a great variety, both the homopolymers and copolymers.

The starting materials for the production of styrene are ethylene and benzene, both of which are products obtained from petroleum sources, although benzene is also available from coal tar distillation. These are first combined to produce ethylbenzene as the intermediate, as shown in the equations below. Benzene and ethylene are fed continuously into the bottom of the alkylating tower at essentially atmospheric pressure, in a moles ratio of 1:0.6, while granular anhydrous aluminum chloride is fed at a constant rate to the top of the tower. The reaction is kept at about 100°C by cooling coils in the tower. The effluent from the top of the tower consists of ethylbenzene, unreacted benzene and a small amount of ethylene which is vented from the coolers, where the temperature is reduced to about 50°C. After settling in storage tanks to remove any entrained catalyst, the liquid is first neutralized and then fed to a series of continuous distilling towers for the separation of benzene, ethylbenzene and diethylbenzenes and final rectification for a 99.9% pure ethylbenzene product. The catalyst coming from the bottom of the alkylating tower is recycled back to the top for reuse. Occasionally it is removed and sent to a high temperature dealkylator to decompose the aluminum chloride complex and regenerate the catalyst. Some ethylbenzene is also obtained from the alkyl benzenes, produced along with benzene, toluene and xylenes in the aromatization of petroleum cracked gases.

The final step in the production of styrene is the dehydrogenation of ethylbenzene at pyrolytic temperatures, thus forming the phenylethylene, or styrene as shown in the equations below. The pure ethylbenzene is heated and mixed with steam in a weight ratio of 1:3 and the mixture fed to a preheater and then to the tubular dehydrogenator reactor containing a fixed bed catalyst consisting of oxides of zinc, chromium, iron and magnesium impregnated on alumina pellets. The reactor is maintained at 600-650°C by the use of superheated steam (700°C) in the shell of the reactor. The reaction products leaving the top of the reactor are cooled by the incoming ethylbenzene-steam mixture in the shell of the heat exchanger and further cooled in a condenser to yield styrene, unreacted ethylbenzene and water as the condensate and hydrogen, carbon monoxide and methane gases which are vented. The organic layer is separated from the water layer, the latter also stripped of any products and the crude products consisting of a 1:2 styrene-ethylbenzene mixture containing traces of benzene, toluene, phenylacetylene and tars, sent to stripping and refining towers for a continuous fractionation and purification. The ethylbenzene is recycled to the dehydrogenator; inhibitors are added to the initial styrene fraction to prevent polymerization during the final rectification and storage of the monomer. Overall yields of 86% styrene are obtained, based on the benzene and ethylene consumed; with respective yields of 95% and 90% for the alkylation and dealkylation steps.

a) $C_6H_6 + CH_2\!\!=\!\!CH_2 \xrightarrow[\text{AlCl3cat.}]{100°C} C_6H_5CH_2CH_3$
(benzene) (ethylene) (ethylbenzene)

b) Petroleum Cracked Gases C_6H_6 (benzene)
$\xrightarrow{\text{Aromaticization}}$ $C_6H_5CH_3$ (toluene)
$C_6H_4(CH_3)_2$ (xylenes)
$C_6H_5CH_2CH_3$ (ethyl-benzene)

c) $C_6H_5CH_2CH_3 +$
(ethylbenzene)

$\xrightarrow[\text{Zn, Cr, Fe oxides}]{\text{steam } 600-650°C} C_6H_5CH\!\!=\!\!CH_2 + H_2$
(styrene)

Since 74% by weight of styrene is benzene and this is the more expensive of the two raw materials, the economics of styrene is closely related to availability and costs of benzene, and is one of the largest outlets for benzene. The physical properties of styrene are shown in Table 1.

TABLE 1. PHYSICAL PROPERTIES OF STYRENE.

Synonyms	phenylethylene, vinylbenzene
Appearance	sweet smelling colorless liquid
Molecular weight	101.14
Boiling point(atm.)	145.2°C
Melting Point	−30.6°C
Density at 20°C	0.908
Flash Point	88°F
Explosive range	1.1 to 6,1% by volume
Toxicity	Tolerable limits 200 ppm
	Fatal 10,000 ppm

Solubility in water at 20°C = 0.001%
Solubility in most organic solvents = miscible in all proportions

Another use for styrene is in polyester resins. Here it serves with the maleate polyesters as a comonomer for cross-linking to form the styrenated polyesters. It is frequently used as a solvent for polyester resins, since its removal prior to utilization of the resin is not essential, and that which does not evaporate during application or curing is polymerized along with the polyester resin, imparting a certain degree of resiliency and toughness to the otherwise brittle resin.

The development of styrene plastics began before World War II, but was greatly accelerated by the availability of styrene in large quantities following the war, with many production units, formerly used for the synthetic rubber program, offering styrene at a low cost for production of plastic. Its use in plastics has steadily grown until, at present, it has reached the billion pound class, third only to polyethylene and polyvinyl chloride. About 40% of the monomer in 1965 was used for production of homopolystyrene resins, with another 20% going into a variety of copolymers in combination with acrylonitrile, butadiene, methylstyrene, polyesters and acrylic esters as comonomers. The balance, 40%, was consumed in the production of GRS synthetic rubbers and rubber latexes for paints. The pattern of use of polystyrene resins shows most of them being molded in a great number of plastic articles, everything from plastic containers to refrigerator door levers. The molded products made from styrene have been predominantly novelties and toys.

Although the homopolymers constitute the majority of the products made from styrene, there is a gradual increase in the consumption of styrene for the production of impact type copolymers, such as the ABS terpolymer containing acrylonitrile and butadiene copolymerized with styrene. Many applications are being found for these copolymers in the replacement of metals in housings, handles, automobile parts and even automobile bodies. They account for much of the recent growth of the polystyrene resin production.

JAMES M. CHURCH

SUCROSE BENZOATE

Sucrose benzoate is virtually insoluble in water and in aliphatic hydrocarbons; sparingly soluble in alcohols and lower glycols; and completely miscible in aromatic solvents. Specific examples follow, showing solubility of sucrose benzoate in g per 100 g of saturated solution at indicated temperature: water, less than 0.01 (67°C); heptane, less than 0.02 (67°C); methyl alcohol, 4.7 (25°C), 13.6 (67°C); ethyl alcohol, 2.3 (25°C). Solvents in which sucrose benzoate is completely miscible include acetic acid, acetone, benzene, butyl acetate, carbon tetrachloride, dibutyl phthalate, diethylene glycol dibenzoate, diisobutyl ketone, diethyl ether, dimethyl formamide, dioxane, dipropylene glycol dibenzoate, dioctyl phthalate, ethyl acetate, ethylene dichloride, isophorone, methyl benzoate, methyl isobutyl ketone, methyl ethyl ketone, methylene dichloride, polyethylene glycol, toluene, tricresyl phosphate, and xylene.

While sucrose benzoate is not compatible with polyethylene, polypropylene, or polyisobutylene, it is compatible with a broad range of polymeric materials which include the acrylics (methyl methacrylate and acrylic ester copolymers), alkyd resins (including phenolic modified and styrenated), amino resins (melamine-formaldehyde, urea-formaldehyde, butylated urea-formaldehyde and butylated benzoguanamine-formaldehyde), cellulosics (nitrocellulose, cellulose acetate-butyrate; ethyl cellulose to 20%), chlorinated rubber (67% chlorine), polyester resins, styrenes, and vinyls (polyvinyl chloride and polyvinyl acetate; limited compatibility with polyvinylidine chloride and polyvinyl butyral). Sucrose benzoate has limited compatibility to 10% level with boiled linseed oil and castor oil, and is not compatible with material such as carnuba wax, Japan wax, mineral oil, and paraffin wax.

Stability

Of the 8 hydroxyl groups originally present on the sucrose molecule, approximately 7 have been esterified with benzoate groups, with the remaining hydroxyl group being essentially nonreactive. While sucrose benzoate has good stability, it is subject to thermal decomposition and hydrolysis similar to other organic esters, as shown below:

Thermal Decomposition. Prolonged heating of sucrose benzoate at elevated temperatures causes increase in acidity and darkening. For example, heating for 8 hrs at 175°C in an aluminum container causes gradual color development from around 60 APHA to around 5–10 Gardner, and causes an increase in acidity from around 0.05 to around 0.35mg. KOH/g. Addition of small amounts of oxirane oxygen containing compounds including epoxy esters and glycidyl phenyl ether imparts improved heat stability to this ester. At temperatures below 150°C, corresponding color and acidity development require a several-fold longer heating time.

Hydrolysis. Sucrose benzoate is resistant to aqueous hydrolysis under mildly acid or alkaline conditions. For example, in 96 hrs at 100°C, no hydrolysis was observed in water, 2.3% hydrolyzed in a 5% solution of sodium carbonate, and 0.6% hydrolyzed in a 5% solution of hydrochloric acid.

Ultraviolet Light. A supported film of sucrose benzoate was prepared from a toluene solution and exposed for 5000 hrs. in an Atlas Fade-O-Meter at around 140°F. There was no color change. Infrared spectrophotometric curves were prepared before and after exposure, and identical curves indicated the probability that no chemical breakdown occurred. The transmittance of sucrose benzoate has been measured in the ultraviolet region between 200 and 400 mμ wavelengths. A major absorption band centers at around 230 mμ. At around 300 mμ, sucrose benzoate approaches 100% transmittance, and this transmittance extends throughout the visible wavelength.

History

Sucrose benzoate was introduced as a developmental chemical in early 1962 at cost of approximately 58¢ per lb. By 1965, this product was available in substantial semi-works quantities, and priced at around 40¢ per lb. A powdered grade (essentially passing a 60 mesh screen) was made available in 1964 selling for 5¢ per lb more than the regular flake material. Sucrose benzoate is manufactured and sold by Velsicol Chemical Corporation, Chattanooga, Tennessee.

TABLE 1. PRODUCT DESCRIPTION.

Form and appearance	noncrystalline solid, flake
Softening point (ASTM—E—28—51—T)	95–101°
Color (ASTM—D—268—48) 50% solution in water white toluene	30 APHA maximum
Ash (ASTM—D—856—49)	0.01% maximum
Specific gravity, 25°/25°C	1.25
Refractive index, 25°C	1.577
Acid number mg KOH/g	less than 0.1
Standard Container is 40 gal fiber drum, net weight 200 lb	

Toxicity

Sucrose benzoate is not classified as a primary skin irritant or as an eye irritant, based on tests on rabbits using terms and procedures outlined in the Regulations (Federal Register, August 12, 1961 et. seq.) under the Federal Hazardous Labeling Act. The product manufacturer reports that this material has been handled in laboratory and in substantial semi-works quantities for over six years. During this lengthy period of time, with normal product handling and exposure, there has been no evidence seen of any toxicity, skin irritation, or allergic reaction. The use of sucrose benzoate as a component in food-packaging adhesives is listed by the United States Food & Drug Administration (CFR pp. 121.2520). Based on the above information, sucrose benzoate would be regarded neither as a "highly toxic substance" nor as a "toxic substance," within the definition provided by the code of Federal Regulations, Title 21, Food & Drugs, sub-chapter D, "Hazardous Substances," pp. 191.1

Uses of Sucrose Benzoate

Sucrose benzoate is a water-clear, UV stable, hard resin modifier. Because of its hard brittle character, it is invariably used in combination with liquid plasticizers such as dioctyl phthalate. Its major areas of use are in the formulation of lacquers based on nitrocellulose, cellulose acetate butyrate, acrylics, and vinyls. Additional uses or areas of interest include gloss additive for alkyd enamels, modification of paper transparentizing systems, modifier in vinyl plastics, and as a dry cleaning textile size. The technical reasons sucrose benzoate is of interest in lacquer systems include:

(1) Unusual clarity and lack of color.

(2) Excellent UV stability. This stability carries over into properties of formulated film. For example, unmodified nitrocellulose will turn yellow in around 40 hrs in an Atlas Fade-O-Meter —films discussed below consisting of nitrocellulose, sucrose benzoate, and DOP do not yellow in over 500 hr under similar exposure conditions.

(3) Low solution viscosity permits higher solids concentration at normal working viscosities.

(4) Excellent depth or fullness of gloss.

(5) Can be formulated to provide good hardness and print resistance, along with good flexibility and cold-check resistance.

(6) Excellent adhesion properties in suitably plasticized systems.

(7) Improved alcohol spot resistance and excellent water spot resistance.

(8) Because of broad compatibility and solubility characteristics, sucrose benzoate can serve as a "mutual compatibility" agent in systems which are of marginal compatibility.

Nitrocellulose Lacquers

In nitrocellulose lacquers, a blend of around 60% sucrose benzoate and 40% DOP plasticizer serves as a modifier comparable in both properties and cost to conventional coconut alkyds. The sucrose benzoate/DOP combination provides advantages of lower solution viscosity, better clarity, possibly better UV yellowing resistance, and usually better alcohol spot resistance. The sucrose benzoate/DOP blend has minor disadvantages in comparison with the coconut alkyds in that the lacquer tends to dry a little more slowly, the dry film has slightly reduced toughness and mar resistance, and the 120°F print resistance is not quite as good in comparing formulations made with the same viscosity grade of nitrocellulose.

Because Sucrose Benzoate is hard and brittle, its use in lacquers requires increased plasticizer level. Several types of ester plasticizers were tested, and dioctyl phthalate was found entirely suitable for the properties and conditions tested. A recommended starting formulation is: 10 parts nitrocellulose $\frac{1}{2}$-second viscosity, 9 parts Sucrose Benzoate, 6 parts DOP plasticizer, and solvent system consisting of 40% n-butyl acetate, 25% xylene, 25% toluene, and 10% ethyl/isopropyl alcohol.

Different proportions of Sucrose Benzoate and DOP permit formulation of a broad range of hardness and flexibility characteristics in a finished lacquer film; however, when formulating for a specific set of properties, the ratio of sucrose benzoate and plasticizer is critical. If a more active plasticizer, such as dibutyl phthalate, is used, then a different modifier blend is indicated. A blend of around 66% sucrose benzoate and 34% dibutyl phthalate is similar in behavior to the blend 60% sucrose benzoate 40% DOP. Because these lacquer films have higher than "normal" ester plasticizer content at a given film hardness, the question of how well this much plasticizer stays in the film must be considered. Films aged several years have not shown evidence of embrittlement or noticeable plasticizer loss. Also, fresh films tested by the "Naugahyde" lacquer lift test show no tendency to lift or to physically gain or lose

plasticizer. All present evidence indicates that the nitrocellulose-sucrose benzoate system effectively "ties in" ester plasticizers at these formulation levels presumably due to the highly esterified structure of the sucrose benzoate which also has a rather high molecular weight of around 1100.

Cellulose Acetate Butyrate Lacquers

Sucrose benzoate in CAB systems provides water-white clarity, excellent UV stability, full compatibility, and ability to serve as a hardening resin. These features are required of a modifier to permit full use of the advantages of excellent clarity and excellent UV stability of these premium polymers.

Sucrose benzoate is fully compatible with several types of CAB, extending from 17%–48% combined butyryl content (EAB-171-2, Half-Second Butyrate, and EAB-500-1, products of Eastman Chemical Products, Inc.). The Half-Second Butyrate was used in evaluating modifier systems.

Addition of sucrose benzoate (without plasticizer) to Half-Second Butyrate permits increased film hardness, as shown below:

Composition of film		Sward hardness
% Half-Second Butyrate	% Sucrose Benzoate	1.3 mil film on glass
100	0	48
84	16	59
67	33	63
50	50	55
40	60	51

Half-Second Butyrate modified with sucrose benzoate (only) results in films unsuitable for conventional wood or metal coatings, because they are of low flexibility and brittle. A blend of around 75% Sucrose benzoate and 25% DOP provides good film properties at levels of around 1 : 1 modification. As with nitrocellulose, if a more active plasticizer such as dibutyl phthalate is used, then the modifier blend should contain a little less plasticizer and a little more sucrose benzoate.

Polyvinyl Chloride-Acetate Solution Coatings

The advantages sucrose benzoate/DOP modification provides solution vinyl systems coatings include (1) reduced solution viscosity (2) increased gloss (3) increased surface hardness (4) improved resistance to organic acids and to alkaline materials and (5) improvement in pigment wetting and dispersion rates. The addition of sucrose benzoate/DOP at increasingly higher levels results in lower film flexibility and less toughness, so this modifier combination is not recommended where ultimate values of both film toughness and flexibility are required.

Sucrose benzoate/DOP modified films showing a good balance of properties have been prepared with polyvinyl chloride-acetate copolymers including bakelite VYHH-1, VMCH, and VAGH (products of Union Carbide Corporation, Plastics Division).

Acrylic Lacquers

With acrylics, Sucrose Benzoate serves as lower cost extender which does not detract from good clarity and UV stability with advantages of (1) reduced solution viscosity (2) increased gloss (3) improved pigment wetting and dispersion rates. Disadvantages of this modifier are slightly longer drying time and less flexibility, noting that increased plasticizer level causes both improved flexibility and greater tendency to show print at elevated temperatures.

ROBERT C. HICKERSON

SURFACTANTS

The term "surfactant" is a general term applied to surface active agents which includes wetting agents, detergents, emulsifiers, dispersants, foaming agents, penetrating agents and spreaders.

Surfactants have varied uses in the field of plastics. Many such uses have been described in the literature. They may be used as dispersants in milling, to improve the clarity of castings, as mold release agents, as antistatic agents, as cell control agents for foams, etc.

A surfactant is a chemical compound which affects the surface forces of a liquid or a solid in relation to other liquids, gases or solids.

Ordinary soap which is the sodium salts of fatty acids, chain length 11 to 17 hydrocarbons, would be an example:

$$CH_3—CH_2—CH_2—CH_2—CH_2—CH_2—CH_2—$$

$$CH_2—CH_2—CH_2—CH_2—\overset{\overset{O}{\|}}{C}—ONa$$

When a soap is added to water, it lowers the surface tension, i.e., it reduces the interfacial tension between water and air. The resulting solution foams readily and has other characteristics of soap solutions. In addition, the soap promotes wetting of solids and the mixing of immiscible liquids etc.

Types of Surfactants

Surfactants are compounds in which one portion of each molecule is hydrophilic (water-miscible) and another portion is lipophilic (oil-miscible) or hydrophobic (water-immiscible). The hydrophilic part of the molecule may be a carboxylate, sulfate, sulfonate, alcohol, or alcohol-ether. The lipophilic portion of the molecule

may be a long hydrocarbon chain as in fatty acids, or a straight, branched, or cyclic hydrocarbon of petroleum or an aromatic hydrocarbon containing alkyl side chains.

Surfactants may be classified as anionic, cationic, amphoteric and nonionic.

Anionic. The anionics bear a negative charge and migrate toward the anode or positive pole while in solution. These are the oldest and best known of surfactants.

$$\left[R—\overset{\overset{O}{\|}}{C}—O\right]^{-} M^{+}$$

Soap

$$\left[R—O—\overset{\overset{O}{\|}}{\underset{\underset{O}{\|}}{S}}—O\right]^{-} M^{+}$$

Alkyl sulfate

$$\left[R—\overset{\overset{O}{\|}}{\underset{\underset{O}{\|}}{S}}—O\right]^{-} M^{+}$$

Alkyl sulfonate

Cationic. The cationic group is the opposite of an anionic group. Its surface activity is due to the presence of a long-chain oil soluble cation. They will neutralize the charges of an anionic surfactant and "break" the emulsion. Cationic surfactants possess germicidal, anti-corrosive, anti-static properties. The following is the structure of a cationic surfactant:

$$\left[R—\overset{\overset{A_1}{|}}{\underset{\underset{A_3}{|}}{N}}—A_2\right] X^{-}$$

"R" represents a hydrophobic group such as a long-chain aliphatic or aromatic group, "X" represents a negative ion such as Cl^{-}, Br^{-}, I^{-} or other monovalent ions, and A_1, A_2 and A_3 represent hydrogen, alkyl/aryl or heterocyclic groups.

Amphoteric. Amphoteric or ampholytic surfactants contain both a positive and a negative charge. These charges may neutralize each other so that at a given pH the surfactant behaves as if

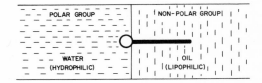

FIG. 1. Emulsion interface.

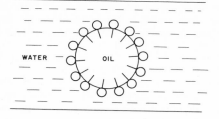

FIG. 2. Oil in water emulsion.

it were nonionic. These surfactants usually exhibit cationic properties in acid solutions and anionic properties in alkaline solutions.

Nonionic. Nonionic surfactants depend chiefly upon hydroxyl groups and ether linkages to create the hydrophilic action.

$$\begin{matrix} O \\ \| \\ RC\!-\!O\!-\!(CH_2)n(OH)n \end{matrix}$$

$$\begin{matrix} O \\ \| \\ RC\!-\!O(C_2H_4)nC_2H_4OH \end{matrix}$$

These compounds achieve solubility by being hydrated in water solutions. When the temperature is raised, the forces of hydration are reduced, and there is a precipitation of the surfactant lowering its effectiveness. This shows up as a turbidity or cloud. This may lead to erratic results when processing produces a higher temperature in the paint.

TABLE 1. CLASSIFICATION OF SURFACTANTS.

I. Anionics
  A. Carboxylic Acid
    (1) Fatty acid, rosin and naphthenic acid soaps
  B. Sulfuric Acid Esters
    (1) Alkyl sulfates, alcohols and olefins
    (2) Sulfated oils and esters
    (3) Sulfated amides and ethers
  C. Sulfonic Acids
    (1) Alkyl sulfonates
    (2) Alkyl-aryl sulfonates
    (3) Sulfonated amides and esters
  D. Miscellaneous—Phosphates, sulfonates, etc.
II. Cationics
  A. Simple Amine Salts
  B. Quaternary Ammonium Salts
  C. Amino Amides and Amidazolines
III. Amphoteric
  A. Amino and Carboxyl Groups
  B. Amino and Sulfuric Ester or Sulfonic Groups
IV. Nonionics
  A. Alkyl, Alkyl-aryl Ethers and Thioethers
  B. Esters and Amides

Dispersing

Surfactants are frequently used for aiding in the dispersion or incorporation of finely divided solids into fluid or plastic matrix. They have been used to aid the incorporation of antioxidants into synthetic elastomers. The viscosity of plastisol and organosol compositions may be lowered by the additions of certain types of nonionic surfactants such as the sorbitol esters, the polyethenoxy ethers of long-chain fatty alcohols and long-chain phenols. These materials facilitate the application of plastisols and organosols in thick layers to base materials such as textile fabrics, paper and metal foil.

Amine soaps, aryl sulfonates and nonionic surfactants have been used to aid the milling of vinyl-type resins. The surfactants are applied to the resins by slurrying the resin in its granular form in a 1–3% aqueous solution of the surfactant.

Mold Release

Surfactants have been used to improve the clarity of coatings and give better mold release.

Anionic wetting agents such as the sulfosuccinates, the fatty alkyl sulfates and the alkyl aryl sulfonates have been added to styrene casting resins in order to eliminate adhesion of the resins to the wall of the mold. Anionic surfactants such as the sulfated fatty alcohols have also been used in the mold release compositions based on polymeric glycols.

Foaming

Foaming and foam production are of very great importance in the production of low density plastic and elastomeric materials such as foam plastics and foamed or sponge rubber. These materials are generally made by whipping air into the polymer formulation before curing or including in the formulation a material which will release a gas such as carbon dioxide or nitrogen during the curing operation. The usual type of foaming surfactant is seldom used in the production of foamed plastics, although they are of some help when the composition contains fibrous reinforcing materials such as glass fibers

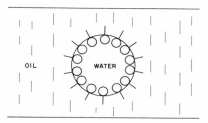

FIG. 3. Water in oil emulsion.

or cellulosic pulp fibers. Surfactants of the oil-soluble type such as metal soaps and mahogony sulfonates have been used to disperse blowing agents of the inorganic carbonate type in sponge rubber compositions. These materials by suspending and dispersing the carbonate help to promote uniformity of bubble size and bubble distribution in the final sponge rubber product.

Chemical Reactions

In the alkaline hydrolysis of esters the primary function of a surfactant appears to be to increase the area of the oil-water interface rather than to exert any specific chemical catalytic activity. Both acid and basic catalytic processes for esters have been described which depend on the presence of a surfactant to promote the hydrolytic reaction. Quaternary amine bases are used as the catalyst for hydrolysing polyvinyl acetate to polyvinyl alcohol. Also used are the alkyl benzene sulfonic acid and the alkyl phosphoric acids.

Antistatic Treatments

Static electricity has always been a problem for the plastics processor or the plastics user since plastic materials acquire electrostatic charges when subjected to friction or contact with other materials. The electrostatic charge causes the plastics to attract dust and lint, causing a cleaning problem, to stick together making finishing and packaging troublesome and even to induce electric shocks in handling. Antistatic agents are sometimes added to the plastics but are usually applied as coatings to the surface. The ideal antistatic agent should:

(1) Eliminate static electricity.
(2) Be stable at elevated temperatures and not color or add odor to the final product.
(3) Be noncorrosive to processing equipment.
(4) Not adversely affect the properties of the plastic.
(5) Be easy to apply.
(6) Be economical.
(7) Be effective in a wide range of plastics.
(8) Be relatively nontoxic to insure F.D.A. approval for food packaging.

Antistatic agents are effective by being electro-chemically charged thus dissipating static electricity by conduction, by being hydroscopic thus depositing an invisible coating of moisture from the atmosphere onto the surface of the plastic which dissipates static electricity by conduction or by acting as a lubricant which will reduce friction and thereby reduce static electricity build-up.

Antistatic agents which have achieved some success are nonionic surfactants and cationic surfactants such as quaternary amines.

CHARLES R. MARTENS

T

"TEFLON" SPONGE POWDERS

Porous or sponge "Teflon" is produced in a variety of pore sizes and void content for use in filtration, electronic, and mechanical applications. First introduced in 1956, the product has been under development and experimental production for many years. Originally sponge "Teflon" was available only in the form of 12 in. square sheets, but powders are now marketed which, when fabricated according to the processing techniques outlined below, give a variety of pore sizes and void contents so that the manufacturer can produce his own sponge "Teflon" to specifications.

The standard products are available in pore sizes ranging from 5–50μ and void contents of from 5–55%. These properties can be varied independently. The anticipated physical and electrical properties of the most common grades are summarized in Table 1, based on sheets produced by Liquid Nitrogen Processing Corporation over a period of several years.

Processing of Sponge Powders. The powder is pressed into a sheet at approximately 500 psi and then carefully placed on a flat screen tray and baked according to the cycle shown in Fig. 1.

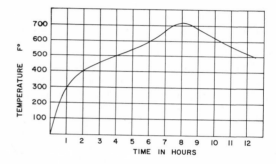

FIG. 1. Baking cycle for sponge powders.

TABLE 1. PHYSICAL AND ELECTRICAL PROPERTIES OF LNP POROUS "TEFLON".

Grade[a]	5–55	18–40	25–55	30–40	35–55	40–40	50–55
Pore size[b]—maximum	10	35	90	60	120	145	150
(Microns)—average	5	18	25	30	35	40	50
% Voids	55	40	55	40	55	40	55
Density	0.97	1.29	0.97	1.29	0.97	1.29	0.97
Hardness Durometer D Scale		31	16				
Tensile strength, psi	260	600	140	740	330	560	250
Flow rate water, 10 psi	7–8	4	9	3	9	3	19
g/m/sq ft, 25 psi	12–15	8	15	7	16	6	24
Flow rate air, 7 psi (CFM/ sq ft)		175	400				
Dielectric Properties:							
1 KC DC		1.53	1.40				
DF		<.0001	<.0001				
5000 MC DC			1.5				
Specific heat			.280				
Thermal conductivity × 10⁻⁴							
cal/cm/cm²/sec/°C			4.5				
Thermal expansion × 10⁻⁵			14.0				
in./in./°C			(40°–290°C)				
Heat of distortion—66 psi			236°F				

[a]The first figure in the grade number refers to the pore size in microns. The second figure refers to the degree of porosity in per cent.
[b]Values are initial product passing through a freshly installed sheet at 2 psi pressure. Values at higher pressure are proportionately smaller due to compression of sheet.

"TEFLON" SPONGE POWDERS

TABLE. 2. DIELECTRIC LOSS PROPERTIES OF LNP POROUS "TEFLON".

Grade	18–40	25–55
Dielectric constant, 1 KC —As received	1.53	1.40
—Bone dry, 24 hr	1.52	1.38
—Moist, 24 hr	1.51	1.36
—Water immersion, 24 hr	1.50	1.46
Dissipation factor, 1 KC—As received	<.0001	<.0001
—Bone dry, 24 hr	<.001	<.001
—Moist, 24 hr	<.001	<.001
—Water immersion, 24 hr	<.001	<.001

Care should be taken in handling at this stage because the preform has very little strength. The cycle shown is satisfactory for sheets from 1/8–1 in. thick. The filler used in the molding powders will explode if not processed according to the cycle shown in the figure. In any case the oven should be tested with an explosion meter* as the first material is run. Shrinkage averages about 15%, depending on the thickness of the sheet.

Applications of Sponge "Teflon"

Filtration. For filtering applications, sponge "Teflon" offers a medium that is completely inert to all chemicals, solvents, bacteria, fungus, and oxidizing agents except metallic sodium in liquid ammonia, molten sodium and fluorine at high temperatures and pressures, and a few fluorinated organic solvents. The inertness is maintained over a temperature range of −400 to +500°F. The pores appear as a uniform integrated network of interconnected air cells. Maximum and average-size particles that will pass through the filter are indicated in Table 1. At higher pressures the maximum and average particle sizes that will pass are proportionally smaller due to the compression of the sponge and consequent reduction of pore size. Because of the inertness of the material, the filter can be cleaned using almost any desired means such as solvents, acids, heat, etc.

Electrical. Sponge Teflon made from powders offers many possibilities in extremely low dielectric-loss applications which are unaffected even at conditions of high humidity. The data in Table 2 illustrate the dielectric-loss properties after various conditioning treatments including drying, controlled humidity, and water immersion. The properties may vary for the larger pore sizes. The unique combination of low dielectric loss and uniformity at various humidities and temperatures indicates its use in ultra high-frequency equipment such as waveguides and radomes. As insulation on coaxial cables or as coaxial spacers it provides low loss yet allows breathing and sparging of the annular free space.

Mechanical. Sponge Teflon made from powders

*Such as that available from Mine Safety Appliances, Pittsburgh, Pa.

offers possibilities in acoustical or thermal insulation and vibration absorption. As a bearing the porous structure combines well with lubricating oils and cooling air or liquids.

J. TRACY O'ROURKE

THIXOTROPIC MATERIALS

The terms thixotropy, pseudoplasticity, false body and shear thinning have in the past frequently been used interchangeably. Until recently thixotropy has been the one term used to describe all materials which exhibit reduced viscosity when subjected to a shearing action. However, rheologists now tend to reserve the term thixotropy to describe materials which remain at a reduced viscosity for a measurable length of time after shearing action ceases.

The other three terms are correctly used interchangeably to describe materials that exhibit reduced viscosity while being subjected to shear but which immediately revert to the original consistency when the shearing action is stopped. False body is probably the most used term but rheologists prefer to use shear thinning.

Both false bodied and thixotropic materials require a measurable shear force before any flow will take place. Consequently the viscosity at zero shear rate is infinite and the materials act as solids until a shear force sufficient to cause flow is applied. However, a decreased viscosity as the shear rate decreases is uniquely a thixotropic characteristic. The change in viscosity as a function of shear rate for a false bodied material is the same for both increasing and decreasing shear rates.

The practical characteristics of both types of materials are best represented by using a brush applied coating as an example. Both thixotropy and false body can provide a relatively high yield value to provide good suspension of fillers and good brush loading. Both will reduce in consistency to allow the brush to slide easily. However, after the coating has been applied, false body will cause an immediate regeneration of viscosity and brush marks will not flow together. Thixotropic materials will remain at a reduced consistency for a short time and permit excellent flow and leveling. However, regeneration of consistency after a short time is effective in preventing excessive flow and sagging.

False body and thixotropy are usually both in evidence at the same time and materials which exhibit one property to the exclusion of the other are extremely rare. Consequently the materials as described below can all be classified as thixotropic modifiers even though some may be much more of a false bodied nature than thixotropic.

Types and Properties

The most commonly used materials for imparting thixotropy to plastics are highly absorptive silicas. Where more false body than thixotropy is desired and clarity is not of importance, the most economical modifier would be diatomaceous silica. Where good clarity or thixotropy is needed, the proper choice would be a synthetic silica aerogel or a pyrogenic silica. These materials are characterized by a particle structure that is very much like a sponge. This provides high surface area and absorptivity so that 2–5% of a high surface area silica, aerogel or pyrogenic, is usually sufficient to impart a significant resistance to flow in a plastic material such as an unsaturated polyester or a liquid epoxy resin.

Other filler materials such as mica, talc and china clay are also frequently used because they will impart some thixotropy but their prime function is that of a filler. Consequently this discussion will not include inorganic materials other than silica. Some typical properties of thixotropic silicas are given in Table 1.

A second class of thixotropic materials is mineral-organic. This includes beatonite clays treated with fatty quaternary ammonium chloride compounds and metallic soaps such as aluminum stearate, zinc stearate and lead stearate. Other fatty acids are also used to form soaps such as octoates and palmitates. Only brief mention is made of this class of materials as they are more often used in greases and paints and are only occasionally used in plastics. These materials produce gels that are more false bodied than thixotropic.

Another class of compounds used to impart thixotropy is the relatively pure organic materials. These include thermoplastic polyamide resins and hydrogenated castor oil as well as a number of derivatives of hydrogenated castor oil. The compounds based on hydrogenated castor oil are usually marketed as proprietary additives and very little is revealed about their chemical make-up or the method in which they function. They are used primarily to provide sag resistance in coatings and are incorporated as part of the pigment dispersing operation.

Much more has been revealed about the use of polyamides as thixotropic agents. Many of the techniques and the chemical background are revealed in U.S. Patents 2,663,649 and 2,861,048. The polyamide modified thixotropic materials are characterized by a high degree of thixotropy with minimal false body. They are the only perfectly transparent thixotropic modifiers. The metal soaps as mentioned earlier may sometimes be fully transparent but their gels tend to have more false body than thixotropy. Table 2 gives the properties of three polyamide resins frequently used to impart thixotropy.

Procedures for Incorporating Thixotropic Modifiers

Thixotropic modifiers are incorporated by one of the following procedures:

(A) Grinding or dispersing to completely wet all particles and essentially absorb the liquid phase into a structure composed of particles of the thixotropic modifier. The materials used in this manner are diatomaceous silica, silica aerogels, pyrogenic silica, the bentonite clays treated with fatty quaternary ammonium chloride complexes and the hydrogenated castor oil based materials. The soaps such as aluminum stearate, zinc stearate and lead stearate may also be incorporated in this manner.

(B) Heating to dissolve a material, followed by cooling to form a gel. The materials incorporated by this process are metallic soaps (primarily aluminum), and some polyamides.

(C) Cooking in a material to chemically alter the thixotropic additive and thereby make an incompatible material compatible with the

TABLE 1. TYPICAL PROPERTIES OF COMMERCIALLY AVAILABLE SILICAS.

	Diatomaceous silica	Silica aerogel	Pyrogenic silica
Physical state	Fluffy powder	Like snowflakes	Powdery snowflake
Apparent density	Approximately 15 lb/ft^3	2.5–6 lb/ft^3	2.2–4.0 lb/ft^3
Silica, %	86–92	90–96	99.9+
Specific gravity	2.65	2.1	2.2
Surface area	—	130–280 sq m/g	225 ± 25 sq m/g
Particle size	1–10μ	0.01–0.02μ	0.015–0.020μ
Color	White to creamy	White	White

TABLE 2. TYPICAL PROPERTIES OF THIXOTROPIC POLYAMIDE MODIFIERS.

	Polyamide "A"	Polyamide "B"	Polyamide "C"
Physical state	Tough transport solid	Frangible solid	Transparent semi-solid
Specific gravity	0.98	0.96	1.00
Color	Light amber	Light amber	Light amber
Melting temperature	112°C	115°C	100°C

resinous system being modified. This procedure is commonly used to incorporate polyamide resins into alkyds, epoxy esters, drying oils and some oleoresinous varnishes. The cooking schedule may vary from 30 minutes to several hours and the reaction temperature may vary from 190°C to as high as 275°C.

Applications for Thixotropic Modifiers

Thixotropic modifiers are nearly always used to provide resistance to flow. Solvent based coatings can depend upon the evaporation of solvent to increase the viscosity of a material and thereby hold the material in place until cured. When very thick applications or solvent free materials must be held in place it is necessary to make use of a thixotropic modifier. Silica is commonly used in 100% solids, epoxy compositions, vinyl plastisols, and polyesters. The silica based materials retain their properties at elevated temperatures and are useful for high temperature cure cycles. Gels based on the organic materials and metallic soaps will melt at elevated temperatures. Consequently they are useful only for moderate temperature cure cycles. Thixotropic modifiers are usually incorporated into organic coatings and may be incorporated into troweling compositions to provide good slip and sag resistance.

Safety Precautions

None of the commonly used thixotropic additives are considered toxic under normal conditions of usage. The silica materials should not be inhaled any more than necessary as they irritate the lungs and prolonged exposure could result in retention of silica in the lungs. The metallic soaps are toxic to the extent that the metallic portion is toxic. Consequently lead soaps and zinc soaps should not be used in situations where they might be ingested.

W. E. SHACKELFORD

TITANIUM DIOXIDE PIGMENT

The predominance of titanium dioxide as the white pigment for plastics is the result mainly of its unsurpassed whitening, lightening or brightening, and opacifying power. This strength is attributable to unusually high refractive index coupled with fine particle size and relatively low specific gravity. Among colorless substances the average refractive index of titanium dioxide is the highest known.

TABLE 1. REFRACTIVE INDEX AND SPECIFIC GRAVITY OF WHITE OPACIFYING SUBSTANCES.

	Mean refractive index, n_D	Specific gravity
Titanium dioxide (rutile)[a]	2.76	4.2
Titanium dioxide (anatase)[a]	2.52	3.9
Zirconium oxide	2.2–2.4	5.68
Zinc sulfide	2.37	4.0
Antimony oxide	2.09–2.29	5.75
Zinc oxide	1.99–2.02	5.65

[a] Crystal structure.

The commanding position of titanium pigments is also the result of universality of application because of physical and chemical stability. Titanium dioxide (TiO_2) is the most stable combination of titanium and oxygen. Titanium peroxide, TiO_3, is highly unstable, as are also the lower oxides, TiO and Ti_2O_3, which oxidize readily. All lower oxides are dark in color, whereas TiO_2 in finely divided form is white.

Physical stability of titanium dioxide is indicated by its high melting point of 1830°C, and its relative invariability when heated to very high temperatures. As a result, titanium dioxide pigments are unaffected by temperatures encountered in most plastic compositions. Although at very high temperatures the color of titanium dioxide may turn yellowish, it usually reverts to white on cooling. Under extremely high vacuum at extremely high temperatures some loss of oxygen and consequent darkening may occur, but this can be eliminated and brightness restored by heating in air.

Chemical stability is indicated by extreme insolubility. Insoluble in water, dilute inorganic acids, organic acids, dilute alkalis and practically any other compound at ordinary temperatures and pressure, titanium dioxide may be brought into solution only by hot concentrated sulfuric acid or hydrofluoric acid; or it may be fused with sodium or potassium carbonate or sodium bisulfate, the melt being dissolved in dilute acid.

Titanium dioxide is unaffected by gases ordinarily encountered in the atmosphere, such as hydrogen sulfide and sulfur oxides, and it is difficultly reducible.

Ordinarily, very high temperatures are required to effect reaction of TiO_2 with other oxides or with reducing agents. Under unusual conditions that may cause reduction of TiO_2 and darkening, such as may occur on exposure to ultraviolet of melamine and urea plastic paper laminates, a special type of titanium dioxide pigment is stabilized to overcome this effect.

Because of its physical stability and lack of chemical reactivity, titanium dioxide pigment is compatible with virtually all of the resins available —natural rubber and natural resins, the synthetics from ABS and acrylics, to cellulosics, phenolics, polyesters, polystyrene, polyolefines, urethanes, vinyls and others.

Currently, two processes for the manufacture of titanium dioxide pigments are being practiced —the sulfate and the chloride. In one, titanium mineral, usually ilmenite concentrate ($FeTiO_3$), is dissolved in sulfuric acid to yield a solution of titanium and iron sulfates from which hydrous titanium dioxide is precipitated by boiling, and thereafter converted to titanium dioxide; in the other, the titanium mineral, usually rutile ($85–95\%$ TiO_2), is reacted with chlorine to form titanium tetrachloride which is converted to titanium dioxide. Through the sulfate process both anatase and rutile titanium dioxide pigments are readily produced, whereas the chloride process generally yields only the rutile crystal structure.

It must be remembered that the name _rutile_, when applied to titanium dioxide pigment, simply indicates crystal structure and does not mean that the pigment has been derived from the mineral rutile. Although refined and ground mineral rutile has been suggested as a pigment, the product is not sufficiently white, and its tinting strength is too low to permit classification as a titanium dioxide pigment, because thus far, suitably small particle size has not been attained.

The white titanium dioxide pigments owe their value to their properties. The manufacturing process is simply a route to these properties, and no single process will necessarily produce titanium dioxide pigment superior to that from any other.

Titanium dioxide pigments do not show 100% TiO_2 upon analysis because additives are needed to influence pigmentary properties. The minima of titanium dioxide content range from $93–98\%$, depending upon the type of pigment. Thus regular anatase type has a minimum of 98% TiO_2, but as modified with alumina for color

retentive effect, may have minimum 96% TiO_2. In the rutile form, the most widely used types may have minimum 97% TiO_2, but the "nonchalking" type, particularly useful in compounds such as electrical insulation, automotive upholstery and exterior coverings that will be exposed to severe weathering, may have minimum of $93\% TiO_2$, such as indicated in Federal Specification TT-P-442.

For the high refractive index of titanium dioxide to effectuate efficient light scattering and, in combination with whiteness, to yield high reflectance and opacity in plastic media, its particle size must be suitably small—usually ranging from $0.2–0.3\mu$ average, while excessive proportions of particles larger than 1μ and smaller than 0.1μ are excluded. As a result, in comparison with some commonly used white pigments, a minimum weight of titanium dioxide will impart a desired level of reflectance (lightness or brightness), opacity or translucency in plastic compositions. This quality is, of course, high tinting strength, and is indicated by relationships such as the one shown in Table 2. The lower the weight, the higher is the tinting strength of the pigment.

TABLE 2. EXAMPLE OF HIGH TINTING STRENGTH OF TITANIUM DIOXIDE PIGMENT.

	Approx. equivalent weights for equal reflectance in white polymeric compounds (other factors constant)
Titanium dioxide (rutile)	1.0
Titanium dioxide (anatase)	1.2–1.7
Zinc sulfide	2.6–3.0
Lithopone	6.6–7.3
Zinc oxide	16.0

The general relationship presented in Table 2, illustrative of the great strength of the TiO_2 pigments accounting for their ascendancy over the others as brighteners and opacifiers, is useful mainly as a guide to the selection of anatase or rutile. However, the relationship between these types in any given case depends upon their concentration, the plastic medium, and the degree of brightening required.

The degree of titanium dioxide pigmentation naturally also depends upon the plastic medium, the thickness of the stock, whether film, sheeting, or thick opaque article, and the brightness needed.

Almost colorless media, such as polyethylene and the vinyls, are readily brightened and whitened by relatively low concentrations, whereas darker stocks require higher amounts and, of course, the thinner the sheeting, the more highly it must be pigmented for high brightness.

It may be noted from Table 3 that over 90%

TABLE 3. EXAMPLE OF REFLECTANCE OR BRIGHTNESS OF SOME WHITE PLASTIC STOCKS
PER CENT REFLECTANCE.

TiO$_2$ pigment (rutile), % by weight of composition	Polyethylene high density, 25 mils	Vinyl sheeting,		Homogeneous vinyl roll type floor covering	Vinyl-asbestos floor tile
		23 mils	5 mils		
1	87.5	77.5	55.0	62.0	40.0
2	89.4	86.0	67.5	67.0	49.0
3	90.6	88.5	73.0	68.5	54.0
4	—	90.5	76.5	69.5	57.5
10		—	88.5	73.5	66.5
12			90.5	74.0	

brightness was obtained with only 3% pigment in a 25-mil polyethylene sheet. In vinyl sheeting, while 4% gave over 90% brightness in a 23-mil sheet, it took 12% to secure this brightness in a 5-mil sheet. The floor covering stocks cited had innately low brightness and for the pigmented product high brightness was not needed—the normal pigmentation being only a few per cent TiO$_2$ pigment. The vinyl-asbestos floor tile sample showed low brightness mainly because it contained dark colored asbestos and other off-colored coarse filler which in a sense acted as tinting color.

The higher brightening power of rutile is strikingly evident in vinyl sheeting when comparison is made with anatase in the parts of pigment required to achieve a given brightness, as may be noted from Table 4. For example, in the 5-mil sheeting, for brightness of 82%, a pigmentation with rutile was 8.2–8.5, but with anatase 14.6; in the 23-mil sheeting, for the same brightness, 2.7 anatase as against 1.9–2.2 rutile. The slightly lower values in parenthesis are for plastic and floor covering grade rutile TiO$_2$ which at lower pigmentation level in this type of composition exerts higher strength than the general utility grade which however is equal at higher TiO$_2$ pigment concentrations. The difference is due to a difference in particle size—the plastic grade

showing an average particle diameter of about 0.2μ and the general utility grade about 0.3μ.

Tinting strength in the sense of ability to lighten colors, rather than to brighten and whiten practically colorless materials, is also naturally much higher for rutile than anatase. This means, of course, that for a desired lightness of color, if the concentration of colored pigment be maintained constant, a lower concentration of rutile than anatase will be required to achieve the lightness; or for a given concentration of TiO$_2$ pigment, colored pigment constant, lightness will be higher with rutile.

Although strictly speaking, gray is not a color, it is most useful to illustrate the tinting strength of these pigments in plastics, for in all tints lightness is involved. The higher tinting strength of rutile is evident from the lighter grays it produced as shown in Table 5. Here again the values in parenthesis are for the plastic or floor covering grade of rutile which, through finer particle size, exerts higher tinting strength in the type of composition involved.

The remarkably high and uniform reflectance of titanium dioxide pigment throughout the visible spectrum accounts for its outstanding whiteness. Yet this whiteness is not perfect, for reflectance at the far blue end is not so high as in the remainder of the spectrum, as may be noted

TABLE 4. EXAMPLE OF BRIGHTNESS OF WHITE VINYL SHEETING.
(no backing)

Brightness (% Reflectance, MgO = 100)	Parts TiO$_2$ pigment per 100 parts resin			
	5 mils thick		23 mils thick	
	Anatase	Rutile	Anatase	Rutile
80	11.8	7.7 (7.1)	2.3	1.9 (1.7)
82	14.6	8.5 (8.2)	2.7	2.2 (1.9)
84	17.9	9.5	3.2	2.6 (2.3)
86	22.0	11.5	4.0	3.2 (3.0)
88	26.0	14.5	5.0	4.0 (3.8)
90	34.0	19.0	7.0	5.0
92	—	27.0	12.0	7.5

TABLE 5. LIGHTNESS (REFLECTANCE) OF GRAY VINYL
SHEETING.

Pts TiO$_2$, pigment per 100 parts vinyl base[a]	Lightness of gray tint, %	
	Anatase	Rutile
5	11.6	14.1 (15.0)
10	19.1	22.4 (23.7)
15	24.1	27.6 (28.8)
20	27.8	31.5 (33.0)
25	30.6	34.8 (35.9)
30	33.0	37.3 (38.2)

[a] Black included.

from Table 6. As the difference in reflectance between the shorter and longer wavelengths is slight in the case of anatase, but pronounced in rutile, the whiteness of rutile is yellowish, while that of anatase is less so.

Inasmuch as the measurements were made on thick compacts of powders that contained no binder, the data of Table 6 represent the color of titanium dioxide pigment itself in its two crystal forms.

The strikingly low reflectance at 390mμ in the violet is indicative of the strong absorption of ultraviolet by rutile.

The fundamental color difference between anatase and rutile manifests itself in plastic compositions. As a result, generally, rutile yields

TABLE 6. REFLECTANCE OF TITANIUM DIOXIDE PIGMENT POWDERS OVER VISIBLE PORTION OF SPECTRUM.

% Reflectance (fumed Mg0 = 100)

Region of spectrum	Wavelength, mμ	Anatase	Rutile
Violet	390	85.0	18.0
	400	92.0	39.5
	410	96.5	66.0
	420	98.0	89.7
	440	98.5	97.0
	460	98.5	97.0
Blue	480	98.5	97.6
	500	98.5	97.7
	520	98.5	97.8
	540	98.5	98.1
Green	560	98.5	98.3
	580	98.5	98.5
	600	98.7	98.7
	620	99.0	99.0
Red	640	99.0	99.5
	660	99.0	99.7
	680	99.2	100.0

a yellowish white, whereas with anatase, whiteness is less yellow, or even bluish. A striking feature of the color effects of these pigments is the fact that the extremely low reflectance of rutile of the shorter wavelengths at the far blue end of the spectrum characteristic of the pigment itself is also strongly evident in plastic compositions. This may be noted from Table 7, which lists reflectance values averaged from numerous spectrophotometric curves of comparable compositions containing anatase and rutile ... reflectance at 400mμ was only 30% with rutile.

TABLE 7. REFLECTANCE OF SOME WHITE PLASTIC COMPOSITIONS OVER VISIBLE PORTION OF SPECTRUM.

(Anatase and Rutile in Comparable Compositions)

% Reflectance (Mg0 = 100)

Region	Wavelength, mμ	Anatase	Rutile
Violet	400	68	30
Blue	450	75	75
	500	80	82
Green	550	82	84
	600	84	86
Red	650	85	88

As with brightness, actual whiteness obtained in a plastic product depends, among other factors, upon the nature of the plastic medium and the concentration of TiO$_2$ pigment.

Dark-colored media not only reduce brightness, but depending upon their color, impart coloration to the white composition, influencing its tone. Naturally, media which are yellowish or brownish promote yellowish whites, and in any case, the dominant color of the medium may be reflected in white.

Following in Table 8 is an illustration of influence of the medium upon whiteness. Here whiteness is expressed in the commonly accepted terms of reflectance and yellowness index as determined with a trichromatic reflectometer ... reflectance or brightness is percent reflectance with green filter, while the yellowness index is the difference in reflectance between red and blue filters as a percentage of the green. The higher this index, the yellower the white; the lower, the less yellow, and when negative, whiteness is usually bluish.

It may be noted from Table 8 that the more colorless vinyl resin gave a less yellowish white than the darker colored natural rubber. Low brightness (despite equal rutile pigment content) of the vinyl-asbestos stock is due to the dark color of the fillers which, however, did not impart yellowness; this stock because of its low brightness should not be considered white.

As brightness is dependent upon pigment concentration so also is whiteness, but usually not to

TABLE 8. EXAMPLE OF EFFECT OF TYPE OF PLASTIC COMPOSITION UPON WHITENESS.

Parts pigment per 100 parts resin	TiO_2 pigment	Natural rubber Brightness	Yellowness index	Vinyl sheeting Brightness	Yellowness index	Vinyl-Asbestos tile Brightness	Yellowness index
10	Anatase	79.8	14.2	91.5	4.8	—	—
8	Rutile	79.9	15.0	92.0	9.2	43.0	0.8

so great a degree. A typical example of the variation of yellowness index with increase in brightness (as effected by increased pigment content) is shown in Table 9.

The greater brightening power of rutile, of course, permits toning with blue and other toners to adjust whiteness.

In tints, of course, other factors being equal rutile is much stronger in lightening effect upon the color as shown in Table 5, but as would be expected, will not yield exactly the same tint as anatase with a given tinting color.

Gray is useful to illustrate the tinctorial effects of these pigments. Yellowness index as used for whites, is applicable as an indicator of the tone of a gray (which also, of course, depends upon the black pigment). In the particular grays used for the data in Table 10, anatase gave definitely bluish grays as shown by the negative values of color index. In these tints the black pigment was maintained at a constant ratio to the unpigmented composition, but TiO_2 pigment content was varied to give lightness varying from dark to light gray.

In general, the lightness and chromaticity of a desired tint is obtained at a selected concentration of titanium dioxide pigment which is held constant while color pigment is manipulated in quantity and for the desired color. Exception to this may come about only with extremely weak colors such as some earth colors, or with fillers that function as tinting colors but are needed in

constant proportion for mechanical effects, so that the TiO_2 pigment content may have to be varied while color or filler is maintained constant.

Note from Table 10 the bluer tone of the plastic grade of rutile as indicated by the negative values. This, of course, is due to its smaller particle size. (Because the refractive index of rutile is higher for blue light, and smaller particles are more reflective of it, less yellowness results.) It should be noted that as in whites as shown in Table 9 in which the chromaticity of the whites was practically constant, chromaticity of the tints varied very little with variation of pigment content with the general utility grade, but at higher lightness the plastic grade also showed small variation.

This plastic grade of pigment finds greatest use in tinted compositions in which TiO_2 pigment is employed with fillers, such as floor coverings in relatively lighter tints, as indicated in the following:

Green floor covering product	Rutile TiO_2 pigment type	%	Lightness of tint, %
Homogeneous vinyl	General utility	3.3	44.7
Homogeneous vinyl	Plastic grade	3.3	45.8
Flexible vinyl-asbestos	General utility	5.3	39.3
Flexible vinyl-asbestos	Plastic grade	5.3	40.3
Rubber tile	General utility	6.0	29.9
Rubber tile	Plastic grade	6.0	30.5

TABLE 9. WHITENESS OF 23 MIL VINYL SHEETING.

At TiO_2 pigment content[a] for % brightness of	Anatase	Yellowness index Rutile[b]	Rutile[c]
80	3.7	8.9	5.4
82	3.9	8.9	5.5
84	4.1	9.0	5.9
86	4.4	9.1	6.4
88	4.6	9.1	6.8
90	4.7	9.2	7.6
92	5.1	9.2	8.0

[a]See Table 4.
[b]General utility grade.
[c]Plastic and floor covering grade.

Although anatase yields less yellowish and more bluish whites and cleaner tints, rutile may promote retention of whiteness and color upon exposure to light. Here is an interesting example in a rigid vinyl composition:

Pigment	Initial whiteness		Whiteness after exposure to sunlight		Decrease in brilliance	Increase in yellowness index
	% Brightness	% Yellowness index	% Brightness	% Yellowness index		
Anatase	82.0	−5.2	67.1	+16.0	5.1	21.2
Rutile, plastic grade	83.5	−2.0	81.3	+04.2	2.2	6.2
Rutile, "non-chalking"	82.9	−0.6	82.2	−00.5	0.7	0.1

Remarkable concerning the foregoing is not only the better whiteness retention of rutile as may be noted from the much lower loss in brightness and smaller increase in yellowness after exposure, but also the exceptional stability imparted by the "non-chalking" rutile pigment as indicated by an insignificant decrease in brightness (only 0.7%) with practically no change in chromaticity. It should also be noted that although with the "non-chalking" grade whiteness was not the best initially, it was so well retained as to make this type of pigment completely preferable in this particular case.

Both anatase and rutile show ultraviolet absorption, but rutile to a greater extent—studies of rutile crystal indicate no transmission of wave lengths in the ultraviolet, and this is particularly true of the "non-chalking" type of pigment.

Usually where durability is most important not only concerning color, but also other qualities such as chalking, crazing and embrittlement, the "non-chalking" grade is first choice. This pigment has been found to impart retention of elasticity and retardation of brittleness in polyvinyl chloride insulating compounds exposed to the weather. In this type of compound, the "non-chalking" grade has been found to be far superior to anatase, and also sufficiently more durable as to be preferable to other types of rutile TiO_2 pigments. Similar experience is reported for other plastic products such as polyethylene.

As to stability and durability of plastics it must be remembered though that the polymer itself, the kind and amount of plasticizers and heat and light stabilizers are all important and can be adjusted to accommodate either anatase or rutile. In other words, for many applications either anatase or rutile can be employed. Naturally for the particular polymer, proper selection of all compounding ingredients and their use in optimum proportions is imperative, as is also suitable degree of dispersion of the pigment.

Opacity of a plastic composition pigmented with titanium dioxide is of paramount importance when the product, if unpigmented, would be undesirably transparent or translucent and too low in reflectance. Film and sheeting either alone or backed, or thin walled containers are naturally the outstanding plastic products for which regulation of opacity is so essential.

Opacity, of course, varies with the thickness of the material and concentration of TiO_2 pigment, and as would be expected, rutile has higher opacifying power than anatase. As a result a lower concentration of rutile will give a desired degree of opacity in a material of constant thickness.

In the foregoing, contrast ratio is, of course, the ratio of the reflectance of the sheeting backed by black to its reflectance backed by white, and expressed in percent. Complete opacity is con-

TABLE 10. EXAMPLE OF EFFECT OF TITANIUM DIOXIDE UPON TONE OF TINT (GRAY).

Lightness of tint brightness[a], %		Yellowness index[b]	
	Anatase	Rutile[c]	Rutile[d]
10	−12.5	−1.9	−13.5
20	−8.2	+1.4	−8.5
30	−6.8	+2.0	−6.0
35	−6.7	+1.6	−5.6
40	−6.8	+0.8	−5.7

[a] Brightness = % Green, % Red, % Blue are reflectance values determined on trichromatic reflectometer.
[b] Yellowness Index = (% Red− % Blue) × 100
[c] General utility grade.
[d] Plastic and floor covering grade.

TABLE 11.

For opacity contrast ratio, %	Polyvinyl chloride sheeting 5 mils thick, parts pigment per hundred resin	
	Anatase	Rutile
70	2.6	1.6–2.2
75	3.8	2.4–2.8
80	5.6	3.4–4.0
85	8.4	5.0–5.4
90	12.5	7.6–8.0
95	20.0	13.4–13.7
98	36.9	20.

trast ratio of 100%, but usually for practical purposes contrast ratio of 98% is considered to express complete opacity.

For films in which opacity to ultraviolet and blue light is of paramount importance, rutile is obviously preferable to anatase.

Plastics are no exception to the principle that opacity of systems pigmented with titanium dioxide may be increased by increasing absorption through addition of color pigment or by increasing scattering within the film. Addition of color pigment naturally reduces reflectance. In plastics,

the use of a minor amount of metallic aluminum pigment in conjunction with TiO$_2$ pigment is often particularly effective, especially when opacity is measured as transmission. At the very high concentration of TiO$_2$ pigment such as 50 parts per hundred of resin to render films highly opaque to transmitted light, metallic aluminum pigment on the order of from .05–0.4% on the TiO$_2$ helps provide complete opacity but, of course, reflectance is decreased. The exceptionally high reflectance obtainable with rutile permits such reduction, so that reflectance after addition of aluminum pigment is still high.

Because of its unsurpassed optical properties and applicability to virtually all types of plastics, titanium dioxide is the truly universal whitener, brightener and opacifier. This status should persist because the appeal of light color in so many plastic products seems to be quite permanent.

While the rutile form because of higher whitening, brightening and opacifying power plus greater inhibition of degradation by heat, light, and the weather, is preferred for the great majority of plastics, anatase is not yet obsolete. It may

TABLE 12. SOME PHYSICAL PROPERTIES OF RUTILE TiO$_2$ OF INTEREST FOR PLASTICS.

Index of refraction at wavelength millimicrons	n_o	n_e
436	2.8499	3.1969
486	2.7305	3.0473
546	2.6503	2.9473
589	2.6126	2.9004
656	2.5720	2.8500
1014	2.4842	2.7418
1530	2.4461	2.6954
Dielectric Constant		
a-direction	86	
c-direction	170	
Breakdown Voltage	600–700 volts mil^{-1}	
Electrical Conductivity		
a-direction	10^{-10} ohm^{-1} cm^{-1}	
c-direction	10^{-13} ohm^{-1} cm^{-1}	
Relative reflectance of compressed powder at wavelength millimicrons	% (MgO assigned 100%)	
Ultraviolet 200	0	
300	0	
400	39	
Blue 500	98	
Infrared 1000	100	
1300	100+	
1500	105	
1900	100	
Melting point	1830± 15°C in air	
Thermal conductivity (cal sec^{-1} cm^{-1} °C^{-1})	.0204–.0256	
100°–1200°C	0.015–0.0079	
Linear thermal expansion (°C^{-1})		
0 to 1000°C	9.0–9.1 $\times$ 10^{-6}	

be selected because of less yellowish whiteness and greater clarity of tints, when with rutile whites have not been adjusted with toners, nor have tints with color pigments. Or, under unique conditions such as in white sidewall tire stocks in which anatase is preferred because it yields greater whiteness and chalking plus resistance to ozone cracking; or where rutile because of its strong absorption of ultraviolet would interfere with fluorescent colors; or where an exceptionally low price for anatase may counteract superiority of rutile in a particular product.

Of course, titanium dioxide will also be utilized for other than the sake of appearance of the plastic product. For electrical insulating compounds for example, the high dielectric constant and low electrical conductivity (high resistivity) of rutile is an important factor in its choice. Rutile also has high reflectance in portions of the infrared which can make it most interesting for many products that must reflect heat while having high visual brightness.

Titanium dioxide pigment serves the plastic industry well because for any plastic use there is a type of pigment to fit the processing conditions and the properties needed in the pigmented product.

In addition to titanium dioxide, there is also available titanium dioxide precipitated upon calcium sulfate known as titanium-calcium pigment in two types, 50% TiO_2 and 30% TiO_2. These extended pigments are useful for compositions requiring a fine particle size filler in addition to titanium dioxide.

The fine particle size and freedom from coarse agglomerates absolutely essential to optical properties of titanium dioxide also promote ease of incorporation in plastics in any type of equipment usually employed. And for unusual cases, a special faster dispersing type of rutile TiO_2 is provided.

Where stability and durability are factors, the "non-chalking" type of rutile TiO_2 pigment is available, and for special cases such as amino plastic paper laminates, special grades are made available. Where particular qualities are needed, for example minimum content of water soluble and high specific resistance, there are readily provided in available grades of rutile TiO_2 pigment.

It may be safely predicted that for almost any conceivable type of plastic a suitable titanium dioxide pigment can be found.

WILLIAM B. ANDERSON

U

ULTRAVIOLET ABSORBERS

As used in the plastics industry, the term "ultraviolet absorber" describes a highly purified specialty chemical that is added to plastics in very small concentrations to protect the plastic from the degrading effects of ultraviolet light.

Ultraviolet light, present in sunlight and some artificial light sources, possesses high energy that is capable of causing chemical reactions in plastics. These photochemical reactions involve the oxidation of the polymer with eventual cleavage of the polymer chain. As a result of loss in molecular weight, the physical properties of the polymer change and elongation and tensile strength are reduced. Frequently chromophoric groups form in the plastic causing undesirable color changes in the polymer.

Early in the development of plastic products it became evident that a solution to the problem of photodegradation would make possible a wide variety of uses. Obviously, if it were possible to prevent ultraviolet light from contacting the plastic, a photochemical reaction could not take place. One solution would be to provide a UV screening area between the light source and the polymer.

Initially it would appear that a simple surface coating containing a UV-absorbing compound would be a successful method. However, this approach presents many practical problems. First, a coating must be found that will bond well to plastic. The coating must be capable of being applied evenly over the surface of the article to prevent striation. Also a compound must be found that has sufficiently strong ultraviolet-absorbing activity and sufficient compatibility in the surface coating to provide satisfactory long-term protection. These criteria are difficult to meet and this technique has not proved commercially feasible to date.

Consequently, a second approach is being used to upgrade the performance of plastics. This system incorporates into the plastic a molecule that has a much greater affinity for ultraviolet light than the plastic and, therefore, preferentially absorbs the UV light. In other words,

the principle is to incorporate a "UV scavenger" that absorbs the ultraviolet light before it is able to activate the polymer chain and cause degradation reactions to begin.

Strong ultraviolet absorption is not the only property necessary for a material that will be used as an ultraviolet absorber in plastics. The material should be colorless so that it will not add color to the plastic. It must be stable to ultraviolet light in order to absorb the energy and convert it to harmless wavelengths without being itself degraded. In addition, the absorber should not affect the polymer's physical properties, such as the melt index or impact strength. To prevent loss of protection from exudation, the absorber must be compatible with the polymer. High heat stability is also required so that the absorber can be carried through the polymer processing steps without degrading.

The earliest known molecules that were used as ultraviolet absorbers in plastics were esters of salicylic acid. These molecules absorb energy in the region of 295–310μ and provide some degree of light stability to many polymers. Usually UV absorbers are chosen whose absorption is strongest in the region 295–400μ since this is the portion of the ultraviolet spectrum that reaches the earth from the sun. The salicylates must be used in relatively high concentrations. But such concentrations have some tendency to rearrange and degrade from light exposure.

The substituted benzophenones are a second, more active group of UV absorbers. In general, the structures are all o-hydroxybenzophenones that are capable of forming a chelate ring between the o-hydroxyl and the carbonyl of the benzophenone. This chelation appears to give strong ultraviolet absorption and a high degree of light stability to the molecule. Another class of compounds with absorption properties similar to the benzophenones is the substituted benzotriazoles. These structures also are capable of forming a 6-member chelate ring that has strong UV absorption and good light stability.

The salicylates, benzophenones and benzotriazoles all appear to function by preferentially absorbing ultraviolet energy and thereby preven the UV energy from causing photochemical breakdown of the polymer. Although no direct evidence is available to confirm the fact, it is believed that all of these molecules act by converting the ultraviolet energy to long wavelength energy. These long wavelengths are so low in energy they cannot initiate photochemical reactions.

In the last few years, a new type of structure, called metal chelates, has been introduced that appears to do a good job of light stabilizing some plastics. Ordinarily they are phenolic chelates of nickel. These molecules absorb little or no ultraviolet light, but they do protect against light degradation. Their mechanism of functioning is not definitely established, but they are apparently able to decompose the activated state of polymer before the degradation can occur. Although the nickel complexes are colored and can add color to the polymer, they are effectively used in pigmented polymers.

Plastics that are heavily colored or pigmented suffer less from the effects of light than do translucent or transparent plastics. However, pigmentation is not always the answer to stabilization problems. Even heavily pigmented films and fibers are subject to photodegradation and are benefited by the incorporation of light stabilizers.

Ultraviolet absorbers are added to polymers in different ways, Some of the more common methods of incorporation are summarized below:

ABS. If ultraviolet absorbers are used in ABS polymers, they are normally incorporated by the polymer manufacturer in the course of other compounding done before production of the molding chip.

Polymethyl Methacrylate. UV absorbers can be stirred into the polymer syrup before polymerization of the finished article.

Polyethylene. Absorbers can be dry blended into the polymer powder before molding or extrusion operations are carried out.

Polypropylene. UV absorbers are normally added with other stabilizing additives by the polymer producer. In other words, the fabricator will buy a light-stabilized polypropylene.

Polystyrene. UV absorbers are normally added by the polystyrene manufactuer, at the same time that other stabilizing and color modifying additives are added to the polystyrene bead before production of the chip.

Polyvinyl Chloride:

Flexible—UV absorbers are normally added by the compounder or fabricator at the same time that the plasticizer and heat stabilizer are added to the formulation.

Rigid—UV absorbers are usually added to rigid vinyl by the polyvinyl chloride producer in his compounding operations.

Cellulosics. UV absorbers are normally added by the manufacturer of the polymer.

It is essential that an absorber be thoroughly and evenly mixed into the system in order to provide uniform protection. Most currently available UV absorbers are low melting solids that can be effectively dry blended with polymer powders at low temperatures. As soon as heat is added to the blended materials, the absorber liquefies and mixes easily with the polymer.

In addition to the thermoplastic materials mentioned above, UV absorbers are commonly used in some thermosets, particularly polyesters and the diallylphthalate resins. In these resins, the absorber is frequently added to the cross-linking monomer of the system. For instance, in polyesters the absorber is dissolved in the styrene monomer or the styrene-methacrylate comonomer system. Because most currently available absorbers are sufficiently soluble in the monomer, by the time the monomer is blended with the polyester, the absorber is also well mixed.

The concentration of absorber required varies from polymer to polymer and also varies within one polymer type depending on the article to be produced. For instance, a thin film of polyethylene will require a higher concentration of UV absorber than will a molded article with a thick cross section. Concentrations used range from a low of 0.1% to a high of 1.0%. Most UV absorbers sell for $4.00 to $8.00 per lb. Therefore, if an absorber costing $4.00 per lb is used at 0.25% concentration, the cost of stabilization is 1¢ per lb of finished plastic.

To evaluate the efficiency of an ultraviolet absorber accurately, the treated plastic should be exposed outdoors for prolonged periods. This is a time-consuming procedure with the added disadvantage that the amount of UV light emitted from the sun not only varies from one location to the next, but also varies from season to season. Exposure in Florida is not equivalent to exposure in Canada or Arizona and exposure in each of these locations would vary from January to July. Despite these variables, outdoor exposure is still considered the best method for determining if a plastic has been adequately stabilized.

However, since it is not always feasible to carry out 2–3-year outdoor exposures, several accelerated weathering devices have been developed for laboratory use. To duplicate sunlight, these units use artificial light sources such as carbon arcs, sunlamps, fluorescent bulbs and xenon arcs.

Because these light sources have a different energy distribution than sunlight, the accelerated tests do not always correlate well with outdoor exposures. Most light sources provide more helpful weathering data for one plastic than another. Several weathering units operate at high ambient temperatures and the possibility of heat causing polymer breakdown can interfere with UV absorber evaluation. Studies are now being carried out by polymer producers and by ultraviolet absorber manufacturers to develop more satisfactory accelerated exposure units that can be depended upon to correlate better with actual outdoor performance.

The art of incorporating ultraviolet absorbers into plastics to upgrade their performance is still a relatively new field of study. Much progress has been made in the last 10 years. Many polymers that could not be used outdoors a few years ago can now be adequately stabilized for outdoor applications. Much work remains to be done and the work is going on at a rapid pace.

J. ARNDT WEICKSEL

UREA

Urea is a white, odorless, water-soluble substance. Urea may crystallize in needles, small prisms, or well-developed large rhombic crystals.

Its formula is

$$NH_2CONH_2.$$

Friedrich Wöhler first synthesized it in 1828 by the isomerization of ammonium cyanate, $NH_4OCN \rightleftharpoons (NH_2)_2CO$. Since he had prepared ammonium cyanate from inorganic compounds, this made obsolete the concept that organic substances could only be produced by animals or vegetables.

During World War I urea was manufactured from calcium cyanamide by a two-step, batch-type process:

$$CaCN_2 + CO_2 + H_2O \rightarrow H_2NCN + CaCO_3$$

$$H_2NCN + H_2O \rightarrow (NH_2)_2CO$$

The synthesis of urea from ammonia and carbon dioxide was suggested by Basaroff in 1868, but it was first accomplished in 1913 by Fichter and Becker. The first commercial plant based on this reaction was designed and operated by BASF at Oppau (Germany) in the early twenties. DuPont started the first U.S. plant for synthetic urea at Belle, West Virginia, in 1933.

Urea, the diamide of carbonic acid, is a hybrid consisting of several molecular resonance forms:

$$H_2N-\underset{\underset{O}{\|}}{C}-NH_2 \longleftrightarrow H_2N-\underset{\underset{O-}{|}}{C}=N^+H_2 \longleftrightarrow$$

$$H_2N^+=\underset{\underset{O-}{|}}{C}-NH_2$$

Urea behaves as a weak base in aqueous solutions but is a strong base in methanol solutions.

Urea heated near or above its melting point, under atmospheric pressure, decomposes to biuret and cyanuric acid with evolution of ammonia. Above 200°C, urea gives cyanuric acid and ammelide. If heating is conducted under 10–15 atm, ammeline is also formed. At higher temperature and pressure (350°C and 200 atm), preferably with additional ammonia, melamine is the main product.

Biuret   Cyanuric acid   Ammelide

Ammeline   Melamine

Urea rapidly heated above 300°C isomerizes to ammonium cyanate which then dissociates into cyanic acid and ammonia. If the vapors are rapidly quenched below 100°C, ammonium cyanate is formed.

Urea-Formaldehyde Resins. Urea reacts with aldehydes to form alkylolureas. The most important of these derivatives are methylolurea, $NH_2CONHCH_2OH$, and dimethylol urea, $OHCH_2NHCONHCH_2OH$, which are obtained when urea is allowed to react with formaldehyde solutions at about 80°C. Additional heating of these compounds causes condensation polymerization which seems to occur by dehydration of the monomers to methyleneurea, $NH_2CON : CH_2$, and dimethyleneurea, $CH_2 : NCON : CH_2$, followed by crosslinking of neighboring molecules. The degree of polymerization of urea-formaldehyde resins can be controlled by adjusting temperature, pH and time. Acid catalysts accelerate the reaction while alkaline catalysts retard it.

The customary method of making thermosetting molding powders is to condense urea with formaldehyde in a kettle at a controlled temperature. Following the initial reaction which is allowed to proceed to a predetermined point, certain fillers (alpha-cellulose is most commonly used) are added together with pigments, catalysts and lubricants, and the composition is thoroughly mixed. The mixture is then carefully dried under conditions of temperature which prevent chemical reaction from advancing to final polymerization or curing of th   ...kes

place at the time of molding, which is performed at relatively high temperature and pressure (280–320°F, and 3000–8000 psi).

By adjusting the urea-to-formaldehyde ratio and the degree of condensation, a broad variety of urea resins can be obtained. Urea-formaldehyde resins used for protective or decorative coatings are generally alkylated by boiling the condensation product with an alcohol. The resulting syrup is diluted with a solvent such as xylol.

The reaction of urea with glyoxal gives a heterocyclic derivative, 4,5-dihydroxy-1,3-imidazol-2-one, which has found application in

$$\begin{array}{c} CHO \\ | \\ CHO \end{array} + \begin{array}{c} NH_2 \\ | \\ CO \\ | \\ NH_2 \end{array} \rightarrow \begin{array}{c} HOCH{-}NH \\ | \qquad\qquad \diagdown \\ | \qquad\qquad C{=}O \\ | \qquad\qquad \diagup \\ HOCH{-}NH \end{array}$$

"permanent press" finishes for garments.

There are a number of processes available today for the manufacture of urea from ammonia and carbon dioxide. Urea production facilities are located next to ammonia plants that furnish both ammonia and carbon dioxide. The latter is a by-product of the preparation of ammonia synthesis gas from gaseous, liquid or solid fuels.

All these processes are based on the same chemistry: ammonia combines with carbon dioxide to form ammonium carbamate which partially dehydrates to urea and water. The differences among the various processes consist in the methods of recovering and recycling the unconverted gases. These methods in turn determine the synthesis conditions and other operating parameters.

The two basic reactions are:

$$2NH_3 + CO_2 \rightleftharpoons NH_4COONH_2; \Delta H = -30 \text{ kcal} \quad (1)$$

$$NH_4COONH_2 \rightleftharpoons (NH_2)_2CO + H_2O;$$
$$\Delta H = +7.7 \text{ kcal} \quad (2)$$

Both reactions are equilibrium reactions; and their combined effect is highly exothermic, although reaction (2) is endothermic. Reaction (1) is quite rapid but (2) is slow. To operate this reaction at practical rates, it is therefore necessary to use high temperatures. Because ammonium carbamate does not exist in the vapor phase, it is necessary to operate at a pressure well in excess of the dissociation pressure of ammonium carbamate. At 374°F for instance, since the dissociation pressure of ammonium carbamate is about 2700 psi, the synthesis should be carried out at a pressure of 3200 psi or higher.

Water, of course, has a detrimental effect on the conversion; but this can be partially overcome by operating with an excess of ammonia. It should be noted, however, that for each set of

conditions there is an optimum NH_3-to-CO_2 ratio beyond which an increase of ammonia causes a decrease of yield.

The following are ranges of operating conditions for the various processes:

Temperature	275–390°F
Pressure	1500—5000 psig
NH_3-to-CO_2 ratio	2 : 1–5 : 1
Conversion to urea	40–60% per pass
Residence time	20–40 min

Figure 1 is a schematic flow diagram of a total recycle process. Major items of equipment are: (1) CO_2 compressor; (2) CO_2 purification train; (3) liquid NH_3 pump; (4) carbamate solution pump; (5) high-pressure synthesis reactor; (6) pressure letdown valve; (7) NH_3 stripper; (8) carbamate decomposer; (9) carbamate condenser; (10) NH_3 condenser.

The process can be described as follows: Carbon dioxide is compressed to the required pressure and purified. Sulfur impurities are removed over activated carbon at about 100°F; and traces of oxygen are removed over a copper catalyst at about 500°F. Carbon dioxide is now introduced at the bottom of the high-pressure synthesis reactor together with ammonia and "recycled" ammonium carbamate solution. Since the reaction is exothermic, the generated heat must be removed. This can be done either by using a water-jacketed reactor or by internal cooling coils.

The reacted liquid mixture consisting of urea, ammonia, carbamate and water leaves the reactor through a pressure letdown valve and enters a medium-pressure ammonia stripper (300–400 psig), where most of the excess ammonia flash evaporates. This ammonia, which is CO_2-free, after condensation, is pumped back to the system together with makeup NH_3.

The bottoms from the ammonia stripper are now introduced into the low-pressure carbamate decomposer (20–60 psig) where heat is added by indirect steam to completely dissociate the remaining ammonium carbamate. Ammonia, carbon dioxide and steam are withdrawn from the top of the column and sent to a condenser where they are cooled and made into a carbamate solution which is pumped back to the high-pressure reactor. The urea solution discharged from the bottom of the carbamate decomposer contains approximately 80% urea. After filtration, the solution is sent to a continuous vacuum crystallizer. The crystals are centrifuged from the mother liquor, dried in a rotary kiln, cooled, bagged and stored.

To make prills (small, hard spheres used mostly for fertilizer or livestock feed), the urea solution is concentrated by evaporation under vacuum to

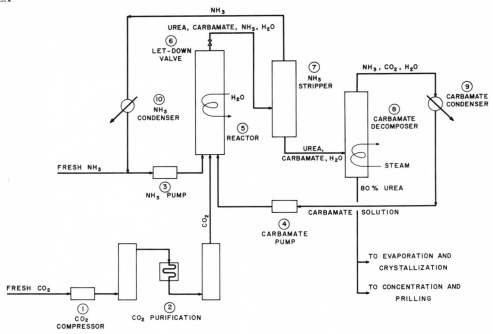

Fig. 1. Urea synthesis. Schematic flow digaram of a total recycle process.

90% and sprayed down a 150–200 ft tower against a rising column of air. The solidified drops discharged from the bottom of the tower are dried, coated with clay or other conditioners, and conveyed to bagging or bulk storage.

The process described above (recycling of ammonium carbamate as an aqueous solution) is only one of the many processes successfully utilizing the reaction of ammonia with carbon dioxide.

The choice of material of construction for urea plants depends on the type of process and specific operating condtions.

The high-pressure reactors are generally made of carbon steel with an internal lining of silver, lead or titanium to withstand corrosion by the hot urea-carbamate mixture. Forged stainless steel reactors are also used.

Stainless steels, aluminium, "Hastelloy" C are extensively used for vessels, valves and piping.

Urea market outlets in recent years were: fertilizers, 69%; livestock feeds, 16%; urea-formaldehyde resins, 11%; others, 4%. Urea resin consumption by type of application was: plywood, 33%; adhesives, 17%; molding, 16%; textile treating, 12%; paper treating, 11%; protective coatings, 8%; others, 3%. Urea plant capacity in the United States by the end of 1965 was estimated to be approximately 2,500,000 tons per year with 35 plants in operation.

M. T. GIACHINO

URETHANE MATERIALS

Urethane polymers (or polyurethanes) are fairly recent additions to the broad field of plastic materials, being the result of research in Germany and the United States during the period 1937–50. They have been produced commercially in the United States since 1954. The term "urethane" or "polyurethane" at present refers to several distinct types of engineering materials produced by common chemical reactions. The types available include rigid and flexible foams, elastomers, coatings, and adhesives.

Polyurethanes are commonly reaction products of polyisocyanates and polyhydroxy compounds. In some cases, the addition of polyamines or water to the reactant mixture produces, by reaction with the polyisocyanate, urea groups in the polymer. Further reaction of urea or urethane groups with polyisocyanates produces biuret or allophanate cross-links, respectively. Expansion of the polymer to form urethane foams is caused by generation of carbon dioxide in the isocyanate —water reaction and vaporization of nonreactive low boiling liquids such as trichloromonofluoromethane. Chemical equations for these reactions are given below.

(1) RNCO + R'OH → RNHCO.OR'
    Isocyanate + *Alcohol*   *Urethane*

(2) RNCO + R'NH$_2$ → RNHCONHR'
    Isocyanate + *Amine*   *Urea*

(3) $2RNCO + H_2O \rightarrow RNHCONHR + CO_2$
   Isocyanate + Water   *Urea*

(4) $RNCO + RNHCONHR' \rightarrow$
   Isocyanate + Urea

$$RNHCORNCONHR'$$
                  Biuret

(5) $RNCO + RNHCOR' \rightarrow$
   Isocyanate + Urethane

$$RNHCORNCO\!-\!OR'$$
                 Allophanate

(6) $n\, OCNRNCO + n\, HOR'OH \rightarrow$
   Diisocyanate   *Dihydroxy compound*

$$\left(\!-CONHRNHCO\!-\!OR'O\!-\!\right)_n$$
              Polyurethane

The rates of these reactions can be controlled over a wide range by addition of catalysts, the most common of which are tertiary amines and organotin compounds. The structure of urethane foams is stabilized by addition of specific surfactants. Silicones, silicone block copolymers, and organic anionic or nonionic types are used, depending on the combination of raw materials.

Urethane polymers are prepared either by the one step or "one-shot" process in which all raw materials are combined simultaneously, or by a two step or "prepolymer" process. In the latter, portions of the polyisocyanates and polyol are pre-reacted to form a prepolymer which can still be easily processed. The prepolymer is then extended and/or cross-linked by further reaction with polyisocyanates, polyols, polyamines, or other reactive curing agents.

Raw Materials

(1) Diisocyanates. The principal commercial diisocyanate at this time is TDI, a blend of 80% 2,4 and 20% 2,6-toluene diisocyanate which is a major raw material of flexible urethane foam, currently the largest single application of urethane polymers. Polymeric polyisocyanates prepared by phosgenation of the products of the aniline-formaldehyde condensation are increasing in use in rigid urethane foams, largely because lower vapor pressures make handling less hazardous. The simplest polyisocyanate of this type, 4,4'-diphenylmethane diisocyanate or MDI, is a component of urethane elastomers.

(2) Polyhydric Alcohols. Polyols employed as co-reactants with polyisocyanates include linear and branched polyesters such as those prepared from adipic and/or phthalic acids and diethylene glycol. Polyesters based on chlorinated carboxylic acids are used in the preparation of flame resistant rigid urethane foams. More widely used in both rigid and flexible urethane foams are low cost polyethers prepared by addition of propylene oxide to glycerol, trimethylolpropane, pentaerythritol, α methyl glucoside, sorbitol, and sucrose as well as ethylene diamine, diethylene triamine and similar compounds. Molecular weights from 200–5000 allow close control of the molecular structure of the final urethane polymer. Polyether urethanes are not only less expensive than polyester urethanes, but are more stable to hydrolysis and, in flexible urethane foams, have more desirable comfort cushioning characteristics. Polyester urethanes are more stable to oxidation and generally have superior mechanical strength.

(3) Polyethers and Polyesters as Intermediates. Most of the polyethers used for the manufacture of urethane foams are the derivatives of propylene oxide noted previously. Poly(tetramethylene ether) glycol derived from tetrahydrofuran is used in the preparation of some solid elastomeric urethanes. Polyether diols are used in some urethane foams as well as in elastomer and propellant binding applications. However, in recent years poly(oxyalkylene) derivatives of polyhydric alcohols have taken over the major portion of polyether production.

Next to the polyethers the most widely used polyhydroxy compounds for urethane plastic production are chemically saturated polyesters, which are for the most part liquids of molecular weight in the range of 1000–3000, and terminate in two or more hydroxyl groups. Low acid numbers and very low water contents are requirements for urethane polyesters.

Modifications of castor oil and ricinoleic acid by means of transesterification (alcoholysis) and esterification have resulted in several potentially useful polyhydroxy compounds for use in the urethane industry. Ricinoleic acid may be esterified with di- or polyalcohols—for example, ethylene glycol, glycerol, or pentaerythritol. These reactions result in polyhydroxy compounds with lower molecular weight than castor oil.

(4) Catalysts. Many metal salts, organometallic compounds, and organic compounds have been found to catalyze reactions of isocyanates. Dialkyltin carboxylates, stannous carboxylates, and tertiary amines are used to speed up the isocyanate-hydroxyl reaction, and tertiary amines are used to catalyze the isocyanate-water reaction. The most generally used tertiary amines are triethylene diamine, triethylamine, N-methyl and N-ethyl morpholine, N,N,N',N-tetramethyl-1,3-diaminobutane, 1-methyl-4-β-dimethylaminoethyl piperazine, dimethyl soya amine, dimethyl cocoamine, and N,N,N',N'-tetramethyl ethylene diamine. The tin compounds most generally used are dibutyltin di-2-ethylhexoate, dibutyltin dilaurate, stannous oleate, and stannous octoate.

Solvents, Fillers, and Pigments

Solvents for use in urethane manufacture are of two types—first for solution of low molecular weight urethanes or raw materials for production of urethanes, and second for solution of the polymerized urethanes. The first includes such solvents as benzene, toluene, xylene, resorcinol, cresylic acid, ethyl acetate, butyl acetate, acetone, ethoxyethyl acetate, and tetrahydrofuran. Typical solvents used to dissolve or swell polymerized urethanes are tetrahydrofuran, dimethylsulfoxide, dimethylformamide, dimethylacetamide, and N-methyl pyrrolidone. Almost any inert filler can be used with urethanes, and some of the more commonly used are carbon black, sawdust, pitch, tall oil, chlorinated hydrocarbons, clay, sand, finely divided silica, silicon carbide, micas, calcium carbonates, barytes, talc, scrap urethane, and granulated or powdered metals.

Pigments of many kinds have been used, but they must be nonreacting with the components used to produce the urethanes, or allowances must be made in the formulation for this reactivity. The most generally used pigments have been titanium dioxide (*q.v.*) and carbon black. Other pigments that have been recommended are lithol reds and lithol rubines, toluidine and cadmium red, iron oxide red, cadmium orange, molybdate orange, cadmium yellow, hansa or toluidine yellows, iron oxide yellow, chrome oxide green, phthalocyanine green and blue, ultramarine blue, bone black, lampblack, iron oxide black, lithopone, antimony oxide, iron oxide brown, umber, and the siennas.

Properties of Tolulene Diisocyanate

Diisocyanates in general can be handled, stored, and used safely if their properties are understood and precautions taken. They are normally respiratory, eye and skin irritants. Oral toxicity is relatively mild. TDI is a serious lachrymator, and the maximum allowable concentration of TDI vapor in the air for extended exposure has been set at 0.02 ppm. Sensitization prevents a small number of persons from working in any contact with the vapor. A rule of thumb is that if TDI can be smelled, the concentration of vapor is already too high for safety. If proper ventilation cannot reduce isocyanate concentration to below 0.02 ppm, then respirators or gas masks should be used by personnel working in these atmospheres.

Urethane Coatings

Second only to those for foam production, the sales of urethane chemicals for coatings have grown steadily since their first introduction in U.S.A. in 1955. Up to the present TDI has been used almost exclusively as the isocyanate in adducts with drying oils, trimethylolpropane, polyethers and polyesters. Five distinct types of coating are recognized suitable for air-drying and baking applications of widely differing properties

and versatility. Three of these are offered as single package products for immediate application, the remaining two are available as two-package systems requiring catalyzation just prior to application. The greater convenience of the one-pack types is offset by the greater versatility of the two-pack types which may be tailored for a large variety of end-uses and application to a multiplicity of substrates whether rigid or flexible. Urethane coatings are being successfully applied to metals, wood, concrete, leather, rubber, fabric, paper and plastics.

Urethane coatings are characterized by unusual toughness, hardness and mar-resistance without loss of flexibility, abrasion resistance and resistance to water, solvents at normal ambient conditions of temperature, and they are capable of accelerated cure rates by the usual means of catalyst addition or higher temperatures.

Further developments are expected in the near future in the production of solventless coatings based on polymeric isocyanates, and in the production of non-yellowing coatings of outstanding durability based on hexamethylene diisocyanate and similar hydrogenated isocyanates. Concurrently with greater usage in the complex coatings industries and lower raw material costs plus more sophisticated application techniques, urethane coatings appear headed for large growth increase in the decades ahead.

Urethane Elastomers

Urethane solid elastomers are made from various isocyanates, the principal ones being tolylene diisocyanate (TDI) and 4,4'-diphenylmethane diisocyanate (MDI), as well as 1,5-naphthalene diisocyanate, the latter more widely used in Europe than in the United States. These diisocyanates are made to react with linear polyesters and polyethers. Various chain extenders such as glycols, water, diamines or aminoalcohols are used in either a prepolymer or one-shot type of system to form a long-chain polymer.

Other Urethane Applications and Materials

Urethane caulks and sealants employ the most inexpensive diisocyanate available and therefore use TDI almost exclusively, although polymeric isocyanates may become very important with further development. In the adhesive fields triisocyanates are preferred over diisocyanates, although some of the triisocyanates are prepared from diisocyanates by reaction with triols, using an excess of the diisocyanate. "Spandex" elastomeric urethane fibers are made using either tolylene diisocyanate or MDI or a combination of the two.

EDWARD R. WELLS
JOHN K. BACKUS

V

VINYL ACETATE

Polyvinyl acetate is obtained when vinyl acetate is polymerized in bulk, solution, suspension, or emulsion systems in the presence of azo- or peroxide catalyst together with heat.

Vinyl acetate monomer is produced by either liquid-phase or vapor-phase reactions—in the former by the catalytic reaction of acetic anhydride and acetaldehyde, or acetylene and acetic acid. In the first process the acetaldehyde and acetic anhydride react to form ethylidene diacetate which, when heated further, yields vinyl acetate and acetic acid;

$$CH_3CHO + (CH_3CO)_2O \xrightarrow{Heat} (CH_3COO)_2CHCH_3$$
Acetaldehyde   *Acetic anhydride*   *Ethylidene diacetate*

$$(CH_3COO)_2CHCH_3 \xrightarrow[Catalyst]{Heat}$$
$$CH_2{=}CHOCOCH_3 + CH_3COOH$$
Vinylacetate

In the vapor phase process, acetylene and acetic acid are reacted at 200°C in the presence of zinc chloride as the catalyst to form vinyl acetate, thusly:

$$CH \equiv CH + CH_3COOH \rightarrow CH_2{=}CHOCOCH_3$$
Acetylene   *Acetic acid*   *Vinyl acetate*

Polyvinyl acetates may best be represented by the following formulas:

$$\left[\begin{array}{c} -CH_2-CH- \\ | \\ O \\ | \\ C{=}O \\ | \\ CH_8 \end{array}\right]_n \left[\begin{array}{c} -CH_2-CH \\ | \\ O \\ | \\ C{=}O \\ | \\ CH_8 \end{array}\right]_n \left[\begin{array}{c} -CH_2-CH- \\ | \\ R \end{array}\right]_m$$
Homopolymer   *Copolymer*

Polyvinyl acetate homopolymer is a hard and brittle polymer with the comparatively low softening point of about 45–50°C. The polymer is colorless, tasteless and nontoxic.

Modified polyvinyl acetates are obtained by copolymerization of vinyl acetate with ethylene, acrylic acid esters, maleic and fumaric acid esters, vinyl esters of higher fatty acids and vinyl chloride. A wide range of properties in the final copolymers can thus be obtained which make polyvinyl acetate and polyvinyl acetate copolymers suitable for a large variety of applications in the coatings and adhesive fields.

Polyvinyl acetate can be externally plasticized by the addition of dibutyl phthalate, chlorinated diphenyls, tricresyl phosphate and sebacic acid esters. Internal plasticization can be achieved by copolymerization of vinyl acetate with ethylene, higher vinyl esters, acrylates, maleates and fumarates. In those applications where plasticizer permanence is important internal plasticization is preferred over external plasticization. Polyvinyl acetate can also be hardened by copolymerization with vinyl benzoate, vinyl pivalate or vinyl chloride. The second order transition temperature for polyvinyl acetate is approximately 30°C. Copolymerization with 20% dibutyl maleate, for example, will reduce this value to about 15°C, with 20% di-*n*-octylfumarate to about −5°C. Molecular weights of the copolymers are generally of the same order as those for vinyl acetate homopolymers.

Polyvinyl acetate resins are soluble in aromatic and chlorinated hydrocarbons, ketones, lower alcohols and esters. They are insoluble in aliphatic hydrocarbons. The stability of polyvinyl acetate to sunlight is excellent which makes these polymers especially useful in surface coatings exposed to the outside.

Manufactured homo- and copolymers are sold under a variety of trademarks such as "Flexbond," "Aircoflex," "Vinac" (Air Reduction Co., Inc.), "Polyco" (Borden Co), "Elvacet," "Elvax" (DuPont), "Resyn" (National Starch & Chemical Co.), "Everflex," "Daratak" (Dewey & Almy Div., W. R. Grace & Co.), "Gelva" (Shawinigan), "Mowilith" (Farbwerke Hoechst), "Vinnapas" (Wacker-Chemie) and "Rhodopas" (Rhone-Poulenc).

Adhesives

A large amount of polyvinyl acetate is being used in the adhesive industry in the form of emulsion, solution, and bulk polymers.

Emulsion polymers are mainly used for bonding cellulosic surfaces such as paper-to-paper or wood-to-wood, or paper-to-plastic materials and wood-to-plastics. The emulsions are usually compounded with plasticizers and tackifiers, polyvinyl alcohol and inert fillers.

Generally small amounts of defoaming agents and fungicides are added to these formulations.

Wood adhesives based on polyvinyl acetates, the so-called "white glues," have displaced the traditional wood glues to a great extent. Typically, a polyvinyl acetate homopolymer emulsion is compounded with partially hydrolyzed polyvinyl alcohol. However, the cold-flow tendencies of polyvinyl acetate are often overcome by incorporating cross-linking agents such as trimethylol phenol or a vinylmethyl ethers maleic anhydride copolymer. A wood glue which is heat- and weather-resistant has the following formulation:

	Parts
Polyvinyl acetate homopolymer emulsion	100
Trimethylol phenol	25

A wood adhesive having high shear strength and resistance to cold flow is made using the following formula:

	Parts
Polyvinyl acetate homopolymer emulsion	145.5
Dibutyl phthalate	4.5
Vinylmethyl ether-maleic anhydride copolymer	12.5
Water	112.0

Film and foil adhesives based on internally plasticized vinyl acetate copolymer emulsions have been suggested. An adhesive composition for film to a porous substrate is formulated as follows:

	Parts
Vinyl acrylic copolymer	85
Plasticizer	10
Methyl isobutyl ketone	5

Usually vinyl acetate-acrylic ester or vinyl acetate maleate ester copolymers are selected for film and foil adhesives. Emulsions such as Flexbond 316 and Flexbond 150 of Air Reduction Chemical and Carbide Co., Gelva TS-100 of Shawinigan Resins Corp. or Daratak B of Dewey & Almy are selected for this purpose and compounded with a plasticizer and solvent.

Hot-melt adhesives are to a great extent based on polyvinyl acetate resins. Usually the polyvinyl acetate resin is extended by rosin materials to reduce the melting point and cost, by plasticizers to increase tack, and by waxes to improve non-blocking properties at normal temperatures. Hot-melt adhesives based on vinyl acetate-ethylene copolymers are being used as bookbinding and packaging adhesives. The Elvax resins of the du Pont Company or the Co-Mer vinyl acetate resins of Union Carbide have been used extensively. Compositions of "Elvax" 150, a copolymer containing 33% vinyl acetate and 67% ethylene, with paraffin wax have the following properties:

HEAT-SEAL BOND STRENGTH OF ELVAX-COATED PAPER

Coating compositions	Elvax 150	
Polymer, %	30	40
Paraffin wax (142–145°F AMP), %	70	60
Coating weight (lb/3000 sq ft)	16	15
Blocking, temp. (°F)	130	130
Grease resistance (hr. to penetration (peanut oil)	112	143

HEAT-SEAL BOND STRENGTH g/in.[a]

Coated paper[b] sealed to:		
Paper	410	470
Aluminum foil	255	300
K-cellophane	235	300
Mylar polyester film	220	260
Polyethylene film	300	335

[a] Determined by delamination of strips 6 × 1/2in. on Instron tensile tester, using cross head speed of 1/2in./min.
[b] Standard 25lb/3000 sq ft sulfite bread wrap.

A heat activated adhesive coating composition is made up as follows:

	Parts
DQD7268 (Union Carbide)	100
Petroleum wax (154° AMP)	90–120
Laminating grade microcrystalline wax	30– 50
Rosin or ester gum	25– 40

The tackiness in this formulation can be varied by using different grades of rosin and by the rosin content. Alkali soluble vinyl acetate-crotonic acid copolymers have also been used for hot-melt adhesives.

The following composition was suggested as a hot-melt bookbinding adhesive:

	Parts
Vinyl acetate-crotonic acid copolymer	49.9
Chlorinated biphenyl	50.0
Inhibitor	0.1

The copolymer was estimated to consist of 93.6 parts of vinyl acetate and 6.4 parts crotonic acid. The chlorinated biphenyl has 42–60% Cl substitution for each part of copolymer. The inhibitor was a tribustituted or "hindered" phenol having a molecular weight of 220 and a melting point of 70°C. A hot-melt adhesive made in rod form which is flexible enough to be unwound from a reel has the following composition:

	Parts
β-Pinene polymer (mp, 125°C)	28.5
Polyvinyl acetate (solid)	14.0
Antioxidant	2.0
Polyethylene	56.5

The solid polyvinyl acetate is obtained by suspension polymerization and solid in bead form. It is available in several viscosity grades.

Remoistenable adhesives consist of a binder which often is polyvinyl acetate or a polyvinyl acetate copolymer and a water soluble component such as polyvinyl alcohol, dextrin or animal glue. A typical formulation is published as follows:

	Parts
Vinac HF-300 (vinyl acetate homopolymer)	68.0
Vinol PA-5 (polyvinyl alcohol) 30% in water	27.2
Dibutyl phthalate	4.1
Ethylene glycol	0.7

Several patents have disclosed formulations for "noncurling tape" remoistenable adhesives. A copolymer of vinyl acetate and crotonic acid or one of vinyl acetate and vinyl pyrrolidone is dissolved in an organic solvent and the water soluble resin such as dextrin is suspended in this solution. After coating paper label stock with this mixture and drying it, the water soluble resin forms a discontinuous phase which on remoistening prevents curling of the label or tape. The vinyl acetate copolymer has to be hydrophillic enough to allow moistening of the dextrin, but should not itself dissolve.

Paints

The use of polyvinyl acetate homo- and copolymers in the paint field is as well established as the use of polyvinyl acetate in the adhesive industry. The first paints based on polyvinyl acetate dispersions were developed in Canada in 1935. By the end of 1945 polyvinyl acetate paints were well established in Europe and in the 1950–1960 decade also in the United States.

Emulsion paints based on polyvinyl acetate have many advantages over other latex type paints. They can be handled very easily, are odorless, dry very rapidly, can be cleaned easily, and are very durable. Plasticizing comonomers used with vinyl acetate are again maleate, fumarate and acrylic esters, fatty acid vinyl esters such as vinyl caproate and more recently vinyl esters of branched carboxylic acids.

A typical paint formulation is listed below:

Ingredients	lb/100gal
Binder	
Polyvinyl acetate emulsion	275–400
Plasticizer	20– 40
Alkyd resin	None or 25% of polyvinyl acetate solid
Pigments	
Titankum Dioxide	100–300
Extender	25–100
Compounding Agents	
Coalescing agent	0– 50
Thickener	3– 6
Pigment dispersant	0– 2
Surface active agent	4
Mold inhibitor	1– 2
Antifoaming agent	0– 3
Water	350–425

A typical formulation for paints with polyvinyl acetate emulsion base is as follows:

	Parts by weight
Polyvinyl acetate emulsion, 50% solids	500
Rutile titanium dioxide	275
Waterground mica, 325 mesh	30
Micronized mica	30
Domestic china clay	30
Diatomaceous earth	35
Water	300
Alkyd resin	35
Ethyl acetate	41
Dibutyl phthalate (plasticizer)	25
Water	4.5

Paper

Polyvinyl acetate homo- and copolymers are being used in large quantities as a pigment binder in clay coated board and paper. The polymer emulsions usually have a very fine particle size.

The following types of paper products are being coated with a latex bound pigment to improve printability and general appearance:

Book covers	Labels
Book papers	Letterpress papers
Coated foodboard	Lithographic papers
Cup stock	Poster and display board
Folding cartons	Wallpaper

Vinyl acetate copolymer emulsions of a somewhat larger particle size have also been used as pigment binders. The following formulation has been suggested:

	Parts
Clay	50
Titanium dioxide	50
Casein (23%)	2
Water	80.7
Polyvinyl acetate emulsion	27.3

Polyvinyl alcohol can be used instead of casein, in which case only 0.7 part of polyvinyl alcohol is needed due to the higher pigment binding efficiency of polyvinyl alcohol. In using vinyl acetate copolymer latexes it is necessary to have fine particle size in the emulsion and high mechanical strength in the polymeric film.

Polyvinyl acetate emulsions have also been used as wet-end additives. Almost complete retention of the emulsion was achieved by modifying the emulsion with anionic or cationic emulsifiers.

Building Products

Polyvinyl acetate emulsions and redispersible powders are added to Portland cements to increase the tensile, compressive and impact strength of the resulting concrete. A typical cement composition is as follows:

	lb
Portland cement (ASTM Type I)	1034
Polyvinyl acetate emulsion (55% solids)	73.3
Ethylene glycol	9.0
Wetting agent (polyglycol)	4.5
Antifoam agent (silicon type)	0.2
Water	442.0

The polyvinyl acetate used is a polyvinyl alcohol protected homopolymer emulsion. The above composition was especially useful as an oil well cementing mixture. A commercial brand of tile cement uses about 1.5% of spray-dried polyvinyl acetate.

Polyvinyl acetate emulsions are also used as an adhesive to bind new mortar to old. Tape-joint cements also contain polyvinyl acetate powders in combination with polyvinyl alcohols. For example, the emulsion is painted onto the old mortar surface and while the resin is not yet completely dry, the new mortar is applied.

Chewing-Gum Resins

Homo- and copolymers of vinyl acetate are being used as chewing-gum bases. For example, 85 parts of a vinyl acetate-2-ethyl hexyl acrylate copolymer was blended with chocolate, sugar, glucose, surface active agents and microcrystalline wax to give chewing-gum composition. Another composition contains a vinyl acetate-vinylether copolymer. A vinyl acetate homopolymer suitable as chewing-gum base has been described in another patent.

Rubbers

Very recently vinyl acetate-ethylene copolymers have been suggested for rubber applications. These rubbers contain about 45% vinyl acetate and can be vulcanized using a dicumyl peroxide-triallyl cyanurate system. These rubbers are being manufactured by Farbenfabriken Bayer and sold under the name "Levapren."

Textiles

Polyvinyl acetate homo- and copolymers have found a number of uses in the textile industry. Resins in general are used to impart "hand" to textile fabrics made of cotton, rayon and synthetic fibers. Polyvinyl acetate is used in this area due to its low price and desirable properties. Copolymers of vinyl acetate and unsaturated carboxylic acids are being used as textile warp sizes. A typical formulation is given as follows:

	lb
Vinyl acetate-carboxylic acid copolymer beads	40
Na_2CO_3	3
"Ivory Snow"	1.5
Urea	10
Water to make	100

MARTIN K. LINDEMANN

VINYL CHLORIDE LATEX

Poly (vinyl chloride) latices, commonly called vinyl latices, are supplied by Borden, Dow, Firestone, Goodrich, Goodyear and National Starch. Goodrich is the largest supplier of this type of latex. There are no readily available government statistics or industrial estimates of vinyl latex usage. However, this usage is small in comparison with resin, organosol or plastisol consumption.

Vinyl latices are produced by means of the same emulsion polymerization technology as that used to produce other elastomeric and plastomeric polymer latices. However, some refinements are necessary to make a commercial vinyl latex. These refinements are required because of the nature of the monomer and polymer.

The emulsion polymerization adjustments deal with the dechlorination of vinyl chloride and the consequent need for stabilization. This need must be considered in both the polymerization and end use of vinyl latices if a non-discoloring polymer is desired. Dechlorination, and consequent discoloration, of vinyl chloride during polymerization is generally caused by certain metal ion contamination, acidity and higher reaction temperatures. Zinc or iron ions should be removed or sequestered in the water phase. Where permitted, suitable buffers should be included in the polymerization to maintain an alkaline pH. Polymerization temperatures should be held to a minimum. Another factor contributing to polymer discoloration which results from polymerization techniques is low molecular weight fractions. The polymerization should be conducted in such a way that the formation of the low molecular weight fraction is minimized.

Due to the high specific gravity, approximately 30% higher than a styrene-butadiene (SBR) or acrylic latex, overly large particles or agglomerates of particles will result in the formation of sediment. The polymerization should be conducted so as to produce smaller and more uniform particles and thereby minimize this sedimentation tendency.

The majority of vinyl latex applications today require that the polymer be film-forming at room temperature or at rapid pass drying oven temperatures. Consequently, rather than vinyl homopolymers, these latices consist largely of copolymer systems in which the end application dictates the polymer composition.

Three principal types of vinyl latex are marketed today:

(1) Externally plasticized (EP) vinyl latex.
(2) Internally plasticized (IP) vinyl latex.
(3) Comparatively high softening point vinyl polymer latex.

EP vinyl latex systems consist of a vinyl latex

to which a quantity of plasticizer has been added by the producer. The polymeric phase of the latex is generally a copolymer containing at least 75% vinyl chloride. The remaining monomer or monomers in the polymer are selected for their ability to facilitate plasticizer acceptance or to simplify the polymerization of vinyl chloride. The bulk of the plasticizer is normally added as an emulsion to the latex. Either monomeric plasticizers such as dioctylphthalate (DOP) or a polymeric plasticizer such as an epoxy may be used. However, because of relative costs, monomeric plasticizers are generally used.

The use of monomeric plasticizers results in plasticizer migration which is the principal deficiency of these latex systems. Since the plasticizer is of comparatively low molecular weight and not chemically bound, the plasticizer is free to migrate to the substrate to which the EP vinyl latex system is applied. This migration can result in either a deterioration of the substrate or a loss of adhesion of the EP vinyl polymer system to the substrate and a stiffening of the vinyl. While not serious, another disadvantage of these systems is that they require fusion at an elevated temperature before maximum properties of the coating can be realized.

IP vinyl latex systems have been developed to overcome the deficiencies of EP vinyl latex systems. These polymer systems are copolymers of vinyl chloride and a comonomer which incorporates flexibility in the polymer chain. The amount of plasticizing comonomer used is determined by the degree of flexibility desired in the copololymer. These polymer systems can be made film-forming at room temperature and do not normally cause deterioration of the coating substrate or loss of adhesion of the coating to the substrate, which is possible with the use of EP vinyl polymers.

The third type of vinyl latex previously mentioned is the comparatively high softening point vinyl latex. These systems are essentially the same as the EP vinyl latex systems, but without the addition of the external plasticizer. The use of this type of vinyl latex permits the latex user to select his own type and quantity of external plasticizer for the preparation of specialized vinyl latex compounds. Another large use of this type of vinyl latex is in blends with nitrile rubber latex. In these blends the nitrile rubber acts as the plasticizer for the vinyl polymer. In the EP vinyl systems, the vinyl latex-nitrile rubber latex blend coating also requires fusion at an elevated temperature to realize maximum properties. Another shortcoming of this blend is the initial color and aging discoloration resulting from the addition of nitrile rubber.

The most desirable properties of coatings obtained with the use of vinyl latex are scuff, abrasion, solvent and flame resistance. These properties suggest a very versatile polymer system.

The nonwoven fabric industry is probably the largest single user of vinyl latex. Nonwoven fabrics are produced by bonding the intersecting fibers of a random web with a binder to produce a cloth-like material having dimensional stability. Vinyl latex is one of the materials this industry uses as a binder. The products of this industry are generally classified as either disposable products, such as wipe cloths, or non-disposable products, such as clothing stiffeners. In this application the vinyl polymer, applied as a latex, accounts for approximately 30% of the finished nonwoven weight.

The second largest industrial use of vinyl latex is probably in fabric coatings. This application involves application of a coat of vinyl polymer in a latex form to the surface of the fabric. After drying and fusion, additional coats of vinyl may be applied to build up the desired depth of vinyl coating. The vinyl coated fabric is either used as produced, as in wallpaper, or overlaid with another polymer.

Nonwoven fabrics and fabric coatings account for approximately 70 per cent of the total vinyl latex usage. Other industrial uses for vinyl latex are paper, polishes, ink, etc.

Vinyl latex has not enjoyed the market growth of the other large volume polymer latex systems such as the acrylics, vinyl acetate, SBR or nitrile-butadiene rubber (NBR). This is probably because of lack of available literature on the manufacture, characteristics and use of vinyl latex, compared with the amount of technical information generated on SBR and NBR latices since World War II. Secondly, the vinyl latices have not enjoyed the vast publicity given the acrylic and vinyl acetate products in recent years.

It is believed that vinyl latex usage will increase in the future. This belief is based on:

(1) The present low cost of vinyl monomer and predictions of even lower costs.

(2) Versatility of the polymer in regard to the degree of flexibility obtainable.

(3) Recognized solvent and abrasion resistance.

(4) Aging characteristics obtainable when properly stabilized.

(5) Fire retardancy possibilities.

The development of new vinyl-based polymer systems for paint, industrial and consumer products and other markets is expected to create a larger demand for vinyl latices.

WESLEY M. GERMON
DALE P. VOGEL

VINYL MONOMERS

A large number of monomers contain the vinyl group ($CH_2=CH-$). All of these may be polymerized but the principal commercial products are vinyl chloride, vinyl acetate, vinyl alkyl ethers, vinyl fluoride and vinyl pyridine. Styrene, acrylic esters and acrylonitirile may also be classed as vinyl monomers but are discussed under their respective headings.

Vinyl chloride $CH_2=CHCl$ was discovered by Regnault in 1838, but was not polymerized until 1872. The polymer was studied intensively by Ostromislenski in the early part of the 20th century. However, there was no commercial interest in this product until it was plasticized by Semon in 1930.

The classical method of preparation is based on the dehydrochlorination of ethylene dichloride in the presence of aqueous sodium hydroxide as shown below:

$$CH_2Cl \cdot CH_2Cl + NaOH \xrightarrow[150 \text{ psi}]{145°C} CH_2:CHCl$$
$$+ NaCl + H_2O$$

In an improved process, ethylene dichloride is dehydrochlorinated at higher temperatures (450–500°C) over barium chloride catalyst at 7–15 psi.

The ethylene dichloride may be produced in a 96% yield by the direct chlorination of ethylene in the presence of ferric chloride at 30°C. Ethylene dichloride may also be obtained by the vapor phase oxychlorination of ethylene by HCl and air in the presence of cuprous chloride, on activated alumina at 285°C. The yield is approximately 90%.

Until recently, most of the vinyl chloride produced annually in the USA was manufactured from acetylene. Acetylene ($HC≡CH$) may be produced by the thermal cracking of hydrocarbons (Wulff process), the partial oxidation (Sasche), or by an electrical discharge process (Schoch). The dilute acetylene produced may be purified by fractional distillation or the mixture may be heated with chlorine to increase the yield and form some hydrogen chloride.

In the liquid process, acetylene is passed into aqueous hydrochloric acid in the presence of cuprous and ammonium chloride catalysts, then the gaseous process a mixture of acetylene and hydrogen chloride gas is passed over carbon or activated alumina impregnated with mercuric salts, such as mercuric chloride, at 150°C. The conversion is about 25% per pass.

The original objection to the use of ethylene as a starting material was the by-product hydrogen chloride, which is not always usable. However, oxychlorination of ethylene yields vinyl chloride without any by-product hydrogen chloride. In this process ethylene and hydrogen chloride are passed over a cuprous chloride catalyst, impregnated on carbon or activated alumina at moderate temperature and pressure. The dichloroethane produced is then dehydrochlorinated to produce vinylchloride and hydrogen chloride which is recycled.

Vinyl chloride (chloroethene chloroethylene) is a colorless gas with a boiling point of 14°C, and a specific gravity of 0.91. This monomer polymerizes readily to polyvinylchloride. One of the best known commercial products is a copolymer of vinyl chloride and vinyl acetate.

Vinyl acetate ($CH_2 : CHO \cdot COCH_3$) may be produced by the liquid or vapor phase reaction of glacial acetic acid and acetylene. In the liquid phase process, acetylene is bubbled through hot glacial acetic acid in the presence of mercuric acetate at 60–80°C. The yields from this process are 75–80%, but this process has been replaced by a vapor phase processes using zinc acetate on activated charcoal at 170–200°C. The ethylidene acetate intermediate decomposes to acetic acid and vinyl acetate.

Vinyl acetate may also be obtained by the oxidation of butane. Polyvinylacetate has been available commercially since 1930. Vinylacetate is a colorless liquid which boils at 72°C. The monomer is usually stabilized with copper salts. It may be polymerized in emulsion to produce a polymer which is used for water based paints and adhesives. The polymer may be saponified to produce polyvinyl alcohol which may be reacted with butyraldehyde to form polyvinylbutyral.

Vinylalkylethers are prepared by reacting acetylene and alcohols at a pressure of 1–15 atm in the presence of sodium alcoholate. The monomers are purified by distilling over sodium metal. Vinylalkylethers may be polymerized in the presence of boron trifluoride. The sticky polymers are used as adhesives.

Vinylmethylether ($CH_2=CHOCH_3$) is a colorless liquid which boils at 6.0°C. It has a specific gravity of 0.75 and a flash point of −60°F. Vinylethylether has a specific gravity of 0.754 and boils at 35.5°C. Vinyl n-butylether has a specific gravity of 0.780 and boils at 94.1°C. Vinyl ether (divinyl ether, divinyl oxide) ($(CH_2=CH)_2O$) has a specific gravity of 0.773 and boils at 29°C. It may be prepared by heating dichloroethyl ether with aqueous alkaline solutions. Its principal use is as an anesthetic—however, it will polymerize, and can be used as a cross-linking agent.

Vinyl fluoride* $CH_2 : CHF$ has been prepared by the dehalogenation of 1, 1, 2-fluorodichloroethane $CH_2ClCHClF$ and by the addition of hydrogen fluoride to acetylene in the presence of a mixture of mercuric chloride and barium chloride. This colorless gas has a specific gravity of 0.85, and boils at −72°C. Polyvinylfluoride is much more resistant to ultraviolet light than polyvinylchloride.

* See Fluorocarbon Monomers.

Vinyl pyridine is prepared by the condensation of vinyl chloride and pyridine in the presence of aluminum chloride. This colorless liquid boils at 159°C, but it is preferable to distill this monomer under reduced pressure. It boils at 71°C at 18 mm pressure. Copolymers of vinyl pyridine and butadiene have excellent adhesion to rayon and nylon fibers.

N-vinyl carbazole is prepared by the reaction of acetylene and carbazole. Polyvinyl carbazole has higher dielectric properties than mica, and has been used as an insulator.

RAYMOND B. SEYMOUR

W

WAXES

The term wax, as used by the plastics industry, is applied to the broad category of wax-like materials found naturally and to the synthetic materials with wax-like properties produced by the chemical industry. This broad utilization of the word wax by those working with plastics is directly related to the usage to which these products are put which in turn is dependent on the physical characteristics of the compound or natural products. The properties of interest are: the low surface tensions of these waxes in contact with various surfaces—principally metal surfaces, the resistance to water and water vapor, the wide range of melting points available and the incompatibility with many plastic products.

Waxes can be classified into the following major categories:

Vegetable. This category includes plant waxes occurring as coatings on the various parts of plants such as leaves, stems, berries, etc. Plants from which these waxes are obtained generally grow wild, usually in hot or tropical climates, and particularly arid regions. The wax acts as a coating to impede the loss of water by evaporation from these plants. Some of the commercially available waxes are: carnauba wax, which is a product obtained from the leaves of the carnauba palm and is produced principally in Brazil. This wax has a high melting point, high hardness, and ability to take a high and lasting polish. Carnauba wax is frequently used as a means of raising the melting point of other wax mixtures.

Candelilla is obtained from the stem or stocks of a weed occurring in Northern Mexico and Southern Texas. It is a hard brittle wax. Others that fall into the vegetable wax category are ouricury, sugar cane, palm wax, Japan wax, esparto wax, and raffia wax.

Insect and Animal Wax. The most common is the beeswax, which is produced by the honeybee. Because of the elasticity and rather low cost of this material, it is largely used in manufacture of models, pattern making, and polishes. Other animal- or insect-designated waxes are spermaceti and shellac wax.

Mineral and Petroleum Waxes. These are derived from various natural occurring mineral sources. Microcrystalline wax is obtained from the refining and purification of oil. Montan wax is obtained from the extraction of brown coal. Ozocerite is a hydrocarbon wax obtained by extraction from shale.

Synthetic Waxes. This category covers a broad, all-encompassing group of compounds which possess physical properties somewhat related to natural waxes. Among the materials that fall into this general category are high molecular weight fatty acids and their derivatives. Among the compounds that fall in this group are octadecyl alcohol or stearyl alcohol; the acids would cover such materials as stearic or myristic; the amides such as stearamides; the amines such as octadecyl amine of both primary, secondary and tertiary types; the nitriles; and other available products manufactured by the condensation of high molecular weight acids with high molecular weight alcohols to form ester or with high molecular weight amines to form fatty acid amides.

A second category of wax-like products produced synthetically includes the esters of polyhydric alcohols, with fatty acids or the hydrogenated vegetable oil derivatives which are fatty acid glycerides. These are generally esters of glycerin, diethylene glycol, polyethylene glycol or sorbitol. The stearic acid esters of these glycols are generally solid with wax-like characteristics.

A third category contains the special low molecular weight polymers, as illustrated by polyethylene, polytetrafluroethylene, polyethylene oxide, polypropylene, and polyethylene-vinyl acetate copolymer.

Another category of wax-like products is obtained by the chlorination of hydrocarbons to produce the chlorinated hydrocarbons "Chlorowax," "Halowax," and "Arochlors."

The vigorous oxidation of "Montan" wax to complex acids and the esterification of the acid produced with various glycols, has created a series of waxes under various trademarks which are available from Germany. A second group of synthetically produced "paraffin" type waxes are a product of the Fischer-Tropsch process. This process yields a variety of derivatives that lend themselves to the manufacture of synthetic waxes.

Waxes are used by the plastics industry for several quite varied and diverse purposes. This goes beyond the normal use of wax as a polish or surface finish for molded parts, or as a mar-resistant additive added to various finishes which have been used with molded plastics parts.

Pattern makers' wax is a blend of waxes generally built around beeswax that is available in sheet form. These sheets are supplied in varying thicknesses to a very close tolerance. The sheets of wax are quite tough and flexible, which enables the pattern maker or mold maker to reproduce both halves of a part from the pattern of the surface of one side of the part, knowing the thickness of the part. For example, the reproduction of the outer and inner surfaces of a hemisphere can be made from a pattern of the outer contour of the hemisphere. The mold is taken off of the pattern as it was produced by the pattern maker. If the hemisphere is $\frac{1}{8}$ in. thick, then this mold is lined with $\frac{1}{8}$ in. thick pattern wax. The whole mold surface is covered. A second reproduction is next made of this inside surface. This produces a mold $\frac{1}{8}$ in. smaller than the original pattern, and would be a true reproduction of the inner surface of the hemisphere.

Flame or fire-retardant characteristics are imparted to various resins by the incorporation of chlorinated paraffin wax ("Chlorowax") in the liquid resin. The addition of 5–10% of a 70% chlorine containing paraffin wax, in the presence of a like amount of antimony oxide (5–10% on the weight of the resin), will convert a freely combustible resin such as a styrene-polyester resin into a self-extinguishing or fire-retardant resin.

Waxes also are used to eliminate the air sensitivity that occurs during cure of styrene-polyester base resins. The styrene based resins when cured in the presence of air give a tacky or sticky surface. This air sensitivity of the resin is the result of air inhibition of the cure. The addition of small percentages (0.1–0.3%) of a paraffinic or microcrystalline wax to the styrene-polyester resin before curing will eliminate the air sensitivity during cure. The small percentage of wax is soluble in the liquid resin. As the resin cures the wax becomes insoluble and is exuded to the surface. As the wax arrives at the surface, it prevents contact of the polymerizing resin with the oxygen of the air and thus eliminates the air inhibition and the stickiness that is a result of this air inhibition. The wax present at the surface also helps in subsequent sanding or buffing that may be needed to finish the molded or laminated part.

Molds for casting or laminating plastics are being made from high melting point microcrystalline waxes and blends of microcrystalline waxes with the low molecular weight polyethylene. Where it is desired to manufacture one or a limited number of prototypes or finished parts, and where a casting technique or a room temperature curing laminate based on polyester or epoxy resins is adequate, then a mold built from wax can be used.

The wax blends are melted to a clear, free-flowing liquid and then brushed or poured over the pattern of the part that is desired. The wax is allowed to cool to room temperature and then the pattern is removed. The mold thus created is used to produce the prototype either by casting or laminating. Care must be taken to see that any exotherm generated during the curing of the resin does not exceed the melting point of the wax, or the form may be destroyed.

The most widely used and recognized application for waxes is as mold releases, mold lubricants and antiblock agents. It is a most common sight in many molding plants to see a metal mold at elevated temperature being lubricated with a stick of wax. This is generally a large chunk of a high quality grade of carnauba wax which is being melted directly onto the mold and the excess being removed with a wiping cloth. A cloth saturated with the wax can also be used to lubricate the mold. Where addition type and condensation type cross-linking resins are being molded, this is a very effective type of mold lubricant or release agent. In addition to carnauba wax, other wax-like materials can be and have been used. Those that can be mentioned are Montan wax and its synthetic derivatives, polyamides, and high molecular weight esters.

A second variation of the use of wax for mold lubrication is the actual incorporation of small percentages of wax or wax-like compounds (0.5–2% on the weight of the resin) in the resin composition for molding operations of the compression, and transfer type; for extrusion operations, and for calendering. For example, it is not unusual to add very finely divided low molecular weight polyethylene, stearyl alcohol, or zinc stearate to a polyester premix molding composition that will be match metal molded. During the molding operation, the wax-like materials are squeezed to the surface and not only lubricate the surface but also aid in the flow of the molding compound over the surface. The result is a part that releases freely from the mold and has a shiny, glossy surface as a result of the presence of the lubricant.

In the extrusion of plastics, wax in the compound eases the material through the die and improves the surface finish. Wax is added to calendering, embossing, and rolled compounds to impart antiblock and antistick characteristics.

Plastic films of all types have coatings containing wax compositions to improve or add water and water-vapor resistance.

ROBERT STEINMAN

WOOD FLOUR

Wood flour as a filler for plastics is most useful when the particles are small and in the form of fibers. It is widely used as a filler in the preparation of thermosetting resin molding compounds, particularly in molded and cast phenolics and ureas. Wood flour contributes improved impact resistance, shrinkage control, and good electrical characteristics at a low cost.

From the processing point of view, uniform size of wood flour particles is important to promote rapid and uniform wetting by the resin during the manufacturing of the molding compound. Freedom from large particles or chips, or pieces of bark or knots is also very important, since such pieces are not wetted thoroughly with resin, showing up either as unsightly dark or light spots in moldings, and thus detract from the physical strength of moldings made from it. Wood flour is obtained by an attrition mill or hammer mill grinding of relatively resin-free fibrous soft woods such as pines, firs, spruces, etc., and, to a lesser extent, of hardwoods. The combination of the grinding process and modern classification and separation equipment now yields wood flour products characterized by controlled narrow particle size distribution and freedom from high density particles or chips. The ultimate results of these process improvements are cleaner, brighter moldings of improved quality.

Wood flour-filled phenolic molding compounds have the natural dark brown color characteristics of phenolic resins and are used extensively in electrical moldings such as receptacles and toggle switches. Urea molding compounds made with flour also are naturally light brown or tan in color, and a typical application for such a compound would be in the molding of salad bowls.

Particle sizes as small as 200 mesh are used in order to obtain smoother surface finishes. However, photomicrographs show that fibrous structures can be destroyed by grinding to very small particles. Wood flour-filled phenolic molding compounds have an Izod impact value of about 0.3 ft lb/in of notch. They are described as CFG under military specification MIL-M-14F. These products are classified as PF 29026 by the SPI and as type 2 by the American Society for Testing Materials (ASTM) under tentative specification D-700-57T. Wood flour chars when heated above 325° F and hence when working with wood-filled plastics it is advisable that they not be used for long periods of time at high temperatures.

RICHARD S. WILNER

INDEX

INDEX